NAME	DEVELOPMENT	LENGTH ft (m)	DIAM ft (m)	MASS lb (kg)	S	ENGINE Designator	Propellant	Thrust lb (kg)	REMARKS
EUROPE continued									
Ariane 5 1995?	ESA/CNES, Aérospatiale	180 (54·8)	37·4 (11·4)	1,583,000 (718,000)	0 1 2	P-230 (x2) Vulcain HM-60 L-5	Solid N₂O₄/MMH LO₂/LH₂	2,954,000 (1,340,000) 229,000 (104,000) 4,400 (2,000)	40,000lb (18 tonnes) to 28·5°, 310 miles (500km), 15,000lb (6,800kg) to GTO. All data for this vehicle are provisional.
Europa I 1964	ELDO HSD, Aérospatiale/ LRBA, ASAT	103·0 (31·4)	10·0 (3·05)	274,000 (124,265)	1 2 3	RR-RZ2 Mk3 (x2) LRBA 7T (x4) ASAT Erno	LO₂/kerosene N₂O₄/UDMH N₂O₄/UDMH + N₂H₄	302,085 (137,000) 59,535 (27,000) 5,250 (2,380)	Payload into CEO 2,000lb (907kg). 3 launches from Woomera — failed.
Europa II 1971	ELDO HSD, Aérospatiale/ LRBA, ASAT	103·0 (31·4)	10·0 (3·05)	246,000 (111,565)	1 2 3 4	RR-RZ2 Mk3 (x2) LRBA 7T (x4) ASAT Erno SEP P.6	LO₂/kerosene N₂O₄/UDMH N₂O₄/UDMH + N₂H₄ Solid	302,085 (137,000) 59,535 (27,000) 5,250 (2,380) 9,260 (4,200)	Payload into CEO 2,536lb (1,150kg); into GO 375lb (170kg). One satellite from Kourou — failed. Project abandoned
FRANCE									
Diamant A 1965	CNES DMA/SEREB	62·0 (18·9)	4·6 (1·4)	39,625 (17,970)	1 2 3	Emeraude L-13 Topaze P-2, 3 Rubis P-0.7	Nit acid/turps Solid Solid	66,150 (30,000) 33,075 (15,000) 11,685 (5,300) max	Launched Asterix etc. Payload into CEO 176lb (80kg).
Diamant B 1970	CNES Aérospatiale	77·0 (23·5)	4·6 (1·4)	55,000 (24,945)	1 2 3	Valois L-17 Topaze P-2,3 Rubis P-0.6	N₂O₄/UDMH Solid Solid	77,175 (35,000) 31,970 (14,500) 11,025 (5,000)	Launched DIAL, Peole and D2. Payload into 186 mile (300km) EO 353lb (160kg).
Diamant BP4 1975	CNES Aérospatiale	71·0 (21·6)	4·6 (1·4)	60,640 (27,500)	1 2 3	Valois L-17 P-4 RITA 1 Rubis P-0.6	N₂O₄/UDMH Solid Solid	88,200 (40,000) max 39,690 (18,000) 11,025 (5,000)	Launched Starlette, Pollux and Castor, Aura. Payload into 186 mile (300km) EO 441lb (200kg). Programme ended after three launches, 1975.
INDIA									
Satellite Launch Vehicle (SLV) 3 1979	ISRO	75·4 (23)	3·28 (1·0)	37,300 (16,900)	1 2 3 4	? ? ? ?	Solid Solid Solid Solid	140,000 (63,500) 60,000 (27,200) 20,000 (9,200) 6,000 (2,700)	First satellite orbited in 1980 after failure in 1979. 92lb (42kg) to 45°, 280-620 miles (450-1,000km). Third flight partial failure, final flight (1983) success.
Augmented Satellite Launch Vehicle (ASLV) 1987	ISRO	77·1 (23·5)	9·8 (3·0)	86,000 (39,000)	1 2 3 4 5	Strap-ons (x2) ? ? ? ?	Solid Solid Solid Solid Solid	265,000 (120,300) 158,000 (71,600) 68,000 (31,000) 20,000 (9,200) 7,900 (3,600)	Launch attempts in 1987 and 1988 failed and programme suspended. 330lb (150kg) to 45°, 248 miles (400km).
Polar Satellite Launch Vehicle (PSLV) 1990?	ISRO	145 (44·2)	10·5 (3·2)	606,300 (275,000)	0 1 2 3 4	Strap-ons (x6) ? Vikas ? ? (x2)	Solid Solid N₂O₄/UDMH Solid N₂O₄/MMH	796,000 (361,000) 1,093,000 (495,600) 130,000 (60,000) 73,900 (33,500) 3,100 (1,400)	2,205lb (1,000kg) to polar 559 miles (900km) orbit. Might be adapted for geosynchronous missions.
ISRAEL									
Shavit 1988	Israeli Space Agency, Israeli Aircraft Industries	24? (11?)	6·5? (2?)	N/A	1 2 3	? ? ?	Solid Solid Solid	N/A N/A N/A	Very little data available: derived from Jerico 2 missile. Launched Offeq 1, mass 344lb (156kg), into a 143°, 155-715 miles (250-1,150km) retrograde orbit.
JAPAN									
Lambda-4S 1970	ISAS Nissan	54·2 (16·52)	2·42 (0·735)	20,905 (9,480)	0 1 2 3 4	SB-310BP2 (x2) 735UP 735BP 500BP 480S	Solid Solid Solid Solid Solid	42,777 (19,400) 81,585 (37,000) 26,460 (12,000) 15,435 (7,000) 1,764 (800)	First Japanese satellite launcher Launched Ohsumi, etc. Payload into CEO 53lb (24kg).
Mu-4S 1971	ISAS Nissan	77·4 (23·6)	4·62 (1·41)	96,140 (43,600)	0 1 2 3 4	SB-310 (x8) M-10 M-20 M-30 M-40	Solid Solid Solid Solid Solid	174,635 (79,200) 161,850 (73,400) 62,840 (28,500) 27,340 (12,400) 4,190 (1,900)	Launched Tansei 1 etc. Payload into CEO 507lb (230kg).
Mu-3S 1974	ISAS Nissan	66·3 (20·2)	4·62 (1·41)	91,730 (41,600)	0 1 2 3	SB-310 (x8) M-10 M-22-TVC M-3A	Solid Solid Solid Solid	171,110 (77,600) 165,375 (75,000) 62,620 (28,400) 12,790 (5,800)	Launched Tansei 2 etc. Payload into CEO 430lb (195kg).
Mu-3H 1977	ISAS Nissan	78·0 (23·8)	4·62 (1·41)	107,385 (48,700)	0 1 2 3	SB-310 (x8) M-13 M-22-TVC M-3A	Solid Solid Solid Solid	171,110 (77,600) 214,545 (97,300) 62,620 (28,400) 12,790 (5,800)	Launched Tansei 3 etc. Payload into CEO 595lb (270kg).
	ISAS Nissan	78·0 (23·8)	4·62 (1·41)	107,825 (48,900)	0 1 2 3	SB-310 (x8) M-13-TVC M-22-TVC M-3A	Solid Solid Solid Solid	171,110 (77,600) 229,320 (104,000) 62,620 (28,400) 13,010 (5,900)	Launched Tansei 4, ASTRO-A etc. Payload into CEO 573lb (260kg).
	ISAS Nissan	92·5 (28·2)	5·41 (1·65)	134,505 (61,000)	0 1 2 3	SB-310-TVC (x2) M-13-TVC N/A N/A	Solid Solid Solid Solid	67,060 (30,414) 252,000 (114,285) 116,775 (52,960) 26,550 (12,040)	Major uprating of Mu-3S. Payload into 124 mile (200km) CO 1,544lb (700kg); into solar orbit 331lb (150kg).
N-I 1975	NASDA Mitsubishi	106·9 (32·57)	8·0 (2·44)	199,025 (90,260)	0 1 2 3	Thio TX-354-5 (x2) Rdyne/Mit MB-3 Mitsubishi LE-3 Thio TE364-3	Solid LO₂/RJ-1 N₂O₄/Aerozine 50 Solid (spherical)	156,575 (71,000) 169,785 (77,000) 11,905 (5,400) 8,820 (4,000)	Based on licence-built Thor. Launched Kiku etc. Payload into 186 mile (300km) CO 2,646lb (1,200kg); into GO 287lb (130kg).
N-II 1981	NASDA Mitsubishi	116·0 (35·35)	8·0 (2·44)	297,675 (135,000)	0 1 2 3	Thio TX-354-5 (x9) Rdyne MB-3 Aero AJ-10-118F Thio TE364-3	Solid LO₂/RJ-1 N₂O₄/Aerozine 50 Solid	470,325 (213,300) 169,785 (77,000) 9,700 (4,400) 14,995 (6,800)	Launched ETS-4 etc. Payload into GO 772lb (350kg).
H-I 1986	NASDA, Mitsubishi Ishikawajima Harima	132·2 (40·3)	8·0 (2·44)	308,400 (139,900)	0 1 2 3	Castor 2 (x9) MB-3 LE-5 ?	Solid LO₂/RJ-1 LO₂/LH₂ Solid	331,000 (150,000?) 194,000 (88,000) 23,150 (10,500) 17,400 (7,900)	Derived from the N-I/N-II vehicles: four successful flights during 1986-1988 with five further flights in 1989-1992. 1,215lb (550kg) to GTO
H-II 1993?	NASDA, Mitsubishi	161·0 (49·0)	13·1 (4·0) core 26·0 (8·0)	586,400 (266,000)	0 1 2	Strap-ons (x2) LE-7 LE-5	Solid LO₂/LH₂ LO₂/LH₂	749,600 (340,000?) 264,600 (120,000) 26,500 (12,000)	Large booster under development in same class as Ariane 5 and Proton. 22,000lb (10 tonnes) to 30°, 186 miles (300km), 8,800lb (4 tonnes) to GTO.
UNITED KINGDOM									
Black Arrow 1969	Ministry of Technology, Westland	42·66 (13·0)	6·56 (2·0)	40,000 (18,140)	1 2 3	RR Gamma Type 8 RR Gamma Type 2 Bristol Aero Waxwing	HTP/kerosene HTP/kerosene Solid	52,075 (23, 615) 15,750 (7,145) 4,927 (2,235)	Launched X-3 Prospero 145·5lb (66kg). Payload into low PO 242lb (110kg). Project cancelled 1971.

SPACE TECHNOLOGY

Kenneth Gatland
Consultant and Chief Author

THE ILLUSTRATED ENCYCLOPEDIA OF
SPACE TECHNOLOGY
—— Second Edition ——

a Salamander book
Published by Salamander Books Limited
LONDON ● NEW YORK

A Salamander Book

Published by Salamander Books Ltd
129/137 York Way.
London N7 9LG,
United Kingdom

© Salamander Books Ltd 1981 and 1989

ISBN 0 86101 449 9

Distributed in the UK by
Hodder & Stoughton Services,
P.O. Box 6, Mill Road, Dunton Green,
Sevenoaks, Kent TN3 2XX.

All correspondence concerning the
content of this volume should be
addressed to Salamander Books Ltd. *TRA*

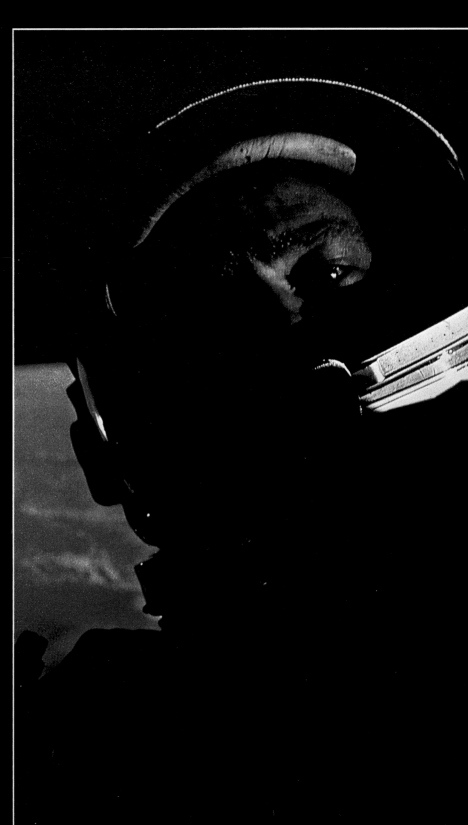

Credits

Editor:
Philip de Ste. Croix

Designers:
Nick Buzzard
SallyAnn Jackson

Colour artwork:
Mike Badrocke © Salamander Books Ltd

Diagrams:
Mike Badrocke, Alan Hollingbery,
Tony Gibbons © Salamander Books Ltd

Maps:
Richard Natkiel © Salamander Books Ltd
Original references for Soviet and
Chinese maps © Charles P. Vick

Filmset:
Modern Text Typesetting Ltd, England

Colour and monochrome reproduction:
York House Graphics Ltd, England

Printed in Belgium by Proost International
Book Production, Turnhout

Acknowledgments

During the preparation of this book Ken Gatland and I have been fortunate to receive help and advice from many people associated with space technology throughout the world. We thank everyone who has answered our requests for pictures and information so patiently, and would particularly like to express our gratitude to the staff of the Novosti Press Agency, London (for pictures and information about Soviet space activities); L.J. Carter, Executive Secretary of the British Interplanetary Society (for the use of original material from BIS archives); Robert Conquest (for permission to quote from "For The 1956 Opposition of Mars"); F.C. Durant, III, of the National Air and Space Museum, Washington, DC (for archive material relating to Dr. Robert Goddard); Rolf Engel (for information about pre-war and wartime German rocket history); Doreen Gatland (for assistance in compiling rocket data); Mike Hammond of RAE, Farnborough (for explaining the finer points of remote Earth-sensing); Dipl-Ing R. Heinrich of the Deutsche Museum, Munich (for information about early German rocketry); Professor Hermann Oberth (for elucidating design features of his Modell B rocket); Louise Parks (for translating Soviet texts), Arthur Rudolph (for explaining the design and applications of his rocket engine); Mitchell Sharpe (for assistance in obtaining information on pre-war German rocket developments); and David Shayler of Astro Info Service (for his help in providing pictures of recent US manned space missions).

A book of this nature relies to a great extent on the quality of its pictures for its overall impact. In this connection, we would like to thank Mike Badrocke for his painstaking work in the preparation of most of the artwork, and the many aerospace companies and space research institutes that have supplied transparencies, diagrams and charts. We are especially grateful to Les Gaver and his colleagues in the Audio-Visual Department at NASA Headquarters in Washington, DC, who supplied a superb selection of photographs. The assistance of Phillip Clark, Theo Pirard, David Skinner and Charles Vick was invaluable in the complex task of compiling the table of launch vehicle data, and preparing the maps.

Philip de Ste. Croix

Contents

Contributors

B. Belitzky

Boris Belitzky is a Soviet science writer who has reported on his country's space programmes from the very beginning: in 1957 he broadcast from Moscow the first announcement of the launching of Sputnik 1.

He has spoken English fluently since childhood, and he acted as interpreter for Yuri Gagarin on his visit to Britain in 1961. During the Apollo-Soyuz flight, he broadcast running commentary on the Soyuz launch, the docking of Apollo and Soyuz in orbit, and other crucial phases of the mission.

A graduate of Moscow University, he combines writing and broadcasting with the translation of mainly scientific literature from Russian into English. He was an early Soviet contributor to *Spaceflight* magazine.

P. Clark

Phillip Clark, FBIS, is one of the world's leading authorities on the Soviet space programme. He was born and educated in Bradford, and holds an Honours Degree in Mathematics and Computing from the Open University. He has written numerous detailed analyses of Soviet space operations which have appeared in the *Journal of the British Interplanetary Society* and *Spaceflight,* and is the author of *The Soviet Manned Space Programme* (Salamander 1988).

D. Dooling

Dave Dooling is currently manager, programme development, for US Space Camp and US Space Academy at the Space & Rocket Center, Huntsville, Alabama producing mission scripts and educational materials for introductory space courses. In 1986 he developed a one-week Space Orientation Course for US Army officers and other ranks. His work includes the preliminary outfitting of mockups and researching specified computer networks and software.

He was formerly, from 1977, Science Editor of *The Huntsville* (Alabama) *Times.* His duties included covering the Space Shuttle and space science and applications in the United States. In 1980 he received the prestigious National Space Club's Press Award and an Aviation/Space Writers' Association Award. He is an associate fellow of the BIS, and member of the American Institute of Aeronautics and Astronautics, the Aviation/Space Writers' Association and National Space Club.

T. Furniss

Tim Furniss is spaceflight correspondent of *Flight International,* Britain's weekly aerospace magazine, which has been covering space activities since 1957. The author of *Manned Spaceflight Log, Space Shuttle Log, Spaceflight — The Records,* and *One Small Step,* the human side of the Apollo programme, he has covered Apollo, Shuttle and Soyuz launches from the Kennedy Space Center, USA and the Baikonur Cosmodrome in the Soviet Union. He has visited the Star City cosmonaut training centre, near Moscow. Tim Furniss is a regular commentator on spaceflight current affairs on TV and radio, and operates from an "electronic base" on the north Devon coast of the UK.

K.W. Gatland

Kenneth W. Gatland — a Past President of the British Interplanetary Society — was in at the beginning of the Space Age. His book, *Development of the Guided Missile* (1952), was immediately translated and republished in Moscow. He has known many of the space pioneers and astronauts personally, and his own contributions to astronautics are recorded in the US space programme.

He was formerly a member of the design staff at Hawker Aircraft Ltd under the late Sir Sydney Camm. During World War II he worked on the Hurricane, Typhoon and Tempest fighters, and on many aircraft from the Hawker stable in post-war years, including the Hunter interceptor.

For the past 45 years he has devoted himself to space studies and writing about space technology. He was member of the BIS Council from 1945 until 1981. For many years he edited the BIS monthly publication, *Spaceflight.* As well as his technical writing, he also contributed as Space Correspondent to *The Sunday Telegraph* and *Telegraph Sunday Magazine.* His many books include *Development of the Guided Missile, Astronautics in the Sixties, Manned Spacecraft, Missiles and Rockets, Robot Explorers* and *Space Diary.*

F. Hussain

Farooq Hussain is a British national who was born in India. Formerly a research associate at the International Institute for Strategic Studies in London (1978-1979), he then became a research fellow in the Arms Control Program at Stanford University, Califorinia. He received his PhD from King's College, University of London. His specialist interests have been concerned with the impact of scientific and technological innovations on military and international affairs. His publications include an Adelphi paper on the effects of weapons test restrictions as a means for arms control, and a number of articles in specialist journals.

N.L. Johnson

Nicholas L. Johnson is an internationally recognised authority on the near Earth space environment with emphasis on space debris, space surveillance, and international space activities. He is co-author of the book *Artificial Space Debris* and has written more than 30 papers and technical reports on space environment issues.

Since 1979 Mr Johnson has conducted space operations analyses for Teledyne Brown Engineering and is presently Advisory Scientist in the Colorado Springs Office, responsible for providing the highest level of technical expertise in organisations performing theoretical, operational, and experimental research functions. Recently, he has been evaluating space environment hazards for the international Freedom Space Station. He was previously Manager, Space Systems Analysis at TBE's Colorado Springs Office, where he directed all space environment, space surveillance, and space defense activities.

He was a principal author of all three editions of the NASA-sponsored technical report *History of On-Orbit Satellite Fragmentations,* and has published works in international journals including *Space Policy, Advances in Space Research, Journal of Spacecraft and Rockets, Space World, Spaceflight, Aerospace America,* and *Journal of the British Interplanetary Society.* He has also written four books about the Soviet space programme and is the sole author of the widely acclaimed annual report on Soviet space activities, *The Soviet Year in Space.*

R.S. Lewis

Richard S. Lewis, a journalist specialising in science and technology, has covered US space programmes since Project Mercury. A former Science Editor of *The Chicago Sun-Times* and Editor of the *Bulletin of the Atomic Scientists,* Mr Lewis wrote the authoritative histories, *The Voyages of Columbia* (1984) and *Challenger: The Final Voyage* (1988). His earlier books include *Appointment on the Moon,* a history of the US space programme from Explorer 1 to Apollo 11; *The Voyages of Apollo;*

and *From Vinland to Mars*, an analysis of exploration over the last thousand years. He is also the author of a history of US Antarctic exploration — *A Continent for Science* — and a work describing the beginnings of the anti-nuclear movement in the USA, *The Nuclear Power Rebellion*. In other fields, he has written books on special education for children with learning disabilities and management of the brain-injured child. He is a graduate of Pennsylvania State University, a member of the US National Press Club and of the British Interplanetary Society.

C. Peebles

Curtis Peebles is a writer who specialises in the history of aerospace technology. He is a Fellow of the British Interplanetary Society and has been a contributor to *Spaceflight* magazine since 1977. He has written on such subjects as the "Big Bird" reconnaissance satellite, the Manned Orbiting Laboratory, the X-15 and Lifting Bodies which were the predecessors of the Space Shuttle, the Soviet Space Shuttle, Extraterrestrial Life and secret Soviet launch failures. He has written several books: *Battle for Space* on beam weapons, *Guardians* — a history of reconnaissance satellites and *The Moby Dick Project* on 1950s reconnaissance balloons.

Mr. Peebles received a BA in history from California State University, Long Beach in December 1985.

T. Pirard

Theo Pirard was born in Belgium in 1947 and graduated from the Catholic University in Louvain with a degree in Modern History. He is currently managing the *Centre d'Information Spatiale* (Space Information Centre) in Belgium, collating data about the development of space activities throughout the world. He contributes to many specialised periodicals and space newsletters, including *Space Calendar*, *Space Business*, *Satellite Communications*, *Spaceflight*, *Avianews International*.

A. Schnapf

Now retired, Abraham Schnapf was, until the early 1980s, the Principal Scientist at RCA Astro-Electronics, Princeton, where he was responsible for future space systems and advanced missions, as well as the growth of current programmes. He was previously Manager, Satellite Programs when he directed all the NASA programmes, including Tiros-N/NOAA, Nimbus and Landsat, and the Atmosphere and Dynamics Explorers. He also directed RCA's Satcom, Telesat and NOVA programmes and the highly successful Tiros, ESSA, ITOS and NOAA satellite programmes.

Mr Schnapf received an MSc in Mechanical Engineering from Drexel University in 1953. He won the RCA David Sarnoff Award for outstanding achievements in engineering in 1970, the NASA Public Service Award in 1969, the Annual Award in 1968 from the American Society of Quality Control and Reliability. He was cited in the *Aviation Week* 1968 Laurels for Tiros Program Management. He was elected a Fellow of the AIAA in 1971.

M. Sharpe

Mitchell R. Sharpe is a science writer and historian who has been concerned with space and guided weapons research for the last 35 years. Born in 1924, he was educated at Auburn University, and he then took postgraduate studies at Emory University.

From 1955-1960 he was a technical writer with the US Army Missile Command, Huntsville, and from 1960-71 a supervisory technical writer at Marshall Space Flight Center, Huntsville. He has been the Consultant in History of the Alabama Space and Rocket Center from 1970 to the present day. In 1968 and 1976 he won the Robert H. Goddard Essay Prize awarded by the National Space Club. He is a member of several societies including the American Institute of Aeronautics and Astronautics, and the National Association of Science Writers. He is a Fellow of the British Interplanetary Society and a member of the History Committee of the International Astronautical Academy in Paris.

Mr Sharpe has written many books on space topics. His titles include *Basic Astronautics; Applied Astronautics; Living in Space; Yuri Gagarin, First Man in Space; Satellites and Probes; Dividends from Space; "It is I, Sea Gull", Valentina Tereskhova, First Woman in Space;* and *The Rocket Team*, with F. Ordway.

D.L. Skinner

David Skinner was born in Indianapolis in 1953. He gained a BSc in Aeronautical and Astronautical Engineering from Purdue University in 1977, and an MSc in Applied Mechanics from the California Institute of Technology in 1979.

He has been employed at the Jet Propulsion Laboratory Pasadena, California, since 1973. His work experience includes the design of both spacecraft and trajectories, and he currently develops software tools in the Mission Design Section of the Systems Division. He is a member of the American Institute of Aeronautics and Astronautics, the BIS, and is a founder member of the World Space Foundation.

C.P. Vick

Charles P. Vick has been a private student of international strategic studies since 1962. He has concentrated on the analysis of US, Soviet and Chinese space hardware, launch vehicle development, and its influence on foreign policy. His illustrations and articles, particularly on Soviet and Chinese rocketry, have been published in *Spaceflight* magazine, and books including *Missiles and Rockets* (by K. W. Gatland). *Spaceflight Directory* (by R. Turnhill), *Analog Science, The Next Man on the Moon* (by James Oberg). He provided data and drawings for the AIAA title *China Space Reports*, and served as consultant reviewer of *Soviet Space Program, 1971-1975*, the Staff Report of the Committee on Aeronautics and Space Science, US Senate, by the Science Policy Research Division of the Congressional Research Service, Library of Congress. He worked on their next five-year study, *Soviet Space Program, 1975-1980*. His drawings of the family of Chinese launch vehicles were published by *Aviation Week & Space Technology* in August 1980.

D.R. Woods

David Woods is a Systems Engineer with the Systems Integration Division of International Business Machines Corporation. In the past, his work has involved the development and simulation of navigation and guidance techniques for precision guided aerospace vehicles at the White Sands Missile Range. More recently, he has worked in data fusion problems associated with tactical intelligence assessments, and simulations associated with high precision coherent location techniques. Currently he is working on a large database problem associated with a classified project.

He maintains an outside interest in the Soviet space programme and has written extensively on the subject, as well as serving as a consultant for others in this area. He is also an accomplished technical illustrator whose works on various Soviet spacecraft have appeared in publications throughout the world. Prior to joining IBM, he was a lecturer and consultant for the National Aeronautics and Space Administration. He received a BSc in Physics from Rensselaer Polytechnic Institute, and an MSc in Computer Science from the State University of New York.

Foreword

When the 20th anniversary of the first Apollo Moon landing was celebrated in July 1989, my thoughts returned almost half a century to a period when small study groups, brought together by the British Interplanetary Society, were struggling to turn dreams of space flight into engineering reality. Everywhere we found scepticism that such things as artificial satellites were possible. Space stations and Moon landings were considered "outrageous fantasy".

We student engineers viewed the matter quite differently. We saw space exploration as the great liberator of the human spirit as inevitable as sailing the high seas. We earnestly believed that some day it would involve all mankind. To the sceptics who asked what use it would have, we could only reply: "What use is a new-born baby?".

It was a young man of the BIS planning group — Arthur C. Clarke — who first proposed that world-wide radio and TV broadcasting could be routed from geostationary orbit. That classic idea of 1945 became the foundation of a multi-billion dollar industry which today links people all over the world.

The "impossible" of yesteryear now touches our lives in many ways. Orbiting "radio stars" help our ships and planes navigate safely in all weathers. Observation satellites keep us informed about weather, ocean conditions, sea ice, destructive storms, pollution and the health of agricultural crops and forests. Others keep watch on military activity around the world and help to police arms limitation agreements.

And still a restless spirit spurs us on. Although mankind has yet to travel beyond the Moon, our robot emissaries have crossed the Solar System to inspect every planet other than Pluto. The use of telescopes and other instruments above the atmosphere has thrown revealing new light upon the Universe.

Now another surge of activity is beginning aboard space stations, shuttles and other specialised spacecraft. We are learning how to fashion unique materials under conditions of microgravity — such things as super-crystals for the electronics industry; light weight/high strength alloys and composites and the purest drugs for the battle against disease.

Taking industry into space could have immense importance if we look far enough into the future. The time is fast approaching when the world must unite to preserve our civilisation in the face of global pollution, rundown of natural resources, depletion of the ozone layer and greenhouse effect warming. Part of the solution must lie, ultimately, in removing polluting activities from Earth and exploiting the "clean" and abundant energies of space.

Competitive studies suggest that the environmental crisis could reach danger level by the year 2050, unless vigorous steps are taken to limit economic growth, energy usage and pollution.

There are few signs that mankind will accept restriction of growth on the needed scale.

Observation satellites have a major role to play in helping us understand the complex interactions between air, land and ocean and the way in which pollution and greenhouse warming affect climatic change. If the well-being of mankind is to be preserved, we must look increasingly beyond the Earth for our salvation. In space energy is clean, non-polluting and free; industry can operate without harming Earth's fragile oasis. Materials of many kinds can be found on the Moon, planets, asteroids and comets with which to fashion a new industrial age.

These will be massive and costly undertakings by any stretch of the imagination, but unless we take the first steps along this path — and do so in a spirit of unfettered co-operation — it may be too late to redress the balance.

President Bush opened the door on 20 July 1989 when he pledged to return Americans to the Moon in the early 21st century. The first step, he emphasised, was to build by 1999 a permanent orbiting space station called "Freedom" which would lead to the "giant leap" into the Solar System. Early next century America would go "back to the Moon. Back to the future, and this time to stay. And then a journey into tomorrow, a journey to another planet — a manned mission to Mars." The Soviets have similar ambitions as we shall see in this book.

The Moon is the key because it constitutes a "storehouse" of raw materials which can be used in construction projects. Samples brought to Earth by the Apollo astronauts show these percentages (by weight): oxygen 42; silicon 21; iron 13; calcium 8; aluminium 7; magnesium 6; others 3. The Moon appears to have sufficient metals and oxygen to satisfy our needs for a considerable period, but hydrogen is scarce and the only hope of finding water appears to be at the poles where it may lie undetected, in permanently shadowed areas, in the form of ice or permafrost. However, nickel, iron and carbon compounds must have fallen over aeons of time in meteoroids and comets.

Opening up this "new frontier" will be slow and difficult, but already automated machines are being designed to tackle the job. One day, on the lunar surface, there will be pressure domes, oxygen to breathe, hydroponic farms and fuels to propel rockets and surface vehicles. New techniques will be developed for manufacturing structures for building into orbiting factories, solar power stations and habitats using the minimum of materials ferried from Earth. Thanks to the Moon's low gravity, it is 20 times easier to launch cargo from the lunar surface than it is from Earth. Electromagnetic catapults are already being developed and tested.

The big question to be answered is how mankind will set about organising this bold new venture. While the 1967 Space Treaty prohibits "land grabbing" in space, a "Moon Treaty" initiated by the Soviets has been largely ignored. Adopted as a Resolution of the United Nations General Assembly and opened for signature on 18 December 1979, parties to it undertake "to establish an international regime...to govern the exploitation of natural resources on the Moon as such exploitation is about to become feasible." Will there be opportunities for private enterprise? Or will exploitation of the Moon's bedrock be restricted by Treaty?

If these problems can be surmounted, the future of astronautics as a fundamental necessity for mankind is assured. "What was once improbable is now inevitable," says President Bush. "We must commit ourselves anew to a sustained program of manned exploration of the Solar System and yes, the permanent settlement of space."

In an ideal world there would be an International Space Agency to plan and coordinate joint activity. These are matters which must be addressed at the highest international level.

Kenneth W. Gatland
Ewell, Epsom, Surrey, England, 1989

The Space Pioneers

In the town of Kaluga south west of Moscow stands a monument to a Russian schoolmaster—Konstantin Eduardovich Tsiolkovsky. Not far away is the brick and timber house in which he lived and which is now a national museum.

At the turn of the century Tsiolkovsky was considered an eccentric dreamer whose theories had little connection with reality. And yet if the Space Age was born anywhere, it was in the quiet rooms of this humble dwelling.

Though he never launched a rocket, Tsiolkovsky's contribution to the science of space travel was immense. He began in 1883 by explaining the principles by which rockets could fly in the vacuum of space. And in *Dream of the Earth and the Sky*, published in Moscow in 1895, he made the first mention of the possibilities of an artificial satellite:

"The fancied satellite of the Earth would be something like a moon, but arbitrarily closer to our planet—only far enough away to be outside its atmosphere, that is, at a distance of some 300 versts."*

---

*Verst: A Russian measure of distance, 3,500ft (1,067m).

> ## "The man with a new idea is a crank—until the idea succeeds."
>
> Mark Twain

Then, in 1903, he began to publish selected chapters of his book, *Exploration of the Universe Space by Reactive Apparatus*, which set out the theory of rocket flight and the prospects for space travel.

There had, of course, been people before who had dreamed of travelling in space but, on the whole, they lacked the depth of understanding that would point the way to practical engineering achievement. Tsiolkovsky's major contribution was to recommend the use of liquid propellants which not only offered greater performance than the solid variety but could be more readily controlled after their ignition.

His first sketch of a spaceship had the shape of a teardrop, with a passenger cabin in the nose and fuel tanks in the rear containing the high-energy propellants liquid oxygen and liquid hydrogen.[1] Within the tank section he drew a long cone-shaped nozzle in which the burning propellants were assumed to expand as a propulsive jet.

The same propellant combination eventually would be used by the United States in the big Saturn V rockets that sent men to the Moon, which illustrates the remarkable quality of Tsiolkovsky's ideas; but then his notebooks and published work were filled with novel concepts which, in one form or another, were to find their way into standard engineering practice.

He suggested controlling a rocket's flight outside the atmosphere by means of rudders impinging in the exhaust, or by tilting the exhaust nozzle. He proposed alternative fuels including gasoline, kerosene, alcohol and methane, worked out methods for controlling the flow of propellants to the combustion chamber by mixer valves, and advocated cooling the combustion chamber and nozzle by passing one of the liquids through a double-walled jacket.

Below: *The house in Kaluga where the great visionary of space travel, Konstantin E. Tsiolkovsky (1857-1935), lived and worked. The house is now a national museum dedicated to his memory.*

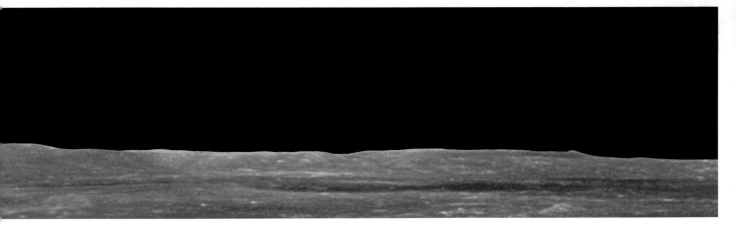

His early designs for a spaceship cabin included consideration of life-support systems which included provision for the absorption of carbon dioxide and odours; and he recognised the importance of having his crew members lie supine with their backs to the rocket engine during periods of acceleration. So seriously did he regard the acceleration problem of rocket flight that, at one stage, he advocated immersing his passengers in a liquid with a density equal to that of the human body!

He also recommended building spaceships of double-wall construction for protection against excessive heat or cold and to serve as a shield against penetration by meteoroids.

Tsiolkovsky also proposed supplying the pressure cabin with gaseous oxygen obtained from the rocket's liquid oxygen tank, and anticipated the use of an airlock to enable men, protected by spacesuits and chain-like tethers, to climb out of their ships into the vacuum of space. He made the mistake, however, of predicting that this would happen in the next century—in fact, 52 years *later* than the first man, Alexei Leonov, actually made a spacewalk.

The Russian pioneer also suggested that the gyroscopic effect of a rotating flywheel could be used to stabilise rockets in flight, and advocated multi-stage rockets—or "rocket trains"—which dropped off spent rockets as the flight progressed, as the only practical means of achieving the high velocities needed for space flight, calculating the optimum amount of propellant required for each stage.

By now he had become convinced of the ability to achieve orbital flight. He wrote:

"When the velocity reaches 8km/sec, the centrifugal force cancels gravity and after a flight which lasts as long as oxygen and food suffice, the rocket spirals back to Earth, braking itself against the air and gliding without explosions."

Tsiolkovsky even anticipated the development of space stations, describing how parts could be taken into space in a folded condition and then opened out and fitted together, and he forecast the time when spaceships and space stations would have closed-cycle life-support systems in which food and oxygen would be derived from vegetation growing within the station.

In his paper, *The Jet Plane* (1930) Tsiolkovsky analysed the merits and shortcomings of rocket planes compared to propeller-driven aircraft for high-speed flight in the upper atmosphere:

"The era of propeller-driven planes must be followed by that of jet aeroplanes or stratospheric aeroplanes."

Goddard's Experiments

In 1909 the American Dr Robert H. Goddard began to make his mark[2] by starting an extensive theoretical investigation of rocket dynamics. Three years later he fired and measured the thrust of a solid-fuel rocket which he had placed inside an evacuated glass tank, proving that a rocket could function in airless space. This finally disposed of the idea, then widely believed, that a rocket could only work in the atmosphere because its gases had to push against the air.

In fact, it responds to Newton's Third Law which states: For every action (e.g. the exhaust of a rocket), there is an equal and opposite reaction (the recoil or thrust). Goddard's experiment showed that the air actually had a "damping" effect, slowing the exhaust gases, and reducing the thrust.

Dr Goddard's further work dealt with the design of a practical sounding rocket capable of obtaining data on the upper atmosphere beyond the reach of aircraft and sounding balloons. And like Tsiolkovsky, he recognised the great potential of rockets propelled by liquid fuels.

His determination was to earn him a lasting place in history; on 16 March 1926 at Auburn, Massachusetts, he succeeded in launching the world's first liquid-propellant rocket. That tiny contraption—the unmanned "Kittyhawk" of Astronautics—made a brief flight of 184ft (56m) lasting just 2·5 seconds. Its average speed was 64mph (103km/h).

The next to succeed—but only just!—was the German Johannes Winkler who fired a rocket near Dessau on 21 February 1931 which burned liquid methane and liquid oxygen. Although on that occasion it succeeded in hopping just 10ft (3·05m), three weeks later, having been fitted with stabilising fins, it climbed to a height of about 295ft (90m).

It has been suggested that another European might have won the laurels had his liquid fuel research been directed towards the propulsion of a projectile instead of a car. The opportunity came about after Max Valier, a German inventor who had previously experimented with cars, ice sleds and railcars fitted with batteries of solid-fuel rockets, won the support of Dr Paul Heylandt who owned a factory that prepared industrial gases including liquid oxygen.

Although Valier did not receive a salary, he was allowed to spend up to 6,000 marks to build and test rockets on the premises though, for reasons of safety, static tests were carried out at night or during the weekends. Assisted by Walter Riedel, one of the engineers at the factory, and a mechanic, Valier built and tested a small steel-cased motor.

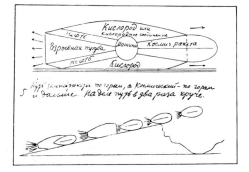

Above: *Sketches from a Tsiolkovsky manuscript depict a liquid propellant rocket and the launch of a two-stage vehicle up a "mountain ramp".*

Right: *Dr Robert H. Goddard (1882-1945) stands beside the liquid oxygen/gasoline rocket which made the world's first flight of a liquid-fuelled rocket on 16 March 1926.*

By 8 March 1930 this uncooled motor, fuelled by ethyl alcohol and liquid oxygen, was producing thrusts of some 17·6lb (0kg) and was installed in the chassis of the car Rak 6. (This was the car that Valier had previously driven around the Heylandt factory propelled by compressed CO_2.)

Another steel-cased rocket motor had by March 1930 been fitted to the car which was rechristened Rak 7. After being tested it was dismounted and modified so that it produced between 20 to 30kg of thrust and in this form it was demonstrated in the car on 19 April at Tempelhof Aerodrome, Berlin.

According to Willy Ley[5] the vehicle made a long lumbering run, its motor burning with a flame that was reddish and smoky, indicating poor combustion. It was shortly after this demonstration that Arthur Rudolph joined the Heylandt company and immediately asked to join the rocket work.

Curiously, Valier believed that the road to space travel lay in a step-by-step evolution from the rocket car to the rocket plane to the spaceship. This explains why Valier did not become the first European to launch a liquid fuel rocket in free flight. He was determined to test his rocket motors in vehicles that a man could operate.

Unhappily, the research had a terrible price. Working late one Saturday night in the empty Heylandt factory on 17 May 1930, Valier, Riedel and Rudolph were making bench tests of a new motor they planned to demonstrate in the car during the forthcoming "Aviation Week" in Berlin.

This time the fuel was a diesel/water mixture and two successful test runs had already been made using a nozzle with a throat diameter of 28mm (1·1in). Valier insisted on making one more run with a 40mm (1·57in) diameter nozzle and increasing the combustion chamber pressure to achieve 100kg of thrust.

As Arthur Rudolph explains:

"While Riedel operated the volumetric flow valves and I managed the feed/pressure valves, Valier himself walked around the engine at very close range (2-5 feet) watching for 'redhot spots', which were indicators of localized overheating and the danger of burnthrough of the combustion chamber wall. To prevent burnthrough, particularly when increasing the combustion chamber pressure, propellant volume and feed pressure had to be constantly balanced. Valier, therefore, by sign language (the engine roar prevented voice communication), gave instructions to Riedel and myself for necessary changes. Valier had signalled to me for higher feed pressure: the combustion chamber pressure reached 7 atmospheres; engine burning was extremely rough with sharp explosive jolts. Then there was a violent explosion and a jagged piece of steel severed Valier's aorta. Riedel grasped Valier to steady him, and then rushed to the guard house of the plant, telephoning the fire brigade, ambulance and doctors for help. When he returned, Valier had bled to death in my arms before anyone could save him."

Rudolph was later to redesign the motor paying particular attention to the fuel and

Above: *Max Valier, the German engineer who began by fitting solid-fuel rockets to racing cars and a sled, later turned to liquid propellants. He is seen here making a bench test at the Heylandt factory.*

oxidant injectors. The solution proved highly efficient and showed the way to a new generation of rocket engines.

In the Valier/Riedel design the fuel entered the thrust chamber through a stem-mounted injector with pin-hole orifices and liquid oxygen flowed down the inside wall. The Rudolph design had fuel and oxidant converging from ring slots. The fuel, being directed toward the combustion chamber wall, had not only a cooling effect on the wall, but protected it also from oxygen impingement (which was one of the causes of burnthrough in the Valier/Riedel design). Further protection of the combustion chamber wall was ensured by directing the liquid oxygen towards the centre of the chamber. The mushroom shape of the fuel injector contributed to an even mixture of the impinging propellants and, therefore, to very even and very smooth burning, "without the slightest danger of explosion".

After the death of Max Valier, the works manager at Heylandt, Alfons Pietsch, was determined to carry on the work that Valier had started. In the words of Arthur Rudolph,

"He held the small team together, protecting and encouraging it in its work. In early 1931 he urged Riedel to design another rocket car, using in its engine the now well-proven Rudolph injector

Above: *"Heylandt" rocket car during a test run at the company's works, Spring 1931. The motor embodied the improved Rudolph propellant injection system (see page 19). Alfons Pietsch is driving.*

design. The team had also made further engine improvements by adding a cooling jacket within which fuel flowed along the outside of the exhaust nozzle and combustion chamber, then entering the chamber as usual in the rear. In Spring 1931 the car was successfully demonstrated at the Tempelhof Aerodrome in Berlin. Pietsch was at the controls, I was standing by. Engine ignition was to be by sparkplug. The sparkplug failed. Recognizing the problem, I alerted Pietsch, then lit a cigarette and popped it into the engine, igniting the fuel. I called to Pietsch: 'Ignition! Full Throttle!' and off he went!"*

Pietsch, unfortunately, argued with Dr Heylandt and was dismissed. The depression of 1932 led to the closing of the plant.

In the Summer of 1932 Pietsch and Rudolph met again at the unemployment office. They agreed to build a rocket-assembly, which was not to fly, but was to have all the essential elements of a rocket for test demonstration on the ground. The main task of Pietsch was to "find a sponsor", that of Rudolph to "design the assembly". Within 8 weeks, Rudolph completed the design ready for manufacture, but no sponsor was forthcoming. Finally, Pietsch got a contract from the Ordnance Department.

Construction was started in small workshops. Unfortunately, Pietsch being unemployed and married had severe financial problems and therefore spent part of the money on his personal needs — and so the work came to a standstill. Rudolph, being himself unemployed, managed to borrow money from a friend, but it was not enough to complete the project.

Repeated requests by Rudolph that they should both go to the Ordnance Department to request more funds were refused by Pietsch and further progress seemed impossible. Finally, Rudolph lost track of his collaborator and went on his own to the Ordnance Department, obtained more money

and completed the project. He demonstrated the rocket-assembly successfully on 18 August 1934 at the Kummersdorf Proving Ground, and became an employee of the German Ordnance Department.

There is a postscript to these events. The Rudolph injection system was easily adaptable to another important rocket engine innovation. By varying the propellant inlet slots during engine burning, the thrust of the engine could be regulated at will. Such a variable thrust rocket engine was built and tested at Kummersdorf and subsequently mounted in a Heinkel He 112 aircraft and successfully flown in 1937 by test pilot Warsitz who changed engine thrust by varying the inlet slots by simple controls in the cockpit.

Hermann Oberth

Oberth, the inspirer of German work on rocketry, was a professor of physics and mathematics. He was born in 1894 in Transylvania, now part of Romania. In 1923 he published a slim volume entitled *Die Rakete zu den Planetraümen* ("The Rocket Into Interplanetary Space") in which he not only set down the fundamentals of a rocket operating in the vacuum of space but explained that, if sufficient thrust could be generated, rockets could be made to circle the Earth. Like Tsiolkovsky and Goddard, he investigated many propellant combinations.

But perhaps most significant of all he described in some detail the form of a rocket —the Modell B—which he believed could be used to explore the upper atmosphere.

Although it was never built, the Modell B was to fire the imagination of other talented people and in 1927 a group of enthusiasts founded the *Verein für Raumschiffahrt e.V.* or VfR—the Society for Space Travel.

That historic first meeting,[4] which took place in an ale-house in Breslau, was to lead to developments of earth-shaking dimensions —for the VfR became the spawning ground for men who were to make the breakthrough into space itself. Early members included Johannes Winkler, Max Valier, Willy Ley, Hermann Oberth, Rudolf Nebel, Walter Hohmann, Guido von Pirquet, Eugen Sänger, Franz von Hoefft, Kurt Hainisch, Klaus Riedel, Rolf Engel and Wernher von Braun (who joined as a youth of 18 in 1930).

In 1928 Oberth had accepted the position of scientific adviser on the UFA-Fritz Lang film, *Frau im Mond* ("Woman On the Moon"), and he was asked to produce a liquid fuelled rocket which could be launched as part of the publicity campaign. Although the rocket was never completed, it served to focus attention upon important technical problems.

Soon the members of the VfR were to begin constructing small liquid-propellant rockets of their own to establish basic principles.[5] The first example, based on a design by Oberth, was the *"Kegelduese"* or cone motor. Made of steel and heavily copper plated on the inside, the motor was uncooled and fuelled with gasoline and liquid oxygen.

Von Braun later explained the carefree fashion in which early tests were made.[3] The equipment was elementary. It consisted of a greengrocer's scale bearing a pail of water from which projected the tiny nozzle. A Dewar flask for oxygen, a bottle of nitrogen with pressure reducer, a petrol tank and copper piping to connect the tank and the Dewar flask to the motor completed the installation. Von Braun reported:

"It was Riedel who performed the somewhat perilous task of igniting the little Kegelduese in its water-filled pail. A dodger or shield had been placed at some distance from the thrust-balance and it was no small trick for Riedel to toss a burning petrol-soaked rag over the gas-spitting Kegelduese and take cover before the motor started with an ear-splitting roar. For a large man of more than 14 stone, his agility on these occasions was little short of miraculous!"

All the same, the *Kegelduese* was to prove an important landmark in German rocketry. To bolster faith in the new technology, Oberth, Rudolf Nebel and Klaus Riedel arranged for a bench test to be made under properly observed conditions at the *Chemisch-Technische Reichanstalt* (the equivalent of the U.S. Bureau of Standards). Wernher von Braun and Rolf Engel helped to set up the test installation and on 23 July 1930 Dr Franz Hermann Karl Ritter, the head of the institution, was able to certify that

"the Kegelduese had performed without mishap for 90 seconds, consuming 6kg of liquid oxygen and 1kg of gasoline, and delivering a constant thrust of 7kg."

Above: *Professor Hermann Oberth explains an aspect of planetary theory.*

Right: *This historic picture was taken on 5 August 1930 after Oberth's successful "Kegelduese" rocket motor test in the grounds of the Chemisch-Technische Reichanstalt. Left to right, Rudolf Nebel; Dr Franz Hermann Karl Ritter; Hans Bermüller; Kurt Heinisch; unknown; Oberth; unknown; Klaus Riedel, holding a model of Mirak I; Wernher von Braun holding the "Kegelduese", and a foreman of the Institute. The partly-finished Oberth/UFA rocket is in the centre.*

Above: *In a bid to obtain support for rocket experiments, members of the VfR approached the German Army. Here a soldier of the Reichswehr holds the group's One-Stick Repulsor at Kummersdorf, 1932.*

Left: *Klaus Riedel (1907-1944), a leading researcher of the VfR, inspects his Zweistab-Repulsor 2 (Two-Stick Repulsor 2) which made successful flights at the Raketenflugplatz in 1931.*

Above: *Johannes Winkler (1897-1947) gives scale to his pioneer HW-I rocket fuelled by liquid methane and liquid oxygen. It is believed it was the first liquid propellant rocket to fly in Europe.*

Nebel, who had worked with Oberth on the UFA rocket, next proposed that the VfR should build a rocket to be called *"Minimum-rakete"*, generally abbreviated to Mirak, to enable members to experiment with liquid fuels at least cost.[4,5]

The first Mirak was tested on a proving stand at Riedel's grandparent's farm near Bernstadt, Saxony. The body took the form of a cylinder of cast aluminium having a streamlined nose fitted with a pressure valve. This was the liquid oxygen tank. Inside at the base was a cone-shaped rocket motor and projecting backwards alongside the nozzle was a metal tube containing the fuel. At the end of the tube was a bulb of compressed carbon dioxide for the purpose of forcing the fuel into the combustion chamber. The liquid oxygen was fed by the pressure of its own expansion.

Nebel possessed boundless enthusiasm and was expert at getting local contractors to donate materials. He was the prime mover in getting the Society to take over as a rocket site a disused Army ammunition dump, which members called the *Raketenflugplatz* or "rocket flying field". At this site in Berlin-Reinickendorf (now Tegal) the group tested Mirak and a series of Repulsor rockets, some of which were fitted with parachutes to assist recovery of the launchers.

The Repulsors came about after repeated troubles with the Miraks. Heat created by the immersed rocket motor caused too rapid expansion of the liquid oxygen which, despite the relief valve, burst the tank. To make the first Repulsor, Riedel merely took two lengths of magnesium tubing, of the same section as the Mirak tail tubes, for liquid oxygen and fuel, and fitted a water-cooled rocket motor at the head. Despite its heavy construction, the rocket rose 60ft (18·3m) into the air and slowly descended, the only damage being a broken fuel line.

In May 1931 a reduced-weight Repulsor with four tail fins of sheet aluminium climbed 200ft (61m), ending its flight in a tree 2,000ft (610m) away.

The following August a new version—a One-Stick Repulsor—made its appearance, the propellant tanks being arranged in line instead of side by side. The motor, fixed in front, was enclosed in a streamlined water jacket and a parachute container was fitted between the tail fins. The first of these rockets reached an altitude of 3,300ft (1,006m) and later versions, although not fuelled to capacity, sometimes climbed over a mile.

Despite these successes, however, the end of the *Raketenflugplatz* was already in sight. Germany was in the grip of economic depression, membership of the VfR fell sharply and objections were raised to rockets being fired within the city limits.

It seemed that the only chance of gaining further support for rocketry was to approach the military authorities, and in 1932 it was arranged for a demonstration to be given before a group of Army officers at the Army Proving Ground at Kummersdorf. As it happened the launch was only partly successful. By the time the rocket had reached a height of 200ft (61m) it was travelling almost horizontally and crashed before the parachute could open.

Johannes Winkler

Before closing this important episode in rocket history, it is appropriate to recall something about the founder and first president of the VfR, Johannes Winkler, who had worked on the problem of rocket flight since 1925. Rolf Engel tells of his first meeting with Winkler in 1931.[10]

"I found myself in the presence of a man who approached his self-appointed task with the utmost modesty but deep sincerity."

He edited the Journal *Die Rakete* ("The Rocket") for the VfR and started his own experiments with powder rockets in 1928. At the Technical University of Breslau he studied problems of heat transfer with a combustion chamber in which he burned liquid oxygen and alcohol, injecting the propellants in the direction opposite to the flow of the exhaust gases.

Under a six-month contract with Junkers, he evaluated all available powder rockets, using special instrumentation to record their characteristics. He then started experiments.

He built a cylindrical combustion chamber with a long conical nozzle, made trials with steel and copper, and used a thin sheet of a refractory material (steatite magnesia) to protect the chamber walls. Oberth, too, had used this material during the UFA period.

Subsequently, under a renewed contract, Winkler made full-scale tests of a rocket-

Above: *The "high technology" HW-II rocket which Winkler built in 1932 in conjunction with Rolf Engel, Hans Bermüller and Heinz Springer. Through no fault of the design, the rocket exploded.*

assisted seaplane for the Junkers company. This contract ended in April 1931.

In the same year a young Austrian engineer Dr Eugen Sänger started a series of rocket experiments using facilities at the University of Vienna. His standard motors had a spherical combustion chamber of 2in (5cm) diameter and a 10in (25·4cm) long nozzle. Surrounding the chamber and part of the nozzle was a jacket into which a light fuel oil was introduced for cooling purposes before being injected into the chamber for combustion with either high pressure gaseous oxygen or liquid oxygen.

A Bosch fuel pump of the kind used in diesel engines forced the fuel through the jacket at high pressure so that the walls of the combustion chamber not only remained cool but could be of thinner construction than the outer casing which absorbed the main combustion pressure through the liquid.

This arrangement worked well. Not only were injection pressures high, raising the motor's efficiency, but long burning times were possible without fear that the thin-walled chamber would develop "hot spots" and burn through.

Fired in a test rig of tubular steel, in which the motor moved horizontally against a spring, Sänger is reported[5] to have achieved thrusts of some 55lb (25kg) and burning times exceeding 15 minutes—in one case half an hour! It was clear, however, from the appearance of the exhaust flame, that combustion was still not complete, which led him to give more attention to the internal geometry of rocket motors and the detailed study of gas dynamics.

Meanwhile encouraged by the results of the HW-I rocket, Winkler determined to build a larger liquid oxygen/methane rocket which he believed could reach an altitude of 16,405ft (5,000m). At the suggestion of his benefactor Hugo Hückel (who also supported some of Rudolf Nebel's rocket work), it was decided to transfer Winkler's laboratory from Dessau to the *Raketenflugplatz* so that the maximum use could be made of limited

resources at the one centre. A completely separate area was set aside as the "Winkler Research Institute for Jet Propulsion". On Hückel's suggestion, too, Rolf Engel joined Winkler to assist development of the HW-II and Engel, in his turn, brought in Hans Bermüller and Heinz Springer.

Together they produced the HW-II, which stood 6·2ft (1·9m) tall and, for its time, was a model of precision engineering. It even had propellant valves made of Elektron, a new aluminium-magnesium alloy.

Winkler had obtained permission to launch the HW-II from the Frische Nehrung on the coast of East Prussia, but when the team filled the rocket with propellants on the morning of 6 October 1932, they were dismayed to find that the liquid oxygen and liquid methane valves were leaking. No one, least of all the manufacturers, had realised that Elektron would corrode under the influence of sea water.

There was little that could be done. Engel reported:

> "Members of the Konigsberg government were on their way, and vessels of the German Navy had already cordoned off the sea area for the launch. We decided to take the risk and to blow the rocket body through with nitrogen under pressure immediately before the launch. This was done, but perhaps not thoroughly enough. When the ignition was switched on, there was still enough explosive gas between the outer skin, the tanks and the combustion chamber to rip our 'beautiful' HW-II to pieces."

The disappointment was tremendous. Winkler returned to Junkers while Engel tried to continue the work independently within the VDI's voluntary service. Had the HW-II succeeded, the course of German rocketry might have been different. As it was, the torch was carried by the other VfR team of Riedel, Nebel—and von Braun.

Despite the Army's obvious interest in this work, however, there was no clamour to take over the activities of the German rocket society. What the Army wanted were details of rocket performance obtained on properly instrumented test stands and, moreover, experiments carried out within the seclusion of a military establishment. Accordingly, von Braun was given an opportunity to work for his doctor's thesis at Kummersdorf.

In 1933 the Army Weapons Department set up a special section under the direction of Capt (later Major-General) Dornberger, a qualified engineer, and the young von Braun was put in charge of liquid-fuel rockets.

This move was eventually to lead to the really big advances from which space flight would blossom—but not before big liquid-fuel rockets had been developed and used in warfare.[6,8]

Russian Researches

The Russians, too, were becoming active.[7] On 17 August 1933, a Moscow group succeeded in launching the GIRD 09, which employed as propellants liquid oxygen and jellified gasoline and which reached an altitude of about 1,312ft (400m). Russia's first fully liquid propellant rocket, the GIRD X, attained almost 262ft (80m) on 25 November 1933.

Above: *GIRD X, the first Russian liquid-propellant rocket to fly on 25 November 1933. In the group (extreme left) is S.P. Korolev who later became Chief Designer of Soviet Spacecraft.*

Left: *Replica of GIRD 09 launched on 17 August 1933. It was designed by M.K. Tikhonravov (1900-1974) who worked on the first Sputniks and Vostoks.*

In the meantime, economic pressures were to deal the German VfR a knockout blow. Nebel and Riedel still believed that the path to astronautics could be pursued without military support but they faced enormous problems and *Raketenflugplatz* activities finally collapsed in 1934.

In the meantime, the young von Braun had become a civilian employee of the Army, charged with the development of liquid rockets. His laboratory was one half of a concrete pit with a sliding roof, the other half being devoted to solid rockets, and at first his staff consisted of a single mechanic to assist him.

His eager researches began in fine style in January 1933 when a water-cooled motor, tested on a stand, developed a thrust of 308lb (140kg) for a full minute.[3]

With the Army willing to pay for the assistance of valve manufacturers, instrument makers and welding experts, he found it was possible to make quite rapid progress. The first rocket intended to be launched, called the A-1, had a 661·5lb (300kg) thrust regeneratively-cooled rocket motor and burned liquid oxygen and alcohol. Frustrations were not long in coming, however. During a series of static tests the motor finally blew up because an explosive mixture had accumulated in the combustion chamber due to delayed ignition (a frequent cause of trouble in early liquid rockets).

Instead of continuing with the A-1, von Braun decided to take advantage of the delay to undertake a complete re-design. One of the changes he made involved

relocating a large flywheel from the nose of the rocket to a position near the centre of gravity between the tanks. The purpose of this flywheel was to stabilise the rocket by brute force; there was no attempt to have it operate rudders of any kind. Nevertheless, two of the improved A-2 rockets launched from the island of Borkum in the North Sea reached altitudes of some 1·5 miles (2·4km) in December 1934.

This led to the A-3, the first German rocket to have gyro-controlled exhaust and aerodynamic rudders, magnetic servo-valves and other refinements. This meant that rockets no longer had to be launched from ramps but could be stood vertically on their tail fins, on the theory that control at low speeds would be catered for by the action of the exhaust vanes.

When launched on test from Greifswalder Oie in the summer of 1937 these rockets were far from successful and the main fault was traced to the gyro control system.

Von Braun had by now expanded his team to include other specialists, including some of the people who had worked with Valier in the late 1920s.

After Valier's death, the group continued under Army auspices in strict secrecy at the *Aktiengesellschaft für Industriegasverwertung*, Britz, near Berlin, under Walter Riedel (who was not, incidentally, related to Klaus). Von Braun later remarked that the standard of work was much more systematic and scientific than anything at the *Raketenflugplatz* and it was a great satisfaction to him that the Army decided to merge this project

with his own at Kummersdorf.

"Thus, Riedel's skill and design experience became complementary to my own preference for formulating specific tasks and outlining problems."

The Army authorities were now pressing for rockets which could be put to practical use in the field and von Braun's group decided to produce another design—the A-5. The designation A-4 was omitted at this stage because of a much more ambitious project which the developers had in mind.

The results of these experiments will be found in the Diary Section of this book, but mention must be made of one other significant event in the story. Hitler, who had come to power in 1933, was beginning to show his influence, and more money became available to the armed services. Not only was the Luftwaffe keen to install rocket motors in aircraft but the Army was interested in ballistic rockets as a means of extending the range of conventional artillery. It was therefore decided to establish a major rocket research centre near the village of Peenemünde on the Baltic coast of Germany where rockets could be launched in safety over distances of more than 200 miles (322km). The huge centre,[3] which took two years to construct, contained elaborate laboratory and test facilities of a kind which only a comparatively short time before had been the stuff of dreams. The rocket team moved into Peenemünde in April 1937, and von Braun was able to recruit into his organisation some of the people who had helped to develop the Mirak and Repulsor rockets at the *Raketenflugplatz*: Klaus Riedel, Hans Huete, Kurt Hainisch and Helmuth Zoike.

It was at Peenemünde that the design of the A-5 rocket was finally settled and the first launchings, made without the guidance systems, took place from Greifswalder Oie in the summer of 1938. The first flight under full gyro-control had to wait until the autumn of 1939—just on the outbreak of the Second World War—and the rocket responded magnificently. In the words of von Braun:[3]

"After weeks of waiting for clear weather on the Greifswalder Oie it was decided to fire the first controlled A-5 despite a prevailing 3,000ft (914m) cloud ceiling. The slim missile rose steadily from its platform and, without the slightest oscillation, disappeared vertically into the cloud. The thunderous roar of its jet smote the ears of the listeners for upwards of a minute. Then all was silence. Some five minutes later the island resounded to cries of joy, as the missile reappeared suspended by its parachute and slowly sank into the Baltic a bare 600 feet (183m) offshore. It was quickly hauled aboard a salvage boat and could have been re-launched immediately, had it not been drenched with sea water."

Goddard's Progress

It must be said, of course, that Goddard—working with much smaller funds—had also achieved success with gyro-controlled rockets and it is of interest to compare progress during this exciting period.

The American engineer began in 1932[2] by fitting a 4in (10·2cm) gyro with its spin axis

Above: *Sergei P. Korolev (1906-1966). Under his direction was built the Soviet R.7 ICBM which launched Sputnik 1.*

Below: *One of Goddard's stabilised rockets built in 1934-35 showing the combustion chamber, nozzle and vane assembly for steering control. It is interesting to compare Goddard's progress with that of von Braun's group in Germany.*

Above: *German A-3 rocket being prepared for a static test at the Kummersdorf proving ground in 1937. A-3 rockets were then launched from the Baltic island of Greifswalder Oie but misbehaved badly.*

on the rocket's longitudinal axis. The spinning gyro maintained its vertical axis and when the rocket tilted 13 degrees from the vertical, electrical contacts were made to supply righting forces; one of the four aerodynamic vanes opened and, at the same time, one of four metal deflector vanes was inserted into the rocket exhaust.

Although the first launch on 19 April 1932 was marred by the rocket motor losing thrust, so that the rocket climbed only about 135ft (41m), it was sufficient to show the effect of the gyro-stabiliser. When the launch crew reached the spot where the rocket had come down, they found the exhaust deflectors warm to the touch, proving that they had operated.

In subsequent years, Goddard made further progress with automatic stabilisers. One of his rockets, launched on 8 March 1935, had a simple pendulum substituting for a gyro which gave corrective signals when the flight path deviated more than 10 degrees from the vertical. The rocket reached a speed of 700mph (1,126km/h) and came down 9,000ft (2,743m) from the launch tower.

Later the same month a 14·8ft (4·51m) rocket reached an altitude of 4,800ft (1,463m) and travelled 13,000ft (3,962m) at an average speed of 550mph (885km/h). It was controlled by a gyroscope working vanes in the exhaust.

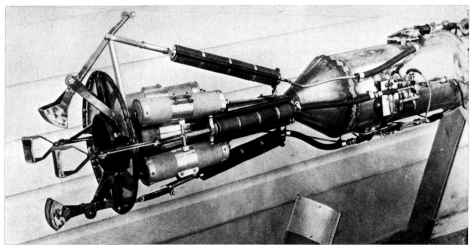

The American rocket pioneer went even further. In the summer of 1937 he succeeded in flying a rocket with gimballed steering to an altitude of 2,055ft (626m), although the flight was marred by the parachute opening prematurely. The 18·5ft (5·6m) long rocket had moveable tailpiece steering, wire-bound tanks, and carried a barograph.

In the meantime, the Russians—like the Germans—had taken liquid-propellant rocket engines to the stage where they were being considered for the propulsion of aircraft. In 1937-38 the ORM-65 nitric acid/kerosene rocket engine developed by V.P. Glushko completed 30 ground tests on the RP-318-1 glider designed by S.P. Korolev.[7]

In 1939 two flight trials were made of a small ramp-launched pilotless rocket air-

craft, the Type 212, powered by an ORM-65, and in 1940 the RP-318-1 glider flew with a modification of the same engine with a pilot at the controls.

More examples of American and Russian pioneer activities appear in the Diary Section. It was in Germany, however, that the really big engineering was to make its mark.

The A-4 Succeeds

The outstanding success of the A-5 opened the way to the large artillery rocket—the A-4—which had been demanded by the Army Ordnance Department. The original specification called for a rocket capable of travelling 171 miles (275km) carrying a warhead of one metric tonne. It had to be limited to a size which could be transported through

17

The big breakthrough in rocket technology was the use of liquid propellants which Konstantin E. Tsiolkovsky, the Father of Soviet Cosmonautics, advocated at the turn of the 19th Century. Broadly, such rockets can be divided into two main types: those which employ bi-propellants in which fuel and oxygen supplies (oxidant) are injected separately into the combustion chamber, and mono-propellants in which fuel and oxygen are combined in a single substance. All solid propellants belong to the latter class, but liquid mono-propellants also exist.

The liquids, stored in separate tanks, are fed into the combustion chamber either under the pressure of a stored gas or by means of pumps. Normally, liquids are more energetic than the solids. They also have the virtue that their thrust can be controlled simply by opening or closing valves. As the rocket pioneers quickly discovered, however, combustion chambers and nozzles can burn through if they are not properly designed. To meet this problem, some of the first motors were provided with water-cooling jackets. But very soon regenerative cooling was introduced in which part of the fuel, after circulating in the jacket, entered the chamber for combustion with the oxidant.

| ■ Oxidant | ■ Fuel | ■ Pressurant |
| ■ Combustion | ■ Water | ■ Framework |

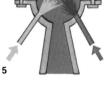
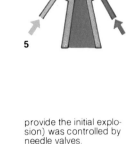

1 Tsiolkovsky's first spaceship design, 1903, envisaged the use of liquid hydrogen (LH_2) and liquid oxygen (LO_2). It incorporated a pressure cabin and exhaust vanes for thrust vector control (TVC).
2 Tsiolkovsky's design of 1914 was a development of the 1903 concept in which the passenger lay supine. It featured double-walled construction, including the pressure cabin, and TVC, and was remarkable in that combustion took place in an offset chamber which exhausted into a curved tube, which would have greatly impaired performance.
3 Tsiolkovsky's design of 1915—taken from the jacket of the book *Lunar*

Travel, On the Moon (Moscow, 1935). Internal detail now shows inlet valves for LO_2 and LH_2.
4 Goddard's design of 1926: the first liquid-propellant (LO_2/gasoline) rocket to fly. An alcohol burner was situated between the tanks to speed vaporising of LO_2. A starting hose (which had to be pulled free as the rocket began to rise) fed oxygen from a ground supply cylinder through the oxygen gas pressure line. Cork float valves prevented the liquid propellants from spilling into the pipes, while still allowing the gas to flow. The supply of fuel/oxidant to the igniter (which contained match heads and black gunpowder to

provide the initial explosion) was controlled by needle valves.
5 Oberth's "Kegelduese" (cone motor) of 1929-30 set the pattern for VfR's early rocket engine experiments. The LO_2/gasoline motor, in two halves secured by bolts, predated those of the Mirak series (see below).
6 Oberth's "Modell B"— a design for a two-stage sounding rocket which inspired early German rocket development. This predecessor of the modern multi-stage rocket incorporated stabilising fins. In the first stage, fuelled by alcohol/water and LO_2, the alcohol/water also functioned as a cooling agent around the thrust chamber and

10 Mirak I of 1930, first of a series of bi-propellant rockets developed by VfR (K. Riedel; R. Nebel). Cone-shaped rocket motor inspired by "Kegelduese". Gasoline/LO_2 propellants, with CO_2 as pressurant (no pressure relief valve above oxidant tank in first version).
11 Mirak III of 1931: improved VfR design with combustion chamber surrounded by water-filled jacket. Nitrogen pressurant for gasoline fuel; note pressure relief valve above oxidant (LO_2) tank.

12 Sänger test motor of 1931-32. This Austrian engine, static-tested, was significant in that fuel ("light fuel oil") was fed into 2in (5·08cm) diameter combustion chamber under high pressure, via cooling jacket, by a pump. Gaseous or liquid oxygen was the oxidant.
13 "Two-stick" Repulsor of 1931, flown by VfR, was nose-driven (like Miraks, from which it developed) by a water-cooled gasoline/LO_2 rocket motor using CO_2 as pressurant.
14 "One-stick" Repulsor

of 1931—Mirak development in which layout/aerodynamics improved by placing propellant (gasoline/LO_2) tanks in tandem. Again nose-driven by water-cooled motor; CO_2 pressurant. Recovery parachute in base container.
15 Repulsor rocket motors of VfR. (Top) Water-cooled gasoline/LO_2 motor of 1931. (Bottom) Fuel-cooled gasoline/LO_2 motor of 1932.
16 GIRD X, second Soviet rocket to fly, after GIRD 09, and first true liquid-

propellant (ethyl alcohol/LO_2) rocket to fly in USSR (design group included S.P. Korolev). Compressed air was pressurant; combustion chamber surrounded by LO_2 cooling jacket. Tsander OR-2 engine developed 154lb

(70kg) thrust.
Rocket length: 7·2ft (2·2m); launch weight: 65lb (29·5kg). Launched 25 November 1933, GIRD X reached nearly 262ft (80m) altitude before the motor burned through.
17 Glushko-designed Soviet rocket engines—advanced for period. (Top) ORM-52 of 1933, kerosene/nitric acid propellants, with regenerative cooling. Designed for experimental rockets and naval torpedoes. Thrust: 551-683lb (250-310kg):

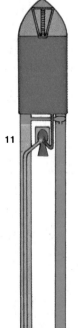
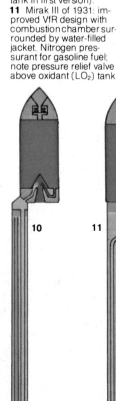
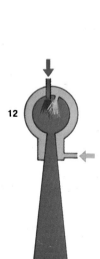
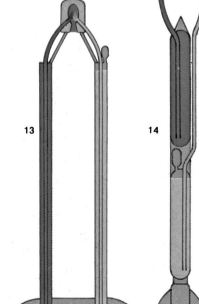
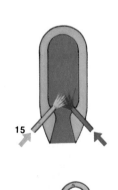
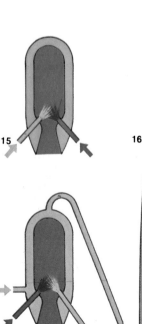
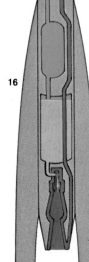

10   11   12   13   14   15   16

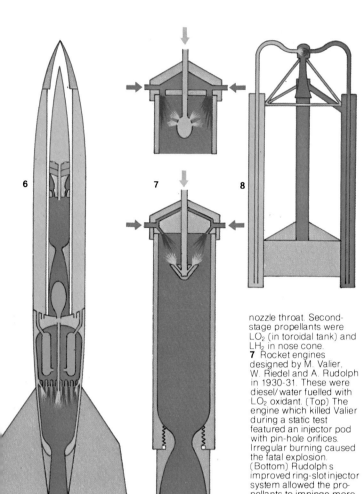

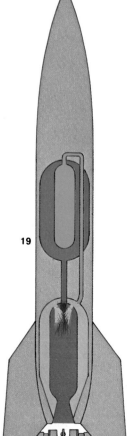

nozzle throat. Second-stage propellants were LO₂ (in toroidal tank) and LH₂ in nose cone.
7 Rocket engines designed by M. Valier, W. Riedel and A. Rudolph in 1930-31. These were diesel/water fuelled with LO₂ oxidant. (Top) The engine which killed Valier during a static test featured an injector pod with pin-hole orifices. Irregular burning caused the fatal explosion. (Bottom) Rudolph's improved ring-slot injector system allowed the propellants to impinge more evenly. Overall length of engine: 15·75in (40cm)
8 Hückel-Winkler (HW)-1 rocket achieved Europe's first flight with liquid propellants (LO₂/liquid methane) in February, 1931.
9 HW-2 "high technology" rocket of 1932, incorporated stabilisers. It featured spark plug ignition 0·5sec after the opening of the LO₂ and liquid methane valves. The rocket exploded on the launch stand because of valve erosion. Length: 6·2ft (1·9m). Diameter: 15·7in (40cm).

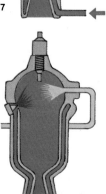

engine weight: 32lb (14·5kg); length: 17·7in (45cm). (Bottom) ORM-65 of 1936, kerosene/nitric acid propellants, featured spark-plug ignition. Designed for RP-318 rocket glider and KR-212 winged rocket. Thrust: 110-386lb (50-175kg); engine weight: 31·4lb (14·26kg); length: 18·1in (46·5cm).
18 A-3 (left) and A-5 (**19**) rockets, built at Kummersdorf and tested at Greifswalder Oie, 1936-39, represented breakthrough to large rocket engineering and were immediate fore-runners of A-4 (V-2). Fuelled by ethyl alcohol/LO₂; nitrogen pressurant. They featured steerable exhaust vanes — TVC.

German A-4 (V-2)

1 Nose fuse.
2 Fuse conduit.
3 Warhead, 2,150lb (975kg).
4 Main electric fuse.
5 Plywood compartment.
6 Nitrogen bottles.
7 Structural frames.
8 Ethyl alcohol/water tank, 9,201lb (4,173kg) max.
9 Servo-control alcohol valve.
10 LO₂ tank, 12,200lb (5,533kg) max.
11 Insulated ethyl alcohol feed pipe.
12 Thrust member.
13 Turbo-pumps.
14 Turbine exhaust.
15 Fuel pipe for regenerative cooling of thrust chamber.
16 Main fuel valve.
17 Combustion chamber, thrust 55,125lb (25,000kg) plus.
18 Main LO₂ valve.
19 Graphite exhaust vane (4).
20 Steerable aerodynamic rudder (4).
21 Antenna.
22 Steam unit to operate pumps.
23 Hydrogen peroxide tank, 379lb (172kg) max.
24 Glass wool insulation.
25 Guidance beam and radio control equipment (when fitted).
26 Guidance compartment: gyro-stabilisers, accelerometers, etc.

Technical Data
Length: 46ft (14m).
Maximum body diameter: 66in (168cm).
Fin span: 11·75ft (3·57m).
Launch weight: 28,373lb (12,870kg).
Cut-off velocity: about 5,200ft/sec (1,585m/sec).
Apogee: 60 miles (96km).
Range: 190-200 miles (306-320km).

Above: This A-4 (Test Vehicle 10), being fired from Proving Stand VII at Peenemünde in January 1943, exploded on the launch table within 2·5 seconds of ignition.

Below: German mobile launch control centre on a half-track tows a launch table for the V-2 (British Operation "Backfire", Cuxhaven, October 1945).

Above: First of three V-2 rockets launched in Operation "Backfire". The "target" was in the North Sea about 46 miles (74km) SW of Ringkoebing, Denmark. Present were Russian observers Gen Sokolov, Col Yuri A. Pobonostev and Col Valentin P. Glushko. An unofficial observer (who viewed the launch from "outside the wire") is said to have been Col S.P. Korolev disguised as a captain.

Right: A-4b winged rocket on the launch pad at Peenemünde, 1944.

railway tunnels in Europe and this was the main factor determining its performance.

It was not then envisaged as a weapon for attacking London; that came later on the whim of Hitler and the German High Command.

The engine had a thrust of 25 tonnes. It burned liquid oxygen and ethyl alcohol and had a turbopump driven by the exhaust products of hydrogen peroxide and potassium permanganate. Guidance and control were obtained by means of a three-axis gyro platform acting upon steering exhaust vanes and aerodynamic rudders.[3,6,8,9]

The first attempt to launch an A-4 in the Spring of 1942 was a big disappointment. The rocket toppled over and exploded. Rocket No 2 took off successfully, penetrated the so-called "sonic barrier", but after 45 seconds veered from course and broke up.

After necessary reinforcement had been made to the instrument compartment, the third A-4 made its ascent from Peenemünde. This time the rocket behaved perfectly, reaching a height of 53 miles (85km) and falling 118 miles (190km) downrange. The date was 3 October 1942.

Von Braun recalled the words spoken to him by Dornberger:

"Do you realise what we accomplished today? Today the spaceship was born!"[3]

Prominent among those who helped develop the A-4 was Dr Walter Thiel (who had taken over von Braun's Kummersdorf facilities in 1937 with the brief of studying and perfecting rocket engines). He was in charge of the A-4 powerplant and lost his life when the RAF raided Peenemünde on the night of 17 August 1943.

Others included Dr Rudol Hermann (supersonic wind tunnel); Dr Hermann Steuding (flight mechanics/computations), and Dr Ernst Steinhoff (guidance and control). Arthur

Rudolph, one of Valier's co-workers, had already joined the group in the Kummersdorf days. He was to manage the model shop at Peenemünde and plan quantity production of the A-4.

Walter Riedel, also from the Valier group, became chief designer at Peenemünde "with hundreds of designers and draughtsmen to do his bidding." And the man in charge of launching A-4s on test was Dr Kurt Debus.

General Dornberger guided the fortunes of the Peenemünde group both from the site and from his Berlin headquarters. In a tribute to his former chief, von Braun wrote:

"Advances in the art of rocket propulsion, present and to come, will owe much to Dornberger's vision, perseverance and sterling character."[3]

It was Dornberger who conceived and promoted the idea of operating A-4s from mobile batteries rather than concrete emplacements which would have been highly vulnerable to air attack. But he, too, was passionately interested in using rockets to explore outer space.

When the V-2 attacks on London began in September 1944, the Goebbels' propaganda machine announced to the world the existence of a second Weapon of Retaliation. (The first such weapon, the V-1, had been the Fieseler Fi 103 flying bomb.)

A winged V-2

Attempts worked out by von Braun and his associates at Peenemünde to extend the range of the A-4 had a double purpose. One was to appease the military; the other reflected the design team's enthusiasm for space flight.

The first move was to fit the basic A-4 airframe with swept wings and to provide enlarged aerodynamic rudders.[3,6,9] In theory this rocket could glide 370 miles (595km).

Two test flights of winged rockets, called A-4b, were made at Peenemünde in 1944 but success was limited. The first launch failed completely. The second rocket made a

successful climb only to have a wing break off when it returned to the atmosphere.

But this was far from being the entire story. When the war in Europe ended in 1945 Allied intelligence officers were astonished to find among Peenemünde documents plans for large two-stage rockets. One of the drawings showed a dart-winged A-4 installed in the nose of a booster intended to have a launch thrust exceeding 400,000lb (181,440kg).

This was the celebrated A-9/A-10 project, which the Peenemünde team had designed in 1941-42.

The A-9, after separating from its A-10 booster, was expected to fly some 3,107 miles (5,000km) by skip-gliding in the upper atmosphere. Suitably uprated, there was the possibility of attacking targets on the Atlantic coast of America from launch sites in Western France or Portugal.

Explaining the circumstances of this work after the War,[6] von Braun said the unbiased visitor to the Peenemünde planning group would have heard little, if anything, discussed which related to matters other than reaching out into space.

He remarked that the second A-4b was probably the first winged guided rocket to penetrate the "sound barrier". The control system had worked perfectly from take-off up to a speed of Mach 4.

For the war-conscious officials, the A-4b was explained as a bid to almost double the range of the A-4.[3] Calculations and wind-tunnel data indicated that this might be done by utilising the tremendous kinetic energy available after cut-off for an extended glide. The wingless A-4 utilised this energy for destruction on impact. In the case of the A-4b, extended range would be at the expense of velocity, which made it more vulnerable to countermeasures. In fact, it would have approached its target at subsonic speed. Von Braun explained[3]

"*Our project drawings for the A-4b showed a pressurized cockpit in place of the warhead—also a tricycle undercarriage. These drawings were always kept out of sight when we entertained visitors from Army Ordnance.*

We computed that the A-4b was capable of carrying a pilot a distance of 400 miles (644km) in 17 minutes. It

might have taken off vertically, like an A-4 and then landed like a glider on a medium-size airstrip!

We even designated it A-4b to give it the benefit of A-4's high priority.

If the A-9—the dart-winged variant—were to be mounted as second stage on a powerful booster rocket it would become a supersonic plane capable of crossing the Atlantic. The A-10 booster was actually a very early concept and with it in view, in 1936, Peenemünde's static test stands were designed to handle thrusts of up to 200 tonnes—some eight times that of the A-4 rocket.

Beyond the A-10, we had not dared to go except in imagination, although there was in our minds another still larger booster, possibly to be designated A-11.

Thus, with slightly improved mass-ratio and better propellants, we might easily have projected the pilot of the A-9 into a permanent satellite orbit around the Earth!"

REFERENCES

1 Michael Stoiko, *Soviet Rocketry: The First Decade of Achievement.* David and Charles, Newton Abbot, 1971.
2 Robert H. Goddard Collection, National Air and Space Museum, Smithsonian Institution, Washington DC.
3 K.W. Gatland (ed), *Project Satellite*, chapter by Wernher von Braun "From Small Beginnings...", Allan Wingate, London, 1958.
4 Frank H. Winter, "Birth of the VfR: The Start of Modern Astronautics", *Spaceflight*, July-August 1977.
5 Willy Ley, *Rockets—The Future of Travel Beyond the Stratosphere*, The Viking Press, New York, 1944.
6 Frederick I. Ordway, III, and Mitchell R. Sharpe, *The Rocket Team*, Thomas Y. Crowell, New York, 1979.
7 V.P. Glushko, *Development of Rocketry and Space Technology in the USSR*, Novosti Press, Moscow, 1973.
8 Walter Dornberger, *V-2*, Viking Press, New York, 1954.
9 Wernher von Braun and Frederick I. Ordway, III, *Rocketry and Space Travel*, Nelson, London, 1966.
10 Rolf Engel, "A Man of the First Hour—Johannes Winkler," paper presented at the IAF Congress, Dubrovnik, 1978.

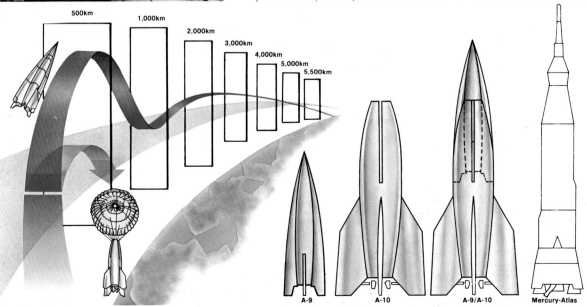

The A-9/A-10 Project
After the booster jettisoned at about 37 miles (60km) altitude, the dart-winged A-9 would reach a cut-off velocity of about 6,214mph (10,000km/h). After reaching the zenith of its trajectory and falling back into denser air, aerodynamic controls terminate the dive; the flight then proceeding in a series of skips. The intention of the skips was to shed frictional heat in space and extend the range to over 3,100 miles (5,000km) though, of course, at the expense of velocity on target. Winged V-2s—A-4bs—were actually flown at Peenemünde. They had swept-back wings and enlarged rudder/elevator surfaces supposedly extending their range by over 160 miles (257km). The A-9/A-10 is here compared in scale to a Mercury-Atlas.

A-9   A-10   A-9/A-10   Mercury-Atlas

Opening the Space Frontiers

It is almost impossible to state precisely where the frontier of space begins—it's really a matter of definition, and could be anywhere in a region between 621 miles (1,000km) and 1,988 miles (3,200km) above Earth. Within it, the random collision of atmospheric gas molecules is negligible, and the particulate density of matter varies greatly.* Also, within the region, the lighter gas molecules can escape the gravity of Earth. From a historical viewpoint, however, the frontier can be considered as being at a much lower altitude: some 99 miles (160km). There, the atmosphere becomes very tenuous and the laws of aerodynamics give way to those of astrodynamics.

It is this region that was first probed by rocket as man began his systematic exploration of space, a voyage that took him from Earth's upper atmosphere, then into cislunar space, to the Moon, and, finally, to the sister planets of the Solar System.

For many years, scientists were denied the *in situ* investigation of the upper reaches of the atmosphere except by observations from Earth and instruments lifted by aeroplane and sounding balloon. Earth observation had obvious limitations. Only a few "windows" were open in the atmosphere for the recording of data, generally those in the optical wavelengths. Additionally, with time, the atmosphere at lower levels above the regions accessible to such observations started to become opaque because of both man-made particulate pollution as well as light pollution from his expanding cities. By the end of World War 2, multi-engine aircraft had a ceiling of only 5 to 6·2 miles (8km to 10km) and the scientific sounding balloon could reach at best some 19·9 miles (32km). (In 1952, and later during the International Geophysical Year, instrumented sounding rockets were launched in the USA from an altitude of some 18·6 miles [30km] by utilising balloons to lift them to that altitude before launch. Such rockets, called "rockoons", carried payloads of 19·8lb [9kg] to altitudes of 62·1 miles [100km]).

With the end of the war, both the USA and USSR found themselves with the means of penetrating to the upper reaches of the atmosphere with sizeable scientific payloads. It was, of course, the A-4 (V-2) rocket.

Plans had been made in Germany during the last two years of World War 2 to utilise the A-4 for such purposes. Special measuring instruments had been developed and tested by the Research Institute for Stratospheric

"The year 1957 arrived ... prototypes of intercontinental ballistic missiles had been created, and there appeared the possibility of achieving orbital velocity."

Academician Anatoli Blagonravov
Vestnik Academii SSSR

Physics for recording the ultraviolet spectra of the Sun, atmospheric pressures and temperatures at various altitudes, cosmic and other radiation fluxes, as well as a device for collecting air samples. Two missiles were launched without instruments to verify flight characteristics for such missions. However, the demands of the war in its latter days brought about cancellations of such missions planned for the A-4.

With the end of the war, A-4 rockets and components fell booty to the USA, UK, France, and the USSR. The Americans and, to a lesser degree, Russians undertook elaborate programmes to utilise the captured weapons as the means of accomplishing what the Germans earlier intended: the scientific investigation of the upper atmosphere[1] by means of a high altitude rocket.

In the USSR for a few years after World War 2, A-4s, including missiles made both in Germany and the USSR, were modified to carry scientific instruments into the upper atmosphere. Several major modifications were made to the A-4 to increase its performance as a sounding rocket. The V-2A, the last of these, made its appearance in 1949. With a payload of 1,896lb (860kg) and a ceiling of 131·7 miles (212km), the rocket saw service well into the mid-1950s.

In the autumn of 1945, parts enough for 100 A-4s had been shipped from Germany to the USA for assembly and launch at the newly established White Sands Proving Ground (now White Sands Missile Range) in New Mexico.[1] The primary purpose of these missiles was to gather data on the physical and radiation environment of the upper atmosphere and to train Americans, both civil and military, in the assembly, checkout, and launch of large rockets.

The first of these A-4s to carry scientific instruments into the upper atmosphere was launched on 10 May 1946. It carried an instrument to record cosmic-ray flux, and reached an altitude of 69·6 miles (112km). It was followed by several more during the year, with failures occurring as often as successes. However, missile tracking, telemetry, and instrumentation, and para-

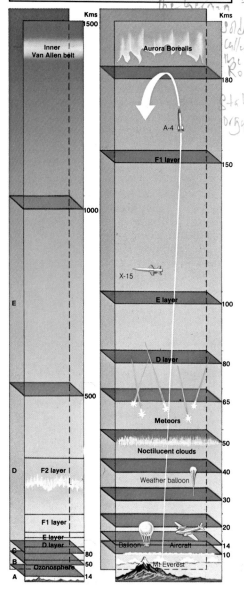

The Earth's Atmosphere
Our atmosphere is made up of several layers; the major divisions are: **A:** Troposphere; **B:** Stratosphere; **C:** Mesosphere; **D:** Thermosphere; **E:** Exosphere. The lower layers are shown enlarged (right) with the maximum altitudes of various research vehicles. The atmosphere both provides the gases which support life and shields us from potentially harmful radiation and particles emanating from space. The ionosphere, an electrically charged region, lies between **B** and **E**. It contains the reflective D, E, F1 and F2 layers created by the penetration of UV and X-radiation. Its structure changes according to temperature and day/night conditions. Satellites enabled Man first to explore these upper regions.

*Between $10^2/cm^3$ and $1/cm^3$ (at sea level, it is approximately $10^{18}/cm^3$).

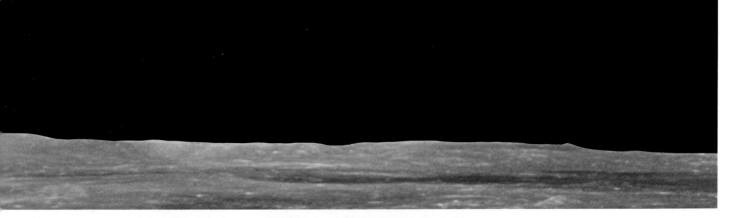

Above: *Captured German A-4 blasts off at White Sands, New Mexico, carrying research instruments into the upper atmosphere. The highest altitude attained by a US A-4 was 132 miles (212km).*

Above: *Soviet geophysical rockets on display in Moscow. In the foreground is the V-2A which carried dogs on sub-orbital flights; behind, the V-5V which ejected an instrument capsule at high altitude.*

chute recovery techniques soon matured to the point where much valuable scientific data from the upper atmosphere began to accrue. Indeed, demands for experimental space aboard the A-4s from government research agencies, armed forces, universities, and industry soon required the formulation of the A-4 Upper Atmosphere Research Panel on 16 January 1947, to arbitrate such requests and allocate priorities for flights.

Seven specially adapted A-4s also took part in Project Blossom, sponsored by the US Air Force Air Materiel Command and the Aero-Medical Laboratory. In these flights, the missile nosecone contained a canister to be returned to Earth by a ribbon-type parachute. The canisters contained a variety of insect and plant life to study the effects upon them of radiation at very high altitudes. Several rockets carried animals such as mice and monkeys; however, the recovery rate was poor because of continuing trouble with the ejection mechanism and parachute recovery system.

The A-4 also gave the United States its first experience with a large, two-stage rocket, a project suggested by Colonel (later Major-General) Holgar N. Toftoy.[1,2] The Bumper missile, of which eight were launched between 1947 and 1950, consisted of the A-4 as a first stage and the 661·5lb (300kg) WAC-Corporal sounding rocket as a second stage. Several of the second stages were instrumented to measure temperatures and cosmic radiation at altitudes denied to instruments of the A-4 alone. Bumper No 5, launched on 24 February 1949, reached an altitude of 244 miles (393km), a record for the time. The last two Bumpers were launched from the newly opened Long Range Proving Ground (now the US Air Force Eastern Test Range).

With the advent of the International Geophysical Year (the IGY, 1957-1958), the sounding rocket came into its own as a means of exploring the regions of space surrounding Earth.

Smaller, lighter, and more sophisticated scientific instruments meant that smaller and more economical sounding rockets could carry useful payloads to specifically desired altitudes. The technology of such rockets spread to nations other than the major or more affluent powers in anticipation of the IGY. As a result, during the period, countries

Left: *First launching from Cape Canaveral LC-3 featured the V-2/WAC-Corporal. There was no downrange tracking and no radio telemetry. The launch pad was a concrete slab, the service structure scaffolding.*

such as France, Japan, Canada, and Australia developed and instrumented sounding rockets for the international programme. Following its official termination, extended into 1959, the spirit of international co-operation in space research continued. The sounding rocket proved especially valuable in performing synoptic meteorological observations on a world-wide basis.

Today, there is a competitive and commercial market well supplied with a variety of sounding rockets that permits the customer to select the vehicle he needs to deliver his payload to its desired altitude.

Age of Satellites

Thus, the sounding rockets sired by the A-4 of World War 2 and the WAC-Corporal became the first in a series of much more powerful rockets that penetrated the frontier of space and sent robot explorers to study and photograph the surface of the Moon, Mars, and Venus as well as to circle the Sun and travel among the outer giants Jupiter, Saturn, and Neptune.

The IGY also introduced a means of studying space beyond the reach of sounding rockets and their payloads.

It was the scientific satellite that could orbit at altitudes where even random collisions with the rare air molecules would exert only a negligible drag upon them. Such scientific observatories could remain aloft for years, limited only by the operational life of their scientific instruments, telemetry systems, and electric power supply.

The concept for an artificial satellite had existed in the USA for several years.[3,4,5,6] As early as 1945, the US Navy's Bureau of Aeronautics undertook a study of such a satellite with the objective of building one to place scientific instruments into space. A year later, the US Army Air Force reviewed a similar study made by Project RAND (at the time a semi-autonomous organisation within the Douglas Aircraft Company). The report included a preliminary design for an "experimental world-circling spaceship".

Also in 1946, the US Navy's Bureau of Aeronautics together with North American

Above: *The Project Orbiter team at ONR on 17 March 1955. Standing (l to r): Lt-Cdr W.E. Dowdell (USN Observatory); A. Satin (ONR); Cdr R.C. Truax (USN); L. Tatum (IBM); A.W. Stanton (Varo Inc); F.L. Whipple (Harvard Observatory); G.W. Petri (IBM); L.O. Anderson (ONR); M.W. Rosen (NRL). Seated (l to r): Cdr G.W. Hoover (ONR); F.C. Durant III (A.D. Little); J.B. Kendrick (Aerophysics Development Corp); W.A. Giardini (Alabama Tool & Die); P.W. Newton (DoD); R.H. Schlidt (ABMA); G. Heller (ABMA); W. von Braun (ABMA). This was the first US space team; their work led to Explorer 1, America's first satellite, launched on the Juno I vehicle.*

Aviation, proposed a spacecraft called the High Altitude Test Vehicle. It was to be a satellite with an integral launching rocket using liquid hydrogen and liquid oxygen and having the capability of placing 992lb (450kg) into an orbit at 149 miles (240km).

Various other satellite proposals were studied in the late 1940s but none was seriously considered beyond that stage. The military services were sponsoring the work, though as yet they could not identify a military role for satellites. Serious consideration as to the utility of artificial satellites did not receive attention until a study

conference sponsored by Project RAND in 1949. The group made certain technical assumptions concerning such a spacecraft and then determined that it would have value as a spectacle, demonstration of US technological superiority, means of communication, means of Earth surveillance, and instrument of political strategy. So described, it is easy to see why funding for such a device was not immediately forthcoming, although the communications aspect had a potential for both civil and military application while the surveillance role had a definite military use.

Project Orbiter

On the eve of the 20th anniversary of the launching of America's first artificial satellite, Explorer 1, three British researchers were told that designs for multi-stage rockets they had produced 27 years before played a role in getting America started into space.

Two of them—Kenneth Gatland and Alan Dixon—at the time were junior members of the famous design team at Hawker Aircraft Limited, responsible, under the late Sir Sydney Camm, for the Hurricane intercepter of World War 2 fame. The third contributor, Anthony Kunesch, worked at Film Cooling Towers (1925) Limited.

Their technical conclusions on satellite launchers, prepared for the British Interplanetary Society, were presented in a paper, "Minimum Satellite Vehicles',[7] before an international gathering of scientists and engineers at the Second International Congress in London in 1951, six years before the first Sputnik.

A letter signed Alexander Satin and dated 23 November 1977 began: "Gentlemen: I have been planning for some time to write to you concerning your excellent paper, 'Minimum Satellite Vehicles', in the book, 'The Artificial Satellite', London, 1951—

Kenneth Gatland compares scale models of the final stage of the "Minimum Satellite Vehicle" with the "metallised" balloon that it was designed to carry. This proposal paved the way for the Explorer 1.

The MOUSE scientific payload subsequently designed in 1953 by Professor S.F. Singer, now on display in the National Air and Space Museum, Washington DC. Again the smallness of the payload is noteworthy.

Proceedings of the Second International Congress on Astronautics.

"May I inform you that this paper was used by me during 1952-54 to direct the first United States Space Project at the Office of Naval Research in Washington,

DC. where I was Chief Engineer of the Air Branch, to an immediate application with available hardware in the United States....

"When I analysed your data I immediately saw that we could make a three-stage rocket with a very small orbiting payload, using hardware available to us at the Office of Naval Research. This eventually became our ONR Project 'Orbiter' and was launched as 'Explorer 1' in January 1958...."[9]

The British theoretical work on minimum satellite launchers had the effect of transforming an otherwise costly and difficult technology into something which could be accomplished with moderate advances in the existing rocket propellants and engineering practice.

This led to the modest satellite payloads with which America opened the space frontier with small multi-stage rockets—Juno I and Vanguard. In Europe the same philosophy was developed in the shape of the French Diamant and British Black Arrow.

By focusing interest upon the smallest scientific satellites that could usefully be sent into orbit, the British forced attention upon the need for lightweight research instruments and radio equipment with all the revolutionary consequences in micro-electronics which were to follow.[12]

One early proposal for a satellite was a joint venture of the US Army and Navy with the co-operation and assistance of industry and university research. Project Orbiter[3] began with a meeting of representatives of the two services as well as participants from various industries, research organisations and universities in Washington on 25 June 1954. The meeting was sponsored by the Office of Naval Research. What came to be proposed was the launching of a small Earth satellite using Juno I, a modified Army Redstone ballistic missile with solid-propellant upper stages. At a later meeting of the group, Wernher von Braun, of the US Army Ballistic Missile Agency (ABMA), elaborated the proposal for modifying the Redstone missile and utilising other available components to construct a satellite-launching vehicle in the minimum time and at a relatively modest cost.

The satellite proposed for the project was to weigh between 4·96lb (2·25kg) and 14·9lb (6·75kg), depending upon the thrust of the rockets used in the launch vehicle's upper stages. While specific and technical details of the satellite were of necessity vague at the time, Alexander Satin, chief engineer of the Air Branch of the Office of Naval Research, and other members of the group were aware of the design for a "minimum" satellite launcher proposed by Kenneth W. Gatland, Alan E. Dixon, and Anthony M. Kunesch, of the British Interplanetary Society in 1951.[7] Thus, all concerned were convinced that such a project was scientifically and technologically feasible.

Despite the enthusiasm, preliminary planning, and some official encouragement at lower levels within the US Navy, Project Orbiter was doomed never to orbit because of a competitor within, of all places, the US Navy itself. The Naval Research Laboratory (a component of the Office of Naval Research) had independently come up with an Earth satellite programme of its own. It was Project Vanguard that was to cause the USA so much embarrassment in both the fields of science and public relations.

Vanguard was officially announced on 9 September 1955. It proposed a three-stage launching vehicle consisting of a modified Viking first stage, a modified Aerobee-Hi second stage, and a solid-propellant third stage to be developed from scratch. The rocket was designed to place a scientific satellite weighing 21·4lb (9·7kg) into an orbit with a perigee of 199 miles (320km). It would weigh 22,600lb (10,250kg) at launch and have a first stage thrust of 28,000lb (12,700kg). (An improved third stage permitted the satellite weight to be increased to 54·5lb [24·7kg] on the last flight.)

The Viking first stage was a sounding rocket developed by the Navy.[8] It had drawn heavily on the technology and experience that went into the A-4; however, it had several advanced features such as a pivotal mounting for the engine. It used liquid oxygen as an oxidiser and kerosene as a fuel. The modified Aerobee-Hi second stage employed nitric acid and unsymmetrical dimethylhydrazine. The third stage could be either of two solid propellant motors developed specially for the Vanguard.

The Vanguard satellites were gold-plated, magnesium-aluminium alloy spheres. They

Above: *Vanguard TV1 test vehicle being fuelled with liquid oxygen for a static test at Cape Canaveral on 15 April 1957. This was a test of the first stage only which was based on the technology evolved in the Viking sounding rocket programme by the Naval Research Laboratory, a part of the Office of Naval Research.*

varied in diameter and weight as well as scientific instrumentation. Vanguard 1 was a test article. It was only 6·4in (16·3cm) in diameter and weighed 3·25lb (1·47kg). It contained a tracking beacon and sensors to measure its internal and external temperatures. Vanguard 2 was 20in (50·8cm) in diameter and weighed 21·6lb (9·8kg). Its scientific instruments included sensors to measure solar X-rays, Earth's cloud cover, magnetic fields, and Earth-energy balances. Vanguard 3 was similar in size to Vanguard 2, but it weighed 99·2lb (45kg) (payload weight was 50·7lb/23kg).

Steps to Sputnik

As early as 4 October 1951, M. K. Tikhonravov, a leading Soviet rocket designer, stated that his nation's technology was on a par with that of the USA and that it could launch an artificial satellite of the Earth. At the World Peace Conference in Vienna, on 27 November 1953, Alexander N. Nesmeyanov, of the Academy of Sciences of the USSR, announced that ". . . the creation of an artificial satellite of Earth is a real 28

Below: *The Vanguard satellite SLV2 being checked out at Cape Canaveral. The solar X-ray satellite was launched on 26 June 1958 but the second stage of the launch vehicle cut off prematurely due to low chamber pressure and ended the mission. The launch was part of the US IGY programme under the direction of the ONR.*

Opening the Space Frontiers

World War II had seen incredible advances on many fronts of technology, not just rockets and guided missiles but a whole range of technical innovations which would greatly influence the future. The German A-4 had been the big advance in rocketry and Dr Wernher von Braun had predicted a coming era of orbital flight.

When the ex-Peenemünde group arrived in the United States, the idea of launching satellites was received with considerable scepticism. After all, the A-4 had a top speed of some 3,355mph (5,400km/h). To get an object into orbit close to the Earth a rocket would have to exceed 17,000mph (27,359km/h). How was this to be done?

First off the mark was the US Navy which produced (in the names of Cdr Harvey Hall and Lt Robert DeHavilland) a report entitled "Feasibility of Space Rocketry" for consideration by the Bureau of Aeronautics (BuAer). The report dated 6 November 1945 recommended setting up a group "for the purpose of constructing and launching an Earth satellite for scientific purposes".

The result was a US Navy/BuAer study for a single-stage, LO_2/LH_2 rocket capable of injecting itself into orbit. The estimated cost of the project (at 1946 prices) was $8,000,000 and, to ease its passage through official channels, the study was given the prosaic title "High Altitude Test Vehicle".

As this amount of money was too much for the Navy to find for such a research task, the Army Air Force (AAF) was invited to join the venture. The AAF, however, elected to have an independent study made and turned to the newly-formed RAND (Research ANd Development) group in California, which included Douglas Aircraft Company, North American Aviation and Northrop. On 12 May 1946, RAND produced the "Preliminary Design of an Experimental World-Circling Spaceship"—a multi-stage rocket to obtain information on "cosmic rays, gravitation, terrestrial magnetism, astronomy, meteorology, and properties of the upper atmosphere". The proposed rocket had four stages and a maximum payload of 500lb (226·8kg).

A second RAND study in late 1946 considered a three-stage LO_2/hydrazine rocket having a launch weight of some 81,570lb (37,000kg). It was to launch the payload into a circular orbit 350 miles (563km) above the Earth. For various reasons, including cost and the higher priority given to strategic bombers and missiles, these studies were abandoned.

It was left to a small study group of the British Interplanetary Society to make the breakthrough. This work carried out between 1948-51 in total ignorance of the RAND studies (which were secret at the time), showed the way to reducing the scale and cost of satellite launching. It was concluded that a properly designed three-stage rocket weighing less than 17 metric tons could orbit a cosmic ray instrument and a radio transmitter.[7] The results were to stimulate interest in "minimum" satellite launchers in the United States, first Project Orbiter, then Vanguard and Juno I.

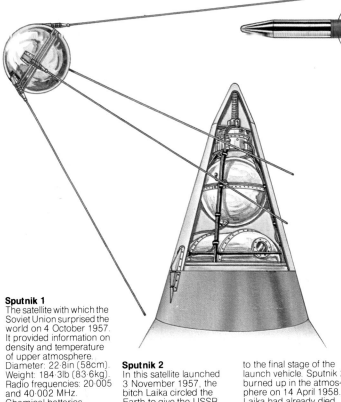

Sputnik 1
The satellite with which the Soviet Union surprised the world on 4 October 1957. It provided information on density and temperature of upper atmosphere. Diameter: 22·8in (58cm). Weight: 184·3lb (83·6kg). Radio frequencies: 20·005 and 40·002 MHz. Chemical batteries. Orbit: 141 x 585 miles (227 x 941km) x 65·1°. Launch vehicle: modified Soviet ICBM (NATO code name Sapwood). Western designation: A-1.

Sputnik 2
In this satellite launched 3 November 1957, the bitch Laika circled the Earth to give the USSR basic information on the biological effect of orbital flight; data were telemetered to Earth. The pressure cabin in which the animal travelled remained attached to the final stage of the launch vehicle. Sputnik 2 burned up in the atmosphere on 14 April 1958. Laika had already died when the air supply ran out. There was no provision for recovery. Payload: 1,120lb (508kg). Orbit: 132 x 1,031 miles (212 x 1,660km) x 65·33°

Explorer 1
First successful United States satellite launched by Juno I on 31 January 1958. Discovered that Earth is girdled by belt of radiation trapped by magnetic field. The project had its origin in Office of Naval Research (ONR). Orbiter developed in conjunction with Army Ballistic Missile Agency. Orbit: 224 x 1,575 miles (360 x 2,534km) x 33·24°. See also drawing, far right.

Vanguard 1
This miniature test-satellite was placed in orbit on 17 March 1958; it was the first to employ solar cells (which recharged mercury batteries). Allowed measurement of atmospheric density; geodetic studies. Revealed Earth to be pear-shaped. Diameter: 6·4in (16·3cm). Weight: 3·25lb (1·47kg). Frequencies: 108 MHz at 10 mW; 108·03 MHz at 5mW. Orbit: 404 x 2,465 miles (650 x 3,968km) x 34·25°

1 EWCS, 1946
A US Army Air Force proposal for "A preliminary design of an Experimental World-Circling Spaceship". Four-stages, launch weight 233,669lb (105,992kg). Propellants: LO_2/alcohol. Payload: 500lb (226·8kg) into 300 miles (480km) circular orbit. Estimated cost (1946 prices) $150 million. Contributors: Project RAND (Research ANd Development): Douglas Aircraft; North American Aviation; Northrop.

2 High Altitude Test Vehicle, 1946
US Navy/BuAer study: single-stage rocket. The HATV rocket design specified nine main rocket engines. Length: 86ft (26·2m). Diameter: 16ft (4·9m). Launch weight: 101,000lb (45,805kg). Launch thrust: 300,000lb (136,080kg). Propellants: LO_2/LH_2. Payload: 992lb (450kg). Contributors: North American Aviation; Glenn L. Martin; Aerojet-General.

3 BIS Study, 1948-51
British attempt to reduce scale, and cost, of launching small scientific satellites. Three stages plus expendable tanks, propellants LO_2/hydrazine. Three-axis gyro-platform plus steerable exhaust vanes, gimballed engine in second stage. Length: 45ft (13·7m). Diameter: 10·5ft (3·2m). Launch weight: 170,000lb (77,112kg). Launch thrust: 275,000lb (124,740kg). Payload: 350lb (159kg).

4 Minimum Satellite Vehicle, 1951
This BIS design study established final design criteria for close-orbit satellite launchers of minimum type. Three stage rocket, pressure stabilised tanks, propellants LO_2/hydrazine. Length: 51ft (15·6m). Maximum diameter: 6·2ft (1·9m). Launch weight: 37,044lb (16,800kg). Three-axis gyro platform plus gimballed engines. Payload: 0-10lb (0-4·5kg).

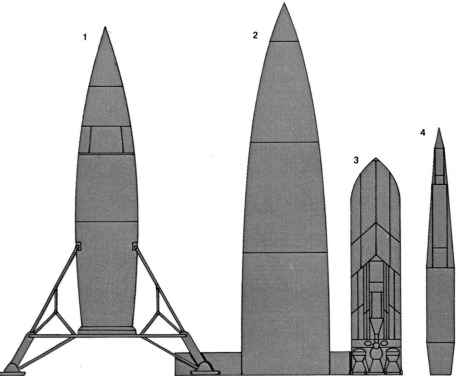

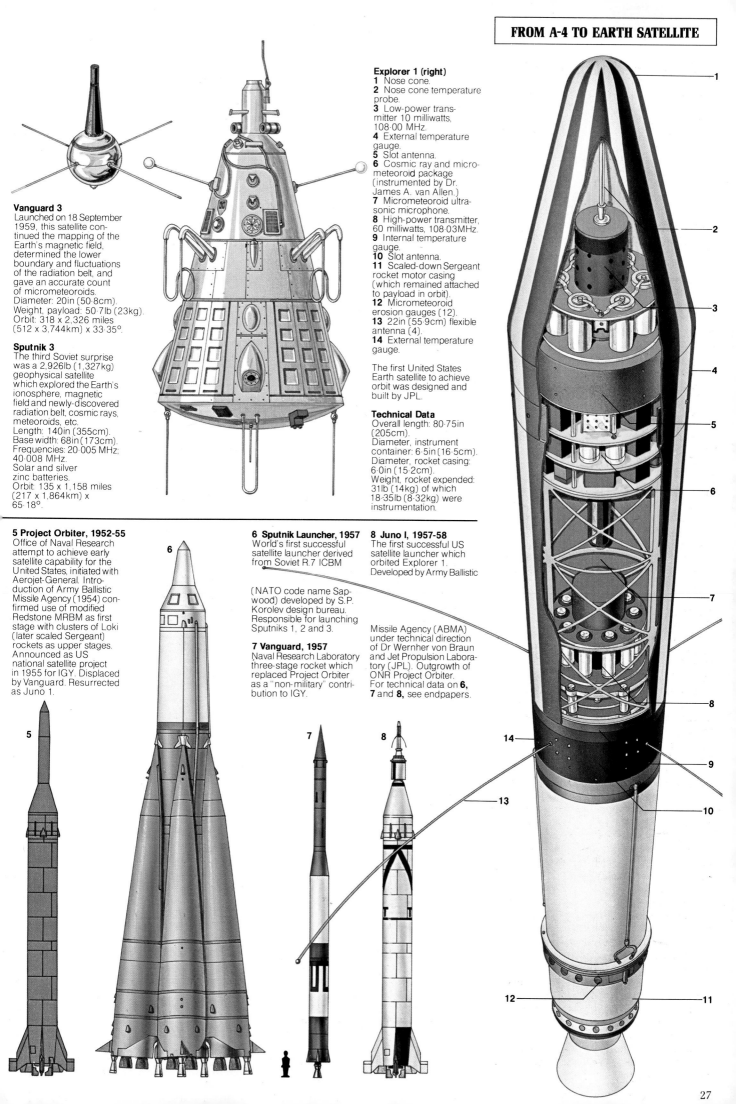

Explorer 1 (right)
1 Nose cone.
2 Nose cone temperature probe.
3 Low-power transmitter 10 milliwatts, 108·00 MHz.
4 External temperature gauge.
5 Slot antenna.
6 Cosmic ray and micrometeoroid package (instrumented by Dr. James A. van Allen.)
7 Micrometeoroid ultrasonic microphone.
8 High-power transmitter, 60 milliwatts, 108·03MHz.
9 Internal temperature gauge.
10 Slot antenna.
11 Scaled-down Sergeant rocket motor casing (which remained attached to payload in orbit).
12 Micrometeoroid erosion gauges (12).
13 22in (55·9cm) flexible antenna (4).
14 External temperature gauge.

The first United States Earth satellite to achieve orbit was designed and built by JPL.

Technical Data
Overall length: 80·75in (205cm).
Diameter, instrument container: 6·5in (16·5cm).
Diameter, rocket casing: 6·0in (15·2cm).
Weight, rocket expended: 31lb (14kg) of which 18·35lb (8·32kg) were instrumentation.

Vanguard 3
Launched on 18 September 1959, this satellite continued the mapping of the Earth's magnetic field, determined the lower boundary and fluctuations of the radiation belt, and gave an accurate count of micrometeoroids.
Diameter: 20in (50·8cm).
Weight, payload: 50·7lb (23kg).
Orbit: 318 x 2,326 miles (512 x 3,744km) x 33·35°.

Sputnik 3
The third Soviet surprise was a 2,926lb (1,327kg) geophysical satellite which explored the Earth's ionosphere, magnetic field and newly-discovered radiation belt, cosmic rays, meteoroids, etc.
Length: 140in (355cm).
Base width: 68in (173cm).
Frequencies: 20·005 MHz; 40·008 MHz.
Solar and silver zinc batteries.
Orbit: 135 x 1,158 miles (217 x 1,864km) x 65·18°.

5 Project Orbiter, 1952-55
Office of Naval Research attempt to achieve early satellite capability for the United States, initiated with Aerojet-General. Introduction of Army Ballistic Missile Agency (1954) confirmed use of modified Redstone MRBM as first stage with clusters of Loki (later scaled Sergeant) rockets as upper stages. Announced as US national satellite project in 1955 for IGY. Displaced by Vanguard. Resurrected as Juno 1.

6 Sputnik Launcher, 1957
World's first successful satellite launcher derived from Soviet R.7 ICBM.

(NATO code name Sapwood) developed by S.P. Korolev design bureau. Responsible for launching Sputniks 1, 2 and 3.

7 Vanguard, 1957
Naval Research Laboratory three-stage rocket which replaced Project Orbiter as a "non-military" contribution to IGY.

8 Juno I, 1957-58
The first successful US satellite launcher which orbited Explorer 1. Developed by Army Ballistic

Missile Agency (ABMA) under technical direction of Dr Wernher von Braun and Jet Propulsion Laboratory (JPL). Outgrowth of ONR Project Orbiter.
For technical data on **6**, **7** and **8**, see endpapers.

The First Sputnik

How the first Sputnik came about was explained in the Soviet publication "New Times" No 40/77 by V. Gubarev ("Pravda", 7 December 1977).

In 1955 the Presidium of the USSR Academy of Sciences mailed to some hundred scientists the following circular:

"Please comment on the use of artificial Earth satellites. What do you think could be conducted in space?"

The answers varied. Some made definite proposals, but others wrote: "Not interested in fantasy; I visualise a space shot only in the year 2000", or "I don't see of what practical use artificial satellites could be".

These remarks came from the pens of quite reputable scientists, and, let it be said, only two years before Sputnik went up. Their replies are quoted, not to reproach them, for many subsequently assiduously advocated space experimentation, but to show how far-sighted a genius was Sergei Korolev when in 1954 he argued that it was quite possible to send up an artificial Earth satellite soon. "In my view," he wrote, "it would be timely and advisable at this present moment to organise

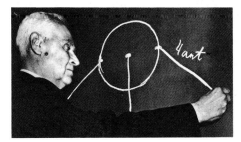

Professor A.A. Blagonravov gives first details of Sputnik 1 during an IGY conference in Washington DC on 5 October 1957, the day after its launch. The satellite, he said, was the simpler of two that the Soviet Union had got in readiness for the launch.

a research division to pioneer a satellite and more thoroughly analyse the range of related problems."

Sputnik was conceived when the man who came to be known as the Chief Designer wrote these lines. However, it took another three years of "crazily intensive effort", as one of Korolev's team put it, for "the Simplest" as its creators dubbed Sputnik, to go up.

On 30 August 1955 in the office of the Vice-President of the Academy of Sciences of the USSR, a "restricted" meeting was held. Taking part were S.P. Korolev, M.V. Keldysh, V.P. Glushko and M.A. Lavrentiev. The Central Committee of the Party put a specific task before the Academy of Sciences—to accelerate the work on an artificial satellite of Earth.

"In one or one and a half years we will have a carrier (launcher)", said Sergei Korolev. "We must not lose time, we must have a scientific programme, we must have institutions which could make instruments and apparatus for five to six satellites".

From the heights of today one might think there was nothing particular about Sputnik. Just a ball from which the antennas of a transmitter jutted out. It carried nothing of the scientific instruments, the sundry sensors, traps and other gadgets that extra-terrestrial laboratories carry into space nowadays. That was all to come—from the dog Laika, carried by the next Sputnik, and the study that was initiated of the Earth's ionosphere.

What Sputnik demonstrated was that Man, that science, now had fundamentally new opportunities to learn more about Nature and the Earth.

---

possibility." Then, on 11 September 1956, a conference of the Special Committee for the IGY, in Barcelona, heard a Soviet delegate say that his nation would orbit an artificial satellite during the forthcoming IGY.

Yet none of the voices appears to have been heard, or, at least, taken seriously in the USA.

On 4 October 1957 the USA and the world realised with shock that those were the voices of prophets rather than propagandists. The USSR orbited Sputnik 1, the first artificial satellite of Earth.[11]

The satellite was an aluminium sphere 22·8in (58cm) in diameter and weighed 184·3lb (83·6kg). It contained instrumentation to measure density and temperature throughout its orbit, which ranged between 141 miles (227km) and 585 miles (941km). It also collected data on the concentration of electrons in the ionosphere. The satellite was launched by a modified R.7 (SS-6 Sapwood), the first Soviet intercontinental ballistic missile.

On the day that Sputnik 1 was orbited, a group of high-ranking individuals from the US Department of Defense and the US Army were visiting the Army Ballistic Missile Agency, in Huntsville, Alabama. Among them were the newly appointed Secretary of Defense Neil McElroy and Secretary of the Army Wilbur Brucker. They were being entertained at a cocktail party when news of Sputnik 1 was announced. Immediately, von Braun and Brigadier General John B. Medaris, Commander of ABMA, resurrected Project Orbiter and approached McElroy for permission to launch America's first satellite. They promised it would be in orbit in 90 days. However, the new Secretary did not want to be hurried into such an important undertaking.

McElroy returned to Washington; and on 3 November the Soviets orbited Sputnik 2. The 1,120lb (508kg) payload contained the dog Laika and instrumentation to telemeter her condition in weightlessness. It also had sensors for measuring the radiation environment of space.

On 6 December an attempt was made to launch Vanguard 1. The rocket ignited and

Above: *Sputnik 2, which carried the dog Laika, was an early indication that the USSR was intent on manned space travel. Top: instruments for measuring short-wave solar radiation; middle: radio capsule.*

lifted off the pad. One second later it lost thrust and fell back on it, exploding upon impact. The satellite, thrown free, rolled across the ground with its beacon transmitter chirping away and clearly discernible by nearby antennas. Five days later, von Braun and his team in Huntsville received approval for launching America's first satellite.

Within 85 days, Explorer 1, America's answer to the Sputniks, was in orbit.[3] In size and weight it was no contender for records. Less than 40in (1m) long and only 6in (15·2cm) in diameter, it weighed only 10·5lb (4·8kg). However, the instrumented payload was attached to the fourth and final stage of the Juno I launch vehicle. Thus, the satellite in orbit was 80·75in (205cm) long and weighed 31lb (14kg).

Like the Sputniks, the satellite carried internal and external thermometers. Addi-

tionally, it had erosion gauges and an impact microphone for detecting the flux of micro-meteoroids, and a Geiger-Mueller counter for recording cosmic rays striking it. Data recorded by these instruments were stored in a miniature tape recorder and "dumped" on command as the satellite passed over tracking stations on Earth. The technological triumph of Explorer 1 lay in the miniaturisation of its instruments and telemetry system, which permitted very small, lightweight equipment to be packed into a low volume.

The scientific triumph of the satellite was its discovery of what later became known as the Van Allen radiation belts around Earth. The Geiger-Mueller counter aboard the spacecraft ceased counting as it passed through apogee at 1,575 miles (2,534km). (The perigee was 224 miles [360km]). Dr James van Allen, a physicist of the State University of Iowa, who had built the counter, theorised that it had been saturated by radiation circling the Earth at that altitude. His hypothesis was verified by subsequent satellites and space probes flown by the USA and USSR.

A second attempt was made to launch a Vanguard 1 on 5 February 1958. It too was a failure. However, on 17 March Vanguard 1 made it into orbit, much to the derision of the Soviets who belittled its small size by referring to it in their press as a grapefruit. Between December 1957 and 18 September 1959, 11 attempts were made to orbit Vanguards. There were only three successes.

Despite the spotty record, both the satellite and its launch vehicle contributed much to space science and aerospace technology. The satellites proved that solar cells could supply electric power for instrumentation, laid the foundation for meteorological satellites, gave geophysicists a truer picturer of the Earth's shape, permitted much more precise mapping of islands in the Pacific Ocean, and provided more accurate data on density changes in the upper atmosphere which influenced the path of satellites. The launch vehicle strengthened the technological base in design and engineering of large, multi-stage space rockets. It also provided the concept of a gimbal-mounted

Above: *A Juno II blasts off from Launch Complex-5 at Cape Canaveral. Rockets of this type launched Explorers 7, 8 and 11.*

Left: *America's first attempt to reach orbit fails disastrously on 6 December 1957 when Vanguard TV3 loses thrust within two seconds. It was left to von Braun and the US Army group at Huntsville, Alabama, to put America into orbit with the launch of Juno I on 31 January 1958.*

engine rather than jet vanes for trajectory control. And it provided experience and confidence in the use of solid-propellant motors as stages for such later space vehicles as the all solid-propellant Scout.

Five additional Explorer satellites were launched between 1958 and 1961 using the Juno I and Juno II launch vehicles. Juno II was a modification of the US Army's Jupiter intermediate-range ballistic missile, with clusters of small solid-propellant rockets for upper stages. However, this vehicle (like its predecessor Juno I) was a stop-gap measure at best. The concept of a cluster of small, spin-stabilised rockets was not precise enough for placing large Earth satellites into orbit.

More powerful launch vehicles were developed from the Atlas ICBM and the Thor IRBM. Utilising them, satellites weighing hundreds and even thousands of kilogrammes could be orbited. Also, with these more versatile launch vehicles, satellites other than those designed solely for scientific research could be realised. The Thor Delta, for example, on 10 July 1962, put into orbit the West's first commercial communications

satellite, Telstar 1. It was followed by the successful Syncom and early Intelsat series using the same type of launching rocket.

The Atlas-Agena vehicles proved especially reliable in orbiting large, complex astronomical and geophysical observatories between 1964 and 1972.

Similarly, in the USSR, successively heavier scientific satellites began appearing in orbit as the technology of launch rockets progressed. As in the USA, these rockets were modifications of early IRBMs and ICBMs. Since those weapons had greater thrusts than their American counterparts, they could orbit heavier payloads.

Typical Soviet missiles adapted for spaceflight missions are the SS-4 (Sandal), SS-5 (Skean), SS-6 (Sapwood) and SS-9 (Scarp). They launched such early scientific satellites as the Cosmos, Elektron, Polyot, and Prognoz as well as communications satellites such as

Right: *The Soviet Union investigated the Van Allen radiation belts with pairs of Elektron satellites put into different orbits by a single carrier rocket.*

Molniya. Highly reliable, most of these vehicles were still in use by the early 80s.

With a stable of such heavy-duty and dependable rockets, it is easy to see how the USSR also took an early lead in the third phase of man's penetration of the space frontier: the dispatch of automatic probes to examine interplanetary space.

On 17 August 1958, the first attempt to send a scientific probe (sometimes known as Pioneer 0) to the vicinity of the Moon was made from Cape Canaveral by the USA. It was a dismal failure.

A Thor-Able launch vehicle with the first American lunar probe for the IGY lifted off and made it only 1/27,400ths of the distance to the Moon, or 10 miles (16km). An explosion in the first stage of the vehicle only 77 seconds after launch put an end to the mission. On 11 October, another attempt (Pioneer 1) failed—and after reaching an altitude of 963 miles (1,550km) on 8 November, yet another Moon probe came to grief.

Pioneer 3, aboard a Juno II vehicle, was launched on 6 December 1958. An early shut-down of the first stage of the launch vehicle doomed the probe to failure, but it did reach a distance of 63,580 miles (102,300km) beyond Earth. It transmitted back valuable data as it passed through the Van Allen belts on its way out and again as it plunged back to Earth.

As with the Earth satellite, the honours for launching the first scientific probe of interplanetary space belong to the USSR. On 2 January 1959, that nation launched the first man-made object to escape the gravitational pull of Earth and take up a trajectory that would carry it relatively close to the Moon and on into orbit round the Sun.

Above: *How Luna 1 was carried in the final stage of the launch vehicle is shown in this full-size exhibition model. The probe missed the Moon by 3,700 miles (5,955km) in January 1959. Luna 2 impacted the Moon.*

Luna 1 or Mechta (Dream) was launched from the Baikonur space centre by a modification of the vehicle that had earlier orbited Sputnik 1. For the interplanetary mission, the SS-6 Sapwood ICBM was fitted out with an additional stage that would permit a payload weighing as much as 882lb (400kg) to escape Earth's gravity. Mechta weighed 797lb (361·5kg) and was probably meant to impact on the Moon. Failing to do so, Mechta passed within 3,700 miles (5,955km) of it on its way into solar orbit.

The probe was instrumented to measure solar and cosmic radiation, interplanetary magnetic fields, and micrometeoroid flux as well as to identify the gaseous composition of the region through which it travelled. Additionally, it carried an experiment to provide observers on Earth with a means of visually checking its trajectory and scientists a means of calculating the density of matter in interplanetary space. At a point 70,000 miles (112,630km) from Earth, a cloud of vaporised sodium was ejected from the rocket stage attached to the probe. Solar radiation caused the cloud to glow, and tracking cameras on Earth photographed it against the constellation Aquarius.

On 3 March 1959 the USA made its last attempt during the IGY to launch a Pioneer probe with a mission similar to that of Luna 1. It was, at best, only a partial success. The 13·2lb (6kg) Pioneer 4, launched by Juno II, was programmed to fly past the Moon at a distance of some 15,000 miles (24,135km). Unfortunately, the second stage solid-propellant rockets burned for a second longer than planned, with the result that it missed the Moon by 37,300 miles (60,016km) and continued on into a solar orbit. Earth

---

Balloon Tank Construction

When the British made their studies of "minimum" satellite launchers around 1950, they described a method of trimming deadweight from the rocket structure which, in conjunction with engine improvements, could significantly boost mission performance. They pointed out that a properly designed propellant tank, with thin walls and hemispherical ends, when pressurised could be made to act as an efficient load-carrying structure.

This made the rocket literally a flying tank with a propulsion unit, a marked improvement over the German A-4 rocket which had a heavy monocoque construction of external skin, frames and stringers with separate tanks for fuel and oxidant. In the new system use would be made of nitrogen gas pressure to serve as a means of stiffening the rocket's skin, similar to an inflated balloon, eliminating internal stiffeners and making the structure still lighter.

As it turned out, however, the idea had been anticipated. Working in secret the US Army Air Force had already contracted Consolidated Vultee Aircraft Company (Convair) to undertake Project MX-774 which sought improvements in rocket technique looking towards an intercontinental ballistic missile.

The pioneering group was headed by Karel J. Bossart, Convair-Astronautics technical director, who remembered the integral tanks which had been incorporated in flying boats.

MX-774 introduced several proven innovations which included:
1 Use of the missile's skin as the wall of the propellant tank.
2 Use of nitrogen gas pressure—required for propellant feed—to serve also as a means of stiffening the missile's skin.

The 60ft (18·3m) tank of an Atlas ICBM at Convair (Astronautics) Division of General Dynamics Corporation in San Diego. All inner support has been removed and the thin-skin "balloon-tank" has been pressurised to enable it to hold its shape while being moved.

3 Development of a separable nose cone, eliminating the need to build the entire missile to withstand the intense heat of re-entry into the Earth's atmosphere—and providing the bonus advantage of a smaller long-range missile.
4 Directional control of the missile by swivelling engines, in contrast to the V-2 method of inserting moveable vanes into the exhaust stream, which robbed the engines of 17 per cent of their thrust.

Despite these innovations, in July 1947 the contract was cancelled for lack of funds but Convair, using its own funds and what little was left over from the original contract, persevered and a year later launched the first of three test rockets.

With the outbreak of the Korean War in 1951, a new Air

Force contract—MX-1593, subsequently Project Atlas—began a study of the relative merits of ballistic and glide vehicles. In September 1951, Convair proposed a ballistic type missile to incorporate features validated by the MX-774.

The thermonuclear breakthrough in 1953 pointed the way to a smaller, lighter, and more powerful warhead, and led to a re-design which finally appeared in January 1955. The same year Convair began fabricating the first test missile.

The first Atlas flight was made in June 1957, and the missile attained operational capability in September 1959. Convair-Astronautics began studies of satellite capability of the Atlas in 1952, a year after the British launcher studies ended. One recommendation called for development of an upper stage rocket powered by liquid oxygen and liquid hydrogen. This was eventually to evolve into Project Centaur under the direction of Dr Krafft Ehricke, a former V-2 engineer who became one of America's chief exponents of space flight.

Atlas with its thin-skin "balloon-tank" construction began its space career when it boosted itself into orbit in Project Score in December 1958 (only the two boost engines being dropped) in a demonstration close to the earlier USAAF concept for a satellite launcher (see page 26).

Later, it became known that the German rocket collective in the USSR under Helmut Gröttrup had also recommended balloon tank construction. Such was the secrecy prevailing at the time that none knew of the others' results. In fact, Oberth himself had proposed balloon-like tanks in 1923 which no one seemed to have noticed, and Glenn L. Martin, North American Aviation and Aerojet-General had used the concept in early designs for satellite launchers. It was a classic case of re-inventing basic technology.

Above: *Pioneer 4 which passed into orbit round the Sun after flying within 37,300 miles (60,016km) of the Moon. The probe was launched by a Juno II rocket from Cape Canaveral on 3 March 1959.*

Above: *Luna 3 which scored another triumph for the Soviet Union by making the first reconnaissance of the Moon's far side in 1959. The trajectory it followed is shown* on the illuminated panel behind the exhibit. *Pictures taken on film, and developed automatically on board, were scanned by television and transmitted to Earth.*

tracking stations lost contact with it when the probe was some 407,000 miles (654,863km) away. As Pioneer 3 had done before, Pioneer 4 provided valuable data on the Van Allen radiation belts since it carried a Geiger-Mueller counter specially designed for the purpose.

Everything considered, the early laurels for the exploration of cislunar space and the Moon went to Luna 2 and Luna 3.

The former of these probes, also popularly known as *Raketa Dostigla Luni*, was launched on 12 September 1959 from Baikonur. The 860lb (390kg) sphere contained instruments to detect and measure magnetic fields and radiations from the Moon. Since it found neither, the probe was a scientific success. The final stage of the launch vehicle, which accompanied the probe to the Moon, also released a sodium cloud that was observed from Earth. The Soviets announced that their probe carried a small, commemorative sphere designed to withstand the impact on the Moon. It was covered with insignia of the USSR and the landing date. Luna 2 crashed into the Moon at a point east of the Mare Serenitatis.

Luna 3, also known in the press as *Automaticheskaya Mezplanetnaya Stantsiya*, was launched on 4 October 1959 from Baikonur, by the same type of vehicle that had launched the two previous Lunas.[11] This 614lb (278·5kg) probe was both an engineering and scientific success and clearly demonstrated that the Soviets were rapidly perfecting the technology for producing very complex inter-

planetary spacecraft. It was instrumented, like its two predecessors, to study the physical and radiation environment of cislunar space. However, it was also designed to do much more. For one thing, it was not destined to crash upon the Moon. Its ambitious mission was to circle behind the Moon and photograph that hemisphere always hidden from Earth. Having done so for a period of some 40 minutes from an altitude of 4,900 miles (7,884km) above the Moon, it swung back toward Earth to telemeter its pictures.

From a mosaic map pieced together by Soviet scientists, it was found that the rear side of the Moon differed greatly from the front side. There were fewer and smaller *maria* and fewer large craters though many more clusters of medium sized ones. Remarkably, some 70 per cent of the hidden half of the Moon was photographed by Luna 3.

With the landing of the first probes upon the Moon and the pictures returned by them of its long-hidden side, man had taken his first long stride in opening the space frontier. His initial implements of exploration were crude by comparison with later probes, but they vastly increased his knowledge of the composition of cislunar space and the nature of the Moon. It remained for the big space launchers to open the frontier to man.

REFERENCES

1 Frederick I. Ordway, III, and Mitchell R. Sharpe, *The Rocket Team*, Thomas Y. Crowell, New York, 1979.
2 Frank J. Malina, "Origins and First Decade of the Jet Propulsion Laboratory", in *History of Rocket Technology*, E.M. Emme (Ed), Wayne State University Press, Detroit, 1964. See also *Spaceflight*, Vol 6, pp. 160-165 and pp. 193-197, 1964; *Spaceflight*, Vol 15, pp. 442-456, 1973.
3 Wernher von Braun and Frederick I. Ordway, III, *Rocketry and Space Travel*, Nelson, London, 1966.
4 K.W. Gatland, *Development of the Guided Missile*, Iliffe & Sons, London, 1952.
5 Lee D. Saegesser, "US Satellite Proposals, 1945-49", *Spaceflight*, April 1977.
6 Rolf Engel, *Moskau Militariisiert den Weltraum*, Verlag Politisches Archiv GmbH, 1979.
7 K.W. Gatland, A.M. Kunesch and A.E. Dixon, "Minimum Satellite Vehicles", *JBIS*, November 1951.
8 Alexander Satin, letter to the BIS on the origin of ONR "Project Orbiter", *Spaceflight*, May 1979.
9 Milton W. Rosen, *The Viking Rocket Story*, Harper & Brothers, New York, 1955.
10 K.W. Gatland, "The Satellite Project", in *Project Satellite*, K.W. Gatland (Ed), Allan Wingate, London, 1958.
11 V.P. Glushko, *Development of Rocketry and Space Technology in the USSR*, Novosti Press, Moscow, 1973.
12 A.T. Lawton, *A Window in the Sky*, David & Charles, Newton Abbot, 1979.

The Space Centres

The premier launch centres for space vehicles in the United States and the Soviet Union have grown up around facilities established at the height of the "Cold War" for the testing and operation of long range missiles. Historically, they have been associated with classified research programmes and, especially in the Soviet Union, information is still heavily restricted.

Early US Missile Facilities

At the end of World War 2, the United States was operating five small missile proving grounds: the Allegheny Ballistics Laboratory (ABL) in Pinto, West Virginia;[1,2] the so-called Goldstone Range north of Barstow, California; the so-called Pendleton Range at Camp Pendleton, California; the Naval Ordnance Test Station (NOTS) at Inyokern, California;[2] and the Hueco Range at Fort Bliss, Texas.[3,4] The maximum range of the missiles being tested at these facilities was less than nine miles (15km).

Three missile facilities were created in the latter half of 1945 to support the greater range requirements of post-war missile activities. The first of these was the Wallops Flight Center* 50-mile (80km) range founded on 27 June at Wallops Island, Virginia by the National Advisory Committee on Aeronautics (NACA) to launch sounding rockets.[31] The second facility was the 100-mile (161km)

> ## "The white sound rising now to fury
> ## In efflux from the hot venturi
> ## As Earth's close down, gives us the endless sky."
> Robert Conquest
> *For the 1956 Opposition of Mars*

White Sands Missile Range† in New Mexico, founded on 9 July adjacent to the Hueco Range. This received the majority of the byproducts of Operation Paperclip: the A-4 (V-2) parts acquired from their Harz Mountain production plant in Germany and the von Braun group of approximately 100 rocket experts from the German Baltic missile range with launch facilities at Peenemünde.[1,32] The third facility was the Naval Air Facility** 60-mile (100km) range at Point Mugu, California, created in December to circumvent the distance limitations and relieve the launch load at NOTS.[5] Beginning in 1960, a 40-mile (64·5km) northern extension of the White Sands Missile Range was

introduced. Not owned by the Army, this extension has been used about 20 times each year, requiring the evacuation of approximately 90 ranch families totalling around 175 people, who are paid individually for both their time and the use of their land. The required absence time is guaranteed to be less than 12 hours during each extended usage of the range facilities.

The most important data retrieved during the flight of the average range-launched missile are acquired near the points of launch and impact: the two ends of the trajectory. Taking advantage of this fact, White Sands pioneered the use of off-range missile flights in 1956, when a Matador winged cruise missile flew from adjacent Holloman Air Force Base, New Mexico, to Wendover Air Force Base, Utah. This technique was employed again beginning in 1963 when Hound Dog air-to-surface missiles were air-launched near Del Rio, Texas, impacting at White Sands. The first ballistic missile off-range launchings also occurred in 1963, when Sergeant short range ballistic missiles were flown from the Hueco Range at Fort Bliss, Texas, and from Datil, Horse Springs, and Fort Wingate, New Mexico, impacting at White Sands. These were followed by launchings of the larger Pershing short-range ballistic missile from Hueco and Wingate as well as from Blanding, Green

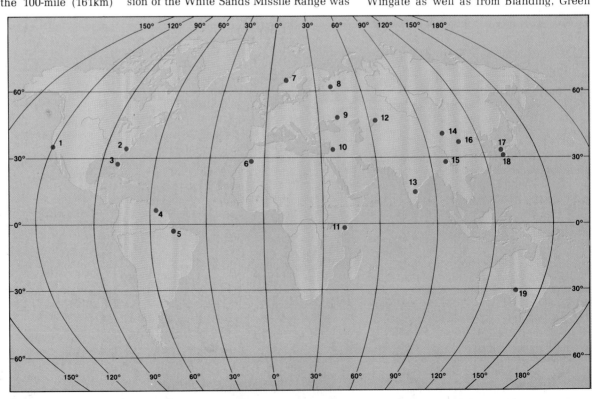

Space Launch Centres
1 Vandenberg AFB.
2 Wallops Island.
3 Cape Canaveral.
4 Guiana Space Centre.
5 Alcantara (under development).
6 Hammaguir (closed 1967).
7 Andoya (under development).
8 Plesetsk (Northern Cosmodrome).
9 Kapustin Yar (Volgograd Station).
10 Palmachim.
11 San Marco Platform.
12 Baikonur Cosmodrome.
13 Sriharikota (SHAR).
14 Jiuquan SLC.
15 Xi Chang SLC.
16 Taiyuan SLC.
17 Kagoshima Space Centre.
18 Tanegashima Space Centre.
19 Woomera (closed 1976).

Until recent years, the space centres of the USA and USSR dominated world space launchings. Now, however, Japan, China and ESA are making significant inroads into the launch market. On a smaller scale. other countries have also established indigenous launch sites.

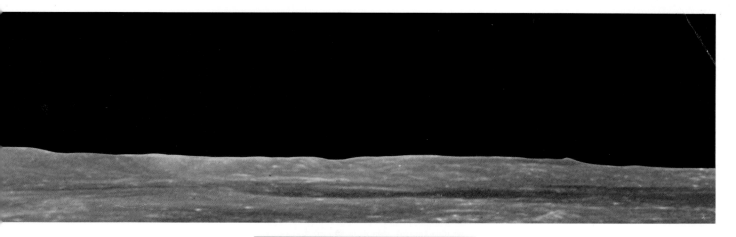

River, and Gilson Butte, Utah. In 1965 the Green River facility began launching Athena missiles to White Sands to simulate IRBMs and ICBMs as part of the Advanced Ballistic Re-Entry Systems (ABRES) tests. The Utah-to-White Sands flights expanded the White Sands range capability from 140 to about 400 miles (225km to about 650km).[32,33]

Even using this launch technique, White Sands, the largest of the American facilities, was still not big enough, and further expansion of any of these three ranges at this early stage in the history of range development was extremely difficult. Admittedly, conducting test flights over the ocean would have been one answer, but expansion of either of the sea ranges at Point Mugu or Wallops Island was hindered by the lack of nearby land masses for tracking sites. The idea of using ships instead of land stations was precluded by the then unsolved problems associated with accurately tracking missiles from the moving decks of ships. White Sands, on the other hand, was both landlocked and surrounded by either foreign-owned or populated areas. Thus it was that the A-4, having been developed in Germany to a range of about 200 miles (300km), was restricted to only half its capability at White Sands. The proposed ballistic missile descendants of the A-4, and winged cruise missile descendants of the V-1 were planned to have ranges of 5,000 to 7,000 miles (8,000 to 11,000km), 50 to 70 times the original length of the White Sands test range. Thus, the development of new, far larger missile ranges was imperative.

History of Cape Canaveral

In response to the missile range size problem, a subcommittee of the Guided Missile Committee of the Joint Chiefs of Staff officially recommended on 9 July 1946 that a location be sought for a long-range missile proving ground.[6] Highlighting the problem

---

* The facility at Wallops Island was known as Wallops Station from its founding on 27 June 1945 to 26 April 1974. On that date the name was changed to Wallops Flight Center, its present designation.[5,31]

+ The original name for the White Sands Missile Range, established on 9 July 1945, was the White Sands Proving Ground, the name it would hold throughout the 1950s.[5,32]

**The facility at Point Mugu was known as the Naval Air Facility, Point Mugu from its founding in December 1945 until 1 October 1946 when the name was changed to the Naval Air Missile Test Center (NAMTC). This name was used until 16 June 1958 when the Pacific Missile Range was activated. The facility name since that date has been the Naval Missile Center, Point Mugu.[5,29]

Above: *Preparing for the launch of Vanguard SLV-3 at Cape Canaveral, Florida. Although the rocket made a perfect take-off on 26 September 1958, the second stage failed to develop sufficient thrust.*

on 29 May 1947, an A-4 launched from White Sands went out of control, travelling 47 miles (76km) only, but landing near Ciudad Juarez, Mexico.[7] Within a month the Committee on Long Range Missile Proving Grounds of the Joint Research and Development Board of the War Department[8] gave its recommendations for the proposed location of the new facility.

To avoid impinging on populated areas, the committee used the Peenemünde approach—sea ranges. Because of the problems of mounting tracking equipment on moving vessels, the committee preferred chains of islands and other land masses at this early point in range history. Favourable weather also played a decisive role. The selection of a launch facility in Washington State with tracking facilities along the Aleutian chain was relegated to third choice because of its adverse climate.[9] This left the first choice: El Centro Naval Air Station in California with tracking facilities on either side of the flight path down the Gulf of California to the South Pacific; the second choice was Cape Canaveral, midway along the Atlantic coast of Florida and 18 miles (29km) north of the already existing Banana River Naval Air Station with initial tracking facilities on the British-owned Bahama Islands. The first choice was abandoned after negotiations with the President of

Below: *"ICBM Row", 1966. In the foreground are the two Atlas-Centaur pads of Launch Complex-36; in the background are the Vertical Integration Building (left) and Solid Motor Assembly Building.*

Mexico in December 1947 failed to secure sovereignty rights for tracking stations.[8] Great Britain was more co-operative, and the Florida choice eventually became the long-range proving ground. The range of the missiles being tested may have caused the selection of a sea range, but the need for tracking stations provided the key for its location. Fortuitously, the final site selected permitted Earth satellites, launched a decade later, partially to take advantage of the Earth's rotation to achieve orbit*; the selection of El Centro would have necessitated retrograde orbital launchings or the subsequent development of a separate space launch range.

The Banana River Naval Air Station, which had been in existence since 1 October 1940, became the Joint Long Range Proving Ground Base on 10 June 1949. The "Joint" refers to the joint development and operation of the new facility by the Army, the Navy, and the USAF. The facility became the sole responsibility of the USAF on 16 May 1950 and its name was changed to the Long Range Proving Ground Base. Finally, on 1 August 1950, the facility was renamed Patrick Air Force Base, the name it still retains. Patrick was the parent facility for the launch site at Cape Canaveral and each of the tracking stations of the new range.

Concurrently, the organisation which operated the launch and range facilities at Patrick was originally called the Joint Long Range Proving Ground (JLRPG) beginning on 1 October 1949. On 16 May 1950 the name changed to Long Range Proving Ground Division. On 30 June 1950, the name changed a second time to Air Force Missile Test Center (AFMTC) and on 15 May 1964 a third time, to Air Force Eastern Test Range (AFETR). On 1 February 1977 the name was officially shortened to Eastern Test Range (ETR),[6, 10] the facility coming under the jurisdiction of the Space and Missile Test Center (SAMTEC) headquartered at Vandenberg AFB in California. Finally, on 1 January 1982, the organization was renamed the Eastern Space and Missile Center (ESMC), and SAMTEC became the Space and Missile Test Organization (SAMTO).

The first launch from Cape Canaveral occurred on 24 July 1950, when an A-4/WAC-Corporal was launched as part of

Project Bumper. A second A-4/WAC-Corporal Bumper launch followed five days later. The pad used for these launchings was later designated Launch Complex-3 and is currently part of the facilities adjacent to the lighthouse.[10, 11] between Launch Complexes 36 and 31/32.

The initial development of the range facilities associated with Cape Canaveral, called the Eastern Test Range**, was accomplished with winged cruise missiles. The first use of Jupiter Inlet and Grand Bahama, which expanded the range to 200 miles (300km), was accomplished with the launch of the first Matador missile on 20 June 1951. Eleuthera Island, 300 miles (500km) distant, was soon added to the Matador testing programme. On 26 November 1955 a Snark became the first missile to use San Salvador, Mayaguana, and Grand Turk providing 700 miles (1,100km) of coverage. On 5 December 1956 Dominican Republic, Puerto Rico, and St. Lucia were added by another Snark flight stretching the range to 1,500 miles (2,500km), enough to handle Intermediate Range Ballistic Missiles (IRBMs). On 31 October 1957 yet another Snark made the flight to Ascension Island, opening the range to Intercontinental Ballistic Missiles (ICBMs) at 5,000-7,000 miles.[11]

Before the outer tracking stations were available Snark and Navaho missiles would occasionally fly the length of the available

range and return several times in a racetrack pattern, sometimes even attempting to land at the skid strip at Cape Canaveral. A Snark first tried this feat on 3 June 1954. The landing skids gave way on impact and the missile exploded. The first successful skid strip recovery occurred on 3 February 1956 with a Navaho X-10.[11] Skid strip recoveries of winged missiles preceded similar recoveries of the Space Shuttle Orbiter on nearby Merritt Island by about 25 years.

After the Redstone missile made its first flight from Cape Canaveral in 1953, the Office of Naval Research in Washington and Wernher von Braun proposed that an augmented version of the Redstone missile be used to place in orbit the first Earth satellite (Project Orbiter).[3] The upper stage additions necessary for an orbital launch became available in September 1956 when the first Jupiter-C was launched.[11] By that time, however, the sounding-rocket-derived Vanguard Programme was already approved as the primary United States contribution to the International Geophysical Year 1957-1958. The non-military nature of the new launch vehicle gave it absolute priority over the proposed modified Jupiter-C, called Juno I, despite the official intelligence reports claiming the existence of long-range ballistic missiles in the Soviet Union capable of orbiting Earth satellites.[3] Jupiter-C launchings were used for ablative warhead testing

---

* The 28·5 deg latitude of Cape Canaveral and the physics of orbiting bodies only permit insertions into orbits (without plane changes) with inclinations between 28·5 deg and 151·5 deg. Additional flight path restrictions make the available range of inclinations even smaller. Such orbits do not gain the full benefit of the Earth's spin, which only equatorial launch sites can utilise to the maximum. Note that a plane change called a "dogleg" is required to reach Clarke orbit from Cape Canaveral,and that plane changes are extremely costly in terms of launch vehicle performance.

**The Eastern Test Range was called the Long Range Proving Ground from its first launch on 24 July 1950 through to the end of 1951. The unofficial but effective title from 1952 until 30 April 1958 was the Florida Missile Test Range. When the Pacific Missile Range was formed on the west coast, the name Atlantic Missile Range was given to the east coast facility. On 15 May 1964 the name was changed to the Eastern Test Range, its present designation.[6, 10, 22]

Cape Canaveral

1 Launch Complex-39B (Apollo/Saturn V: Skylab/Saturn IB: ASTP: Space Shuttle).
2 LC-39A (Apollo/Saturn V: Skylab/Saturn V: Space Shuttle).
3 C-41 (Titan IIIE-Centaur).
4 C-40 (Titan IIIC).
5 C-37A and B (Apollo/Saturn IB). dismantled.
6 C-34 (Apollo/Saturn IB). dismantled.
7 C-20 (Titan). deactivated.
8 C-19 (Gemini-Titan II). deactivated.
9 C-16 (Titan I).
10 C-15 (Titan I) deactivated.
11 C-14 (Mercury-Atlas). dismantled.
12 C-13 (Atlas-Agena).
13 C-12 (Atlas-Agena). deactivated.
14 C-11 (Atlas). deactivated.
15 C-36 (Atlas-Centaur).
16 C-31 and -32 (Minuteman). deactivated.
17 C-18 (Blue Scout). deactivated.
18 C-17 (Delta).
19 USAF Space Museum (ex C-5, C-6 and C-26).
20 C-30. deactivated.
21 C-25 (Trident).
22 C-29. standby.
23 Missile assembly area.
24 Antenna field.
25 Missile propellants.
26 Command control building.
27 Spin test facility.
28 Liquid-fuel storage.
29 Control centre.
30 Propellant inspection area.
31 Solid-propellant storage.
32 Engine storage.
33 Spin test facility.
34 Solid motor assembly building.

Road
Railway
Base facility
Launch complex
Rivers and lakes

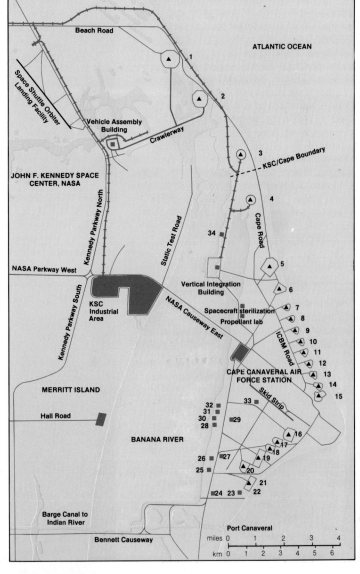

in support of the forthcoming IRBMs and ICBMs. The decision to promote Vanguard to the exclusion of all competitors resulted in the first Earth satellite being Russian.

On 4 October 1957 Sputnik 1 was orbited by the USSR. Before Vanguard made its first orbital attempt, a second Russian satellite was orbited.[12] On 6 December 1957 in front of a live television audience, the first Vanguard orbital attempt lifted-off from Launch Complex-18 Pad-A.[11] A second later the rocket lost thrust, fell back onto the pad, and exploded. The von Braun team was finally given the go-ahead and at 10:48:16 p.m. Eastern Standard Time on 31 January 1958[3] the first American satellite Explorer 1 was orbited by a Juno I from LC-26 Pad-A.[11]

The Russians had released the masses of their two Sputniks in 1957 as 184·3 and 1,120·8lb (83·6 and 508·3kg)* respectively. When compared to a 3·25lb (1·47kg) Vanguard satellite and 31lb (14kg) Explorer 1, it was quite evident that the Russians had developed large ballistic missiles.[12] This fact accelerated the IRBM and ICBM activities, which had been in slow motion behind the winged cruise-missile programmes of the 1950s. The slow development of IRBMs and ICBMs in the United States was the result of low military budgets resulting from a feeling of superiority that emerged after World War 2, when the United States alone had the atomic bomb (a feeling that disappeared in 1949 when the Soviet Union exploded its first nuclear weapon) and the larger number of technical problems, especially in the area of terminal guidance, that plagued ballistic missiles far more than winged missiles.[1] The first step was the cancellation of the Navaho Programme with the last Navaho X-10 flight on 26 January 1959.[11] The Navaho launch complexes numbered 9 and 10 were the only such sites in the history of Cape Canaveral to be completely replaced by new launch facilities on the old sites. The new launch complexes, numbered 31 and 32, were for the Minuteman ICBM.[9] Meanwhile, the first four Thor IRBM flights all occurring in 1957 from Launch Complex-17 had ended in explosions. The first successful Thor launch finally took place on 20 September from Launch Complex-17 Pad-B, just 14 days before Sputnik 1.[11]

*Less attached rocket stage.

Eleven days after the embarrassing Vanguard explosion, and after two explosions of its own earlier in the year, the first successful Atlas A flight occurred on 17 December 1957 from Launch Complex-14. Two and a half years later an operational version of the Atlas ICBM, known as the Atlas D opened the Eastern Test Range to extended ICBMs at 9,000-10,000 miles (14,000km-16,000km).[11]

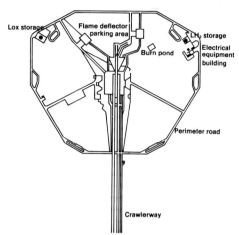

Launch Complex-39 Pad-A
LC-39A was the main launch pad for the Apollo Moon project. It was later modified for the launching of Skylab. At lift-off the flames from the five Saturn V F-1 engines were directed onto a flame deflector that diverted the blast length-ways into the flame trench. Both LC-39 Pads-A and -B have now been adapted for launching the Space Shuttle.

Above: A Saturn V engineering test vehicle designated Saturn 500F, moves towards LC-39A on the "giant crawler" during checkout procedures at KSC, 1966.

IRBMs and ICBMs have been used in 83·5% of all United States orbital launchings up to the end of 1988, either as the only stage or as the primary stage of the launch vehicle.[12, 13, 14]

Cape Canaveral has utilised a variety of launchers in its history. The Matador and Snark flights were launched from mobile ramp launchers like the operational V-1s in the field. The various ballistic missiles and launch vehicles were launched from permanent vertical pads, like the A-4s (V-2s) at Peenemünde. The vertical pad launchers at both Peenemünde and Cape Canaveral each had a moveable service structure, often called a gantry, which was rolled away from the missile prior to launch, and a concrete blockhouse from which the launch operation was controlled. The ramp launchers gave way to the so-called zero-length launchers at Launch Complexes-21 and -22, where the first Bull Goose missiles were launched in 1957.[10, 11] Effectively, a zero-length launcher is an above-ground silo for ramp launched missiles. After successful launchings of the Polaris missile from the ship simulator at Launch Complex-25, a Polaris A1P became the first missile to be launched from a submerged submarine when on 20 July 1960 the USS George Washington performed the launch while situated approximately 25 miles (40km) due east of the Cape at a depth of 91·5ft (27·9m). The first in-silo launch of a United States ICBM occurred on 30 August 1961 when a Minuteman I was launched from the silo at Launch Complex-32.[11]

The space launchings at Cape Canaveral include all United States Clarke orbit launchings which are dominated by communications satellites, but also include the post-1966 early-warning type reconnaissance satellites[15] used to detect IRBM/ICBM launchings, and recently National Oceanic and Atmospheric Administration (NOAA) meteorological satellites. Unmanned space launchings at Cape Canaveral also include all United States lunar and planetary spacecraft launchings, as well as assorted other scientific and applications satellites.

Cape Canaveral has also been the site of all United States manned space launchings. Launch Complex-5 was the site of the Mercury sub-orbital Redstone flights of Shepard and Grissom in 1961. Launch Complex-14 was the site of the four Mercury orbital Atlas D flights beginning with John

Below: The VAB of LC-39 with the Barge Turning Basin in the foreground. The Launch Control Center is the low building at the corner of the VAB.

Glenn on 20 February 1962. The third pad north of Launch Complex-14 along the eight-gantry array called "ICBM Row" located on the north shore of Cape Canaveral and beginning at Launch Complex-11, is Launch Complex-19 where all ten manned Gemini flights were launched in 1965 and 1966 using the Titan II ICBM as a launch vehicle.[16] The proposed X-20 Dynamic Soaring (Dyna-Soar) vehicle, a forerunner of the Space Shuttle, was also scheduled for launch in 1965 on a Titan IIIC[17] from either Launch Complex-40 or -41 before that programme was cancelled on 10 December 1963.[9] The "Apollo 1 Fire" occurred atop a Saturn IB at Launch Complex-34 on 27 January 1967. Twenty-one months later the first manned Apollo mission into Earth orbit took place from the same pad, also using a Saturn IB.

The Saturn Vs and Saturn IBs launched from Launch Complex-39 were assembled on mobile launchers in the Vehicle Assembly Building (VAB) and then hauled to either Pad-A or Pad-B on top of crawler transporters along a specially built crawlerway. A similar system is currently used for Space Shuttle missions. It permits a more efficient and flexible utilisation of the launch facilities. All Saturn V launches, except for Apollo 10, took place from Launch Complex-39 Pad-A.[18] The first 24 Space Shuttles were also launched form Pad-A. Apollo 10, the three manned Skylab Saturn IBs and the Saturn IB for the Apollo-Soyuz Test Project (ASTP) mission lifted off from Launch Complex-39 Pad-B.[19] The first launch of a Space Shuttle from Pad-B is an inauspicious memory: on 28 January 1986 *Challenger* and its 7-member crew were destroyed in a violent explosion, 73 seconds after liftoff. Now both Pad-A and Pad-B are used to launch Space Shuttle missions. It is planned to convert one Pad for the launching of automated heavy lift vehicles, the Shuttle-C transportation system, which should be operational in the mid-1990s.

Launch Complex-39 was patterned after its predecessor to the south, the Titan IIIC launch facility. The Titan IIIA central core of the Titan IIIC launch vehicle is erected on a mobile service structure inside the Vertical Integration Building (VIB) which is located on a man-made island in the middle of the Banana River. From there the mobile service structure is carried along a causeway to the Solid Motor Assembly Building (SMAB), where the two solid boosters are side-mounted and then the entire vehicle is hauled to either Launch Complex-40 or -41 by diesel locomotives simultaneously pulling the mobile service structure along two parallel sets of railroad tracks. Launch Complexes-40 and -41 were both used for the first time in 1965.

Launch Complex-41 is operated by the USAF to boost heavy military spacecraft utilising the Titan IV vehicle, which has about the same payload capability as the Space Shuttle. Using the General Dynamics Centaur G-Prime upper stage, Titan IV is capable of putting about 10,000lb (4·5t) into geosynchronous orbit. Commercial space transportation services, facing competition from Arianespace launch operations, are reviving some Eastern Test Range Launch Complexes: Delta II launch services of McDonnell Douglas Astronautics from LC-17, Atlas-Centaur operations of General Dynamics Space Systems Division from LC-36, and Titan III launches of Martin Marietta Commercial Titan, Inc., from LC-40 are proposed mainly to reach geosynchronous transfer orbits. During the 90s, new facilities will be required by the USAF to operate the powerful ALS (Advanced Launch System) which is planned to be partially reusable.

Vandenberg Air Force Base

An operational training facility under field conditions was needed to train crews to handle the Cape Canaveral developed IRBMs and ICBMs. The decision to create such a facility was made in January 1956. After canvassing more than 200 available tracts of government-owned land, the Department of Defense decided on the old Army facility called Camp Cooke[21] which occupied a strip of land approximately halfway along the Pacific coast of California from Los Angeles to San Francisco running from the hills of Point Arguello in the south across the Santa Ynez River, the Burton Mesa, and into the Casmalia Hills on the north. The area of Camp Cooke north of the Santa Ynez River became Cooke Air Force Base on 7 June 1957 and then on 4 October 1958 the name was changed to Vandenberg Air Force Base. The area of Camp Cooke south of the Santa Ynez River became the Naval Missile Facility, Point Arguello until the National Range Division was created in 1964, when the Point Arguello facility became part of Vandenberg.[21] The two portions of the base are now known as North Vandenberg Air Force Base and South Vandenberg Air Force Base. The range facility associated with the Vandenberg is called the Western Test Range. A corridor exists between North Vandenberg and South Vandenberg for civilian passage to and from the beach at Surf. Moving from facilities in North Vandenberg to facilities in South Vandenberg involves leaving and re-entering the base. Vandenberg activities are also known for the synchronisation of launch operations around the passage of Southern Pacific Railroad trains through the base.[21,24]

The first launch from the new facility occurred on 16 December 1958 when a Thor IRBM was launched from SLC-2E (then called 75-1-1). The first orbital launching, a Thor-Agena A from SLC-1W (then known as 75-3-4), occurred on 2 February 1959 and was only the second missile to be launched from Vandenberg.[25] The significance of this orbital launch was that the satellite Discoverer 1. an area survey reconnaissance satellite, was both the first man-made satellite to go into a polar orbit around the Earth and the first United States reconnaissance satellite. Vandenberg is ideally suited for polar orbit launchings as the nearest land mass when launching due south is Antarctica. In the thirty years since Discoverer 1, Vandenberg has launched all United States reconnaissance satellites except Clarke orbit early warning satellites. The number of such launchings totalled 308 by the end of 1988. This figure includes 147 area survey satellites, 106 close-look satellites, 20 so-called "Big Bird" and 9 KH-11 area-survey/ close-look satellites, 17 independently launched elint satellites, and 9 ocean surveillance satellites. Vandenberg also launched 11 polar-orbiting early-warning satellites, eight successfully, until mid-1966 when that activity was shifted to Clarke orbit.[14,15] When NOAA began launching Clarke orbit meteorological satellites from Cape Canaveral rather than the lower-altitude high-resolution polar-orbiting variety from Vandenberg, the USAF began launching its own low-altitude polar-orbiting meteorological satellites.[26] The Navy Navigation Satellites, formerly known as Transits, have all been launched from Vandenberg. In addition to the military launchings, NASA has launched a variety of satellites into polar orbits from Vandenberg including its own surveillance satellites, namely the Landsats and single Seasat,

The Pegasus Launcher

During autumn 1989, two American companies — Orbital Sciences Corporation (OSC) and Hercules Aerospace Company — plan jointly to inaugurate a new type of space transportation system: named Pegasus. It will be a 3-stage solid propellant vehicle which will be air-launched at an altitude of 39,370ft (12,000m) from the NASA B-52 which is based at the Dryden Flight Research Facility, Edwards AFB (California). Pegasus, the first stage of which is winged but not recoverable, will be able to place up to 606lb (275kg) into a polar orbit of some 310 miles (500km).

More important than the union of aeroplane and rocket is the symbiosis of techniques which have evolved since the 1950s. The idea of launching a satellite from an aircraft is not new. In 1957, the Americans tried in vain to launch a 4-stage rocket into space from a sounding balloon above Eniwetok Atoll; this was the Far Side Project carried out by Ford Aerospace for the USAF. The B-52 itself dates back to the 1950s and has launched some 450 winged craft — including the famous manned X-15 rocket plane. This time it will launch Pegasus carrying a payload 4ft (1·2m) in diameter and 6ft (1·8m) in length. Pegasus design was started in 1987 by OSC and Hercules; it uses an advanced propulsion system, composite materials technology, and computer-aided design techniques. Its delta wing is made of a graphite composite by Scaled Composites Inc., in Mojave

(California), whose chief executive is Bert Rutan, builder of the ultra-light Voyager aircraft which flew non-stop around the world.

Pegasus' advantages lie in its simple operation, its modest development cost of 45 million dollars, plus 10 million for a launch, and its great flexibility which suits it for a wide range of applications with light satellites. This air-launched space booster has already attracted the attention of the DARPA (Defense Advanced Research Projects Agency) which will be the first user of this original launch system. Pegasus' promoters propose to introduce another heavy civilian aircraft in late 1990 for high-altitude release of the booster, so that its performance can be upgraded.

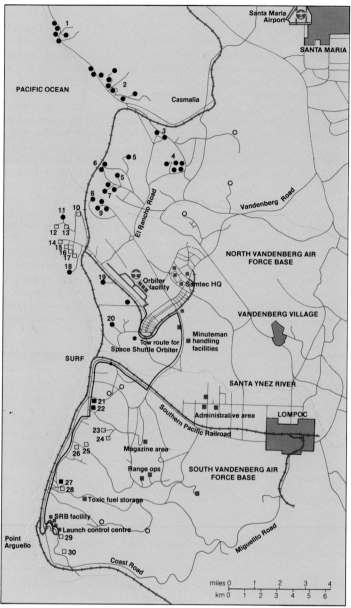

Vandenberg AFB

Vandenberg AFB
1 Minuteman III silos.
2 Minuteman III and Peacekeeper (MX) silos.
3 Atlas F decommissioned (decom.).
4 Titan I, decom.
5 Atlas E coffin-type launcher, decom.
6 Bomarc launchers.
7 Atlas D coffin-type launchers, decom.
8 Titan II, decom.
9 Atlas D and F, decom, and inactive.
10 4300-C pad (Scout Jr). decom.
11 Thor. decom.
12 SLC-10W (Thor/Burner) inactive.
13 SLC-10E (Thor) inactive.
14 SLC-1W (Thor/Agena) decom.
15 SLC-1E (Thor/Agena) decom.
16 SLC-SW (Thor-Delta).
17 SLC-2E (Thor-Delta), decom.
18 Atlas F, decom.
19 Titan II.
20 Titan II, decom.
21 Probe Launch Complex-A (sounding rockets), decom.
22 Point Arguello Launch Complex (PALC)-B (sounding rockets), decom
23 SLC-3W (Thor/Agena; Atlas/Agena).
24 SLC-3E (Atlas/Agena; Atlas).
25 SLC-4W (Atlas/Agena; Titan IIIB/Agena).
26 SLC-4E (Atlas/Agena; Titan IIID).
27 PLC-C (sounding rockets), inactive.
28 SLC-5 (Scout).
29 SLC-6 LE-1 (Space Shuttle: originally designed for Titan IIIM/MOL).
30 SLC-6 LE-2 (proposed second Titan IIIM/MOL pad) never constructed.

—— Road
+++ Railway
■ Base facility
▬ Town
✈ Airport
● Missile facility
■ Probe launch complex
□ Space launch complex
░ Tracking/communication
▒ Rivers and lakes

Below: *Shuttle launch support systems being evaluated at Vandenberg. To the left is the Shuttle Assembly Building, designed to protect the vehicle systems as they are mated at the launch mount, while to the right is the mobile service tower.*

which was lifted into orbit by an Atlas F booster on 26 June 1978.[12, 25]

The use of Vandenberg as a space-launch centre so rivalled its usage as a ballistic missile launch centre that for four years the facility averaged an equal number of both types of launchings. In fact, on 29 January 1962 when a Titan I was launched from the vertical lift silo at Launch Complex 395 A-1 becoming the 158th Vandenberg launch, it was also the 79th non-orbital launch, exactly 50 per cent. This was the sixteenth and last time that the number of orbital launchings matched the number of non-orbital launchings. From that date to the present the non-orbital launchings have dominated.[25] During ten of the last 16 years Cape Canaveral has witnessed more orbital launchings than Vandenberg which is significant because Vandenberg completely dominated the United States orbital launchings during the period from 1961 to 1972 and still maintained a 533 to 432 overall dominance at the end of 1988.[12, 13, 14] Vandenberg provided ICBMs for Nike Zeus and the subsequent Spartan and Sprint Anti-Ballistic Missiles (ABMs) being tested at the Kwajalein Missile Range* in the late 1960s and early 1970s. The 12 Minuteman silos in the Casmalia Hills[27] are part of the 1,000-Minuteman nuclear deterrent force distributed throughout the United States.

The variety of launch facilities at Vandenberg has been almost as diverse as at Cape Canaveral. The launch facilities are divided into five major types: 18 vertical-silo launchers for the Minuteman and Titan II ICBMs, seven vertical-lift silos for the old Titan I and Atlas F ICBMs, five coffin-type emplacements for the old Atlas E ICBMs, the two ramp launchers for the Bomarcs which are currently used as target drones, a mobile ramp launcher for the GLCM, and the 20 assorted vertical launch pads which have been used at one time or another.[27] In addition to the 53 pads and silos just mentioned, the southernmost launch facility at Vandenberg is SLC-6, which was intended to have two pads for the launching of the Titan IIIM/ Manned Orbiting Laboratory (MOL). Construction work on SLC-6 was halted when MOL was cancelled in 1969.[27, 28] On the basis that up to 100 million dollars could be saved by reusing the existing facilities, it was decided in 1975 to make it the West Coast Shuttle launch site, for polar mission launches. Since 1979, some 3 billion dollars have been spent on extending the runway to 2·8 miles (4·5km), on building the Orbiter maintenance and checkout facility, on modifying SLC-6 or "Slick Six" to include a Launch Control Center, a Shuttle Assembly Building (SAB), access tower, launch mount, mobile service tower and three exhaust ducts. Space Shuttle preparation procedure will be different from Kennedy Space Center operations at Launch Complex-39: the various Shuttle components are to be erected one by one on the launch pad in the same way as all

---

* The Kwajalein Missile Range was originally part of the Pacific Missile Range, founded on 16 June 1958. On 15 May 1964 the Kwajalein portion of the Pacific Missile Range became the Kwajalein Test Site operated by the Army as an independent range. On 15 April 1968 it became Kwajalein Missile Range; today it is known as the US Army Kwajalein Atoll (USAKA).[30]

non-mobile launcher pads are operated. At the end of 1986, the Shuttle Launch Complex at Vandenberg AFB was completed but then mothballed. According to USAF, it is to be "maintained in an operational caretaker state until 1992".

After the *Challenger* accident, it appeared that SLC-6 would face serious competition from SLC-4 where the powerful Titan IV was due to be launched at the rate of two per year. However on 18 April 1986, the two

Titan pads of Space Launch Complex-4 suffered 60 million dollars' worth of damage when a Titan 34D exploded 16 sec after liftoff, damaging ground support equipment. Atlas and Titan II launch vehicles are still regularly used to place spacecraft in Sun-synchronous orbit, while the USAF is planning to build a Titan IV launch facility called SLC-7 adjacent to the dormant SLC-6. The USAF views Titan IV as the heavy cargo carrying replacement for the Shuttle.

Wallops Island

The use of Wallops Island for sounding rockets has continued since 1945. By the end of 1988, over 13,000 sounding rockets had been launched from the facility. The first of the rare orbital launchings at Wallops Island took place on 4 December 1960 using a Scout launch vehicle.[12] The Scout is a sounding-rocket derivative, like its predecessor Vanguard. Until now, only 4-stage Scout vehicles have been used to launch small spacecraft from NASA Wallops Station.[23] DARPA (Defense Advanced Research Projects Agency) is considering this site to put into

LEO light satellites for military communications. The private company Space Services Inc. of America, managed by astronaut Deke Slayton, signed an agreement with NASA in September 1986 to launch commercial Conestoga vehicles from Wallops.

The Future

A new generation of heavy launchers with reusable elements, such as the ALS (Advanced Launch System) or the Shuttle-C, will certainly require impressive new launch complexes. Medium-class expendable vehicles with upgraded capabilities will continue to coexist alongside the fleet of manned Space Shuttles for the launching of commercial spacecraft operated by the private sector. But the great hope for the future is a revolutionary, fully reusable, one-stage-to-orbit spaceplane which could convert the present launch centres into real spaceports which might handle passengers and cargo like conventional airports. Operational SSTO (Single-Stage-To-Orbit) carriers are hoping to start spaceflights around 2010.

Above: *An aerial view of Wallops Island Main Base looking towards the north-east. Wallops Station occupies three separate areas of Virginia: the Main Base, the Wallops Island Launch Site and the Wallops Marshland Site. The Italian crews for the San Marco platform trained here.*

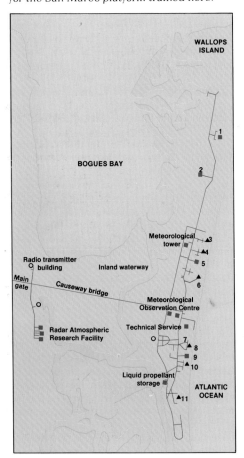

Wallops Island
1 Dynamic balance facility.
2 Payload checkout and assembly area.
3 Launch area No. 5.
4 Launch area No. 4.
5 Blockhouse No. 3.
6 Launch area No. 3.
7 250ft (76.2m) meteorological tower.
8 Launch area No. 2 and blockhouse No. 2.
9 Assembly shop No. 1.
10 Launch area No. 1.
11 Launch area No. 0.

- — Road
- ■ Base facility
- ▲ Launch area
- ○ Tracking/communications
- ▨ Rivers and lakes

REFERENCES

1 von Braun, Wernher, and Ordway, Frederick I., III, *History of Rocketry and Space Travel*, New York, Thomas Y. Crowell Company, 1969.
2 Buchard, John E., editor, *Rockets, Guns, and Targets*, Boston, Little, Brown, and Company, 1948.
3 Ley, Willy, *Rockets, Missiles, and Men in Space*, New York, The Viking Press, 1968.
4 Emme, Eugene M., editor, *The History of Rocket Technology*, Detroit, Wayne State University Press, 1964.
5 Emme, Eugene M., *Aeronautics and Astronautics 1915-1960*, Washington, DC, Government Printing Office, 1961.
6 Patrick Air Force Base Historical Staff, *Chronology of the Joint Long Range Proving Ground, Florida Missile Test Range, and Atlantic Missile Range 1938-1959*, History Office, 6550th Air Base Group, Air Force Eastern Test Range, Florida, 1960.
7 Jarrett, Francis E. Jr. and Lindemann, Robert A., *Historical Origins of NASA's Launch Operation Center 1 July 1962*, KSC Historical Monograph No 1, Florida, National Aeronautics and Space Administration, 1964.
8 Kennedy Space Center Historical Staff, *Utilization of Cape Kennedy Launch Complexes*, Florida, National Aeronautics and Space Administration, 1972 (unpublished).
9 US Congress, House of Representatives, Committee on Science and Astronautics, Subcommittee on Manned Space Flight, *1963 NASA Authorization, Part 2, Appendices 8, 9 and 10 ("The AFMTC Story")*, Washington, Government Printing office, 1963.
10 Patrick Air Force Base Office of Information, *Facts Book of the 6550 Air Base Wing and Eastern Test Range*, Florida, 1979.
11 Whipple, Marvin R., *Index of Missile Launchings by Missile Program July 1950-June 1960*, Patrick Air Force Base, Florida, Office of Information Historical Branch, 1961.
12 Thompson, Tina, editor, *TRW Space Log*, Volume 23, Redondo Beach, California, 1988.
13 Thompson, Tina, editor, *TRW Space Log*, Volume 24, Redondo Beach, California, 1989.
14 Cartwright, Edie Scott, editor, *TRW Space Log*, Volume 15, Redondo Beach, California, 1978.
15 Kenden, Anthony, "US Reconnaissance Satellite Programmes", *Spaceflight*, Volume 20, Number 7, 25 June 1978.
16 John F. Kennedy Space Center Historical and Library Services Station, *A Summary of Major NASA Launchings October 1, 1958-September 30, 1970*, Florida, National Aeronautics and Space Administration, 1970.
17 NASA Historical Staff, Office of Planning,

Astronautics and Aeronautics 1963, NASA SP-4004, Washington, DC, 1964.
18 Benson, Charles D. and Faherty, William Barnaby, *Moonport, A History of Apollo Launch Facilities and Operations*, NASA SP-4204, Washington, DC, 1978.
19 Library of Congress Science and Technology Division, *Astronautics and Aeronautics 1973*, NASA SP-4018, Washington, D.C., 1975.
20 "Military Studies Closing of Eastern Test - Range", *Aviation Week and Space Technology*, 12 September 1977.
21 Berger, Carl and Howard, Warren S., *History of the 1st Strategic Aerospace Division and Vandenberg Air Force Base 1957-1961*, Strategic Air Command, 1962.
22 NASA Historical Staff, Office of Planning, *Astronautics and Aeronautics 1964*, NASA SP-4005, Washington, DC, 1965.
23 Sharpe, Mitchell. R., Jr. and Lowther, John M., "Progress in Rockets, Missiles, and Space Carrier Vehicle Testing, Launching, and Tracking Technology, Part 1: Survey of Facilities in the United States", *Advances in Space Science and Technology*, Volume 6, New York and London, Academic Press, 1964.
24 Space and Missile Test Center Headquarters, *SAMTEC Capability Summary Handbook*, Vandenberg Air Force Base, California, 1973.
25 1st Strategic Aerospace Division Headquarters, *Vandenberg AFB Launch Summary*, Vandenberg Air Force Base, California, 1978.
26 Klass, Philip, *Secret Sentries in Space*, New York, Random House, 1971.
27 1st Strategic Aerospace Division History Office, *Vandenberg Air Force Base Launcher Status and History* (Revised 1 March 1977), Vandenberg Air Force Base, 1977.
28 Library of Congress Science and Technology Division, *Astronautics and Aeronautics 1969*, NASA SP-4014, Washington, DC, 1970.
29 Menkin, Arthur, *History of the Pacific Missile Range*, Naval Missile Center, Point Mugu, California, 1959.
30 Kwajalein Missile Range Directorate, *Kwajalein Missile Range Historical Summary July 1964-June 1970*, Huntsville, Alabama, 1972.
31 Shortal, Joseph Adams, *A New Dimension, Wallops Island Flight Test Range—The First Fifteen Years*, Wallops Flight Center, Virginia, NASA Reference Publication 1028, 1978.
32 White Sands Missile Range Information Office, *White Sands Missile Range at a Glance*, White Sands Missile Range, New Mexico, 1974.
33 White Sands Missile Range Information Office, *History of White Sands Missile Range*, White Sands Missile Range, New Mexico, 1974.

The "Secret" Cosmodromes

Photographs of the Soviet Union obtained by US Air Force reconnaissance satellites are classified—the layman would be astonished by the wealth of detailed information they contain. It is an open secret, for example, that under optimum conditions the high-resolution camera of the "Big Bird" satellite can discriminate objects on the ground smaller than 1ft (0·3m) across from altitudes above 100 miles (161km).

In seeking to discover details of the Soviet cosmodromes for publication, therefore, reliance has to be placed on other available sources, in particular the images obtained by the NASA Landsat and French SPOT remote sensing satellites (Chapter 8). Charles P. Vick, the American analyst, using the best available space photographs, has precisely located the Soviet and Chinese launch facilities. He has prepared references for the maps which appear on these pages. Until such time as the authorities concerned feel able to release more definitive information on cosmodrome layout and usage, it is inevitable that this survey must contain elements of speculation. To reduce this to a minimum, Charles Vick has spent a great deal of time matching Landsat and SPOT imagery with information obtained from specialised Soviet publications and officially released photographs and documentary films. He has also taken into account verbal descriptions of cosmodromes actually visited by people from the West.

Baikonur

Although the Soviets call their premier cosmodrome "Baikonur", this should not be confused with the town of that name (47·48°N, 65·50°E). The cosmodrome itself can be seen clearly in photographs of the area taken by Landsat and SPOT spacecraft, and lies due north of the railway junction town of Tyuratam east of the Aral Sea.

Work on this sprawling complex began in early 1955 when test facilities were required for Sergei Korolev's R.7 ICBM sufficiently remote from US Air Force surveillance posts in Turkey. Engineers started by building a branch line of the railway which runs between Moscow and the Soviet eastern regions. This extended the apex of the railway triangle above Tyuratam a distance of some 11·8 miles (19km) due north into desolate scrubland.

Within two years the site, which had begun as an outpost of tents, shacks and caravans showed the results of their labours —a huge launch platform of reinforced prefabricated concrete connected by a mile-long (1·6km) railway to a two-bay horizontal assembly building.[19]

The Soviets had greater plans for the area. With what must have been a huge labour force, the base was extended in a Y-shape system of roads and railways to link other pads for new-generation missiles extending east and west of the original R.7 launch site.

To the south, immediately adjacent to Tyuratam and contrasting strangely with the primitive buildings of the old town, were the beginnings of a "science city" to be known as Leninsk.

Already in 1975 Leninsk was a thriving community with a population of around 50,000 and the whole area including the adjoining territories of the launch complexes had the green freshness of vegetation with trees that reached the roofs of five-storey buildings. The entire city is interlaced by a complex irrigation system. The climate is variable, hot in summer and cold in winter sometimes with temperatures down to −40°C and violent snow storms

Leninsk, like other Soviet cities of the new era, has many schools, several "palaces of culture", cinemas, a 164ft (50m) swimming pool, a large stadium and cafes, restaurants and hotels. The local radio/TV station broadcasts its own programmes.[2]

Below: *Soyuz 31 spacecraft mated with the A-2 launch vehicle leaves the horizontal assembly building on its way to the launch pad at the Baikonur cosmodrome.*

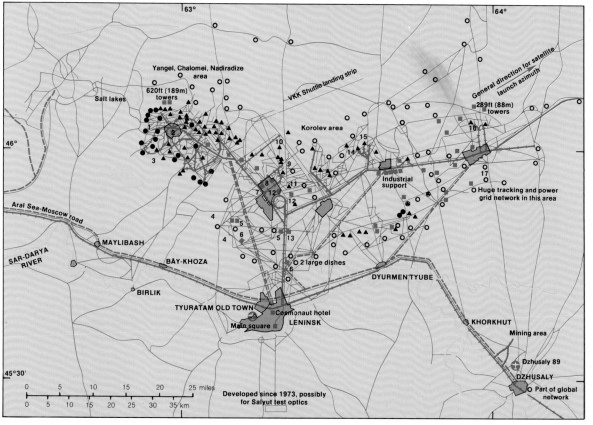

Developed since 1973, possibly for Salyut test optics

Baikonur Cosmodrome
1 F-1-r FOBS silos?
2 Probable centralised launch control facility.
3 Military launch complex.
4 Tracking and power grid.
5 Fuel storage area.
6 Major tracking and mission control centre.
7 Area devoted to Type G development.
8 Type G assembly buildings?
9 Type G pads? (Position suggested by *AW and ST*).
10 Pad facilities for Energiya.
11 A-class booster complex used for Sputnik 1, Vostok 1 and ASTP Soyuz 19.
12 Soyuz assembly buildings (2).
13 Lox production.
14 Venera, Progress, Cosmos, Soyuz 9 pads.
15 ASTP back-up pad.
16 Huge facilities believed to be Proton pads.
17 These facilities may be related to solid-fuel military rockets.

- Road and/or railway
- Primary railway
- Power line
- Support area/test facility
- Town, village or industrial
- Airport
- Silo facility
- Pad facility
- Silo or pad facility
- Tracking or range support
- Rivers and lakes

However, the total population working at the cosmodrome does not live entirely in the city. Close study of the Landsat pictures reveals several dormitory areas near industrial centres on the extreme western and eastern sectors and also near the original facilities developed in the mid-1950s.[2,11]

Cosmonauts taking part in early space missions were accommodated in "comfortable cottages" and in recent years they have been able to make use of their new hotel training complex located between Leninsk and Tyuratam.[2] The complex has all the necessary facilities for medical examinations, a swimming pool and a gymnasium.[2]

The cosmodrome itself lies to the north, not far from the main gateway to the city where a blue sign with a white arrow points "To Baikonur". The highway which passes close to the Tyuratam railway station, is lost among hills and then radiates towards numerous launch complexes.

This huge sprawling facility is highly dependent on its extensive railway system and airports; that part covered by the "Y" configuration is some 85 miles (137km) long and 55 miles (88·5km) wide. In addition to materials and equipment needed to support launch operations, the cosmodrome must require several train loads of foodstuffs and other domestic freight every day.

The First Launches

Launch tests of the R.7 ICBM (SS-6, NATO code name Sapwood) began in May 1957. During the following weeks a Lockheed U-2 reconnaissance aircraft flew over the area and photographed the launch site. Finally, the Soviet official news agency Tass announced

"A super long-distance intercontinental multi-stage ballistic rocket flew at . . . unprecedented altitude . . . and landed in the target area."

That particular launch took place on 21 August 1957 and, according to Western sources, the rocket travelled a distance of about 4,000 miles (6,436km). It was from the same pad that Sputnik 1 was launched on 4 October 1957 and Yuri Gagarin ascended in Vostok 1 on 12 April 1961.

Two small houses not far from the large industrial buildings in which the launch vehicles and spacecraft are assembled and checked out have been preserved because of their historical association with Sergei P. Korolev, the late "Chief Designer". In one of them Gagarin spent the night before starting his historic space journey. Korolev stayed in the other during his frequent visits.[11]

As already mentioned the launch complex —a huge platform of steel and reinforced concrete overhanging a deep flame pit—is linked by rail with a two-bay horizontal building in which launch vehicles are prepared for flight. This, however, is only part of the pre-launch procedure.

The spacecraft to be launched first undergoes thorough checkout in the Space Vehicle Assembly—Test Building (MIK-KO). It then proceeds on a special transporter to the fuelling facility where non-cryogenic propellants and pressurant gases are loaded. The craft then returns to the main Space Vehicle Assembly—Test Building where it is mated to the launch vehicle on a rail-mounted transporter-erector for final checkout.

Above: *The Soyuz 33 launch vehicle backing onto the launch pad at Baikonur in 1979. The erector raises it vertically.*

When all is ready the big doors of the preparation building are opened and the vehicle is taken out to the launch platform by a diesel locomotive. The rocket is backed up to the pad. Hydraulic jacks stabilise the erector and securely anchor it to the pad foundation; the vehicle then can be lifted bodily by the erector into the vertical launch position, again by the use of hydraulics. It actually sits on a turntable which can be rotated to the desired launch azimuth.[17]

Hinged steady arms—which fall away at the moment of lift-off—support the vehicle on the pad[2] and service towers and a service mast are elevated so that launch crews can complete the final checkout and fuelling.

Fuelling facilities are located in separate "subterranean rooms" some hundreds of metres from the pad, a complex of pipes and conduits running underground from the storage tanks to positions beneath the pad and thence through the service structure to the rocket.[18]

Next to the original launch pad is a shallow underground command bunker with periscopes which convey the appearance of a submarine. This facility has been greatly modernised since the early days and now incorporates automatic systems. On top of the blockhouse are many concrete pillars which resemble "tank traps" designed to break up a misbehaving launch vehicle and reduce any impact loads should they occur.[2] The same ICBM/Sputnik/Vostok pad was used to launch the Soyuz 19 spacecraft involved in the ASTP docking exercise with an Apollo CSM in July 1975.

The Soviets indicated to ASTP personnel that they do not spend much time on the pad and that the major preparatory work for launching is performed in the controlled climate of the horizontal assembly building.[2] In view of the harsh winter conditions of the region, one can readily appreciate why only minimal work is done outside.

The map (page 39) gives some idea of the distribution of various launch complexes at the cosmodrome which covers an area far bigger than the Kennedy Space Center.

Two additional launch complexes not including the ASTP back-up complex, which makes three complexes in total for the A-1, A-2 and A-2-e rockets, seem to be located out

on the north-eastern spurs of the railway system.[5,14,15] Today, these sites are used for launching Soyuz, Progress and Soyuz T/TM spacecraft to Salyut and Mir space stations. The same facilities are used to launch various scientific, applications and reconnaissance missions that require use of the A-1 (SL-3) and A-2 (SL-4) and A-2-e (SL-6) launch vehicles.

On the opposite side of the "Y"—to the north-west—are the support and launch facilities for the large ICBMs tested at Baikonur. At the extreme western end is a series of what seem to be very isolated facilities which may be related to SS-18 test and training.

Other parts of the cosmodrome are above-ground pads and silos for a whole range of ballistic missiles fired on test towards target areas in the north-east of the country, the Kamchatka Peninsula or into the Pacific Ocean. Launch facilities include those for the SS-8 Sasin, SS-9 Scarp, SS-11 Sego, the solid-propellant SS-13 Savage and the new family of liquid-fuelled ICBMs, the SS-17, SS-18 and SS-19. Some of the earlier sites have been modified to accept new missile systems.

At the extreme eastern end of the cosmodrome is a major industrial support complex with four launch pads for the large Proton D-1-e (SL-12) rocket used for launching "new generation" Luna, Zond, Mars, Venera, Vega and Phobos spacecraft.[6,7,8,9] The same facilities are used for launching space stations by the Proton D-1 (SL-13).

The first launchings of a Proton D (SL-9) 2½ stage booster took place in 1965 when a 26,900lb (12,200kg) orbital laboratory (Proton 1) was placed in Earth orbit for research in high energy particle physics.

Thanks to still photographs and film footage released by the Soviets it is possible to describe the basic layout of the Proton rocket's launch facility.[1,12] Like Korolev's R.7, the booster is rolled out to the launch pad from a large horizontal assembly building, fully assembled with the spacecraft payload in position ready for launching.

Left: *The first Energiya booster waits on the pad in May 1987; a second pad is available for Energiya VKK launches.*

Above: *The Buran VKK mated to its Energiya booster is hauled towards the pad in anticipation of its first launch in 1988.*

The launch pad does show some differences, however; it uses a two-directional flame deflector similar to that of Saturn I, although the flames are directed upward from below ground level at about 30°. Each pad has two tall towers which support floodlights, cameras and lightning conductors. The gantry is uniquely different from those used for previous Soviet boosters in that it resembles the old Mercury-Redstone gantry with a crane. From the circumlunar Zond and Salyut 1 launch pictures, it can be seen that the rest of the launch complex broadly resembles a scaled up version of the facility for the "A" booster.

Two major complexes were built in the mid-1960s to handle the Type G-1-e, SL-X-15 "Super-Booster". One of these pads had to be re-built after the first development vehicle caught fire and exploded seconds after launch in July 1969. The "before" and "after" events are said to have been observed by US Air Force reconnaissance satellites.

After two launch failures in June 1971 and November 1972 respectively, the super-booster seemed to be on the verge of cancellation; but its importance as a means of advancing the Soviet space programme—especially the assembly of a major space station in Earth orbit—suggested at that time that development would continue after an extensive design review. But Soviet thinking and programme requirements were changing dramatically in the early 1970s.

After the 1972 failure effort seems to have been concentrated on achieving systems reliability and more extensive ground testing. In the spring of 1974 static and dynamic testing was reported to have been resumed at the cosmodrome in a 400ft (122m) structure. The tests may have led to the Soviets putting the project into temporary suspension. The two launch pads and associated facilities were apparently mothballed in 1973 and 1974.[3, 13, 14]

This impressive ground infrastructure was modified during the 1980s to support the preparation of the new Energiya heavy launch vehicle and of the VKK (Vozdushno-Kosmicheskiy Korabl, or Air-Space Vehicle system). The development of both Energiya and VKK Shuttle elements was begun in 1978 in order to create an Universal Space Transportation System which could be operated automatically to help with the establishment and maintenance of large orbiting facilities, which might provide the springboard for a manned expedition to Mars. The first Energiya launch took place on 15 May 1987 from the new complex at Baikonur, and on the first anniversary of this event some Western journalists were invited to visit it. *Aviation Week & Space Technology* published pictures in its 6 June issue showing a panoram of the overall Soviet Energiya/VKK launch and support facilities. They look as large or perhaps even larger than those for the Space Shuttle at NASA Kennedy Space Center and Marshall Space Flight Center. There are two Energiya/VKK pads, and a third one may be converted from a mothballed support structure for the old Soviet Type G rocket.

Energiya/VKK facilities are relatively close to the main base of Baikonur, where the original ICBM/Sputnik launch complex is located; in contrast, integration and launch facilities for Proton and other vehicles are established many miles away from this central zone. Two Energiya/VKK pads are available: the first one, used for the first flight, allows the launch of Energiya carrying conventional spacecraft, while the second is mainly designed for preparation and launch of the VKK. This was used for the first flight of VKK-1 *"Buran"* on 15 November 1988. The launch facilities are connected by a double railway track to an impressive assembly and checkout building. The Energiya and VKK elements are assembled in horizontal position, in the same way as Soyuz and Proton vehicles are prepared for launch. In addition to the high-bay Energiya/VKK checkout building, a large hangar-like assembly building is used for assembly of the large Energiya booster components. Many rail tracks converge into it.

Two VKK space shuttles and their Energiya carrier rockets can be prepared simultaneously. Once assembled horizontally on the Mobile Launcher-Mating Unit, Energiya and shuttle are hauled to the launch pad by four diesel locomotives. At the pad, powerful machinery tilts the vehicle into the vertical position. At the centre of the pad is a concrete flame pit up to five storeys in depth; it has three vents to channel Energiya's rocket exhaust away from the pad. However, the original Energiya launch pad had only one of these vents. This explains why it suffered major damage during the first Energiya blast-off; as a result the VKK pad has been improved. Huge pipes deluge thousands of gallons of water onto the pad from two reservoirs located next to the service towers. In addition to cooling the ferro-concrete structure, the water helps to prevent sound waves reflecting off the pad and damaging the ascending vehicle. In the event of a fire breaking out, water, foam and inert gases can be directed at the pad.

To the right of the VKK pad is a service tower similar to the structure seen on the Energiya pad. This tower carries all the facilities for an Energiya launch. To the left of the VKK pad is the tower with the crew access arm. A third tower, described by Soviet media as "the main tower"[21], rises to a height of 328ft (100m). Its purpose is to enclose the Soviet shuttle in maintenance gantries. It moves into position on rails. Installed on the launch tower, two tubes about 10ft (3m) in diameter run from the crew access arm to an underground bunker. The upper tube is the route cosmonauts take to the VKK cabin. Special trolleys carry the crew from the underground bunker up to a spacious white room; from here they enter the orbiter through the side hatch. The lower tube, which is set at a much steeper angle, is an emergency egress chute for the cosmonauts. According to Soviet reports, the escape from the orbiter to the bunker takes only 15 seconds!

The VKK runway, successfully tested by *Buran* on 15 November 1988, is located 7·5 miles (12km) from the launch pad; it is 15,000ft (4·5km) long. Its landing system allows an automated approach and touch-down, even when the shuttle is unmanned, as it was on its first flight.

Unlike the American Space Shuttle, the VKK propulsion system is not ignited at liftoff. Energiya develops 3,500 tonnes of thrust at launch. The four units of the first stage are wrapped round the second stage core unit. Each first stage unit has four single-chamber motors developing a total thrust of 800 tonnes, burning kerosene and

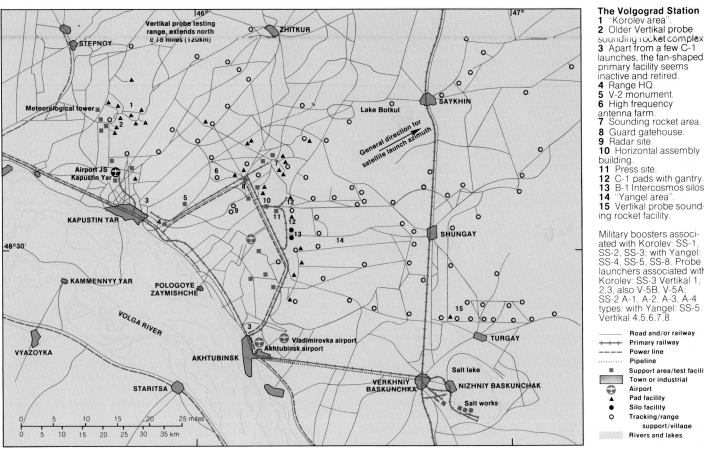

The Volgograd Station
1 "Korolev area".
2 Older Vertikal probe sounding rocket complex.
3 Apart from a few C-1 launches, the fan-shaped primary facility seems inactive and retired.
4 Range HQ.
5 V-2 monument.
6 High frequency antenna farm.
7 Sounding rocket area.
8 Guard gatehouse.
9 Radar site.
10 Horizontal assembly building.
11 Press site.
12 C-1 pads with gantry.
13 B-1 Intercosmos silos.
14 "Yangel area".
15 Vertikal probe sounding rocket facility.

Military boosters associated with Korolev: SS-1, SS-2, SS-3; with Yangel: SS-4, SS-5, SS-8. Probe launchers associated with Korolev: SS-3 Vertikal 1, 2,3, also V-5B, V-5A; SS-2 A-1, A-2, A-3, A-4 types; with Yangel: SS-5. Vertikal 4,5,6,7,8.

——	Road and/or railway
+++	Primary railway
- - -	Power line
······	Pipeline
■	Support area/test facility
▬	Town or industrial
✈	Airport
▲	Pad facility
●	Silo facility
○	Tracking/range support/village
▒	Rivers and lakes

oxygen. The second stage, which looks externally rather like the main tank of the Space Shuttle, has four single-chamber motors developing a thrust of 200 tonnes each, using cryogenic propellants (oxygen and hydrogen) for the first time on a Soviet rocket. After burn-out, the first stage units are jettisoned in pairs and land in a predetermined area; they are due to be fitted with landing equipment to ensure their reusability. The second cryogenic stage is jettisoned at suborbital speed and splashes down in a predetermined area of the Pacific Ocean. Energiya, according to Soviet sources, can continue controlled flight even in the event of failure of one sustainer motor of the first or second stage.

Initially, Glavkosmos, which is the agency responsible for civilian space activities in the USSR, plans to launch the Energiya/VKK system four times a year. Two missions will carry heavy modules into low Earth orbit for the automated assembly of a large space facility. The other two will use the VKK shuttle in either automated or manned mode. The Energiya/VKK system is an essential part of Soviet plans to place men on Mars at the beginning of the next century. Outlined in a film shown during the 39th IAF Congress at Bangalore (India), the Soviet manned Martian landing programme will depend on a complex combination of Earth orbital rendezvous and Mars orbital rendezvous manoeuvres. The manned spacecraft, its final stage powered by a nuclear reactor, will have to be assembled in Earth orbit, before the departure to Mars.

The Volgograd Station

This L-shaped rocket range, called the Volgograd Station by the Soviet authorities, is an outgrowth of the site from which Russian and German rocket engineers con-

ducted flight trials of some twenty V-2 type rockets in the last quarter of 1947. The Soviet design bureau under Sergei P. Korolev rapidly absorbed the experience of the German collective working in the USSR (page 22) and began to develop improved V-2s and an entirely new family of ballistic rockets.

The improved V-2s are identified in the West by the NATO codes Scunner and Sibling; they were followed by the Pobeda, or Victory-class medium-range ballistic missiles identified by the NATO codes Shyster and Sandal. One impact area for the medium-range missiles was in the Kyzl Kum Desert to the south-east of the launch site and the rockets' trajectories and telemetry were monitored by US Air Force stations located in Turkey and later Iran.

It was not long before Soviet researchers were using some of these rockets to carry geophysical payloads into the upper atmosphere and by 1949-1952 the first animal passengers (dogs and rabbits) were being flown on high altitude, short-range trajectories, a clear indication of interest in space travel.

Since that time the base has been greatly expanded and primary facilities appear to stretch in a wide arc between the towns of Kapustin Yar and Akhtubinsk. Launch pads and silos are widely separated and some of them seem to have been abandoned. Since 1961 the centre has taken on the equivalent importance of the Wallops Island (Virginia) station and White Sands facilities combined.

Today the Volgograd Station is mainly associated with the SS-5 Skean and the C-1 (SL-8) variant of the SS-5 used for launching scientific satellites of the Cosmos and Intercosmos families and certain military satellites also under the Cosmos label. Launchings were also made of the large Vertikal sounding rockets.

An SS-5 variant has been used to launch dummy warheads as targets for anti-ballistic missiles launched from a test centre near Sary Shagan far to the east.

The smaller B-1 (SL-7) satellite launcher, derived from apparently re-cycled SS-4 Sandal MRBMs, is now phased out of the programme; it was used between 1961 and 1975 to launch small scientific satellites (typical inclinations 48°-49°).[16]

The Russians actually used an old SS-4 Sandal silo to launch the two-stage B-1 satellite rocket from the Volgograd Station in a clever adaptation of existing facilities, whereas normal above-ground pads were used at the Northern Cosmodrome.[16]

As can be seen from the map (page 42) the Volgograd Station does not have the extensive railway network of the Baikonur cosmodrome although supplies are delivered by rail and there is some internal linkage.

Launch vehicles of the sounding rocket programme are moved between preparation buildings and launch pads on road transporters of the kind seen in Red Square military parades, while the B-1 and C-1 have been observed to use the same transporters except that they are placed on railway wagons. Using an American-style diesel switcher engine the Soviets back the C-1 booster out of its horizontal preparation building fully assembled. The rocket is erected onto its launch table enclosed in a gantry which somewhat resembles the old Atlas gantry used in the United States.

The Northern Cosmodrome

South of Archangel lies a major military rocket base known to the Soviets as the Northern Cosmodrome. This most secret centre located near the town of Plesetsk (62°43'N, 40°18'E) can be compared with Vandenberg Air Force Base in the United

States in that it contains a large number of launch pads and underground silos for ballistic missiles, and like Vandenberg it is responsible for launching satellites into high inclination orbits. It is the world's busiest launch centre: after only 22 years of space operations, total satellite launches numbered some 1,200 — more than all the US, European, Japanese and Chinese space launches combined.

The Northern Cosmodrome, however, is smaller and more concentrated than Vandenberg and industrially appears to be linked to the town of Kochmas.

The centre was first publicly identified by Geoffrey Perry of the Kettering Group in England when radio tracking of Cosmos 112 in 1966 traced the point of origin to an area close to the town of Plesetsk far from the location of known cosmodromes.

The first officially released pictures of the Northern Cosmodrome showed the preparation and launch of the Intercosmos-Bulgaria 1300 satellite atop a Vostok launch vehicle. The main difference from the Baikonur Cosmodrome was the wooded character of the surrounding countryside. Other photographs appeared — along with the official announcement of Plesetsk — in the beautiful book *Kosmonautika CCCP*.[20] They showed activities in an assembly and checkout building, and in a launch control bunker, during the preparation of a Vostok rocket.

Since that time the base has been used for the launching of satellites for a wide variety of purposes, e.g. photo-reconnaissance, meteorological, Earth resources, scientific (62°, 63°, 65°, 67°, 69-76°, and 82°); telecommunications, early warning, "ferret", and navigation (74° and 83°). Some military communications satellites have been launched eight at a time by the C-1, SL-8 rocket. Molniya satellites are also launched from Plesetsk by the A-2-e.

Orbital targets for "hunter-killer" satellites launched on test from Baikonur also have originated from the Northern Cosmodrome launched by the C-1 booster.

The Cosmodrome contains both operational and training facilities for the Strategic Rocket Forces. Military rockets possibly launched from the Northern Cosmodrome are, according to design bureau: SS-2, SS-3, SS-6 (S.P. Korolev); SS-4, SS-5, SS-7, SS-8, SS-9, SS-17, SS-18 (M.K. Yangel); SS-13, SS-14, SS-15, SS-16, SS-20 (V.N. Nadiradze); SS-11, SS-19 (V.N. Chalomei). The Chalomei bureau is also primarily responsible for the SS-N series which are launched from the land base test facility at Nonoksa. Development flights of the SS-13 and SS-14 were launched from the Baikonur Cosmodrome. Subsequently the SS-13 was installed in the Northern Cosmodrome region from which both operational training and development flight tests were launched. The SS-16 and SS-20 were exclusively flight tested from the Northern Cosmodrome where the SS-13 was operationally deployed.

Satellite launch vehicles include the A-1 (SL-3), A-2 (SL-4), A-2-e (SL-6), B-1 (SL-7), C-1 (SL-8), F-1-m (SL-11) and F-2 (SL-14). Prominent are launch complexes for the A-1, A-2 and A-2-e rockets which follow the same pattern of railway interconnection with preparation buildings as seen out on the

Northern Cosmodrome

1 This military centre is primarily concentrated around Kochmas. Much secret R&D has been transferred here from Baikonur.
2 "Yangel area": believed to be associated with B-1 and C-1 launchers. Similar to Volgograd facilities.
3 Possible Type-F facilities for the F-1-m and F-2. They presumably once accommodated the SS-7, which was replaced by the SS-9, and now the SS-17 and SS-18.
4 These unidentified facilities may be connected with the Yangel bureau or may be military facilities.
5 "Korolev area": at least four of these facilities are believed to be SS-6 Type-A launch pads. The configuration resembles the Baikonur "A" booster pad arrangements.
6 These may be area defence, facility support, or national defence related areas. They may not be directly associated with the Northern Cosmodrome.

Road and/or railway
Primary railway
Power line
Support area/test facility
Town, village or industrial
Airport
Pad facility
Silo facility
Silo or pad facility
Tracking or range support
Area of pads
Rivers and lakes

north-east wing of the Baikonur cosmodrome. According to Nicholas L. Johnson, the American author of the annual publication *The Soviet Year in Space*[22], activity at Plesetsk will decrease during the 1990s. This decline is linked to several evolutionary changes in different space programmes with military purposes. He writes:

"When the Glonass high altitude navigation network (launched by Baikonur) is operational in the 1990s, the smaller, low-altitude navigation

satellites, which account for about nine launches each year, will probably be phased out. Similarly, by the end of the century, the Plesetsk-launched, highly elliptical early warning satellites may give way to a new constellation of geostationary satellites . . . In addition, the number of 2-week photographic reconnaissance satellites, which primarily come from Plesetsk, is expected to be curtailed — perhaps substantially — in the 1990s."

REFERENCES

1 *Soviet Union*, July 1971, No 7, 256, photographs, p6.
2 George M. Low, "Notes from visit to Soviet Union, May 17-23 1975", NASA, 5 June 1975, pp. 1-17.
3 Craig Covault, "Astronauts' Tyuratam Tour Restricted", *Aviation Week and Space Technology*, 12 May 1975, pp. 19-21.
4 "Portrait of Baikonur", *Flight International*, 12 June 1975, p. 957.
5 "Progress 5 Tanker/Transport Launched", *Aviation Week and Space Technology*, 9 April 1979, p. 21.
6 "Tyuratam and Leninsk Separate Communities", *Soviet Aerospace*, 9 June 1975, pp. 39-41.
7 "Tyuratam and Leninsk Separate Communities," *Defense Space Business Daily*, 5 June 1975, pp. 193, 194.
8 "First Map of Baikonur Cosmodrome", *Defense Space Business Daily*, 16 April 1975.
9 "Leninsk — Growing Baikonur Cosmodrome Support City", *Defense Space Business Daily*, 1 May 1975, pp. 1-3.
10 Robert F. Kennedy, *Thirteen Days*, W.W. Norton & Co Inc., New York, January 1969 (photographs section).
11 Various ASTP releases and Soviet film footage, photographs of tours, rollout of launch vehicle, launch, etc.
12 Soviet documentary film, "Steep Road Into Space."

13 "CIA/Soviet Technology," *Science Trends*, 15 March 1976, pp. 1-3.
14 *Kosmodrome (The Space Port)*, Rakety-Mositele, Kosmicheskiye Letatec/nyye Apparaty, General editor Professor A.P. Vol'skiy; authors V.M. Karin; V.N. Nikolaev; N.I. Prigozhin; A.V. Ekhaldeev; I.A. Shuiskii. Veyenizdat Publishing House (Military Publishing House), Moscow 1977, pp. 1-312 (Specifically readers should consult pp. 39, 112, 125, 126 and 128).
15 Lev Levedev, Alexander Romanov, *Rendezvous in Space*, Progress Publisher, Moscow, 1979.
16 Craig Covault, "U.S. Hardware Carried on Intercosmos," *Aviation Week and Space Technology*, 19 April 1976, pp. 40-41.
17 B.P. Vladimirov, "Rocket Launching Facilities at Baikonur Described," in Translations on USSR Science and Technology, Physical Sciences and Technology, No 37, JPRS-71181.
18 R.Z. Sagdeyev, et al, "How They Fuel Space Ships," in *The Conquest of Outer Space in the USSR, 1974*, NASA TT-F-17259, pp. 106-117.
19 *Spaceflight*, July-August 1977, cover photograph (lower left).
20 *Kosmonautika CCCP*, Moscow, 1986.
21 *Spaceflight*, December 1988, Soviet Shuttle, pp. 450-453.
22 Nicholas L. Johnson, *The Soviet Year in Space 1987*, Teledyne Brown Engineering, Colorado Springs, 1988.

Jiuquan Launch Centre

In the early 1960s the People's Republic of China began the construction of a modest test centre for ballistic rockets on the edge of the Gobi desert near the town of Shuang-ch'eng-tzu (40°25'N, 99°50'E) in Inner Mongolia. The desert launch facility, located on both sides of the seasonal Jo Shui river, was initially developed for short-to-medium range missiles modelled on the Soviet pattern before the collapse of Sino-Soviet relations.

A small but talented team of Chinese rocket engineers, some of whom received their training in the United States, the Soviet Union and England, began to develop a small family of ballistic missiles alongside the programme to develop nuclear weapons.

The Chinese nuclear test at Lop Nor in October 1966 involved the use of a rocket,[7] clear confirmation of substantial progress in the related sciences.

We now know that China's first liquid-propellant ballistic missile, known in the West as the CSS-1, was a totally redesigned version of the Soviet SS-3 Shyster, a follow-on to the SS-2 Sibling. This is borne out by photographs officially released by the Chinese authorities, which show a rocket which had been erected on a launch table by a transporter-erector similar to that of the German V-2. Another picture shows the rocket in flight displaying frost on the section above the engine bay, indicating the presence of liquid oxygen. The fuel is believed to have been kerosene following the Soviet practice. The rocket is controlled from a three-axis autopilot acting on steerable exhaust vanes and aerodynamic rudders and has a range of 600 to 750 miles (965 to 1,207km). According to the US Department of Defense, it has been operational since 1966. There are some indications that China may also have received the Soviet V-2 variant known in the West as the SS-2 before the rift with the USSR.

Next to be developed was the CSS-2, an intermediate-range ballistic missile (IRBM) with a range of 1,491 to 2,013 miles (2,400 to 3,240km). This is said to be more akin to the Soviet SS-5 Skean in size and capability but not necessarily in its design. Its nearest parallel in the West would be the Jupiter IRBM or a long-tank version of the Thor although the Chinese are known to have used hypergolic (self-igniting) storable propellants to enable the weapons to be installed in silos in a fully fuelled condition.[1,2,3,10] They are thought to have nuclear warheads of 1 MT yield.

Development of the CSS-2 started in 1960-61 and apparently reached the flight test stage in 1966-67.[9] The rocket was subsequently deployed in late 1971.[1,2,3] This in turn led to the two and three-stage CSS-3, work on which appears to have begun in the years 1966-67.

From 1966 through 1970 the Chinese carried out dozens of test firings of the CSS-1, CSS-2 and CSS-3 over ranges of 400 to 1,000 miles (644 to 1,609km).[11,12]

The first stage of development of the

Right: *China launches a CSS-4 ICBM on test from the Jiuquan launch centre. This firing in May 1980 launched a dummy warhead some 5,000 miles (8,046km) downrange into the South Pacific.*

Shuang-ch'eng-tzu "East Wind" launch centre appears to have been completed in 1967 with the building of prototype test stands and launch pads for the first examples of the CSS-2 and CSS-3. The facility had already been used for the development of the CSS-1. The Ministry of the Aerospace Industry (MOA) and the CGWIC (China Great Wall Industry Corporation) now describe this northern site as the Jiuquan Space Launch Centre, and it is currently used to put into orbit recoverable capsules for earth observations and non-recoverable spacecraft.

Part of the rocket facilities was dismantled and re-built between 1968 and February 1970.[1,2] And two months later, on 24 April, the Chinese used a variant of the CSS-2, known as Long March 1, to launch their first artificial satellite on a south-easterly course. The orbit ranged between 273 and 1,481 miles (439 and 2,383km) above the Earth and was inclined at 68·5° to the equator.

Militarily, the two- and three-stage CSS-3 LRICBMs have a range of 3,453 to 4,095

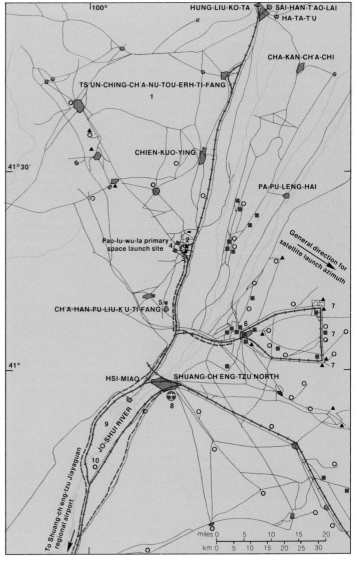

Jiuquan Launch Centre
1 This whole triangular area has undergone major development since 1973, with the addition of paved defence highways and construction that may be related to facility support.
2 CZ-2 (FB-1) pad. The China 3-8 series of satellites were launched from here. CZ-2 is a CSS-4 variant.
3 CZ-1 (Long March 1) pad. The China 1 and 2 satellites were launched here. Long March 1 is a CSS-3 with a solid motor third stage. Possible CZ-3 (Long March 3) test pad? Long March 3 is an LM-2 with addition of a hydrogen/oxygen third stage. The two pads (2 and 3) are served by one central gantry. Each has an umbilical work tower and flame trench.
4 Blockhouse.
5 A series of two-storey support buildings were spotted here.
6 Major industrial support buildings.
7 Believed to be primary military launch facilities for CSS-2, CSS-3 and CSS-4. Some scattered facilities may be able to accommodate CSS-1.
8 "East Wind" Shuang-ch eng-tzu North airport, abandoned.
9 Nomads and camels seen in this area.
10 Da-Shu-Li three-dish tracking station.

— Road and/or railway
+--+--+ Primary railway
----- Power line
■ Support area/test facility
▬ Town or industrial
⊕ Airport (abandoned)
▲ Pad facility
○ Tracking/range support
▨ Rivers and lakes

miles (5,556 to 6,590km) sufficient to reach Western regions of the USSR.[1,2] The CSS-2 and CSS-3, in their turn, were to lay the foundation for the full-range intercontinental ballistic missile (FRICBM) known by China as the FB-1 and by the West as the CSS-X4. It has a design range of about 6,835 miles (11,000km) and should be able to carry a thermonuclear warhead of 3MT yield.[13, 14]

In 1974, the two-stage Long March 2 (CZ-2A) was ready for lift-off from Jiuquan. This liquid rocket, 115·3ft (35·15m) high, has a lift-off mass of 421,000lb (191 tonnes) and is able to launch some 4,400lb (2 tonnes) in low Earth orbit, with 63 degree inclination. The first flight test was carried out in November 1974, but it failed. Analysis of the telemetry revealed a broken section in a wire which delivered the pitch rate gyro signal. As a result, improvements were made in the electric circuit design and better quality control was introduced in the process of design and production. Between 1975 and 1988, 11 launchings of Chinese spacecraft— most of them recoverable satellites, now promoted as the Chinese FSW platform for microgravity tests — have been made by Long March 2 vehicles, apparently with high success.

In the 1970s, another two-stage launch vehicle was also developed. Named FB-1, (Feng Bao or Storm Booster), this liquid rocket looked very much like the Long March 2, but, according to official Chinese reports, it contained different subsystems. However, the FB-1 was no better in performance or reliability than the Long March 2, and the FB-1 launcher programme was eventually stopped in 1981. The first and second stages of Long March 2, using respectively four and one YF-2 engines of 154,320lb (70 tonnes) thrust each (with N_2O_4 and UDMH propellants), are manufactured in Beijing and transported by rail to the launch sites.

Seen from space by Landsat remote sensing satellites, the Jiuquan Space Launch Centre (see map) incorporates road and rail systems linking various launch complexes and towns and villages bordering the Jiayaguan (Chiu ch'uan) airport built to handle jets where the American space officals landed during their tour of May 1979.[15] The nearby town has barrack-like buildings and the Chinese militia are much in evidence.

After leaving the aircraft the Americans were taken to a railway station about half a mile from the airport where they boarded a train for the journey north to the launch facility. On the two-hour journey they crossed a bridge and passed a drain-off lake about three-quarters of the way up, about 10 minutes from the town called "East Wind" near a seasonal river. Near this town their train swung to the right at a place marked on publicly available maps as Hsi-miao and pulled into an area signposted "Shuang-ch'eng-tzu North/51". Here they transferred to a bus which travelled to the NNE along a rough black-top road which turned parallel with the railway. For about 45 minutes to an hour the bus kept parallel with this railway at an estimated speed of 20 to 25mph (32 to 40km/h), until it passed a railway spur turning off to the left.

Shortly afterwards the bus turned left across the railway and went on for about a mile. This brought the Americans to a place called Pao-lu-wu-la some 68 miles (109km) NNE of the regional airport.[5,15]

Here the party was able to inspect one of the two launch pads set about 656ft (200m) apart. The launch facility consisted of two concrete tables of approximately 100ft (30·5m) diameter each equipped with an underground deflector trench.

The two pads were served by a single gantry over 164ft (50m) tall with many open work platforms which could be moved between them on rails. Each pad had a fixed umbilical "work tower" also with many open platforms. The tower used for the FB-1 was estimated to be between 148 and 164ft (45 and 50m) tall, that for the Long March 1 booster being about 33ft (10m) shorter.

Unlike Western and Soviet facilities there was no major industrial area in the vicinity of the pads. Instead, the launch vehicles are brought to the pad and offloaded from a railway spur which circles behind the double launch facility. Across the railway for each launch pad was an igloo-type blockhouse built partly underground which contained the firing rooms with various consoles. The complex also had facilities for propellant storage with a refrigeration room and power system, including motor-driven generators to back up the local electricity supply. The whole complex was reminiscent of the early US launcher programme.

Above: *A Long March 2 (CZ-2C) launch vehicle lifts off from Jiuquan on 21 October 1985. It is carrying the China 17 Earth observation satellite.*

Below: *Preparation of a Long March 2 at Jiuquan. The rocket's stages and payload are brought to the pad horizontally and then assembled ready for launch.*

Xi Chang Launch Centre

To launch spacecraft into geosynchronous orbit, China initiated development of a cryogenic third stage for the Long March 2 vehicle and began building a new launch complex in a mountainous area in the South. The Long March 3 (CZ-3) is derived from the two-stage Long March 2 version with the addition of a cryogenic third stage powered by the YF-73 engine,[4] which has four thrust chambers and produces 9,920lb (4·5 tonnes) of thrust. This YF-73 engine, which is reignitable, fires twice, first for a period of 425 seconds, and then for a 318 second burn. With a lift-off mass of some 445,300lb (202 tonnes), the 144·2ft (43·95m) high Long March 3 is able to deliver 3,086lb (1·4 tonnes) into geostationary transfer orbit with 31·1 degree inclination. The first test flight of Long March 3 was conducted on 29 January 1984 with partial success. It took place at a new launch site in China, Xi Chang (Sichuan province) which is linked by air, railway and highway to Chengdu city.

The Xi Chang Launch Centre is China's door to geosynchronous orbit. The second Long March 3, launched from Xi Chang on 8 April 1984, successfully lifted into geostationary transfer orbit an experimental telecommunications satellite (STW-1). The Chinese authorities, through CGWIC, have since decided to market launch services for commercial geosynchronous spacecraft. The first commercial launch of Long March 3, for the refurbished Westar 6 satellite, was scheduled to take place in 1988. However, international regulations concerning technology transfer had to be overcome. The Chinese had established facilities at Xi Chang to prepare, checkout, and integrate satellites to standards acceptable to Western customers. The British company Vega Space Systems Engineering Ltd acted as technical advisers to the CGWIC for the Long March family of launch vehicles.

The technical area at Xi Chang consists of buildings for the horizontal assembly and checkout of the three stages for Long March 3, and for the preparation of the payload (apogee engine testing, payload hydrazine filling, pyrotechnics systems etc). The launch site, which is surrounded by mountains, was originally equipped with a fixed 213·25ft (65m) high launch service tower, with rotating platforms on the tower, plus propellant charging and draining facilities, cryogenic handling systems, and pyrotechnics store. A clean room platform was installed on the launch service tower for the integration of the satellite with the third stage.

A second launch complex, consisting of two separate launch pads linked by a mobile service tower, will be ready for use during the 1990s — mainly for commercial launch services. They will launch Long March 2E (19,400lb, 8·8 tonnes in LEO or 6,610lb, 3 tonnes in GEO) and Long March 3A (5,510lb, 2·5 tonnes in GTO). The second generation Aussat communications satellites of Australia, made by Hughes Aircraft, are candidates for launch on Long March 2E vehicles. With three launch pads operational at Xi Chang, China will be able to offer up to nine Long March flights to geosynchronous orbits per year. Beijing Wan Yuan Industry Corporation, in association with the Shanghai

Above: *A Long March 3 launch vehicle is assembled on the pad at Xi Chang launch centre. The rotating service platforms equipping the launch service tower are clearly visible in this photograph.*

Left: *A Long March 3 lifts off from Xi Chang on 8 April 1984 carrying STW-1 (China 15), the PRC's first experimental telecommunications satellite for positioning in geostationary orbit.*

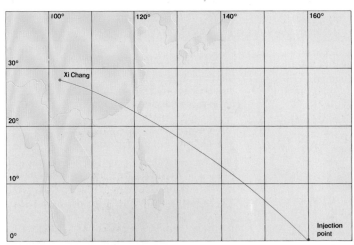

Xi Chang Launch Trajectories

Situated in a mountainous area some 40 miles (64km) north of Xi Chang city in Sichuan Province, Xi Chang Satellite Launch Centre is China's door to geosynchronous orbit. The diagram shows a typical launch azimuth for a communications satellite that is to be propelled towards geosynchronous transfer orbit by a CZ-2 or CZ-3 Long March launch vehicle. The satellite (e.g. an HS-376) would be equipped with an upper stage such as a PAM-D to boost it into GTO. The orbital inclination for the launch of such a mission is typically 28·5 degrees.

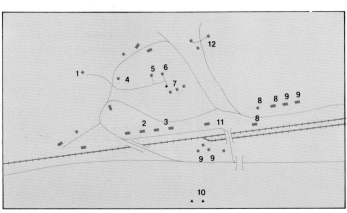

Xi Chang SLC

1. Launch control technical centre.
2. Compressor.
3. Gas bottle storage.
4. Fuel store.
5. Power room.
6. Launch tower.
7. Pad.
8. Lox storage.
9. Laboratories.
10. LM-2E/LM-3A pads (under construction).
11. LH₂ storage.
12. Pyrotechnic store.

———— Road
+—+—+ Railway
■ Base facility
▲ Pad facility

Bureau of Astronautics, have the entire responsiblty for the production of the Long March family of launchers. Two other versions are being marketed: Long March 1D (1,545lb, 700kg in LEO) from Jiuquan, and Long March 4 (3,307lb, 1500kg into a 560 mile, 900km Sun-synchronous orbit) from Taiyuan.

Taiyuan Launch Centre

While Xi Chang is used for geo-synchronous missions, on 6 September 1988 Taiyuan (in Shanxi Province) became the third Chinese launch site with the flight of the first Long March 4 rocket. The Taiyuan space launch centre was built in the 1960s to test ballistic missiles; it has been selected as the launch site for Sun-synchronous missions to be launched by Long March 4, which is also capable of circular and elliptical orbit mission launches. The Long March 4 vehicle, 137·8ft (42m) high and with a lift-off weight of 548,950lb (249 tonnes), is an improved Long March 3 with a storable propellant third stage (N_2O_4) and UDMH); it is especially designed to place 3,307lb (1,500kg) payloads in Sun-synchronous orbit at 560 miles (900km) altitude. Designed, developed and manufactured by the Shanghai Bureau of Astronautics, it can launch Chinese weather and remote sensing satellites. The first Long March 4 launch put into polar orbit the Fengyun 1 (Wind & Cloud) meteorological satellite, which was also designed and manufactured in China.

REFERENCES

1 Charles H. Murphy, "China's Nuclear Deterrent", *Air Force Magazine*, 19 April 1972, pp. 22-26.
2 Niu Sien-Chong, "Communist China's Capacity for Nuclear Attack", *NATO's Fifteen Nations*, April/May 1974 (19 July), pp. 3F, 4F, 5F.
3 William Beecher, "Peking Said to Deploy Atomic Missiles", *The New York Times*, 23 November 1970, p. 4.
4 James J. Harford, "PRC Space Work Surprises AIAA", *Astronautics and Aeronautics*, January 1980, pp. 7-11.
5 Various notes of C.P. Vick from US: NASA. AIAA, etc., delegation visits to PRC facilities.
6 William Beecher, "Chinese ICBM Bid Reported by US", *The New York Times*, 4 March 1973, p. 17.
7 Murrey Marden, "Peking Shot Calculated at 400 miles", *The Washington Post*, October 29 1966, pp. 1 and 6.
8 Robert S. Allen and Paul Scott, "China May Test New Missile", *Northern Virginia Sun*, 3 February 1966, p. 4.
9 William Beecher, "Improved Missile in China Reported", *The New York Times*, 1 January 1972, pp. 1 and 6.
10 William Beecher, "Russians and Chinese Continue Wide Military Build-up Along Disputed Border", *The New York Times*, 22 July 1970, p. 5.
11 William Beecher, "Soviets Said to Add Forces Near China", *The New York Times*, 10 September 1972, p. 19.
12 William Beecher, "China's ICBM Test Said to be Closer", *The New York Times*, 31 May 1971.
13 PRC Fails in Attempt to Launch Satellite. 15:48 Moscow Tass in English 15:27 GMT. Lo. New York, August 1. Tass (29 August 1979) reports.
14 George C. Wilson, "Chinese Halted Missile Work, General Says", *The Washington Post*, 25 February 1976, p. A4.
15 Craig Covault, "US Team Tours China Space Facilities", *Aviation Week and Space Technology*, 25 June 1979, pp. 77-82.

Italy

Since the mid-60s Italy, under the auspices of the Aerospace Research Centre (CRA-*Centro Richerche Aerospaziali*) of the University of Rome, has operated the first civil, mobile, equatorial launch site in the Indian Ocean. The San Marco Range was developed with the initial purpose of launching the Italian San Marco 2 satellite into equatorial orbit by means of a four-stage NASA Scout vehicle. The first launch of an equatorial satellite was made on 26 April 1967 for the Italian San Marco 2. The last use of the platform for an Italian satellite was the launch, on 25 March 1988, of San Marco 5 for the University of Rome and NASA.

The San Marco Range comprises two different off-shore platforms some three miles (5km) off the African coast, beyond Kenya's territorial limits, at roughly 3°S. The San Marco launch platform and the Santa Rita control platform are about 1,640ft

San Marco
1 Santa Rita control platform.
2 San Marco launch platform 2°56'S. 40°12'E.
3 Base camp.

The mobile range consists of two large platforms. The launch vehicle is the

four-stage, solid-propellant Scout, which derives maximum benefit from the Earth's rotation by being launched so close to the equator.

— Road
■ Base facility
▲ Pad facility

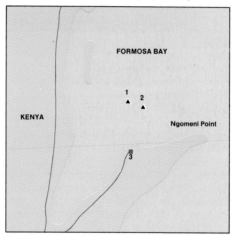

Below: *The two platforms of the San Marco Equatorial Range in Formosa Bay, Kenya. The control platform Santa Rita is in the foreground; nearer the coast is the San Marco launch platform.*

(500m) apart, independently organised but linked by 23 cables. The two platforms communicate by radio with ground facilities in Kenya (a main station at Mombasa and a mobile telemetry station near Nairobi).

The Santa Rita control platform is a triangular three-legged sea-rig of the type used for drilling; each side measures 137ft (40m) in length and the trestle-like steel legs are operated electrically. Electricity is provided by six 100kW diesel generators mounted on a small sea platform. Functioning as the heart of the range, it supports the major facilities: the range control centre containing radar and telemetry plotboards, TV monitors and communication equipment, the vehicle control centre and telemetry stations, the radar and command destruct transmitter systems, and support for 80 people.

The San Marco launch pad and the support equipment needed to assemble and test Scout rockets are carried on a large floating steel pontoon which weighs 3,000 tons (2,953 tonnes). This 98ft x 328ft (30m x 100m) rectangular hull is equipped with 20 steel caissons which can be embedded in the ocean floor by means of a pneumatic system. Electrical power is supplied by eight 100kW diesel generators; however, during final countdown power is provided by Santa Rita generators through the submarine cables. The vehicle is assembled and tested as it lies horizontally under a shelter at the rear of the platform. For the pre-launch work the shelter is pulled along rails to the pad. The launcher and rocket are then set to the azimuth that will put the scientific payload into equatorial orbit. The San Marco launch platform is located at 2°56'18''S and 40°12'45''E in Formosa Bay, so little correction is needed.

Perhaps the most remarkable spacecraft launched from the San Marco Range has been NASA's Small Astronomy Satellite, alias Explorer 42, named Uhuru after its successful launch on 12 December 1970. It is the first US spacecraft to have been put into orbit from a foreign launch base. Uhuru information on X-ray sources has provided a new insight into the nature of the Universe, and other data have enabled the first mysterious "Black Hole"—known as the Cygnus X-1 source—to be identified.

Europe in French Guiana

In 1964 France established an equatorial launch base on the coast of French Guiana, just north of Brazil. The choice of French Guiana for space activities came about because CNES (*Centre National d'Etudes Spatiales*, the French national space agency) was required to terminate its launches from the military base of Hammaguir in the Algerian Sahara. The site of what was to become the Guiana Space Centre was selected after a comparative study of 14 possible sites across the world, because of its political and geological stability, its favourable weather conditions, and its attractive location allowing launches to all-inclinational orbits (geosynchronous and Sun-synchronous missions).

The Guiana Space Centre conducted its first launch in April 1968, this being a Veronique sounding rocket. On 10 March 1970 two technological satellites (one French, the other German) took off together from Kourou on the first Diamant B vehicle. Until 26 September 1975—when the final launch of the French Diamant programme took place—six other French satellites were put into orbit from Guiana. During its first decade of operation the Kourou space facilities fired some 355 rockets.

However in the 70s the progress of space activities was slower than expected. The launch pads successively became inactive; the equatorial base for Europa II was closed in April 1973, and the Diamant facilities ceased operation in September 1975. But since 1977, after the decision taken in 1976 by the European Space Agency to launch the Ariane rocket from Kourou, the centre has entered a new lease of life. New facilities and equipment specific to Ariane (launching site, E-band telemetry system) have been established and some installations and systems, obsolete after a decade of use, have been refurbished.

The Guiana Space Centre covers 386 sq miles (1,000 sq km) of land; it stretches along a north-west/south-east savannah coast some 37 miles (60km) long and and 12·5 miles (20km) wide, and is located 5°14'N and 52°46'W. It includes the city of Kourou, which incorporates both the old Kourou village situated on the riverside and the modern town built on the shore. Upstream on the Kourou river are a private harbour which can only be approached by low draught ships (small tankers) and an industrial area which is basically occupied by manufacturers working for the Space Centre. A few kilometres north-east of the town, along the main road which connects Cayenne with St Laurent du Maroni, is the Technical Centre. This houses the management and administrative offices and the Control Centre, which is equipped for directing the launch operations. Stretching north-west for some 12·5 miles (20km) between the main road and the Atlantic, are the launch sites, buildings and facilities for checking, assembling and launching three types of vehicle: sounding rockets, the Diamant family and Ariane.

The sounding rockets launch complex has three launch pads for solid rockets and one launch site for liquid rockets. The Diamant launch complex has been unused since September 1975 and its facilities now

Above: *A view from the ELA-2 assembly zone towards the launch zone. Ariane rockets are transported to the pad on mobile platforms along the double rail track visible. In the background is ELA-1.*

Below: *Part of C.D.L.2 (Centre de Lancement Ariane No 2), a control centre from which technicians monitor vehicle functions during the countdown, and exercise control of the actual launch.*

are space relics where French firemen store their equipment. Towards the north, along the Atlantic Ocean, lies the impressive Ariane launch complex about 11 miles (18km) away from Kourou city. The ELA (*Ensemble de Lancements Ariane*) is the property of ESA (European Space Agency) but its facilities are currently leased to the Arianespace company for commercial space transportation services. Two separate launch areas are operational as of 1989: ELA-1 which has been used since 1979 by Ariane 1, 2 and 3 versions, and ELA-2, operational since early 1986 for Ariane 2, 3 and 4 configurations. A third launch site is under construction for the 1990s: this is ELA-3 which will be used for Ariane 5 tests and launches of automated and manned spacecraft.

ELA-1 will be taken out of service after the last Ariane 3 launch during 1989. Originally, it was built to launch the Europa 2 vehicle of the 1960s. When the Europa 2 programme was halted in 1972 by ministerial decision, after many launch failures, the facility was modified to launch Ariane vehicles. The first Ariane launch area comprises the launch platform, containing the equipment for vehicle checkout, the servicing tower (fully air-conditioned) which moves on rails and encloses the rocket on its launch table, the umbilical mast, facilities to store and transfer propellants and water, and a plant for storing liquid nitrogen and producing high-pressure gaseous nitrogen.

Launch preparation, propellant loading and final activation are monitored and

controlled from a heavily protected, blockhouse-type building, sited about 650ft (200m) from the launch table; this bunker provides protection for personnel and checkout equipment, and is completely isolated during the potentially hazardous operation of filling Ariane's third stage with cryogenic propellant. After Ariane lift-off, control passes from this launch centre to the mission control room of the Technical Centre over 6 miles (10km) away. The first Ariane was launched successfully on 24 December 1979; it put a 3,527lb (1,600kg) technological payload into geostationary transfer orbit.

Above: *The maiden flight of an Ariane 4 blasts away from ELA-2 at Kourou on 15 June 1988. This configuration is an Ariane 44LP which mounts two liquid and two solid propellant strap-on boosters.*

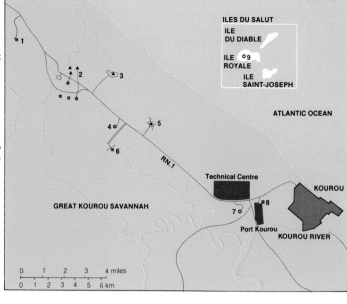

Guiana Space Centre
1 Iris TM/TC interfero-metry station. Diane station.
2 Ariane launch complex.
3 Diamant launch complex.
4 Meteo. radars.
5 Sounding rocket launch site.
6 Motor storage facility.
7 Radio relay.
8 Nitrogen/oxygen plant.
9 IR kinetheodolite.

French launch centre near Kourou, French Guiana, 5° north of the equator. ELDO used the facility briefly for Europa II and after that project was abandoned. the centre was modified to launch Ariane rockets for ESA.

Road
Town
Base facility
Pad facility
Tracking/communication
Rivers and lakes

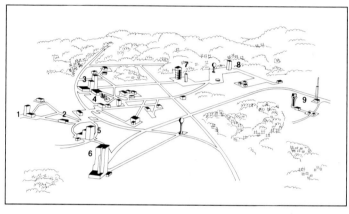

The Ariane Launch Areas
1 Booster integration building.
2 Control centre.
3 ELA-2 vertical assembly building.
4 ELA-2 launch preparation zone.
5 Launcher integration building.
6 Final assembly building.
7 ELA-2 launch pad.
8 ELA-1 launch pad (now deactivated).
9 ELA-3 launch area (first launch due 1995).

The drawing shows the Ariane complex marked **2** on the map above.

The Ariane development programme is administered and funded by ESA (European Space Agency). On 26 March 1980, the French space agency CNES, 36 European manufacturers in the aerospace and electronic industries, and 13 European banks became the shareholders in the world's first commercial space carrier. The company is called Arianespace and is based in France. The success rate of Ariane launchings, the flexibility offered by Arianespace services, the tragedy of the Space Shuttle *Challenger* and the subsequent unavailability of launch vehicles in USA, all aided the marketing of Ariane throughout the world, not least in the USA. On 22 May 1984, the first commercial spacecraft launch by the ninth Ariane was carried out from ELA-1 by Arianespace. It successfully injected the American GTE Spacenet-1 satellite into geosynchronous transfer orbit. To be able to meet the high demand for commercial launch operations and competition from American launch vehicles, it was then decided to establish a second improved launch area at Kourou and to develop a family of modular (tailored) Ariane 4 launchers.

The development of ELA-2 was agreed by the ESA Member States in July 1981. The new facility became operational with the successful launch, on 28 March 1986, of Ariane 3 (V17) carrying the American G-Star 2 and the second Brazilsat communications satellites. Especially designed to support Ariane 4 flights, ELA-2 comprises two distinct zones: the launcher-preparation zone and the launch zone. The two zones are linked by a double rail track 0·6 miles (1km) long along which a mobile platform can be rolled by a MAN truck. In this way, one launcher can be prepared and checked out in the preparation zone, while a second vehicle is in the final checkout and countdown phase on the launch pad. Two launch tables are available which allows two Ariane vehicles to be prepared simultaneously. This optimises operating costs and accelerates launch operations by reducing to 1 month the interval between launches.

The main facilities in the launcher-preparation zone are the destorage hall, the erection hall, the assembly dock (66x100 x220ft; 20x30x67m), and associated air-conditioning, fluid supplies, offices, workshops and stores. Nearby stands the heavily-protected launch centre, a two-storey, reinforced concrete building covered with a 6·6ft (2m) thick concrete slab and a 13·2ft (4m) deep layer of earth to protect personnel and equipment during launches. Two systems, the electrical monitoring and command (EMC) system and the fluids monitoring and command (FMC) system, constitute the main elements of the control rooms. For transfer to the launch pad, Ariane is assembled upright on its mobile table which rolls on bogies; transfer to the pad takes less than one hour. The launch table (mass about 1,102,000lb, 500 tonnes) supports the launcher release system.

In the launch zone, two impressive facilities are used to complete preparations for an Ariane launch. The launch pad, onto which the mobile table carrying the launcher is attached, is surrounded by handling platforms; an uncooled jet deflector, with two slopes coated with refractory concrete, is integrated in the foundation. The umbilical tower, measuring 26x49x243ft (8x15x74m), houses the equipment for the electrical and fluid connections between the launcher and the ground facilities. As the Ariane 4 family comes into service, the ELA-2 complex will be the only operational launch pad at Kourou between 1989 and 1995, when the Ariane 5 heavy launch vehicle will first be test flown from the ELA-3 area which is currently under development.

ELA-3 Is Established

ELA-3 construction started in late 1988. Its configuration is similar to that of ELA-2. It comprises two parts: the preparation zone consisting of solid booster assembly building, and vehicle assembly and payload integration buildings; and the launch zone with the mobile launch table carrying the umbilical mast, which allows a rapid return of the launcher to the vehicle assembly building. Ariane 5 and its payload — which can be the Hermes spaceplane — will be assembled on the mobile table and will roll along the twin-track rail line to the launch pad. ELA-3 will be used to test the cryogenic Vulcain engine. In addition, it will be equipped with facilities for the development of the powerful solid boosters and will also incorporate a landing strip for the return of Hermes from space.

Japan

In 1955, when the restriction on the building of indigenous aircraft and rockets was lifted, Japanese scientists began to test "Pencil" and "Baby" rockets at the Akita Range on the Sea of Japan. The man responsible for this pioneer activity was Professor Hideo Itokawa of the University of Tokyo. Thirty years later, following the development of space science and applications programmes. Japan operates two satellite launch centres, both in the south of the country. The Institute of Space and Aeronautical Science of the University of Tokyo has developed a family of solid rockets for the Ministry of Education and is working on scientific payloads launched from its Kagoshima Space Centre. The National Space Development Agency (NASDA) working for the Science and Technology Agency is more interested in the industrial and commercial aspects of space technology and is conducting practical experiments with applications satellites launched from its Tanegashima Space Centre.

Science at Kagoshima

During the 50s the first Japanese sounding rocket launches were made at Akita Rocket Range. Because the Sea of Japan was too narrow for the large sounding rockets of the University of Tokyo, the launch site was moved to Japan's East Coast, facing the Pacific. During the 60s the Institute of Space and Aeronautical Science selected a new launch site on hilly and uninhabited land near Uchinoura in the Kagoshima Prefecture. Construction of facilities on several hills facing the Pacific began in February 1962 and the Kagoshima Space Centre was officially opened in December 1963. By 1965 it was fully equipped to launch the solid-fuel Kappa and Lambda sounding rockets, and by 1966 could meet the demands of launching a small satellite with a Lambda-type four-stage rocket. Since 1964 the site has been upgraded to launch the more powerful Mu satellite launch vehicle. After four unsuccessful attempts in 1966, 1967 and 1969, the Lambda 4S-5 rocket put into 209 x 3,195 miles (337 x 5,141km) orbit, the first Japanese payload, a technological satellite weighing 53lb (24kg). It was named Ohsumi (after the peninsula where the launching site is located). This first successful launch occured on 11 February 1970. Since then, at a rate of about one per year, spacecraft for scientific purposes have been launched by Mu vehicles, initially in a four-stage configuration, and later in a three-stage improved version.

With its launch facilities sited on level hilltops at different heights, the Kagoshima Space Centre at 31°14'N, 131°04'45"E looks unique. Covering an area of approximately ·274 sq miles (0·71 sq km) it consists of eight levels where specific facilities are established. Arranged on Nagatsubo Plateau, 1,050ft (320m) above sea level, are the range control centre, the telemetry receivers (with a 59ft [18m] dish antenna), the radio tracking station for satellites and the payload assembly shop. The Lambda centre is 908ft (277m) above sea-level and includes several mobile launch pads for Kappa and S rockets and an explosives handling room. The Lambda pad formerly located here has been

Above: *An aerial view of Kagoshima Space Centre which is constructed on hilly terrain overlooking the Pacific Ocean. The launch facilities for Mu rockets can be seen in the foreground of the picture.*

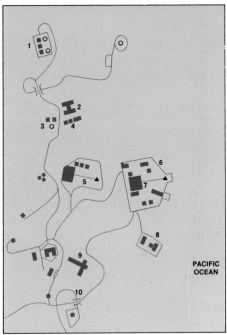

Kagoshima Space Centre
1 Satellite tracking centre.
2 Control centre.
3 Telemetry centre.
4 Payload assembly shop.
5 Lambda launch complex.
6 Mu launch complex.
7 Mu assembly building.
8 Satellite preparation building.
9 Administration offices.
10 Main gate.

The Kagoshima Space Centre was established in 1962 for launching and receiving data from sounding rockets and scientific satellites. The various facilities – launch pads. control and telemetry centres etc – were built on plateaus facing the Pacific. The two Halley's Comet probes were launched from here.

—— Road
▪ Base facility
▲ Pad facility
○ Tracking/communication

moved to the Mu Centre, about 722ft (220m) above sea-level. The Mu launch area is the largest of the Kagoshima Space Centre; it contains the Mu service tower, assembly shop, launch control blockhouse (about 262ft [80m] away from the launch pad), satellite test shop, dynamic-balance test shop, and propellant store.

The Mu launch vehicle is assembled in a vertical position on its launcher inside the service tower. Upon completion of the vehicle and spacecraft assembly, the tower is orientated towards the launch direction and the launcher with the Mu rocket is drawn out of the tower and tilted to the appropriate launch elevation angle

(75°-80°). Once in flight, rockets are tracked by two radars, one working at L-band, the other at C-band, and by an optical tracker on Miyabaru Plateau some 1·24 miles (2km) to the southwest of the control centre.

During the 1980s, the Mu launch area was improved and adapted to accommodate the more powerful four-stage Mu-3SII vehicle; this latter launched the Japanese Halley's Comet probes Sakigake (Pioneer) and Suisei (Comet) respectively on 8 January and 19 August 1985. ISAS (Institute of Space and Astronautical Science, under the Ministry of Education) is currently investigating the Mu-3SIII with improved launch capability, and it is doing basic research on winged launch vehicles with small-scale models.

Applications at Tanegashima

On 1 October 1969 NASDA became Japan's principal agency for space development. It integrated the functions of the National Space Development Centre and the Ionosphere Sounding Satellite Development Division of the Ministry of Posts and Telecommunications. Funded mainly by the Government, with financial contributions from non-governmental bodies, it promotes space technology projects whose aims are to explore the peaceful utilisation of space; these include research into liquid propulsion, communications satellites, spacecraft for Earth observation and for aeronautical and maritime surveillance. NASDA's first task was to acquire an independent launch capability for geostationary applications satellites. From the beginning it was planned that Japan would gradually develop a heavy launch vehicle composed of liquid-propelled stages. Since 1964, using the facilities on Niijima island (in the Bay of Tokyo), multistage rocket technology has been developed through the operation of sounding rockets employing a second liquid stage.

For the development of a satellite launch vehicle, it was necessary to replace the Niijima Test Centre by new launch facilities on Tanegashima Island, in the south of

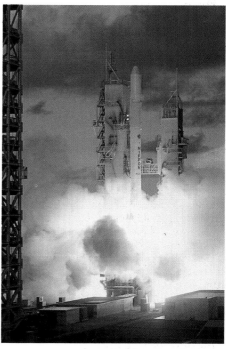

Above: *The Osaki launch site on Tanegashima Island. To the right is the N launch pad and in the centre the Q launch pad. In the background is a weather observation tower.*

Right: *An H-I launcher lifts off from NASDA's Osaki range at Tanegashima on 27 August 1987. A new launch complex for the heavier H-II vehicle is being developed for operations in the early 1990s.*

Tanegashima Launch Site
1 Spin test facility.
2 Solid propellant storage facilities.
3 Static firing test facilities for first stage main engine.
4 H-II Yoshinobu launch complex.
5 H-I/N-II launch pad.
6 ETV (Q) launch pad.
7 Liquid propellant storage facilities.
8 Weather tower.
9 Launch vehicle assembly building.
10 Range control centre.
11 Telemetry station.
12 Spacecraft checkout building.
13 Water supply.
14 Electric power plant.

— Road
■ Base facility
▲ Pad facility
○ Tracking/communication
░ Rivers and lakes

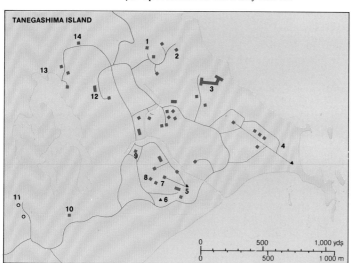

TANEGASHIMA ISLAND

Japan, about 62 miles (100km) south of the Kagoshima Space Centre developed by the University of Tokyo. Construction work on the south-east coast of Tanegashima began in September 1966 with the erection of the Takesaki launch site for small rockets at 20°22'20"N, 130°57'55"E; these facilities were ready for launch operations in 1968.

While NASDA was establishing at Osaki (north of Takesaki) the major centre in Japan for launching large liquid-propellant rockets, the decision was taken to augment Japan's own development capability with important technologies and equipment purchased from the USA, so as to shorten the overall timescale. The Osaki Launch Site at 30°23'N, 130°58'E was established especially to operate the N-I, a vehicle based on the Thor-Delta first stage and employing a Japanese engine(LE-3) for its second stage. On 23 February 1977, the third N-I rocket placed the Kiku-2 test satellite in geostationary orbit at 130°E; Japan had become the third country — after the USA and USSR — to reach geosynchronous orbit. Between 1975 and 1982, a total of seven satellites were launched by the N-I. When NASDA decided to develop an improved N-II vehicle

with an inertial guidance system and with higher performance (772lb, 350kg to GEO), the Osaki facilities were upgraded to accommodate this more powerful launch vehicle. Between 1981 and 1987, the N-II launched a total of eight satellites, including Japan's first Sun-synchronous satellite, the Momo-1 for remote sensing observations.

To launch heavier spacecraft for Earth observations, direct TV broadcasts, and high data traffic, NASDA has done considerable research into cryogenic propulsion. Its objective for the 1990s is to make Japan autonomous in terms of domestic satellite launchings and competitive for commercial space transportation services. The three-stage H-I vehicle was accordingly developed by replacing the N-II second stage with a cryogenic stage powered by a 10-tonne thrust engine (LE-5) with re-ignition capability. The Osaki complex was modified to handle cryogenic propellants. It includes a launch deck 375,000lb (170 tonnes) in mass, with a cantilever steel structure, as well as two umbilical masts that support the feed pipes and conduits for liquid oxygen and hydrogen, electrical power, air conditioning and high-pressure gases. Another

facility is a mobile service tower (MST), 220ft (67m) high, 85ft (26m) wide, 82ft (25m) deep and 6,614,000lb (3,000 tonnes) in mass, that moves backward some 328ft (100m) before launch. The first H-I test launch, in a two-stage configuration, was successfully made on 13 August 1986. H-I is currently used to launch Japanese applications satellites into geosynchronous (1,212lb, 550kg) and Sun-synchronous orbits (3,307lb, 1,500kg).

For early 1993 NASDA is developing a new heavy launcher named H-II to meet the demand for larger satellite launches at a lower cost with a high degree of reliability. The two-stage cryogenic rocket, equipped with two large, solid, strap-on rocket boosters for thrust augmentation, will be able to launch 4,409lb (2 tonnes) into geostationary orbit, or 8,818lb (4 tonnes) in GTO, or 22,046lb (10 tonnes) into LEO. Its first stage will use the new liquid hydrogen/liquid oxygen LE-7 engine developing some 220,460lb (100 tonnes) thrust. Its second stage employs an improved LE-5 engine.

A new complex for the H-II is scheduled for completion during 1990 on Tanegashima Island. Located near the Osaki site, it will be called Yoshinobu Launch Complex. Its main facilities are a vehicle assembly building, a mobile launcher, a pad service tower, cryogenic propellant storage facilities and a blockhouse. In order to achieve a higher launch rate than the present two a year, the H-II will be assembled in the vehicle assembly building and transported to the pad service tower on a mobile platform. Another mobile table will be available so that one vehicle can be assembled while another is actually on the pad. The payload will be checked at a spacecraft test building and then transferred to a fairing/spacecraft assembly facility. The Yoshinobu launch complex also includes a static firing test stand for the LE-7 engine.

Launches from Japanese territory are limited to the January-February and July-August periods each year. These restrictions resulted from objections of local fishermen to launch noise and associated hazards.

India

The manifest practical applications that research into space technology can offer a developing country have prompted the Indian authorities to fund their own space programmes. Since 15 August 1969 the management of space research and its utilisation for peaceful purposes has been controlled by the Indian Space Research Organisation (ISRO). In June 1972 the Indian Government set up the Space Commission and entrusted a Department of Space (DOS) with responsibility for conducting that country's space activities. The DOS is directly under the Prime Minister's control, and ISRO projects are conducted at four space centres.

VSSC and TERLS

The Vikram Sarabhai Space Centre (VSSC) is ISRO's main research and development establishment. Its facilities were built near the Thumba Equatorial Rocket Launching Station (TERLS), on the west coast of India, about ten miles (16km) north of the city of Trivandrum in Kerala State.

Named after the late Professor Vikram A. Sarabhai (1919-1971), founder of the Indian space programme, VSSC is an entirely national facility working on the development of sounding rockets (Rohini and Menaka), satellite launch vehicles (SLV-3) and ground-based and vehicle-borne instrumentation.

TERLS is now a United Nations sponsored station, located on the sandy coast of the Arabian Sea. The location of Thumba (8°32'34"N, 76°51'32"E) is ideal for the furtherance of low-altitude upper-atmosphere and ionosphere studies which are of special importance in the region of the magnetic equator (just north of Thumba). Because of this factor, with the assistance and co-operation of France, the USA and the Soviet Union, TERLS has become an international launch site for sounding rockets.

The normal launch area covers about 0·78 sq mile (2 sq km) and the range has capabilities for launching rockets up to 1·83ft (0·56m) in diameter. Its three launch pads have facilities for a variety of sounding rockets. The VSSC is the largest of the ISRO Centres and currently employs over 5,000 people; it provides the technology base for the country's indigenous satellite launch vehicle development programme. The most ambitious activities are the development of the PSLV rocket which aims to lift 2,205lb (1 tonne) spacecraft to Sun-synchronous orbits, and the preparation of the GSLV rocket which will provide India with indigenous capability to launch geosynchronous satellites of 2,205lb (1 tonne) mass.

ISRO Satellite Centre

The ISRO Satellite Centre (ISAC) is the main Indian laboratory for the development of satellite technology. It is located near Bangalore airport (Karnataka State), has a staff strength of around 2,000 people, and is responsible for the design, development, fabrication, integration and testing of Indian spacecraft. It built the country's first scientific satellite, Aryabhata which was launched by a Soviet Cosmos rocket on 19 April 1975. It is currently building Earth observation (IRS or Indian Remote Sensing),

geosynchronous multipurpose (Insat-II), and light technological and scientific satellites (SROSS).

SHAR

The Sriharikota Launching Range (SHAR) is developing into the most important centre, with test, assembly and launch facilities for large multi-stage rockets and satellite launchers, and tracking, telemetry and telecommand stations for Indian spacecraft. It is situated in Sriharikota Island, on India's east coast, about 62 miles (100km) north of Madras at 13°47'N and 80°15'E.

Sriharikota, an island in the Nellore District of Andhra Pradesh State, lies along the east of Pulicat Lake and is reached by road from Madras. Prior to its acquisition for ISRO by the Indian Government it was a firewood plantation of Eucalyptus and Casuarina trees. This island is affected by both the south-westerly and north-eastern monsoons, but rains are generally only heavy during October and November; thus many sunny days are available for out-door static tests and launchings.

SHAR covers a total area of about 56 sq miles (145 sq km) with a coastal length of 16·7 miles (27km). The range became operational when three Rohini 125 sounding rockets were launched on 9 and 10 October 1971. Since then, the ISRO facilities at SHAR have expanded. The Solid Propellant Space Booster Plant processes large size propellant grains for the satellite launch vehicle and stage motors programmes. The Static Test and Evaluation Complex tests and qualifies different types of solid motor for launch vehicles. The Sriharikota Launch Complex consists of three separate assembly and launch areas whose construction shows the evolutionary growth of Indian launch capabilities. The first and now mothballed launch site was built in the 1970s for the four-stage SLV-3 rocket, which could put satellites of up to 88lb (40kg) into LEO.

Below: *The first ASLV being prepared for launch at Sriharikota Range. The rocket is assembled vertically under a mobile service tower, here seen rolled back*

After an unsuccessful first launch in August 1979, the SLV-3 orbited three light satellites for technological purposes: in July 1980, in May 1981 and in April 1983.

The second site, designed for the ASLV rocket (331lb, 150kg in LEO), has a mobile service structure with a clean room for the integration of the satellite with the vehicle; the ASLV is vertically assembled under this structure on the launch pad itself. Two ASLV rockets were launched unsuccessfully in March 1987 and July 1988. Despite these failures, ISRO is progressing toward the first test launch of the PSLV (Polar Satellite Launch Vehicle), capable of placing a 2,205lb (1 tonne) class satellite in Sun-synchronous orbit at some 620 miles (1,000km) altitude. The PSLV launch facility, based on the concept of the Mobile Service Tower, is equipped for the preparation of the liquid second and fourth stages of the four-stage vehicle. For the 1990s, ISRO is developing the GSLV (Geosynchronous SLV), required to place 5,510lb (2·5 tonnes) class Insat-II satellites into geosynchronous transfer orbit. In the next decade, India plans to launch from SHAR some 10 indigenous spacecraft.

Sriharikota (SHAR)
1 Explosives storage.
2 Accommodation
3 Technical centre.
4 Telemetry building.
5 Sounding rocket complex.
6 Explosives storage
7 SLV-3 and ASLV launch complex.
8 Polar SLV (PSLV) launch complex.

9 Geosynchronous SLV (GSLV) launch complex.

The Sriharikota centre also includes a solid propellant plant and static rocket test facilities.

———— Road
■ Base facility
▲ Pad facility
▨ Rivers and lakes

Alcantara in Brazil

In 1981, the Instituto de Atividades Espaciais (IAE) decided to build a satellite launch site near the equator, on the coast of Northern Brazil. The Centro de Lançamento de Alcantara (CLA) with its modern facilities is located in a forest covering some 130 sq miles (520sq km). Before the establishment of CLA, Brazilian sounding rockets, named Sonda, were fired from a small launch complex near Natal, at Barreira do Inferno (Barrier of Hell). With the development of the indigenous VLS *(Veiculo Lancador de Satellite)*, a four-stage solid rocket which will be able to launch a 441lb (200kg) satellite into circular orbit at 310miles (500km), IAE needs a more complex infrastructure with laboratories, preparation halls, test facilities, checkout buildings and an airport. A city will also grow up near CLA.

While the Instituto de Pesquisas Espaciais (INPE) is developing within the planned schedule the first Brazilian MECB satellite (MECB means *Missao Espacial Completa Brasileira*) for a launch in 1989-1990, the IAE has encountered some delays in the acquisition of components for the VLS rocket. Brazilian authorities are seeking co-operation from West Germany, China and USSR to help them achieve their national ambitions in space. The CLA site, located at 2°24'S, has also been proposed for use by non-Brazilian launch vehicle operators.

Israeli Achievements

On 19 September 1988, Israel sprang a real surprise with the successful launch of its first satellite, named Offeq-1 (Horizon-1). This spin-stabilized, solar-powered, 344lb spacecraft, developed by Israel Aircraft Industries (with the assistance of German electronics industries) for the Israeli Space Agency (ISA), was launched by an indigenous solid rocket, the Shavit-2 vehicle, using ballistic missile systems and engines. Israel thus became the ninth country in the world to orbit a payload by its own means, from its territory. Israeli authorities did not publish detailed information about Shavit-2's characteristics and performances, nor about the

Below: *Israel's Shavit-2 launch vehicle after launch from Palmachim in the Negev desert on 19 September 1988.*

military launch site. However, we do know that Offeq-1 was launched in a retrograde trajectory (142·87° inclination) over the Mediterranean Sea from a Israeli Air Force Base at Palmachim, south of Tel Aviv. ISA plans to launch a satellite every year not only for scientific and technological experiments, but also for governmental and strategic purposes.

Private Launch Services

Since the late 1970s, a number of audacious entrepreneurs in the USA and Europe have tried to enter the satellite launch market by means of the private development of commercial space transportation services at competitive prices! Their hopes are vanishing because of lack of orders, of money and of public support. Geosynchronous spacecraft have found reliable launch vehicles in Europe's Ariane 4, the US Delta II, Atlas II and Titan III, H-I in Japan, and Proton in USSR. However, light spacecraft for technological purposes and for specific applications are seen by space investors as a potentially attractive and lucrative source of business. Other investors are looking for the most profitable locations of launch sites around the globe; sites in the Pacific Ocean, on equatorial islands, and on Cape York peninsula (Australia), are currently proposed as international spaceport candidates.

OTRAG *(Orbital Transport-und Raketen Aktiengesellschaft)* was a surprising German venture to market low-cost modular liquid rockets for satellite launch services. The first single propulsion modules were tested with partial success in 1977 and 1978 from a high plateau in North Shaba, then in 1980 from the Libyan desert, finally in 1983 from the Nordic Esrange (Kiruna in Sweden). OTRAG ceased activities during 1987.

Space Services Inc., based at Houston and supported by Texan investors, announced in 1980 the development of a Redstone-type rocket, named Percheron, but the first rocket was destroyed during a static test. SSI, under the management of NASA astronaut Deke Slayton, chose to develop a solid-propellant launcher, named Conestoga. Combining Morton Thiokol Castor and Star motors, the Conestoga family is conceived as a series of expendable launch vehicles for low-orbiting spacecraft with masses from 0·5 to 1 ton. SSI signed a launch agreement with NASA in 1986 to use facilities at Wallops Station. Fighting to survive, it claimed reservations for eight launches but did not identify them. The Celestis Group of Florida announced its particular interest in Conestoga vehicles for placing in orbit highly reflective satellites containing cremated human remains.

Pacific American Launch Systems, Inc. (PALS), founded in 1982, is introducing a small launch vehicle system called Liberty I. This privately funded, Californian enterprise started development tests in 1988 of its simple pressure-fed, coaxial-pintle injector rocket engine. It plans to launch a 441lb (200kg) satellite on a two-stage liquid vehicle from Vandenberg Air Force Base.

AMROC (American Rocket Company), also based in California, was incorporated in 1985 to continue the development work of Arc Technologies/Starstruck on a hybrid propulsion engine for the Dolphin launch

Above: *Space Services Inc. are trying to market the Conestoga family of modular launchers. This is Conestoga 2.*

vehicle. With private funding, it started a new project to develop a modular ILV or Industrial Launch Vehicle. This ILV-1 rocket will consist of four stages using hybrid motors (solid hydrocarbon fuel and liquid oxidizer). AMROC plans to test a single ILV module on a sub-orbital trajectory during 1989 from Vandenberg AFB. If it succeeds, and if major financing can be secured through private placement or launch order, AMROC will demonstrate its ability to put a 496lb (225kg) payload into a 155 mile (250km) circular polar orbit.

LittLEO (Little launch vehicle for Low Earth Orbit) is a four-stage solid propellant satellite launcher, being developed with European industrial participation. Conceived by British consultancy General Technology Systems (GTS), LittLEO is intended to put payloads of the order of 661lb-1,100lb (300-500kg) into polar orbits at 186 miles (300km) and higher altitudes. The Industrial team includes British Aerospace, MBB-ERNO, Royal Ordnance, SAAB Space and the Norwegian Space Centre. In addition to providing Europe's first satellite launch site — located at 69°17'N, 16°01'E, the Andoya Rocket Range has been operational since 1962 launching sounding rockets — Norway will be also be involved in the vehicle design and manufacture. The first launch of LittLEO carrying a Norwegian spacecraft may be expected in 1992.

Astra launch vehicles are proposed by E'Prime Aerospace Corporation, formed in Florida during 1987; they would be derived from the MX-Peacekeeper ballistic missiles that might be decommissioned under the Strategic Arms Reduction Talks (START). The E'Prime initiative represents a recent effort to convert decommissioned missiles into space launchers. The young company plans to take over two of the three MX production lines from the US Air Force, to develop a vehicle which would be able to put 16,000lb (7·2 tonnes) into LEO or 6,200lb (2·8 tonnes) into GTO. It is looking at Cape Canaveral and Cape York (Australia) as possible launch sites.

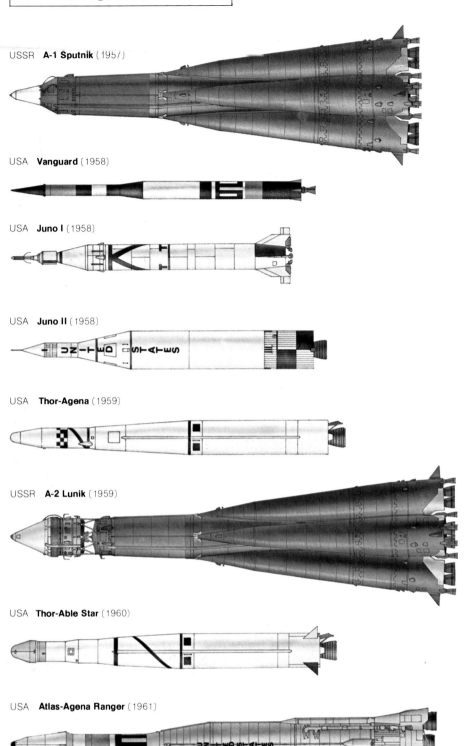

USSR **A-1 Sputnik** (1957)

USA **Vanguard** (1958)

USA **Juno I** (1958)

USA **Juno II** (1958)

USA **Thor-Agena** (1959)

USSR **A-2 Lunik** (1959)

USA **Thor-Able Star** (1960)

USA **Atlas-Agena Ranger** (1961)

USSR **A-2-e Mars/Venus** (1961)

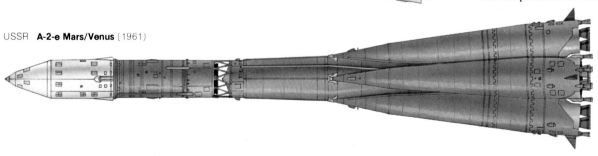

USA **Mercury-Redstone** (1961)

The Space Age followed strenuous efforts by the Soviet Union and the United States to develop ballistic missiles in the years following World War II. It was the Russians who took an early lead with the big R.7 intercontinental ballistic missile (SS-6 Sapwood) which received the go-ahead before scientists had achieved a "light weight" thermonuclear warhead. The Americans, on the other hand, waited for the thermonuclear break-through with the result that their first ICBM, the SM-65 Atlas, was smaller and more efficient.

Although inferior as a weapon — and highly exposed on its launch complex— it was the Russian rocket's greater lifting capacity that scored when it came to the launching of satellites and space probes. In contrast, America's decision to build a non-military rocket for launching satellites during the International Geophysical Year (1957-58) had got off to a poor start when the attempt to launch a 3·25lb (1·47kg) Vanguard test-satellite ended in humiliating failure.

For several years Russia enjoyed supremacy and incredibly the same basic rocket that launched the first Sputnik has been developed to launch whole families of space vehicles— from unmanned Earth satellites and lunar and interplanetary probes to the manned spacecraft Vostok, Voskhod, Soyuz, Soyuz T and Soyuz TM and the Progress unmanned cargo craft which supply Salyut and Mir space stations.

The United States replied by adapting a whole range of ballistic missiles for space purposes, including the Redstone, Jupiter, Thor and Atlas which, together with America's superiority in the miniaturisation of scientific instruments and electronic equipment, began to show remarkable progress. The advent of manned spaceflight had seen adaptations of the Redstone (for sub-orbital lobs) and Atlas and Titan II for orbital missions.

In these pages some of the launch vehicles that opened the space frontier are compared to scale. It is interesting, for example, to contrast the American Juno I and Vanguard with the Russian ICBM/ Sputnik launcher. At the other extreme we have the Saturn rocket that launched America's astronauts to the Moon. Soviet launch vehicles are based on studies by the American analyst Charles P. Vick who is also responsible for the maps of Soviet and

Chinese launch centres in this chapter.

Tiny multi-stage rockets like America's four stage Scout, France's Diamant series, Japan's Lambda-4S, Mu-4S and Mu-3C, Britain's Black Arrow, and India's SLV-3 enabled small satellites to be launched at least cost. China entered the field with the heavier launchers Long March 1 and FB-1, and Europe with Europa and Ariane.

In the military field the principal US launchers were Thor-Agena and Atlas-Agena which enabled the US Air Force to embark on programmes of reconnaissance, surveillance and early warning in the Sixties. Counterparts in the Soviet Union have been launched by A-1 and A-2 boosters — derivatives of the old Sputnik launcher — and adaptations of the second-generation ICBM known to the West as the SS-9 Scarp. The Scarp has been used with appropriate upper staging to launch the Fractional Orbit Bombardment System (FOBS), the Satellite Interceptor System (SIS) and ocean-surveillance satellites.

Much effort in recent years has gone into upgrading the performance of launch vehicles mainly by improving the performance of upper stages and fitting strap-on solid-fuel boosters to increase the launch thrust. Particularly successful has been the large family of reliable Delta rockets.

The need to get satellites, particularly those used for relaying telecommunications, into Clarke orbit 22,300 miles (35,880km) above the equator led in the United States to improved models of Delta and Atlas-Centaur, the latter making use of high-energy propellants (LO_2/LH_2) in the top stage. Atlas-Agena and Atlas-Centaur became the means of sending space probes to the Moon, testing the ground for man, and also launched space probes to Venus and Mars. Russia had begun her quest for the planets with the A-2-e launcher, following this with an adaptation of the larger Proton D-1 satellite launcher introduced in 1965. Rockets of the D family also became the means of sending robot spacecraft to the Moon. Later, similar launchers were used to send second-generation probes to Venus and Mars. The D-1 launched the Salyut and Mir space stations.

Meanwhile, great strides had been made in the United States through the development of the Titan fitted with large solid-fuel strap-on boosters of 10ft (3·05m) diameter, which resulted in another important rocket family responsible for launching a wide variety of civilian and military payloads. Titan IIIC put up a series of military communications satellites and Titan IIID was responsible for launching the Lockheed "Big Bird" and KH-11 "Keyhole" reconnaissance satellites. Combination of the Titan IIIC and the Centaur upper stage led to the powerful Titan IIIE-Centaur which launched the Viking and Voyager spacecraft. More recently, Titan 34D, Commerial Titan III and Titan IV — a still heavier launcher — have emerged.

All previous rockets had been expendable, throwing off non-retrievable stages as they proceeded into orbit.

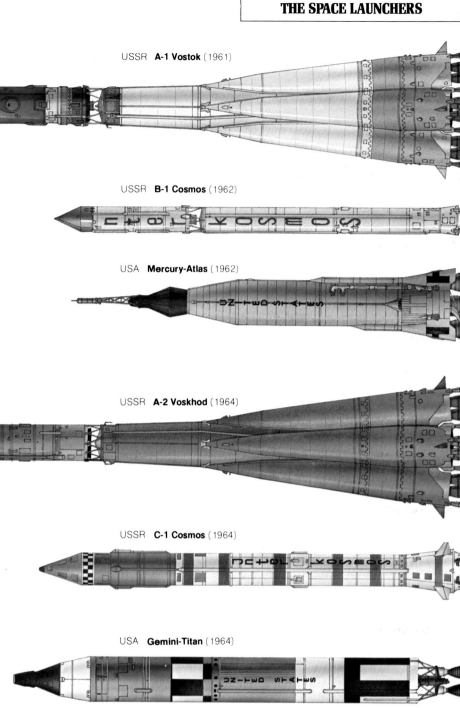

USSR **A-1 Vostok** (1961)

USSR **B-1 Cosmos** (1962)

USA **Mercury-Atlas** (1962)

USSR **A-2 Voskhod** (1964)

USSR **C-1 Cosmos** (1964)

USA **Gemini-Titan** (1964)

USA **Delta E** (1965)

France **Diamant A** (1965)

USSR **D-1 Proton** (1965)

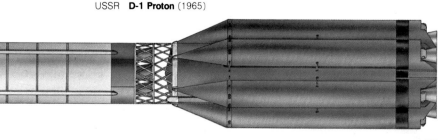

55

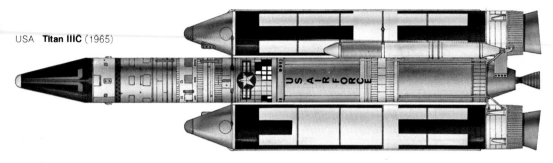

USA   **Titan IIIC** (1965)

USA   **Titan IIIB-Agena** (1966)

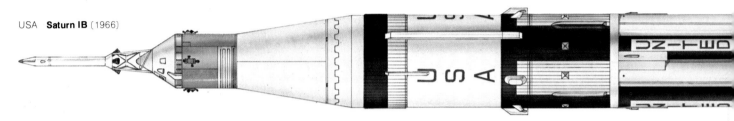

USA   **Saturn IB** (1966)

USSR   **F-1-r FOBS** (1967)

USSR   **A-2 Soyuz** (1967)

USSR   **F-1-m SIS** (1967)

USA   **Saturn V Apollo** (1967)

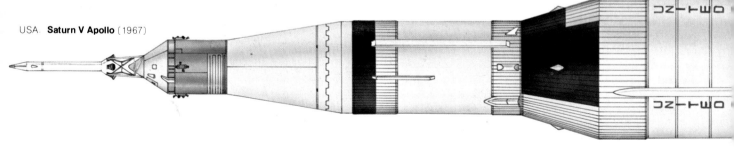

USSR   **D-1-e Zond** (1968)

For a long time designers dreamed of ending this wasteful procedure by making space flight more like normal aircraft operations. America's Space Shuttle was the first to exploit this technique in 1981. The Soviet Union followed with *Buran* in 1988, the first of a series of winged shuttles launched by the newly-developed Energiya rocket. The Energiya designers aim to recover parts of the launch vehicle, first the big liquid propellant boosters using parachutes, retro-rockets and cushioning devices. In a later version of this versatile rocket, there is even talk of fitting wings to the core.

Energiya is based on a modular design philosophy which allows steady development well into the 21st century. It

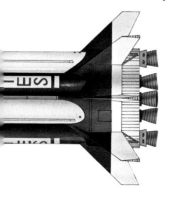

will operate with combinations of two, four and six strap-on boosters and can carry a wide range of alternative payloads, mounted piggyback, including large manoeuvrable rocket stages.

The ultimate development is a lengthened core vehicle with eight strap-

ons, raising payloads delivered into low Earth orbit to a massive 440,900lb (200 tonnes). This cannot be achieved without some redesign and strengthening of the basic structure but it does show how farsighted Soviet designers have been in setting the specifications. Energiya, they

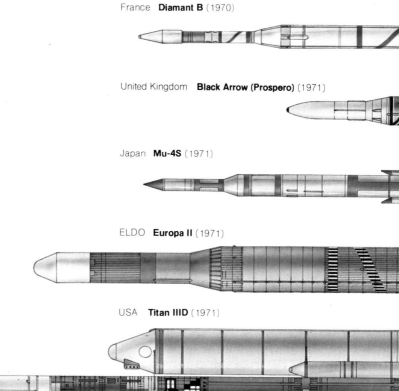

Japan **Lambda-4S-5** (1970)

China-1 **CSL-1 Long March 1** (1970)

France **Diamant B** (1970)

United Kingdom **Black Arrow (Prospero)** (1971)

Japan **Mu-4S** (1971)

ELDO **Europa II** (1971)

USA **Titan IIID** (1971)

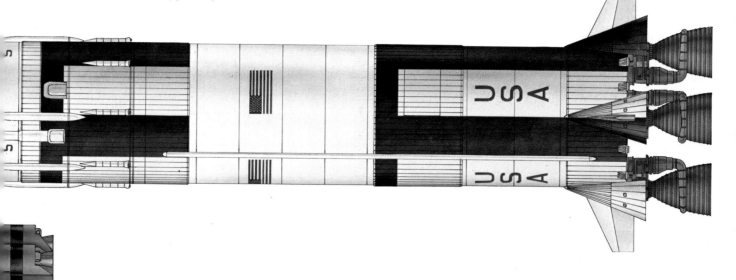

feet	100	90	80	70	60	50	40	30	20	10	0
metres	30			20				10			0

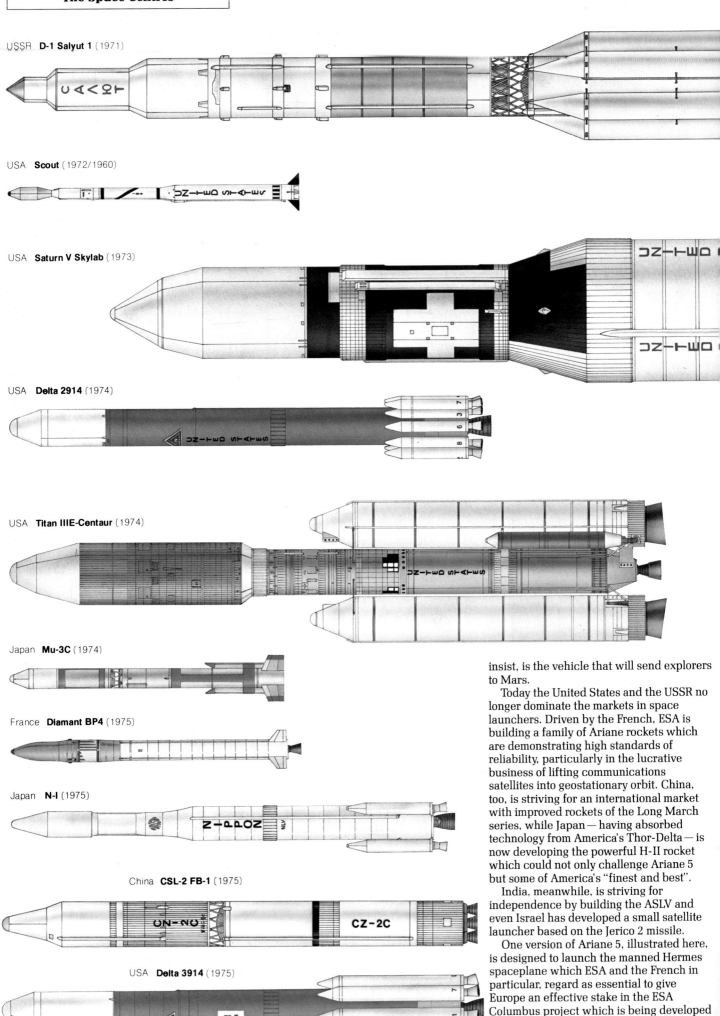

USSR **D-1 Salyut 1** (1971)

USA **Scout** (1972/1960)

USA **Saturn V Skylab** (1973)

USA **Delta 2914** (1974)

USA **Titan IIIE-Centaur** (1974)

Japan **Mu-3C** (1974)

France **Diamant BP4** (1975)

Japan **N-I** (1975)

China **CSL-2 FB-1** (1975)

USA **Delta 3914** (1975)

insist, is the vehicle that will send explorers to Mars.

Today the United States and the USSR no longer dominate the markets in space launchers. Driven by the French, ESA is building a family of Ariane rockets which are demonstrating high standards of reliability, particularly in the lucrative business of lifting communications satellites into geostationary orbit. China, too, is striving for an international market with improved rockets of the Long March series, while Japan — having absorbed technology from America's Thor-Delta — is now developing the powerful H-II rocket which could not only challenge Ariane 5 but some of America's "finest and best".

India, meanwhile, is striving for independence by building the ASLV and even Israel has developed a small satellite launcher based on the Jerico 2 missile.

One version of Ariane 5, illustrated here, is designed to launch the manned Hermes spaceplane which ESA and the French in particular, regard as essential to give Europe an effective stake in the ESA Columbus project which is being developed to complement the US International Space Station "Freedom".

USA **Atlas E/F** (1977/1961)

USSR **F-2 Tsyklon** (1977)

Japan **Mu-3H** (1977)

USA **Atlas-Centaur** (1977/1962)

ESA **Ariane I** (1979)

India **SLV-3** (1979)

USA **Space Shuttle** (1981)

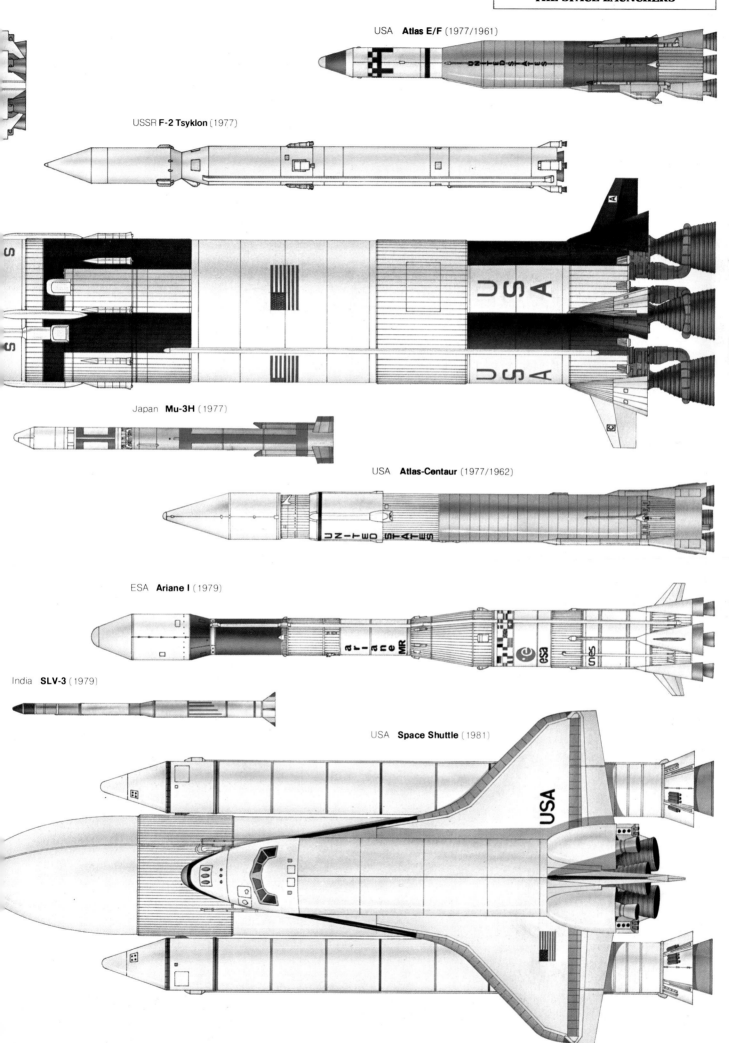

USA **Titan 34D** (1982)

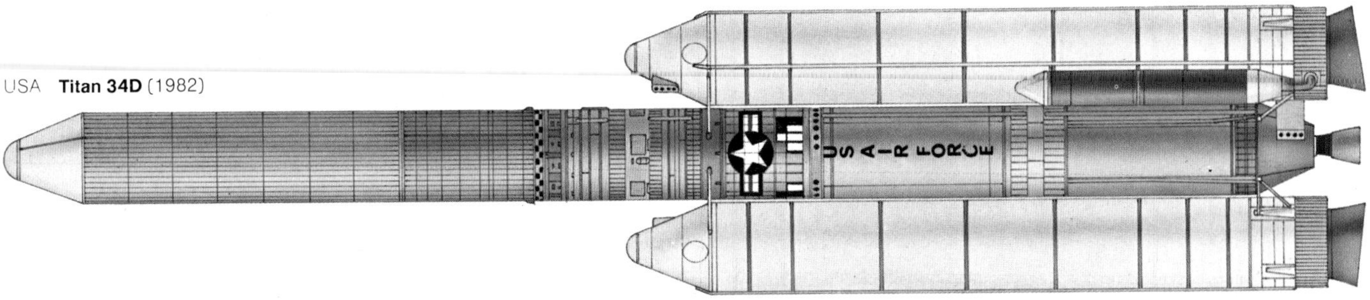

USA **Delta 3920** (1982)

Japan **N-II** (1981)

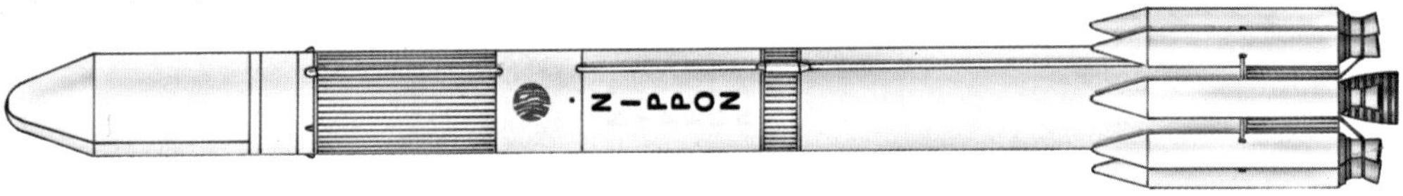

China **CZ-3** (1984)

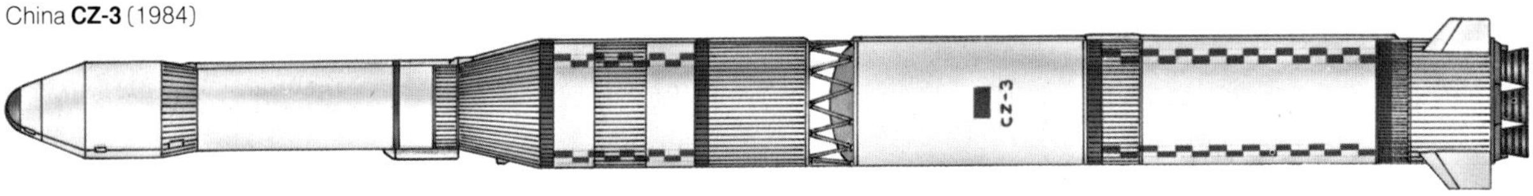

ESA **Ariane 3** (1984)

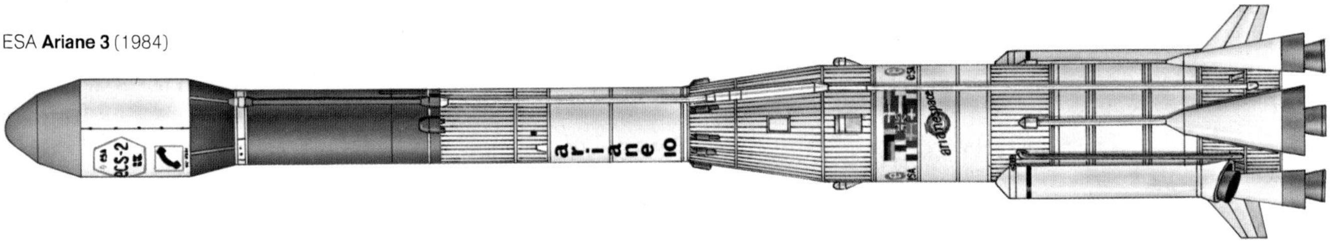

India **ASLV** (1987)

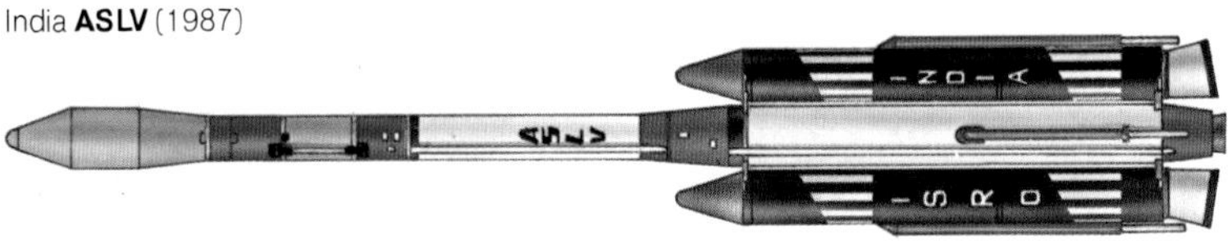

Japan **H-I** (1987)

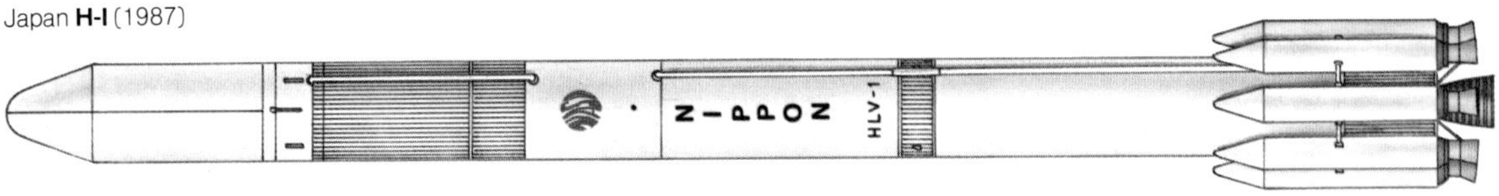

ESA **Ariane 4** (44LP) (1988)

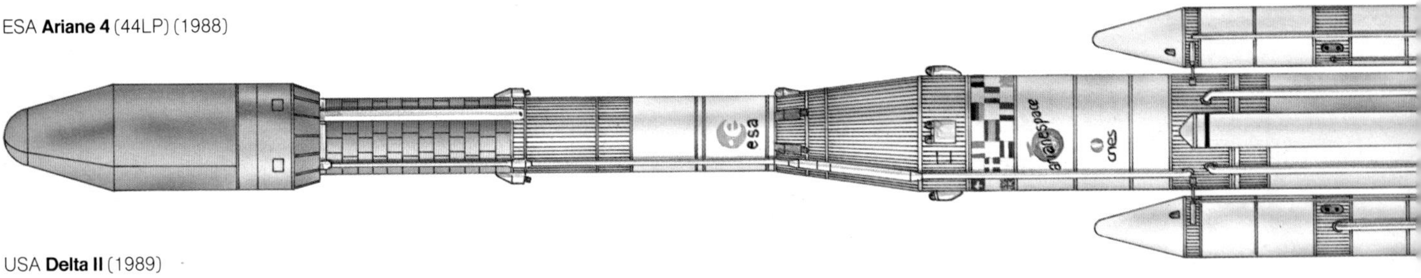

USA **Delta II** (1989)

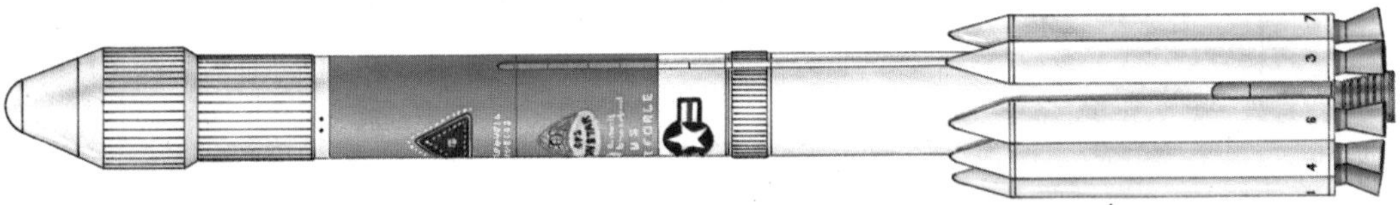

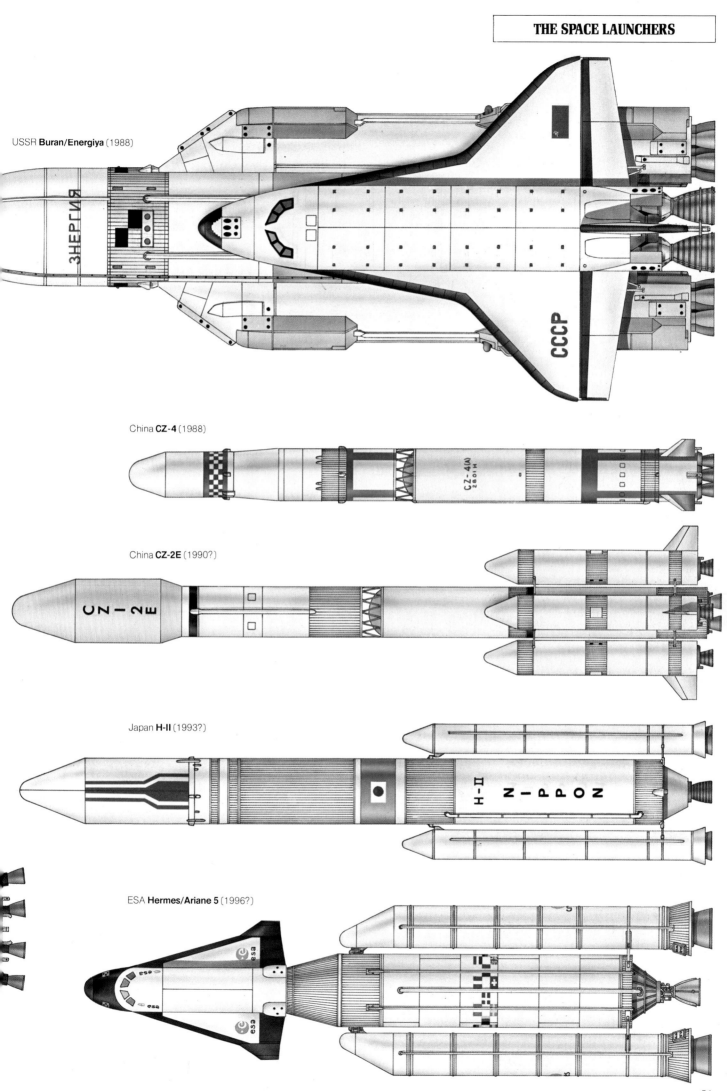

USSR **Buran/Energiya** (1988)

China **CZ-4** (1988)

China **CZ-2E** (1990?)

Japan **H-II** (1993?)

ESA **Hermes/Ariane 5** (1996?)

Man in Space

Dawn of 12 April 1961 was a typical spring day on the steppes of Kazakhstan. There were few clouds, and the day promised to be a warm one. The peasants of Tyuratam hamlet were heading for work in their melon and grain fields, except for a few who decided it would be a good day for fishing in the Syr Darya River.

However, the scene was not so tranquil some four or five kilometres to the north. There, in the Soviet Union's growing space and missile centre, a huge white rocket stood out against the bright blue sky. It was an SS-6 (Sapwood) intercontinental ballistic missile, but there was no nuclear warhead on top of it.

In the place of a warhead, a Vostok manned spacecraft (named *Swallow*) held Lieutenant, soon to be Major, Yuri A. Gagarin, of the Soviet Air Force, who was busy making last-minute checks before being launched at 0907hr Moscow time. The launching went smoothly. He entered an orbit with a perigee of 112·4 miles (181km) and an apogee of 203 miles (327km). The Swallow made one orbit of Earth in 89min at an inclination of 65°. In 108min after launching, he was back on Earth, having landed near the small village of Smelovaka.

Within four years of orbiting the Earth's first artificial satellite, the USSR had placed the first man into space.

Gagarin, born 9 March 1934, was the son of a carpenter. He joined the air force in 1955 and won his wings as a jet pilot in 1957. He was accepted for cosmonaut training in 1959, but died in an air crash on 27 March 1968 and his ashes were buried in the wall of the Kremlin: a mark of his prestige.

Vostok Spacecraft

The Vostok spacecraft[1] was the work of a team of scientists and engineers led by the Soviet Union's pioneer aerospace engineer, Sergei P. Korolev. It consisted of two sections or modules. The manned module was a sphere 7·5ft (2·3m) in diameter covered with an ablative material to protect it during re-entry into the atmosphere. It contained automatic and ground-activated controls, but there were emergency manual controls for the cosmonaut. The atmosphere environment was a mixture of oxygen and nitrogen at a pressure of one atmosphere. The pilot sat in an aircraft-type ejection seat with a parachute and communications equipment. Small rockets at its base could propel the seat through a circular hatch in the module in case of emergency.

The manned module was held by metal straps to an equipment module, 8·46ft

> "They felt that their bodies were absolutely without weight. Their arms, fully extended, no longer sought their sides.... Their feet no longer rested on the floor. In their efforts to hold themselves straight they looked like drunken men trying to maintain the perpendicular."
>
> Jules Verne
> *De la terre à la lune*

(2·58m) in diameter and 10·17ft (3·1m) long. Everything not actually required within the manned module was stowed in the equipment module. It held high-pressure nitrogen and oxygen bottles for use in the manned module, chemical batteries for radios and instruments, the retro-rocket used to brake the Vostok out of orbit, and small attitude control thrusters for orientating the spacecraft. Vostok 1 weighed 10,419lb (4,725kg), but the weights of other craft in this series varied from mission to mission.

After a mission, Vostok was prepared for return to Earth by a computer programme that sent specific radio commands to the spacecraft. The attitude-control thrusters orientated the craft with respect to the Earth for the proper re-entry angle. Once in the proper attitude, the retro-rocket fired and reduced its orbital velocity. At the same

Below: *Yuri Gagarin makes a check of vital systems in the Vostok capsule before his epic 108 minute space flight on 12 April 1961. In charge of the mission was the space pioneer Sergei P. Korolev.*

Above: *A Vostok launcher on display in the Soviet Union. When first revealed in 1967, Western observers were surprised to find that 32 thrust chambers—20 main and 12 vernier—had to ignite at lift-off.*

Above: *Rocket-propelled ejection seat which was installed at an angle in the Vostok capsule behind a jettisonable hatch. After ejection, the cosmonaut separated from the seat and used his own parachute to land.*

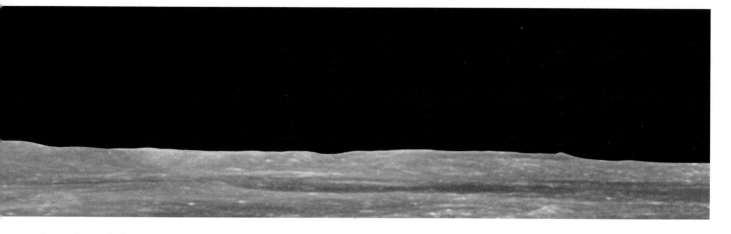

time, the explosive bolts severed the straps holding the Vostok to its equipment section, and the spacecraft began its fiery plunge back through Earth's atmosphere.

At an altitude of some 4·3 miles (7km), the cosmonaut's hatch was blown from the capsule, and he ejected from it in his seat. A parachute opened and the cosmonaut descended for a certain distance before jettisoning the seat so he would not be injured by it in landing. The Vostok capsule came down separately by its own parachute. It was initially reported that Yuri Gagarin had actually landed inside his capsule, but it was later officially confirmed that he had, in fact, ejected and followed the standard landing procedure.

The Vostok had been tested five times in space before it was declared safe for men. Between 15 May 1960 and 25 March 1961 these spacecraft were orbited under the name of *Korabl Sputnik*. They contained dogs, mannequins, and various biological experiments. Four of these Vostoks had recovery capsules mounted in the cosmonaut's seat. Three were recovered. The

last two in the series made just one orbit before re-entry, as did Vostok 1. The others made 17 orbits, as would Vostok 2.

The second man into space did not orbit Earth, nor did the third.

Mercury Flights
Following Gagarin's historic flight, two American astronauts made sub-orbital flights to test the Mercury spacecraft, their nation's answer to Vostok. On 5 May 1961 less than four weeks after Gagarin's flight, Commander Alan B. Shepard, an American naval officer, became its first astronaut on a technicality. While he did not orbit Earth, he reached an altitude of some 116 miles (186km) above it. By American ground rules, anyone who went above 50 miles (80km) would be awarded astronaut status. (Thus, several pilots of the X-15 rocket-propelled aircraft actually became astronauts.) Shepard, launched from Cape Canaveral in Mercury 3 (*Freedom 7*) atop a modified Redstone ballistic missile, spent 15min and 22sec in flight before landing in the Atlantic. He proved that a man could manually

control a spacecraft though he is weightless. On 21 July Shepard's fellow astronaut, Major Virgil I. Grissom, US Air Force, duplicated his ballistic flight in Mercury 4 (*Liberty Bell 7*), but very nearly drowned when his Mercury sank following the unscheduled blow-out of the escape hatch.

The Mercury spacecraft differed markedly from the Vostok. It consisted of only one module, the manned capsule. It had the shape of a truncated cone and was 9·51ft (2·9m) long and 6·17ft (1·89m) in diameter at the base. Its nickel-alloy pressure vessel had an outer shell of titanium for protection against the heat of re-entry. A special heatshield on the base was made of an ablative material similar to that of Vostok. The retrorocket unit consisted of three solid-propellant rockets, each producing 1,160lb (526kg) of thrust. The retro-rocket package 66

Below: *Marine Sikorsky UH34 helicopter lifts Alan Shepard's Mercury capsule Freedom 7 from the Atlantic after its flight on 5 May 1961. Note marker dye and the deployed landing bag venting water.*

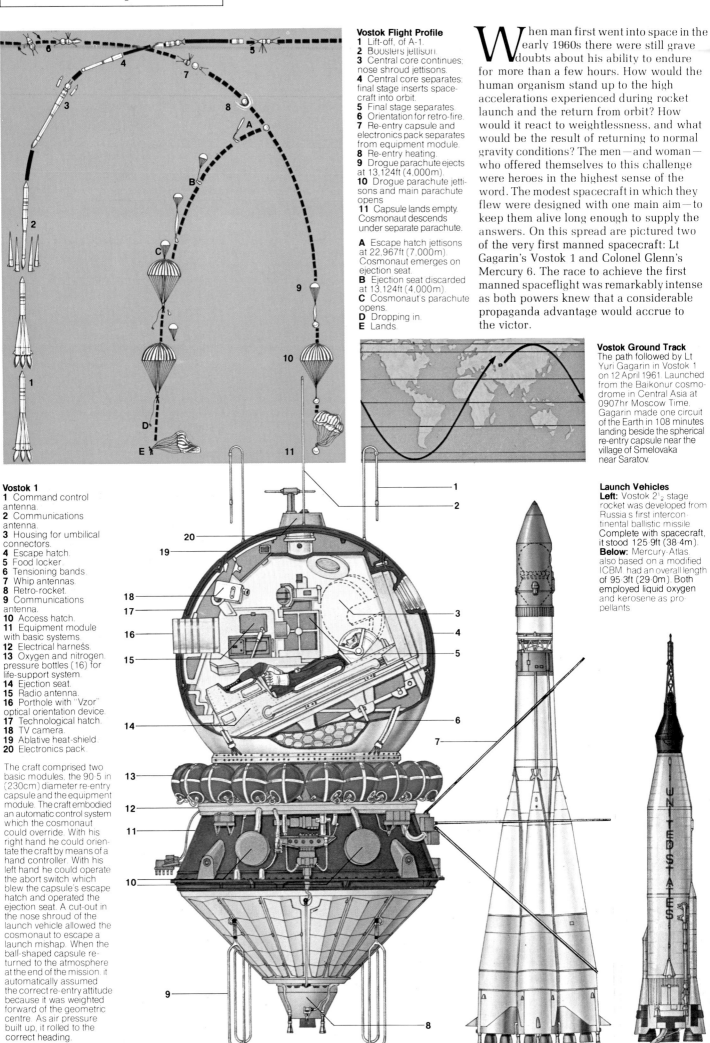

Vostok Flight Profile
1 Lift-off, of A-1.
2 Boosters jettison.
3 Central core continues; nose shroud jettisons.
4 Central core separates; final stage inserts space-craft into orbit.
5 Final stage separates.
6 Orientation for retro-fire.
7 Re-entry capsule and electronics pack separates from equipment module.
8 Re-entry heating.
9 Drogue parachute ejects at 13,124ft (4,000m).
10 Drogue parachute jettisons and main parachute opens.
11 Capsule lands empty. Cosmonaut descends under separate parachute.

A Escape hatch jettisons at 22,967ft (7,000m). Cosmonaut emerges on ejection seat.
B Ejection seat discarded at 13,124ft (4,000m).
C Cosmonaut's parachute opens.
D Dropping in.
E Lands.

When man first went into space in the early 1960s there were still grave doubts about his ability to endure for more than a few hours. How would the human organism stand up to the high accelerations experienced during rocket launch and the return from orbit? How would it react to weightlessness, and what would be the result of returning to normal gravity conditions? The men—and woman— who offered themselves to this challenge were heroes in the highest sense of the word. The modest spacecraft in which they flew were designed with one main aim—to keep them alive long enough to supply the answers. On this spread are pictured two of the very first manned spacecraft: Lt Gagarin's Vostok 1 and Colonel Glenn's Mercury 6. The race to achieve the first manned spaceflight was remarkably intense as both powers knew that a considerable propaganda advantage would accrue to the victor.

Vostok Ground Track
The path followed by Lt Yuri Gagarin in Vostok 1 on 12 April 1961. Launched from the Baikonur cosmo-drome in Central Asia at 0907hr Moscow Time, Gagarin made one circuit of the Earth in 108 minutes landing beside the spherical re-entry capsule near the village of Smelovaka near Saratov.

Vostok 1
1 Command control antenna.
2 Communications antenna.
3 Housing for umbilical connectors.
4 Escape hatch.
5 Food locker.
6 Tensioning bands.
7 Whip antennas.
8 Retro-rocket.
9 Communications antenna.
10 Access hatch.
11 Equipment module with basic systems.
12 Electrical harness.
13 Oxygen and nitrogen pressure bottles (16) for life-support system.
14 Ejection seat.
15 Radio antenna.
16 Porthole with "Vzor" optical orientation device.
17 Technological hatch.
18 TV camera.
19 Ablative heat-shield.
20 Electronics pack.

The craft comprised two basic modules, the 90·5 in (230cm) diameter re-entry capsule and the equipment module. The craft embodied an automatic control system which the cosmonaut could override. With his right hand he could orientate the craft by means of a hand controller. With his left hand he could operate the abort switch which blew the capsule's escape hatch and operated the ejection seat. A cut-out in the nose shroud of the launch vehicle allowed the cosmonaut to escape a launch mishap. When the ball-shaped capsule returned to the atmosphere at the end of the mission, it automatically assumed the correct re-entry attitude because it was weighted forward of the geometric centre. As air pressure built up, it rolled to the correct heading.

Launch Vehicles
Left: Vostok 2½ stage rocket was developed from Russia's first intercontinental ballistic missile. Complete with spacecraft, it stood 125·9ft (38·4m).
Below: Mercury-Atlas, also based on a modified ICBM, had an overall length of 95·3ft (29·0m). Both employed liquid oxygen and kerosene as propellants.

Mercury Flight Control
1 Pitch thrusters.
2 Lock pin.
3 Pitch control linkage.
4 Roll control linkage.
5 Yaw control linkage.
6 Locked position.
7 Trigger.
8 Roll thrusters.
9 Yaw thrusters.

Compared with the highly computerised systems used in today's spacecraft, the Mercury astronauts had only basic instrumentation and were encouraged to use manual controls. This drawing shows the action of the three-axis stick which the astronaut used to achieve control in pitch yaw and roll. Control actions released gas from appropriate thrusters on the spacecraft. When problems arose with the automatic attitude system, John Glenn switched to manual control to fly *Friendship 7*.

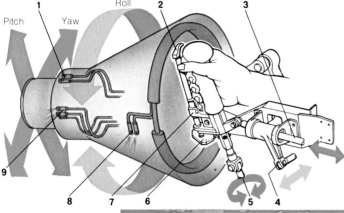

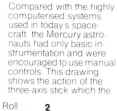

Mercury Ground Track
The path followed by Col John Glenn after his launching from Cape Canaveral, Florida on 20 February 1962. Black spot represents the pre-staging abort zone; hatched area the abort zone following booster separation. White spots represent preferred contingency landing places from orbit.

Mercury Splashdown
When the capsule returned to Earth it was first braked by drogue parachute. The main ring-sail parachute opened in a reefed condition, then inflated fully. A landing bag deployed ready for splashdown. This involved detaching the heat shield which dropped down 4ft (1·2m) pulling out a perforated skirt of rubberised glassfibre. This served as an air-cushion to reduce the landing shock. Immediately after landing, the main parachute was automatically disconnected and the capsule had sufficient buoyancy to float upright in the water. The astronaut waited inside until retrieved by a naval vessel.

Mercury Capsule
1 Aerodynamic "spike".
2 Escape rocket with three angled nozzles.
3 Infra-red horizon sensors.
4 Aerodynamic fairing.
5 Yaw thrusters.
6 Main and reserve 63ft (19·2m) diameter ring-sail parachutes.
7 Periscope.
8 Double-walled pressure cabin.
9 Instrument panels.
10 Three-axis attitude controller (*see above left*).
11 Roll thrusters.
12 Form-fitting couch and restraints.
13 Ablative heat-shield.
14 Retro-rocket restraint strap.
15 Separation rockets.
16 Retro-rockets.
17 Hydrogen peroxide tank.
18 Abort control.
19 Skin shingles.
20 Titanium top-hat stringer.
21 Pitch thrusters.
22 Hydrogen peroxide bottles.
23 6ft (1·8m) diameter conical ribbon drogue parachute.
24 Tower separation rockets.

In this drawing the astronaut's tight fit in the pressurised capsule is clearly illustrated. The escape tower was designed to pull the capsule clear of the launch vehicle in the event of a mishap on the launch pad or after take-off. It jettisoned from the rocket when a safe altitude had been reached, after separation of the boost engines. During re-entry the heat shield was subjected to a maximum temperature of about 1,650°C at an altitude of 25 miles (40.2km) as the capsule moved at some 15,000mph

Mercury Cabin Arrangement
1 Astronaut's window.
2 Hatch release initiator.
3 Main instrument consoles.
4 Periscope display.
5 Escape hatch.
6 Small pressure bulkhead.
7 Astronaut's toe guards.
8 Map and chart kit.
9 Tape recorder.
10 Nitrogen bottles.
11 Astronaut observer camera.
12 Left console.
13 Flood lights.

This is the layout of the Mercury cabin in which John Glenn was launched from Cape Canaveral, Florida. The astronaut was tightly wedged into the capsule and so all the instrument displays were designed to be easily visible, while the fly-by-wire and abort controls were readily to hand. He circled the Earth three times in a flight lasting 4 hours 55 minutes and 23 seconds, splashing down in the Atlantic about 210 miles (338km) northwest of San Juan, Puerto Rico. The later manned Mercury flights were: MA 7 (Scott Carpenter); MA 8 (Walter Schirra); MA 9 (Gordon Cooper). A 3-day MA 10 mission was finally turned down. It is interesting to note that while John Glenn's mission lifted off some 22 months late, Cooper's flight took place only 4 months after the decision to go ahead with it. Total cost of the programme was $392,100,100.

Technical Data
Overall height (including escape tower and aerodynamic spike): 26ft (7·9m). Width (across the heat shield): 74·5in (189cm). Weight at lift-off (including escape tower): 4,265lb (1,934kg). Weight in orbit: 2,987lb (1,355kg). Weight at splashdown: 2,493lb (1,130kg).*
*Figures refer to the MA 6.

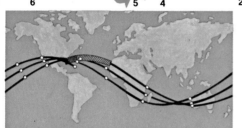
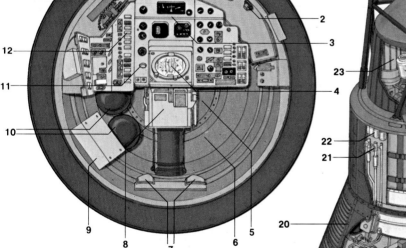

was attached by metal straps to the heat-shield. The spacecraft also had 18 small thrusters for attitude control. Mercury had a cabin environment of pure oxygen at a pressure of 5lb/sq in (·36kg/sq cm). Instead of an ejection seat, astronauts depended upon an escape rocket mounted on a tower attached to the top of the spacecraft. If not required, the tower was jettisoned.

The re-entry sequence was much the same as that of Vostok. The attitude-control thrusters orientated Mercury to the proper angle, and the retro-rockets fired and were then separated. Mercury entered the atmosphere base down. Because of its shape, a degree of aerodynamic control was available during the transit of the atmosphere because the spacecraft produced some lift. By using the manual controls, the astronaut could vary his flight path and so his touchdown point. In the final stage of descent, a parachute deployed and lowered the Mercury and the astronaut gently into the sea.

The second man to orbit Earth was Soviet Air Force Maj Gherman S. Titov, who was launched from the Baikonur cosmodrome on 6 August 1961. Unlike the single orbit made by Gagarin, Titov made 17 orbits, spending 25hr and 18min in space.

On 20 February 1962 America made it into orbit. Lt-Col John Glenn, US Marine Corps, was launched in Mercury 6 (*Friendship 7*) by a modified Atlas ICBM from Cape Canaveral. His mission, like Gagarin's, was a cautious one. Glenn spent only 4hr and 55min circling the Earth, completing just three orbits before landing safely.

Glenn's objective was to evaluate man in Mercury. The spacecraft had previously been tested unmanned in space—although two monkeys and a chimpanzee had flown in it—and it was felt ready and reliable enough for its pilot. Although he had some trouble adjusting to the use of the hand control during re-entry, the mission was a success. On 24 May Mercury 7 (*Aurora 7*), with Lt-Cdr M. Scott Carpenter, US Navy, flew an almost identical mission to corroborate Glenn's performance.

On 11 August 1962 the Soviets returned to space with Vostok 3 (*Falcon*). The cosmonaut was Major Andrian G. Nikolayev, who was joined in space on the following day by Lt-Col Pavel R. Popovich in Vostok 4 (*Golden Eagle*). Their spacecraft passed within four miles (6·5km) of each other. While the mission made for a good stunt, it did little to advance the state-of-the-art of astronautics; neither Vostok nor Mercury had the rocket motor and control system necessary to permit two spacecraft to rendezvous in orbit. However, the Soviets logged valuable experience. Nikolayev made 64 orbits in 94hr 22min, while Popovich rounded out 48 orbits after 70hr 57min.

Honours returned to the USA on 3 October when Cdr Walter M. Schirra, US Navy, was orbited in Mercury 8 (*Sigma 7*). His mission was to verify the man-machine concept upon which the Mercury was designed.

Right: *Nearly 10 months after Yuri Gagarin had triumphed with Vostok 1, Lt-Col John Glenn heads for orbit aboard the Mercury capsule* Friendship 7. *After the 3-orbit flight Glenn was given a ticker-tape welcome in the Lindbergh tradition.*

Above: The original seven Mercury astronauts pose for posterity in front of a USAF F-106B. Left to right: M. Scott Carpenter; Leroy G. Cooper, Jr.; John H. Glenn, Jr.; Virgil I. Grissom; Walter M. Schirra, Jr.; Alan B. Shepard, Jr.; and Donald K. Slayton. Grissom was later to die at Cape Kennedy in the Apollo fire while Shepard led the Apollo 14 mission, and Slayton flew in the Apollo-Soyuz Test Project.

Above: The interior of L. Gordon Cooper's Mercury capsule Faith 7. Note the fairly rudimentary structure of the spacecraft. At the time the Soviets were increasing their lead with Vostok.

Above: Valentina Tereshkova was the courageous woman who flew in Vostok 6 in June 1963. She completed 48 revolutions of the Earth. Several Soviet and US women have now followed her into space.

While Glenn and Carpenter had proved that man could function in space with no serious difficulties owing to weightlessness, Schirra was to prove that man and Mercury could work together for longer periods of time than previously demonstrated. He spent 9hr 13min in making six orbits and turned in a successful mission.

Mercury made its last appearance in space on 15 May 1963, when Major L. Gordon Cooper, US Air Force, orbited in Mercury 9 (Faith 7). It was to be an extension of Schirra's mission lasting more than a day. Cooper made 22 orbits during his 34hr 20min aloft.

Woman in Space

During the same year, Vostok also made its last appearance, and it did so with characteristic Soviet élan.

On 14 June 1963 Vostok 5 (Hawk) was launched from Baikonur with Lt-Col Valery F. Bykovsky aboard. For two days he manually controlled the spacecraft, performed medical experiments, and made observations of Earth and the stars. As he passed over Baikonur on 16 June, Vostok 6 (Sea Gull) lifted off into an orbit that closely matched his.[2] In it was Valentina V. Tereshkova, a civilian who had been given the Air Force rank of junior lieutenant shortly before the flight. Thus, woman had taken her first steps across the space frontier. Though Tereshkova, and the world, thought that she

was to be the first of many, it was not until 1982 that another woman went into space. She had spent 70hr 50min in space; Bykovsky remained aloft for 119hr 6min.

Tereshkova was born 6 March 1937 the daughter of a tractor driver on a collective farm. Something of a hoyden as a young girl, she was fiercely competitive, especially against boys and their physical activities. As a young woman, she worked first in a tyre factory and then as a textile worker. Tereshkova joined a parachutist club in Yarolslavl and through it applied for training as a cosmonaut in 1962. Accepted with four other women, she went through an abbreviated training programme with her male counterparts. After her mission, she married cosmonaut Nikolayev. On 8 June 1964 she gave birth to a daughter Yelena, who had the distinction of becoming the first child born on Earth both of whose parents had been in space. Tereshkova later completed her formal technical education and became a staff member at the Yuri A. Gagarin Training School for Cosmonauts near Moscow.

With the completion of the Vostok and Mercury programmes, it would be more than a year before man next went into space. When he did, it was again the Soviets who led the way. They did so in a short-lived spacecraft called Voskhod. In fact, it was a Vostok capsule greatly modified for missions impossible with the original design.

Voskhod 1 (Ruby) was launched on 12 October 1964 with three men aboard—another Soviet first in the competition with the USA. These cosmonauts were Dr (of medicine) Boris B. Yegorov; Dr (of science) Konstantin P. Feoktistov, and Col Vladimir M. Komarov. Feoktistov, who was a spacecraft designer, made the mission apparently with only minimal cosmonaut training but great faith in his handiwork.

For the mission, the interior of the Vostok had been modified to accept three couches for cosmonauts who, because of the cramped quarters, would not be wearing bulky space-suits. Vostok had proven the pressure integrity of the vehicle sufficiently to take such a seemingly daring departure from usual procedures. Because of the additional weight of the crew and their environmental needs, Voskhod weighed 11,730lb (5,320kg).

The three men spent 24hr and 17min in space, making 16 orbits. For the first time, there was a physician aboard who could, and did, make *in situ* medical examinations and experiments. Feoktistov was also able to make first-hand observations in flight of a spacecraft with whose operation he had formerly been acquainted only in design, fabrication and testing. Komarov was the military commander of the craft and had been through the complete cosmonaut training programme.

Since there was no way to deploy three ejection seats from the Voskhod, the cosmonauts were obliged literally to go down with their ship. To cushion the impact of landing, a special arrangement of retro-rockets fired just before touchdown, greatly reducing the landing velocity.

Voskhod 2 (*Diamond*) was even more of a surprise to the world and, again, gave the Soviets another first in space. It was launched from Baikonur on 18 March 1965, with only two cosmonauts aboard. They were Col Pavel I. Belyaev and Lt-Col Alexei A. Leonov. For their mission, the interior of the manned compartment was again redesigned. Since the primary objective of the mission called for both men to wear spacesuits, only two men could be accommodated. The space that could have been

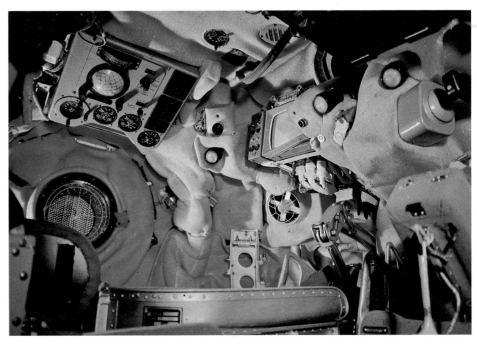

filled by a non-spacesuited cosmonaut was occupied by a collapsible airlock.

Once in orbit, the crew purged themselves of nitrogen by breathing pure oxygen. Then they depressurised the Voskhod and deployed the airlock. Leonov entered it, sealed the hatch to the spacecraft, and after spending some 10 minutes inside the airlock emerged as the first man to walk in space. He did so for 10 minutes and returned to the airlock preparatory to re-entering the Voskhod. During his venture, he was connected

Above: *Inside the cabin of Voskhod 1 in which three men of different specialisation gained experience of space flight: Col Vladimir Komarov (cosmonaut); Boris Yegorov (medical doctor) and Konstantin Feoktistov (spacecraft designer).*

to the spacecraft only by telephone and telemetry cables. His oxygen came from a back-pack on his spacesuit.

While his time outside Voskhod was relatively brief, Leonov's activities reinforced

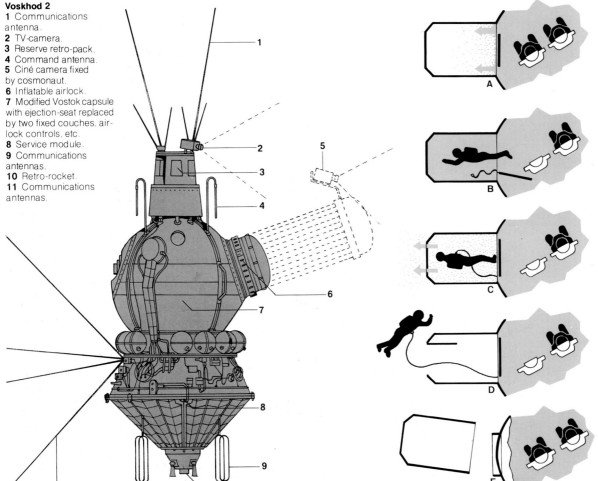

Voskhod 2
1 Communications antenna.
2 TV-camera.
3 Reserve retro-pack.
4 Command antenna.
5 Ciné camera fixed by cosmonaut.
6 Inflatable airlock.
7 Modified Vostok capsule with ejection-seat replaced by two fixed couches, airlock controls, etc.
8 Service module.
9 Communications antennas.
10 Retro-rocket.
11 Communications antennas.

EVA Procedure
A Cosmonauts (both in spacesuits) deploy and pressurise airlock.
B Leonov enters airlock sealing hatch behind him.
C Depressurises airlock, attaches tether and after 10 minutes opens external hatch.
D Leonov (supplied by oxygen bottles on his back) emerges from airlock to spend some 10 minutes in free space.
E After returning to the airlock, the outer hatch is closed and the airlock is repressurised; the cabin hatch is opened and Leonov returns to his seat. Finally, the airlock is jettisoned.

Russia gained another spectacular 'first' with Voskhod 2 which had been modified to accommodate an inflatable airlock to enable Lt-Col Alexei Leonov to make the world's first 'space walk' from an orbiting spacecraft. His companion (who remained in the cabin) was Col Pavel I. Belyaev. The airlock control panel in the cabin was duplicated in the airlock so that Leonov could assume control of it in case of emergency. TV pictures of his EVA were transmitted continuously to Earth as he somersaulted in space. How the mission was accomplished is illustrated in the diagram.

the Soviet belief that man could do useful, perhaps even necessary, work outside his spacecraft. Voskhod 2 also proved that man can react to emergency and take over control of a malfunctioning spacecraft, if it is so designed.

The mission was scheduled to terminate on the seventeenth orbit, when the spacecraft's path would take it over the designated landing ground. However, a malfunction in the attitude-control system at the time prevented proper orientation of the Voskhod for retro-rocket firing and re-entry. As a result, the crew had to make an additional orbit in order to prepare for a manually controlled manoeuvre and descent. Although the necessary actions were successfully executed, the spacecraft landed some 746 miles (1,200km) northeast of Moscow in a remote and snow-covered region. Since an antenna had been damaged during re-entry, communications with the descending spacecraft were interrupted and the two cosmonauts had to shiver for two and a half hours before the first rescue helicopter appeared.

The year 1965 saw the appearance of the first multi-manned American spacecraft. While not so versatile in interior appointments, it was a technological advance over the Voskhod *cum* Vostok.

Gemini

Gemini, as the name implies, was designed for two astronauts. While it superficially resembled Mercury, it was an entirely new spacecraft, although it had the same type of construction. Like Vostok, it consisted of two sections; a manned capsule and an adapter section. The former had the same truncated cone shape as Mercury. However, there was no escape rocket tower; instead, the two astronauts had ejection seats. The atmospheric environment of the capsule was the same as Mercury: pure oxygen at a pressure of 5lb/sq in (0·36kg/sq cm). The forward end of the capsule was a cylinder designed for docking with another spacecraft. It contained the re-entry parachute and had the attitude-control thrusters for the capsule. Four solid-propellant retro-rockets were attached to the heatshield as they were with Mercury. The capsule was 11ft (3·35m) long and 7·5ft (2·3m) in diameter.

The adapter section, like that of Vostok, contained all equipment not required inside the manned capsule. Thus, it held the fuel cells for generating electricity and drinking water, oxygen tanks, eight attitude-control thrusters, orbital manoeuvring engines, propellant tanks for the thrusters, and reactant tanks for fuel cells. There also was room for experiment stowage. The section was 7·4ft (2·25m) long and 10ft (3·05m) in diameter across the base.

Since Gemini was designed for orbital missions of up to a fortnight, its weight varied accordingly. A typical spacecraft (Gemini 12) weighed 8,297lb (3,763kg). Since such weight was beyond the orbital capacity of the Atlas launcher for Mercury, the Americans turned to their more powerful Titan II ICBM for the Gemini launch vehicle.

Between March 1965 and November 1966 ten manned Gemini spacecraft were orbited. (Two unmanned ones were launched before the manned flights began.) The objectives of Gemini were to gain experience in extended

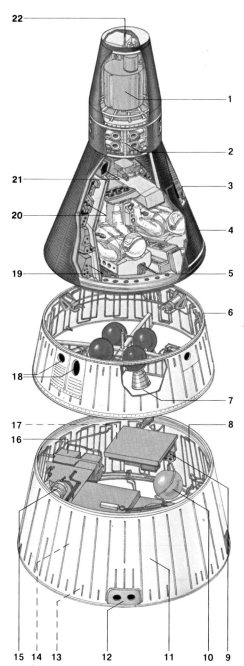

Above: *Titan II lifts a two-man Gemini spacecraft from the pad at Cape Canaveral. Longest flight of the series was that performed by astronauts Borman and Lovell in Gemini 7 in December 1965. They were aloft 330hr 35min.*

Gemini Spacecraft
1 Parachute landing system.
2 Re-entry attitude control system (duplicate sets of 8 x 25lb (11·3kg) thrusters.
3 Port hole.
4 Re-entry module.
5 Ejection seats.
6 Retro-module.
7 4 x 2.500lb (1.134kg) solid-fuel retro-rockets.
8 Coolant radiators.
9 Communications equipment.
10 Propellant tanks.
11 Equipment module.
12 8 x 25lb (11·3kg) attitude control thrusters.
13 Coolant pumps.
14 Cryogenic oxygen tank.
15 Drinking water.
16 Electrical power system.
17 Instrumentation equipment.
18 6 x 100lb (45·3kg) manoeuvre thrusters and 2 x 85lb (38·5kg) deceleration control thrusters.
19 Inertial guidance system.
20 Electrical equipment.
21 Horizon sensors.
22 Rendezvous radar assembly.

This two-man spacecraft gave American astronauts vital experience during 10 manned missions flown in 1965-66. Although in appearance basically an enlarged Mercury, there were many differences. Experience had shown that much equipment could be placed outside the pressurised cabin and left behind at re-entry. Gemini propulsion systems allowed changes in orbit, as well as re-entry manoeuvres for pin-point landings. The cylindrical nose section had docking capability with ADTA and Agena target vehicles which embodied docking receptors.

Technical Data
Length: 18·4ft (5·6m), re-entry module only 11ft (3·35m).
Maximum diameter re-entry module: 7·5ft (2·3m).
Maximum diameter adapter module: 10ft (3·05m).
The orbiting mass of Gemini 12 was 8,297lb (3,763kg).

mission times, perfect and practise orbital manoeuvring, rendezvous, and docking techniques; and to train astronauts in extravehicular activity.

The first manned mission was launched on 23 March 1965. It was Gemini 3, also unofficially known as "Unsinkable Molly Brown", the name of a popular musical play at the time. The spacecraft was so referred to by its commander Virgil I. Grissom, who had lost his Mercury 4 (*Liberty Bell 7*) in 1961. Alongside him was Lt-Cdr John W. Young, an irrepressible officer of the US Navy. Following the cautious approach to spacecraft testing earlier adopted by both the USSR and the USA, their mission lasted only 4hr 53min. It was designed primarily to check out the spacecraft and man's ability to control it, to perform three science experiments and photograph the Earth.

Since both astronauts were test pilots, they devoted most of their energies to their primary objectives, checking out their spacecraft. However, science did not suffer. For the first time a manned spacecraft made an orbital plane change. During the mission, Young made headlines by presenting Grissom with a corned beef sandwich he had smuggled aboard the ship, an unscheduled event in the mission of which NASA expressed extreme disapproval.

On 3 June Gemini 4 was launched with Captains James A. McDivitt and Edward H. White both of the US Air Force. During the mission, which lasted 97hr 56min, the Americans once more caught up with the Soviets. White emerged from the spacecraft and spent 21mins outside it, testing the ability of an astronaut to manoeuvre in space with a small, hand-held rocket-gun powered by compressed gas. On being ordered back into Gemini, everyone listening on radio heard him say: "It's the saddest moment of my life." The crew performed a variety of scientific and engineering experiments and took many photographs of interest to meteorologists and geologists. They exercised with an elastic strap to maintain muscle tone. On the 62nd orbit the crew made a Mercury-type rolling re-entry because Gemini's computer had failed. They arrived some 50 miles (80km) off-target, but touched down safely.

Gemini 5 was orbited on 21 August. Its crew consisted of L. Gordon Cooper, who became the first American astronaut to make two space flights, and Lt Charles "Pete" Conrad, US Navy. Their mission was primarily to demonstrate the capability of the spacecraft and crew to perform adequately for eight days and to investigate the physiological effects of weightlessness for such a period. Additionally, they were to evaluate the rendezvous guidance and navigation system with a system rendezvous evaluation pod. Again there were a number of scientific and engineering experiments.

The pod was a small, battery-powered unit weighing some 66lb (30kg). It had a radar transponder, beacon, and flashing light. It was designed to be ejected from its stowage in the adapter section and used as a target for Gemini astronauts practising the technique of rendezvous. Gemini 5 was also the first spacecraft to utilise fuel cells to provide electricity. Unfortunately, a fault in the fuel cells made it impossible to proceed with the planned manoeuvres with the pod, and it was lost in space. Indeed, the problem threatened to cut the mission short until the engineers on the ground provided a solution. The mission continued with the astronauts performing assigned experiments, among them several to test the visual acuity of man in space. As a result, the crew reported seeing the launching of Minuteman missiles and the smoke from a rocket-powered sled at Holloman Air Force Base in New Mexico. Despite problems, Gemini 5 completed its 120-orbit mission.

Agena Docking

The original flight plan for the next mission, Gemini 6, called for it to rendezvous and dock with a specially adapted Agena rocket stage that was to be orbited by an Atlas vehicle 90 minutes before the manned craft lifted off. The Atlas was launched on 25 October, but the Agena apparently failed to ignite its engine and achieve orbit. There was no other Agena available at the time and the launch of Gemini 6 was called off.

Then NASA demonstrated the flexibility inherent in the Gemini programme. Why not launch Gemini 7 to be the target for Gemini 6 which would fly at a later date? True, the two craft could not dock, but four astronauts could practise the crucial rendezvous phase of orbital operations. Thus on 4 December, Gemini 7 with Major Frank Borman, US Air Force, and Lt-Cdr James A. Lovell, US Navy, was sent into space as a target for Gemini 6. They were provisioned for a 14-day stay.

Gemini 6 was re-scheduled for launch on 12 December, but in the event, a fault on the launching pad "scrubbed" the mission. It was three days later before Gemini 6 with Walter Schirra and Capt Thomas P. Stafford, US Air Force, left for their rendezvous.

As they waited for their fellow astronauts, the crew of Gemini 7 performed a number of medical experiments, some of which looked forward to Project Apollo. To make life as comfortable as possible during their fortnight in space, Borman and Lovell had been fitted out with special lightweight spacesuits. Since they would not be leaving the spacecraft, there was no need for the bulky Gemini suit designed for that purpose. Their suits weighed only 16lb (7·3kg).

Once in orbit, Gemini 6 found itself some 1,238 miles (1,992km) behind Gemini 7. But 3hr 15min later the spacecraft received a radar signal from the Gemini 7 indicating a range of only 270 miles (434km). At a distance of 62 miles (100km), Schirra saw what he thought was the star Sirius, but it turned out to be Gemini 7. In 7hr 15min the

Above: *Gemini 7 photographed from Gemini 6. Although they could not dock, their close manoeuvring in Earth orbit was a key step on the road to the Moon.*

Left: *Ed White leaves the Gemini 4 spacecraft as his umbilical unreels from a black bag. He carries a gas-gun to assist his free-space manoeuvres.*

Right: *Gemini 8 astronauts David Scott and Neil Armstrong await pick-up after making an emergency landing in the Pacific some 690 miles (1,100km) south-east of the island of Okinawa.*

two craft had made rendezvous and were only 131ft (40m) apart, with no relative movement between them. For several orbits the two spacecraft practised drawing apart and then drawing near, sometimes closing to within 1ft (0·3m).

On the following day, after 25hr 51min in space, the astronauts of Gemini 6 exercised their option to end the mission since all its objectives had been accomplished. Also one of the fuel cells in Gemini 7 was performing erratically, and the problem required the full attention of ground controllers. In returning, they performed the first controlled re-entry, landing only eight miles (13km) away from their designated target.

Gemini 7 had almost three days to go. The astronauts by that time were somewhat weary, especially as the excitement of rendezvous and stationkeeping with Gemini 6 had worn off. They drifted silently to conserve energy and read frequently from novels they had taken along. On December 18, they returned to Earth only 7·3 miles (11·8km) from their target after spending 330hr 35min in space, making 206 Earth revolutions.

Gemini 8, launched on 16 March 1966, provided what almost became America's first catastrophe in space. Neil A. Armstrong, a civilian, and Capt David R. Scott, US Air Force, were to perform a rendezvous and docking with an Agena stage that had been

launched by an Atlas D some 101 minutes previously. Gemini 8 was to be a three-day mission, and it got off auspiciously as the spacecraft came up with the Agena on the fourth orbit. Docking went smoothly enough, and then Scott noted the position of his attitude indicator and said, "Neil, we are in a bank!" The two joined spacecraft were rolling rapidly instead of being stable. The astronauts thought that the trouble must be with the Agena. For a brief period Armstrong managed to stabilise the craft, but then the gyrations returned. He withdrew the Gemini from the Agena, but the Gemini began rolling even faster. The hand controllers failed. As the astronauts tried everything, mission control studied the problem. Finally, the hand controllers began to function, and the astronauts were able to stop the tumbling. All the same the decision was made to return Gemini 8 on its seventh orbit. The re-entry and recovery went without event, and the mission ended after only 10hr 41min. Later investigations disclosed that one of the attitude-control thrusters had failed to obey the order to cease firing.

Gemini 9, with Thomas P. Stafford and Lt Eugene A. Cernan, US Navy, was launched on 3 June. The plan had been for it to rendezvous and dock with an Agena that had been launched on 17 May. However, the Agena was lost. Plans also called for Cernan to perform a space-walk to test out a manoeuvring unit carried in the adapter section. An alternative docking device was orbited on 1 June and awaited Gemini 9 on its third

Vostok   **Voskhod**   **Mercury**   **Gemini**

The First Space Suits
Vostok: This rather cumbersome pressure suit had an orange coverall to aid recognition of the cosmonaut in the open tundra of Kazakhstan after landing.
Voskhod: Drawing shows the Voskhod 2 pressure suit worn by Alexei Leonov during the first space walk.
Mercury: The "lightweight" suit worn by John Glenn and other US astronauts in Mercury capsules.
Gemini: The improved suit worn by astronauts of America's first two-man spacecraft.
Helmet visors could be opened during orbital flight because spacecraft cabins were pressurised. The three Soyuz 11 cosmonauts died because they were not wearing space suits.

orbit. However, when they approached it Stafford and Cernan were dismayed to find that a metal band had failed to release the nose shroud of the docking mechanism. There was no way they could dock with it. However, the two made simulated docking manoeuvres, including one that would be required in the Apollo mission. Then, on 4 June Cernan emerged from the spacecraft. His schedule called for several exhausting manoeuvres on the end of a tether before he was to move to the adapter section and place himself in the manoeuvring unit stowed there, remove it from the spacecraft, and then test it. A bulky arm on the unit refused to deploy; and his efforts to move it soon tired him to the point that he was ordered back inside the Gemini, and the experiment was abandoned. He had remained outside for 128min instead of a planned 167min. The remainder of the mission was spent in performing scientific and engineering experiments. The spacecraft returned to Earth during its 45th orbit and landed only 3,000ft (0·7km) from its target after spending 72hr 21min in space.

Gemini 10 had the complex task of intercepting two vehicles in orbit. Launched on 18 July with John W. Young and Capt Michael Collins, US Air Force, the spacecraft was to rendezvous with the Agena still in orbit after the ill-fated Gemini 8 mission,

and a new one launched just prior to Gemini 10. The plan was for Gemini to dock with its Agena, fire the Agena's engine and climb to a rendezvous with Agena 8. Since an Agena boost had never been tried before, there was an element of risk. However, it had to be taken because the end of the Gemini programme was within sight. Additionally, Collins was required to leave the spacecraft to retrieve samples from the Agena 8 and perform other tasks.

Further Successes

It took some 6 hours to rendezvous and dock with the Agena, and its engine fired perfectly for 80sec, sending Gemini 10 to an apogee of 474 miles (763km). Another burst of the Agena's engine lowered the Gemini's apogee to 237 miles (382km), and a final thrust circularised its orbit at 234 miles (377·6km), only 11 miles (18km) below Agena 8. Before the final burn, Collins stood up in the open hatch of the spacecraft but did not leave it. Gemini was on the night side of its orbit, and he was taking photographs of ultraviolet stellar radiation.

After being attached to the Agena for 39 hours, the crew backed away from it; and Collins made preparations for his walk in space. They first sighted Agena 8 at a distance of some 23 miles (37km) and began manoeuvring toward it. Two hours later,

they were hovering only 10ft (3m) above it. Collins left the spacecraft, and attached the propellant line for his hand-held manoeuvring gun to the nitrogen supply in the adapter section of the spacecraft. Using it, Collins moved to the Agena, removed a micrometeoroid experiment from it and returned to the Gemini. The crew continued scientific and engineering experiments until re-entering the atmosphere on 21 July and landing safely after 70hr 46min in space, only five miles (8km) from their target.

On 12 September, Gemini 11 with "Pete" Conrad and Lt-Cdr Richard F. Gordon, US Navy, was launched. The primary task of this mission was to demonstrate a technique that would be required during the forthcoming Apollo project. As in previous Gemini missions, an Agena was launched into orbit about an hour and a half before the Gemini. On this occasion, however, the rendezvous had to be made on the first orbit! It was accomplished some 94min after launch. Gordon was scheduled to make an extensive space walk; but, like Cernan and Collins, he had difficulty and ultimately cut short his activities. However, he succeeded in accomplishing his major task: attaching a 109ft (33·3m) fabric tether from the Gemini to the Agena. The purpose of this procedure was to demonstrate that spacecraft could be stabilised in orbit by using Earth's gravity

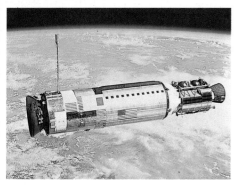

Left: *"The angry alligator" observed by Gemini 9 astronauts over Isles Los Roques, Isla Orchila, and the coast of Venezuela. It was the Agena Target Docking Adapter (ATDA) with which they planned to dock.*

Above: *A 100ft (30·5m) nylon tether links the Agena Docking Target Vehicle (ADTV) with Gemini 12 during its 32nd orbit of the Earth. It was fixed during a space walk by Edwin Aldrin.*

Left: *Lockheed Agena target vehicle.*

Above: *(L to r) Virgil "Gus" Grissom; Roger Chaffee, and Ed White. After his Gemini 3 flight, Grissom had said: "If we die we want people to accept it.... The conquest of space is worth the risk...."*

gradient. It also was a means of station-keeping and of producing artificial gravity by rotating the two craft about their common centre of gravity. The gravity-gradient experiment could not be achieved, but the 'spin-up" mode of station-keeping worked to a degree. On the 26th orbit, Conrad fired the Agena's engine to raise the orbit to 850 miles (1,368km), from which altitude he reported; "I'll tell you it's go up here, and the world's round ..." Two orbits later the Agena fired, lowering the apogee to 161 miles (259km). The remainder of the mission was spent in performing scientific and engineering experiments and taking many photographs of Earth and stars. On their 44th orbit, the Gemini re-entered and landed within 1·5 miles (2·4km) of its target after spending 71hr 17min in space.

The final Gemini mission began on 11 November with the launching of Gemini 12. James Lovell and Maj Edwin E. Aldrin, US Air Force, were aboard. Again, this space-craft was preceded into orbit by an Agena. Drawing on the experience of Cernan, Collins, and Gordon, Aldrin came better prepared for working in space. He had a pair of body tethers that could secure him to either the Agena or Gemini. A work area inside the adapter section was fitted out with foot restraints to secure him while he worked on a panel using a variety of space tools. He

used the body tethers in performing similar tasks on the forward end of the spacecraft. In all, he remained outside the Gemini for 2hr 29min, and experienced none of the fatigue that earlier astronauts had. He made three EVAs in all, totalling 5hr 30min. The mission ended with an uneventful re-entry and landing only 1·5 miles (2·4km) from the target after 94hr 34min in space.

While 1966 ended on a note of triumph for Gemini, 1967 opened in tragedy for Apollo.

First Spacecraft Fatalities

On 27 January the crew of what would have been the first manned Apollo mission perished in a fire inside their spacecraft at the Kennedy Space Center. Virgil I. "Gus" Grissom, Edward H. White, and Lt-Cdr Roger B. Chaffee, US Navy, became the first American astronauts to die in a spacecraft. They were sitting inside the Apollo on top of its Saturn IB launch vehicle at Launch Complex-34. The situation was not deemed hazardous since the Saturn contained no propellants; neither did the Apollo, and all pyrotechnic components had been either disconnected or removed. A fire broke out. Within 15 seconds the three were dead and the fire was out. An investigation board made an exhaustive inquiry, but it could come to no explicit cause for the fire. However, the opinion was expressed that an electrical short-circuit in the spacecraft wiring was the most probable cause. The severity of the fire was laid to the fact that the Apollo spacecraft used a 100 per cent oxygen atmosphere. Compounding the tragedy was the fact that the crew entrance hatch required some 90 seconds to open. The fire also instigated an extensive re-evaluation of the materials inside the Apollo. As a result, much time and expense went into fireproofing before a capsule was flown by the next team on 11 October 1968.

The year 1967 also opened with tragedy for the Soviet Union. On 23 April Colonel Vladimir M. Komarov, who had been commander of the Voskhod 1, was launched from Baikonur aboard the first manned Soyuz ("Union"). The launching went off smoothly as did the orbital mission itself through its 13th orbit. Komarov periodically reported to ground control that he was well and that the Soyuz was functioning as planned. Sometime later, he apparently began having trouble manoeuvring or stabilising the Soyuz. On the 18th orbit, 26hr 45min after launch, Komarov began re-entry orientation and retro-rocket firing. What happened after that will probably never be known. It is assumed that violent orbital manoeuvres or perhaps gyrations during re-entry snarled the shroud lines of the recovery parachute which tangled and became a "streamer" when deployed. The cosmonaut was killed instantly when his Soyuz impacted at a velocity of some 400mph (644km/h).

Because of the two catastrophes, the momentum of manned spaceflight slowed down, but it was not checked in either the USA or USSR. The Apollo, like the phoenix, rose from the flames to transport the first men around the Moon and then to a landing on its arid surface.[4] In a similar manner, extensive redesign and testing of the Soyuz resulted in a highly reliable spacecraft that found primary use as a ferry for cosmonauts to the Soviet Union's Salyut, its first family of space stations.

REFERENCES

1 K.W. Gatland, *Manned Spacecraft* (3rd ed), Blandford Press, Poole, Dorset, 1976.
2 Mitchell R. Sharpe, "*It Is I, Sea Gull*", *Valentina Tereshkova, First Woman in Space*, Thomas Y. Crowell, New York, 1975.
3 Peter Sullivan, "The Voskhod Spacecraft", *Spaceflight*, November 1974, pp. 404-409.
4 Michael Collins, *Carrying the Fire*, Farrar, Straus and Giroux, New York, 1974.

Military Space Systems

Satellites have always had important military roles but in recent years dependence on them has grown dramatically. As a result defence analysts have been concerned that a selective attack on even a few specialised satellites might easily have catastrophic effects, greatly reducing the capacity for effective crisis management and military operations. The most widely known types of military satellites are those used to verify the extent and composition of military forces. These reconnaissance and intelligence gathering functions, while very important, represent, however, only a small fraction of the true scope and diversity of the capabilities of military satellites.

To sense the competing pressures that will shape the future of military space programmes it is necessary to appreciate the extent to which satellite technology has irreversibly superseded other methods of communication, remote sensing, and navigation, all of which were formerly constrained in some way by being land-based or dependent on specialised aircraft and surface ships. Satellites are now able to provide the capacity for instant communications between operational forces and their national command authorities irrespective of distance or time of day. The weather forecasting that is vital to successful military operations is nowadays based largely on data gathered by satellites. Additionally, navigational satellites are currently capable of providing data of such accuracy that a receiver can establish its position to within a few hundred metres anywhere in the world. In a few years this will have further improved to enable position-fixing to be made to within a few metres.

Dependency on space techniques for these missions has grown because satellites can accomplish them in a technically superior manner and more economically than would otherwise be possible. Moreover, the early methods have been abandoned to an extent which would make it very difficult now to turn away from the convenience of satellite-based systems. In the commercial sector familiar examples of this pattern of development are live satellite-linked television and telecommunications.

Some attention has been given to controlling military activities in space, but initial concerns were to prohibit the testing and deployment of nuclear or other weapons of mass destruction in space. The two treaties presently in effect that prohibit such activity are the Limited Test Ban Treaty (LTBT) signed in August 1963, and the Outer Space Treaty signed in January 1967. The LTBT prohibits the testing of nuclear weapons in

"Human history becomes more and more a race between education and catastrophe."
H.G. Wells
Outline of History

Above: *Washington, DC, photographed on infra-red film from an aircraft at 50,000ft (15,240m). Landmarks are identifiable, but it is the reconnaissance satellite which really puts the world under the microscope.*

space, in the atmosphere, and under water, but has not been signed by two of the nuclear powers (France and China) or India, which has tested a nuclear device. All three countries also conduct space programmes.

The Outer Space Treaty is important in that it contains an undertaking by the signatories (the US and Soviet Union in particular) not to place in orbit around the Earth, install on the Moon or any other celestial body or otherwise station in space, nuclear or other weapons of mass destruction. This treaty also limits the use of the Moon and other celestial bodies exclusively to peaceful purposes and expressly prohibits their use for establishing military bases and for the testing of weapons. The Outer Space Treaty has been signed by a number of countries including all the states which

maintain active space programmes. Another important arms-control treaty which constrains the militarisation of space is the Anti-Ballistic Missile Agreement of 1972. Under the terms of this agreement both the United States and the Soviet Union are prohibited from the development, testing, and deployment of space-based anti-ballistic missile systems such as charged particle, ion, or laser beam weapons, though research on these systems is permitted.

While these treaties are of great value in restraining the military competition in space between the two superpowers they do not in any way prevent the development of anti-satellite (ASAT) systems designed specifically to destroy satellites or significantly to impair their performance by the use of jamming techniques or induced failures in the satellites' components. Both the United States and the Soviet Union had made some effort to develop such hunter-killer satellite systems during the middle to late 1960s. But American interest waned after a few unsuccessful tests and following evaluation of the technical difficulties and expense involved. The expense was an especially important factor at that time because of the emphasis on defence priorities related to the US involvement in Vietnam. Soviet development of ASATs has followed a more ambiguous course by comparison. The Soviet development of a Fractional Orbit Bombardment (FOB) system—initially a method of delivering nuclear warheads to targets using near-orbital trajectories—has now gone on to include sporadic series of tests with manoeuvrable satellites, some of which have carried explosive charges and which have been intentionally steered towards and detonated in the vicinity of target satellites.

It was not surprising then that the US Department of Defense should have been alarmed by the Soviet resumption of this kind of testing during 1976, especially as no comparable programme existed in the United States. However, the Soviet ASAT system was technically unsuited to eliminating a significant number of critical US satellites by surprise attack, and the precise nature of the Soviet ASAT development remained difficult to interpret from a study of the tests. One suggestion was that the Soviet programme was directed against Chinese reconnaissance satellites. At first, it was possible to show that the orbits of Soviet ASAT tests were more suited to the interception of Chinese satellites than US military craft. But later Soviet testing proved this view to be too simplistic, since the variety of orbits and manoeuvring techniques utilised

were much too sophisticated to be required solely for the purpose of an anti-Chinese anti-satellite system.

US ASAT Systems

The United States' response was to embark on the development of an ASAT programme (which had by now become technically and economically feasible) to counterbalance Soviet developments and to take the initiative on opening negotiations towards an arms-control agreement limiting the further development and deployment of ASAT systems. These secretive discussions began in Helsinki on 8 June 1978 and continued at Geneva and Vienna during 1979. Although very little is reported from these meetings, both the US and the Soviet Union have an important interest in restraining arms competition in space, though neither will have much incentive to enter into an ASAT treaty in the absence of an agreement to limit strategic weapons through SALT II. There are also many technical difficulties involved in negotiating an ASAT treaty. The exact

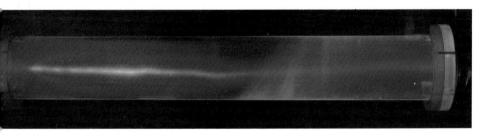

nature of these difficulties has never been officially stated but they are considered to relate to the development of systems with prospective anti-satellite capabilities such as the US Space Shuttle, and to the prohibition of non-destructive interference with satellites (in the form of jamming and deception measures). Perhaps the most important difficulty of principle relates to the arrangement of provisions which would adequately cover the safety of satellites once hostilities have begun at some other level of escalation—possibly with the outbreak of a conventional war. At such a time satellite-based C³ (command, control and communications) and intelligence-gathering functions, for example, would be of great importance, and the ability suddenly to disable a significant number of key satellites associated with such functions would provide an aggressor with significant military advantages. It is very difficult to design the provisions of an ASAT agreement to cover the likelihood that its terms will not be adhered to under such circumstances, parti-

Above: *Russia and America are now in a race to produce charged particle beam weapons. This relativistic electron beam was produced by the USAF Kirtland Weapons Laboratory FX-25 accelerator.*

Below: *Experiments which may lead to the first American laser weapons have already taken place. A vital role is played by this Airborne Laser Laboratory—a modified NKC-135—which carries test equipment.*

cularly since the greatest advantages of an ASAT capability would be forthcoming from their employment during such periods.

It would be also very difficult to establish without some means of inspection whether a satellite designated for some benign purpose did not also carry an offensive capability, for example a high-energy laser for use against an opponent's satellites in times of war. But it is the potential of the US Space Shuttle to verify an ASAT agreement by close external inspection of those satellites within the limited range of its orbital manoeuvring capability that has brought objections from the Soviet delegation at the talks. The Soviet Union did not have a comparable spacecraft in 1978 and wanted to restrain the US military use of this system. However, the United States developed the Shuttle in order to make the launching of both military and civilian satellites more economic and did not intend to forfeit these benefits and revert to traditional launching methods until the Soviet Union developed a similar Shuttle.

Nevertheless, the United States does accept that spacecraft like the Shuttle could be employed for unacceptable espionage in the form of close external inspection and even internal examination of components by temporarily taking the satellite aboard the Shuttle. While acceptance of a principle of non-interference would overcome this problem it does not solve the difficulties of verification which would permit some basic non-destructive external examination of satellites designated for non-military purposes but which could conceivably take on military roles in a potential satellite war in space. In order to overcome this problem—which applies to a lesser extent to Soviet manned space operations from orbital laboratories—the United States has continued to press for acceptance of the principle of non-interference at all times with satellite systems that could be verified by national technical means including the Shuttle, specialised satellites, ground-based radars and telescopes, and other methods.

The United States and the Soviet Union have also been considering the practicability of high-energy lasers and particle beams as anti-ballistic missiles and ASAT weapons. The novel feature of such systems is that the destruction of a target can be caused by a pulse or beam of intense radiated energy which travels at the speed of light. Within the atmosphere, however, a number of limitations inhibit the propagation of such beams reducing their destructive capability at ranges much in excess of six miles (10km). But if located in areas where the

atmospheric conditions are ideal, a ground-based laser or particle beam ASAT system with a range of 435 miles (700km) might be feasible and this type of system is being studied. In the near-vacuum of space the range limitations of lasers are due more to the natural spreading of the beam with the distance it travels—resulting in a proportionate reduction in energy density. Particle beams, by comparison, are susceptible to being bent by the Earth's magnetic field and this creates additional targetting problems.

Even though initial experimental tests have been quite impressive, the technical difficulties associated with laser and particle-beam weapons are so great that it is difficult to predict whether these will become viable weapon systems in the foreseeable future. But it is already apparent that space-based high-energy lasers could become ASAT weapons, and both superpowers are spending a significant amount of money evaluating the destructive potential of both lasers and particle beams. The unrestrained deployment of these systems as ASAT weapons would cast doubts on the survivability of satellites in both the Soviet Union and the United States. Thus an important priority for future arms-control measures to regulate military activity in space would be to seek ways of restraining the further development and prohibiting the deployment of lasers and particle beams as ASAT weapons.

The US/Soviet concern over the prospective development of ASATs has had the important secondary effect of arousing interest in the peaceful utilisation of space through international collaboration. In part this interest has arisen owing to the costs of

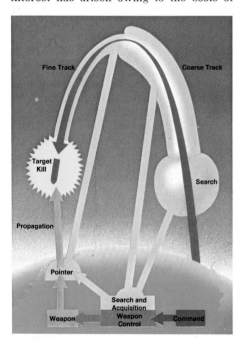

Future ABM Systems?
Can a "death ray" be devised capable of destroying ballistic missiles in flight? According to certain US intelligence sources, the Soviets have made big progress with high-energy particle beams. However, claims that such weapons are nearly operational are premature. It would need a huge investment to take such systems beyond the experimental stage. The

drawing shows a hypothetical weapon system. First, the incoming warhead is identified and tracked. After a period of coarse tracking, the beam projector is locked on and the weapon discharges to achieve a "kill". Closer to operation are high-energy lasers, but the atmosphere seriously limits their efficiency, causing the beam to bloom or defocus, so losing its target lethality.

Above: *Part of the wreckage of the Cosmos 954 satellite that fell over northern Canada in 1978. This incident focussed public attention on possible dangers consequent upon the militarisation of space.*

independently developing satellite and space programmes for third-world countries which could benefit greatly from satellite technology, especially that developed for remote sensing. Equally, public concern over the character of orbiting spacecraft was aroused in January 1978 following the crash of the Soviet Cosmos 954 satellite which spread debris from its nuclear power source over a remote part of northern Canada. Some months later the US Skylab—the largest object ever placed in orbit—fell to Earth. Although it too was mostly burnt up during re-entry, considerable interest was created by the remote prospect that debris from this satellite might impact in a densely populated area. Public alarm helped to draw attention to the more serious problems of regulating civilian and military activities in space.

Such incidents have helped to spur interest in the development of international co-operation in the space activities of many nations. The suggestions proposed so far have been of two kinds, the first dealing exclusively with the verification of military capabilities of nations and the second trying to approach the problem of the militarisation of space by addressing issues connected with the collaborative development of civilian space programmes and the possibilities for an agreed system of international verification of military capabilities.

If it could be agreed, the major powers might set up an independent satellite verification system and contribute to an International Verification Agency (IVA) which would interpret data collected by satellites which had either been specifically developed for an IVA or which had been assigned to such duties by their national authorities. But the grave limitations of such a scheme would be in the virtually insurmountable political difficulties involved in devising acceptable methods by which an international agency (however disinterested or unbiased) might be trusted with sensitive and detailed information about the military capabilities of every nation on Earth. But collaboration in multi-national space programmes might be encouraged through the establishment of a major United Nations agency, for example.

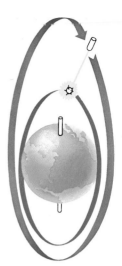

Lasers in Space
Laser beams directed from satellites might be used to knock out enemy satellites, either by destroying them outright or by damaging sensitive equipment. In this case the laser equipment pursues an elliptical orbit some 4,300 x 6,000 miles (6,920 x 9,650km) above the Earth to counter low-to-medium altitude satellites on reconnaissance or other military duty. Satellites relaying strategic communications would be other prime targets and to be wholly effective it would be necessary for lasers to reach targets in geostationary orbit. Study has also been made of using high-energy lasers for ABM purposes.

This could help to curb military activity in space by increasing the mutual interest and value of space exploration for nations that cannot afford independent space programmes, or which would benefit greatly from technical and economic assistance given by the major powers. If the major powers were drawn into a large-scale co-operative utilisation of space to help other nations the incentive and available resources for military space activities could be reduced.

Such a proposal was made in June 1979 by US Senator Adlai Stevenson, chairman of the Senate sub-committee on Science, Technology and Space. He suggested that, as a first step, an international system of remote sensing satellites should be developed as part of a world-wide effort to explore energy resources and raw materials, as well as monitor environmental pollution and weather. Progress has already been made in the co-operative development and utilisation of satellite-based communications and for meteorological forecasting. But in the absence of a strong initiative to develop greater co-operation the United States, Europe, the Soviet Union, Japan, China, and India will probably develop independent remote sensing satellites—duplicating research and development and consequently wasting intellectual and economic resources.

Because the technology of remote-sensing satellites shares common origins with the technology developed for verification of military capabilities, an international programme to develop and jointly operate an Earth-resources satellite might help to build the experience and mutual confidence between nations that will be needed to promote the establishment and operation of an IVA. Even without such an agency broad international agreement on the value to all nations of the peaceful utilisation of space may help to reduce the incentive for military activity in space, particularly if this interest is expressed in formal treaties and firm commitments to long-term co-operation in space activities for which there are already many useful precedents. But it is unrealistic to expect that the many useful military functions that are currently undertaken with the aid of satellites can now be abandoned, or that such drastic measures are even reasonable. The following section describes the military uses of satellites and though it is certainly true that some developments could be considered provocative and destabilising, the majority of the military applications of satellites are benign and arguably conducive to stability and peace.

Military Space Systems

The fact that the Soviet Union launches more military satellites than the United States does not mean there is a great disparity between them in such activities. The Soviet practice has been to build individual, single-mission satellites while a single American satellite frequently accomplishes multiple missions. Thus, launch rate alone is not a reliable indicator of the relative intensity of military space programmes of either side. There are, however, indications that the USSR will build more multi-role satellites in the future.

One very important role of military satellites is the verification of agreed limitations of strategic arms and the monitoring of new military developments. This is achieved by a variety of electronic and photographic means.

The development of photo-reconnaissance satellites in the United States began in the late 50s within the US Air Force's Discoverer programme. The Discoverer satellite was an Agena upper-stage which could be equipped with a camera and high-resolution optics. When a camera was carried, exposed film was returned to Earth in a re-entry capsule. This capsule had a retro-rocket and could be recovered, as it descended by parachute, by specially equipped transport aircraft.

The test programme started on 28 February

MAJOR WESTERN POWERS MILITARY SATELLITES				
NAME	**PROJ AUTHORITY/ PRIME CONTRACTOR**	**LAUNCH VEHICLE**	**PAYLOAD MASS** lb (kg)	**PURPOSE**
Aquacade	DoD/TRW?	Space Shuttle/IUS	N.A.	Ferret satellite in geosynchronous orbit. Deploys two large dish antennae sensitive enough to pick up discreet microwave communications of military and diplomatic interest. Launched (STS-51C) January 1985. Also reported as Magnum.
"Big Bird"	DoD/USAF/Lockheed	Titan IIID, Titan 34D	25,000 (11,340) est.	Radio transmission + film returned in recoverable capsules. Typical orbit 100×155 miles (161×249 km)×96·4°. Ejects "elint" sub-satellite/s e.g. May 1982, orbit 435×439 miles (701×707 km)×95·99°.
"Clipper Bow"	DoD/USN	Space Shuttle	N.A.	Ocean surveillance with active radar.
Defense Meteorological Satellite Program (DMSP)	DoD/RCA Astro-Electronics (now GE Astro Space)	LV-2F, Atlas E Atlas E Titan II SLV	Blk 5D-1 1,058 (480)* Blk 5D-2 1,445 (660)* Blk 5D-3 3,775 (1,712)†	Two satellites survey same area of Earth's surface every 12 hours by line-scanning radiometer in visual and IR. Orbit is Sun-synchronous at 513 miles (825 km)×98·7° *In orbit; † at launch.
Defense Satellite Communications System (DSCS 2)	DoD/TRW Defense & Space Systems	Titan IIIC, Titan 34D (Oct 1982)	1,345 (610)	US strategic communications satellite, geostationary, spin stabilised, two steerable spot-beam antennae. Height 13·lft (4m); width 8·9ft (2·7m).
Defense Satellite Communications System (DSCS 3)	DoD/General Electric	Titan 34D or Space Shuttle	1,950 (885)	US strategic communications, with S-band and SHF transponders at 7/8 GHz, geostationary, 3 axis stabilised. First DSCS 3 launched with penultimate DSCS 2 on first Titan 34D October 1982. Height 6·6ft (2m); width 8·9ft (2·7m).
Defense Support Program (DSP) Code 647	DoD/USAF/TRW Aerojet	Titan IIIC Space Shuttle Titan IV	2,000 (907) 5,200 (2,359)	Detect launch of ICBMs, SLBMs by IR sensors in synchronous orbit. First DSP Block 14 launched by Titan IV on 14 June 1989
Ferret	DoD/USAF/ Lockheed, Sanders	Thor-Agena LTTAT-Agena	2,000 (907) est.	Electromagnetic surveillance of military/diplomatic communications (2nd generation) was superseded by new satellite concept by Hughes (Program 711/Jumpseat) in 1975.
FLTSATCOM	DoD/US Navy/TRW Defense & Space Systems	Atlas-Centaur	4,189 (1,900) at launch 2,293 (1,040) in orbit	Provides UHF communications between land bases, ships, submarines, aircraft — also links SAC with USAF aircraft. Geostational, three-axis stabilised, 23 transponders operating at 244-400 MHz; dish antenna 16ft (4·9m) diameter. Height 4·2ft (1·3m), width 7·5ft (2·3m); span solar arrays 43·3ft (13·2m), Power, end of life, 1·3 kW.
Helios	French MoD/Aérospatiale/ Matra/SEP/Alcatel	Ariane 4	N.A.	Reconnaissance/signal intelligence utilizing SPOT platform, optical resolution 3·28ft (1m). Launch 1993-94.
High-resolution reconnaissance satellite	DoD/USAF/ Lockheed	Titan IIIB-Agena D	N.A.	Orbital reconnaissance. Formerly used as high resolution satellite with film-return capsule. Later "search and find" type which seeks out new targets for Big Bird and KH-11s. Has demonstrated lifetime in excess of 50 days.
Jumpseat	DoD/Hughes?	Titan IIIB	N.A.	Ferret satellite launched into orbit similar to those of the SDS satellite (qv).
KH-11	DoD/USAF/TRW	Titan IIID, Titan 34D Space Shuttle	25,000 (11,340) est.	Strategic reconnaissance, digital imagery, manoeuvrable. Typical orbit 155×329 miles (250×530 km)×96·95°. Upgraded KH-11 launched KSC, 8 Aug 1989.
KH-12 Ikon	DoD/USAF/TRW	Space Shuttle	N.A.	Strategic reconnaissance, digital imagery, with capability of being serviced and refuelled in orbit. Cancelled 1988?
Lacrosse	DoD/USAF/ Martin Marietta	Space Shuttle	N.A.	All-weather day/night reconnaissance with synthetic aperture radar. Launched (STS-27) December 1988. Solar arrays/planar antenna span some 150ft (45·7m).
Leasat	DoD/USN/Hughes	Space Shuttle	17,508 (7,942) at launch 2,899 (1,315) in orbit	Fleet communications, 13 transponders-6 for relay, one wideband, five narrow band, one fleet broadcast. Geosynchronous at 22,210 miles (35, 740 km)×3°. Height, with antennae deployed 20·3ft (62m); width 13·78ft (4·2m). Power, end of life, 1·2kW.
Milstar	DoD/USAF/US Army USN/Lockheed	N.A.	N.A.	Strategic & tactical communications including personnel receiver/transmitters. Systems highly-resistant to jamming. Employs Extra High Frequency (EHF) which recover relatively quickly from electro-magnetic pulse due to nuclear explosions. Deployed both in geostationary & polar orbits.
N-ROSS	DoD/US Navy	Titan II SLV	N.A.	Oceanographic survey.
NATO 3	NATO/Philco-Ford	Delta	1,543 (700) at launch 789 (358) in orbit	Military communications. Three channels for secure voice data and telex links. Height overall 10·2ft (3·1m); width 7·2ft (2·18m).
NATO 4	DoD/BAe/ Marconi	N.A.	N.A.	Provide NATO members with secure military and diplomatic communications. Contract for two geostationary satellites awarded January 1987, almost identical to Skynet. Fixed and mobile terminals. First launch 1990.
Navstar	DoD/Rockwell	Block 1: Atlas E/F Block 2: Delta 2	1,157 (525) 2,000 (907)	Global positioning system. First Block 2 satellite (Navstar 2-1) launched 14 February 1989.
Nova	DoD/USN/GE Astro Space	Scout	364 (165)	Navigation satellite. Height 3·3ft (1m); width 1·64ft (0·5m). Stabilised by a gravity gradient boom. Orbit 717×747 miles (1,154×1,202 km)..
Relay Mirror	DoD/Ball Aerospace	Delta	2,300 (1,043)	Relay mirror experiment.
Rhyolite	DoD	Atlas-Agena D	N.A.	Ferret satellite in geosynchronous orbit. First launched 1973. Monitors telemetry from missiles fired on test from Soviet Baikonur and Plesetsk launch sites.
Satellite Data System	DoD/USAF/Hughes	Titan IIIB	N.A.	UHF communications between Satellite Control Facility ground stations; strategic data relay; e.g. reconnaissance electro-optical image data from satellite KH-11 to USAF ground terminals.
Skynet 2	MoD/Marconi	Thorad-Delta	959 (435) launch mass 517 (235) in orbit	Military communications satellite. Single transponder split into two channels to allow contact with ground stations and shipborne units. Height 6·8ft (2·1m); width 6·25ft (1·9m).
Skynet 4	MoD/BAe/ GEC-Marconi	Ariane 4 (Skynet 4A) Titan III (Skynet 4B) Ariane 4 (Skynet 4C)	2,800 (1,270) launch mass	Military communications between ships, mobile terminals on land and command bases; both UHF and SHF frequencies. Skynet 4A launched 11 December 1988; 4B 1989; 4C 1990. Evolved from OTS/ECS technology.
Syracuse	French MoD	Ariane 3	2,607 (1,182)	Military utilisation of Telecom I using X-band frequencies; later upgraded Telecom II. Provides cover of Atlantic and Indian Oceans.
Tacsat 1	DoD/US Army	Titan IIIC	1,600 (726)	Tactical communications between US forces in the field using small transmitters. Geostationary; length 25ft (7·6m); diameter 9ft (2·7m).
Vela (Data refer to Vela 11 & 12)	DoD/USAF	Atlas-Agena D Titan IIIC	770 (349) 2 per launch	Detection of nuclear detonations on Earth's surface, within the atmosphere and out to 100 million miles (161 million km), solar flares and space radiation. Vela 11 orbit 69,106×69,696 miles (111,210×112,160 km)×32·4°. Role subsequently taken over by Integrated Missile Early Warning Satellites (IMEWS).
White Cloud	DoD/USN/ Martin Marietta	Atlas F	N.A.	All weather, ocean surveillance, 1976, three per launch tethered by wires. Satellites pick up Soviet naval radio/radar transmissions. Orbit 700 miles (1,126 km).
Zircon	UK MoD	N.A.	N.A.	Reported signal intelligence for deployment geosynchronous orbit 53°E; based on US sigint technology (e.g. Aquacade/Magnum). Project possibly terminated.

1959, when a Thor-Agena was launched into polar orbit from the Pacific Missile Range, California. However, the Agena developed a stabilisation fault and ended in an elliptical orbit which rapidly decayed. This was the first of 12 consecutive failures of various types. Finally, on 10 August 1960, Discoverer 13 was launched and the next day a re-entry capsule was recovered from the Pacific.

By the summer of 1961, Discoverer satellites were returning very high quality photos which were instrumental in ending US fears of a massive Soviet ICBM buildup. For example: Discoverer 29 is credited with photographing the ICBM base at Plesetsk.[2]

The other half of the US orbital reconnaissance effort is the "search-and-find" satellite—principally an endeavour to locate and identify new weapon developments and deployments within the Soviet Union from photos transmitted to ground stations. The first experiment was called Samos 1 (Satellite And Missile Observation System), but its Atlas-Agena failed during launch on 11 October 1960. Samos 2, launched on 31 January 1961, operated for a month. Because of their importance, in mid-November 1961, a heavy curtain of secrecy descended on both the reconnaissance satellites and the Midas (Missile Defense Alarm System) early-warning satellites.[1] Not until a 1 October 1978 speech by President Jimmy Carter was there any official acknowledgement that satellites were conducting photo-reconnaissance missions, even though it was well-known that such missions were taking place. The closest to an acknowledgement was an off-the-record comment by President Johnson in 1967 that such photos were worth ten times the $35 to $40 billion* spent on space up to that time.

The second-generation US reconnaissance satellites began to appear in 1963; approximately 12 search-and-find satellites and nine recoverable types were launched per year. The recoverable satellites stayed up for an average of 4·5 days; the search and find for two to three weeks. Boosters were TAT-Agenas and Atlas-Agenas.[3]

The third-generation recoverable satellites launched by Titan IIIB-Agenas were first flown in mid-1966. By 1968 they were staying in orbit for 15 days or longer. On some flights the high resolution camera was replaced by either a mapping camera or cameras which scanned wavelengths in the infra-red spectrum.

Also, in mid-1966, a new generation of search-and-find satellites was launched by the Long Tank Thrust Augmented Thor-Agena. Their cameras had improved resolution and infra-red scanners were also carried. Time in orbit was three to four weeks. About six to ten recoverable and search-and-find satellites were launched per year.[4] Each year the total number of US satellites fell, though total time in orbit increased indicating improvements in the technology.

The fourth-generation reconnaissance satellites were a departure in that they combined the functions of both earlier types of satellites. This new satellite—the so-called "Big Bird"—made its debut in June 1971. It was 50ft (15·2m) long and 10ft

*U.S. billion = 1,000 million.

Above: *A converted C-119 transport makes a mid-air snatch of a capsule ejected from a Discoverer satellite near Hawaii in 1961. This was the technique used to return exposed reconnaissance film.*

Below: *Titan IIID—the powerful Big Bird reconnaissance satellite launcher—thunders into the sky from Vandenberg. The Big Birds are believed to have uncovered many Soviet military secrets.*

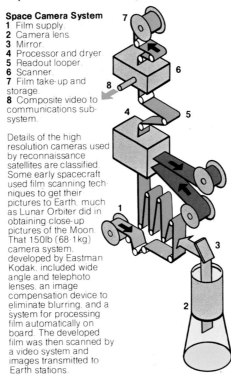

Space Camera System
1 Film supply.
2 Camera lens.
3 Mirror.
4 Processor and dryer.
5 Readout looper.
6 Scanner.
7 Film take-up and storage.
8 Composite video to communications sub-system.

Details of the high resolution cameras used by reconnaissance satellites are classified. Some early spacecraft used film scanning techniques to get their pictures to Earth, much as Lunar Orbiter did in obtaining close-up pictures of the Moon. That 150lb (68·1kg) camera system, developed by Eastman Kodak, included wide angle and telephoto lenses, an image compensation device to eliminate blurring, and a system for processing film automatically on board. The developed film was then scanned by a video system and images transmitted to Earth stations.

(3·05m) in diameter and weighed approximately 30,000lb (13,608kg). Two-thirds of this consists of a large camera, with a resolution better than 1ft (0·3m) from an altitude of 100 miles (161km). It carries six re-entry capsules. A modified Agena is used to prevent premature orbital decay. Its launch vehicle is a Titan IIID. An average of one or two Big Birds was launched per year and their time in orbit increased from 60 to 90 to 180 days.

In addition, two or three Titan IIIB-Agena search-and-find satellites were also launched per year as gap-fillers or ocean surveillance test satellites.[5]

In December 1976 a new US reconnaissance satellite was launched—the KH-11 (for Key Hole-11, the CIA code name). It was about the same size and used the same launch vehicle as Big Bird but was fired into

a higher orbit. Unlike photo-reconnaissance satellites which supply high-resolution images of surface targets by ejecting film capsules, KH-11 obtains its high-resolution imagery by digital transmission. In March 1978, a former CIA clerk, William P. Kampiles, sold the Russians a KH-11 manual. This manual detailed its characteristics, capacities and limitations. It cost the Russians $3,000, but Kampiles was sentenced to 40 years' imprisonment[6,7] Although information on the KH-11 and the Rhyolite satellites had been compromised, compensatory measures were quickly taken.

Soviet reconnaissance satellites account for the largest percentage of Russian space launches. The Russian reconnaissance programme began with Cosmos 4 (launched on 26 April 1962), which was recovered after three days. The camera equipment was

Above: *A Gemini 5 photograph of some 30 miles of dykes, an engineering project at the Israel-Jordan end of the Dead Sea. Military reconnaissance satellites are capable of much higher resolution.*

carried aboard an unmanned Vostok spacecraft, the same type as had been used for early Russian manned missions. The use of a proven spacecraft enabled reconnaissance missions to be undertaken quickly, with increased reliability, avoiding the US Air Force's incredible string of disasters with Discoverer.

In 1962 five recoverable satellites were launched, staying up an average of 4·5 days. In the next year, seven more were orbited. In 1964 launches occurred with almost clock-like regularity, each satellite staying in orbit for eight days.

The number of launches accelerated through the mid-1960s, finally stabilising at approximately 30 per year. Unlike US satellites, both the high resolution and the search-and-find satellites ejected a capsule for recovery. The satellites could be destroyed if the retro-rocket should fail, thereby preventing them from falling into unfriendly hands.[8]

Starting in 1968, an improved version was gradually introduced. The first was Cosmos 208 launched on 21 March 1968. These were high-resolution satellites; they stayed in orbit 12 days and, shortly before recovery, jettisoned the manoeuvring engine that was used to adjust the orbital ground path to pass closer to a target. Four of this type were launched in 1968. The number increased until they constituted half the reconnaissance satellites launched. The low-resolution satellites now also have a lifetime of 12 days.[9]

Since 1976 an advanced reconnaissance satellite has been under development which may take the form of a modified Soyuz spacecraft. The first was Cosmos 758 launched on 5 September 1975. After 20 days in orbit it exploded. Initially there were about two launches per year. The satellite's lifetime was approximately 30 days, although there have been some mission failures.

During the 1980s, the Soyuz-based reconnaissance satellite has undergone a growth both in numbers (now about 10 per

Above: *The USAF project for a Manned Orbiting Laboratory got off to a good start at Cape Canaveral on 3 November 1966 when this mock-up was launched by a Titan IIIC rocket.*

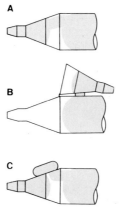

MOL Crew Transfer
Proposed methods for transferring USAF astronauts into the Manned Orbiting Laboratory (MOL) from the Gemini spacecraft in which they travelled. The chosen method **(A)** involved cutting a hatch in Gemini's heat shield. The alternatives ranged from **(B)** rotating the Gemini capsule to line up with a transfer hatch, **(C)** an inflatable tunnel, and **(D)** extra-vehicular activity. The unmanned Gemini capsule carried by the Titan IIIC above was actually modified to include a hatch in the heat shield. It was successfully recovered from the Atlantic after separating from the vehicle during the climb into orbit.

year) and in lifetime. In 1982, the standard lifetime was increased to 44 days, and by 1985 to 54 days. The Soviets have also developed a fifth generation photo-reconnaissance satellite, also based on the Soyuz. It uses digital imagery like the KH-11. It was first introduced on 28 December 1982 with the launch of Cosmos 1426 which operated for 67 days. By the mid-1980s, this type had achieved lifetimes in excess of 200 days.

The Soviets have also tested use of manned orbital reconnaissance. This used the military adaptation of the Salyut space station (e.g. Salyut 3 and 5). The most easily recognised characteristic of a military station is its orbit: 150 miles (241km) high as opposed to more than 200 miles (322km) in the case of a scientific station. Exposed film is returned in a re-entry capsule at the end of the mission. Although no operational system was developed, military experiments have been conducted on the Salyut 6 and 7 and the Mir space stations.

The MOL Project
Interestingly enough, the US Air Force was developing a similar capacity in the mid-1960s. The Manned Orbiting Laboratory (MOL) was a modified Gemini attached to a cylindrical lab and launched as one unit. It was to make 30-day missions with a two-man crew. The programme was begun in 1965 but the funding demands of the Vietnam War caused delays, and MOL was cancelled in 1969.[10]

China, also, has a reconnaissance satellite programme. The first was China 3, a radio transmission type, followed by China 4, a recoverable satellite. The recovery capsule represents approximately two-thirds of the satellite's weight, variously estimated at 6,000lb to 10,000lb (2,722 to 4,536kg). The re-entry capsule looks like a larger version of that used on the Discoverer project. The camera is fitted in a cone-shaped service module.

At first it seemed the NASA Space Shuttles would have considerable military significance. The next generation US reconnaissance satellite KH-12 Ikon was being designed for deployment and recovery by them. There were plans to service and refuel the satellites in orbit.

However, the *Challenger* disaster of January 1986 highlighted the folly of "placing too many eggs in one basket" and the still unfinished USAF Shuttle facility at Vandenberg AFB was mothballed. The USAF began placing orders anew for big expendable rockets.

In 1988, the KH-12 was reportedly cancelled and separate programmes were set up to meet the different (and incompatible) needs of the CIA and Air Force. An up-rated manoeuvrable satellite of the KH-series was launched from Kennedy Space Center by the Shuttle *Columbia* (STS-28) on 8 August 1989, being delivered into an orbit of 188 x 196 miles (302 x 315km) inclined at 57° to the equator. It remains to be seen if the Soviet Space Shuttle will be used to extend the military arts, perhaps for reconnaissance.

At the end of 1988, another reconnaissance technique made its debut — radar. The radar signals from a satellite penetrate cloud cover. The reflected echoes can then be processed to produce images that resemble

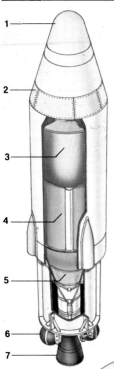

Discoverer Spacecraft

1 Re-entry capsule.
2 Equipment bay including computer, inertial reference package, propellant pressurisation and horizon scanner.
3 Fuel (UDMH).
4 Oxidant (IRFNA).
5 Destruct charge.
6 Nitrogen and helium bottles.
7 Bell 8096 rocket engine. Agena B: Length 25ft (7·6m).

The Discoverer vehicles were based on the Lockheed Agena orbiting stage launched by a modified Thor intermediate range ballistic missile (IRBM) from Vandenberg AFB, into near-polar orbit. Most of the 5ft (1·52m) diameter Agenas had a nose-mounted recovery capsule 27in (68·6cm) long x 33in (83·8cm) diameter containing a radar beacon and aluminium radar chaff to aid recovery. Project contributed significantly to Midas, Samos and Transit programmes.

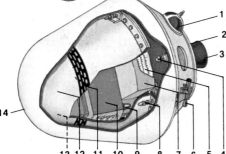

Discoverer Capsule

1 Cold gas storage tank.
2 Thrust cone.
3 Retro-rocket.
4 Explosive bolt.
5 Recovery parachute and chaff.
6 Stabilization jets.
7 Parachute cover.
8 Explosive pistons.
9 Flashing light.
10 Instrumentation package.
11 Dye markers.
12 Recovery capsule.
13 Radio beacon (inside).
14 Ablating re-entry shield.

The re-entry capsule, built by General Electric Co.,

weighed about 300lb (136kg). The part recovered by parachute was enclosed within a protective heat shield. Capsule contents varied from launch to launch. Discoverer 14, launched 18 August 1960, was first to eject film from reconnaissance camera. Capsule of Discoverer 32 investigated effect of radiation on (a) metal samples; (b) genetic properties of seed corn; (c) shielding materials, and (d) silicon solar cells. Discoverer 36 had a biopack with human and animal tissue, spores and algae.

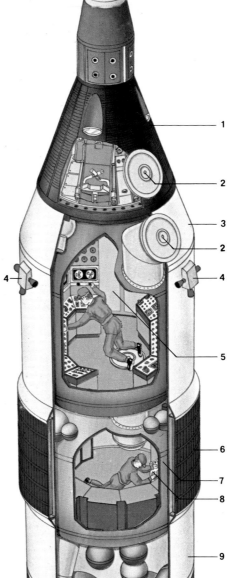

The first military satellites were developed to pick up intelligence information around the world using reconnaissance cameras, infra-red sensors and electronic devices of various kinds. An early start was made in the 1959-62 period under the US Air Force Discoverer programme using the Lockheed Agena orbiting rocket stage which returned exposed film and other data in a re-entry capsule. The Discoverers led to the photo-reconnaissance satellite Samos and the advance warning satellite Midas.

The Soviet Union developed a simple yet effective reconnaissance system based on an unmanned version of the Vostok spacecraft which returned a re-entry capsule within eight days. Later models of Soviet spy satellites, spending longer in orbit, are believed to have evolved from the Soyuz spacecraft. Both American and Russian spy satellites have manoeuvre engines which allow their orbits to be adjusted to pass over specific targets. Their orbits also can be raised to offset

Manned Orbiting Laboratory (MOL)

1 Gemini B spacecraft.
2 Hatches for external inflatable tunnel (one of four different crew transfer methods considered).
3 Gemini adapter.
4 Attitude control jets.
5 Pressurised lab with control consoles, air-purification and circulation systems, toilet (commode) and hygiene area, main control consoles, food storage and preparation, bio-med sleeping couches, spare spacesuit and other emergency equipment.
6 Solar panels (stowed).
7 Pressurised lab with control and telemetry consoles, attitude control TV, extra emergency gear, spare spacesuit, food and water, second commode, etc.
8 Console for pointing and tracking telescope.
9 Test module for experiments and/or equipment.
10 Aft tunnel.

The MOL project, sponsored by the USAF in the 1960s, was based on the ability of two Air Force officers to perform up to

30 days of experiments in Earth orbit related to the military uses of space, mainly reconnaissance and surveillance. The 10ft (3·05m) diameter laboratory was intended to be launched by a Titan IIIM booster fitted with a Gemini B spacecraft containing the crew. Several internal arrangements were considered in designing the laboratory section and docking facilities were being worked out to enable crews to be replaced in separately-launched Gemini capsules. A number of methods were considered for achieving mooring or docking of spacecraft (page 79). One included an inflatable tunnel for transferring the crew on the outside of the vehicle. The favoured solution was direct access to the MOL through a hatch cut in the Gemini heat shield. As the programme developed, it was considered possible to assemble two MOLs in orbit to provide greater capacity. Three methods were suggested: tail to tail, side by side, nose to tail.

Capsule Recovery

1 Pitch down.
2 Separation and retro-fire.
3 Re-entry heating.
4 Recovery by patrolling C-119 or C-130 aircraft.

The Discoverer spacecraft released its capsule at a backward angle while passing over Alaska. After

re-entering the atmosphere, protected by a disposable heat shield, the capsule was recovered by parachute near Hawaii. A patrolling C-119 (later C-130) aircraft snagged the parachute as it descended. If the capsule was missed it floated just below the surface of the sea.

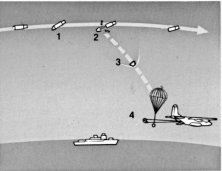

"Big Bird"

1 Agena propulsion module.
2 Recovery capsules.
3 Central body with high resolution camera and main equipment.
4 Radio antenna.

Details of this US Air Force reconnaissance satellite are secret. The

drawing (above) is purely conjectural based on known dimensions of the nose shroud of the Titan IIID launch vehicle. Launched from Vandenberg AFB in California "Big Bird" pursues a near-polar orbit which takes it over the whole of the Communist World. Its Perkin-Elmer high-resolution

camera can spot people on the ground from over 100 miles (161km) up. Film is ejected in separate capsules for recovery. Electronic picture transmission is also possible. Other equipment is believed to include a powerful array of electronic intelligence devices. A manoeuvre

engine is used to adjust the orbit. "Big Bird" is thought to have played a key role in tracking down and identifying new Russian aircraft and ballistic missiles including the mobile IRBM SS-20. Weight, fully fuelled, exceeds 25,000lb (11,340kg). "Big Bird's" lifetime is c. 180 days.

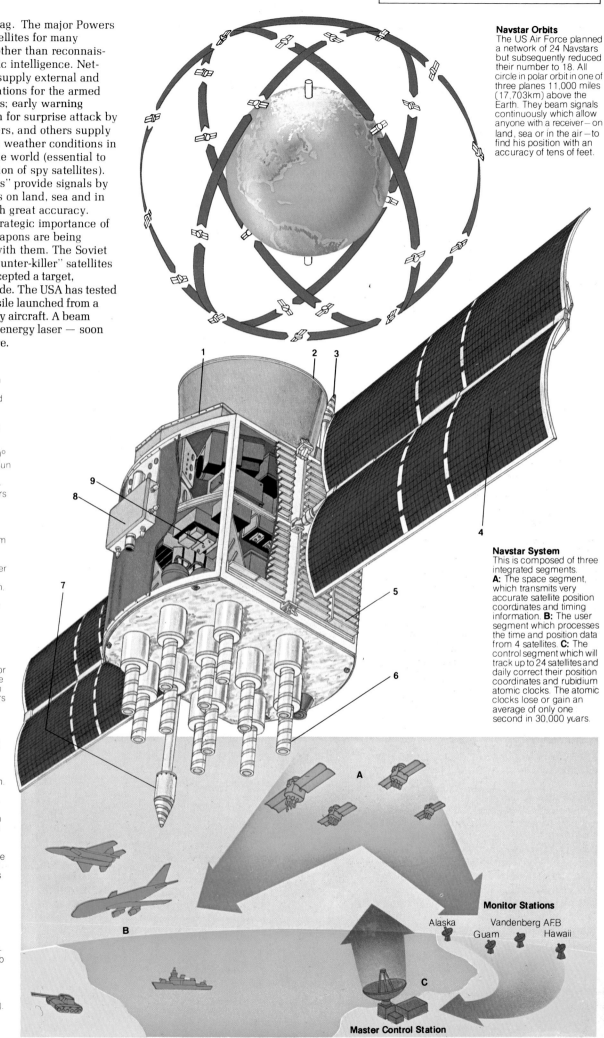

the effects of air drag. The major Powers now depend on satellites for many defence purposes other than reconnaissance and electronic intelligence. Networks of satellites supply external and internal communications for the armed forces in all theatres; early warning systems keep watch for surprise attack by missiles and bombers, and others supply vital information on weather conditions in different parts of the world (essential to the efficient operation of spy satellites). Orbiting "radio stars" provide signals by which military units on land, sea and in the air navigate with great accuracy.

Because of the strategic importance of satellites, space weapons are being developed to deal with them. The Soviet Union has tested "hunter-killer" satellites which, having intercepted a target, explode like a grenade. The USA has tested an anti-satellite missile launched from a fast-climbing military aircraft. A beam weapon — the high-energy laser — soon may enter the picture.

Navstar Orbits

The US Air Force planned a network of 24 Navstars but subsequently reduced their number to 18. All circle in polar orbit in one of three planes 11,000 miles (17,703km) above the Earth. They beam signals continuously which allow anyone with a receiver — on land, sea or in the air — to find his position with an accuracy of tens of feet.

Navstar Satellite

1 Three nickel-cadmium batteries to maintain power during eclipse and peak load periods.
2 Apogee rocket motor, maximum thrust 6.470lb (2.935kg).
3 S-band antenna.
4 Solar panels swivel 360° in 12 hours for tracking Sun.
5 Louvre panels assist thermal control. Thermostatically controlled heaters for navigation, reaction control, orbital injection, and electrical power components.
6 Navigation shaped-beam helix array antenna.
7 S-band antenna.
8 Reaction control thruster module.
9 Attitude control system, consisting of 4 skewed reaction wheels, reaction jet control, manoeuvre and attitude control.

Each Navstar user set includes a radio receiver with an omni-directional antenna, a signal processor and a readout unit. As the sets operate passively, an unlimited number of users can engage the system without saturating it or revealing their position. The set automatically will select four satellites most favourably located, lock onto their navigational signals and compute the approximate range of each. It then will form 4 simultaneous equations with 4 unknowns: the 3 coordinates of the user's position (U_x, U_y, U_z) and the clock bias factor (C_B). A small computer in the set will solve the equation for the user's actual position and the time and determine his velocity. It is also known as GPS: Global Positioning System.

Technical Data

Weight (at boost-satellite separation): 1,705lb (773kg). Weight (at insertion into final orbit): 1,020lb (462kg) including empty case, 55lb (24.9kg) of apogee motor.
Width (solar arrays deployed): 17.5ft (5.33m).
Design life: 5 years.
Life of consumables: 7 years.

Navstar System

This is composed of three integrated segments.
A: The space segment, which transmits very accurate satellite position coordinates and timing information. **B:** The user segment which processes the time and position data from 4 satellites. **C:** The control segment which will track up to 24 satellites and daily correct their position coordinates and rubidium atomic clocks. The atomic clocks lose or gain an average of only one second in 30,000 years.

Monitor Stations
Alaska   Vandenberg AFB
Guam   Hawaii

Master Control Station

photographs. The advantage is that neither superpower can use bad weather or darkness any longer to hide their military activities. This is important as many areas of the Soviet Union particularly are cloud covered for most of the year. According to press reports, the STS-27 Shuttle mission carried a radar reconnaissance satellite which could cover 80 per cent of Russia.

There are two other types of mission that come under the general category of surveillance. The first of these is electromagnetic reconnaissance, or "ferret". This deals with the location and cataloguing of military radio and radar stations. Both the US and the USSR ferret programmes use two separate types of satellite.

The US employs small instrument packages carried piggy-back aboard photo-reconnaissance satellites. They are boosted into a circular 300-mile (483km) orbit by an on-board rocket engine. Once a source is located, a detailed examination of its characteristics, such as antenna rotation speed, pulse duration and frequency is made by a larger, more extensive, package launched on-board an Agena. Two to five of the piggy-back satellites and one or two of the larger satellites were launched per year starting in 1963.[12] The larger ferret satellites were retired after 1971. According to some reports, it was replaced by a ferret satellite called "Jumpseat". These were launched by Titan IIIB boosters into highly elliptical orbits identical to those used by the Satellite Data System communication satellites.

Another ferret system has the code name Rhyolite. The satellites, which are placed in geosynchronous orbit, have a network of antennas which can intercept the telemetry signals from Soviet and Chinese missile test launchings.[13] The first, of a total of four, was launched on 6 March 1973. A follow-on system, Aquacade[14], was under development. It was described as a multipurpose system. The first of these was launched by Space Shuttle *Discovery* on 24 January 1985 during mission STS-51C, a dedicated military Shuttle flight. The ferret satellite successfully reached geosynchronous orbit and unfolded its two large dish antennas. Although the satellite was referred to by the code name "Aquacade" at the time of launch, subsequent press reports called it "Magnum". There have also been reports of a series of geosynchronous ferret satellites called "Chalet" and later "Vortex". The number, dates, and even their existence is unclear due to confusion that exists in the public record between early warning and military communication satellite launches. The British also began development of a system like Aquacade/Magnum called "Zircon". It was apparently cancelled after its existence was publicised in a magazine article in January 1987.

The smaller Soviet ferret satellites are launched by a C-1 vehicle about four times per year into similar orbits. The first launch

was Cosmos 189 (October 1967). As with American practice, larger ferrets are used for a detailed examination of the sources. They are launched by an A-1 booster at a rate of about one per year. The first such launch was Cosmos 389 (December 1970). By 1983, the booster for these satellites was switched to the F-2. On 28 September 1985, the Soviets launched Cosmos 1603, the first of a new very heavy ferret satellite. The first two launches used the D-1 booster while subsequent flights were launched by the J-1 medium lift booster.[15]

In ocean surveillance, at first sight, the Russians appear to have a clear lead. The United States is nevertheless able to conduct ocean surveillance from a number of overseas bases and from allied territory, e.g. Diego Garcia and Ascension Island, and so does not require so many satellites for this purpose. The Soviet Union lacks such bases from which to fly long-range patrol aircraft, and those that are available to it (e.g. Cuba) provide limited logistical support for such missions. Satellites therefore offer the best technical solution to the problems of ocean surveillance for the USSR. Cosmos 198 (December 1967) was the first in a series of large ocean surveillance satellites.

Development continued at a slow pace until 1974 when the system became operational. Satellites were launched into a 174 x 162 miles (280km x 260km) orbit by an F-1-m rocket. One distinctive feature is that a pair of them was launched within a period of a few days. Each carried a powerful radar for locating shipping in any weather conditions; and a radioisotope thermal generator was carried to provide the power. The complete satellite was about 45·9ft (14m) long and 6·6ft (2m) in diameter. The reactor unit was about 19·7ft (6m) long and contained 110lb (50kg) of slightly enriched uranium 235. After the satellite had completed its mission, lasting typically 60 or 70 days, the reactor package was boosted by an on-board rocket into a 590-mile (950km) circular orbit.

Although known to the US Navy since the early 1970s, this type of satellite came to public attention in January 1978 when

Cosmos 954 failed to separate its reactor and re-entered over Canada, necessitating a multi-million-dollar clean-up of the radioactive debris.

The Soviets also use a smaller, non-nuclear ferret-type ocean surveillance satellite. It is an F-1-m launched satellite placed into a 280 × 273-mile (450km × 440km) orbit —higher than the nuclear satellites. The first was Cosmos 699, launched in December 1974. One was flown each year between the pairs of nuclear-powered satellites.[16]

In the wake of Cosmos 954, the Soviet ocean surveillance programme underwent a re-orientation (no such satellites were launched in 1978). In April 1979, a pair of the non-nuclear type was launched, signalling a resumption of effort.[17]

Launch of the nuclear ocean surveillance satellites resumed with Cosmos 1176 in April 1980. The satellite was modified both to double its lifetime to about 140 days and to incorporate several safety measures. The reactor core could now be separated. In the event that the boost failed, the core would burn up during re-entry. Also added was a back-up system that would propel the reactor unit automatically into a safe parking orbit if the reactor depressurized, attitude control fuel ran out, or re-entry heating began. Regular operations of the nuclear and ferret ocean surveillance satellites continued through 1982 when another nuclear satellite, Comos 1402, failed to make the correct boost manoeuvre. The core was separated and both satellite and core burned up safely. Flights of the nuclear satellites halted until the launch of Cosmos 1579 in June 1984.

In the spring of 1988, it appeared that a third uncontrolled re-entry was about to occur. The Soviets lost radio contact with Cosmos 1900, so they were unable to order either a boost or core separation. The satellite continued to orbit until October 1988 when the automatic system activated and boosted the reactor to the final, higher orbit.[17]

The US Navy's effort began later. During the 1970s, several Titan IIIB Agena reconnaissance satellites were used to gain

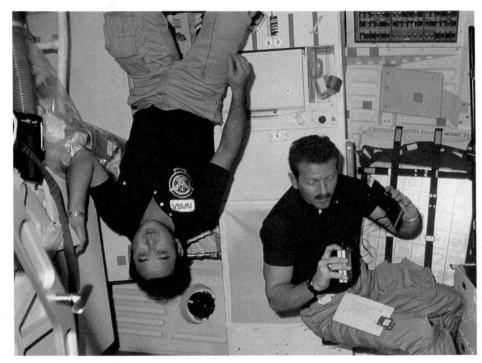

Right: *The Shuttle mission STS-51C was a dedicated military flight. Flown in January 1985, it deployed the first of the Aquacade geosynchronous ferret satellites which can monitor military and diplomatic communications. Seen here are crew members Ellison Onizuka (left) and Loren Shriver.*

experience in ocean surveillance. The first such Navy satellite was launched on 30 April 1976. It used radar, passive radio listening devices and infra-red. The system involves a main satellite and three subsatellites, each carrying its own sensors and transmitting its data to the main satellite for relay to Earth.[18]

Early Warning Satellites

Experiments looking towards the development of early warning satellites began under the US Air Force's Midas programme (MIssile Defense Alarm System), the idea being that an Agena would carry infra-red sensors capable of detecting the hot exhaust of a rising ICBM. The complete system was expected to comprise 12 to 15 satellites in 2,000-mile (3,218km) polar orbits, increasing the warning time of an ICBM attack from 15 to 30 minutes and thus lessening the chance that US strategic missile and bomber forces would be caught by surprise on the ground. Midas 1 (26 February 1960) was a launch failure. Midas 2 (24 May 1960) suffered a telemetry failure after two days. Midas 3 (12 July 1961) was the first successful mission. However, tests with this satellite, as well as Midas 4 (21 October 1961) and two Discoverers (19 and 21), which carried infra-red sensors, indicated that the system was prone to false alarms. In late 1961 therefore the Midas programme was cut back to a development effort. Twice, in 1963 and 1966, satellites were launched into Midas-like orbits to develop more advanced sensors. In the mid-1960s emphasis shifted to placing satellites in synchronous orbit. These satellites were part of the BMEWS (Ballistic Missile Early Warning System). Four were launched between August 1968 and September 1970 and a fifth failed in December 1971.

On 6 November 1970 the first IMEWS (Integrated Missile Early Warning Satellite)

Below: *Satellites play a critical role in monitoring ICBM launches, principally by using infra-red sensors to detect the heat of the rocket efflux. This is a US Defense Support Program satellite.*

IMEWS

The effort to provide advance warning of missile attack against the USA began with the USAF's Midas. In these experiments IR sensors were expected to register the heat emissions produced by ICBM rocket engines, but results were frustrated by sunlight reflected from clouds and the planned operational system was abandoned. Since that time great strides have been made with IMEWS which has means of discriminating between real missiles and spurious effects. Late models also carry Vela-type equipment.

was launched. It was to have been placed in synchronous orbit but a failure in the Titan IIIC transtage left it in the transfer orbit. The second, launched in 5 May 1971, was successful. Further launches have been carried out at the rate of approximately one a year. The satellites carry large infra-red telescopes and television cameras to transmit photos of the detected ICBMs. This is to prevent the false alarms which plagued Midas (a particular problem was sunlight reflecting off high-altitude clouds). They can detect an ICBM within seconds of ignition. The warning is transmitted to ground stations in Australia and Guam and relayed to NORAD (North American Air Defense Command) headquarters within Cheyenne Mountain near Colorado Springs. With the move to operational status, the programme was renamed the Defense Support Program. By the mid-1980s, a four satellite network was established — one over Russia, two over the Pacific and Atlantic, and the fourth over South America. Although various options for future early warning satellites have been explored, in the near term a modified DSP satellite has been developed for Shuttle launches.[19]

Soviet early warning satellites are placed in elliptical 12 hour orbits at a height of 311 by 24.856 miles (500km by 40.000km) because of the difficulty of launching satellites into geostationary orbits from launch sites so distant from the equator. It is difficult to say which was the first Soviet early warning satellite launch. For a long time it was thought Cosmos 159 (May 1967), Cosmos 174 (September 1967) and Cosmos 260 (December 1968) were early warning test missions. Subsequent research indicates that Cosmos 159 may have been a Soyuz propulsion module test, while the other two were failed Molniya communication satellites. The first Soviet early warning satellite now appears to have been Cosmos 520 (19 September 1972). The Soviets were rather slow to move to operational status. Possibly they were having problems similar to Midas; launchings were carried out at the rate of one per year until 1977 when there were three launched, indicating a move to operational status. The Soviets used a three satellite early warning network until 1980 when it was expanded. By the end of 1982, a nine satellite network had been established. Despite the effort, the early warning satellites have shown poor reliability — the Soviets launch nearly enough satellites each year to replace the entire network.[20]

Nuclear Detection

In late 1959 studies were undertaken in America of ways to police a nuclear test ban treaty. The solution was the Vela satellite, which could detect a nuclear explosion at the distance of Venus or Mars and report its yield and characteristics. Its instruments also provide scientific data on the space environment. The first pair of Velas was launched on 16 October 1963 into a circular 60,000-mile (96,540km) orbit. The satellites were placed 180° apart so that they viewed simultaneously opposite sides of the world. Two more pairs were launched on 17 July 1964 and 20 July 1965. A more advanced design, launched on 28 April 1967, extended Vela's capacity to include atmospheric tests. Two additional pairs were launched on 23 May 1969 and 8 April 1970. Vela 11 and 12 were the last of the series. Thereafter, the IMEWS early warning satellites shouldered the task of carrying nuclear detection instruments.[35]

On 25 October 1979 there were reports that United States satellites had detected a nuclear explosion in the atmosphere in the region of South Africa. A statement issued by the State Department gave the following information:

"The United States Government has an indication suggesting the possibility that a low-yield nuclear explosion occurred on 22 September in an area of the Indian Ocean and South Atlantic including portions of the Antarctic continent, and the southern part of Africa. No corroborating evidence has been received to date. We are continuing to assess whether such an event took place."

Some observers believed a nuclear test had taken place at a test site in the Kalahari Desert, some 400 miles (644km) west of Pretoria, but this was quickly denied by the

Below: *Vela satellites which had the task of detecting nuclear explosions in the Earth's atmosphere and outer space. Their role has now been taken over by the Integrated Missile Early Warning Satellite.*

Above: *The first FLTSATCOM was launched in 1978. Four, plus a spare, link US Navy aircraft, ships and submarines, SAC and the Presidential command network.*

Above: *The 19-beam waveguide lens transmit antenna assembly in DSCS 3. These advanced military communications satellites have multiple channels.*

South African authorities. Another theory, that a nuclear accident had occurred in a Russian submarine, was firmly denied by the Soviet Government. Was it possible that a missile launched from a South African warship had exploded a nuclear device at high altitude? There was mention of the possibility of collaboration between Israel and South Africa, but no admission of responsibility was forthcoming.

There have been no readily identifiable Soviet nuclear detection satellites. If a Soviet Vela programme exists, it may be as piggy-back instruments on other military or civilian satellites.

Command and Communications

Not all military satellites have such Doomsday missions as reconnaissance or early warning. Some, in fact, are available for such civilian uses as communications, navigation, weather and nuclear detection. The first military communication satellite was Courier 1B, launched on 4 October 1960. It weighed 500lb (227kg) and was powered by 20,000 solar cells. It demonstrated the active repeater concept: signals were received on one frequency, amplified and re-transmitted on another. It lasted 17 days before suffering a power failure.[21]

Ambitious plans for military communication satellites were delayed by a combination of political problems and lack of sufficiently powerful boosters. The Air Force therefore began to investigate lighter, passive satellites. The result was Project West Ford: a 77lb (35kg) canister would be carried aboard a Midas satellite. After separation, it would slowly release 400 million copper dipoles, each 0·7in (1·8cm) long and about one-third the thickness of a human hair. They would slowly spread out to form a ring around the Earth, 2,000 miles (3,218km) high, five miles (8km) wide and 25 miles (40km) deep.[22] Radio messages could be bounced off the ring. However, Project West Ford was bitterly attacked, particularly by British and Russian scientists. It was claimed that it would seriously impede both optical and radio astronomy research.

Despite the protests, Midas 4, carrying a

West Ford canister, was launched. Anti-climactically, the canister separated but the needles failed to disperse. The experiment was repeated on 9 May 1963. This time deployment was successful and communication tests were conducted.[23] Although no detrimental effects on astronomical research were noted, no further launches were made.[24] By early 1966, when most of the West Ford needles had re-entered the atmosphere, the next US effort was underway.

This was the Initial Defense Communication Satellite System (IDCSS), later renamed Defense Satellite Communication System 1 (DSCS 1). It employed small satellites only 34in (86cm) in diameter and weighing 100lb (45kg). The first batch was placed in sub-synchronous orbit by a Titan IIIC in June 1966. Up to eight satellites were launched at one time; they appeared to drift slowly across the sky, staying in view of particular ground stations for about four days. The complete 26-satellite network was completed after three more flights, the last on 13 June 1968. The design was later improved for use in the NATO and Skynet series. A rocket engine was added to place them in geostationary orbit.

The next system was DSCS 2, employing a much more advanced satellite weighing 1,151lb (522kg); it had multiple channels and could use smaller ground stations. In

November 1971 the first pair was launched into synchronous orbit by a Titan IIIC; both then developed problems and subsequently failed. The next launch took place in December 1973. One of the two DSCS 2s failed after a few months in orbit. The next pair ended their lives in a launch failure during May 1975. Subsequent launches have been more successful. By the late 1970s, four satellites plus three spares were operating. The first DSCS 3 launch was not made until October 1982. It used the first Titan 34D booster. This has been followed by additional launches such as those undertaken during the STS-51J Space Shuttle mission in October 1985, when *Atlantis* placed two DSCS 3s into geosynchronous orbit.

For communicating between US vessels, the US Navy has developed the Fleet Satellite Communication system (FLTSATCOM). The first launch, by an Atlas-Centaur, was made on 9 February 1978. Four satellites plus one spare make up the operational system, each having 30 voice and 12 teletype channels.[25,26]

Another Navy communication satellite is the Leasat. It was designed to take advantage of the full width of the Space Shuttle's cargo bay and can be launched by no other booster. The first Leasat 2, was launched on STS-41D in August 1984. The next, Leasat 3, (STS-51D in April 1985) was deployed successfully but did not fire its own engine to boost itself into geosynchronous orbit. It was repaired by the crew of STS-51I (August 1985) which also deployed Leasat 4.

Ironically, the most mysterious satellite is not a reconnaissance craft but a military Comsat—the Satellite Data System. Launched into a highly elliptical orbit similar to that used by the Russian Molniya Comsats, it is used to communicate with US nuclear forces in the polar regions. No photos of this satellite have been released and disclosure of orbital elements is delayed. The first was launched in August 1973.[27]

The largest communication satellite is TACSAT 1, launched in February 1969. It is used to link, by means of small transmitters, aircraft, ships, land vehicles, using even hand-held equipment.

Satellite-based tactical communication techniques were first demonstrated with LES 5 (Lincoln Experimental Satellite) in 1967 and LES 6 in 1968. They were built by the Massachusetts Institute of Technology's Lincoln Laboratory. Another unusual type of Comsat is LES 8 and 9, launched in March 1976 into a 25° synchronous orbit. It tested

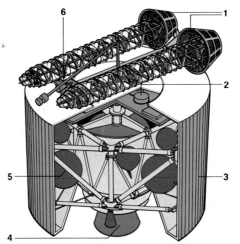

Leasat
1 UHF antennas.
2 Despun platform.
3 Solar cell array.
4 Solid propellant apogee motor.
5 Liquid propellant storage.
6 SHF antennas.

This spin-stabilised satellite – to be launched by the Space Shuttle – will be used primarily by the US Navy for communications with mobile tactical units, ships, submarines, aircraft and ground services. Four satellites, to be distributed around the world in Clarke orbit, will be controlled by four ground stations and a master operational control centre.

Technical Data
In launch configuration:
Height: 169·3in (430cm).
Diameter: 166·1in (422cm). With antennas deployed in orbit:
Height: 242·5in (616cm).
Spin rate on station: 30rpm.
Design lifetime: 10 years.
Prime contractor: Hughes.
The spinning section of Leasat contains the propulsion, attitude control and power subsystems. The despun section contains the telemetry, command and communications subsystems and the spacecraft's Earth-pointing antenna. The solar cell array will generate 1,260 watts after 5 years (11 per cent over requirements) and 1,210 watts after 10.

Above: *One of the Navstar satellites that will make up the Global Positioning System. Such a satellite has more than 33,000 parts; it also carries three atomic clocks.*

techniques to reduce vulnerability to killer satellites. It also tested direct satellite-to-satellite communications.[28]

The array of Russian military Comsats is less complicated, falling as it does into three groups. For direct point-to-point communication, it is believed that the Soviet military uses Molniya 1 satellites. They are placed into highly elliptical orbits, 24,856 by 311 miles (40,000km by 500km). This looping orbit allows about 8 hours of coverage during a single pass. It is also preferable for a northerly located country, such as the USSR, to an equatorial orbit. About three of these satellites are launched per year, interspersed with the later model Molniya 2 and 3 series. They are equipped to carry radio, telephone and telegraph signals.

The Soviet military also uses a series of storage/dump-type satellites. Placed in orbit eight at a time, they are used to pass information to Soviet forces when real-time transmission is not possible. Launches occur about two or three times a year; approximately 30 such satellites are operating at a time. The third, and least understood, type of Soviet Comsat is launched singly by a C-1. It is believed also to be a storage/dump satellite used to record data from clandestine sensor equipment and secret agents and then replay it to Soviet tracking stations.[29]

Navigation Satellites

The US Navy Transits were designed to provide navigational fixes, accurate to 1/10th of a mile (161m) for Polaris submarines in any weather conditions. It carries two ultra-stable oscillators transmitting on 150MHz and 400MHz. Positions are obtained by using the satellite's known orbit and the signal's Doppler shift.

The first launch took place in September 1959, and operational missions began with Transit 5A in December 1962. Shortly afterwards the Transit programme was classified. At least ten Transit-related satellites were launched during the next four years, and in 1967 they were released for civilian use.

Soviet navigation satellites use exactly the same procedures and frequencies as the Transits. The Soviet system was first

launched in November 1967 (Cosmos 192). Like Transit, it went through distinct phases, becoming operational in 1971. About five per year are launched.[30]

Transit's successor is the Navstar Global Positioning System. It originated from several US Air Force test satellites and the Navy's Timation 1, 2 and 3 (May 1967, September 1969 and July 1974) and Triad satellites (September 1972).

The Navstar's receiver measures signal delay and is accurate to 33ft (10m). It will be able to provide navigational information for space, air, sea and ground operations, both military and civilian.[31][32]

The first Navstar was launched on 22 February 1978, beginning a series of pre-operational tests. It was hoped that the final 24-satellite network, in three orbital planes, would be completed in 1984, but budget cuts announced in April 1980 envisaged reducing the number of satellites in the Navstar constellation to 18 with a corresponding decrease in accuracy of 19·7ft (6m).

The road to the full network proved difficult; there was a total of four Navstar launches in 1978 and two in 1980. Problems with the Atlas F booster then caused a halt and it was not until February 1983 that the next Navstar lifted off. By October 1985, a total of 11 had been launched. It was planned that more Navstars would be launched on the Space Shuttle, but they were delayed when *Challenger* exploded. In the tragedy's aftermath, it was decided to develop a number of expendable boosters, and when the first Delta 2 left the pad on 14 February 1989, it was carrying a Navstar. By late 1992, 19 Navstars will have been launched on Delta 2s and two more are scheduled for a 1991 Shuttle flight.

The Soviet counterpart to Navstar is the GLONASS (Global Navigation Satellite System). They are launched in threes aboard a D-1-e booster. The first trio were Cosmos 1413, 1414 and 1415 launched on 12 October 1982. As before, the "Navstarsky" uses exactly the same methods and orbits as the corresponding US system.

Meteorology Satellites

One of the earliest benefits of the space programme was the provision of accurate weather information from satellites. In addition to providing long-range forecasts for military planners, weather satellites play a key support role in reconnaissance satellites. They tell the mission planners whether or not an area of interest will be clear of cloud cover when a reconnaissance satellite makes its pass. Because the amount of reconnaissance film carried is limited, none can be wasted on photos of clouds. From 1960 until 1965, the US civilian Tiros weather satellites provided this information. The Air Force then began in early 1965 to launch its own weather satellites. The reason was a decision to raise the orbit of future civilian weather satellites from 300 miles (483km) to 800 miles (1,287km) high. This decision was unacceptable to the Air Force which needs higher resolution photos for planning military operations as opposed to large-scale photos that satisfy civilian forecasters.

These satellites built by RCA were launched by Thor-Burner. The latest Air Force weather satellite is RCA's Block 5D,

Above: *The Block 5D meteorology satellite. From a near polar orbit it supplies weather information to the USAF. Data are used for strategic and tactical planning.*

providing infra-red and visual imagery, temperature/moisture soundings, auroral detection and upper-atmosphere soundings. Two are operational at any one time.[33]

In contrast to the US programme, Russia was slow to fly weather satellites. A number of engineering test flights were made from 1963 to 1965, possibly indicating either engineering problems or a low priority. In any event, it would appear that up to 1966 or 1967, Soviet reconnaissance satellites were flown with little or no support from weather satellites. Since 1967, the Meteor weather satellites have been operational. Soviet military authorities have full access to them.[34]

ASAT

In times of international crisis, the foregoing satellites would make tempting targets, and this consideration has prompted the USA and USSR to study methods of satellite interception and destruction. In the US, studies of such a concept began in 1959. In the following years RCA received a contract to develop the SAtellite INTerceptor (SAINT), which involved the development of a final stage and inspection package. It would co-orbit, inspect, and possibly destroy a target. The programme was cut back in December 1962 due to schedule slippage and cost increases and because a less sophisticated concept would be ready much sooner.

In 1962 work was begun on adapting the Nike Zeus ABM (anti-ballistic missile) for use as a direct-ascent anti-satellite system. The first successful shot was made on 23 May 1963 when a Nike Zeus, fired from Kwajalein Atoll in the Pacific, intercepted an Agena-D in orbit. A handful of these nuclear-equipped missiles were operational during 1964. They were replaced by nuclear-armed Thors on Johnston Island, also in the Pacific, which were operational from 1964 until 1975 when the project was closed down.[36]

In October 1967 Russia began hardware-testing a satellite interceptor system. On 20 October 1968 their first attempted intercept was successfully made. The previous day, Cosmos 248 had been launched by an F-1-m rocket. This was the target; it may have carried the instruments to report back miss-distance information.

The next day Cosmos 249 was launched, also by F-1-m. This was the interceptor. After several orbital adjustments to achieve an eccentric path, it made a fast fly-by of the target before blasting itself into a cloud of metal shards. This was probably the kill mechanism, the target being peppered.

In the first series, between 1967 and 1971, seven successful interceptions were made. Starting in 1971, the target satellites were launched by a C-1 vehicle. All but one of the interceptions followed the pattern of the first mission. The exception was the interception of Cosmos 400 by Cosmos 404 in April 1971. Cosmos 404 was manoeuvred into a near co-orbit, resulting in a slower fly-by. It was then de-orbited over the Pacific. After 1971, there was a pause in interceptor flights.[37]

US studies of various concepts had continued through the 1960s and early 1970s. The only one to be built was an infra-red guided, direct-ascent package developed by the Vought Corporation. Only one test flight was made (April 1970) and it ended in failure when the Thor booster collided with the payload after separation.

Soviet interceptor tests were resumed in February 1976, when Cosmos 803 was intercepted by Cosmos 804. The next test in April employed a new intercept technique. Cosmos 814 was placed in orbit and almost immediately fired an on-board engine that put it into a pop-up trajectory. It made a fast fly-by of that target, Cosmos 803, then re-entered over the Pacific. The whole mission occupied less than one orbit. This profile reduced the warning time during which evasive action might be taken by the satellite under attack. Unlike the two other profiles, there was no extensive manoeuvring before interception.

The second series consisted of nine tests made from February 1976 through May 1978. Several were possible failures. The tests indicated that the Soviets had the ability to destroy low-altitude reconnaissance, ferret and navigation satellites. These renewed efforts caused deep concern in Washington[38], which was further fuelled in April 1980 when single orbit intercept tests — Cosmos 1,171 and 1,174 — were resumed. The final Soviet ASAT test was made on 18 June 1982 when Cosmos 1379 intercepted the Cosmos 1375 target. This was part of a seven hour exercise involving the firing of two SS-11 ICBMs, an SS-11 IRBM, a submarine-launched missile and two ABM X-3 interceptors. It was a simulation of a nuclear attack on the US and Western Europe.

In late 1976 the Air Force began a new series of ASAT studies, arguing that without a comparable US system, the Russians would enjoy an unacceptable advantage.

A contract for research was given to the Vought Corporation, who had worked on earlier ASAT studies, and two separate concepts are now under consideration. The first is air launch reaction, based on the Short Range Attack Missile (SRAM). It could be fired from an F-15 aircraft during a high speed climb and make a direct-ascent attack. It would carry a 12in x 13in (30 x 33cm) cylindrical miniature homing device which separates from the missile, and using an infra-red seeker, is guided to a collision

Above: *An ASAT vehicle being carried under the centreline of an F-15 aircraft. Though tested successfully, the ASAT programme was cancelled in 1988.*

with the target. The other is larger, 700lb-1,500lb (317kg-680kg), mounted either on a missile or satellite. It would co-orbit and destroy its target with impacting fragmentation warheads. This is considered a back-up to the air-launch system.[39] The F-15-launched ASAT was tested successfully several times. This included one interception and destruction of a target satellite in September 1985. However, the programme ran into Congressional opposition that labelled it "destabilizing". In 1988, it was cancelled and the remaining rockets were put into storage. At the present time the Soviet Union possesses the only operational ASAT system.

For the future, speculations are centred on a science fiction weapon: an energy beam, either a chemical laser or a charged-particle beam.

Lasers produce very powerful and narrow beams of coherent light. The name is the acronym of Light Amplification by the Stimulated Emission of Radiation. In the laboratory they have been shown to burn through steel but their potency, like that of other forms of radiation, diminishes with distance.

One of the key centres of laser weapon research in the United States is the Air Force Weapons Laboratory (AFWL) at Kirtland Air Force Base, Albuqerque, New Mexico, which operates two laser ranges and an airborne laser laboratory. The first successful use of a laser beam against a flying target occurred at AFWL in 1973.

In 1974 the US House Appropriations Committee was told in secret testimony that high-energy chemical lasers were already within reach of advanced technology. There was concern that Russia was in the race.

TRW Systems of Redondo Beach, California, had the task of building a prototype laser projector, and a target tracking and aiming platform was contracted out to Hughes Aircraft Company. The first successful test came in 1973 when the Air Force used a high-energy gas-dynamic laser to shoot down a winged drone at Kirtland AFB. In 1976, the Army destroyed winged and helicopter drones at Redstone Arsenal with a high-energy electric laser, while in 1978 a

chemical laser developed by the Defense Advanced Research Projects Agency for the Navy engaged and destroyed a TOW anti-tank missile in flight. Air Force Secretary Hans Mark stated during Congressional hearings that the Air Force hoped to demonstrate the feasibility of a laser aboard a KC-135 by the end of 1980.

It was anticipated that laser beams could burn through vulnerable parts of low-flying aircraft such as cockpit canopies and cause significant damage to internal equipment. Cruise missiles would be another potential target.

Early studies indicated that laser satellites might be capable of blunting a mass ICBM attack. The satellites would need a 2 megawatt chemical laser and a 33ft (10m) mirror or a 5 megawatt laser with a 13ft (3·96m) mirror and could destroy an ICBM 4,000 miles (6,436km) away. Each satellite would have enough fuel for the chemical laser to destroy 1,000 targets. The US has conducted lab tests which indicate that an ICBM would explode within one second of being hit.

However, the step from short-range laser weapons to ones capable of providing a defence against ballistic missiles is a large one. An anti-satellite application would be easier because beams of moderate strength could damage highly sensitive electronic equipment. Much contemporary research is concerned with the problem of protecting satellites from the disabling effects of beam weapons. Several methods are being investigated. They range from the shielding of electronic circuits to the use of components less sensitive to radiation, and the redundancy of other components. Efforts have also been made to produce "dark" satellites by reducing their optical and radar responses.

The alternative — a charged-particle beam in which subatomic particles (protons or electrons) are accelerated to very high velocities (and therefore energies) in an electromagnetic field — is also limited.

Not only does the beam require very high power to generate but its installations are likely to be massive and expensive. Its directional control must be precise and losses due to interaction with the atmosphere complicate the problem of aiming. Additional problems arise from the Earth's magnetic field, which bends the beam. Mutual repulsion of the beam's charged particles increases beam spread and so the beam loses intensity.

Broadly, the advantages of directed particle beams as distinct from lasers (both operating in the atmosphere) are that they work with greater efficiency, being less affected by weather and less attenuated by moisture in the atmosphere. Moreover, there is the prospect that electronic equipment in the target will be damaged by ionising radiation.

If the beams could be directed at their ICBM targets from the vacuum of space, they would be still more effective. A beam weapon has the advantage that it can engage multiple targets rapidly. However, since both laser and charged-particle systems are still in the laboratory phase, their limitations are not yet fully understood. For example: a beam must be aimed much more accurately than a conventional ABM or anti-satellite system. They would also be highly vulnerable to enemy anti-satellite missiles launched from the ground, and other beam-weapon-equipped satellites.

The Russians have been carrying out fundamental research into particle beams for a number of years. Much of this has to do with the development of controlled nuclear fusion for future power-stations. But a large installation at Semipalatinsk is believed to be conducting research into particle-beam weapons. Recent published reports indicate that the Russians have tested the effects of charged-particle beams on metal targets and high explosives. The Russians have also tested a 500 KV "switch ring" which could be used to aim a charged-particle beam, and have generated magnetic fields with a strength of several million gauss.[40 41]

SDI

These possibilities came forcefully to public attention in March 1983 when President Ronald Reagan made his celebrated Strategic Defense Initiative speech. The years that followed saw intensive research into a wide range of technology; from the conventional to the exotic. One approach tested was to use a conventional ABM rocket with a non-nuclear warhead to intercept incoming missiles. This was tested in the HOE (Homing Overlay Experiment) programme. A Minuteman ICBM was fitted with a number of long metal blades. When unfurled, they formed an umbrella-like disc. In one flight test in June 1984, a HOE missile proved itself able to intercept and collide with a dummy warhead, destroying it.[40] The advantages of a "hit-to-kill" warhead are several. It uses technology that is well proven. Moreover, it avoids the problems inherent in using a nuclear weapon to destroy incoming RVs. The fireball from an ABM's nuclear warhead exploding in space can blackout radar signals, so making it impossible to track and intercept subsequent warheads. A low altitude interception, within the atmosphere, may destroy the incoming RV but the blast from the ABM's own warhead could cause damage on the ground.

Under the ABM Treaty up to 100 interceptors could be deployed to defend an ICBM field or the national capital. An ABM of this type would be used for the terminal phase (ie as the warheads re-enter the atmosphere). A similar hit-to-kill warhead

Below: *The non-explosive, umbrella-like "warhead" as used in the HOE experimental missile intercept mission that was successfully flown on 10 June 1984.*

Above: *An artist's impression of a space-based electromagnetic railgun which might fire hypervelocity missiles, or "smart rocks", at up to 60 rounds per second.*

has also been tested for use during the boost phase (while the ICBM's engines are still firing), and the mid-course phase (after the engines have shut down and the warheads have been released). The interceptors would be carried aboard satellites and fired when the ICBMs came within range.

Boost and mid-course interception was tested in September 1986. The third stage of a Delta booster was fitted with the infra-red sensor from a Maverick anti-tank missile, and the radar and computer from a Phoenix air to air missile. It also carried a laser, radar and other camera and electronic sensors. The second stage also carried sensor equipment to watch the third stage. During the flight, the third stage monitored the exhaust plume of the second stage and an Aries sounding rocket. The Aries was tracked while it was still within the atmosphere. The second stage sensors monitored the third stage as it coasted through space — simulating an ICBM just before the warheads are released. As the final demonstration, the third stage successfully manoeuvred to collide with and destroy the second stage.[41]

A more advanced ABM system is the "railgun", which has been ground tested. Unlike a conventional gun, it uses electromagnetic power rather than powder to accelerate projectiles. The principle is the same as for a particle beam weapon, except that a projectile, rather than a stream of atoms, is being accelerated. The interceptor, called a "Smart Rock" or "Brilliant Pebble". would be similar to the F-15 ASATs miniature vehicle. A railgun is capable of a very high "muzzle velocity" — indeed, it has been suggested that an orbiting railgun could launch small planetary probes to escape velocity from Earth orbit.

Testing of the sensors for such space interceptors was carried out on two Delta flights. The first was conducted in February 1988 in which the satellite released 14 sub-satellites which simulated warheads. For a March 1989 Delta launch, the satellite carried systems to observe rocket plumes against a wide range of backgrounds. Other tests and observations are to be made on the StarLab Shuttle mission in 1990.

Above: *The potential lethality of a high-power laser is graphically illustrated here as a MIRACL beam destroys the second stage of a target Titan I booster.*

Above: *The US Navy's laser beam director at White Sands Missile Range. It is designed to track targets in flight, and direct a high energy laser beam at them.*

Lasers and X-Rays

Most of the interest and research effort in strategic defences, before the 1983 SDI speech, was carried out in the area of high power lasers. Extensive ground tests have been made since then. Lasers have been fired at targets ranging from drones, a Titan ICBM stage under the simulated stress of powered flight and a Talos surface to air missile travelling at supersonic speed. Much of the work was done by the US Navy to develop a laser defence against anti-shipping missiles. The tests were made at the White Sands Missile Range, New Mexico, with the Sea Lite mirror and beam director system and the MIRACL (Mid-Infrared Advanced Chemical Laser). This is the most powerful laser in the western world. In early 1989, it was proposed to modify the MIRACL to act as a prototype ASAT laser.[42, 43] Orbital tests will be made by the Zenith Star laser which is being built by TRW.

Underground nuclear tests have also been conducted for the most exotic defence system — the X-ray laser. A small nuclear bomb is used as the power source. When the weapon is detonated, a burst of X-rays are emitted at the speed of light. The X-rays travel down long metal rods. This generates an intense beam, not of laser light but of X-rays. In effect, the power of a nuclear bomb is focused onto the target ICBM. The energy of the beam would, in theory, be so great that the ICBM would be irradiated, incinerated and fragmented.[44]

By late 1988, a plan for the first phase of SDI's deployment had been formalized. It envisioned a limited number of orbital weapons with the bulk of the defences resting on ground-based ABMs. They would defend US ICBM silos. The space shield foreseen by President Reagan as the means of defending the civilian population of the United States, would come later. The final outcome of this ambitious enterprise is not clear. The programme may flounder; both due to cost and technical difficulties, and because of the bitter opposition of academics, arms controllers and the media to the very idea of strategic defences.

Soviet Research

The Soviets have also been busy — their strategic defence activities predate the SDI speech. At the end of the 1960s, they deployed ABM sites around Moscow. These were upgraded in the late 1980s with 100 improved interceptor missiles, the SA-4 which would destroy the warheads at long range and the SA-8 for interceptions within the atmosphere. Incoming warheads are detected by the Pushkino large phased-array radar near Moscow. Once within range of the ABMs, they are picked up by the Flat Twin engagement radars; the ABM missiles are guided to their targets by Pawn Shop radars.

The Soviets have also tested SA-5 surface to air missiles as ABMs; and the SA-12 SAM has destroyed an ICBM warhead in a test. The SA-12 launchers and Grill Pan radar are mounted on several tracked vehicles and could provide an ABM defence for a limited area. They have also ground tested a powerful laser similar to the MIRACL, and are building what has been labelled an ASAT laser site at Dushanbe near the Afghanistan border. A huge radar site is being constructed at Krasnoyarsk in central USSR in violation of the ABM Treaty. All this suggests the Soviets may be planning a country-wide ABM defence.[45, 46] The Russians claim, for their part, that the station is for tracking satellites.

If SDI and its Soviet counterpart are successful, it will mean a profound shift in nuclear policy. Today the US holds to the principle of MAD (Mutual Assured Destruction). This is the belief that even if the Soviet Union launches a surprise attack, they would still be destroyed by the surviving US nuclear forces. Deterrence would be preserved as both sides would be destroyed — there would be nothing to gain by launching a nuclear attack. The flaw in MAD is that should deterrence break down, and either side come to believe a surprise attack was possible, their adversary would be faced with the choice of submitting to nuclear blackmail or total destruction.

With SDI there could be a shift to MAS (Mutual Assured Survival). Under MAS,

SELECTED SOVIET MILITARY SATELLITES

NAME	LAUNCH VEH	ORBIT miles (km)	PURPOSE
ASAT	F-1-m	Example: Cosmos 1174 77x252 (124x405); then 225 x 637 (362x1,025) to intercept Cosmos 1171	Hunter-killer satellite interceptor. World's first operational anti-satellite (ASAT) system tested 1967-1985. First interception of orbiting target by Cosmos 249. Shrapnel-effect warhead.
Early warning	A-2-e	Example: Cosmos 520 2,718x22,281 (4,375x35,857)x67·6°	Possibly first experimental early warning satellite employing IR surveillance was Cosmos 159 launched into high elliptical orbit with apogee over Northern Hemisphere.
Ferret (large)	A-1, F-2	391x404 (630x650)x81·2°	Detailed survey of operational characteristics of military radar and radio stations.
Ferret (large)	D-1/later J-2	—	Heavy multi-purpose satellite with ferret capability, late 1980s-1990s.
Ferret (small)	C-1	311x342 (500x550)x74°	General survey of military radar and radio stations.
FOBS	F-1-r	Example:Cosmos139 89x130(144x210)	Fractional-Orbit Bombardment System (FOBS) tested 1966-1971, subsequently cancelled. Aimed to develop orbital ICBM capable of entering United States through "backdoor" of the Southern Hemisphere.
GLONASS	D-1-e	11,869 (19,100)x64·8°	Global Navigation System (GLONASS), first Cosmos 1413, 1414, 1415 — with civil and military applications, similar to USAF Navstar. To comprise 18 satellites in three groups in different orbital planes; 3 more in reserve 1989-1995.
Military communications (strategic/tactical)	A-2-e	311x24,856 (500x40,000)	Molniya 1 satellite in highly-elliptical orbit serving Northern Hemisphere. Molniya 3 "hot-line" communications Moscow-Washington.
Military communications (tactical)	C-1	932 (1,500)	Storage-dump satellites, launched eight at a time to produce 30 satellite network.
Nuclear-powered ocean surveillance satellite	F-1-m	159x168 (256x270)	Locate shipping by use of radar. Pair of satellites launched a few days apart. Uses nuclear-reactor to power equipment. After completion of 60-75 day mission, nuclear reactor unit is fired into higher orbit.
Reconnaissance satellite, Soyuz-based	A-2	106x218 (171x352)	Introduced 1975, lifetime 30 days, increased to 44 days 1982, 54 days 1985. Fifth-generation satellite employs digital imagery (first Cosmos 1426) achieves lifetimes of 200 days plus.
Reconnaissance satellite, Vostok-based	A-1/A-2	130x154 (210x248) high-resolution 223x258 (360x415) search and find	Orbital reconnaissance by modified, unmanned Vostok spacecraft carrying high-resolution camera plus manoeuvre engine. Began 1962, at first being recovered after 3-8 days. Improved version 1968, lifetime 12-14 days.
Salyut/Mir space stations	D-1	150/225 (241/362)	Extensive photography with both civil and military applications. Salyut 3 and 5 used known "reconnaissance" frequencies.

NOTES: Many other Soviet satellites have both civil and military functions, e.g. Meteor satellites providing advance warning of weather conditions around the world, and certain communications satellites in geostationary orbit.

deterrence would be preserved both by offensive and defensive systems. A Soviet attack would fail because not enough warheads would get through to destroy US nuclear forces or American society. A Soviet attack would be deterred both because the probability of success was too low and the penalty for failure too high.

FOBS

There is a mission even more threatening than killer satellites—the establishment of nuclear weapons in orbit. It was the threat of such weapons which spurred the early US killer satellite effort. The US had studied orbital nuclear weapons in the early 1960s but soon abandoned the effort. The studies showed that, in addition to profound reliability and control problems, such weapons would be inaccurate and would have only a small payload. The Soviet Union was not so restrained. In September and November of 1966 the Russians conducted space missions which they did not acknowledge, something they had not done since the 1963 planetary failures. The flights were directed into a new orbital inclination by means of a launch vehicle—the F-1-r. Apparently they were precursor flights in some new programme.

In 1967 there were nine more flights, all carried out anonymously within the Cosmos programme. The satellites were launched into a low Earth orbit; then shortly before the completion of one orbit, they would retro-fire and land back on Soviet territory.

On 3 November 1967 US Defense Secretary McNamara revealed that they were unarmed test flights of a Fractional Orbit Bombardment System (FOBS). Such a weapon would shorten warning time as it does not describe a high arc into space (unlike an ICBM) and could approach from any direction, rather than from the northerly route over the Pole.

After the frantic development effort of 1967, only one or two FOBS flights per year were made.

One of these, Cosmos 316 (launched on 23 December 1969) was a failure. A few months later it decayed over the American midwest. Several large chunks were recovered. According to unconfirmed reports, they resembled a bomb casing. Tests stopped after 1971, when a total of 18 flights had been conducted.[42] A limited number of FOBS were deployed in silos but are now considered obsolescent. The Soviet Union indicated its intention to dismantle these systems in accordance with the broader reductions of strategic missile systems that would be made if SALT II were ratified by the US Congress. In any case, deployment of weapons of mass destruction in space is prohibited by Treaty.

Impact

From the earliest days of the US and Russian reconnaissance effort, these satellites have had a profoundly beneficial effect on international relations. Before their advent, the US had a minimal understanding of Soviet military strength. Projections were made, not from data recorded by instruments but from information provided by agents, which had been notoriously unreliable. The Russians were quick to exploit this uncertainty. Now each side knows more precisely the size of its opponent's forces, lessening the chance of miscalculation, bluff or reaction through fear. New threats can be discovered early and countermoves prepared before the threat matures. The status and location of military units can be monitored, so lessening the chance of surprise attack. There is no question of the importance the US places on reconnaissance satellites. The US insisted that the SALT treaty guarantee non-interference with "national technical means of verification".

Reconnaissance satellites are both the guarantors of arms treaties and the means to make such treaties possible, as they eliminate the need for that old sticking point—on-site inspections. Clearly, the Russians feel the same way, otherwise they would not countenance the cost of launching over 30 satellites per year. Also, during crises like the 1969 engagements with China and the October 1973 Middle-East War, the launch rate of Soviet reconnaissance satellites

Below: *The effect of laser radiation on various materials is investigated in laboratory experiments as this 15 kilowatt carbon dioxide electric discharge laser burns through a sheet of acrylic plastic.*

doubled, indicating the importance of up-to-date information for crisis management.

It is interesting to note that the first military satellites launched by the three sides— the United States, the USSR and China—were for reconnaissance purposes. Yet despite all their powers, such space techniques have their limitations. They can reveal the capacities of a country but not its intentions. They provide raw data. It is up to people to interpret these data and draw conclusions. This interpretation can be affected by views, beliefs, knowledge and perceptions even when there is an attempt to be impartial and objective. Yet, within these limitations, reconnaissance satellites provide a measure of reassurance in what is otherwise an uncertain and dangerous world.

REFERENCES

1 Philip Klass, *Secret Sentries in Space*, Random House, 1971, Chapter 10.
2 Laurence Freedman, *US Intelligence and the Soviet Strategic Threat*, Westview Press, 1977, Chapter 4.
3 *Secret Sentries in Space*, Chapter 14.
4 *Secret Sentries in Space*, Chapter 15.
5 *Spaceflight*, November 1978.
6 *Aviation Week & Space Technology (AWST)*, 9 April 1979.
7 *New York Times*, 18 November 1978, 23 December 1978.
8 *Secret Sentries in Space*, Chapter 16.
9 *Soviet Space Programs 1971-1975*, US Library of Congress, pp. 457-478.
10 Curtis Peebles, *Guardians*, Presido Press, Chapters 9, 13 and 14.
11 *Spaceflight*, October 1977.
12 *Secret Sentries in Space*, Chapter 19.
13 *AWST*, 14 May 1979.
14 *AWST*, 4 June 1979.
15 *Guardians*, Chapter 12.
16 *Soviet Space Programs 1971-1975*, p 430.
17 *Guardians*, Chapter 15.
18 *Spaceflight*, July 1978.
19 *Guardians*, Chapter 17.
20 Curtis Peebles, *Battle for Space*, Beauford Books, 1983, Chapter 4.
21 Richard S. Lewis, *Appointment on the Moon*, Viking Press, 1969.
22 Reginald Turnill, *The Observer's Book of Unmanned Spaceflight*, Frederick Warne & Co, 1974.
23 *Astronautics & Aeronautics*, NASA SP 4004, 1963.
24 *Astronautics & Aeronautics*, NASA SP 4005, 1964.
25 T. M. Wilding-White, *Jane's Pocket Book of Space Exploration*, Macdonald and Jane's, 1976.
26 David Fishlock (Editor), *A Guide to Earth Satellites*, Macdonald and Jane's, 1971.
27 *Armed Forces Journal*, January 1978.
28 *AWST*, 22 March 1976.
29 *Soviet Space Programs 1971-1975*, pp 381, 407, 408.
30 *Soviet Space Programs 1971-1975*, pp 407, 453-456.
31 T. M. Wilding-White, *Jane's Pocket Book of Space Exploration*, Macdonald and Jane's, 1976.
32 Richard W. Porter, *The Versatile Satellite*, Oxford University Press, 1977.
33 *Secret Sentries in Space*, Chapter 14.
34 *Soviet Space Programs 1971-1975*, p 357
35 *Secret Sentries in Space*, Chapter 19.
36 *Battle for Space*, Chapter 3.
37 *Soviet Space Programs 1971-1975*, pp 424-429.
38 *AWST*, 26 April 1976.
39 *AWST*, 25 June 1979.
40 *San Diego Union*, 12 June 1984, A-1.
41 *Reader's Digest*, July 1987, pp 59-64.
42 *San Diego Union*, 1 January 1989, A-2.
43 *San Diego Union*, 4 March 1989, A-5.
44 *Battle for Space*, Chapter 6.
45 *Reader's Digest*, July 1986, pp 149-153.
46 *Soviet Military Power 1988*, Department of Defense, 1988, Chapter 4.

Voices from the Sky

"Live via satellite."

This phrase is used less and less in television broadcasts, even though transmissions are increasingly carried by satellite. It is an odd indication of the tremendous success of the first space industrialisation effort, and the way it has become an accepted part of everyday life.

Communications satellites tie the world together, quite literally, on invisible threads. If broken, many economies would slow. In another decade those threads may mean life itself, not just to the industrial world, but to many of the less developed nations.

Communications satellites were born shortly after World War II when a far-sighted British writer realised that Hitler's rocket technology might make possible a wedding of the laws of Newton and Kepler with the inventions of Marconi. In the October 1945 issue of *Wireless World*, Arthur C. Clarke elaborated on his idea for a communications relay station to be placed 22,300 miles (35,880km) above the Earth.

The idea of satellites was not new. Clarke's achievement was to discover a place in the sky where objects would stand still. More properly, he found an orbit in which a satellite can remain stationary with respect to the Earth. This path is called a geosynchronous, geostationary or Clarke orbit. The greater the distance a satellite orbits, the longer it takes to complete one circuit. At 22,300 miles (35,880km), a circular orbit takes 24hr to complete—the same

> ## "We the globe can compass soon Swifter than the wandering moon."
>
> William Shakespeare
> *A Midsummer Night's Dream*

Above: *In the early 1960s long-range communications experiments were made by bouncing radio signals from balloon satellites like this 135ft (41m) Echo 2.*

period as one rotation of the Earth. A satellite in such an orbit will stay over the same spot day after day (though the effects of tidal forces require continual adjustments to keep the satellite on station).

Clarke proposed this as the ideal position for global communications relays. From it, three satellites could see most of the Earth's surface (excluding the polar regions). No longer would radio communications be tied to the vagaries of the ionosphere.

The idea did not catch on right away as no means existed to boost a satellite into low Earth orbit, let alone such a high one. In fact, the first communications satellite turned out to be the Moon. US Army engineers used it as a reflector during experiments in 1951, and during a communications blackout caused by an intense solar storm in 1955.

Man's first artificial satellite, Sputnik 1, was a communications satellite of sorts by virtue of its radio beacon. It was launched in 1957. The first human voice to be returned from space was that of US President Dwight D. Eisenhower when in 1958 Project Score orbited an Atlas ICBM minus its booster with a tape-recorded Christmas message from the leader who saw little practical use for space. The recorder could also store messages for dumping later; this was known as a delayed repeater satellite. A later delayed repeater was Courier 1B, launched on 4 October 1960. This military satellite could store and retransmit up to 68,000 words a minute. It used solar cells rather than the limited batteries of Score.

Balloon Satellites

Passive systems, mimicking the US Army's earlier use of the Moon, were briefly tested. Echo 1 and 2 were large reflective balloons made of aluminized Mylar. Their use was limited to pairs of ground stations that could both see the balloons at the same time. In the end, geodetic scientists found them of greater use as extraterrestrial mapping beacons.

Engineers recognised that what was needed was an active relay system, ie, orbital versions of the microwave relay towers used by telephone systems. For some time they debated whether it was more desirable to put a few satellites in geostationary orbit—and pay a higher price to launch them—or place a multitude of satellites in lower orbits—and pay a higher price for the satellites. In the end, the geostationary proponents won, if for no other reason than that such vehicles would be easier to track. Low-orbit satellites require continual motion of large antennas, plus

Clarke Orbit

Arthur C. Clarke presented his original proposals for a geostationary satellite in the form of a Memorandum to the Council of the British Interplanetary Society. This document, dated 25 May 1945, is now in the archives of the Smithsonian Institution in Washington, DC. The Society immediately recommended wider dissemination of the proposals, which resulted in the publication of an article in "Wireless World" the following October.

In his Memorandum Clarke emphasised the importance of the 24-hour orbit, so permitting a satellite that maintains station above a fixed point on the Earth at the equator. He showed how three satellites spaced at equal intervals above the equator at a height of some 22,300 miles (35,880km) could spread a web of communications around the world, and how a single satellite could broadcast to several regions simultaneously.

Speaking to the Society 23 years later—with a global satellite network obeying just these principles in being—Clarke said that in 1945 he had taken it for granted that communications satellites would be large manned space stations assembled in orbit and staffed by servicing crews.

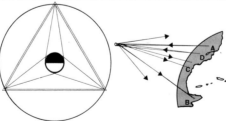

Diagrams from Clarke's original 1945 Memorandum to the BIS explaining the principles of geostationary communications satellites. Left, the classic three-satellite distribution; right, programmes from A being relayed to point B and area C. Programmes from D being relayed to the entire hemisphere.

Thanks to the incredible advance in electronics miniaturisation, the first ones have turned out to be automatic devices about the size of beer barrels. However (he continued) the ultimate communications satellites were likely to be large manned assemblies which would be regularly serviced for maintenance and the replenishment of fuel supplies for station-keeping. Thus, in the "orbital antenna farm", Clarke's ideas are now seen to be coming full circle.

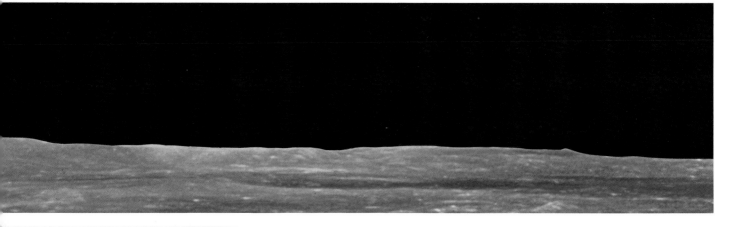

handing-off as one satellite sinks below the horizon and another rises. Geostationary satellites on the other hand require only one setting of the ground antenna.

Telstar

Notwithstanding this, the first true communications satellite, Telstar 1, was launched into low Earth orbit at 592 × 3,500 miles (952 × 5,632km). It was also the first commercially-funded satellite, being paid for by American Telephone & Telegraph.

Telstar 1 was launched on 10 July 1962 and was followed almost a year later by Telstar 2. Ground stations were located at Andover, Maine (USA), Goonhilly Downs (UK), and Pleumeur-Bodou (France). The first broadcast showed the American flag flapping in the New England breeze with the Andover station in the background. This image was relayed to Britain, France, and a US station in New Jersey, just 15hr after launch. Two weeks later, millions of Europeans and Americans watched as a con-

Left: *Telstar, the 170lb (77kg) "private venture" satellite which began the revolution in global TV communications from low orbit. It linked the United States and Europe for periods of about 20 minutes.*

versation was conducted by people on opposite sides of the Atlantic. They not only talked, but watched each other, live via satellite. Many historians may date the birth of the "global village" from that day.

Telstar was an engineering test only, a proof of concept project, sent up to find the "unknown unknowns" that might make the whole gamble a footnote in history. No insurmountable problems were found, although scientists became aware of how damaging radiation can be to solar cells. This problem has been alleviated through intense research, but it continues as the major limiting factor on satellite life (satellites are launched with more solar cell capability than they need at first, with the expectation that the cells will degrade to minimum acceptable levels at the end of life).

Telstar 1 was followed by Relay 1, another low-orbit satellite, launched on 13 December 1962, and Relay 2, orbited on 21 January 1964. These were experimental vehicles, like Telstar, designed to discover limits of satellite performance. As such they were just a prelude to greater events.

On 26 July 1963 Syncom 2 went into synchronous orbit over the Atlantic. Syncom 1 had been placed there in February, but its radio gear failed. The orbit of Syncom 2 was inclined to 28° so it appeared to describe a figure-of-eight over the Earth. Nevertheless, it was used on 13 September, with Relay 1, to link Rio de Janeiro, Brazil, Lagos, Nigeria, and New Jersey in a brief three-continent conversation.

Syncom 3 was placed directly over the equator near the international dateline on 19 August 1964 and broadcast live the opening ceremonies of the Olympics in Japan. "Live via satellite"—the world started to learn the potential of communications satellites.

From the start, the commercial potential was not lost on the politicians. In 1961 US President John F. Kennedy invited

> "All nations to participate in a communication satellite system in the interest of world peace and closer brotherhood among people throughout the world."

His call was answered, and in August 1964 Intelsat—the International Telecommunications Satellite Organisation—was formed. The system is owned by member nations, pro-rated by their share of the

Left: *One of the big dishes at Britain's satellite Earth station at Goonhilly Downs, Cornwall. The station took part in the historic Telstar experiment in July 1962.*

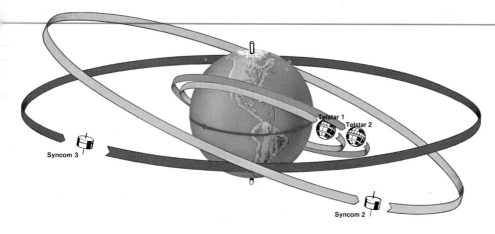

Telstar/Syncom Orbits
A satellite in geostationary orbit matches the period of the Earth's rotation above the equator. It moves neither east nor west relative to a fixed point on the surface. A single satellite, therefore, can provide uninterrupted communications service 24 hours a day. Lower altitude systems (like Telstar 1 and 2) required that ground stations should follow the satellites as they crossed the sky. Then the stations had to switch from satellite to satellite as one slipped below the horizon and another came within range. Telstar 1 orbit was 592 x 3,500 miles (952 x 5,632km). Telstar 2 orbit was 604 x 6,713 miles (972 x 10,800km). The first steps toward Clarke orbit were taken by NASA with Syncom 2, an inclined satellite, which traced a figure-of-eight ground track, and Syncom 3, a geostationary satellite. These pioneer experiments led to the development of Early Bird (Intelsat 1), the first commercial satellite operating in Clarke orbit.

rising another 8·1ft (2·46m). Like Intelsat 3, the antenna was despun, but spot-beams were added to increase broadcast efficiency. Intelsat 4 also passed another milestone of sorts. Rather than being limited to the power of its solar cells (400W), it was limited by the available frequencies. To have crowded more circuits into the satellite, which was possible, would have meant listeners having to sort out other calls from their own. Intelsat 4A, a modified version of the 4 series, partially solved this problem through the use of more spot-beams and polarised signals, and boosted to 6,000 the number of circuits, while holding the cost to $1,000 per circuit. Both the 4 and 4A series were the first to use the larger and more capable Atlas-Centaur launcher instead of the Thor-Delta family used earlier.

In 1980 the first of the Intelsat 5 series satellites was launched. Breaking with past traditions, it is three-axis stabilised rather than spin-stabilised. While more complex attitude controls are required, fewer solar cells are needed. On a drum the Sun effectively illuminates less than half the cells, whereas flat panels can be repositioned always to face solar radiation. The first Intelsat 5s were launched by Atlas-Centaur. Later ones used Ariane.

Intelsat 5 has 12,000 telephone circuits plus two colour TV channels. It also operates in the 14/11 gigahertz band as well as the 6/4GHz band used by most satellites (one Hertz equals one cycle per second; one GHz equals 1,000 million cycles per second), as well as using other techniques to increase use of the radio spectrum.

In April 1982, a new generation of Intelsat satellites was born. Hughes Space and Communications Group were awarded a contract to build at least five Intelsat 6 satellites. These reverted to the spin stabilised, drum shape of Intelsat 4 and incorporated a drop-skirt solar array. Stowed, the satellite measures 17·4ft (5·3m) tall but in space, with its solar array skirt and C band antennas deployed, the satellite is 38·4ft (11·7m) tall. The Hughes satellites will carry 120,000

annual traffic. (US ownership had declined from 53 per cent in 1964 to 24 per cent in 1986. The decline of industrial nation ownership reflects increased membership, 110 in 1986, especially among developing nations.) The 800 or so ground stations remain the property of the 165 user countries. The consortium's operational arm is Comsat, the Communications Satellite Corporation, in Washington, DC.

The first satellite launched by this unique venture was Intelsat 1, better known as Early Bird. On 28 June 1965 it went into regular service with 240 telephone circuits. The satellite was a cylinder 2·36ft (0·72m) wide and 1·93ft (0·59m) high, and had a mass of just 86lb (39kg) on station. Solar cells wrapped around it provided 40W of power and to simplify systems design it was spin-stabilised, like a toy top. Early Bird was designed to operate for 18 months, but stayed in service for four years. By today's standards the venture was modest, but in 1965 it was revolutionary.

In 1967 Intelsat 2 was launched. It was somewhat larger and weighed 189·6lb (86kg) with 75W of power. But more important, the cost per circuit had dropped from $30,000 to $10,000. Intelsat 2 also became the first

commercial communications satellite over the Pacific, and permitted access by many stations in northern and southern hemispheres, rather than just the two north stations connected by Early Bird.

With Intelsat 3 capacity jumped to 1,500 circuits and power to 120W. The cost per circuit dropped to $2,000. Each of the eight satellites in the series used a mechanically despun horn antenna. Intelsats 1 and 2 had used omni-directional antennas, meaning that much of their power was radiated into space. Intelsat 3's horn pointed upward into an elliptical reflector mounted on a turntable, so the horn only radiated towards the Earth. This was a significant step forward because long-life space-rated motors were required if the satellite was to function for its 5-year design life. They generally worked well (though there were some problems) and in 1969 Intelsat 3 was used to relay data from tracking stations when man landed on the Moon.

The next step in the series was Intelsat 4, providing 4,000 telephone circuits or 2 colour television circuits (normally it is a combination of the two). The satellite's drum was 7·8ft (2·38m) wide and 9·25ft (2·82m) tall, with the antenna assembly

Below: *Early Bird, the world's first geostationary communications satellite in commercial service, being inspected in space-simulated vacuum at Hughes. It was launched on 6 April 1965.*

The Intelsat Series
The International Telecommunications Satellite organisation, Intelsat, launched its first satellite Early Bird into Clarke orbit in 1965. The tiny 86lb (39kg) satellite provided 240 circuits for continuous service between Europe and North America for more than three years. Since that time Intelsat has provided the global community of nations with four additional generations of communications satellites, each generation larger and with greater capability than its predecessor.
Intelsat 1, 1965
240 circuits or 1 TV channel.
Design life: 1·5 years.
Intelsat 2, 1967
240 circuits or 1 TV channel.
Design life: 3 years.
Intelsat 3, 1968

332lb (150kg), 1,500 circuits, up to 4 TV channels.
Design life: 5 years.
Intelsat 4, 1971
1,585lb (719kg), 4,000 circuits plus 2 colour TV channels.
Design life: 7 years.
Intelsat 4A, 1975
6,000 circuits plus 2 TV channels.
Design life: 7 years.

Intelsat 5, 1980
2,205lb (1,000kg), 12,000 circuits plus 2 TV channels.

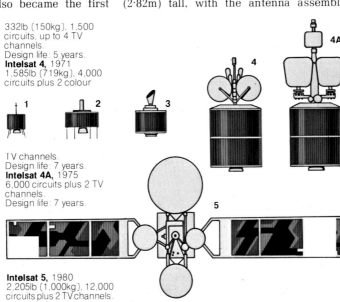

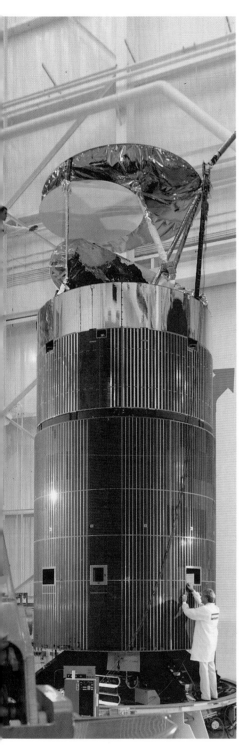

Above: *A satellite of the Intelsat 4A family during checkout at the Hughes factory. It was launched by an Atlas-Centaur rather than a Thor-Delta vehicle.*

Above: *Intelsat 6 is currently the world's largest communications satellite. Even with its C band multiple beam antennas stowed, it stands nearly 39ft (11·7m) tall.*

telephone circuits and three TV channels, operated with advanced modulation digital techniques. Intelsat 6 has 48 transponders operating in the C band (6/4 GHz) and K band (14/11 GHz). Solar power output is 2,600W. The operational lifetime is planned to be 14 years. These satellites were to have been launched on both Ariane 4 and the US Space Shuttle, starting aboard the latter in September 1986. The *Challenger* disaster in January 1986 resulted in all Intelsats being taken off the Shuttle. Ariane 4 will now carry the first in 1989, three years late, while other launchers, including the Commercial Titan III are configured to carry those not contracted to Ariane.

Above: *This satellite named Anik, meaning Eskimo "brother", began the process of linking Canada's 3,800,000 square miles by communications relayed from space.*

In 1988, the Intelsat network operated 12 Intelsat 5 satellites situated between 307°E, over South America and 180°E over the mid Pacific. That year, Intelsat announced plans for an Intelsat 7 series and awarded a contract to Ford Aerospace to build five spacecraft, starting in November 1991, with the first launch set for the summer of 1992. These three-axis stabilised satellites have C and K band transponders with multiple re-use capability and other enhancements such as solid state power amplifiers instead of TWTAs. Intelsat 7 will weigh 8,030lb (3,643kg) at launch and will operate at 2,526W. Launch can be by Ariane 44P, Atlas-Centaur, Titan or Long March 2E.

Intelsat is by no means the only communications satellite system in operation and it is coming under increasing competition. As technology advanced and prices dropped, the desirability of operating dedicated communications satellites, particularly for domestic purposes, became greater. It was commercially attractive to tailor satellites to the needs of large, sparsely populated nations, businesses, shipping lines, or organisations that had large volumes of communications traffic to move more than a few hundred miles.

The first nation to have a domestic system was Canada, which launched Anik communications satellites. The parent company is Telesat Corporation, which operates telephone and television systems. Three Anik A, 1,240lb (562kg) satellites were launched between 1972 and 1975, by which time the third had upgraded capability to handle 10 TV channels and 9,600 telephone circuits. These were used primarily to improve communications within the sparsely populated areas of the Canadian outback and Alaska. A new series, the 12/14 GHz, Anik B was introduced in 1978 to provide similar services, augmented by educational, medical and teleconference facilities to the Eskimos of Alaska. A new series, Anik C, was built by Hughes. These operated at 12/14 GHz and had 16 channels providing several TV and over 21,000 voice circuits. All these were deployed successfully by the US Space Shuttle during the fifth, seventh and sixteenth missions between November 1982 and April 1985.

Anik D, a joint venture between Hughes, providing a 376 model satellite bus, and Canada's Spar Aerospace, provides 24 transponders. The economics of the system were such that it was cheaper for Telesat to place Anik D2 into a storage orbit aboard Shuttle 14 in 1984 rather than to keep it on the ground. The first Anik D was launched by a Delta in 1982. Spar Aerospace became prime contractor for two Anik E satellites, using GE Astro Space three-axis-stabilised Satcom buses. These will incorporate three antennas for C band and Ku band voice, data and broadcast transmissions.

The Soviet System

The world's biggest domestic satellite network was developed by the Soviet Union, starting in April 1965 with a series of Molniya (Lightning) satellites which pursued highly elliptical orbits reaching their zenith over the northern hemisphere. In this way various centres across the enormous landmass of the USSR were linked by black-and-white television programmes, telephone and telegraph. The 12hr orbit took the satellite high over the Soviet Union during the prime periods of communication, thus giving ground stations a target with very slow apparent motion. Each series (Molniya 1 and 2) comprises four pairs of each type of satellite spaced at 90° intervals around the orbit. The Molniya 3 series is the most capable, carrying colour television in addition to telecommunications.

Molniya 2 (1971) and Molniya 3 (1974) differed from their predecessors in that they could handle signals of higher frequencies in the centimetre band, from 4GHz to 6GHz.

Voices from the Sky

Communications satellites appeared only 27 years ago. Today they are part of our everyday lives and it is difficult to think how we could do without them. Almost every country in the world is linked by telephone, telex and data services and our television screens show world events as they happen. The world has become a "global village" in which political and cultural frontiers have been crossed as never before.

After the pioneer developments of Score, Courier, Telstar and Relay in the United States, and Molniya in the Soviet Union, the new era of space communications came of age when satellites were placed in Clarke orbit which allowed them to keep pace with the Earth's rotation. This enabled communications links to be established between ground stations 24 hours a day through a new generation of satellites: Syncom, Early Bird and the Intelsat series, and in the USSR, Raduga ("Rainbow") and Gorizont ("Horizon").

Soon these intercontinental links were joined by systems of communications, also involving satellites in Clarke orbit, which served groups of countries (regional systems) and individual countries (domestic systems). The Soviet Union was first to use satellites domestically with Molniya satellites in 12-hour orbits which allowed the relay of a large volume of radio and TV traffic, telephone conversations and telex, facsimile and newspaper matrices. One of the first geostationary satellites in a domestic role was Comstar, serving the United States.

The future is bright with promise when large "antenna farms" are placed in Clarke orbit. However, the economics of operating communications satellite systems in the 1980s, and parallel improvements in terrestrial systems, such as fibre optics, have resulted recently in a slightly more conservative prediction of future developments.

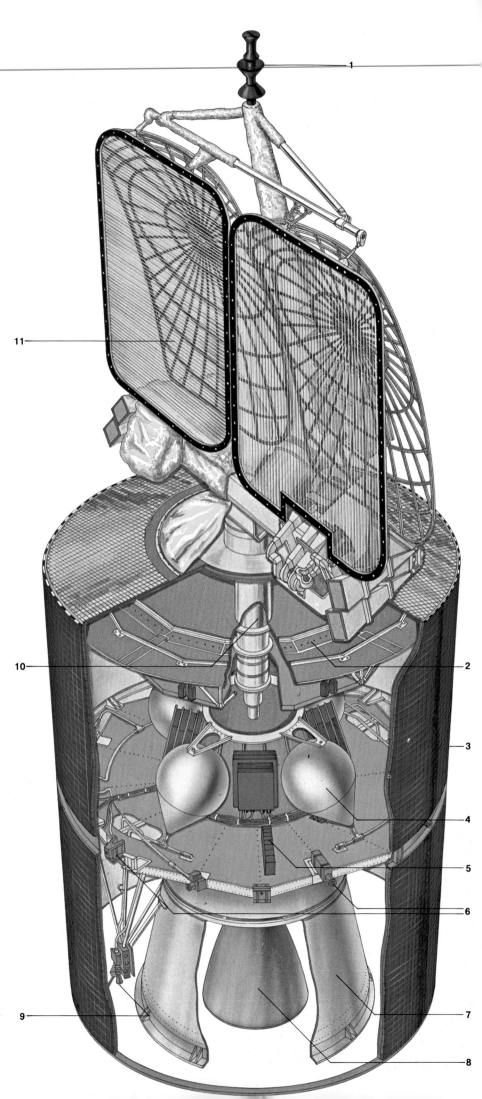

Comstar 1

1 Telemetry and command antenna – transmits data on the satellite and receives commands from ground stations.
2 Electronic equipment compartment with communications receivers, amplifiers and transmitters.
3 Drum spins at about 60 rpm to give gyroscopic stability; surface is covered with solar cells which generate electricity from sunlight.
4 Positioning and orientation system.
5 Battery pack. Stores electricity from solar cells to power the satellite when in the Earth's shadow.
6 Sun and Earth sensors, the reference devices by which Comstar is kept in position.
7 Booster adapter.
8 Apogee motor, which lifts satellite to geostationary orbit after separation from launch vehicle.
9 Axial jets.
10 Bearing and power transfer assembly. A bearing is fitted between the spinning tub and the top section which does not spin because the antennas must be kept pointing at the Earth.
11 Communications antennas which receive and transmit the communications signals. Fitted with horizontal and vertical polarising screens which allow the same frequency to be used twice, thereby doubling the effective capacity of the satellite. Comstar 1 domestic satellites, designed to operate for seven years, receive, amplify and retransmit telephone calls and TV broadcasts between ground stations within the USA as well as Puerto Rico. Like their global equivalents, they are positioned in geostationary orbit.

Technical Data

Height: 17ft (5·2m).
Diameter: 7·5ft (2·3m).
Launch weight: 3,109lb (1,410kg).
Capacity: will relay up to 6,000 telephone calls or 12 television programmes or combinations of the two.
Prime contractor: Hughes Aircraft Company.
Operated by COMSAT General and leased by American Telephone and Telegraph Company.

Ekran (below)
1 Deployable boom.
2 Three-axis stabiliser.
3 High-power transmitter.
4 Pencil-beam antennas permit TV signals to be transmitted to home TV sets through collective-use ground antennas.
5 Solar panels providing total of 2kW of power.

Ekran ("Film") was introduced in October 1976 to transmit programmes of the Central Television Service to isolated communities in Siberia and the Far North. Serving about 40 per cent of the USSR, satellites are located over the Equator above the Indian Ocean. Ekran relays colour or black and white TV programmes to an area of approximately 3,500,000 miles² (9 million km²).

Technical Data
International designation: "Statsionar T".
Frequencies:
  Uplink 6,000 MHz.
  Downlink 702-726 MHz.
Location: Clarke orbit: 99° E.

Gorizont—a more powerful geostationary satellite—was introduced in December 1978 to provide telephone, telegraph and television coverage of the 1980 Moscow Olympics. After the Games satellites of this series were used to expand Soviets links with other friendly countries.

Ekran System
This transmits programmes of the Soviet Central Television Service between Moscow, Siberia and the Far North. Ships in arctic waters within range of Ekran also pick up transmissions.
1 Moscow TV tower transmits programmes to local population.
2 Earth station transmits TV signals to Ekran satellite in Clarke orbit for wider distribution.
3 Community receivers in thinly populated areas of USSR distribute TV signals to low-power relay stations.
4 Direct reception by TV sets through roof-top antennas.

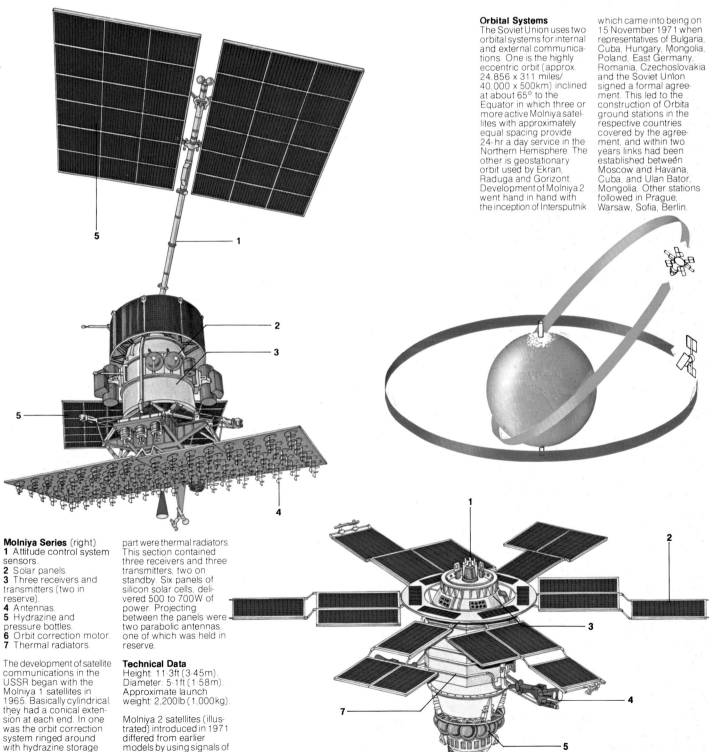

Orbital Systems
The Soviet Union uses two orbital systems for internal and external communications. One is the highly eccentric orbit (approx. 24,856 x 311 miles/40,000 x 500km) inclined at about 65° to the Equator in which three or more active Molniya satellites with approximately equal spacing provide 24-hr a day service in the Northern Hemisphere. The other is geostationary orbit used by Ekran, Raduga and Gorizont. Development of Molniya 2 went hand in hand with the inception of Intersputnik which came into being on 15 November 1971 when representatives of Bulgaria, Cuba, Hungary, Mongolia, Poland, East Germany, Romania, Czechoslovakia and the Soviet Union signed a formal agreement. This led to the construction of Orbita ground stations in the respective countries covered by the agreement, and within two years links had been established between Moscow and Havana, Cuba, and Ulan Bator, Mongolia. Other stations followed in Prague, Warsaw, Sofia, Berlin.

Molniya Series (right)
1 Attitude control system sensors.
2 Solar panels.
3 Three receivers and transmitters (two in reserve).
4 Antennas.
5 Hydrazine and pressure bottles.
6 Orbit correction motor.
7 Thermal radiators.

The development of satellite communications in the USSR began with the Molniya 1 satellites in 1965. Basically cylindrical, they had a conical extension at each end. In one was the orbit correction system ringed around with hydrazine storage bottles; in the other were sensors for attitude control. On the cylindrical part were thermal radiators. This section contained three receivers and three transmitters, two on standby. Six panels of silicon solar cells, delivered 500 to 700W of power. Projecting between the panels were two parabolic antennas, one of which was held in reserve.

Technical Data
Height: 11·3ft (3·45m).
Diameter: 5·1ft (1·58m).
Approximate launch weight: 2,200lb (1,000kg).

Molniya 2 satellites (illustrated) introduced in 1971 differed from earlier models by using signals of higher frequency. Molniya 3 satellites were introduced in 1974.

Working with the satellites are the "round-house" Orbita ground stations, each employing a low-noise 39·37ft (12m) diameter dish antenna on a rotating mount. The antenna is directed at the satellite by means of a tracking electric drive.

The Molniya satellites had a major social, political and economic impact on the development of the Soviet State, bringing peoples in remote parts—often with different cultures and customs—into closer contact with Moscow, and making links, via the Intersputnik organisation, with other socialist countries from Eastern Europe to Mongolia.

The wide-ranging network is now being developed still further. In December 1975 the family of Soviet communications satellites was augmented by Raduga which bears the international designation Statsionar 1. This served the same purpose as the Molniya series with the exception that it operated in geostationary orbit.

This was followed by Ekran, another stationary-orbit satellite having the international designation Statsionar T. It has the special function of relaying TV programmes from the central studios in Moscow to areas with simpler ground stations. This is possible because Ekran transmitters have several times the power of other communications satellites, and the on-board pencil-beam antennas make it possible to relay TV signals directly to home TV sets through "collective-use" (community) aerials, and directly to home receivers via roof-top aerials.

Soviet engineers have also developed a mobile ground station, Mars, which is transportable in three containers. Although primarily intended for live TV reception, it has a 23ft (7m) dish antenna and is completely automatic in operation. It can also be used for telephone and telegraph relays.

Special facilities for relaying the 1980 Moscow Olympics via space brought a world audience of 2,000 to 2,500 million people as close as possible to the sports events. These included new geostationary satellites of the Gorizont type embodying improved relay equipment. The first was launched in December 1978. Up to the end of 1987, 17 Ekran, 21 Raduga and 14 Gorizont satellites had been launched by the highly reliable Proton booster. This reliability was a key factor in Soviet attempts to offer the vehicle for commercial service in the West. Another commercial service being offered is the lease of transponders on a Gorizont, or indeed the whole spacecraft, delivered in orbit. During this same period, the Molniya 2 programme was phased out, but Molniya 1 and 3 launches continued, with there having been 62 Molniya 1 and 13 Molniya 3 satellites orbited to the end of 1987. The Soviet Union also tested a data relay satellite under the Cosmos satellite label in 1986/87 before it apparently malfunctioned. This provided, from geostationary orbit, real time communications between cosmonauts in the Mir space station and the ground more frequently than the existing system of ground stations and ocean-deployed tracking ships previously allowed.

Other Systems

Indonesia also quickly recognised the potential of communications satellites, and had Palapa 1 and 2 on station by March 1977

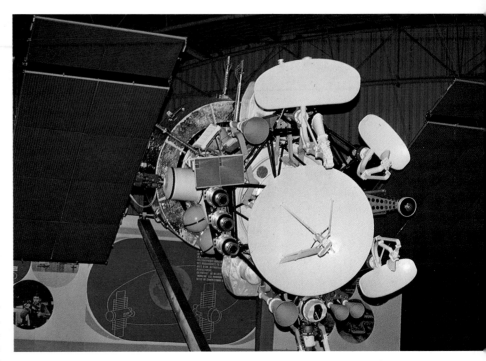

to link her scattered island nation. Indonesia comprises over 6,000 islands with a population of 150 million. Palapa A satellites provided 12 transponders with 4,000 voice circuits and 12 simultaneous TV programmes to 125 Earth stations situated on these islands. Another series, Palapa B, entered service in 1983. These were twice the size and four times as powerful. Built by Hughes, they carry twenty-five, 10W transponders. B1 was launched by the seventh US Space Shuttle in June 1983. B2 was deployed successfully by the tenth Shuttle the following February but was left stranded in orbit, together with Westar 6, when their PAM-D stages malfunctioned. Both satellites were recovered and brought back to Earth in 1984 by the fourteenth Shuttle. NASA launched Palapa B3 on a Delta in 1987 and the refurbished B2, flying B2R, will also fly a Delta—on a commercial basis—in 1989.

India, China, Saudi Arabia, Brazil, Mexico, Australia and Japan have followed suit with domestic satellite systems, while other countries from South America to Iran have considered similar programmes. Ford Aerospace provided India with the Insat 1 series of satellites which also doubled as meteorological spacecraft. Insat 1 had 12 transponders capable of communicating with over 100,000 small Earth terminals, reaching 70 per cent of the Indian population relaying entertainment as well as educational TV programmes—including information on birth control techniques. The first, launched in 1982, had to be abandoned. The second, deployed by Shuttle 8 in 1983, hit trouble when a solar panel almost failed to deploy. Insat 1C, launched on an Ariane in 1988, suffered an electronics failure and operated at only 50 per cent capacity. Insat 1D will follow in 1989-90 on a commercial Delta II and India plans eventually to orbit an autonomous Insat II system, built in India and launched on the Indian GSLV.

China has launched is own communications satellites using its home-grown Long March 3 geosynchronous launcher. There have been three launches, with two successes, of small 1,984lb (900kg) experi-

Above: *Russia's latest geostationary satellite with improved multi-channel relaying equipment, Gorizont (Horizon), broadcast coverage of the 1980 Moscow Olympics throughout the world.*

Below: *TDF-1, a direct broadcast satellite, during integration tests at Aérospatiale's Cannes facility. In geostationary orbit, the solar arrays unfold to a maximum span of more than 62ft (19m).*

mental communications satellites. These will be followed by larger more versatile spacecraft in the later 1990s but in the meantime, China is collaborating with international partners, including Britain's Cable and Wireless company in Asiasat 1. This is the refurbished Westar 6 satellite recovered by the Shuttle in 1984. It will provide communications services to the Far East region.

Saudi Arabia ordered three Arabsat communications satellites from France's Aérospatiale in 1981. These provide C band communications to the 22 countries in the Arab League. The first was launched by Ariane in 1985 and the second by Shuttle 17 the same year, accompanied by a Saudi prince as a payload specialist passenger. These two satellites have not been fully utilised and the third ground spare may not be launched.

Two Hughes 376 satellites were ordered by Mexico in 1982 to provide TV, data, telephone and facsimile services to an increasing number of the nation's 75 million population. The first of the eighteen C band and four Ku band transponder satellites was launched by Shuttle 17 in June 1985 and the second by the 23rd Shuttle in November that year, accompanied by a Mexican passenger-astronaut.

Australia ordered three of the popular Hughes 376 communications satellites for launch in the 1985-88 period. These 15 transponder satellites, incorporating four direct broadcast TV channels, were used primarily to provide communications for the sparsely populated regions of Australia but have been enhanced to provide services to the SW Pacific region and to New Zealand. Two Aussats were deployed by Shuttles 20 and 23 in 1985 and the third by Ariane in 1988. Two second generation Aussat series were ordered from Hughes in 1988 and these are likely to be launched by Chinese Long March 2E boosters. After launching a test series of development communications satellites, Japan, for its part, has launched its series of BS2, CS2 and CS3 comsats, providing full services including DBS TV to Japan and its outlying islands.

Domestic US systems came about as commercial ventures with Westar (Western Union), Comstar (AT&T and Comsat), and Satcom (RCA Globcom). Westar is based on the Anik design (spin-stabilised, single antenna) and Comstar is based on Intelsat 4. Satcom is a new design with three-axis stabilisation and overlapping antennas. Later satellites included the commercially unsuccessful Satellite Business Systems (SBS), and GTE Spacenet's G Star and Spacenet satellites. G Stars incorporate a piggyback payload provided by Geostar which offers a radio determination positioning satellite system for mobile users in the USA. American Satellite Corporation launched two ASC communications satellites on Shuttle in 1985 to provide specialist business services to the USA, Puerto Rico and Hawaii.

Following highly successful experiments with the two Franco-German Symphonie communications satellites Europe moved into the field more comprehensively with the European Communications Satellite (ECS).

When these Clarke-orbit satellites are fully operational they will carry a large part of future inter-European telephone, telex, television and data-transmission traffic. Pre-operational tests were made with the Orbital Test Satellite (OTS) launched in 1978. Five ECS satellites were ordered by the European Space Agency from British Aerospace. These 20W spacecraft with 14 transponders are leased by the European communications organisation Eutelsat. ECS 1 and 2 were launched by Ariane in 1983-84, but ECS 3 was lost in the Ariane V15 failure of 1986. ECS 4 followed in 1987 and the fifth and final ECS was launched by Ariane in 1988 on the 24th Ariane mission. Eutelsat will now move into a new phase of operations with a series of Eutelsat II proprietary satellites ordered from Aérospatiale. Three are being built and an option exists for a further five. The first of the 50W, 24 transponder satellites will be launched in 1989 by Ariane.

A maritime satellite, Marecs, which employs the same spacecraft platform as ECS, will provide much-improved telecommunications between ships in distant waters and European shore stations. Marecs A and

Above: *Aussat K1 is gently nudged from its launch cradle on 27 August 1985 during Space Shuttle Mission STS 51-I. The motor beneath the satellite is the PAM stage that fires to inject it into its transfer orbit.*

B2 (B1 was lost in an Ariane failure) are used by the international maritime communications agency, Inmarsat, to provide global communications services for over 5,000 ships and other mobile users of its member nations. These 20W satellites, based on the ECS bus, are complemented by the lease of services of Marisat and Intelsat 5 satellites. Like Eutelsat, Inmarsat is moving into the proprietary business with the Inmarsat F2 series being built by British Aerospace. These satellites, based on the Eurostar satellite bus, provide 250 two way circuits on C and L band. Inmarsat is also leading the effort to provide aircraft telephone communications services as well as a global positioning system service for mobile users, using Inmarsat F2. Developments such as this illustrate the growing applications of the communications satellite.

Indeed, communications satellites have been taking on new roles envisaged many years before, but requiring maturity in the system for actual operation. United Press International and the Associated Press, the two major US newspaper wire services, both started experimenting in 1979 with news transmissions via satellite.

Major advances are being made by TV satellites, initially providing programmes to cable TV networks. Television itself started taking on a new look and the traditional role of the networks was challenged by "super stations". Following an FCC (Federal Communications Commission) ruling — opposed by the networks — individual stations were given permission to transmit their signals to communications satellites which then relay the signals to

cable TV networks serving communities across the US, but not to actual broadcast stations. Thus, cable subscribers in Alaska are well familiar with the Atlanta Braves baseball team via Channel 17 in Atlanta, Georgia.

Growth of cable TV satellites was described by RCA in 1980 as having gone from two Earth stations on 30 November 1975, to 3,400 in 1980, of which an estimated 2,500 were operated by cable TV systems. Cable TV subscriptions grew, RCA estimated, from 9·8 million in 1974 to an estimated 19·5 million in 1981. Indeed, the growth has been so rapid that RCA leased space aboard AT&T's Comstar D-2.

In 1979 direct TV programme distribution experiments started with RCA American Communications, Viacom International Inc, and the Washington Post-Newsweek Stations.

An attempt in early 1980 to develop the first commercial direct broadcast TV system providing pictures direct to individual homes fell through for economic rather than technical reasons. The original thinking behind DBS TV envisaged that it would require very high power satellites broadcasting to receiver dishes as small as 3·28ft (1m) in diameter. As a result, several countries in European embarked on satellite projects such as TV Sat, TDF and Olympus to develop the technology. However, technology improvements in ground equipment seemingly overtook these high power satellite projects, enabling programmes from smaller, less powerful satellites to be received by smaller dishes. As a result, satellites such as TV Sat and TDF are largely under-utilised while new, medium power efforts, such as Luxembourg's Astra are leading the market. Astra, the first privately funded DBS concern in Europe, is using a second hand GE Astro Space 2000 Satcom bus with 45W transponders. Viewers in the centre of the satellite's footprint in Europe require dishes only 3·28ft (1m) in diameter to receive 16 channels.

The future of pan-European TV broadcasting is far from assured, however. The major problems lie in differences in language, culture and reception to unified advertising campaigns. The trend has, therefore, been toward national DBS systems — which have proved to have been relatively successful in the USA — such as the one being offered by British Satellite Broadcasting, which is to launch two Hughes 373 communications satellites in 1989 and 1990. That the business is largely a gamble is reflected in the fact that BSB needs to invest over £600 million in the project and does not expect to yield a profit for at least five years, if at all.

Technology Satellites

Much of the TV relay technology now in use was made possible by NASA's series of applications technology satellites. The last in the series, ATS-6, was a direct-broadcast TV satellite. It carried a 30ft (9·1m) antenna and a powerful TV relay module. Designed to operate for two years, it functioned from May 1974 until mid-1979, when it was removed from geostationary orbit: failing control systems meant that engineers were no longer confident in keeping ATS-6 on station.

Over India ATS-6 was used to bring farming, hygiene, and safety lectures to an uneducated population. The Satellite Instructional Television Experiment — SITE — used conventional TV sets with 9·8ft (3m) antenna made of chicken wire and signal converters costing a few hundred dollars. The programme did not match the sophistication of the satellite's technology; puppet shows brought back the old miracle plays of an earlier era of communication. But communication it was, on a level that people understood, and they learned from it. Over the United States, ATS-6 was used for long distance medical diagnoses in Alaska (it saved at least two lives) and for teachers' conferences in the Appalachian region of the continental US.

Other direct broadcasting TV experiments soon followed, however. Japan is already operating its broadcast satellite experimental (BSE), which covers virtually all of the main islands with two colour TV channels. Canada in 1976 launched its Communications Technology Satellite, a cooperative venture with NASA. CTS can be received through 3·28ft (1m) antennas on the 14/11GHz band. And the European Space Agency has developed Olympus, a large direct-broadcast TV satellite.

Orbital Slots

The rapid growth in the number of operational communications satellites has caused concern over a potential "traffic jam" in geostationary orbit. In 1980, following the 1979 World Administrative Radio Conference, the US FCC and National Telecommunications Information Administration abandoned support of the "evolutionary approach" to rights for direct broadcast TV satellite slots. That concept essentially was first-come, first-served. However, other nations in the Western Hemisphere sought assurances that there would

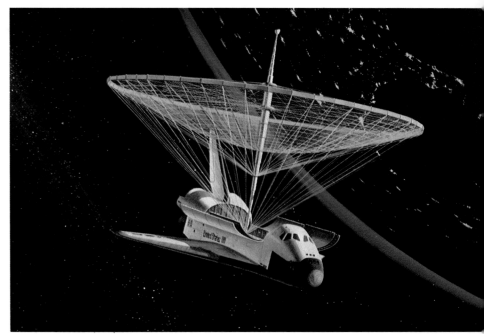

Above: *Shuttle-deployed antennas of this type will have many uses, both civilian and military. This light-weight structure which unfurls like an umbrella takes its inspiration from the applications technology satellite ATS-6 which deployed in like manner.*

be slots available to them, and so the method for fixing slots remains unresolved.

Indeed, the problem of crowding is one that is apparent even today as engineers seek to find ways to open new channels without flooding the radio spectrum. Intelsat alone is expected to need 400,000 new two-way circuits by the end of this century.

Problems of frequency and slot allocation were highlighted again in early 1980 when a NASA study concluded that demand for telecommunications will grow fivefold by the year 2000. By then, 25 per cent of all long-distance voice traffic will be carried by satellite, saturating the 6/4 and 14/11 GHz bands and placing demands on the 30/20 GHz band early in the 1990s. NASA estimated that 90 per cent of all telecommunications will then be real-time, with the remaining 10 per cent operating on delayed transmission, such as electronic mail.

Continued research into future developments in communications satellite technology has centred on extending the capacities of existing wavebands, and looking at exploiting the relatively unused Ka band (30/20 GHz). A major experiment, to be flown aboard a Spacelab mission, is Goddard Space Flight Center's adaptive multibeam phased-array antenna. Such aerials are used in military radar and use phase and amplitude differences to steer beams without physically moving the antenna. In communications, they will make more efficient use of the band width available and permit simpler ground stations.

To expand the bandwidths available for communications satellites, in late 1979 NASA initiated the 30/20 GHz project, ACTS. This should lead to orbiting two demonstration satellites to test advanced technology for this band, which can handle 50-100 times as much data as the lower frequencies. Advanced studies at NASA's Lewis Research Centre are concentrating on multi-beam antennas, onboard signal processing and switching, high-power transmitters, and low-noise amplifiers. In June 1980, Lewis awarded parallel $1 million definition contracts to Hughes Aircraft and TRW Defense and Space Systems Group for design work on the 30/20 GHz satellites. TRW was

selected to build at least one ACTS. The launch will not take place until the early 1990s, if at all, since NASA has been hit by a budget crisis that threatens the ACTS programme.

At NASA's Marshall Space Flight Center, the large space structures programme led to parallel definition studies by Grumman Aerospace and Harris Corp on a 164ft (50m) deployable antenna intended to be flown by the Space Shuttle.

TDMA Relays

Also developed in the late 1970s is a concept known as time-division multiple access. In simple TDMA, data from each of, say, four stations is broadcast only at selected periods. Each station transmits a burst of data, and the satellite relays it, interleaved with other bursts, in a wide-area transmission. The whole sequence takes about 0·75 second. In satellite-switched TDMA, separate stations transmit bursts of data to the satellite, with each burst carrying the address of another station. The satellite acts as a switchboard, packages the appropriate bursts and retransmits to the designated stations. A variation on this has groups of stations sending data intended for other groups. In the ultimate form the beam itself does the switching, with a phased-array antenna continually re-pointing from one station to another to deliver data.

This is the forerunner of the giant switchboard in the sky predicted by Clarke.

*"The 1990s, we predict, could see a
small number of very large platforms
in geostationary orbit replacing
many smaller satellites,"*
wrote Burton Edelson and Walter Morgan of Comsat Laboratories in 1977. They predicted that, if single-mission satellites continue to be launched, there would be 110 operating by 1980. The orbital antenna farm, or OAF, harks back to Clarke's original concept.

"I'm delighted to know that my
original concept of a large manned
space station is coming back,"
Clarke wrote after reviewing Edelson and
Morgan's paper.

The potential impact on human society,
even measured by what we can estimate
today, is unlimited. Ivan Bekey of NASA
noted,

"Rather than leading to 'wired cities',
these developments could create
'wireless cities' and thus allow
developing nations to leapfrog 100
years of technology."

Such super satellites do not blindly follow
the "bigger is better" dictum. Rather they
are the result of careful engineering studies
based on fundamental principles. Firstly,
combining satellite operations on one platform permits berthing space and rent of

Below: Proposed Geostationary Communication Platform (GCP) would replace large
numbers of conventional specialised
satellites with one system capable of
performing multiple services.

Above: TDRS-D rises slowly from
Discovery's payload bay on 13 March 1989.
The attached IUS rocket stage is used
to boost it to geostationary orbit.

utilities to other firms wanting to install
special communications systems. Maintenance will be easier, the Shuttle is expected
to make tele-operator systems — "repair
robots" — available.

Applications seen by Edelson and Morgan
include trunking systems and fixed networks
for intercontinental, regional, and domestic
service; mobile systems for maritime, aeronautical, and ground service; and high-
power transmissions for public services,
educational TV, and the growing network of
business communications.

An early geostationary platform under
study by NASA's Marshall Space Flight
Center at Huntsville, Alabama, is TDRS. It
weighs almost 11,025lb (5,000kg) and is
launched by a single Shuttle mission plus an
Inertial Upper Stage to boost it to geosynchronous orbit. It is a tracking and data
relay satellite (hence TDRS) with experi-

mental packages attached. At the core is a
TDRS module for housekeeping functions
plus TDRS operations. Radiating from it are
six arms, a product of large space structure
technology being developed at Marshall.

At the ends of two arms are solar arrays
delivering 7·5kW. The span across these
arms is 164ft (50m). Another pair of arms
holds a 16·4ft (5m) Ka-band multibeam
antenna (experimental) and a 13·1ft (4m) S-
band TDRS antenna. The last pair holds a
39·3ft (12m) Ku-band antenna (experimental)
and a second 13·1ft (4m) TDRS S-band
antenna. In addition, a 6·56ft (2m) Ku-band
TDRS antenna is mounted on the solar
array panels. The first TDRS satellite was to
have been launched in 1981, but the Space
Shuttle was delayed. The first launch,
therefore, actually came on the first
Challenger mission in 1983. However, the
IUS upper stage malfunctioned and TDRS
limped to its geosynchronous orbit with the
help of its stationkeeping thrusters. The
second TDRS was lost in the *Challenger*
disaster in 1986, but the third was
successfully deployed by Shuttle *Discovery*
in late 1988 on the first mission since the
disaster. A fourth was launched in March
1989, and this should be followed by a
minimum of two more in the early 1990s. The
major advantage of the TDRS satellite is that
it allows more real time communications
between the Shuttle and other NASA — and
DoD — satellites and ground control.

TDRS is regarded as a learning tool for
the larger platforms that are expected to be
built in the 1990s. Following this proof of
concept, a "Big Comsat" envisioned by
Bekey might be built. It would be almost
541ft (165m) long, using a 220ft (67m)
"bootlace" lens to help focus the multi-
beam array. An electronic mail satellite
would use a 31·5ft (9·6m) lens and weigh
5,512lb (2,500kg); and an education TV
satellite would weigh 10,806lb (4,900kg)

The design of each is basically the same — a
bus module containing all systems, paddle-
like solar arrays to either side, and the lens
in front of the satellite. Even before large
space structures become operational, the
Space Shuttle could make medium-scale
antenna farms possible. Its 14·8ft (4·5m)
wide payload bay will accommodate solid
antennas up to that width with 2·8 times the
surface area of satellites launched by Atlas-
Centaur. Larger bus designs are expected,
too, as witnessed by the 13·8ft (4·2m) wide
Leasat developed by Hughes Aircraft.
It was the first satellite designed for the wide
Shuttle payload bay and with other Shuttle
capabilities being offered, was expected to
lead the way towards reduced satellite
launch costs, a goal that has proved
unrealistic. However, we cannot begin to
guess at ultimate shapes or applications,
although here again Clarke may have seen a
little farther than the rest of us. On 20
August 1971, at ceremonies finalising the
establishment of Intelsat, Clarke (a featured
speaker) told the audience that:

"For today, gentlemen, whether you
intend it or not, whether you wish it or
not — you have signed far more than
yet another intergovernmental agreement. You have just signed the first
draft of the Articles of Federation
of the United States of Earth."

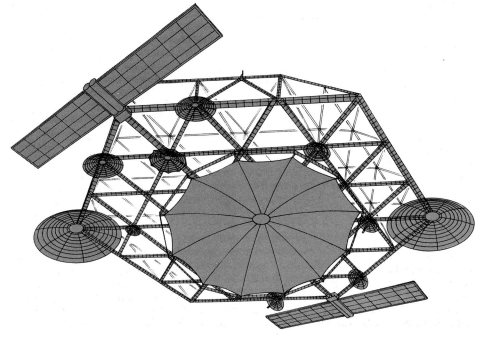

Weather Patrol in Space

After the first scientific satellites had been placed in orbit by the Soviet Union and the United States, the next step was to think about practical applications of the technology that had been developed. The early results from sounding rockets had shown the value of examining the Earth's atmosphere with instruments, and the opportunity to fly cameras and other sensing apparatus aboard satellites quickly alerted meteorologists to the possibility of obtaining information on the world's ever-changing weather on a routine basis.

The lead was taken by the United States with a family of satellites known as TIROS, the acronym for Television and Infra-red Observation Satellite. The Tiros system matured from a research and development programme, marked by the successful mission of Tiros 1 in April 1960, which demonstrated the feasibility of using satellites for weather observation. The system soon evolved to a semi-operational satellite programme in which nine additional Tiros satellites were successfully launched in the period from 1960 to 1965. Each satellite carried a pair of miniature television cameras and approximately half of the missions included a scanning infra-red radiometer and an Earth radiation budget instrument which monitors the amount of radiation received and re-radiated by the Earth.

ESSA

The commitment to provide routine daily worldwide observations without interruption in data was fulfilled by the introduction of the Tiros Operational System (TOS) in February 1966. This system employed a pair of ESSA (Environmental Science Service Administration) satellites, each configured for its specific mission. One satellite provided global weather data to the US Department of Commerce's stations in Wallops Island, Virginia, and Fairbanks, Alaska, which were relayed to the National Environmental Satellite Service at Suitland, Maryland, for processing and forwarding to the major forecasting centres of the United States and to nations overseas.

The second satellite provided direct, real-time readout of its APT (automatic picture transmission) television pictures to simple stations located around the world.

Nine ESSA satellites were successfully launched between 1966 and 1969. One of them, ESSA 8, remained in operation until March 1976. Larger television cameras (1in [2·54cm] vidicons) developed for the Nimbus satellite programme were adapted for use on the ESSA series, significantly increasing

Above: *The weather satellite ESSA 3. It was the first TOS satellite to carry two Advanced Vidicon Camera systems each capable of complete daily picture coverage of the Earth's weather.*

the quality of the cloud cover pictures over that obtained from the earlier Tiros cameras, which used 0·5in (1·27cm) vidicons.

ITOS

The second decade of meterological satellites was ushered in by the successful orbiting on 23 January 1970 of ITOS-1*, first of the second-generation operational weather satellites. This satellite dramatically surpassed the capabilities of its ESSA predecessors, moving rapidly closer towards the objectives of the US National Operational Meteorological System (discussed later).

ITOS-1 provided in a single spacecraft the combined capability of two ESSA space-

*This spacecraft was originally designated Tiros-M. After being placed into orbit, it was redesignated ITOS-1 (Improved Tiros Operational Satellite-1). Subsequent spacecraft in this series were named NOAA-1 etc. by the National Oceanic and Atmospheric Administration, the successor to ESSA.

craft—direct-readout automatic picture transmission, and storage of global images for later transmission and processing. Additionally, ITOS-1 supplied, for the first time, day-and-night radiometric data, either in real time or stored for later playback. Global observation of the Earth's cloud cover was provided every 12 hours by the single ITOS spacecraft as compared to every 24 hours by two of the ESSA satellites. A second ITOS spacecraft, NOAA-1 (ITOS-A), was launched on 11 December 1970.

The ITOS system evolved into the ITOS-D which carried a more sophisticated array of environmental sensors. The new instruments provided day-and-night imaging by means of very high resolution radiometers (VHRRs) and medium resolution scanning radiometers (SRs). Also included were vertical temperature profile radiometers (VTPRs) for temperature soundings of the atmosphere and a solar proton monitor for measurements of proton and electron flux. Six spacecraft (ITOS-D, E-2, F, G, H and I) were planned for the ITOS-D series. NOAA-2 (ITOS-D), the

Right: *High resolution infra-red photograph of the Arabian Peninsula from Nimbus 3. Yellow areas show high reflectivity coming from the bright desert sand. Almost white areas in the desert follow major sand dune formations. Olive areas indicate moisture. Red denotes a fairly fertile soil with vegetation.*

Below: *First complete view of the world's weather obtained by Tiros 9, February 1965.*

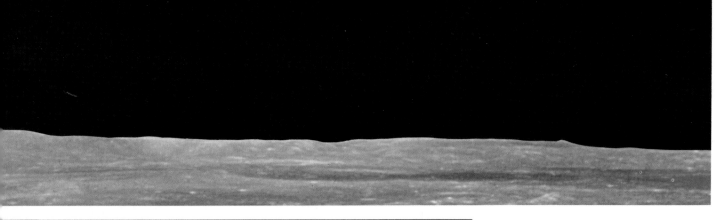

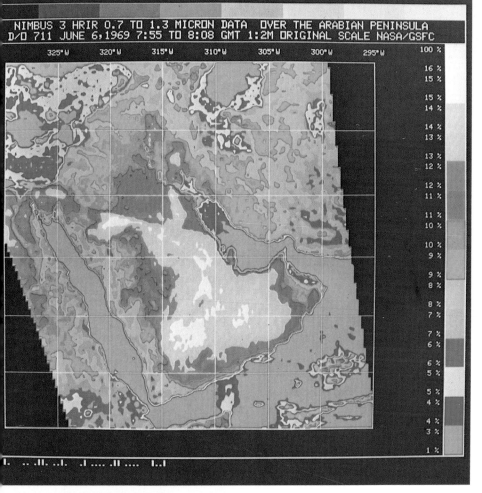

NIMBUS 3 HRIR 0.7 TO 1.3 MICRON DATA OVER THE ARABIAN PENINSULA
D/O 711 JUNE 6,1969 7:55 TO 8:08 GMT 1:2M ORIGINAL SCALE NASA/GSFC

first satellite in this series, was successfully launched on 15 October 1972. Three additional satellites of this type (NOAA-3, NOAA-4, and NOAA-5) were placed into orbit in 1973, 1974, and 1976, respectively. E-2 and I were not launched due to the longevity in orbit of their predecessors. The ITOS system, as it matured, brought closer to realisation the goals of the National Operational Meteorological System.

The ITOS satellite system evolved from the proven technology of the Tiros and ESSA spacecraft. Many devices and techniques employed on the earlier series were improved and utilised. This orderly evolution permitted growth from a spin-stabilised spacecraft to a 3-axis stabilised Earth-oriented de-spun platform.

Tiros-N

The third-generation operational polar-orbiting environmental satellite system, designated Tiros-N, completed development and was placed into operational service in 1978 with the expectation that eight spacecraft would provide global observational service from 1978 to 1985. A second satellite, NOAA-6, was put in orbit in June 1979. A third satellite, which was intended to be NOAA-7, ended up in an unusable orbit after launch on 29 May 1980. This was followed by what became NOAA-7 on 23 June 1981.

This series has a new complement of data-gathering instruments. One of these instruments, the advanced very high resolution radiometer (AVHRR), is designed to increase the amount of radiometric information for more accurate sea-surface temperature mapping and identification of snow and sea ice, in addition to day-and-night imaging in the visible and infra-red bands. Other instruments included are a high-resolution infra-red sounder, a stratospheric sounder and a microwave sounder to improve vertical sounding of the atmosphere. A data collection system (DCS) receives environmental data from fixed or moving platforms such as buoys or balloons and retains it for transmission to ground stations. A solar environmental monitor is included to measure proton, electron, and alpha particle densities for solar disturbance prediction.

In the meantime, a fourth generation Tiros series had been introduced. Seven Advanced Tiros-N satellites were ordered from RCA Astro Space — which became GE Astro Space in 1986. The first, designated NOAA-8, was launched on 28 March 1983 but was destroyed when its battery exploded in December 1985. NOAA-9, 10 and 11 followed in 1984, 1986 and 1988. The remaining

NOAAs, designated D, I and J, were in various stages of development at GE Astro Space in 1989. Three more Advanced Tiros-N satellites, designated NOAA-K, L and M, were ordered in 1988 to fulfill the USA's needs for polar-orbiting civilian weather satellites in the 1990s.

Nimbus Technology Satellite

The Nimbus satellite programme was initiated by NASA in the early 1960s to develop an observational system capable of meeting the research and development needs of the nation's scientists.

The objectives of the programme were: (1) to develop advanced passive radiometric and spectrometric sensors for daily global surveillance of the Earth's atmosphere and thereby provide a data-base for long-range weather forecasting; (2) to develop and evaluate new active and passive sensors for sounding the Earth's atmosphere and mapping surface characteristics; (3) to develop advanced space technology and ground techniques for meteorological and other Earth-observational spacecraft; (4) to develop new techniques and knowledge useful in the exploration of other planetary atmospheres; (5) to participate in global observation programmes (notably the World Weather Watch) by expanding daily global weather observation capability; and (6) to provide a supplemental source of operational meteorological data.

The Nimbus system was intended to be both the test-bed for advanced instruments for the future operational Tiros polar-orbiting satellites, and the research system for remote-sensing and data-collection. The Nimbus spacecraft system was developed under NASA/GSFC management, with the General Electric Company as the spacecraft integration contractor. RCA, Hughes, ITT, Texas Instruments, and a number of other companies and universities provided sensors and data processing and storage equipment.

Seven Nimbus spacecraft were successfully placed in orbit between 1964 and 1978. The final example, Nimbus 7, was launched in October 1978. This spacecraft was instrumented to monitor atmospheric pollutants.

ATS Technology Satellite

The increased launch-vehicle performance available during the middle 1960s permitted satellites to be placed at geostationary altitudes some 22,300 miles (35,880km) over the equator. At this altitude the satellite moves about its orbit at the same rate as the Earth rotates on its axis. Hence, the satellite moving at the same relative speed as the Earth appears to be stationary and is able to observe the same area continuously.

These satellites provided atmospheric scientists with a new dimension in observations, namely continuous observation of almost one-third of the Earth's surface. A NASA research programme involving geostationary satellites was implemented in the Applications Technology Satellite (ATS) series (see also chapter 6). Although primarily designed to demonstrate communications satellite technology, several of the ATS series carried high-resolution cameras for atmospheric observation.

On 7 December 1966 ATS-1 was placed into geostationary orbit. One function of this

Above: *Tiros-N satellites being prepared for launch in high bay areas at GE Astro Space's plant in Princeton, New Jersey. The sensors are mounted on the instrument platform above the central satellite bus.*

Below: *Synchronous Meteorological Satellite 2 was placed in geostationary orbit at 135°W longitude south of Sitka, Alaska, from where it viewed the western half of the United States.*

technology satellite was to demonstrate the capability of providing a picture of the western hemisphere every 20 minutes through the use of a spin-scan camera. Useful data was provided from approximately 55°N to 55°S. The ability to receive sequential photographs of the same area improved the possibility of detecting severe storms and tornadoes, and provided real-time coverage at an earlier stage of cloud and frontal movements.

A second technology satellite, ATS-3, was launched in November 1967. This satellite, using a multispectral spin-scan camera, returned the first colour images of the full Earth disc. Such pictures have been used for many applications in addition to meteorology. ATS-1 and ATS-3 were developed by NASA's Goddard centre, with Hughes Aircraft as the prime contractor.

SMS/GOES Series

The success of the atmospheric-observations test programme at geostationary altitudes led to NASA's development of an operational satellite designed specifically for that purpose. The prototype for the SMS/GOES series (for Synchronous Meteorological Satellite/Geostationary Operational Environmental Satellite) was called SMS-1 and was designed and integrated by the Aeronutronic Ford Corporation. NASA's prototype Synchronous Meteorological Satellite, SMS-1, was successfully launched in

May 1974. Placed over the equator at 45°W, it provided continuous hemispheric coverage. The principal instrument for SMS is a 16in (40·6cm) aperture telescope for visible and infra-red scanning. Built by Hughes Aircraft Company and called VISSR (visible and infra-red spin-scan radiometer), this sensor permits day and night observation of clouds and the determination of temperatures, cloud heights, and winds.

SMS also relays data received from remotely located data-collection platforms such as river gauges, ocean buoys, ships, balloons, and aircraft. Its space environmental monitor (consisting of an X-ray sensor, an energetic-particle sensor, and a magnetometer) detects unusual solar activity, such as flares, and measures the flow of electron and proton energy and the changes in the geomagnetic field. Observation and forecasting of atmospheric phenomena not specifically related to meteorology are thus possible on an operational basis.

Four additional satellites of the SMS/GOES design were launched: SMS-2 on 6 February 1975; the first operational version, GOES-1, on 16 October 1975; GOES-2 on 16 June 1977; and GOES-3 in June 1978. These satellites were owned and operated by the National Oceanic and Atmospheric Administration.

Subsequently, the GOES programme suffered a series of setbacks which resulted in only one satellite being fully operational in 1988, and likely to remain so until July 1990. GOES-4 was launched on 4 September 1980 and orginally placed at 135°W. This was lent to the European Space Agency to replace its first Meteosat satellite and was moved from its orginal orbital slot. It was then boosted out of GEO in 1986. GOES-5, went into orbit on 22 May 1981 and was placed at 75°W. It suffered a data loss and was used as a relay satellite for GOES-4. GOES-6 then had to perform the work of two operational satellites, moving around in GEO after its launch on 28 April 1983. GOES-7 was a victim of the tragic space year of 1986 when it was lost in the Delta launch failure, one of four major launch failures that year. Finally, GOES-8 was successfully orbited on 26 February 1987 and placed at 83°W. A new, advanced series of GOES satellites, designated I, J, K, L and M, was ordered from Ford Aerospace, but the first of these will not be launched until 1990.

The Operational System

The US National Operational Meteorological System achieved full capability in the second decade of space operations. The system required, in addition to the polar-orbiting Tiros satellites, geostationary satellites for continuous viewing of the Earth's cloud cover, a data relay for weather facsimile to users, and the ability to collect data from remote-sensor platforms. The research and development that produced these current observational systems evolved out of the Tiros, Nimbus, and Advanced Technology Satellites.

International Satellites

The USSR has developed a low Earth-orbiting meteorological satellite in the Cosmos series, which orbits the Earth at an altitude of 559 miles (900km) and an 81·3° inclination to the equator. Over the past ten years Meteor satellites have become the USSR's operational meteorological spacecraft. Two or three of this series operate in orbit simultaneously. The Meteor satellites provide data relating to the state of the atmosphere, the Earth's thermal radiation, and charged-particle measurements. They have a direct-readout capability to over 50 stations in USSR. The payload generally consists of optical-mechanical television equipment for the visible spectrum. Also included is infra-red scanning equipment to obtain data on the moisture content of the atmosphere as well as the vertical temperature profile. Warnings of abrupt weather changes, com-

bining data from meteorological radar and satellites, are broadcast by Moscow, Leningrad and other centres, and a special service links ships and aircraft to the network.

The Soviet Meteor weather satellites, like many other civilian and military operational space systems, began with experiments carried out within the Cosmos programme. Early examples were Cosmos 44, 58, 100, 118, 122 and 144.

After Cosmos 122 was launched in June 1966, the Soviet authorities disclosed that the satellite had two systems of orientation. One kept the cylindrical centre-body with its TV cameras and IR sensors pointed vertically at the Earth; the other kept a pair of large solar panels constantly facing the Sun so that the maximum amount of electricity is generated to run on-board systems. For orientation the craft depended on a three-axis system of momentum wheels.

Cosmos 156 appears to have carried out pre-operational tests for a national meteorological distribution network. Meteor 1 was launched from the Northern Cosmodrome on 26 March 1969 into an orbit of 400 x 443 miles (644 x 713km) inclined at 81°.

Today Meteor satellites developed from these early models routinely scan the Earth from pole to pole, taking in an area of some 11,584 sq miles (30,000 sq km) in an hour. While over the night side of the Earth they obtain imagery by means of IR sensors responding to thermal emission from the

ground, oceans and clouds.

Typical of this family is the Meteor 2-04 satellite launched from the Northern Cosmodrome on 1 March 1979 which entered an orbit of 521 x 557 miles (839 x 897km) inclined at 81·22°. Three satellites are normally in orbit spaced 90° to 180° apart and pass over a given area at intervals of 6 to 12 hours. They store data for transmission to ground stations on command.

At the end of 1987, Meteors 2-14, 15 and 16 were fully operational. A new series, Meteor 3, was introduced on 24 October 1985 and was placed into a higher operational orbit. Presumably these satellites carry enhanced equipment. The first Meteor 3 did not function well, however, and this explained why there was then a delay until 1988 before the next was launched. These satellites are intended to take over from Meteor 2s in the 1990s.

Reception centres of the USSR Hydrometeorological Service provide the greatest possible spread of meteorological information. The main centres are in Moscow, Novosibirsk (Siberia) and Khabarovsk (Soviet Far East).

Below: *Exhibition model of a Soviet Meteor weather satellite which is three-axis stabilised by momentum wheels and powered by solar energy. The principal Earth-facing sensors are an imaging TV system and an infra-red radiometer.*

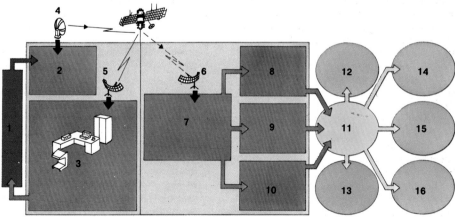

The Meteor System
1 Command centre.
2 Command radio link.
3 Automatic processing of satellite performance data.
4 Command link antenna.
5 Satellite performance data.
6 Satellite meteorological data.
7 Receiving station for meteorological data
8 Processing of TV data.
9 Processing of solar heating data.
10 Processing of infra-red data.
11 To Hydrometeorological Centre of USSR.
12 Data for aircraft.
13 Data for farmers.
14 Data for shipping
15 Advance warning of dangerous weather conditions.
16 Assessment of snow and ice cover

Large claims have been made for the Meteor satellite system, which provides routine forecasts of weather phenomena including warning of fast-developing tropical storms. The data-service is said to be especially valuable in the prediction of snowmelt from mountains and in the planning of irrigation schemes in remote places. It also has been of great benefit in the routing of shipping to avoid major storms, rough seas, high winds and pack ice with savings estimated in "millions of roubles".

A new Soviet weather satellite was being developed to survey the Earth from geo-stationary orbit. The Soviet Union committed itself to the GARP programme in 1977, announcing its intention of launching a spin-stabilised GEO weather satellite called GOMS. Technical difficulties cropped up, however, and GOMS was never launched. As a result, the Soviets withdrew from GARP.

International programmes include Eole, the result of co-operation between France (CNES) and the United States (NASA).

The ITOS System

The ITOS satellites operate in a Sun-synchronous* near-polar circular orbit at an altitude of 909 miles (1,463km). During the satellite's 115-minute orbital period the Earth rotates 28·5°. The sensor view angles give contiguous coverage between adjacent orbits as well as observation in the orbit track, providing global imaging during the 12·5 orbits daily.

The ITOS/NOAA system provides both real-time direct data to APT-type receiving stations throughout the world and stored data to the two United States CDA (command and data acquisition) stations for retrans-mission to NESS, the National Environmental Satellite Service at Suitland, Maryland, for processing and distribution. The real-time data provided to local users consist of SR visible and infra-red data, with a resolution of 2·3 and 4·6 miles (3·7km and 7·4km) respectively; VHRR infra-red and visible data with a resolution of 0·56 miles (0·9km); and VTPR temperature profiles of the atmos-phere from the surface of the Earth to about 100,070ft (30,500m).

The data stored for playback to the CDA stations consist of SR, VHRR, and VTPR information. It also includes SPM (Solar Proton Monitor) data on proton and electron flux at orbit altitude. The SR, VTPR, and SPM data are recorded on a global basis. The storage of VHRR data is limited to 9 minutes of viewing of a selected area of the Earth on each orbit.

The attitude-control subsystem of the ITOS satellite continuously orientates the satellite so that its sensors are pointed directly toward the Earth and scanning at a 90° angle to the satellite's orbital path. This orientation of the satellite's roll, yaw, and pitch axes is maintained to better than ±0·5° at all times.

The satellite is a rectangular, box-shaped structure, approximately 40in x 40in x 48in (101·6cm x 101·6cm x 121·9cm). The ITOS-D series spacecraft weigh c750lb (340kg).

*Sun-synchronous orbit: a near polar orbit which has its plane directed at the Sun. A satellite in such an orbit is ideal for observing the Earth.

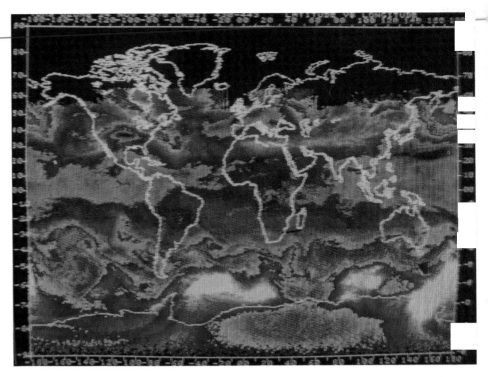

The Tiros-N System

In March 1983 NASA and NOAA in-troduced Advanced Tiros-N, the fourth-generation operational meteorological polar-orbiting satellite. This spacecraft is equipped with improved sensors and in-struments, and its data-collection system permits it to gather information from balloon and buoy platforms deployed about the planet. The NOAA satellites, in conjunction with three GOES satellites, were intended to constitute the USA's contribution to FGGE (First Global GARP Experiment), an inter-national programme. Additionally, they provided NOAA with the global meteoro-logical data required to support both the operational and the experimental portions of the World Weather Watch Programme.

Data collected by the satellites' advanced instruments are processed and stored on board for transmission to the central process-ing unit at Suitland, Maryland, via the CDA stations. Data are also transmitted in real-time to remote stations.

Advanced Tiros-N operates in a near-polar circular Sun-synchronous orbit with nominal altitude of either 518 or 541 miles (833km or 870km). In the operational configuration, two satellites positioned with a nominal orbit plane separation of 90° are used.

The instrument payload consists of:

1 The Advanced Very High Resolution Radiometer, a four-channel, cross-track scanning instrument providing image and radiometric data in the visible, near-infra-red, and far-infra-red portions of the spectrum. This instrument was pro-vided by ITT.

2 The Tiros Operational Vertical Sounder, a subsystem consisting of:

a The High-Resolution Infra-red Sounder (HIRS/2), a 20-channel step-scanned, visible and infra-red radio-meter, used to produce tropospheric temperature and moisture profiles. This instrument was also provided by ITT.

b The Stratospheric Sounding Unit (SSU), a three-channel, pulse-modu-lated, step-scanned, far-infra-red

Above: *Three images from Nimbus 7's TOMS (Total Ozone Mapping Spectrometer) were combined and processed in false colour to produce this map of the global ozone field in 1978. Black and red represent low total ozone values, while blue and white signify high values. Yellow and green are mid-scale in total ozone amount.*

spectrometer, used to produce tem-perature profiles of the stratosphere. It was provided by the British Meteoro-logical Office.

c The Microwave Sounding Unit (MSU), a four-channel, step-scanned spectrometer with response in the 60GHz oxygen band, used to produce temperature profiles in the atmosphere in the presence of clouds. This was provided by JPL.

3 The Data Collection System (DCS), a random-access system for the collection of meteorological data from in-situ plat-forms, both movable and fixed, such as buoys, balloons, and remote weather stations. Provided by CNES of France.

4 The Space Environment Monitor (SEM), a multi-detector unit used to monitor solar electron and proton energy in the vicinity of the satellite. Provided by Aeronutronic Ford Corporation.

5 The Search and Rescue (SAR) pay-load is used in a joint US-Canadian-French-Soviet SARSAT programme, providing data for identifying and locating downed aircraft and ships in distress. SAR detects distress signals from emergency locator transmitters. ELTs, on aircraft and from emergency position identification radio beacons, EPIRBs, on ships.

6 Some Advanced Tiros-N satellites carry the Solar Backscatter Ultraviolet Instrument, SBUV, to measure the Earth's ozone distribution.

7 Some satellites also carry the Earth Radiation Budget Experiment, ERBE, to determine radiation gains and losses to and from the Earth.

DMSP

The US Department of Defense has operated the DMSP (Defense Meteorological Satellite Program) since the mid-sixties. The DMSP polar-orbiting satellite system is under the management of the US Air Force, SAMSO (Space & Missile Systems Organization, Air Force Systems Command).

The DMSP spacecraft was designed and built by RCA and the primary sensor subsystem was provided by Westinghouse.

The mission of DMSP is to provide to the Air Weather Service global meteorological data in support of world-wide military operations, to advance spaceborne meteorological sensing technology to meet DoD (Department of Defense) requirements, and to provide DoD tactical support through direct transmission of local area weather data.

The Defense Meteorological Satellite Program's space segment consists of two satellites in 518 miles (833km) Sun-synchronous polar orbits, each carrying a payload of meteorological sensors. Primary cloud imaging sensors capable of globally viewing the Earth in the visible and infra-red spectrums are carried by every satellite. Each satellite collects data by continuously scanning a crosstrack swath 1,841 miles (2,963km) wide. The final data product is either in computer programme format or film product directly usable for imagery analysis.

The satellites are commanded and controlled from sites located at Loring Air Force Base, Maine, and Fairchild Air Force Base, Washington. These sites also receive stored data from tape recorders on board the spacecraft. These data are relayed to the Air Force Global Weather Central at Offutt Air Force Base, Nebraska, over a communication satellite link. They are also transmitted directly from the DMSP satellite to Air Force and Navy ground terminals and Navy aircraft carriers located throughout the world.

SMS/GOES

The capabilities of the SMS/GOES system include day-and-night Earth imaging, retransmission of imaged data, data collection and relay from terrestrial data-collection platforms, and space environmental monitoring. However, the geostationary satellite's most important contribution may be its ability to show, in virtual real time, violent weather disturbances at several scales of size and motion.

The diagram (pages 106-7) shows the image coverage area and communications range of two SMS/GOES satellites stationed at approximately 75°W and 135°W. From these vantage points they view all of North and South America and the adjacent oceans.

The SMS/GOES spacecraft consists of a Visible and Infra-red Spin-Scan Radiometer (VISSR) for high-resolution infra-red imagery, a communications subsystem for data-collection and relay, and a Space Environment Monitoring (SEM) subsystem. The VISSR scans from west to east in eight identical visible channels and two redundant infra-red channels. The resulting visible images have a resolution of nearly half a mile (0·8km). The infra-red images have a resolution of 4 miles (6·4km).

The GOES data-collection system collects and distributes environmental data acquired by remotely located, manned or unmanned,

Tiros 1

Tiros 1
The original meteorological satellite, launched on 1 April 1960, gave meteorologists their first pictures of Earth. Its surface covered with solar cells.

Tiros 1 weighed 283lb (128kg) and had a cartwheel configuration — 22in (0·56m) in height: 42in (1·07m) in diameter — rolling along in orbit like a wheel. Two 0·5in (1·27cm)

Vidicon TV cameras — wide angle (104°) and narrow angle (12°) — were mounted 180° apart on the rim. It operated successfully for nearly three months.

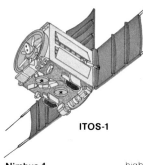

ITOS-1

ITOS-1
The second-generation operational weather satellite ITOS-1 was successfully orbited on 23 January 1970 and was followed by NOAA-1 (ITOS-A) on 11 December 1970. The ITOS/NOAA satellites operated in Sun-synchronous orbit with an orientation system which pointed sensors at the Earth, giving full meteorological coverage of land and oceans. ITOS-1 weighed 690lb (313kg), was 49in (1·24m) in height and had a width of 40 x 40in (1·02 x 1·02m). Its array span was 14ft (4·3m). It carried two automatic picture transmission TVs and two advanced 1in (2·54cm) Vidicon camera systems.

Nimbus 1
The first of seven Nimbus spacecraft launched between 1964 and 1978. Nimbus 1 was successfully orbited on 28 August 1964. A large, automated spacecraft, it was stabilised on three axes so that its sensors — including a

Nimbus 1

high resolution infra-red radiometer — always pointed at the Earth. Its big butterfly "wings", spanning 11ft (3·35m), were covered with solar cells. Nimbus 1 was 10ft (3·05m) in height and 5ft (1·52m) in diameter. Compare Landsat (Chapter 8).

Tiros-N
The first of a planned total of eight third-generation polar orbiting satellites. Tiros-N was launched on 13 October 1978. It is 12ft (3·66m) long and weighs 3,127lb (1,418kg). Its improved sensors and instruments include an advanced very high resolution radiometer; high resolution infra-red sounder; high energy proton and alpha particle detector; and medium energy proton and electron detector.

Tiros-N

Advanced Tiros-N

Advanced Tiros-N
These satellites, some 14ft (4·3m) long and weighing around 3,800lb (1,724kg), have increased still further the scope of weather/environment study. Among the instruments of the Advanced

Tiros-N are search and rescue (SAR) antennas which provide data for locating and identifying ships in trouble or aircraft which may be stranded in remote places, and directing rescue forces.

data-collection platforms on land, at sea, or in the atmosphere. The data-collection platforms include instrumented buoys, river gauges, automatic weather stations, seismic and tsunami stations, and ships. Some examples of their uses are: (1) fixed stations in remote land areas transmit information on earthquakes, wind direction and velocity, humidity, and rainfall; (2) river platforms measure currents, weather levels, and temperatures; (3) marine platforms (either fixed or floating) measure tides, water and air temperatures, and provide tsunami (large waves caused by undersea earthquakes) warnings.

Many photographic and computer-generated products are derived from SMS/GOES images. One unique to the geostationary satellite data is derived from the ability to generate time-lapse cine frames from a series of registered GOES images

(visible or infra-red) of the full Earth disc. By the use of both manual and computer techniques, selected cloud tracers are tracked in successive GOES images to determine wind speeds and directions.

China Joins In

China entered the weather satellite business in 1988, launching Feng Yun 1 on the first Long March 4 booster from a new launch site at Taiyuan in Shanxi Province on 6 September. Feng Yun was placed into a circular, Sun-synchronous orbit inclined at 99·12° deg at an altitude of 562 miles (904km). The 1,543lb (700kg) satellite is equipped with two "very high resolution" scanning radiometers.

Benefits

Over the past 30 years the quantity, quality and reliability of satellite coverage

When major hurricanes David and Frederic struck the Caribbean and moved towards the East and Gulf Coasts of the United States in August-September 1979 hundreds or thousands of lives may have been saved because weather satellites were in orbit. With the data they supplied meteorologists were able to track the hurricanes with great precision and give timely warning of their approach to local populations. The retinue of satellites making observations at this time included geostationary satellites forming part of the 1978-79 Global Atmospheric Research Program (GARP) to improve knowledge of global processes that bring about changes in weather and climate, and so supplement the existing World Weather Watch which generates over 40,000 observations daily. Some 147 member countries of the World Meteorological Organisation and the International Council of Scientific Unions contributed to this major experiment—the largest co-operative space effort—which included observations and measurements by ships, aircraft, buoys, balloons, sounding rockets and satellites to trace air and moisture movements over every region of the Earth's surface. The intention was to determine the practical limits of weather forecasting and so design an appropriate world observation system. The satellites, operating in the visible and infra-red parts of the spectrum, produced pictures of the Earth's cloud cover by day and night. The images they transmitted at regular intervals, enabled meteorologists to identify, track and monitor severe storms, snow cover, sea surface and atmospheric temperatures, hurricanes and typhoons. Five geostationary satellites of the international network (see diagram below) included three SMS/GOES (Synchronous Meteorological Satellite/Geostationary Operational Environmental Satellite System) supplied by the United States, one Meteosat (built in Europe) and one Japanese GMS (Geo-stationary Meteorological Satellite) (built in the USA). The map (right) shows the relative positions of these satellites and what measurements they can take in the various arcs of coverage. The ellipses indicate: 10° elevation, communication range; 20° elevation, useful cloud information; 30° elevation, 10 knot wind accuracy measurements; 40° elevation, 5 knot wind accuracy measurements.

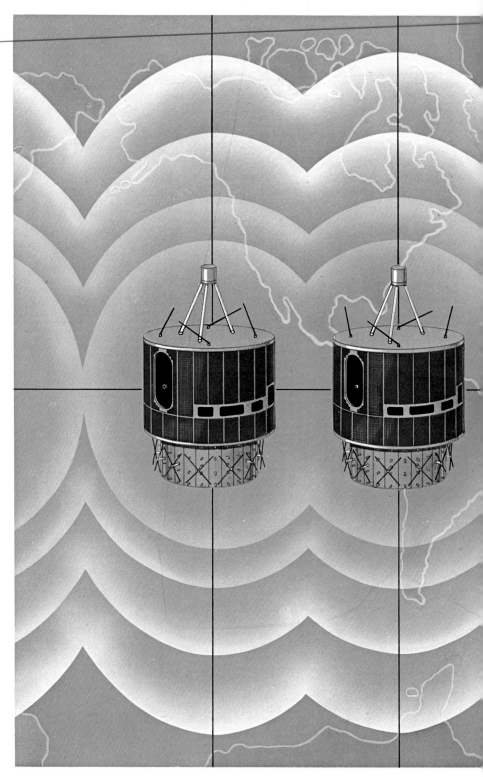

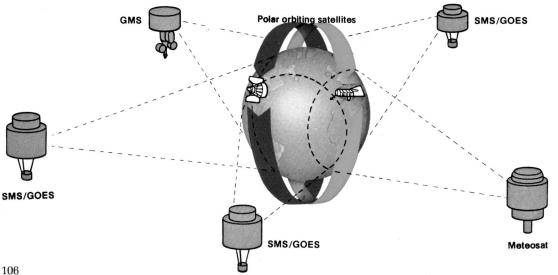

GMS · Polar orbiting satellites · SMS/GOES

SMS/GOES

SMS/GOES

Meteosat

GARP
Space Segment
Apart from satellites circulating in polar orbit, five satellites were operating in Clarke orbit as part of the GARP experiment which took place between 1 December 1978 and 30 November 1979. Meteosat 1, supplied by the European Space Agency, looked down from a position above the Gulf of Guinea at longitude 0°. Two SMS/GOES were stationed respectively at approximately 75°W and 135°W longitude to observe North and South America and adjacent oceans. GOES 1 was above the Indian Ocean (60°E). Japan's Geostationary Meteorological Satellite, Himawari 1, was at 140°E longitude.

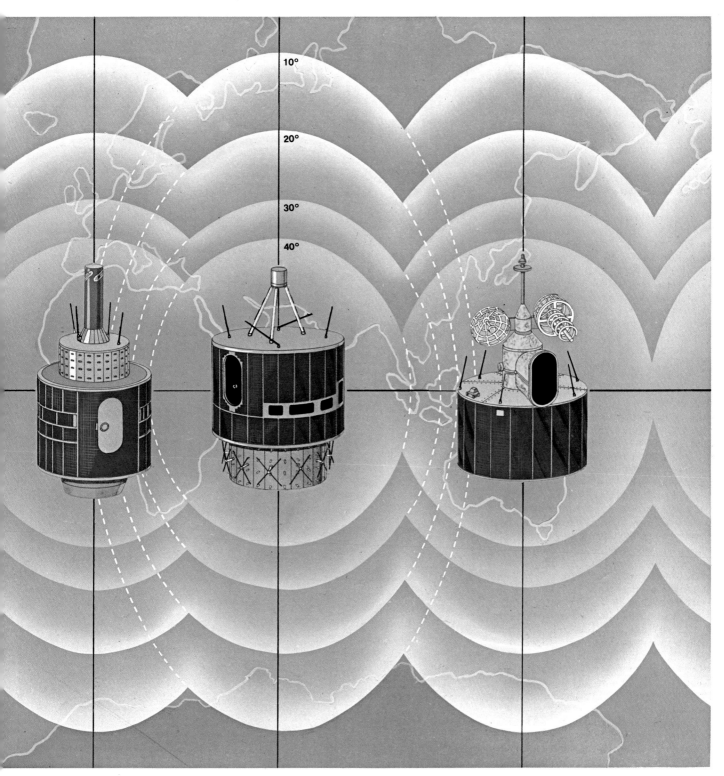

10°
20°
30°
40°

Meteosat System
1 Meteosat.
2 Central Station.
3 User ground stations.
4 Ocean liner.
5 Hydrological station.
6 Ship (data collection).
7 Transmitting buoy.
8 Low-orbit satellite.
Raw weather pictures (red arrows) are transmitted to the European Central Ground Facility in West Germany and main user stations. Corrected and processed images plus APT (Automatic Picture Transmission) and WEFAX (Weather Facsimile) data (blue) are distributed via the same satellite to users in the coverage zone using small ground receivers. Locally obtained data (green) are also collected and disseminated by Meteosat.

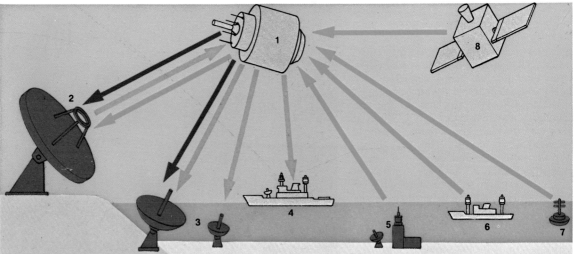

have improved greatly. Since 1966 the entire Earth has been photographed at least once a day on a continuous basis. The photographs are used in daily operations and are also placed in archives from which they can be retrieved for use in research case studies. From its inception as a new research tool with a potential not fully realised, satellite-derived data have steadily increased in importance. They are now being used by meteorologists and environmental scientists on a wide-spread basis in routine operations throughout the world, and are considerd almost indispensable for analyses and short-range forecasts.

The meteorological information from around the Earth is received at the National Environmental Satellite Service in Washington, transformed into a broad variety of products and distributed worldwide.

Satellite information has proved particularly useful in two research fields. First, extensive areas of the Earth exist from which conventional weather reports are sparse, namely the oceanic regions of the northern and southern hemispheres, deserts, and the polar regions. Satellite information fills such voids by locating large-scale features revealed by cloud formations. These features include storm systems, fronts, upper-level troughs and ridges, jet-streams, fog, stratus, sea-ice conditions, area of snow cover, and (to some extent) upper level wind directions and speeds.

Secondly, satellite data are usefully applied for tracking hurricanes, typhoons, and tropical storms. Coastal and island stations with little or no adjacent conventional weather information can make maximum use of APT data and the processed stored data from facsimile circuits. The satellite data provide information on the presence and position of frontal patterns, storms, and general cloud cover.

However, weathermen do not depend on satellites alone to provide advance warning of approaching storms. For example, when a major hurricane is found to be heading in the direction of the United States, USAF and NOAA weather-reconnaissance aircraft are called upon to support the satellite data and provide detailed measurements of meteorological events in and around the storm. When a hurricane moves in close to the United States, coastal radars keep the storm centre under close surveillance. In this way precise information on the path and ferocity of the storm is passed to communities which lie along its predicted track. Other sources feeding data into the network are ships, ocean buoys and weather stations located on various islands and along mainland coasts.

Since 1966 coverage of the world by the Tiros satellites has been completed on a daily basis, and no tropical storm has escaped detection and daily tracking. Storms are usually spotted while developing, often at distances beyond the normal range of reconnaissance aircraft. The APT, direct-readout infra-red, and processed stored visible and infra-red data are available at most offices with tropical storm forecast responsibilities. All the tropical regions of

Above: *From its lofty vantage point of 140°E, GMS-1 viewed all of the Far East, Australia and New Zealand, and even a substantial portion of India.*

Right: *Japan's GMS-2 undergoing tests in Hughes' anechoic chamber. The VISSR scan mirror is visible beneath the antennas.*

Above: *Meteosat 1 being checked out with the nose fairing of the Delta 2914. Beneath the satellite is the apogee rocket which transfers it from low to geostationary orbit.*

the world are completely monitored through satellite data received by the National Environmental Satellite Service.

The infra-red data from the ITOS/NOAA satellites can be used to produce charts showing the sea-surface temperature over a larger area and with more frequency than is possible from any other source. This information is useful to shipping interests and the fishing industry, and is a vital input to meteorological forecasts.

Satellite pictures also display the extent and character of ice-fields in the Arctic and Antarctic Seas, and on the Great Lakes, with a frequency of geographic coverage never before approached.

Worldwide atmospheric temperature soundings provided by satellites result in more complete and accurate analyses for use in weather forecasts because they monitor oceans and remote areas not covered by conventional sounding instruments. Continuous soundings help to measure atmospheric temperature gradients for use in studying atmospheric phenomena. Individual soundings aid the interpretation of satellite picture data by providing correlation at specific geographical locations.

Above: *"Earth disc" as seen by the ESA Meteosat 1 from geostationary orbit above the Gulf of Guinea. Cloud patterns can be identified over a very wide area.*

Future Expectations

The Tiros–ESSA–ITOS–NOAA polar-orbiting meteorological satellites have been the mainstay of the US meteorological satellite programmes. The Advanced Tiros-N series is now operational, and is the mainstay of NOAA's global weather gathering satellite data system. They have fulfilled United States operational requirements by providing a reliable in-orbit system that transmits routine observations on a timely basis without interruption in service. Its evolutionary design has permitted programme objectives to be achieved cost-effectively and has gradually and effectively improved service with existing worldwide receiving stations. Advanced Tiros-N, the fourth generation operational system, provides further improvements in observation and in the processing and dissemination of the polar-orbiting data required by the long-term goals of the National Operational System.

The complementary geostationary environmental satellites will be improved by the addition of an atmospheric sounding capability on the latest GOES satellites. The real-time temperature and thermal gradient data provided by these soundings are expected to improve the meteorologist's ability to forecast the areas where severe thunderstorms and tornadoes are likely to occur.

As part of the international co-operation and participation within the World Meteorological Organization, Japan, the European Space Agency (ESA), and the USSR are placing satellites in service to support FGGE. Japan's geostationary satellite (Himawari-1) was launched on 14 July 1977 and positioned over the western Pacific Ocean. ESA's geostationary satellite (Meteosat) was launched on 23 November 1977 and positioned over the eastern Atlantic Ocean. Both were launched by NASA Delta launch vehicles from Cape Canaveral.

When the USSR deferred the launch of its geostationary satellite, the United States (NOAA) filled the gap with a GOES satellite. This satellite had been positioned over the Indian Ocean and was operated by ESA with a US-loaned ground station.

In 1988, the picture had changed, however. Only one GOES and one GMS, GMS-3, launched in 1984, were fully operational. The second Meteosat, launched in June 1981 to replace Meteosat-1, which suffered electrical failure, was being complemented by a refurbished prototype launched in 1988, in preparation for the launch of the first of three planned Meteosat Operational Programme (MOP) satellites which happened on 6 March 1989. The first of five new GOES will be launched in 1990 and one more GMS is due for launch in 1989. A fifth GMS is being studied by Japan.

These geostationary satellites are complemented by the polar-orbiting Advanced Tiros-N satellite series, which provide the global data, particularly filling in the data for the far polar regions.

As a result of this pioneering effort, the satellite is now an established tool of the meteorologist in most countries of the world. To the public at large, the weather charts which appear nightly on our television screens are visible evidence of the value of satellite observations in providing a clear idea of developing weather systems.

New satellite instruments for probing the Earth's atmosphere by day and night in all weathers are being developed, and it is not only the Americans and Russians who are providing them; much important work in this field is now being carried out in Europe.

The developing world has also shared the benefits of this research, which has made possible advance warning of hurricanes, tornadoes, monsoons and flood-producing rain storms. Countries like Japan, India and China are now developing their own special instruments of "weather watch". Much of this research overlaps the still broader area of Earth observation.

Observing Planet Earth

Man first became aware of the value of satellites for monitoring agriculture, forests and other natural resources some years after the Space Age began. The first hint came in 1960 when Tiros weather satellites showed map-like outlines of the world beneath the clouds.

These early black and white television images revealed little about human activities until someone spotted on a picture of Northern Canada faint patterns in the snow which turned out to be places where lumberjacks had been clearing forests.

Even so it was not until men went into space that the ability to observe relatively small details on Earth from altitudes above 100 miles (161km) was fully recognised. Astronaut Gordon Cooper during his flight in a Mercury capsule in May 1963 astonished space officials by claiming that he had seen roads, buildings and even smoke from chimneys. He was accused by ground control of being hallucinated!

Subsequent space missions were to show the truth of Cooper's observations. Colour photographs taken by the Gemini astronauts passing over the launch centre at Cape Canaveral showed changes in urban structure and progress in the building of new roads during a six-month interval between flights. Gemini 4 provided pictures of water drainage patterns in Western Texas and wheat fields were clearly identified on images returned by Apollo 6.

Another space photo showed where rain had fallen the previous evening in a dry region of Texas, not because the ground was visibly damp but because the vegetation had begun to "uncurl", throwing up a different colour response to the camera.

Apollo 9 photos showed snow concentrations on a mountain range in Arizona and extensive flood damage could be seen over an area of 165 square miles (427 sq km) along the Ouachitra River in Louisiana following a major storm.

Soon new techniques were developed to enhance the value of this type of operation, and profit was made from military research which aimed to increase the scope of high-flying reconnaissance aircraft using different film and specialised electronic sensing equipment.

Information was obtained through multi-spectral imagery in visible light or infra-red (IR) which made it possible to detect minute variations in IR radiation on the ground invisible to the human eye but containing vital information. The two basic type instruments were infra-red cameras loaded with film sensitive only to IR, and infra-red radio-

---

> **"This fragile miracle of life;**
> **spinning blue in the sea of black;**
> **precious beyond compare;**
> **sacred in its wondrous possibility."**
>
> Dean Francis B. Sayre
> *On the occasion of the dedication of a "space window" at the Washington Cathedral in which is preserved a rock from the Moon*

---

meters which are special radio receivers tuned to pick up only IR wavelengths.

For example, in early IR photographs taken by research aircraft it was possible to tell the difference between fields containing healthy agricultural crops and ones afflicted by blight. The healthy crops stood out in pink or red while the blighted ones registered in blue/black. And frequently it was possible to identify the onset of disease before it was apparent to the farmer on the ground.

The multi-spectral sensors now in general use in observation satellites work on the same principle—features on the Earth's surface can be identified in general by the energy they emit or reflect from the Sun. The spectral signature for vegetation is different from that of rock, soil or water.

These differences are registered by the sensing equipment aboard the satellite and they can be interpreted in different (false) colours defining these variations within the region surveyed. So effective has this type of "civil reconnaissance" become that it is possible to recognise specific crops under cultivation and changes in their spectral signature indicating such information as poor soil condition, moisture content of the soil as well as crops affected by disease or insect infestation.

The first satellites to give detailed attention to these opportunities were the Landsats developed by General Electric for NASA.

The early Landsats travel in north-south circular orbits at an altitude of about 570 miles (917km) and their coverage of land and ocean shifts westward as the Earth rotates beneath them. The orbits are such that a single satellite can report on nearly every area of the world every 18 days.

Images are digitised and transmitted to dish antennas at receiving stations on the Earth's surface, where they are stored on magnetic tape for conversion to photographic prints in colour and black and white.

Landsat 4, the fourth in the series, was designed to survey the Earth from an altitude of more than 398 miles (640km) using improved sensing equipment. As well as having a multi-spectral scanner (MSS) of the kind carried by the first three Landsats, it was designed to carry a sensor known as the thematic mapper (TM) capable of discriminating features as small as 0·2 acre—as compared with 1·2 acres previously—enabling users to extract much more detailed and timely information.

The project is unusual in being the first to employ the Multi-Purpose Modular Spacecraft (MMS) which is intended to be retrieved by the Space Shuttle for possible repair and re-use. It consists of a general-purpose satellite "bus" which supplies the basic functions of power, propulsion, attitude control, communications and data handling and a structure capable of accepting a broad range of scientific and applications type payloads.

Above: *Landsat 3 being prepared at General Electric. It is one of a growing family of satellites used to monitor agricultural crops and assist the search for deposits of minerals, oil and fresh water.*

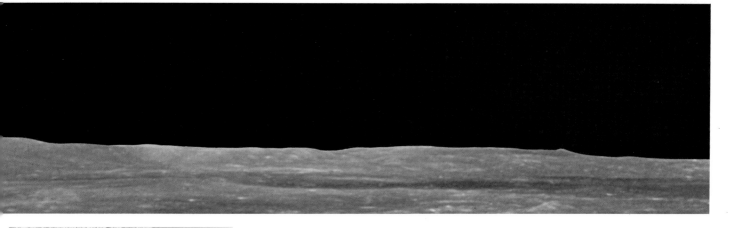

With the Thematic Mapper Landsats 4 and 5 were able to depict surface scenes in natural colour so that the ground appeared green instead of MSS red. The addition of a blue-green band enabled analysts to see considerable depth in clear water, making it possible to map reefs and survey uncharted islands and atolls. Extra IR channels enabled geologists to identify a wider variety of rock and soil types, especially those bearing clay minerals. One prospector in Oklahoma found in the images evidence of oil near the surface and immediately staked a claim!

Cartography

One of the first applications for Earth-resources imagery has been in map-making. Before the era of satellites, many areas even in developed parts of the world had been imperfectly mapped.

Landsat imagery helped to correct and update certain features of existing United States maps at scales of 1:250,000 or smaller. The fresh information provided immediate evidence of urban development since existing maps were made and modifications made to roads and railways. In the Soviet Union imagery obtained from Salyut space stations proved invaluable for checking the route of the BAM strategic railway, then under construction north of the existing trans-Siberian route.

Satellite imagery has also been used to produce detailed maps for the construction of roads, railways and irrigation channels. It has also been possible to chart underwater features such as coral reefs which are potentially dangerous to shipping.

More than half of Asia, Africa and Latin America had not been mapped at scales larger than 1:1,000,000 before satellites got to work. With Landsat, uncharted areas could be quickly and cheaply mapped and existing maps updated with acceptable accuracy; and decisions could be made regarding areas where higher resolution imagery from aircraft was required.

The speed with which space surveys can be made compared to alternative methods has been a major factor in reducing costs. For example, a plan to make a new geological map of Egypt at a scale of 1:1,000,000 in ten years — at an estimated cost of $2·4 million — using black and white aerial photographs was changed when Landsat offered roughly three times more geographical detail and allowed the task to be completed in half the time at considerably less cost.

Agriculture

In the mid-1970s NASA, the Department of Agriculture and NOAA (the National Oceanic and Atmospheric Administration) combined in a major experiment to demonstrate how a satellite system could help forecast the yield of an important world crop—wheat.

What the researchers did was to calculate total wheat acreage from Landsat surveys and compare this with the potential yield per acre based on knowledge of past meteorological data between crop harvests. The survey, which proved to be remarkably accurate, was later expanded to include other crops.

Researchers using Landsat images of California's Imperial Valley in just 40 man-hours succeeded in identifying more than 25 separate crops in 8,865 fields. The total area covered in this particular survey was 185,150 hectares (643 sq miles), and among the crops which could be picked out were corn, popcorn, soya beans, sorghum, oats, grasses

Above: *Forty-six infra-red pictures obtained by Landsat 1 during four seasons in 1972-73 make up this cloud-free view of Italy, Sicily, Corsica and Sardinia. The red areas show healthy areas of vegetation.*

Below: *Death Valley, California: an infra-red Thematic Mapper image taken by Landsat 4. The picture has been processed with a false colour technique to identify rock types by their spectral characteristics.*

Observing Planet Earth

Landsat 4 and 5
1 RF compartment
2 TDRS high-gain antenna.
3 Powered hinges.
4 Solar array jettison mechanism.
5 Solar array.
6 Sun sensors.
7 Multi-spectral scanner.
8 Wideband module and antennas.
9 X-band antenna.
10 S-band antenna.
11 Communications and data-handling module.
12 Thematic mapper.
13 Signal conditioning and control unit.
14 Earth sensor.
15 Propulsion system thruster.
16 Propulsion module (hydrazine).
17 Power module.
18 Multi-mission modular spacecraft (MMS) support structure.
19 Attitude control module.
20 Adapter.

21 S-band omni antenna (2).
22 Instrument module primary structure.
23 Global Positioning System (GPS) antenna.
24 2 axis gimbal.

Landsat 4, launched on 16 July 1982 and its sister craft, Landsat 5, launched 1 March 1984, are the most advanced of NASA's Earth resources satellites. The craft comprises a Multi-mission Modular Spacecraft (MMS), which provides power, attitude control, communications and data handling, and propulsion; and an Instrument Module (IM). The satellite improves considerably the technology of remote sensing of the Earth, thereby aiding resource management. In some senses, it is a test vehicle: for example, it has

assessed the capabilities of the new Thematic Mapper (TM) and also demonstrated the feasibility of the system in respect of user participation. However, it also ensures the continued availability of MSS data — previously available from similar equipment aboard Landsat 1, 2 and 3 — and offers users a transition from MSS to the high-resolution TM. A transition adapter provides the mating structure for the IM and MMS. It also provides 3 mounting points to a cradle which in turn mounts in the Shuttle cargo bay for retrieval. Power is generated from a solar array, for conditioning and regulation by the MMS; output is 2200 watts, with storage in 50 amp/hr batteries for night use. Data transmission is performed in a variety of

bands, both directly to ground stations and also using TDRS. Attitude control is very precise and achieved by an inertial reference unit, updated from two star trackers. Torquer magnets unload the momentum wheels 5lb hydrazine thrusters enable orbital altitude to be varied for Shuttle rendezvous and to repeat ground swath coverage. For the first time in a NASA satellite a Global Positioning System (GPS) is incorporated: using data supplied by navigation satellites, Landsat's computer can calculate the craft's position and velocity, signals being received by means of a GPS antenna. In August 1983, loss of electrical power on Landsat 4, and TM direct ground link failure forced NOAA to authorize the launch of the backup Landsat

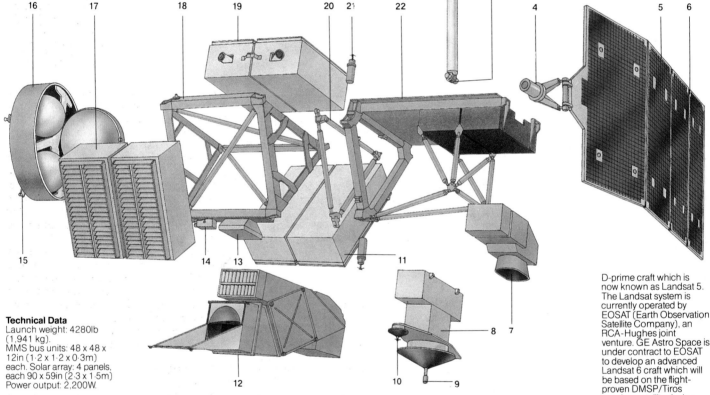

Technical Data
Launch weight: 4280lb (1,941 kg).
MMS bus units: 48 x 48 x 12in (1·2 x 1·2 x 0·3m) each. Solar array: 4 panels, each 90 x 59in (2·3 x 1·5m) Power output: 2,200W.

D-prime craft which is now known as Landsat 5. The Landsat system is currently operated by EOSAT (Earth Observation Satellite Company), an RCA-Hughes joint venture. GE Astro Space is under contract to EOSAT to develop an advanced Landsat 6 craft which will be based on the flight-proven DMSP/Tiros weather satellite design.

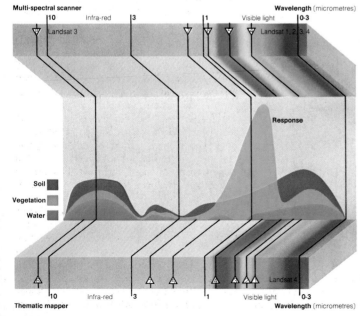

The Sensors
The diagram shows how the remote sensing instruments aboard Landsat 4 obtain their information. Light and heat reflected or emitted from land and oceans are picked up in selected wavebands. Each band, from the visible to the far infra-red, contains specific information on living and non-living things. The sensors are "tuned" to the wavebands of vegetation, soil, water and other surface materials and are thereby able to identify (by repeated observation) any changes that occur in their properties. The other instrument aboard Landsat 4 is a Multi-spectral Scanner (MSS) of 262ft (80m) resolution and with four channels, identical to the sensors in Landsats 1 and 2. The diagram compares the waveband range of Landsats 1, 2 and 3 with the waveband range of Landsat 4.

(rye, Bermuda, Alicia and Sudan), lettuce, mustard, tomatoes, carrots, and onions.

The scientists distinguished between wet-planted fields and bare earth in areas as small as ten acres (4·5 hectares). The remote sensing devices installed on the latest generation of operational Landsats are able to locate and identify these characteristics on a one-acre plot.

From this ability may come a global food watch which could help mankind avoid disastrous food shortages. A 25 per cent improvement in the accuracy of forecasting foreign wheat harvests could, according to one estimate, yield benefits to the United States worth $200 million and avoid many of the difficulties brought about by under- or over-production.

The researchers also pointed to the possibilities of achieving better management of crop and timber resources. From the regular survey made by satellites the best time to plant and harvest for maximum yield

Thematic Mapper
1 Electronics module.
2 Multiplexer.
3 Thermal control louvres.
4 Radiative cooler.
5 Cold focal plane.
6 Relay optics.
7 Prime focal plane.
8 Primary mirror.
9 Telescope assembly.
10 Secondary mirror.
11 Scan mirror assembly.
12 Power supply.

Band 1 (0·45-0·52um) aids assessment of water quality and forestry mapping. Band 2 (0·52-

0·60um) is green reflectance band. Band 3 (0·63-0·69um) is chlorophyll absorption band for signature analysis. Band 4 (0·76-0·90um) measures biomass and plant stress. Cutoff at 0·90um avoids H₂O absorption. Band 5 (1·55-1·75um) for soil moisture and geologic study. Separates snow from clouds. Band 6 (10·40-12·50um) moisture content and geo-chemical classification. Band 7 (2·08-2·35um) aids urban land use study.

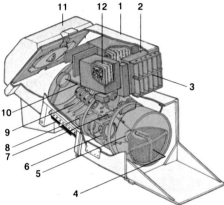

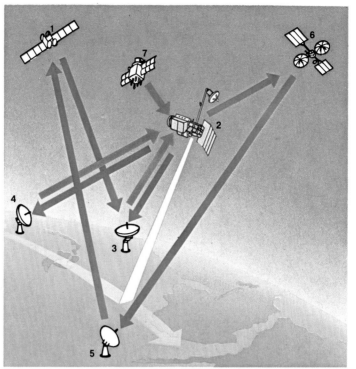

Landsat 4 Mission
1 Synchronous Communications Satellite.
2 Landsat 4 (launched 16 July 1982). Altitude 438 miles (705km).
3 Landsat ground station (foreign).
4 Goddard Space Flight Center ground station.
5 TDRS ground station.
6 Tracking and Data Relay Satellite (TDRS).
7 Navstar GPS.

Landsat 4 carried a wide band communications system capable of operating through NASA's Tracking and Data Relay Satellite System as well as directly to US and foreign ground stations. Apart from a Multi-Spectral Scanner, it operated a Thematic Mapper (TM), a third-generation precision multi-spectral instrument for Earth resources study from low-orbit satellites; it is a seven-channel radiometer, designed to provide scenes of Earth with 98ft (30m) resolution. Information from Landsat's scanning instruments is digitized for transmissions to Earth.

Above: *Landsat 3's MSS—a technician examines the instrument's aperture housing a reflecting mirror and telescope optics which receive reflected IR and visible light spectral images.*

can be found by checking soil condition and moisture content; an inventory of crops can be kept during the growing season and advance warning given of drought.

The same type of "agricultural watch" would allow an inventory to be made of tropical areas which could be potentially productive if cleared, and data obtained on fertile and arid regions which could be made more productive by irrigation.

So effective has Landsat's potential become that farmland of an entire region can be sorted crop by crop in a matter of hours in combination with high-speed computers on the ground. The end result is a computer-printed terrain map showing precise location and area of each crop.

Rangelands

An example of the way in which remote sensing can be brought to bear on the most severe human problems occurred in the case of the Sahel, a vast African prairie just south of the Sahara Desert.

A number of countries in the area asked for the area to be surveyed by Landsat in order to find ways of alleviating starvation due to prolonged drought. Not only were many regions identified as being suitable for farming, but Landsat imagery pointed to a valuable lesson in conservation. The satellite found an irregularly shaped area of vegetation that stood out from the surrounding parched land. The patch was identified as a ranch where careful management had prevented the livestock from denuding the land.

The lesson here, as in semi-arid lands elsewhere, is that grazing rotation and other methods of livestock management can prevent the encroachment of desert and dust bowls.

More generally, a system of rangeland monitoring from space allowed people to decide the best times to turn out cattle in grazing areas. Plans were prepared to prevent overgrazing and to open up new areas for this purpose, and it was possible to assess the amount of additional investment needed to be made in range improvements by draining, irrigation, seeding and the application of fertilizers.

Forestry

Similarly, Landsat data has shown clear advantages in estimating the volume of timber across large areas of a given country. When forests are being cut it has been possible to monitor this and, if necessary, to recommend changes in the cutting pattern in the best interests of conservation.

Developing countries are increasingly aware of the need to manage their forest resources not only to meet their timber requirements but also to preserve the ecological balance and to prevent erosion, silting of dams and pollution of coastal waters. In

Brazil Landsat imagery has been used to monitor a programme for controlled development of the Amazon forests for various purposes, including cattle grazing. Landowners—with the help of government subsidies—are allowed to cut down trees up to a third of their land holdings and systematic use of Landsat imagery has proved to be the only economic way of enforcing the terms of the government-assistance contracts and of monitoring and controlling the volume of tree-cutting.

From satellite imagery it has also been possible to make rapid assessment of places where forest fires have burnt the ground, especially the "crown type" fire common in western regions of North America. One Canadian survey using Landsat imagery found 42 burns across north Saskatchewan, indicating the extent of damage.

Oceanography

Apart from photography of the oceans various satellite techniques can be used to wrest information directly from the sea. Automatic buoys in major oceans can measure local air and water surface temperatures, temperature, pressure and salinity at depth, and wave heights and the speed of surface currents. The data transmitted on command to a satellite then can be stored and re-transmitted to a ground station for rapid assimilation.

It is now possible to obtain data on sea conditions directly from the satellite by radar microwave (backscatter) techniques. The scope for ocean reconnaissance by this method was demonstrated when NASA in June 1978 launched Seasat 1 from Vandenberg Air Force Base. Though it operated for only four months, Seasat 1 swept over 95 per cent of the world's oceans every 36hr, taking more measurements in a single day than had previously been obtained in decades of scientific observation.

From its 500 miles (805km) orbit, Seasat pointed five instruments at the world's oceans as it made 14 orbits of the Earth each

Above: *Seasat 1 in the payload fairing of the Atlas-Agena launch vehicle that placed it in a near polar orbit in June 1978. Here it is being mated to the second stage of the Atlas-Agena launcher.*

day penetrating fog, rain, sleet and darkness. Just as the human eye registers in the visible regions between 4,000 and 7,000 Angstroms*, microwave instruments "see" in a radio portion of the spectrum between 1,000MHz and 300,000MHz, corresponding to wavelength between 30cm and 0·1cm. Such instruments provide data which can be translated into sea-surface temperature, wind speed, wind direction and the amount of water in the atmosphere. They can also take pictures of ocean waves, ice fields, icebergs, ice leads (linear openings in ice through which ships may navigate), and sea conditions along the coastlines.

Ocean currents often meander and change course and size. For example, "El Nino" is a warm current that flows south along the coast of Ecuador, usually beginning just after Christmas. NASA reports that in exceptional years, El Nino may extend down the coast of Peru to 12°S latitude. When that occurs, plankton and fish are killed in vast numbers, devastating the fishing industries of many nations. Large concentrations of *Dinoflagellates* (single-celled sea creatures) increase the fish kills, perhaps because of toxins they carry.

The water turns a red colour similar to the "red tides" along the Southern California and western Florida coasts. Ocean monitoring satellites help chart the vagaries of such currents and provide useful information to those who need it.

Fishermen in the Pacific Ocean use satellite-derived information on the location of thermal boundaries in the ocean where salmon and albacore tend to congregate because of the high nutrient levels in the waters. According to NASA, the combination of fuel saving and "additional catch advantage" afforded by satellite IR data has an estimated annual benefit of $2,440,000.

Profit has also been made from satellites supplying information on the ever-changing

*1 Angstrom = 10^{-8}cm, or 1/100,000,000cm

positions of the Gulf Stream and Gulf Loop Current. As early as 1975, seven oil tankers owned by the Exxon Corporation used satellite data to ride the northbound currents of the Gulf Stream and to avoid the current on southward passages. The fuel saving for the company's total fleet of 15 tankers was estimated to be about $360,000. The oil company now uses satellite data for all its vessels plying the east-coast route.

As far as deep-water surveys are concerned, sensing instruments on present Landsats are able to penetrate clear water surfaces to a depth of about 65ft (20m). In the Caribbean, for example, this has made possible the charting of shallow underwater features that were previously unknown.

Russia, too, is studying the oceans from Salyut and Mir space stations and has launched satellites which measure the sea surface electromagnetic radiation in the visible, infra-red and microwave bands. The first was Cosmos 1076, launched on 12

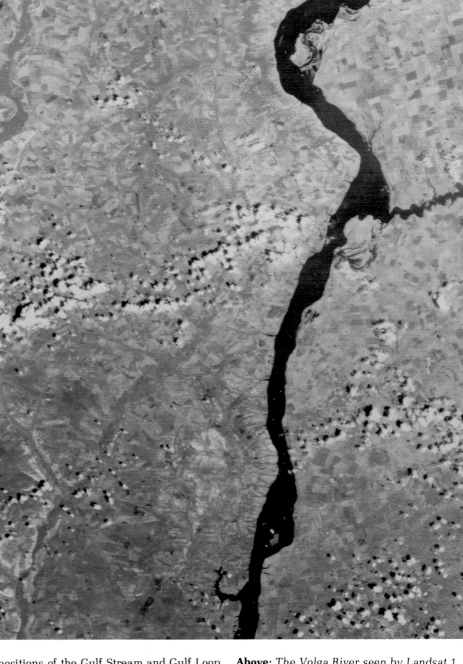

Above: *The Volga River seen by Landsat 1 from an altitude of 568 miles (914km). A reservoir "lake" created by a dam at Volgograd (bottom) extends 200 miles (320km) upstream past Saratov. To the east is low-lying, intensely-cultivated steppe; to the west, higher ground is broken by streams.*

February 1979 into an orbit of 396 x 414 miles (637km x 666km) inclined at 81·5°.

Research of this kind is leading to observation systems in which different satellites collect different types of data from land and sea surfaces to allow better use to be made of the Earth's resources.

Sensors under consideration for the early 1990s to equip a proposed Earth Resources Survey Satellite System by the European Space Agency, for example, are a multi-spectral ocean colour monitor/infra-red mapper; a synthetic aperture radar, and an imaging radiometer. They would be expected to pull together data on such subjects as:

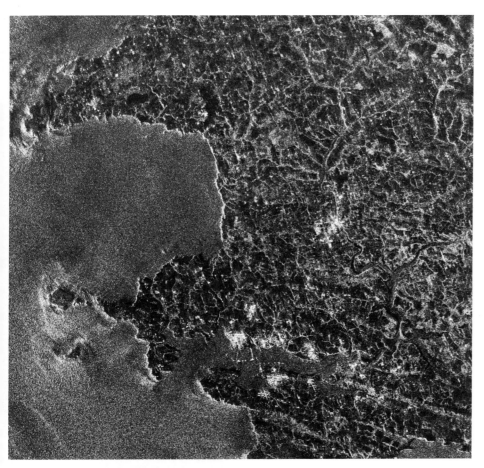

Above: *Synthetic Aperture Radar imagery of geological structure and topographic variability around Milford Haven, Wales, from Seasat 1. From such imagery, it is also possible to obtain sea-state information.*

Above: *This gigantic iceberg was spotted by Landsat on 31 January 1977. It was nearing the end of a 1,800 mile (2,896km) journey along the Antarctic coast toward the open sea east of South America. Here it is temporarily grounded near the tip of the Palmer Peninsula.*

1 Coastal sedimentation and pollution.
2 Conservation and use of fish stocks.
3 Ship routing, making use of ocean currents.
4 Wave forces for use in the design of off-shore structures and wave-power generating systems.
5 Mapping of polar ice caps, ocean temperatures and winds for improved climate and weather forecasting.

Ice Reconnaissance

From the beginning of satellite observation it has been possible to monitor sea lanes used by shipping. Four types of satellites have been working in conjunction with the Russian nuclear-powered icebreaker *Sibir* in a bid to open up safer and more economical routes for shipping in the Northern Seas. In one typical voyage the vessel travelled from Murmansk to the Bering Strait.

Cosmos 1000 — a navigation satellite — provided the information used by the ship's computer to fix an exact position. Meteor satellites gave the crew pictures of cloud cover, and forecasts of snow and sea ice allowing them to choose the best route. Molniya satellites allowed the ship to maintain regular contact with base and Ekran, the Soviet television satellite in geostationary orbit, sent the crew entertainment from Moscow.

Navigation of ships in these cold waters depends crucially upon knowledge of the properties, distribution, variability and behaviour of ice and icebergs. Forecasts require knowledge of air and sea temperatures, precipitation, wind and currents.

Data on ice thickness in lakes and rivers, and sea-ice coverage, can be obtained by infra-red sensors aboard satellites under cloud-free conditions. Passive microwave radiometry shows promise for all-weather systems while high-resolution photography monitors the coast and in-shore areas.

One of the most spectacular pictures of an iceberg—a giant one— was obtained by Landsat 1 as it pased over Antarctica on 31 January 1977. The shoe-shaped 'berg, nearly the size of Rhode Island, which looks to be in a bay actually is in open water and temporarily grounded north of James Ross Island. On the left of the picture is the Palmer Peninsula pointing into the Weddell Sea towards South America.

The big iceberg was first noticed on weather-satellite photographs taken in 1971 and a search of the files of earlier pictures showed that it first appeared on satellite imagery in March 1967. They indicated clearly that its source was an ice tongue which projected from the Princess Martha coast of Antarctica, a formation still to be seen on some maps but in fact no longer there; it was broken off the ice shelf either by winds or by an iceberg collision.

Over the years during the 1,800 miles (2,896km) journey along the coast, its progress was continually monitored from space. In August 1975 it rammed into the Larsen Ice Shelf breaking off another huge iceberg nearly 13 x 36 miles (21 x 58km) across. It was then temporarily grounded near the tip of the Palmer Peninsula and was expected to drift slowly out of Antarctic waters. Then, after being exposed to warmer waters, it should slowly disintegrate.

Oil Pollution

The oil tanker captain who insists on washing out his tanks in coastal waters in future may have to contend with satellites which discreetly observe his anti-social activities. Although oil slicks are difficult to see from aircraft which, in any case, are restricted in vision to narrow bands of ocean because of their low altitude, they can be spotted quite effectively by satellites on a global scale except in places of persistent low cloud. To do so the space-borne sensors measure the amounts of sunlight reflected from the ocean surface.

Spilled oil stands out starkly from ordinary ocean water in the near-ultra-violet of about 3,800 Angstroms and in near red light at about 6,000 Angstroms. Polarisation measured from reflected light of oil spills also shows sharp contrast.

Not only can light and heavy oils be distinguished in any one slick (the light oils appear brighter) but the volume can be assessed by repeated observation; knowledge of the type and quality of oil would be important in tracing the source.

Air Pollution

Closely related to changes in atmospheric circulation (and satellite weather survey) is the problem of air pollution. Each year industrial activity, car exhausts and other sources generate hundreds of millions of tons of noxious gases. Smog clouds over Los Angeles and other cities are clearly seen in photographs obtained from space.

The odd thing is that despite the huge quantities of carbon monoxide added each year, the total concentration does not seem to be increasing at a steady rate. So there must be some natural mechanism for removing most of the gas as it is generated.

An instrument known as a correlation interferometer—an optical device capable of detecting minute amounts of gas constituents—permits global mapping of those parts of the atmosphere which have high, low and average concentrations of the gas. By repetitive scanning over long periods, it is hoped to identify the so-called "removal 118

Observing Planet Earth

When a new view of Planet Earth was required to cope with problems posed by the rundown of natural resources, expanding population and a deteriorating environment, scientists found the answer in the Earth Resources Technology Satellite (ERTS). Only from space is it possible simultaneously to collect global data on the condition of the atmosphere and oceans, on agriculture and geology, and the way in which man's activity is constantly changing the quality of life (not always for the better!).

The first satellites specifically designed for this purpose were the Landsats built for NASA by the General Electric Company of Valley Forge, Philadelphia. They worked on the principle that everything—living and non-living—emits, absorbs and reflects, in its own distinctive way, electromagnetic radiation which gives different objects their own particular spectral "signatures". These different signatures—registered by special TV cameras and radiometric scanners aboard the satellite—provide information related to such things as crop species, crop health, geological structure, rock types, soil quality, moisture content of the ground, surface water distribution and the spread of industrial pollution. The images are digitised and transmitted to dish antennas at receiving stations on the Earth's surface where they are stored on magnetic tape for conversion to photographic prints in colour or black and white.

Although Landsat could wrest information from the oceans as well as the land, Seasat derived information almost entirely from the sea. NASA explains:

"The sea covers 70 per cent of our planet. There are regions where man seldom ventures, vast and lonely areas where huge currents flow unseen, storms are born and mature, and fleets of icebergs drift in cold and lonely splendour."

Eighty seven per cent of the fresh water on Earth is tied up in the polar ice caps. Huge schools of fish swarm the seas; some species follow regions where the temperature varies no more than two degrees— a difference which a satellite like Seasat can detect. From its 500-mile (800km) orbit, Seasat pointed five instruments at the world's oceans as it made 14 orbits of the Earth each day penetrating fog, rain, sleet and darkness. Just as the eyes see in the visible region of the spectrum between 4,000 and 7,000 Angstroms, microwave instruments "see" in a radio region between 1,000 and 300,000 MHz. Such instruments provide data which can be analysed to determine sea-surface temperature, wind speed, wind direction, and the amount of water in the atmosphere. They also take pictures of ocean waves, ice fields, icebergs, and ice leads—linear openings in ice through which ships may navigate.

To date, five Landsat and one Seasat spacecraft have been launched. Landsats 4 and 5, developed by General Electric, carried a new sensor, developed by Hughes, called a thematic mapper, as well as a multi-spectral scanner. This system produces data in seven colours with significantly improved resolution.

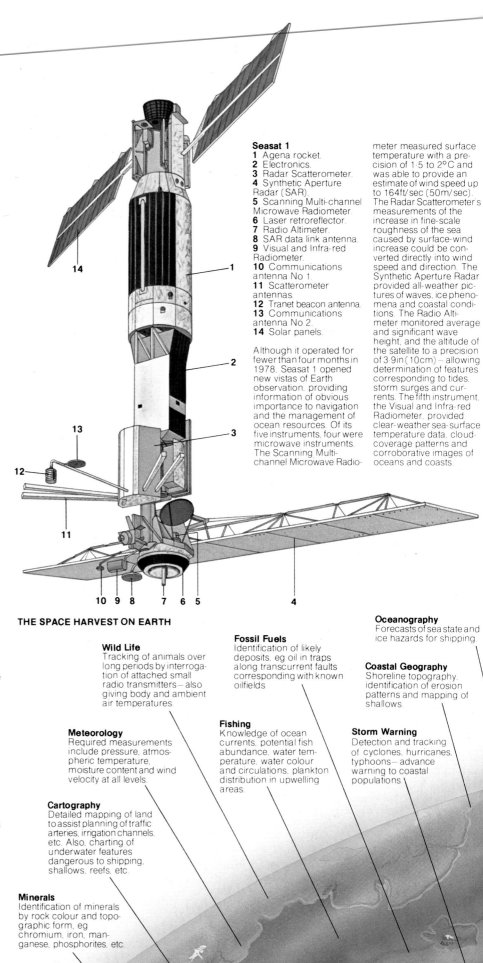

Seasat 1
1 Agena rocket.
2 Electronics.
3 Radar Scatterometer.
4 Synthetic Aperture Radar (SAR).
5 Scanning Multi-channel Microwave Radiometer.
6 Laser retroreflector.
7 Radio Altimeter.
8 SAR data link antenna.
9 Visual and Infra-red Radiometer.
10 Communications antenna No 1.
11 Scatterometer antennas.
12 Tranet beacon antenna.
13 Communications antenna No 2.
14 Solar panels.

Although it operated for fewer than four months in 1978, Seasat 1 opened new vistas of Earth observation, providing information of obvious importance to navigation and the management of ocean resources. Of its five instruments, four were microwave instruments. The Scanning Multi-channel Microwave Radio-meter measured surface temperature with a precision of 1·5 to 2°C and was able to provide an estimate of wind speed up to 164ft/sec (50m/sec). The Radar Scatterometer's measurements of the increase in fine-scale roughness of the sea caused by surface-wind increase could be converted directly into wind speed and direction. The Synthetic Aperture Radar provided all-weather pictures of waves, ice phenomena and coastal conditions. The Radio Altimeter monitored average and significant wave height, and the altitude of the satellite to a precision of 3·9in (10cm)—allowing determination of features corresponding to tides, storm surges and currents. The fifth instrument, the Visual and Infra-red Radiometer, provided clear-weather sea-surface temperature data, cloud-coverage patterns and corroborative images of oceans and coasts.

THE SPACE HARVEST ON EARTH

Wild Life
Tracking of animals over long periods by interrogation of attached small radio transmitters—also giving body and ambient air temperatures.

Meteorology
Required measurements include pressure, atmospheric temperature, moisture content and wind velocity at all levels.

Cartography
Detailed mapping of land to assist planning of traffic arteries, irrigation channels, etc. Also, charting of underwater features dangerous to shipping, shallows, reefs, etc.

Minerals
Identification of minerals by rock colour and topographic form, eg chromium, iron, manganese, phosphorites, etc.

Fossil Fuels
Identification of likely deposits, eg oil in traps along transcurrent faults corresponding with known oilfields.

Fishing
Knowledge of ocean currents, potential fish abundance, water temperature, water colour and circulations, plankton distribution in upwelling areas.

Oceanography
Forecasts of sea state and ice hazards for shipping.

Coastal Geography
Shoreline topography, identification of erosion patterns and mapping of shallows.

Storm Warning
Detection and tracking of cyclones, hurricanes, typhoons—advance warning to coastal populations.

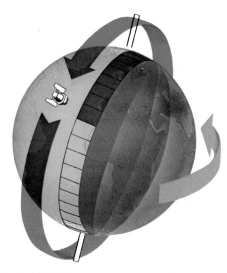

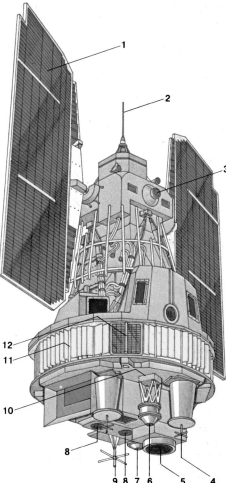

Landsat 3 Observatory

1 Solar panel.
2 Command antenna.
3 Attitude control system.
4 Wide band antenna.
5 Five-band multi-spectral scanner.
6 Unified S-band antenna.
7 Attitude measurement sensor.
8 Return-beam vidicon cameras (2).
9 Data collection systems antenna.
10 ERTS command auxiliary memory (ECAM) subsystem.
11 Sensory ring.
12 Beacon antennas (4).

Landsat 3 consists of integrated subsystems that provide the resources required to support the payload in orbit. Its two solar panels track the Sun and provide 630 W/hr of electrical energy to power the subsystems. An active attitude control subsystem maintains the observatory within ±1.0° of the local vertical and ±1.0° in the orbital plane (yaw). Data are furnished to ground acquisition stations at a rate of 18,000 million bits/orbit.

Technical Data

Weight: approximately 2,100lb (953kg).
Height overall: approximately 10ft (3.05m).
Diameter at base: 5ft (1.525m).
Solar paddles extend 13ft (3.96m) maximum; each driven independently by identical drive units so only partial power loss results from a drive failure.

Landsat 3 Orbit

The satellite travels in a north-south circular orbit at an altitude of about 570 miles (917km). As the Earth rotates beneath it, its coverage shifts westward in longitude at the equator by 1.43° — ie. 98.8 miles (159km) — each day. On any given day Landsat 3 makes approximately 14 revolutions of the Earth; a complete coverage cycle, during which the satellite reports on every area of the Earth between 81°N and 81°S, consists of 251 revolutions and takes exactly 18 days. The coverage pattern provides 14 per cent imagery overlap at the equator.

Multi-spectral Scanner (MSS) (above right).

A line-scanning device which uses an oscillating mirror to scan continuously the ground passing beneath the spacecraft. In Landsat 1 the scanner produced four synchronous images, each at a different waveband: Band 4 (green) 0.5 to 0.6 micrometres;

Band 5 (lower red) 0.6 to 0.7; Band 6 (upper red/lower infra-red) 0.7 to 0.8; Band 7 (infra-red) 0.8 to 1.1. The MSS of Landsat 3 has a fifth band: Band 8 (thermal infra-red) 10.4 to 12.6 micrometres. Bands 4 to 7 each have six detectors; Band 8 has only two. Of the original wavebands, Band 7 is best

for land-water distribution: Band 5 for showing topographic detail; Band 4 may qualitatively discriminate the depth and/or turbidity of standing water; and Band 6 best shows tonal contrasts reflecting land usage and also gives maximum land-water contrast (see also diagram on p112).

Return Beam Vidicon (RBV) (above)

In the RBV camera system of Landsat 3, two panchromatic cameras produce side-by-side images of the Earth beneath the spacecraft. Both cameras have the same broad-band response (green to the near infra-red) of 0.505 to 0.75 micrometres. Each

covers an area some 58 x 58 miles (93 x 93km) with a ground resolution twice that of the earlier Landsats — 131ft (40m) instead of 262ft (80m). The cameras can operate independently for either single-frame or continuous coverage. Four RBV images approximately coincide with one MSS

frame. In Landsats 1 and 2, three television cameras sensitive to spectral bands from 0.48 to 0.83 micrometres were mounted side-by-side for simultaneous operation. The individual frames of RBV images covered approximately 115 x 115 miles (185 x 185km) and overlapped by 10 per cent.

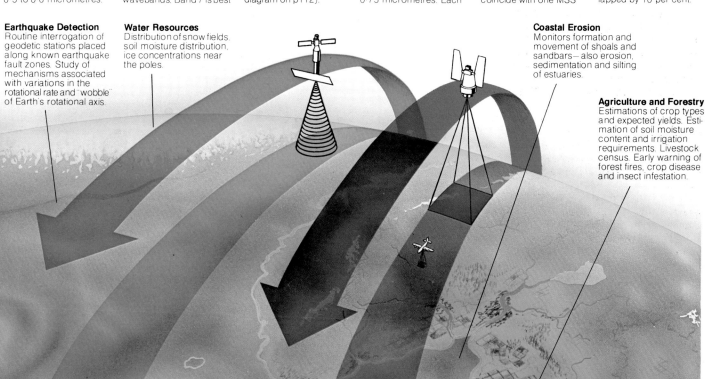

Earthquake Detection

Routine interrogation of geodetic stations placed along known earthquake fault zones. Study of mechanisms associated with variations in the rotational rate and "wobble" of Earth's rotational axis.

Water Resources

Distribution of snow fields, soil moisture distribution, ice concentrations near the poles.

Coastal Erosion

Monitors formation and movement of shoals and sandbars — also erosion, sedimentation and silting of estuaries.

Agriculture and Forestry

Estimations of crop types and expected yields. Estimation of soil moisture content and irrigation requirements. Livestock census. Early warning of forest fires, crop disease and insect infestation.

sinks" in which the gas is changed to another compound.

Unless the removal mechanism can be defined, there is no way to predict whether the carbon monoxide concentration will increase in the future and by how much.

There is also concen that the amount of carbon dioxide in the atmosphere is increasing world-wide because 20th century Man continues to burn so much fossil fuel. As Dr Glen Werth, Associate Director for Energy and Research Planning at the Lawrence Livermore Laboratory, near San Francisco, points out, this has the effect of putting an increasingly thick blanket over the Earth which allows sunlight to reach the surface as before but would reduce the escape of its heat by reflection back into space, thus trapping ever more heat near the surface.

"If one extrapolates our present rate of burning fossil fuels, it could very well be that by the year 2025 the Earth's temperature could rise by as much as 10°F, according to the theory. That's a very worrisome matter, because even with a few degrees rise, climate changes."

Today's lush food-growing areas could turn into deserts and other areas now barren could become production centres for crops.

Contrary to expectations, the results are not all gloomy. There are indications, for example, that carbon monoxide initiates a complex series of chemical reactions which may actually lead to the production of beneficial ozone in the low atmosphere, or troposphere, at altitudes from six to nine miles (10km to 15km).

So it is vital that scientists continually monitor the highly variable effects that pollutants can have on the atmosphere on a global scale—and once again satellites provide the key.

It is, of course, well known that sunlight, humidity and rainfall change the character, amount and distribution of airborne pollutants. Satellite observations not only make it possible to pin-point contamination concentrations but also the drift of contamination and the relationship with local weather conditions.

One of the most important satellite studies concerns that region of the stratosphere which contains the ozone layer protecting the Earth and its inhabitants from the harmful effects of the Sun's ultraviolet rays.

The stratosphere, which extends from above the clouds to an altitude of some 30 miles (50km), also contains a layer of dust-like particles and minute liquid droplets called aerosols which lie below the maximum concentration of ozone. Jet aircraft are constantly injecting aerosols and gases directly into the stratosphere and even the fluorocarbons used as propellant gas in aerosol spray-cans eventually find their way there. For this reason, fluorocarbon spray-can propellants have been banned in the United States but no good substitute has been found for fluorocarbons used in refrigerators, air conditioners, plastic foams, fire retardants and other commercial products.*

The aerosol layer 13·7 to 17·4 miles (22km to 28km) above the Earth has the effect of filtering the amount of sunlight reaching the Earth's surface and the amount of reflected sunlight that eventually escapes to space.

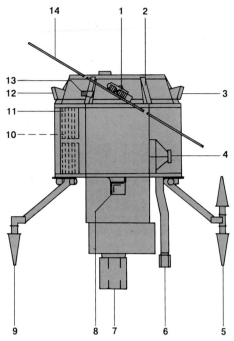

Stratospheric Aerosol and Gas Experiment (SAGE)
1 Solar array deployment mechanism.
2 "Yo-Yo" despin support (4).
3 Sun sensor No 3.
4 Scan wheel "A".
5 S-band telemetry antennas "B".
6 Magnetometer.
7 SAGE instrument.
8 Sun sensor No 4, near side: No 5, far side.
9 S-band data antenna "A".
10 Louvre panel (under).
11 Thermal control radiator.
12 Sun sensor No 2.
13 Electrical umbilical connector.
14 Deployable solar arrays.

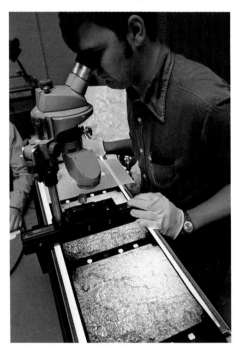

Above: *Thomas H. Pieper of Purdue University examines Landsat images for evidence of disease in corn growing areas. The Corn Blight Experiment covered several states of the North American corn belt.*

Scientists are therefore concerned that an increase in aerosol concentration and the chemical changes that take place under the influence of sunlight could bring about a gradual change in world climate, perhaps sufficient to cause melting of the polar ice and change the world's ecological balance.

One of the studies specially designed to investigate this problem is SAGE, an atmospheric aerosol measurement experiment,

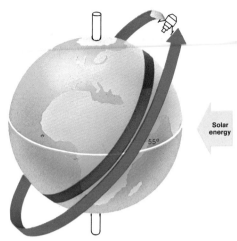

Solar energy

Concern that industrial pollution may be leading to an excessive build-up of aerosols and gas in the stratosphere, causing adverse changes in the Earth's weather and climate, has led to investigation by specialised satellites. The stratosphere begins above the cloud tops at about 8 miles (12km) and extends to about 30 miles (50km) altitude. Ozone in this layer protects us from the Sun's harmful ultra-violet radiation. The stratosphere also contains a layer of aerosols – small particles or liquid droplets – concentrated below the ozone peak. To investigate these regions NASA flew the 324lb (147kg)

Explorer-B satellite with SAGE instruments in 1979. Operating in a 373 miles (600km) circular orbit, the SAGE photometer "looked" at the Sun through the stratospheric gases and aerosols each time the satellite entered and left the Earth's shadow. The device "saw" 15 sunrises and 15 sunsets each 24-hr day. The photometer recorded, in four colour bands, the light as it faded in a sunset and brightened in a sunrise. This information was converted to define concentrations of ozone and aerosols. The four SAGE colour bands were centred at 1·0, 0·60, 0·45 and 0·38 micrometres from the near IR to blue.

which was launched in the satellite Applications Explorer Mission-B. Operating in a 373 miles (600km) high circular orbit inclined at 55°, the SAGE photometer "looked" at the Sun through the stratosphere's gas and aerosols each time the satellite entered or left the Earth's shadow.

Each 24hr day the instrument "saw" 15 sunrises and the same number of sunsets while it recorded in four colour bands the light as it brightened or faded. From repetitive observations the concentrations of ozone and aerosols could be determined.

Dr M. Patrick McCormick of NASA's Langley Research Center explained that the satellite's ozone measurements, when combined with other data, would help to confirm or deny the predicted chlorofluormethane (CFM) effect on ozone depletion. It had been predicted that if all the CFM releases into the atmosphere were to continue at the 1975 rate, between 8 and 30 per cent of the global ozone would eventually be destroyed, the greatest effect taking place at 21·7 to 28 miles (35km to 45km) altitude.

A decline of as little as 1°C in the average global temperature would affect northern region agriculture.

Major natural contributors to the aerosol layer are volcanoes, the gas from which injected into the stratosphere, turns into heat-reflecting sulphuric acid droplets, blocking solar radiation.

The most recent temperature decline occurred during the Little Ice Age of AD 1450 to AD 1615 when in England the River Thames froze over so thickly that fires could be built on the ice to roast oxen for ice fairs.

---

*It is estimated that the United States accounts for something less than 50 per cent of the world's fluorocarbon production.

In Greenland the Norse Colony established centuries before perished because of pack ice in the North Atlantic and the disappearance of most agriculture there due to cold.

According to NASA, the evidence suggests that this was the result of an almost continuous series of huge volcanic eruptions combined with some other influence, perhaps a short-term variation in solar radiation.

If this is the correct explanation, it illustrates most graphically how finely balanced is the ecology of our planet and how important it is that we understand how man is adding to atmospheric pollution.

Minerals and Oil

Orbital space also can be used to probe the land mass and continental shelves for oil, minerals and natural gas, and indeed the oil and mining industries have been to date the largest purchasers of Landsat data.

Geologists can see Earth's interlocking features, including large folds and ruptures which give clues to mineral deposits, and searches can be made for unknown deposits of oil along trans-current faults corresponding to known oil fields. Minerals can be identified by rock colour and topographic form, e.g. chromium, manganese, phosphorites, etc.

An early revelation (according to US Senator Frank E. Moss) was the "geological inference" that the oil and gas deposits of the Alaskan North Slope were much larger than previously believed. The satellites obtained multi-spectral images of "large lineaments and structural breaks" that were invisible before and bear no relationship to surface geology.

Information about faults and fracture zones derived from Landsat imagery has also been used in selecting sites for nuclear power stations and routes for pipelines.

Snow-melt

Another important service provided by ERTS satellites is routine photography of snow-covered ground and mountains. Accurate predictions of snow-melt are important in planning the best use of water for power generation, irrigation, controlling flood water, and estimating future water supplies for major cities.

Until quite recently such predictions— useful in deciding whether to hold or release water in reservoirs—have been based on less accurate observations made by people on foot, or by land-vehicle penetration of remote areas, or by aircraft.

Landsat has shown a capability of measuring snowline and extent of snow within 5 per cent of the accuracy obtained by aircraft measurements. The area of snow cover, multiplied by its depth and density, represents the storage of water that may be available for use. For example, clear evidence of the drought in the west of North America was apparent in satellite photographs of the snow-bare Sierra Nevada mountains in February 1977. A similar picture taken in 1975 revealed that the snowline had been 2,000ft (610m) higher.

Again, the rapidity with which surveys can be made by satellite saves a great deal of time and money.

In Florida, for example, imagery from a NOAA geostationary satellite is routinely computer-processed to provide a tem-

perature map every 30 minutes showing the southward progression of crop-killing frost on winter nights. Using the computerised prediction system, forecasters are able to provide information which allows the citrus growers to decide when they should start the costly effort of heating their groves ($833,000 per hour for fuel across the State). It was estimated that possible savings to Florida citrus farmers could reach $45 million at 1979 prices.

Space Station Images

Multi-spectral cameras have also been used most effectively in the American Skylab and Russian Salyut space stations. The Russian programme, which is continuing, uses an MKF-6M battery of six "multi-zonal" cameras developed by Carl Zeiss Jena the famous optical firm located in East Germany which obtain the same number of images of a given area in different parts of the spectrum. After the films have been processed, the images are projected one upon another using special Zeiss equipment.

Each camera has its own special film and lens filter registering different information. For example one brings out details of the soil structure, including moisture content and rock composition. Another captures information on the types of vegetation in the picture, such as forests or plants on cultivated land. Another concentrates on water quality in lakes and oceans and the extent of pollution.

The space scan, say the Russians, is so effective that as much information can be obtained in five minutes as an aerial survey could gather in two years.

Photographs are quite startling in their 3-D effect. A shot of the rugged Pamir-Alai region obtained by a test camera in the

Above: *Landsat 1 image of New York. Major landmarks are clearly visible: Central Park near the lower end of Manhattan and the runways of JFK, LaGuardia and Newark Airports. In this false colour composite picture, red areas are vegetation, orange is swampland, pale blue urban areas, brown-green high-density industrial areas, and white is concrete and roads.*

spacecraft Soyuz 22 shows the glacier Fedchenko in great detail, making it possible to identify more than 100 lesser glaciers in the area whereas only about 30 were known before. Not only has knowledge of the region been greatly advanced but areas which appear rusty-brown in the photos have been found to be well suited to the breeding of cattle in an otherwise unlikely region of the country.

Another task of the Salyut crews has been to study the world's oceans, ice and snow cover, and global weather conditions.

Dr Andrei Monin, director of the Soviet Institute of Oceanography, also points out the value of such observations to the fishing industry. Infra-red sensors carried by space laboratories, he says, can measure the temperature of the ocean surface and detect zones of warm and cold currents very rapidly. The movement of fish shoals and other marine organisms depends on the state of masses of water which also determine the concentration and distribution of different fish species. It would take tens of thousands of research ships to obtain the same information on a world scale.

Today the resolution of space-borne cameras is so good that civil and military observations are closely linked. Such activity became routine aboard Salyut and Mir space stations and related missions are flown independently within the Cosmos programme. With the onset of Glasnost (openness) in the Gorbachev era, in 1987 the Soyuzharta foreign trade organisation offered to sell photographs with a resolution of 19·7ft (6m) taken from the Salyut stations.

Soviet Ocean Observation Platforms are also in regular operation within the Cosmos programme yielding basic data in support of shipping (e.g. ice monitoring and ocean surface condition). After Cosmos 1766 (1986) and Cosmos 1869 (1987)—the antenna of which did not open fully—it became known that these satellites have a five-segment side-looking radar operating at a wavelength of 3·15cm.

In a short time the Soviets had compiled a radar map of the Antarctic ice cover. They found unknown ice cupolas under Queen Maud Land and buried beneath the ice, the crater of an extinct volcano. Beneath the sand of the Sahara they discovered ring structures (21°N, 11°W), remnants of the fortresses of an ancient civilisation. None of these were visible in ordinary photographs.

Other Countries Join In

In the meantime the value of Earth-resources studies has been recognised more widely and satellites are being developed by other countries serving specific needs. In 1979 India had her own experimental observation satellite launched by the Soviet Union as a step towards a more permanent system.

As in other countries, India looks upon the observation satellite as being particularly useful for studying resources which change with time and are renewable, like cultivated land, forests, rivers, coastal erosion, snow and wetlands in coastal areas. One of the aims is to predict the onset of the monsoon, crucial to the transplantation of rice.

India's Remote Sensing Satellite, IRS-1A, launched by the Soviets into a near-polar orbit in March 1988, enabled specialists to up-date maps of the sub-continent and obtain a revealing new picture of flora, soil state, water resources and also to predict water

run-off from snow-clad mountains important to the operation of hydropower schemes.

Dr U. R. Rao, chairman of the Indian Space Research Organisation (ISRO), speaking in New Delhi on 25 December 1988, said that IRS-1A had helped detect promising deposits of diamonds and rubies near the village of Najranagar; also deposits of zinc and copper near Wantimata in Andhra Pradesh State and copper reserves in the State of Karnataka.

In 1978 France announced the go-ahead for SPOT, an acronym for *System Probatoire d'Observation de la Terre*. The long-term aims of this project are to maintain an inventory of non-renewable and slowly renewable resources such as minerals and fossil fuels, water resources, agriculture and the atmosphere. SPOT looks towards the ability to identify, predict and, in certain cases, control some of the process relating to oceanography, climatology, soil erosion and water pollution as well as keeping track of potentially dangerous natural phenomena such as floods, droughts, storms, earthquakes and volcanoes.

SPOT 1, launched by Ariane 1 on 22 February 1986, had a fuelled mass of some 4,035lb (1,830kg). It achieved a Sun-synchronous polar orbit and returned well-defined picture data. France anticipates a series of four Matra-built remote sensing satellites, with SPOT technology branching into the military reconnaissance satellite Helios, and ERS-1.

After developing expertise in communications satellites, Britain turned towards Earth resources observation as the next positive step promising commercial rewards. Having set up ground analysis facilities at the National Remote Sensing Centre, Farnborough, taking input from Landsat, SPOT and other satellites, Britain took a major stake in ESA's Earth Resources Satellite (ERS) which uses radar technology to monitor crop development, weather patterns, shipping movements and mineral deposits.

UK support for ERS-1, scheduled for launch in 1990, and the Columbus Polar

Platform, gives Britian a key role in Earth observation alongside the new Earth Observation Data Centre (EODC) to be completed at Farnborough in 1993. The Polar Platform, originally conceived by British Aerospace as being serviceable in orbit, was subject to re-design and simplification, reducing cost estimates from $500 million to $315 million. Then Matra stepped in with a still cheaper design based on SPOT technology which led to more competitive studies. Finally it was decided that the Polar Platform would be built by a consortium of European companies led by British Aerospace.

Japan, too, is getting into the business with elegant technology, the first example being

Above: *ESA's ERS-1 will use a remote sensing radar to monitor ocean and coastal regions and improve our knowledge of oceanography, glaciology and climatology.*

Below: *A simulation of SPOT imagery, this is a view of Toulouse. The old town centre (green) sits between the Garonne and the Canal du Midi.*

the Marine Observation Satellite MOS-1 (Peach Blossom). Launched into a Sun-synchronous polar orbit by the newly-developed N-II rocket in February 1987, on-board instruments registered ocean colour and temperature with implications for agriculture, forestry, fishing and environmental preservation. In 1994 the Japanese Advanced Earth Observation Satellite is to measure wind speed and direction including in its payload a NASA Scatterometer (NSCAT).

Such satellites are becoming increasingly important for monitoring long-term changes to the Earth's environment, building on the results of Seasat, Geosat and the Stratospheric Aerosol and Gas Experiment (SAGE). The Solar Backscatter UV (SBUV) instrument aboard Nimbus 7 confirmed that ozone depletion followed a seasonal cycle, at its worst above Antarctica around October. Now a US-made ozone measuring spectrometer is to fly in the Soviet satellite Meteor 3. More co-operative ventures will follow.

China, for her part, had begun by building simple recoverable satellites which returned photographs and other data. The capsules were distinctive. Instead of having heat shields of ablative plastic, they were protected by machined oak which charred in the approved manner. The first such satellite, SKW-4, achieved orbit on 26 November 1975, returning its capsule by parachute after six days.

In an effort to improve understanding of the large-scale circulation of ocean currents, which relate to climatology, the French national space agency CNES, ESA and NASA-JPL co-operated on the Ocean Topography Experiment (TOPEX). The satellite, to be launched in 1992, uses a radar altimeter to measure height variations on the sea surface —variations that could reveal not only details of currents, eddies and other features of ocean circulation, but also information on the seafloor geologic structure, winds and waves. As the satellite passes over the Earth, the altimeter bounces the signals off the ocean's surface. The time required for the signal to return to the satellite gives a precise measurement of the distance between the satellite and the ocean's surface.

Mission plans call for the TOPEX satellite to be launched into an 810 miles (1,300km) x 65° orbit by an Ariane rocket. In support are two primary tracking systems, NASA's TRANET and France's DORIS, with laser backup.

Mission to Planet Earth

Exploration of the home planet is taking shape as one of the most important space ventures for the 21st century. Although it need not be tied to the manned base, a programme called the Earth Observing System (EOS, for the goddess of the dawn) has been developed as a major element of the US "Freedom" Space Station. Through EOS it is hoped that the Earth will be studied and understood as a unified system rather than as an aggregation of parts. The instruments to be carried aboard the EOS platforms are natural descendants of those aboard the weather satellites, Landsats, and SPOTs, but with a major difference: for the first time the instruments will be grouped aboard a series of platforms in comple-

mentary orbits so that measurements can be taken at the same times and thus compared on an equal footing.

Major Earth science tasks to be tackled by EOS scientists are understanding the hydrologic cycle, biogeochemical cycles, climatological processes, geophysical processes (including atmospheric, oceanic, and solid Earth).

In human terms, the problems being addressed include the greenhouse effect, holes in the ozone layer, the El Nino phenomenon that alters drought and monsoon cycles, and even whether there is a link between solar activities and climate.

Four polar-orbit platforms will comprise the EOS space segment, two from NASA and one each from ESA and Japan. Additional instruments will be placed aboard the manned base for increased coverage of the tropics.

The first EOS platform will be launched by the US atop a Titan IV from Vandenberg AFB in 1995. It will be placed in a 512 mile (824km) Sun-synchronous orbit that crosses the equator at 1.30pm. ESA's platform will be in a similar orbit descending across the equator at 10am. The second US platform will pursue an orbit identical to the first although it will be offset so that it provides complementary rather than duplicate coverage.

Above: *The Polar Platform is a major element in the Columbus programme, ESA's contribution to the US Space Station Freedom project now under development.*

Below: *Topex will use a radar altimeter to measure sea surface height variations. This should reveal details of ocean circulation and even seafloor topography.*

Space Science

The celebration in 1979 of the 100th anniversary of the birth of Albert Einstein paid homage to a scientist who drastically altered our conception of the Universe as no man had done since Copernicus showed a doubting world that the Sun, not the Earth, was the centre of our planetary system. Fittingly, the same year also marked the first twenty-one years of the space-age during which man not only probed the planets and walked on the Moon, but also experienced a revolution in space-science unparalleled in our history. Along with the great technological feats consequent upon the advent of spaceflight has come knowledge of Earth and nearby worlds.

Prior to the development of high-altitude and orbital rockets, our access to the Universe was severely limited by that same mantle which sustains all life—the Earth's atmosphere. Due to the immense distances which separate Earth and Sun and the planets as well as the incredibly more distant stars and galaxies, one of the few means available for the study of the celestial sphere is by the electromagnetic radiation emitted by each body. But until recently astronomers have been restricted to only a very small portion of this spectrum owing to the atmospheric absorption of a majority of electromagnetic wavelengths. Without observation posts above the atmosphere most of the lower frequency radio waves (greater than 328ft, 100m wavelength), middle and extreme frequency ultraviolet radiation (100A-3,000A), X-rays (·01A-100A) and gamma rays (less than ·01A) are inaccessible. Even conventional optical studies of the night sky are severely hindered by hazy and cloudy weather conditions, man-made light pollution, and the background heat radiation of the Earth itself. As will be seen, these previously inaccessible electromagnetic frequencies are exactly those which reveal the truly violent nature of the Universe.

Early Experiments

One of the first departures from conventional visual observations of the Universe began shortly before the start of World War I when the Austrian V. F. Hess piloted a balloon to high altitudes and discovered, contrary to expectations, that the seemingly isotropic cosmic rays (high-energy atomic nuclei) increased sharply with altitude after passing a threshold level. In 1946 an ultraviolet (UV) spectrum of the Sun was obtained during a short rocket flight and by the early 1950s sounding rockets and extremely high altitude, unmanned balloons were opening the doors to a hitherto undisclosed Universe.

> ## "The universe is full of magical things patiently waiting for our wits to grow sharper."
> Eden Phillpotts

In 1952 and 1953 Dr James Van Allen coordinated the scientific investigation of low-energy cosmic rays by launching small rockets from 12 to 15 mile (19km to 24km) high balloons (affectionately dubbed "rockoons") near the Earth's magnetic north pole. First postulated in 1600 by William Gilbert, the geomagnetic field was believed to be similar to the magnetic field lines set up around an ordinary lodestone or dipole. Hence deflection of the electrically charged cosmic rays should be minimal near the poles from which the field lines emanate, allowing a deeper penetration of this radiation to the Earth's surface. The results of these experiments led Van Allen in 1956 to petition government officials to include simple cosmic ray detectors on the early US artificial satellite attempts.

The world scientific community designated 1957 the International Geophysical Year (IGY) with the announced intention of both the US and the USSR to place a man-made body in orbit about the Earth before the end of the year. The Soviets, of course, were the first to succeed with the launching of Sputnik 1 on 4 October 1957. Along with evaluating the effects of spaceflight on the dog Laika, Sputnik 2 launched a month later carried the first true orbital space sensors with the assigned mission of detecting solar UV and X-rays and cosmic rays.

Although the first US orbital attempt was a public humiliation, the small Explorer 1 satellite finally orbited on 31 January 1958, more than compensated for its size and tardiness. Together with Explorer 3 which was orbited two months later, the two spacecraft revealed an apparent abrupt decrease in cosmic rays above 590 miles (950km). Initially puzzled by these results, Van Allen and his associates quickly concluded that their limited equipment was being saturated by an enormous and unexpected flux of charged particles. This discovery of highly energetic protons and electrons trapped in the geomagnetic field, soon christened the Van Allen radiation belt (see diagram), was the crowning achieve-

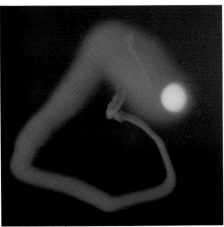

Above: *Nike-Apache-launched sodium/ lithium (red) and barium (white) cloud experiment to reveal upper atmosphere wind. Similar tests advanced auroral studies.*

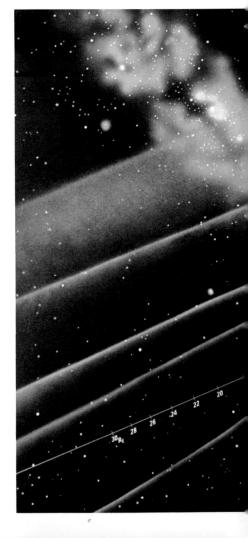

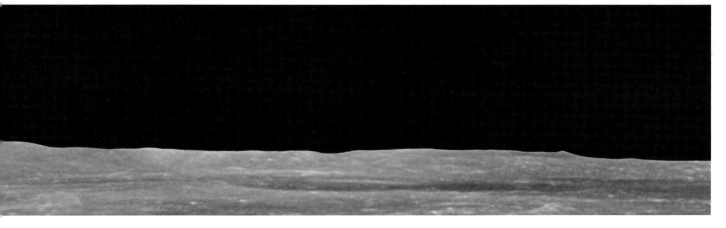

ment of the IGY and ushered in a whole new era in scientific exploration.

Before 1958 had come to a close Pioneer 3, which fell far short of its goal of reaching the Moon, climbed over 60,000 miles (100,000km) during its day-long flight and detected a second and higher radiation belt encircling the globe. Subsequent explorations have disclosed that, in fact, electrons and protons with energies as high as 700 MeV (700 million electron-volts*) surround the Earth in a continuous cloud as far away as ten Earth radii (40,000 miles/64,000km) and oscillate between the northern and southern hemispheres along the magnetic field lines.

Aside from the excitement exhibited by scientists, the existence of this intense

---

*The electron-volt is a measure of energy. One eV is the energy acquired by an electron travelling across a potential difference of 1 volt.

radiation about the Earth was of great interest to the US and Soviet engineers and doctors who were then investigating the feasibility of manned spaceflight. The newly detected radiation levels would prove lethal to unprotected spacemen flying through the region, and the amount of shielding required to safeguard any future astronaut was unclear.

The situation grew worse when in March 1959 US officials revealed that three 1·5 kiloton atomic weapons had been detonated above 200 miles (320km) altitude in August and September of the previous year. The object of the exercise, code-named Project Argus, was to evaluate the possibility of jamming radio and radar transmissions and neutralising incoming nuclear missiles. The unfortunate result was the formation of a new artificial belt of radiation stemming from the trapping in the geomagnetic field of electrons released in the explosion. Luckily, the doughnut-shaped belt extending from a

few hundred kilometres to over 6,000km (3,700 miles) above the Earth had largely dissipated by the end of 1958. Before the atmospheric and space nuclear test-ban treaty of 1963 a series of high-altitude tests in 1962 led to even greater contamination through longer-lasting radiation belts, which interfered with the launching of the dual manned Vostok 3 and 4 missions and which precipitated the early failure of several artificial satellites, including the first British satellite, Ariel 1.

The flights of Lunas 1-3 and Pioneer 4 to the Moon in 1959 disclosed another largely unsuspected phenomenon: the solar wind. Although the Norwegian Olaf Birkeland had postulated in 1896 the existence of solar corpuscular rays to account for the Aurora Borealis, the magnitude and penetrating power of these particles came as a surprise. Due to the rotation of the Sun and its violent surface activity, particles are flung off into

The Magnetosphere
The magnetosphere is that region of space surrounding the Earth which is dominated by the magnetic field. This field is much more complicated than that revealed by the familiar experiment of holding a piece of paper over a bar magnet and sprinkling iron filings on top to show the lines of force. The Earth's magnetic field is not uniform. On the Sun-facing side it is compressed by electrically charged particles which stream continuously from the Sun (the solar wind) which create a bow wave and distort the field into a long flowing tail. The boundary between interplanetary space and the magnetosphere is called the magnetopause. As the diagram shows its distance is about 10 Earth radii (R_E) (37,300 miles or 60,000km) on the Sunward side and considerably more in other directions. Within the magnetosphere is a complex system of magnetic fields which vary with distance from the Earth and with the degree of solar activity. The first scientific satellite to investigate these fields and particles from a constant distance was the ESRO geostationary satellite GEOS 1 (shown in this diagram). Nearer the planet is the doughnut-shaped ring of charged particles (protons and electrons), trapped by the magnetic field, called the Van Allen radiation belt. This was discovered by America's first artificial satellite Explorer 1.

interplanetary space in spirals at average velocities between 200 and 350 miles/sec (300km/sec and 550km/sec). This solar flux literally blows the Earth's magnetic field into a teardrop shape exactly as it does the gaseous components of comets when they venture close to the Sun. Recently Pioneers 10 and 11 discovered a similar distortion of the strong magnetic field of Jupiter while Mariner 10 has revealed that the strength of the solar wind actually blows a hole in the dense cloud structure of Venus.

Since the energy density of the Sun's own magnetic field is less than the energy density of the solar wind flow, the solar magnetic field is carried along with the particles, permeating interplanetary space and interacting with the geomagnetic field. The reduction of galactic cosmic-ray flux during periods of high solar activity results from an umbrella-like effect when the interplanetary magnetic field (IMF) inflates and deflects these extra-solar particles. Experiments have shown that the solar magnetic field itself is distorted as the entire solar system speeds through the interstellar medium at a velocity of approximately 12 miles/sec (20km/sec). Pioneers 10 and 11, which are on trajectories respectively to leave the solar system and to pass Saturn, are expected to emerge from this magnetic heliosphere somewhere past the orbit of Pluto, and measurements of total galactic cosmic rays, uninfluenced by the Solar System, will be possible.

Solar Probes

Investigations of the Sun dominated many of the early Earth and interplanetary satellites. Between November 1963 and October 1973 ten spacecraft called IMPs (Interplanetary Monitoring Platforms) were launched to make detailed surveys of the Sun during an entire eleven year solar cycle and to warn Apollo and Skylab astronauts of solar flare hazards. IMP 1 discovered the interplanetary magnetic field to be even more complex than originally thought, and in fact consisting of several sectors of alternating polarity. Continued experiments carried on Earth-orbiting and interplanetary

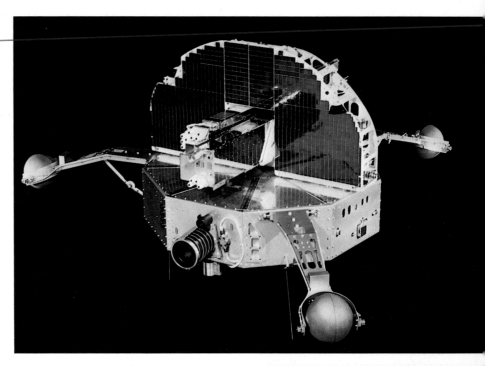

Above: *One of the family of Orbiting Solar Observatory (OSO) satellites designed to study the Sun and its influence on the Earth and its magnetosphere.*

Right: *Solar storm activity shown by the spectroheliograph aboard OSO-7. White indicates the most intense storm activity; yellow and red, lesser intensities.*

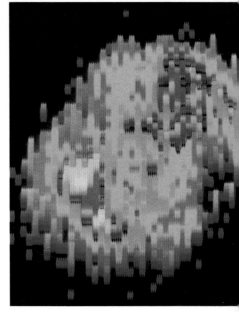

spacecraft indicate that when a sector boundary crosses the Earth's magnetosphere, geomagnetic and auroral activity increases.

From their solar orbits Pioneers 4, 5, 6, 7, 8 and 9 (1959-1968) radioed back vital information about the structure of the Sun and how the solar wind interacts with the Earth. Pioneer 5 found a correlation between solar-flare activity and the strength of the IMF, revealing that such activity could prove harmful to spacemen unprotected by the near geomagnetic field. With the IMPs stationed at Earth distances, the Pioneers

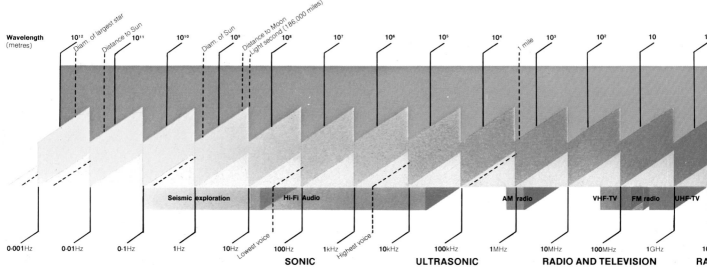

Wavelength (metres)	10^{12}	10^{11}	10^{10}	10^9	10^8	10^7	10^6	10^5	10^4	10^3	10^2	10	1

Diam. of largest star · Distance to Sun · Diam. of Sun · Distance to Moon (186,000 miles) · Light second · 1 mile

Seismic exploration · Hi-Fi Audio · AM radio · VHF-TV · FM radio · UHF-TV

Lowest voice · Highest voice

0·001Hz	0·01Hz	0·1Hz	1Hz	10Hz	100Hz	1kHz	10kHz	100kHz	1MHz	10MHz	100MHz	1GHz	100

SONIC · **ULTRASONIC** · **RADIO AND TELEVISION** · **RA**

The Electromagnetic Spectrum
Early man registered the Universe only through the visible spectrum. Science has taught us that this optical band is but a narrow slot in the total

range of electromagnetic radiation. Beyond the violet end of the visible spectrum is light with waves too short for our eyes to register. We call it ultraviolet light. Beyond the red end of the spectrum is

a region we cannot see because its waves are too long. We call it infrared. When we switch on an electric fire and feel its heat before the element starts to glow, we are registering the effect in

infra-red. To "see" these radiations, we must invent new "eyes" (or sensors) tuned to the band of radiation we wish to examine. For example, the "eyes" we use to detect infra-red radiation

(measuring an object's low heat value or the amount of thermal radiation it reflects) are called infra-red radiometers. We use them in weather satellites to observe the Earth's cloud cover at night, and

in interplanetary spacecraft to find "hot spots" in planetary atmospheres. In deep space, astronomical objects (eg. stars, nebulae, galaxies) emit radiation over a wide range of wavelengths and fre-

MAJOR US SPACE SCIENCE PROGRAMMES

NAME	LAUNCH DATE	MAJOR DISCIPLINE STUDIED
VANGUARD		
TV3	6 Dec 57	Launch failure
TV3A	5 Feb 58	Launch failure
Vanguard 1	17 Mar 58	Geodesy
TV5	28 Apr 58	Launch failure
SLV1	27 May 58	Launch failure
SLV2	26 Jun 58	Launch failure
SLV3	26 Sep 58	Launch failure
Vanguard 2	17 Feb 59	Intended weather satellite: data reduction hindered by satellite motion
SLV5	13 Apr 59	Launch failure
SLV6	22 Jun 59	Launch failure
Vanguard 3	18 Sep 59	Solar X-radiation: meteoroids
EXPLORER		
Ex 1	31 Jan 58	Earth radiation: discovered Van Allen Belt
Ex 2	5 Mar 58	Launch failure
Ex 3	26 Mar 58	Earth radiation: meteoroids
Ex 4	26 Jul 58	Analysed Argus radiation
Ex 5	24 Aug 58	Launch failure
S-1	16 Jul 59	Launch failure
Ex 6	7 Aug 59	Earth radiation: first Earth photo
Ex 7	13 Oct 59	Geomagnetic field: solar flares

S-46	23 Mar 60	Launch failure
Ex 8	3 Nov 60	Ionosphere
Ex 9	16 Feb 61	Atmospheric density
S-45	24 Feb 61	Launch failure
Ex 10	25 Mar 61	Geomagnetic field
Ex 11	27 Apr 61	Gamma rays
S-45A	24 May 61	Launch failure
S-55	30 Jun 61	Launch failure
Ex 12	15 Aug 61	Earth radiation: solar wind
Ex 13	25 Aug 61	Meteoroids
Ex 14	2 Oct 62	Geomagnetic field
Ex 15	27 Oct 62	Analysed "Starfish" radiation from a high altitude nuclear explosion
Ex 16	16 Dec 62	Meteoroids
Ex 17 (AE A)	3 Apr 63	Earth atmosphere
Ex 18 (IMP 1)	26 Nov 63	Geomagnetic field
Ex 19	19 Dec 63	Atmospheric density
S-66	19 Mar 64	Launch failure
Ex 20 (IE A)	25 Aug 64	Ionosphere
Ex 21 (IMP 2)	3 Oct 64	Geomagnetic field
Ex 22 (Beacon)	9 Oct 64	Ionosphere
Ex 23	6 Nov 64	Meteoroids
Ex 24	21 Nov 64	Atmospheric density
Ex 25 (Injun)	21 Nov 64	Earth radiation
Ex 26	21 Dec 64	Earth radiation
Ex 27 (Beacon)	29 Apr 65	Ionosphere
Ex 28 (IMP 3)	29 May 65	Geomagnetic field
Ex 29 (GEOS 1)	6 Nov 65	Geodesy

Ex 30 (Solrad)	18 Nov 65	Solar radiation: associated with IQSY (International Quiet Sun Year)
Ex 31 (DME A)	28 Nov 65	Ionosphere
Ex 32 (AE B)	25 May 66	Earth atmosphere
Ex 33 (IMP 4)	1 Jul 66	Geomagnetic field
Ex 34 (IMP 6)	24 May 67	Geomagnetic field
Ex 35 (IMP 5)	19 Jul 67	Lunar and geomagnetic fields from lunar orbit
Ex 36 (GEOS 2)	11 Jan 68	Geodesy
Ex 37 (Solrad)	5 Mar 68	Solar radiation
Ex 38 (RAE 1)	4 Jul 68	Radio emissions
Ex 39	8 Aug 68	Atmospheric density
Ex 40 (Injun)	8 Aug 68	Earth radiation
Ex 41 (IMP 7)	21 Jun 69	Geomagnetic field
Ex 42 (SAS 1)	12 Dec 70	X-rays
Ex 43 (IMP 8)	13 Mar 71	Geomagnetic field
Ex 44 (Solrad)	8 Jul 71	Solar radiation
Ex 45 (SSS 1)	15 Nov 71	Geomagnetic field
Ex 46 (MTS)	13 Aug 72	Meteoroids
Ex 47 (IMP 9)	23 Sep 72	Geomagnetic field
Ex 48 (SAS 2)	15 Nov 72	Gamma rays
Ex 49 (RAE 2)	10 Jun 73	Radio emissions from lunar orbit
Ex 50 (IMP 10)	26 Oct 73	Geomagnetic field
Ex 51 (AE C)	16 Dec 73	Earth atmosphere
Ex 52 (Injun)	3 Jun 74	Solar wind
Ex 53 (SAS 3)	7 May 75	X-rays
Ex 54 (AE D)	6 Oct 75	Earth atmosphere
Ex 55 (AE E)	20 Nov 75	Earth atmosphere
DE 1 and 2	3 Aug 81	Dynamics Explorer, magnetosphere, ionosphere, atmosphere
SME	6 Oct 81	Mesosphere

Note: the following abbreviations have been used in this table — Ex: Explorer: AE: Atmospheric Explorer: DE: Dynamics Explorer: IE: Ionospheric Explorer: IMP Interplanetary Monitoring Platform: DME: Direct Measurement Explorer: RAE: Radio Astronomy Explorer: SAS: Small Astronomy Satellite: SME: Solar Mesosphere Explorer: SSS: Small Scientific Satellite: MTS Meteoroid Technology Satellite. Beacon, Injun, and Solrad Explorers are a part of larger programmes of the same names.

and Mariners probing regions from within the orbit of Mercury out to Saturn, and a host of other international observatories travelling between Mars and the Sun, knowledge about the IMF and its effects on Earth and man has increased tremendously, although much remains to be learnt.

Since 1962 eight sophisticated US Orbiting Solar Observatories (OSO) and six Orbiting Geophysical Observatories (OGO) have been placed in Earth orbit for geomagnetic surveys and for advanced solar-physics studies in far-ranging regions of the electromagnetic spectrum. Similar experiments have been undertaken by the Soviet Elektron satellites in 1964 and the Prognoz series of satellites beginning in 1972 and still continuing.

International efforts to develop a better understanding of the relationship between solar activity and Earth weather patterns, radio communications, and its effects on man-made chemical pollutants, have been extensive. The first British satellite, Ariel 1, launched in 1962 was devoted in part to examining solar radiation in the ultraviolet and X-ray portions of the spectrum. The 1969 West German Azur satellite was placed in a solar synchronous orbit to study solar particle fluxes and their effects on the Earth's radiation belts, while the same country orbited Aeros 1 and 2 in 1972 and 1974 to examine solar UV radiation. West Germany extended its solar investigations further with the two solar probes, Helios 1 and 2,

which approached the Sun to within the orbit of Mercury in 1975 and 1976, respectively. The French Tournesol and Aura spacecraft and the Japanese Shinsei and Taiyo satellites expanded these solar studies by spectrophotometry in the UV range, along with measuring radio and X-ray emissions and cosmic rays. The objectives of the first Indian satellite, Aryabhata, were solar physics and the investigation of stellar X-ray sources in the Milky Way and beyond.

As the sophistication and expense of these projects grew, multi-national efforts became more frequent. The European Space Agency (ESA) and its predecessor, the European Space Research Organisation (ESRO), were responsible for the extremely

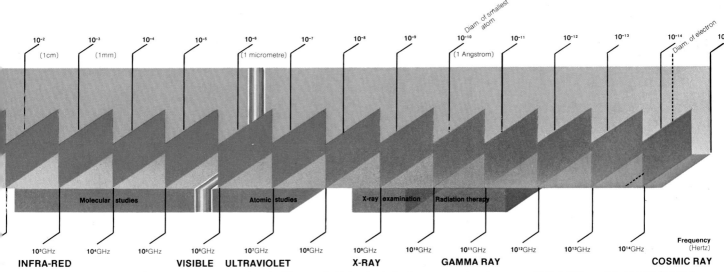

10^{-2}	10^{-3}	10^{-4}	10^{-5}	10^{-6}	10^{-7}	10^{-8}	10^{-9}	10^{-10}	10^{-11}	10^{-12}	10^{-13}	10^{-14}	10^{-1}
(1cm)	(1mm)			(1 micrometre)				(1 Angstrom)				Diam. of electron	

Diam. of smallest atom

Molecular studies   Atomic studies   X-ray examination   Radiation therapy

10^3GHz	10^4GHz	10^5GHz	10^6GHz	10^7GHz	10^8GHz	10^9GHz	10^{10}GHz	10^{11}GHz	10^{12}GHz	10^{13}GHz	10^{14}GHz	Frequency (Hertz)

INFRA-RED   **VISIBLE** **ULTRAVIOLET**   **X-RAY**   **GAMMA RAY**   **COSMIC RAY**

quencies, mostly invisible to us. (Wavelength and frequency are the units of measurement in the spectrum. Wavelength is the distance from wave peak to wave peak; frequency is the number of waves, or

cycles, passing a fixed point in a given time.) Stars of different age and type emit several kinds of radiation. We can investigate these emissions only with instruments tuned to specific wave-

lengths. The "eyes" which detect radio waves from the Universe are radio-telescopes. But only the narrow band of the visible spectrum and some of the longer wavelengths penetrate Earth's atmosphere

to study others, we must make observations from space. This chart covers the breadth of the electromagnetic spectrum from very short, high frequency gamma and cosmic rays to very long waves of low

frequency. Each major division represents a factor of ten, also known as an order of magnitude. The 28 orders of magnitude in wavelength extend from the size of the electron to beyond the distance

between the Sun and Earth, called the Astronomical Unit. This dimension is small in astronomical terms. The next unit, the light year, would extend the scale five more orders of magnitude.

MAJOR US SPACE SCIENCE PROGRAMMES

NAME	LAUNCH DATE	MAJOR DISCIPLINE STUDIED
PIONEER		
Thor Able 1	17 Aug 58	Launch failure; first lunar attempt
Pioneer 1	11 Oct 58	Insufficient thrust to reach Moon
Pioneer 2	8 Nov 58	Launch failure
Pioneer 3	6 Dec 58	Insufficient thrust to reach Moon; returned radiation data on outer Van Allen Belt
Pioneer 4	3 Mar 59	Geomagnetic field studies and solar flare monitoring
Atlas Able 4	26 Nov 59	Launch failure
Pioneer 5	11 Mar 60	Solar radiation from solar orbit
Atlas Able 5A	25 Sep 60	Launch failure
Atlas Able 5B	15 Dec 60	Launch failure
Pioneer 6	16 Dec 65	Solar wind and activity from solar orbit
Pioneer 7	17 Aug 66	Solar wind and activity from solar orbit
Pioneer 8	13 Dec 67	Solar wind and activity from solar orbit
Pioneer 9	8 Nov 68	Solar wind and activity from solar orbit
Pioneer E	27 Aug 69	Launch failure
Pioneer 10	3 Mar 72	Meteoroids, solar wind, and cosmic rays from trans-Solar System trajectory
Pioneer 11	5 Apr 73	Same as Pioneer 10
Pioneer 12	20 May 78	Interplanetary space en route to Venus
Pioneer 13	8 Aug 78	Interplanetary space en route to Venus
ORBITING SOLAR OBSERVATORY (OSO)		
OSO 1	7 Mar 62	Solar flares and activity
OSO 2	3 Feb 65	Solar UV, X, and gamma radiation and solar activity
OSO C	25 Aug 65	Launch failure
OSO 3	8 Mar 67	Solar flares and activity
OSO 4	18 Oct 67	Extreme UV radiation and solar activity
OSO 5	22 Jan 69	Solar flares and activity
OSO 6	9 Aug 69	Solar corona, flares, and activity
OSO 7	29 Sep 71	Solar corona, flares, and activity
OSO 8	21 Jun 75	Solar UV radiation and cosmic X-radiation
SOLAR MAXIMUM MISSION (SMM)		
SMM 1	14 Feb 80	Solar UV, X, and gamma radiation and solar activity at peak of Sun's 11-year cycle
ORBITING GEOPHYSICAL OBSERVATORY (OGO)		
OGO 1	4 Sep 64	Geomagnetic field and radiation
OGO 2	14 Oct 65	Geomagnetic field and radiation mapping: solar UV and X-radiation
OGO 3	7 Jun 66	Earth radiation, geocorona, solar wind, cosmic rays and radio emissions
OGO 4	28 Jul 67	Geomagnetic field, ionisation of atmosphere, and aurora
OGO 5	4 Mar 68	Geomagnetic field and solar activity; hydrogen cloud surrounding comet Bennett
OGO 6	5 Jun 69	Earth radiation, ionosphere, and aurora
PEGASUS		
Pegasus 1 Pegasus 2 Pegasus 3	16 Feb 65 25 May 65 30 Jul 65	Distribution, size, and velocity of meteoroids for evaluation of manned space-craft requirements
ORBITING ASTRONOMICAL OBSERVATORY (OAO)		
OAO 1	8 Apr 66	Equipment failure on second day
OAO 2	7 Dec 68	Stellar infra-red, UV, X, and gamma radiation; comet hydrogen halos
OAO B	30 Nov 70	Launch failure
OAO 3 (Copernicus)	21 Aug 72	Stellar UV and X-radiation; Cygnus X-1 "black hole"
HIGH ENERGY ASTRONOMY OBSERVATORY (HEAO)		
HEAO 1	12 Aug 77	Full sky survey to map all X-ray sources; cosmic gamma sources
HEAO 2 (Einstein Observatory)	13 Nov 78	Found X-ray emitting quasar over 10 billion light years away
HEAO 3	20 Sept 79	Seeks celestial gamma ray and cosmic ray data

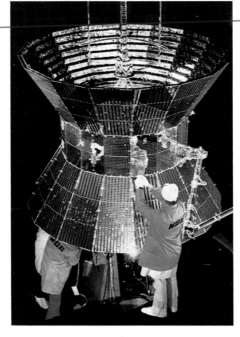

Above: *German space probe Helios 1 which flew within 30 million miles (48 million km) of the Sun's surface in 1975 enduring temperatures hot enough to melt lead. Helios 2 made an even closer inspection.*

productive HEOS 1 and 2 space probes. From highly elliptical Earth orbits these spacecraft studied the IMF during a seven-year period, establishing the strength and direction of solar corpuscular radiation and discovering the geomagnetic plasma mantle (a region of rarefied, high-temperature ions). The earlier Iris and Aurorae satellites had plotted the travel of solar particles through near-Earth space and had monitored the events surrounding magnetic storms. They were both launched by ESRO in 1968.

Meanwhile the thus far 22 satellites of the Intercosmos series, financed by a number of communist countries (Bulgaria, Cuba, Czechoslovakia, German Democratic Republic, Hungary, Poland, Romania, USSR), have been almost exclusively oriented toward solar and near-Earth studies. Intercosmos 1, launched in 1969, was instrumental in the study of the polarisation of solar flares. A recent probe, Intercosmos 18, carried along with it a small Czechoslovakian satellite for the purpose of joint experiments concerned with the ionosphere and magnetosphere.

Exploring Solar Activity

By international agreement the period 1976 to 1979 was designated the International Magnetospheric Study (IMS) for the purpose of determining the effect of solar activity on Earth weather patterns, the long-term effects of solar wind and the IMF on the world's climate, and the relationship between the Sun and the ionosphere regarding communications, navigation, and ozone levels. As part of this effort in 1977 and 1978 NASA and ESA orbited three International Sun-Earth Explorers (ISEE) to augment instruments carried on GEOS (ESA), the Japanese EXOS, Prognoz 4 and 5, Intercosmos 14 and 18, and Venera 9 and 10. ISEE 1 and 2 were placed in highly elliptical Earth orbits, while ISEE 3 was programmed for an unusual orbit around the first Lagrangian point some 900,000 miles (1,500,000km) from Earth. This arrangement allows solar activity seen by ISEE 3 to be viewed by ISEE 1 and 2 one hour later, providing information on temporal and spatial variations.

Even with versatile automated spacecraft directed by alert ground personnel, many observations and studies can still best be conducted by humans in space. Thus, the Soviet Salyut and the US Skylab manned orbiting platforms provided a unique opportunity for solar and other astrophysical investigations. The Orion 1 stellar spectrograph on Salyut 1 and the Orbital Solar Telescope (OST-1) carried by Salyut 4 offered scientists a chance to record solar activity over an extended period, with virtually no reprogramming problems due to the man-machine interface, to catch unusual solar fluctuations. During the Soyuz 18B mission to Salyut 4 this versatility was taken advantage of when the orbiting cosmonauts received a special request from the Crimean Astrophysical Observatory to record a solar disturbance which had just been detected by ground observatories. During their flight these spacemen snapped hundreds of solar photographs and spectrograms.

Below: *One of a number of scientific satellites launched under the Intercosmos programme of scientific co-operation between the USSR and other countries.*

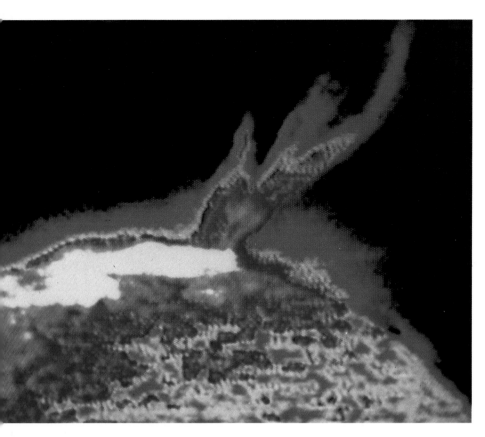

The Skylab space station contained no less than eight solar telescopes: five for X-ray and UV radiation, two for television solar pictures, and one for photographing the solar corona. Three manned missions and a total of six months occupation of Skylab provided over 180,000 photographs, including astronaut Gibson's fortunate first recording of the birth of a solar flare.

In the early days of spaceflight scientists and engineers were concerned that meteoroids as well as space radiation might present a serious hazard to both manned and unmanned spacecraft. In 1946 a Harvard University astronomer had predicted that one in twenty-five spaceships travelling to the Moon would be destroyed by these particles of space debris. Thankfully, artificial satellites such as Explorers 1 and 6 and Sputnik 3 quickly showed that the actual meteoroid flux almost certainly did not pose a major threat to passing spaceships. The flights of the three huge Pegasus satellites in 1965 provided the refined data needed for the planning of extended Earth orbital and lunar manned spaceflights.

Since the Sun represents man's only opportunity to examine a star at first-hand, what is learned about it can be applied to the larger questions of stellar and galactic evolution. Our next nearest stellar neighbours are found in the Alpha/Proxima Centauri system some 1·3 parsecs away (1 parsec = 3·26 light years = $3·08 \times 10^{13}$km) and can only be resolved as small points of light in the best of Earth-based telescopes. With the discovery in 1784 that the star δ Cephei (namesake of the Cepheid class of variable stars) fluctuated regularly in brightness astronomers soon realised that not all stars were as stable as our own. Since then space research has revealed a multitude of fantastically exotic celestial bodies.

In 1963 the significance of a new class of star-like objects (quasi-stellar sources or

Above: *A large eruption on the Sun photographed by the Skylab 3 astronauts on 21 August 1973 using an NRL Spectroheliograph. In just 90 seconds clouds of helium gas have blasted out some 350,000 miles (563,270km) from the solar surface.*

quasars for short) became apparent when it was discovered that the spectral lines of two objects known as 3C273 and 3C48 were red-shifted (moved toward the longer wavelengths of the electromagnetic spectrum) 16 and 37 per cent, respectively, indicating that the latter was over 4×10^9 light years away. For these bodies to show up so brightly at such great distances, their energy output must be extraordinarily great. Conventional theories required collisions of whole galaxies to account for the enormous energies emitted. OAO 2 launched in December 1968 with eleven telescopes and two scanning spectrometers was only one of several spacecraft designed further to investigate these strange objects. Current UV, X-ray, and gamma-ray orbiting observatories are continuing to reveal new characteristics of quasars in the hope of deciphering their true nature.

One of the justifications for observing these and other very distant bodies is that by virtue of the great time required for their light (and other electromagnetic radiation) to reach us we are in fact looking into the past history of the Universe. Whereas the observations of an entire human lifetime will detect virtually no change in most stars whose own lifetimes are measured in millions and billions of years, by examining quasars we may be viewing conditions present shortly after the birth of the Universe. Examinations of these phenomena, therefore, should lead to a better understanding of the evolution of the Cosmos. Quasars have also been used as precisely located reference points in highly accurate geodesy studies

MAJOR USSR SPACE SCIENCE PROGRAMMES		
NAME	**LAUNCH DATE**	**MAJOR DISCIPLINE STUDIED**
COSMOS (Selected Missions) 1967-73		
Cosmos 1	16 Mar 62	Ionospheric structure
Cosmos 3	24 Apr 62	Solar and cosmic radiation; atmospheric density
Cosmos 5	28 May 62	Earth radiation following US "Starfish" tests
Cosmos 7*	28 Jul 62	Solar flare activity before and during Vostok 3 and 4 flights
Cosmos 8	18 Aug 62	Meteoroids
Cosmos 26	18 Mar 64	Geomagnetic field
Cosmos 49	24 Oct 64	Geomagnetic field
Cosmos 51	10 Dec 64	UV and gamma radiation; stellar background luminosity
Cosmos 97	26 Nov 65	Earth radiation; test of theory of relativity
Cosmos 163	5 Jun 67	Cosmic rays
Cosmos 166	16 Jun 67	Solar X-radiation
Cosmos 208*	21 Mar 68	X-ray and gamma-ray fluxes
Cosmos 215	19 Apr 68	Visible, UV, and X-radiations with nine telescopes
Cosmos 230	5 Jul 68	Solar observatory
Cosmos 251*	31 Oct 68	Extragalactic gamma-ray sources
Cosmos 262	26 Dec 68	UV and X-radiation
Cosmos 264*	23 Jan 69	Extragalactic gamma-ray sources
Cosmos 321	20 Jan 70	Geomagnetic field and ionosphere
Cosmos 381	2 Dec 70	Diffuse cosmic background; ionosphere
Cosmos 461	2 Dec 71	Diffuse cosmic background
Cosmos 477*	4 Mar 72	Radiation and particle fluxes
Cosmos 481	25 Mar 72	Geomagnetic field
Cosmos 484*	6 Apr 72	Solar and cosmic radiation
Cosmos 490*	17 May 72	Primary cosmic rays and high energy electron fluxes
Cosmos 561*	25 May 73	Galactic gamma radiation
*These scientific experiments were secondary to the spacecraft's primary photographic reconnaissance mission.		
ELEKTRON		
Elektron 1	30 Jan 64	Simultaneous investigation of inner (Elektron 1) and outer (Elektron 2) Van Allen Belts; cosmic rays; galactic radio emissions
Elektron 2	30 Jan 64	
Elektron 3	11 Jul 64	Identical to Elektron 1
Elektron 4	11 Jul 64	Identical to Elektron 2
PROTON		
Proton 1	16 Jul 65	Largest spacecraft to that date 26,900lb (12,200kg), investigated energy spectrum and chemical composition of primary cosmic rays, gamma radiation, and galactic electron flux
Proton 2	2 Nov 65	Similar to Proton 1
Proton 3	6 Jul 66	Similar to Proton 1, but also searched for fractionally charged quarks in cosmic particles
Proton 4	16 Nov 68	Largest spacecraft of series 37,485lb (17,000kg); looked for high-energy primary cosmic rays and energy spectrum of high-energy electrons
PROGNOZ		
Prognoz 1	14 Apr 72	Solar wind, neutrons, and X-radiation; outer magnetosphere
Prognoz 2	29 Jun 72	Similar to Prognoz 1 in a complementary orbit
Prognoz 3	15 Feb 73	Solar flares; solar X-and gamma radiation
Prognoz 4	22 Dec 75	Solar radiation and geomagnetic field; associated with International Magnetospheric Study (IMS)
Prognoz 5	25 Nov 76	Solar wind; solar X-and gamma radiation; associated with IMS
Prognoz 6	22 Sep 77	Effect of solar activity on IMF and geomagnetic field; galactic UV, X-, and gamma radiation
Prognoz 7	30 Oct 78	Geomagnetic field; UV and gamma radiation
Prognoz 8	25 Dec 80	Solar wind/magnetosphere
Prognoz 9	1 Jul 83	Interstellar space
Prognoz 10	26 Apr 85	Solar wind/magnetosphere

because when viewed by us their motions across the sky are virtually zero.

A further development in the early 1960s was the detection by sounding rockets and the later pinpointing by orbiting spacecraft of celestial X-ray emissions. Initially, they were thought to emanate from the shock front of the hot expanding gas produced by supernovae explosions colliding with interstellar clouds such as those found in the constellations Puppis and Cassiopeia, and the Crab Nebula. The eminently successful Copernicus satellite (OAO 3), still working since its launch in 1972, confirmed this theory for the first two, but found that the Crab Nebula had a more discrete source of radiation which emitted hundreds of times more energy than Cassiopeia A even though the former, the site of a supernova in AD 1054, is over 650 years older. ESA's COS-B satellite found the Crab Nebula to be a powerful source of gamma and X-rays.

The explanation for the behaviour of the Crab Nebula can probably be found in the 1967 discovery of pulsars. These physically small bodies (only tens of miles in diameter) are unique by virtue of their extremely regular radio pulsations of two seconds or less. By the following year the Crab Nebula was confirmed to be the location of a very energetic pulsar. Current explanations envisage the source of these signals to be a rapidly rotating neutron star which formed after the collapse of a supernova remnant. Postulated in 1934, a neutron star consists of matter so dense that free electrons and protons have been recombined into neutrons to form a body with the mass of the Sun (over 330,000 times the mass of the Earth) squeezed into a six-mile (10km) diameter ball. The X-ray source Hercules X-1, discovered by the Uhuru satellite (SAS 1) and monitored by OSO 7, also appears to meet these specifications.

Black Holes

The discovery of neutron stars rekindled the interest in complete gravitational collapse of a star first aroused in 1916 by Schwarzschild following the publication of Einstein's general theory of relativity. If a star very much more massive than the Sun undergoes a supernova explosion, the weight of the remaining material might exceed all existing nuclear forces, and the star would undergo complete gravitational collapse to form what is popularly called a black hole. Such an object's gravitational field would be sufficiently strong to prevent light and other electromagnetic radiation within it from escaping, rendering the body invisible and thus accounting for its colourful name.

These characteristics, of course, would preclude the detection of black holes by ordinary methods. In fact, the presence of a black hole can be verified only by its effect on a nearby body. A possible condition for observing a black hole would occur if it were an invisible partner in a binary system with a conventional star. In such a case, X-rays generated by matter falling from the normal star should be detectable.

Although prior to 1960 most scientists did not believe the detection of X-radiation from stars or extragalactic sources possible, the advent of quasars, neutron stars, pulsars, and black holes has thrust X-ray astronomy

Black Holes
Cygnus X-1, a possible black hole, was discovered by the SAS 1 Uhuru satellite in 1972. The theory assumes that a neutron star in the final stages of collapse is the component of a binary star system. The atoms of the neutron star are so densely packed, and the gravitational force so great, that its material is being crushed out of existence. Ultimately, it creates a kind of "cosmic drain" from which no object, light or radio waves can escape. The black hole is invisible but still exerts immense gravitational force, sucking off material from its companion star into a rotating disc. In the process atom stripping takes place creating X-rays (purple rings in diagram) which can be detected by artificial satellites.

Above: Celestial Observation Satellite (COS-B). Developed by ESRO (now ESA), it carried a spark chamber for studies in gamma-ray astronomy; X-ray studies were also made by this satellite.

Above: NASA's first High Energy Astronomy Observatory at TRW Systems. It was designed to map systematically all significant high-energy sources over the entire celestial sphere.

to the forefront of space research. Since X-rays are absorbed by the Earth's atmosphere, a fleet of satellites has been developed to explore this new science frontier. The SAS 1, 2 and 3, OSO 7 and 8, HEAO 1 and 2, and Ariel 5 satellites are but a few of many observatories orbited to investigate steady and transient X-ray sources.

In April 1975 the British Ariel 5 detected an X-ray nova which soon flared to become the brightest X-ray source in the sky before fading out within a few months. SAS 3 and Ariel 5 also discovered and monitored a new phenomenon called X-ray bursters for their periodic, intense X-ray emissions. Shorter period bursts (milliseconds) should indicate the presence of a black hole, while longer period bursts (seconds) should be characteristic of rotating neutron stars. An X-ray experiment conducted during the Apollo-Soyuz Test Project (ASTP) found the first known extragalactic pulsar. HEAO 1 made the startling discovery of a pervasive background X-radiation, the origin of which has yet to be conclusively determined.

One of the most studied X-ray sources in

the heavens is Cygnus X-1. This emitter was first found to be an X-ray source by SAS 1 and its identification as a black hole was later suggested by OAO 3 data. Cygnus X-1 was the subject of HEAO 1's first observations and is viewed by many scientists as the best prospect for verifying the existence of black holes. If indeed this object is a black hole, it has a mass close to ten times that of the Sun, but a diameter only one-millionth as great. Three other possible black hole candidates (Circinus X-1, GX 339-4, and V861 Scorpii) have been suggested from studies using satellite-supplied data.

One of the many reasons for the keen interest in black holes is their contribution to theories concerning the evolution of the Universe. The single biggest question facing cosmologists today is whether the expanding Universe will continue to expand forever or will slow down and eventually contract again. The deciding factor in the equation is the amount of mass present in the Universe. The observable mass (visible stars, galaxies, clouds, etc) has insufficient gravitational influence to prevent the Universe from

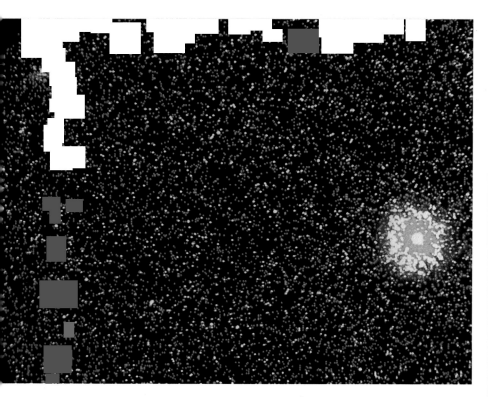

Above: *This X-ray picture taken by NASA's High Energy Astronomy Satellite (HEAO 2) reveals a newly discovered object (upper left) which, at the time, appeared to be the most distant and brightest quasar (quasi-stellar object) yet observed to emit X-rays. Its red shift indicates that the light reaching us began its journey more than 10,000 million years ago. The bright object (lower right) is quasar 3C273.*

flying irretrievably apart. However, if there are extensive black holes throughout the Universe, their mass may be enough to assure that the Universe will someday fall back on itself and perhaps begin again. Present theories already propose the existence of supermassive black holes in quasars and galactic cores. Recent returns from the orbiting Einstein observatory (HEAO 2) suggest that black holes also reside in the centre of associations of elderly stars called globular clusters.

A second method for solving this riddle of a single-shot or a pulsating Universe is to examine the amount of deuterium (an isotope of hydrogen, with one proton and one neutron in the nucleus) in interstellar clouds. If large quantities are found, this would imply an initial density in the Universe too low to stop the observed expansion. On the other hand, small amounts of deuterium should indicate a high initial density and a resultant closed Universe. The Copernicus satellite (OAO 3) has already undertaken this experiment and preliminary findings point to the open Cosmos as being more likely.

A better understanding of the extent of intergalactic gas will also aid in calculating the actual mass of the Universe. To detect these clouds and young, hot stars which both radiate heavily in the UV and X-ray bands the ESRO TD-1A conducted a full sky survey in the UV band, cataloguing over 15,000 stars. The OAO 2 satellite found the first UV radiation from the centre of M31, the Andromeda galaxy, and another ASTP experiment detected the first extreme UV sources outside the Solar System along with the hottest known white dwarf star. OAO 3 and The Netherlands' first satellite, ANS 1, continued these investigations in the UV and X-ray bands. OAO satellites have

furnished in half a day data equivalent to that from forty sounding rockets over a research period of fifteen years.

The ultraviolet spectrum was fully exploited with the launch of the joint NASA-ESA-UK International Ultraviolet Explorer (IUE) in January 1978. With exposures lasting up to several hours this amazingly successful spacecraft has already accumulated a number of "firsts", first high-resolution UV spectrum of a star in another galaxy, first UV recording of a supernova, first detection of absorption and emission lines from faint sources, and the unexpected penetration into the centre of globular clusters over 15,000 light years away.

Radio frequencies which have longer wavelengths than those in the UV range are monitored by both Earth and space based detectors. Denpa, Ariels 2, 3 and 4, and RAE 1 and 2 have been devoted to such investigations. RAE 1 supported four 755ft (230m) antennas and subsequently discovered that the Earth emits radio waves similar to those of Jupiter. RAE 2 was inserted into a lunar orbit in 1973 to permit studies of solar and galactic radio signals with the Moon acting as a shield against the background Earth "noise" that would otherwise interfere.

The high-energy end of the electromagnetic spectrum (the gamma-ray region) was investigated in detail as early as 1961 by Explorer 11, but its existence gained new import with observations in 1967 by the US Vela satellites which had been designed to detect nuclear-weapon detonations under the Nuclear Test Ban Treaty. Finally declassified in 1973, the readings from these satellites showed what appeared to be hydrogen bomb blasts originating in deep space. Further analysis revealed these recordings to be associated with astronomical, not

MULTI-NATIONAL SPACE SCIENCE PROGRAMMES		
NAME	**LAUNCH DATE**	**MAJOR DISCIPLINE STUDIED**
ESA (European Space Agency)		
ESRO 2A	29 May 67	Launch failure
ESRO 2B (Iris)	17 May 68	Solar corpuscular radiation in near-Earth space
ESRO 1A (Aurorae)	3 Oct 68	Geomagnetic field and ionosphere
HEOS 1 (Highly Eccentric Orbit Satellite)	5 Dec 68	Studied IMF over large portion of eleven-year solar cycle; solar corpuscular radiation
ESRO 1B (Boreas)	1 Oct 69	Identical to ESRO 1A
HEOS 2	31 Jan 72	Similar to HEOS 1
TD 1A	12 Mar 72	Full sky UV survey; X- and gamma rays
ESRO 4	22 Nov 72	Earth polar atmosphere
COS-B	9 Aug 75	X- and gamma ray astronomy
GEOS 1	20 Apr 77	Geomagnetic field; associated with International Magnetospheric Study (IMS)
GEOS 2	14 Jul 78	Same as GEOS 1
Exosat	26 May 83	X-ray sources
ESA/NASA		
ISEE 1 (International Sun-Earth Explorer)	22 Oct 77	ISEE 1 and ISEE 2 launched simultaneously into slightly different orbits to investigate magnetosphere, magneto-tail, bow shock, plasma pause, and solar wind
ISEE 2	22 Oct 77	
ISEE 3	12 Aug 78	Provided temporal data on the solar wind in conjunction with ISEE 1 and 2
IRAS	26 June 83	Infra-red sources
AMPTE	16 Aug 84	Magnetosphere, ionosphere, atmosphere interaction
ESA/NASA/UK		
IUE (International Ultraviolet Explorer)	26 Jan 78	Detailed UV astronomy with 17·7in (45cm) Cassegrain telescope; high resolution UV spectrum of extra-galactic stars; UV detection of super-novae; faint UV sources
INTERCOSMOS		
Intercosmos 1	14 Oct 69	Solar UV and X-radiation (C, GDR, USSR)
Intercosmos 2	25 Dec 69	Ionosphere (B, C, GDR, USSR)
Intercosmos 3	7 Aug 70	Geomagnetic field (C, USSR)
Intercosmos 4	14 Oct 70	Solar UV and X-radiation (C, GDR, USSR)
Intercosmos 5	2 Dec 71	Geomagnetic field (C, USSR)
Intercosmos 6	7 Apr 72	Cosmic-ray particles; recovered after four days (C, H, P, R, USSR)
Intercosmos 7	30 Jun 72	Solar radiation absorbed by atmospheric molecular oxygen (C, GDR, USSR)
Intercosmos 8	1 Dec 72	Geomagnetic field and ionosphere (B, C, GDR, USSR)
Intercosmos 9 Copernicus 500	19 Apr 73	Solar radiation and ionosphere (C, P, USSR)
Intercosmos 10	30 Oct 73	Geomagnetic field and ionosphere (C, GDR, USSR)
Intercosmos 11	17 May 74	Solar UV and X-radiation (C, GDR, USSR)
Intercosmos 12	31 Oct 74	Ionosphere and meteoroids (B, C, GDR, H, R, USSR)
Intercosmos 13	27 Mar 75	Geomagnetic field and polar ionosphere (C, USSR)
Intercosmos 14	11 Dec 75	Geomagnetic field and ionosphere; associated with International Magnetospheric Study (IMS) (B, C, GDR, H, USSR)
Intercosmos 15	19 Jun 76	Tested systems for new-generation Intercosmos (C, GDR, H, P, USSR)
Intercosmos 16	27 Jul 76	Solar UV and X-radiation; upper atmosphere (C, GDR, Sweden, USSR)
Intercosmos 17	24 Sep 77	Energy spectrum of charged particles (C, H, R, USSR)
Intercosmos 18	24 Oct 78	Geomagnetic field and ionosphere (C, GDR, USSR)
Intercosmos 19	27 Feb 79	Augmented ionospheric and magnetospheric studies of Intercosmos 18 (B, C, H, P, USSR)
Intercosmos 20	1 Nov 79	Meteorological
Intercosmos 21	6 Feb 81	Oceanographic/terrestrial
Intercosmos 22	7 Aug 81	Ionosphere/magnetosphere

Note: the following abbreviations have been used in this table — B: Bulgaria; C: Czechoslovakia; GDR: German Democratic Republic; H: Hungary; P: Poland; R: Romania; USSR: Union of Soviet Socialist Republics.

Space Telescope (ST)

1 Forward shell.
2 Magnetic torquers.
3 Crew handrails.
4 Aperture door.
5 Light shield.
6 Secondary mirror assembly.
7 Solar panels.
8 Reaction wheel assembly.
9 Scientific instruments

command and data handling electronics.
10 RMS grappling fixture.
11 Equipment section.
12 Batteries and charge controller.
13 Primary mirror.
14 Optical Telescope Assembly access.
15 Fixed head star trackers (3) and rate gyro assembly.
16 Aft shroud.

17 Tip docking probe (3).
18 Vent.
19 Coarse sun sensor.
20 Low gain antenna.
21 Fine guidance sensor (3).
22 Central baffle.
23 Pointing and control computer.
24 Transponder.
25 Tape recorders.
26 Digital interface.
27 High gain antenna.

This 94in (240cm) optical telescope is similar in size to the 120in (305cm) telescope at Lick Observatory. It consists of three parts: (a) an Optical Telescope Assembly (OTA) containing primary and secondary mirrors; (b) the Scientific Instruments (SI) which convert the telescope images to useful scien-

tific data; (c) the Support Systems Module (SSM) which contains a very precise stabilisation system, and the power system. Electrical power is derived from solar panels. A meteoroid shield and sunshade protect the optics. The open front end of the Space Telescope is similar to most Earth-based

Launch and Deployment

The Space Telescope (ST) is designed to be launched by the NASA Space Shuttle. It fits inside the cargo bay of the Orbiter and is deployed in space for independent operation. **A:** Launch from Kennedy Space Center. **B:** After orbital insertion and circularisation, the Orbiter is manoeuvred into the correct position and the Telescope is raised ready for deployment. **C:** After preliminary checkout, it is positioned by the remote manipulator arm into the correct alignment for release. **D:** The Telescope separates while the Orbiter remains close at hand. A comprehensive check is made to ensure that all systems are working normally. If it is necessary to retrieve the Telescope, the

deployment sequence is reversed. **E:** After the Telescope has been operating for 2 to 3 years — earlier if it has seriously malfunctioned — it can be retrieved by a Space Shuttle and placed in the cargo bay. Astronaut engineers can perform EVA to make repairs and replace equipment. In cases of major repair and refurbishment, the Telescope can be returned to Earth with the Orbiter. It can then be launched again with new equipment.

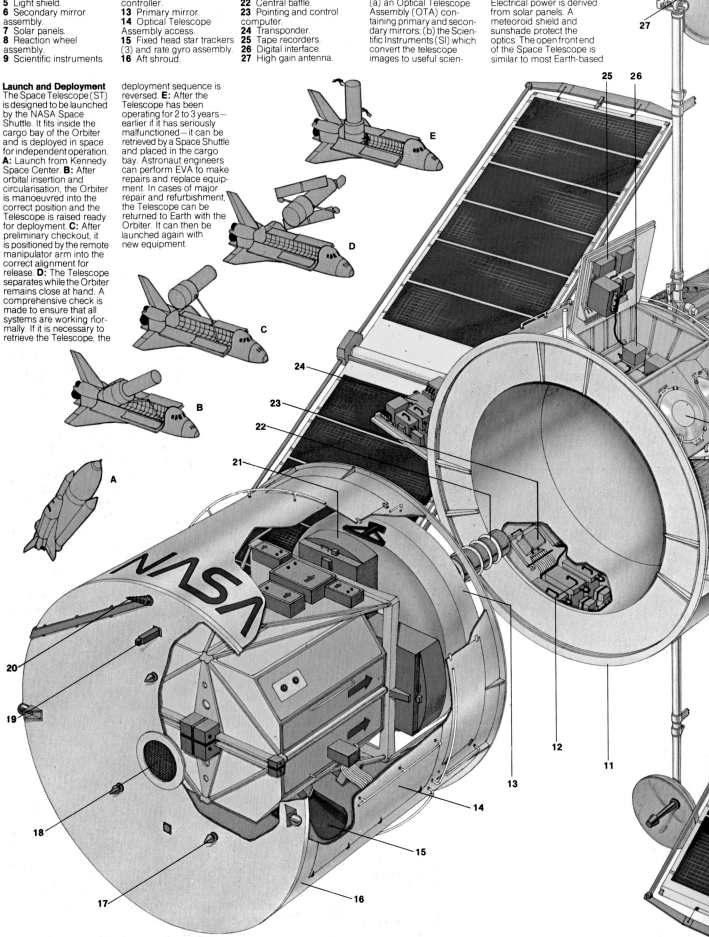
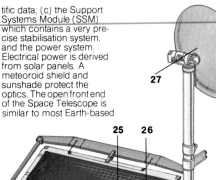

telescopes and admits light to the primary mirror in the rear of the telescope. The primary mirror projects the image to a smaller secondary mirror in the front (see page 126). The beam of light is then reflected back through a hole in the primary mirror to the Scientific Instruments in the rear which provide the means of converting the telescope images to useful scientific data. The instruments, and their sensors, communicate images in various ways. The modular instruments contain imaging systems, spectrum analysers (to find out about atomic structure and make-up of objects observed).

temperature controls and light intensity and polarisation calibrators.

Technical Data:
Length: 43ft (13·1m). Diameter: 14ft (4·26m) Weight: 24,000lb (11,000kg) approx. including 94in (240cm) reflecting cassegrain-type telescope. Ritchey-Chretien folded optical system with the secondary mirror inside the prime focus. Prime contractor: Lockheed Missiles and Space Company. Perkin-Elmer Corporation is responsible for the Optical Telescope Assembly. The scientific instruments include two cameras, two spectrometers and a photometer.

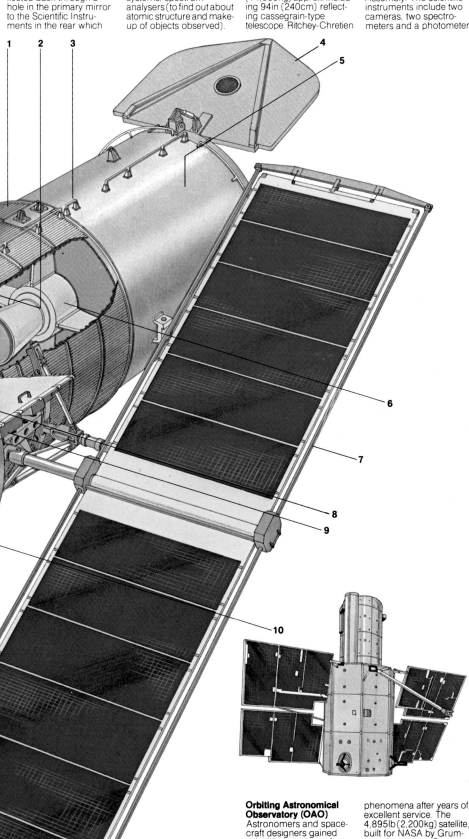

1   2   3

4

5

6

7

8

9

10

Orbiting Astronomical Observatory (OAO)
Astronomers and spacecraft designers gained valuable experience for the design of the Space Telescope and its directional stability from the success of an earlier project, the OAO. The third of these observatory satellites called "Copernicus" was still supplying data on stellar and interstellar phenomena after years of excellent service. The 4,895lb (2,200kg) satellite, built for NASA by Grumman Aerospace Corporation, was launched on 21 August 1972 into an orbit of 457 x 462 miles (736 x 744km) inclined at about 35 deg to the Equator.

Technical data:
Length: 10ft (3·05m). Diameter: 7·05ft (2·15m).

THE SPACE TELESCOPE

Our understanding of the Universe has undergone remarkable changes since the Space Age began, largely because of our ability to make observations from artificial satellites. The Earth's atmosphere, while transparent to visible light, filters out much of the electromagnetic spectrum cutting off vital clues to the true nature of radiation-producing bodies in the depths of space. Even in the optical regime, it blurs the telescope's image. Warm air rising from the surface causes shimmering or "twinkling" and haze and the light pollution from towns and cities also degrade the view of cosmic phenomena.

Because of this dramatic opening out of the spectrum, and other significant advances made possible by radio-astronomy, a violent Universe has been revealed to us. We have begun to understand far more about the birth of galaxies and the death of stars. Neutron stars, pulsars, quasars and the so-called "black holes"—all are mysteries we can now explore in depth.

To this exciting quest now comes a space instrument of such sensitivity that we anticipate improvements in knowledge comparable with those of Copernicus some 500 years ago. This is the Space Telescope, which will allow us to observe light over the entire range from the far ultra-violet to the far infra-red (from wavelengths of approximately 1,100 Angstroms to about 1 millimetre or 10,000,000 Angstroms). Most of this range is inaccessible to ground-based observatories. The remarkable instrument will "see" objects that are 50 times fainter and seven times farther away than anything we now observe from the ground. The pointing and stabilisation system can point the telescope to an accuracy of 0·01 arc-second and can hold onto a target for extended periods within 0·007 arc-second. The space agency points out that this angle is only slightly larger than that made by a dime when viewed at the distance between Washington, DC, and Boston, nearly 400 miles.

In theory the Telescope could resolve a coin at a distance of some 372 miles (600km), or features of about 186 miles (300km) width in the clouds of Jupiter. In practice a search could be made for planets which may be associated with other nearby stars.

We can investigate young stars, perhaps no more than 75,000 years old, which have surface temperatures as great as 50,000°C. Under such circumstances most of the radiation occurs in the ultra-violet part of the spectrum. On the other hand, we can also observe cool stars which emit largely in the infra-red wavelengths.

Observing the Universe means looking back in time. Light from the nearest star beyond the Sun takes more than four years to reach us. From the Gamma Boötes it is 200 years. What we are picking up is "dead light" giving us information of physical conditions on these bodies as they existed in the past. Most remarkably, for the first time, the Space Telescope may enable scientists to see distant galaxies as they appeared when they were formed. In effect this means looking back nearly 14,000 million years when, according to one theory, the Universe was created.

man-made, events. A relatively new field, gamma-ray astronomy is fast developing with the first manned space gamma-ray telescope, Anna 3, installed on board Salyut 1 in 1971. HEAO 1 and 2 joined forces first to conduct an all-sky survey of gamma-ray sources and then to examine in more detail those subjects of particular interest. SAS 2 (Small Astronomy Satellite 2) and COS-B (Celestial Observation Satellite-B) have also contributed much new information to this field.

Aside from answering questions of astronomical interest, the Cosmos also provides a unique physics laboratory for the testing of nuclear theories which may one day find use here on Earth. The FEK-7 photo-emulsion camera used on the Salyut space-stations observed primary cosmic rays in a search for Dirac monopoles (particles with only a single magnetic pole, either north or south) and nuclei of anti-particles. The large 1966 Proton 3 observatory was capable of detecting fractionally charged quarks (another species of elementary particles) had they been a component of cosmic rays. High-altitude balloon flights in November 1977 found what appears to be electron-positron annihiliation processing in space in what may be the first step to measuring the amount of anti-matter* in the Universe.

*Anti-matter: the mirror image of ordinary matter, having exactly the same appearance but mutually destructive upon contact. An atom of anti-hydrogen would have as its nucleus an anti-proton with an orbiting positron (positive electron). The creation of larger atoms of anti-matter requires anti-neutrons. Such anti-particles have been produced in high-energy particle accelerators. However, it seems anti-matter does not occur naturally in the Universe.

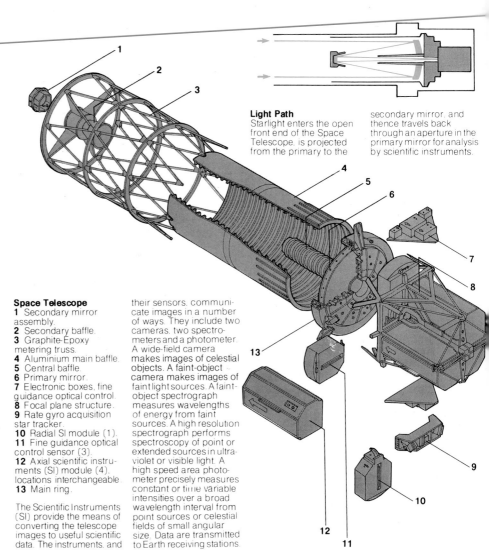

Light Path
Starlight enters the open front end of the Space Telescope, is projected from the primary to the secondary mirror, and thence travels back through an aperture in the primary mirror for analysis by scientific instruments.

Space Telescope
1 Secondary mirror assembly.
2 Secondary baffle.
3 Graphite-Epoxy metering truss.
4 Aluminium main baffle.
5 Central baffle.
6 Primary mirror.
7 Electronic boxes, fine guidance optical control.
8 Focal plane structure.
9 Rate gyro acquisition star tracker.
10 Radial SI module (1).
11 Fine guidance optical control sensor (3).
12 Axial scientific instruments (SI) module (4), locations interchangeable.
13 Main ring.

The Scientific Instruments (SI) provide the means of converting the telescope images to useful scientific data. The instruments, and their sensors, communicate images in a number of ways. They include two cameras, two spectrometers and a photometer. A wide-field camera makes images of celestial objects. A faint-object camera makes images of faint light sources. A faint-object spectrograph measures wavelengths of energy from faint sources. A high resolution spectrograph performs spectroscopy of point or extended sources in ultraviolet or visible light. A high speed area photometer precisely measures constant or time variable intensities over a broad wavelength interval from point sources or celestial fields of small angular size. Data are transmitted to Earth receiving stations.

Assembling a Giant Radio-Telescope in Space

How such giant structures would be assembled was explained by Yuri Kolesov in July 1979. To begin with, separate 656ft (200m) units would be put into low Earth orbit in a collapsed condition for assembly into the antenna either by robots or by the crew of an orbital station. Some 10 to 15 men would be needed for manual assembly. The completed radio-telescope would measure between 0·6-6 miles (1-10km) across and would be able to operate on its own or in combination with another similar instrument located elsewhere in space, thus forming an interferometer.

The technique of using radio telescopes in different and perhaps widely separated countries to receive and compare radio signals from the same celestial object is now well established. The resolving power of the combined telescope system acting as an interferometer then depends not only upon the performance of individual antennas but on the distance separating them. When the largest telescopes of different countries — Australia, Britain, the Netherlands, West Germany, Canada, the United States and the USSR — are used in this way their resolving power is immense. An object on the Moon can be determined within a distance of 7·9in (20cm). However, the present system cannot be extended as it is already using the full width of the Earth as the baseline. The next move, therefore, must be into space. A first such experiment was carried out in August 1979 when the KRT-10 radio telescope with a 32·8ft (10m) erectable antenna was deployed from the Salyut 6 space station and used in conjunction with the 229·6ft (70m) radio telescope in the Crimea.

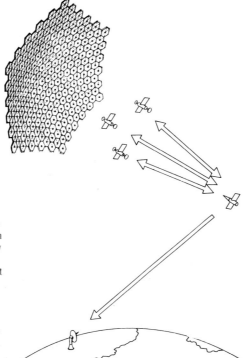

Observations could begin with the assembly of an antenna constructed from 656ft (200m) modules as shown in this Soviet design. Automated spacecraft keeping station with the dish would act as antenna feeds. The control module (extreme right) has facilities for communicating with Earth. In theory two such instruments could produce holograms of the Universe.

With modern space communications, says Kolesov, it would be possible to place one of the big 0·6-6 mile (1-10km) antennas into orbit near Saturn. One of the telescopes would be accelerated into its path by "special rocket engines" (presumably employing low-thrust electrical propulsion) and transferred into a heliocentric orbit. The final distance between the two radio-telescopes would be something like 932 million miles (1,500 million km), giving the system a resolution "many hundred thousand times" greater than the best interferometers available to us on Earth.

Soviet astronomers believe this would open the door to studies of remote objects, including planets revolving round other stars. One of the main objectives of the USSR Academy of Sciences programme of studies on problems of contact with extra-terrestrial civilisations includes "the detection of planets, planet-like bodies and cooled stars". Orbital telescopes of this kind would greatly increase the chances of detecting artificial radio signals from other civilisations in the Universe, assuming that such civilisations exist.

Their value in general astronomy would be immense, particularly in probing pulsars, quasars and active galactic nuclei, all of which have extremely small angular dimensions when observed from Earth.

Kolesov points out that until now observers on Earth have only had a flat, two-dimensional representation of the Universe. "Cosmic telescopes," he says, "will enable us to view everything from a new angle. With their aid, radio-astronomers will, for the first time, have the opportunity to view distant objects from their previously 'blind side' and thus obtain a three-dimensional picture of the Universe."

Programmes for the 1980s

During the first 21 years of the Space Age, spaceflight awakened man to a previously unknown Universe. Theories held prior to Sputnik 1 now seem as antiquated to scientists as did those of Ptolemy to Copernicus. Exploration in the '80s brought us closer to the scientific truths which we seek; it also saw space scientists themselves travelling into space. The effectiveness of manned observations and actual human intervention in space was also demonstrated.

An example of the latter was provided by the Solar Maximum Mission (SMM) satellite launched on 14 February 1980 to study the Sun during the most active period of its 11 year cycle, as part of an International Solar Maximum Year. SMM observed solar flares in ultraviolet, X-ray and gamma regions of the spectrum and measured the Sun's total radiation output within one tenth of one per cent. SMM carried seven instruments: gamma ray spectrometer, ultraviolet spectrometer and polarimeter, hard X-ray burst spectrometer, hard X-ray burst image spectrometer, X-ray polychromator, coronagraph polarimeter, and active cavity radiometer irradiance monitor.

On 23 November 1980, three fuses on the spacecraft attitude control thrusters blew, severely affecting its observations. SMM was the first spacecraft to be designed to accommodate attachments to enable it to be retrieved by the Space Shuttle. So, a rescue and repair operation was set in motion. This dramatic mission, flown by Orbiter *Challenger* (STS-41C), eventually took place in April 1984. The five man crew rendezvoused with SMM and NASA astronaut-astronomer

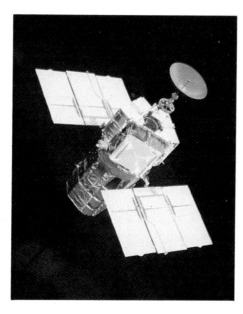

Above: *The Solar Maximum Mission Satellite is seen here after its repair and subsequent deployment from Shuttle Challenger's payload bay on 12 April 1984. The scientific instruments are mounted in the bus section at the base of SMM.*

Below: *The Sun's flaring corona prepared from data supplied by NASA's Solar Maximum Mission satellite. The colours represent densities of the corona and go from purple (densest) to yellow (least dense). The purple coronal region overlies sunspot regions far below on the Sun's surface. Shortly after this picture was taken, a solar flare occurred.*

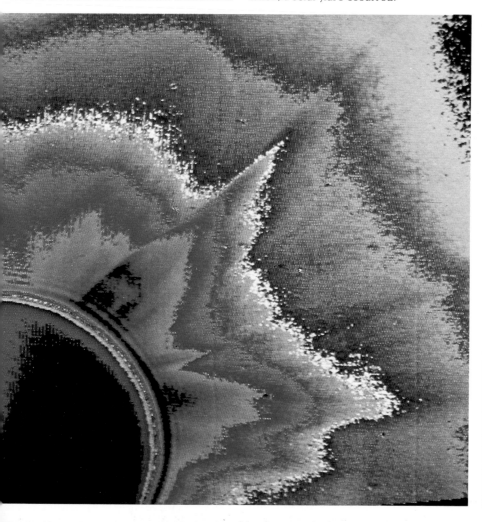

OTHER NATIONAL SPACE SCIENCE PROGRAMMES		
NAME	**LAUNCH DATE**	**MAJOR DISCIPLINE STUDIED**
UNITED KINGDOM		
Ariel 1	26 Apr 62	Solar UV and X-radiation; energy spectrum of primary cosmic rays
Ariel 2	27 Mar 64	Radio astronomy; galactic noise, interaction of ionosphere and solar radiation
Ariel 3	5 May 67	Radio astronomy, galactic noise
Ariel 4	11 Dec 71	Radio astronomy, ionosphere
Ariel 5	15 Oct 74	X-ray astronomy, X-ray sources, polarised X-rays, and pulsed X-rays
Ariel 6	2 Jun 79	Ultra-heavy cosmic rays; fluctuating X-ray sources; discrete X-ray sources
WEST GERMANY		
Azur	8 Nov 69	Earth radiation; solar particles
Aeros 1	16 Dec 72	Ionosphere, solar UV radiation
Aeros 2	16 Jul 74	Similar to Aeros 1
Helios 1	10 Dec 74	Interplanetary probe passed within 30 million miles (48 million km) of Sun to investigate solar wind, solar surface conditions, IMF cosmic rays, and zodiacal light
Helios 2	15 Jan 76	Similar to Helios 1, passed within 28 million miles (45 million km) of Sun
FRANCE (launched by France)		
France 1 (FR-1)	6 Dec 65	Ionospheric structure
Diapason (D-1A)	17 Feb 66	Geodesy
Diademe 1 (D-1C)	8 Feb 67	Geodesy
Diademe 2 (D-1D)	15 Feb 67	Geodesy
Péole	12 Dec 70	Geodesy
Tournesol (D-2A)	15 Apr 71	Solar radiation; geocorona
Auréole 1	27 Dec 71	Auroral phenomena
Auréole 2	26 Dec 73	Auroral phenomena
Starlette	6 Feb 75	Geodesy
Pollux/Castor (D-5A/D-5B)	17 May 75	Geodesy
Aura (D-2B)	27 Sep 75	Solar and stellar UV radiation; celestial gamma emissions
JAPAN		
Shinsei	28 Sep 71	Solar and cosmic radiation
Denpa	19 Aug 72	Geomagnetic field and radio exploration
Taiyo (SRATS)	24 Feb 75	Solar UV and X-radiation
Ume (ISS 1)	29 Feb 76	Ionospheric structure
Kyokko (EXOS A)	4 Feb 78	Auroral phenomena
Jikiken (EXOS B)	16 Sep 78	Magnetospheric charged particles, plasma, and electric and magnetic fields
Hakucho (CORSA)	21 Feb 79	Cosmic X-rays
Hinotori (Astro A)	21 Feb 81	X-ray sources
Tenma (Astro B)	20 Feb 83	X-ray sources
Ozora (EXOS C)	14 Feb 84	Upper atmosphere studies
Ginga (Astro C)	5 Feb 87	X-rays, gamma rays
NETHERLANDS		
ANS 1 (Astronomical Netherlands Satellite)	30 Aug 74	Stellar and cosmic UV and X-radiation
INDIA		
Aryabhata (Indian Scientific Satellite)	19 Apr 75	Solar neutron flux; stellar X-rays in Milky Way and extragalactic regions; ionosphere
Bhaskara 1	7 Jun 79	Utilised Aryabhata back-up equipment for Earth-oriented studies
Bhaskara 2	20 Nov 81	Remote sensing prototype; returned more than 300 TV images of Indian sub-continent.

George Nelson, wearing a Manned Manoeuvring Unit, flew over to the satellite with a view to docking with it and bringing it back for repairs inside the Shuttle's payload bay. This was not a success but the astronauts managed to catch the satellite at the first attempt using the Shuttle's remote manipulator system arm. SMM was then repaired by Nelson and astronaut James van Hoften, and subsequently redeployed in space to continue its observations.

In 1981, two more Explorer satellites were launched, to provide data on the combination of energy, electric currents, electric fields and plasmas between the Earth's magnetosphere, the ionosphere and atmosphere. Launched together on a Delta booster on 3 August 1981, Dynamics Explorers DE1 and 2 entered different orbits. DE1 studied the interaction of energy between the ionosphere and magnetosphere, while DE2 measured energy streams travelling as fast as 1,000mph (1,600km/h), between the atmosphere and ionosphere.

Another Explorer satellite, Solar Mesosphere Explorer, SME, was also launched in 1981 to conduct a comprehensive study of atmospheric ozone and the processes that form and destroy it. This was the first spacecraft to explore the ozone layer after it had become generally known that man-made pollution in the atmosphere could be degrading it. The satellite carried an ultraviolet ozone spectrometer, nitrogen dioxide spectrometer, infra-red radiometer and a solar ultraviolet monitor. SME was launched into a Sun-synchronous orbit from Vandenberg. Riding piggyback with it was a British radio research satellite, UOSAT.

The Soviets launched the French Oreol 3 satellite on 21 September 1981 to study the magnetosphere and ionosphere. In the same year, Japan launched the first in a series of Astro satellites. Astro 1 (Hinotori), launched on 21 February, made observations of solar hard X-ray flares. Astro 2 (Tenma), which followed on 20 February 1983, investigated X-ray sources in active galaxies. The third

satellite (Ginga), launched on 5 February 1987, continued this research using a British soft X-ray mirror and a gamma ray detector supplied by the USA.

IRAS Scans the Sky

After the unusually barren space science year of 1982, 1983 saw the launch of the revolutionary IRAS, the first satellite to conduct an all-sky survey to search for astronomical objects emitting infra-red radiation. IRAS was an international venture involving the UK, US and the Netherlands. The 2,372lb (1,076kg) satellite was launched on 25 June 1983 on a limited five month mission that was to revolutionise astronomy.

Its limited lifetime was due to the consumption of on-board liquid helium needed to cool the sensitive infra-red telescope to 2°K (−271°C). Its sensitivity, 1,000 times better than other telescopes, was such that it could detect small, dim and dwarf stars at a distance of 32 million light years.

Another astronomical satellite of European origin, Exosat, was launched on 26 May 1983. This ESA spacecraft made

Below: *A recently discovered newborn star (arrowed) is seen embedded in a cloud of dust and gas in this IRAS image. The young protostar, called B5-IRS 1, is no more than 100,000 years old.*

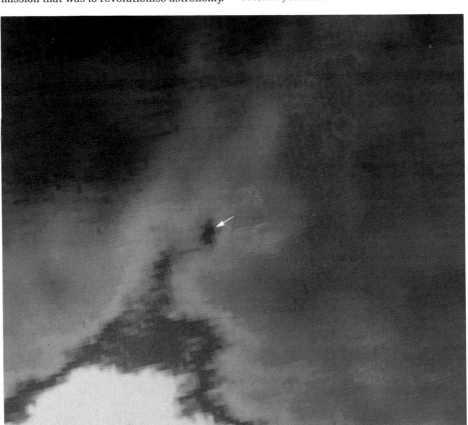

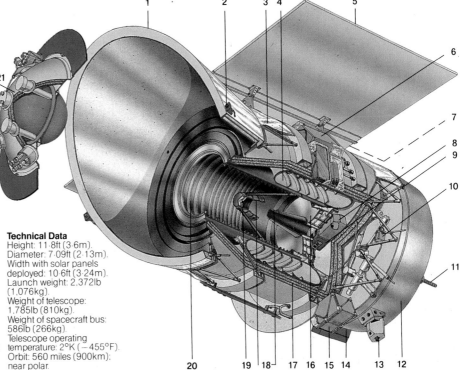

Infra-Red Astronomical Satellite (IRAS)
1 Gold-plated sunshade (to reflect solar and Earth IR radiation).
2 Coarse Sun sensor (6).
3 Evacuated main shell.
4 125gal (475l) superfluid helium tank (for telescope cooling).
5 Deployable solar panel.
6 Experiment electronics.
7 Fine Sun sensor (2) (behind solar panels).
8 Dutch Additional Experiment (DAX).
9 Focal plane assembly: 62 rectangular detectors.
10 Cryogenic valves and manifold.
11 S-band antenna.
12 Spacecraft telemetry, attitude control and command module.
13 Horizon sensor (60° field of view).
14 Nickel-cadmium battery.
15 DAX electronics.
16 22.4in (57cm) beryllium primary mirror.
17 Mylar and Dacron net insulation.
18 Baffles.
19 Secondary mirror.
20 Baffle.
21 Helium-cooled telescope aperture cover (ejected after IRAS check-out in orbit).

Launched on 25 January 1983, IRAS was designed to perform the first all-sky survey in the infra-red portion of the electromagnetic spectrum, and so detect the emission of infra-red radiation from stars that cannot be seen by telescopes limited to observations in the visible light wavelengths. Thus it has proven possible to detect protostars (newly coalescing stars), which means that scientists will be able to study new data concerning the formation of stars, and even of solar systems. IRAS is a joint US-Dutch-British venture: JPL designed and built the telescope, provided the Delta launcher, and processes the data; Fokker and Hollandse Signaalapparaten, under Dutch National Aerospace Laboratory management, designed and produced the spacecraft; and the British Rutherford Appleton Laboratory provides tracking and data acquisition systems. An additional experiment (DAX), for measuring the spectra of bright objects, was designed by the Dutch Groningen University.

Technical Data
Height: 11.8ft (3.6m).
Diameter: 7.09ft (2.13m).
Width with solar panels deployed: 10.6ft (3.24m).
Launch weight: 2,372lb (1,076kg).
Weight of telescope: 1,785lb (810kg).
Weight of spacecraft bus: 586lb (266kg).
Telescope operating temperature: 2°K (−455°F).
Orbit: 560 miles (900km); near polar.

detailed studies of known and new X-ray sources in our and other galaxies. The 1,124lb (510kg) spacecraft conducted over 2,000 observations, mainly of the physics of neutron stars and black holes, continuing observations begun by NASA's HEAO satellites. Exosat discovered quasi-periodic oscillations in the star GX5-1, 30,000 light years away, hundreds of times more energetic than our Sun.

The Soviet Union launched the largest ultraviolet telescope to date on 23 March 1983 aboard the observatory satellite Astron. This comprised the Spika UV instrument, jointly designed with France. It was 16·4ft (5m) long with a 31·5in (800mm) diameter mirror. Astron also carried out X-ray observations and discovered a possible binary star in the Andromeda constellation. It was launched by a D-1-e Proton into an unusual 51° inclination orbit, with a perigee of 1,212 miles (1,950km) and an apogee of 124,900 miles (201,000km), ensuring that the spacecraft made the bulk of its observations outside the Van Allen radiation belts and far from Earth-induced orbital perturbations.

Three more Explorer satellites were launched on 16 August 1984 under the name of AMPTE 1, 2 and 3 (AMPTE standing for Active Magnetosphere Particle Tracer Explorer). These US, British and West German satellites measured the transfer of charged particles from the solar wind into the Earth's magnetosphere. The US Charge Composition Explorer, CCE, detected lithium and barium trace ions released into the magnetosphere by the West German IRM satellite, AMPTE 2. The British, UKS satellite, flying in formation with the IRM, measured disturbances as the ions were released.

The AMPTEs were followed by the deployment in Earth orbit of the Earth Radiation Budget Satellite, ERBS, from the thirteenth Shuttle mission on 5 October 1984. ERBS was designed to study Earth radiation and the interaction of the Earth with radiation energy received by the Sun. Japan's EXOS C (Ozora), meanwhile, began upper atmospheric studies in 1984.

Manned Observations

The first fully dedicated manned astrophysics and astronomical observation mission, by *Challenger*, designated STS-51F, was launched on 29 July 1985, after a tense launch pad abort, only to limp into an orbit 70 miles (113km) short after losing thrust from a main engine during launch. *Challenger's* thrusters reduced the shortfall to 50 miles (80km) and the seven man crew set to work. The crew included five NASA career astronauts, among them astronomer Karl Henize, at 58 the oldest man in space, after 18 years in the astronaut corps, and two career astrophysicist astronomers, John David Bartoe and Loren Acton, who designed equipment being flown on the mission. STS-51F carried Spacelab 2, a pallet-mounted array of instruments exposed to space in the open payload bay. The four major telescopes were mounted on a delicate Instrument Pointing System, which after some initial problems, achieved a 1-arc-sec pointing accuracy. The telescopes included a British X-ray instrument and a US solar ultraviolet telescope.

Although several Soviet manned occupations of Salyut space stations had been taken up with astronomical observations, the launch of the new uprated Salyut, Mir, in 1986, began a new phase of astronomy from space. The first add-on module to be attached to Mir was Kvant in 1987. This astrophysics module was equipped with a series of Soviet and international telescopes, including the British-Dutch TTM. For much of their year long mission in 1987-88, cosmonauts Vladimir Titov and Musa Manarov spent many hours on Kvant experiments, performing two EVAs in 1988 to replace TTM detectors.

Summarising the results, Soviet astronomers drew these conclusions: unique information was recorded of the emission spectra of a supernova in the Large Magellanic Cloud. For the first time, the nuclear synthesis of chemical elements was studied during a stellar explosion, providing data of great scientific importance. Photographs of part of the celestial sphere made with the Glasar telescope were being used to compile a comprehensive atlas of stars radiating in the ultraviolet.

Before leaving Mir/Kvant on 27 April 1989, cosmonauts Volkov, Krikalev and Polyakov recorded radiation from the X-ray pulsar in the constellation Hercules and continued investigation of the X-ray source Swan X-1.

Above: *Exosat at ESTEC in Holland where it underwent final functional tests before its launch from Vandenberg AFB by Delta 3914 on 26 May 1983. Exosat operates both by direct observation of X-ray sources and using a technique of lunar occultation.*

Below: *The cluster of hardware visible in Challenger's payload bay constitutes the Spacelab 2 package. Prominently on view in the foreground are the three solar telescopes and the atmospheric research instrument mounted on the IPS.*

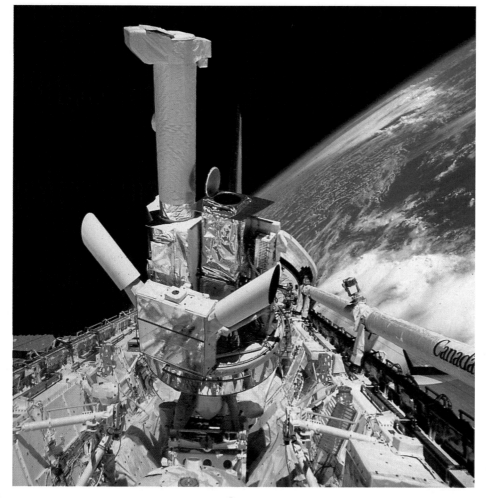

Space Science in the 1990s

Several eagerly awaited space science projects are planned for the 1990s but the star of the decade is surely going to be the Hubble Space Telescope. This should have been launched in the mid 1980s; it was then re-scheduled for August 1986, but the *Challenger* disaster left it Earthbound until March 1990 at the earliest. Hubble is equipped with a 94in (2·4m) diameter mirror which should allow the observation of stars as faint as the 27th magnitude, fifty times fainter than those seen by the 200in (508cm) Mount Palomar telescope. This complex will be refurbished during Space Shuttle missions, running repairs being planned to include the replacement of its solar arrays.

The Soviet Union has announced an ambitious programme of space science for the 1990s which will start with the launch — possibly in 1989 — of two projects which have been delayed considerably beyond their original launch dates. The first of these is the Gamma 1 high energy gamma ray observatory. Calibration of the satellite's instruments, using laboratory accelerators has shown the angular resolution will be 100 times better than previous satellites. The US Gamma Ray Observatory is due to be deployed from the US Space Shuttle in 1990-91. This $250 million TRW-built satellite, mass 24,000lb (10,886kg), will be serviced during later Shuttle missions.

Another delayed Soviet project is Granat, an astrophysics observatory incorporating two gamma ray telescopes, one called Sigma, being supplied by France. Granat will be placed into an orbit with an apogee of 124,278 miles (200,000km). Its 5,070lb (2,300kg) of instruments include an instrument pointing system. Another planned launch is that of Aktivny, a plasma wave laboratory with a 65·6ft (20m) diameter antenna which will transmit very low frequency radio waves into the magnetosphere to study the interaction with charged particles in radiation belts. Czechoslovakian sub-satellites will make observations. Another plasma laboratory called Apex is also planned. More studies of the magnetosphere will be conducted using the Interball project which will use two Prognoz type satellites.

Solar observations in the Soviet programme will be conducted by two Corona satellites, to be launched by 1992, which will incorporate X-ray telescopes and heliometers. The orbits of the satellites will enable 20 days' continuous solar observations to be made. Similar projects are planned by Japan, the USA and ESA. Japan is studying the Solar A project and will be participating in the Soho-Cluster multi-satellite project being handled by NASA and ESA. Further astronomical observations will be conducted by the Soviet Relikt 2 which will be dedicated to understanding the basic physical processes which have taken place in the Universe since the Big Bang. A Spectrum-Roentgen-Gamma project will involve two satellites.

1993 should see the start of a highly ambitious Soviet project to erect giant radio telescopes in orbit. The first, Radioastron CM, will actually consist of two Spekte satellites in deep 435,000 miles (700,000km) Earth orbits. These will have dish aerials

Above: *The Hubble Space Telescope during systems integration at Lockheed's plant. Lockheed make the Support Systems Module that will shield the telescope from extreme temperature variations in orbit.*

Below: *ESA's Soho-Cluster project. Soho will observe the Sun, its corona, and the solar wind, while the four Cluster spacecraft will study the reactions of the magnetosphere to varying solar conditions.*

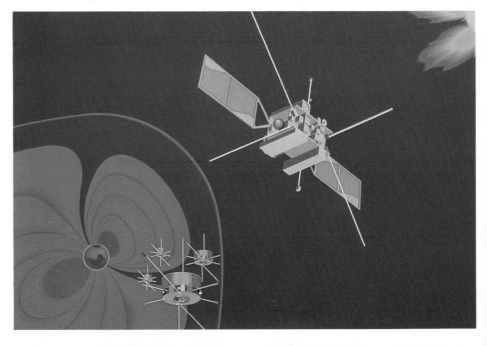

Above: *Developed by a consortium led by Matra Espace, Hipparcos was to enter geostationary orbit above 12° W to fix the position of 115,000 stars. Launched 8 August 1989, the apogee motor failed to ignite, curtailing its mission.*

Below: *The Advanced X-ray Astrophysics Facility (AXAF) is evidently related to the Hubble Space Telescope in basic design. It will carry an X-ray telescope of exceptional power and precision to carry out spectroscopic studies.*

Above: *The Extreme Ultraviolet Explorer is planned to conduct the first all-sky survey at extreme ultraviolet wavelengths. The first detection of an EUV star was made in 1975, and it is hoped that EUVE may reveal more than 1,000 new sources.*

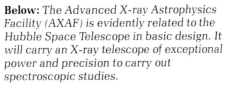

of auroras and the magnetosphere; Muses A will study gravity-assist fly-by techniques by flying round the Moon and placing a small subsatellite into orbit around it; Geotail will study the effect of the solar wind on the tail of the magnetosphere; Solar A will make studies of the Sun and solar flares from Earth orbit; and Astro D will conduct X-ray astronomical observations.

In addition to the Hubble Space Telescope and the Gamma Ray Observatory, several other major projects are being planned by the USA. NASA hopes to receive funding for an X-ray telescope, AXAF, based on the Hubble design. The Space Shuttle STS-35 mission in 1990 will carry the Astro 1 observatory — and two more career astronomers as payload scientists, Ronald Parise and Sam Durrance. Astro 1 is configured to conduct ultraviolet astronomy but will include a Broad Band X-ray telescope brought forward two years from a later Shuttle mission. A second Astro mission is also planned.

Another Shuttle mission will be used to deploy the Upper Atmosphere Research Satellite which will make a detailed study of the natural and human related mechanisms that control the structure and variability of the atmosphere. Expendable launch vehicles are slated to launch Cobe. Rosat, CRESS, Geotail, EUVE and small Explorer satellites through the 1990s. Cobe, the Cosmic Background Explorer, will investigate the Universe's microwave radiation, "seeing" the aftermath of events that occured some 15,000 million years ago, the time of the Big Bang. The Extreme Ultraviolet Explorer will investigate one of the last remaining regions of the electromagnetic spectrum to be systematically explored, mainly to study stars at an advanced stage of development, including collapsed stars.

32·8ft (10m) in diameter. Operating together, they will create a "radio telescope" hundreds of thousands of kilometres in diameter. Further Radioastrons may follow, two in 1996 and three enormous Radioastron KKs in 2000. These will have 98·4ft (30m) diameter dishes. One may be placed in geosynchronous orbit, and the three functioning together should provide a three-dimensional picture of the Galaxy. In 1994, the Soviets plan to launch Aelita, a cryogenically cooled telescope similar to

IRAS. Another infra-red observatory scheduled for the 1990s is ESA's ISO (Infra-red Space Observatory), which will be more sensitive even than IRAS. ESA's other science project is Hipparcos, an astrometry satellite intended to make accurate measurements of the parallaxes, proper motions and positions of 115,000 selected stars in our Galaxy. Regrettably, in August 1989 it failed to achieve geostationary orbit.

Japan also has several planned science projects. EXOS D will make further studies

Probes to the Moon

The Moon has always fascinated man. Our literature is full of countless fanciful journeys there, the earliest dating back nearly 2000 years. Until recently, however, such flights were beyond man's capability: he had to satisfy himself with exploring it at a distance through a telescope. Galileo Galilei was the first of the Renaissance astronomers to scan the Moon through a telescope. He saw large, dark, relatively smooth plains mixed with lighter areas covered with mountains and craters. In time, cartographers would use the term *mare* or sea to name these plains, although it was obvious they were not oceans as we know them. The advent of photography greatly aided the mapping process. By the late 1800s the entire hemisphere that always faces the Earth had been photographed to a resolution of less than one kilometre, and huge atlases prepared as a result. Even so, many basic properties remained unknown.

It was established that the Moon is about one-quarter the diameter of the Earth and that it travels in a nearly circular orbit about the Earth with a period of one month. It possesses no atmosphere or detectable water, so there was no hope of finding life there comparable to life on Earth. Its average density, only 61 per cent that of Earth, implied a completely different internal structure; but how different? Even more basic than that: what was it made of, and how did it get there? In the thousands of millions of years since the Earth was formed, its original surface features have long since been completely transformed by the actions of wind, water, glaciers and biological forces. The lunar surface has undergone bombardment by solar winds and meteoroids, as well as weathering due to extremes in temperature. But these effects have been minimal. The Moon is really a very well preserved relic from the days when it was formed; a fossil record of the past. A direct examination of it could help provide a better understanding of the origin of the Earth-Moon system and possibly of the origin of the Solar System itself. It was to this end that the United States and Soviet Union prepared to launch robot exploring craft towards the Moon in the late 1950s.

Direct Ascent

The first lunar probes had a very modest objective: simply to achieve a high enough velocity and sufficient pointing accuracy to ensure that they would pass close enough to the Moon to be able to return significant data. To achieve this goal at such an early stage of space technology was no easy

matter. Visualise the Earth to be a giant merry-go-round and the Moon as a target 239,000 miles (384,000km) away travelling once its diameter every hour. Using a rifle mounted on the merry-go-round try to hit the target with a bullet that will take several days to get there, travelling in a long arc and with a speed that decreases the farther it goes. The firing of the bullet must be timed to within seconds to assure a hit, or near miss if only a fly-by is intended.

The United States was first to attempt to launch a series of probes to the Moon. The first three USAF Pioneer attempts all fell short of the required escape velocity, as did the first US Army effort. The final Army attempt did achieve a distant lunar fly-by, but only after Soviet success.

Below: *Space scientists decontaminate the Pioneer 1B spacecraft in case it should land on the Moon and spread earthly microbes which might prejudice the findings of future exploration. This procedure was later abandoned.*

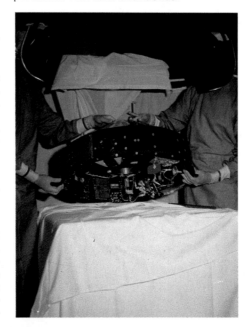

The first American Pioneer space probes, while not achieving their primary goal of passing close to the Moon, did provide the first measure of the extent of the Van Allen radiation belt, and made the first measurements of the interplanetary magnetic field. Russia's Luna finally achieved the first successful fly-by in 1959, passing within 3,100 miles (5,000km) of the lunar surface. Luna 2, just nine months later, was a phenomenal success, impacting approximately 500 miles (800km) north of the visual centre of the Moon to become the first man-made object to reach another celestial body. Just before impact onboard instrumentation transmitted back information indicating the absence of a strong magnetic field or radiation belts around the Moon.

One month later Luna 3 was launched on a slower trajectory that sent it 4,900 miles (7,890km) to the south of the Moon. The lunar gravitational field whipped it around so that it appeared high in the northern sky on its return trajectory back around the Earth: an ideal geometry for Soviet tracking stations. The mission had been timed to take place when nearly all of the lunar far side was illuminated by sunlight so that it could be photographed by a camera system aboard the probe. With the Sun on its back, the stabilised probe took a series of pictures showing about 30 per cent of the side visible from Earth, together with 70 per cent of the face never before seen. Known features from the visible side were used to map new features on the far side. It was hoped that the photographs could be scanned several times, with stronger and stronger signal strength as the probe got closer to Earth. Unfortunately, this process stopped early in the return trip at a distance of about 292,000 miles (470,000km), while the image quality was still rather poor. Nevertheless, an atlas of some 30 images was published, documenting man's first view of the Moon's far side.

NASA attempted to launch a further five heavier, solar-powered "paddle-wheel" Pioneer spacecraft in 1959 and 1960. These were fitted with liquid hydrazine monopropellant engines designed to brake the craft into lunar orbit. Unfortunately each of the Atlas-Able boosters experienced problems either in static firings or during launch, and their payloads were lost.

The 1950s ended with Soviet space spectaculars far outclassing anything produced by the Americans. In three successful missions the Soviets sent 2,271lb (1,030kg) of payload to the Moon or its vicinity, while only one 13lb (6kg) American probe succeeded. At this time, competition between

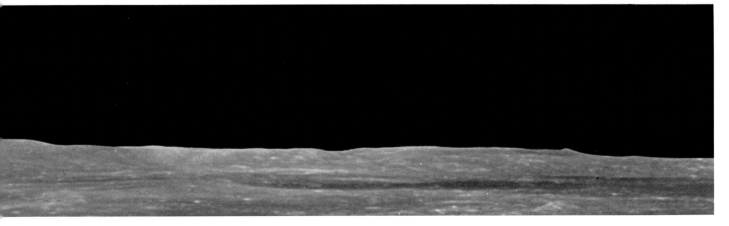

US democracy and Soviet communism was intense, and the success of the space programmes of the respective countries could be interpreted by a watching world as a relative indication of "who was ahead". With national pride and prestige at stake, both nations entered an undeclared race that would put the first man on the Moon.

Close-up Views

The early Pioneer spacecraft had a very limited potential for growth. For the 1960s, therefore, NASA embarked on a completely new programme to develop a much larger standardised spacecraft capable of conducting detailed studies of the Moon and planets. The Ranger programme was originally to consist of five flights: two engineering and three operational. When the landing of a man on the Moon became a national goal, more flights were added.

Rangers 1 and 2 were the first of the basic, standardised spacecraft and were configured for engineering studies and some environmental sampling from high Earth orbits. These first two missions each experienced booster upper-stage restart failures and only achieved low, short-lived Earth parking orbits. The missions were sufficient, however, to return some scientific and engineering data.

BASIC LUNAR DATA	
Diameter	2.160 miles (3.476km)
Orbital Radius—max	252.667 miles (406.610km)
—min	221.423 miles (356.330km)
Sidereal Period	27 days 7hr 43min
Mean Orbital Velocity	2.287mph (3.680km/h)
Surface Gravity	⅙ Earth's 5·31ft/sec² (1·62m/s²)
Surface Temp Range	+130°C day. −150°C night

The next set of craft were fitted with retro-engines that, it was hoped, would brake a survivable, hard-lander seismometer onto the lunar surface. After an impact of up to 125mph (200km/hr) it would right itself and transmit seismic and meteorite impact data from the Moon for the next 60 to 90 days. Unfortunately, Ranger 3's booster imparted an excessive velocity to it, making lunar contact impossible. All spacecraft systems remained operational, however, and an extensive in-flight performance evaluation was conducted, including the first mid-course correction manoeuvre. Rangers 4 and 5 each experienced problems early in their missions. Using the lander capsule transmitters as beacons, Ranger 4 was tracked to a crash landing on the lunar far side; the first American probe to reach the Moon. Ranger 5 was tracked for 11 days, through a 450-mile (725km) lunar fly-by and on into solar orbit.

An extensive review of all spacecraft systems was then conducted to detect and upgrade low-reliability components and to add redundancy to critical elements to guarantee success for the next series. The Ranger 6 mission proceeded flawlessly right up to the moment of camera activation. It was later determined that it had experienced high voltage arcing during the launch

Below: *The small Pioneer 4 payload, built by the Jet Propulsion Laboratory, California, weighed only 13lb (6kg). It made a 37,050-mile (60,500km) lunar fly-by in 1959 and then passed into solar orbit.*

Above: *Ranger 1 is prepared for a test of the basic space system. After it had been placed in a parking Earth orbit, its Agena B stage failed to eject the craft into a far-ranging elliptical Earth orbit.*

Below: *Replica of the 860lb (390kg) Soviet Luna 2, the first man-made object to reach the Moon, which impacted about 1°W, 30°N between the craters Archimedes, Aristillus and Autolycus in September 1959.*

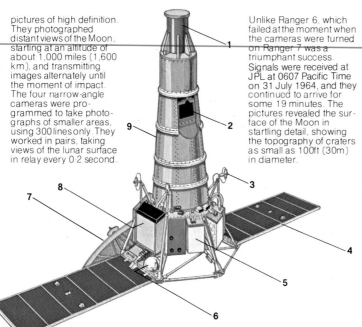

Ranger 7

1 Omni-directional antenna.
2 Aperture for six television cameras (two wide-angle, four narrow-angle).
3 Solar panel latch.
4 Extensible solar panel (2).
5 Batteries.
6 Attitude control gas storage bottle.
7 High-gain antenna.
8 Attitude control electronics.
9 Television sub-system.

Launched on 28 July 1964 by an Atlas-Agena D, Ranger 7 carried a battery of six television vidicon cameras on a lunar impact trajectory. During the last 13 minutes of flight, it obtained no fewer than 4,306 TV pictures before impacting the Sea of Clouds (10°38'S, 20°36'W) at 5,800mph (9,334km/h). Two of the six cameras had wide-angle lenses and used 1,150 lines per image to achieve

pictures of high definition. They photographed distant views of the Moon, starting at an altitude of about 1,000 miles (1,600 km), and transmitting images alternately until the moment of impact. The four narrow-angle cameras were programmed to take photographs of smaller areas, using 300 lines only. They worked in pairs, taking views of the lunar surface in relay every 0.2 second.

Unlike Ranger 6, which failed at the moment when the cameras were turned on Ranger 7 was a triumphant success. Signals were received at JPL at 0607 Pacific Time on 31 July 1964, and they continued to arrive for some 19 minutes. The pictures revealed the surface of the Moon in startling detail, showing the topography of craters as small as 100ft (30m) in diameter.

phase, destroying the television package in the process. It fell on target without returning a single picture.

After a system redesign, Ranger 7 was launched, and unlike its predecessors, was an outstanding success returning over 4,300 close-up, crystal-clear TV pictures of the Moon before impact. The final picture, taken at 5,250ft (1,600m) altitude, was of an area of just 100ft x 165ft (30m x 50m), and clearly showed craters as small as a metre in diameter. The picture resolution of that final image was about 1.3ft (0.4m).

Rangers 8 and 9 followed in early 1965 and performed perfectly, returning respectively 7,137 and 5,814 TV images of the lunar surface. Ranger 8 was targeted to approach Mare Tranquillitatis at a shallow 42° approach angle so that its pictures would sweep over a much larger area. Even with the high lateral velocity the image resolution on the final picture was under 6.5ft (2m). Ranger 9 was targeted to the 80 mile (130km) diameter crater Alphonsus, and impacted within 3 miles (5km) of its aim point, achieving a final image resolution of 1ft (0.3m).

A detailed analysis of the Ranger images showed the mare plains to be nearly devoid of any features, other than smooth-rim craters. The absence of boulders and all but small rubble, and any crevasses, was a reassuring sign that it would be possible to proceed with the next phase of the exploration of the Moon: soft landings.

Soviet Soft Landers

Soft landing a payload on the Moon required all the precision of the previous missions as well as the added necessity of dissipating at least a 1.6 miles/sec (2.6km/sec) approach velocity. Landing on Earth from orbit is made easier because almost all of a satellite's orbital velocity can be dissipated by friction experienced during re-entry. The Moon, without an atmosphere, permits only a retro-rocket and large propellant supply as a means to reduce this speed.

The Soviets were the first to prepare for a soft lunar landing when they resumed their Luna series in 1963. These bigger Luna spacecraft, weighing up to 1.8 tons (1.6

Below: *Ranger 9 took this high-definition picture of the Moon 170 seconds before impacting within the crater Alphonsus. This programme helped US scientists to narrow down possible Apollo landing sites.*

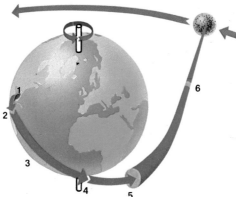

Typical Launch Corridor Ranger 6-9
1 Launch by Atlas-Agena.
2 First Agena burn.
3 Agena coasts in circular parking orbit at 18,000 mph (28,962km/h); altitude 115 miles (185km).
4 Agena second burn into trans-lunar trajectory.
5 Spacecraft enters 10 miles (16km) diameter corridor within 16 mph (26km/h) of desired injection velocity. Mid-course motor adjusts trajectory for lunar impact.
6 Mid-course manoeuvre corrects initial guidance errors of position and velocity.

tonnes), were designed to deliver a survivable 220lb (100kg) instrument package to a point on the surface between 62° and 64°W, near the equator. This was the only point on the Moon where the Luna's approach trajectory would fall perpendicular to the surface; ie, it would be a completely vertical drop. This compromise was made to simplify the guidance scheme.

A typical mission would start with a launch into an Earth parking orbit. The Luna and its escape stage would remain there for one orbit until it was once again over the Soviet Union. The escape stage would then fire, sending the Luna on a three and a half day flight to the Moon. At about 46 miles (75km) from the Moon, strap-on radar and celestial navigation gear that was no longer needed would be cast off and powered descent would begin. A spherical payload would separate from the propulsion unit a moment before touchdown, and after coming to rest, four petal-like panels over the upper hemisphere would open, deploying antennas and uncovering a TV camera.

Three attempts in 1963 and five more in 1965 each failed to achieve this goal. Luna 9 in 1966 finally succeeded in soft-landing the first man-made object on the Moon. Its turret-like mechanical-scan TV camera transmitted several medium-resolution panoramas of the surrounding landing site over a four-day period. Radiation data were also obtained before its battery power supply ran out.

One additional landing mission was made in this series: Luna 13. When its four protective cover panels opened, they released two folded, mechanical arms each fitted with a soil-testing instrument. A soil penetrometer on one and a soil irradiator on the other both measured surface soil density and consistency.

All other Lunas of this second series were orbiters, not intended to land.

Placing an object just into lunar orbit requires a propulsion system with about a 0.6 miles/sec (1km/sec) velocity change capability. This compares with a 1.6 miles/sec (2.6km/sec) requirement for a direct descent to the lunar surface. Stated simply, this means that an orbiter requires much less propellant than a lander. Rather than develop an all-new orbiter series, the Soviets chose to take the basic lander's propulsion system core, load it with only about two-thirds of the regular propellant supply, and use the remaining weight to increase the delivered payload. Luna 9's surface payload had weighed about 220lb (100kg) while Luna 10's, the first spacecraft ever placed in lunar orbit, weighed 540lb (245kg). It carried instrumentation to measure the radiation and micrometeoroid environment in circumlunar space for a period of about eight months. It also carried a recording of the Communist Party anthem "Internationale" which was transmitted back to Earth, an event of more political than scientific value. Luna 11 had approximately the same payload, but with refinements based on Luna 10 data. Lunas 12 and 14 remained attached to their propulsion modules after completion of the lunar orbit insertion manoeuvre. Strap-on modules that would be jettisoned to lighten a lander vehicle were retained to provide celestial attitude control on these missions since at least Luna 12 was fitted with a camera system to return pictures of the lunar surface. Few pictures were ever released.

One additional Soviet lunar mission was conducted during this period, but in this instance using a planetary spacecraft. Zond 3 was sent on a fly-by of the Moon to take pictures of the remaining portions of the far side not seen by Luna 3. Of 28 pictures taken, 23 contained images of the lunar surface, three of them in the ultraviolet region of the spectrum. These pictures, combined with those of Luna 3, left only 5 per cent of the far side remaining to be seen.

Prelude to Apollo

The rapid-fire sequence of Soviet Luna launches leading up to the successful Luna 9 mission was a direct response to its American competitor, Surveyor. This was a far more sophisticated craft than the Lunas, and had it been first to soft-land, would have left little for the Soviets to capitilise on. As it was, only one more Luna lander mission was made after Surveyor started to operate.

Surveyor was originally intended as a two-part programme consisting of orbiters and landers to support requirements for the Apollo manned lunar landing programme. The orbiter portion was later developed separately under the Lunar Orbiter series.

Surveyor 1 was launched to the Moon four months after Luna 9 on a direct-ascent trajectory. It was powered by four engines: three liquid-propellant variable-thrust verniers and one solid-propellant main retro. Following a midcourse correction using the verniers, preparations were made for a landing. The main solid retro was ignited at 48·6 miles (75km) distance, and used with the verniers to slow the craft to 230ft/sec (70m/sec). The heavy, burned-out retro engine was then cast off, leaving the verniers to complete the descent to a near hover at 13ft (4m). A free fall from that height without engines was made to minimise surface contamination and disturbance from exhaust gases. Shock-absorber legs and crushable pads on the frame softened the blow of impact. Surveyor 1, the first attempt of the series, successfully soft-landed on the Moon. Over the next six weeks, including a shut-down for the fortnight-long lunar night,

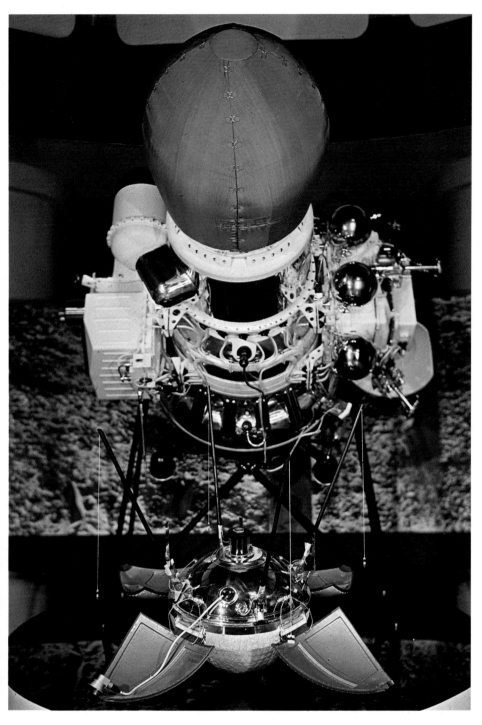

Above: *Exhibition model of Luna 9. The small landing capsule it carried (the pod at the top) is shown below in deployed form. It housed a small TV camera which took 360° panoramic pictures.*

Right: *First picture from the surface of the Moon obtained by the Luna 9 automatic station in February 1966. Part of a 360° scan it shows a section of the station and rocks 3·9 to 7·9in (10 to 20cm across).*

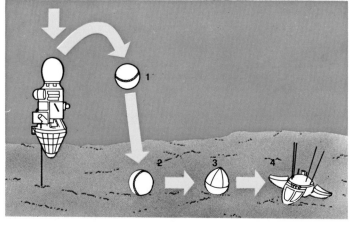

Luna 9 Landing Technique
1 Instrument capsule separates after rocket-braking of mother craft when hinged arm touches lunar surface.
2 Capsule bounces and rolls on the Moon. The weighted base causes it to assume the correct attitude.
3 Capsule starts to deploy.
4 Petal-like panels set capsule upright exposing TV camera; antennas deploy. Signals are sent to Earth.

Weight, including 220lb (100kg) rough-landing capsule: 3,490lb (1,583kg).
Lifetime: four days.

Probes to the Moon

a total of 11,237 pictures were transmitted back to Earth, almost all being at high resolution and in colour using filters.

Surveyor 2 was lost when one of its three vernier engines failed to fire. Surveyor 3 gave mission controllers a brief scare during landing when highly reflective surface rock apparently confused its landing radar, causing it to bounce twice before engine shutdown, first to 33ft (10m) and then to 9·8ft (3m). Over the next two weeks remaining in the lunar day, it transmitted some 6,300 pictures of its landing site back to Earth. Many of these were of its mechanical scoop that was used to dig into the soil down to a depth of 7in (18cm). Observations and readings indicated that the lunar surface soil consistency was similar to that of wet beach sand on Earth: adequate to support a

Right: *Surveyor Moon Lander. Built for NASA by Hughes Aircraft Company, these robot spacecraft were pathfinders for the subsequent landing of men on the Moon. Some carried a mechanical soil scoop.*

LUNAR MISSION UNMANNED SPACECRAFT					
NAME		**DATE**	**BOOSTER**	**WEIGHT** lb (kg)	**MISSION**
Pioneer 0	(USA)	17 Aug 58	Thor-Able	84 (38)	Lunar orbit attempt. Booster exploded at ten miles (16km)
Pioneer 1	(USA)	11 Oct 58	Thor-Able	84 (38)	Lunar orbit attempt. Reached 70,700 miles (113,830km), fell back over South Pacific
Pioneer 2	(USA)	8 Nov 58	Thor-Able	87 (39)	Lunar orbit attempt. Reached 965 miles (1,550km), fell back over central Africa
Pioneer 3	(USA)	6 Dec 58	Juno II	13 (6)	Lunar fly-by attempt. Reached 63,580 miles (102,320km), fell back over central Africa
Luna 1	(USSR)	2 Jan 59	A-1	797 (361)	Lunar impact attempt. Solar orbit after 3,100 mile (5,000km) fly-by
Pioneer 4	(USA)	3 Mar 59	Juno II	13 (6)	Lunar fly-by at 37,050 miles (60,500km). Into solar orbit
Luna 2	(USSR)	12 Sep 59	A-1	860 (390)	First lunar impact
Pioneer/Orbiter	(USA)	24 Sep 59	Atlas-Able	375 (170)	Lunar orbit attempt. Destroyed in booster static test explosion
Luna 3	(USSR)	4 Oct 59	A-1	614 (278)	Final stage instrumentation=345lb (156kg) ∴ mission payload 959lb (434kg). Photographed 70 per cent of lunar far side
Pioneer/Orbiter	(USA)	26 Nov 59	Atlas-Able	373 (169)	Lunar orbit attempt. Destroyed when booster shroud lost 45 sec into launch
Pioneer/Orbiter	(USA)	25 Sep 60	Atlas-Able	388 (176)	Lunar orbit attempt. Destroyed when booster second-stage oxidiser system malfunctioned
Pioneer/Orbiter	(USA)	15 Dec 60	Atlas-Able	388 (176)	Lunar orbit attempt. Destroyed when booster first-stage exploded 70 sec into launch
Ranger 1	(USA)	23 Aug 61	Atlas-Agena	674 (306)	High Earth orbit test vehicle attempt. Achieved only low Earth orbit when Agena failed to restart
Ranger 2	(USA)	18 Nov 61	Atlas-Agena	674 (306)	High Earth orbit test vehicle attempt. Achieved only low Earth orbit when Agena failed to restart
Ranger 3	(USA)	26 Jan 62	Atlas-Agena	727 (330)	Hard land seismometer attempt. Lunar fly-by at 22,872 miles (36,808km) when Agena imparted excess velocity
Ranger 4	(USA)	23 Apr 62	Atlas-Agena	730 (331)	Hard land seismometer attempt. Timer failure. Tracked to indicated impact on lunar far side
Ranger 5	(USA)	18 Oct 62	Atlas-Agena	752 (341)	Hard land seismometer attempt. Power failure. Solar orbit after 450 mile (725km) lunar fly-by
Luna	(USSR)	4 Jan 63	A-2-e	3,080 (1,400)*	Unannounced soft-landing attempt. Earth orbit only
Luna	(USSR)	3 Feb 63*	A-2-e	3,080 (1,400)*	Soft-landing attempt. Failed to achieve Earth orbit
Luna 4	(USSR)	2 Apr 63	A-2-e	3,135 (1,422)	Soft-landing attempt. Solar orbit after 5,280 mile (8,500km) lunar fly-by
Ranger 6	(USA)	30 Jan 64	Atlas-Agena	805 (365)	TV close-up before impact attempt. Crashed on target but no pictures returned
Luna	(USSR)	9 Apr 64*	A-2-e	3,142 (1,425)*	Soft-landing attempt. Failed to achieve Earth orbit
Ranger 7	(USA)	28 Jul 64	Atlas-Agena	806 (366)	Returned 4,306 high-resolution pictures before impact on Mare Cognitum
Ranger 8	(USA)	17 Feb 65	Atlas-Agena	809 (367)	Returned 7,137 high-resolution pictures before impact on Mare Tranquillitatis
Cosmos 60	(USSR)	12 Mar 65	A-2-e	3,240 (1,470)*	Soft-landing attempt. Earth orbit only
Ranger 9	(USA)	21 Mar 65	Atlas-Agena	807 (366)	Returned 5,814 high-resolution pictures before impact inside crater Alphonsus
Luna 5	(USSR)	9 May 65	A-2-e	3,255 (1,476)	Soft-landing attempt. Crashed at 31°S x 8°E
Luna 6	(USSR)	8 Jun 65	A-2-e	3,180 (1,442)	Soft-landing attempt. Solar orbit after 100,000 mile (160,000km) lunar fly-by
Zond 3	(USSR)	18 Jul 65	A-2-e	2,095 (950)	Lunar fly-by, into solar orbit. Returned pictures of remaining portions of lunar far side
Centaur 3	(USA)	11 Aug 65	Atlas-Centaur	2,100 (952)	High Earth orbit of Surveyor dynamic model. Engineering development flight of Centaur
Luna 7	(USSR)	4 Oct 65	A-2-e	3,321 (1,506)	Soft-landing attempt. Impact at 9°N x 40°W
Luna 8	(USSR)	3 Dec 65	A-2-e	3,422 (1,552)	Soft-landing attempt. Impact at 9°8'N x 63°18'W
Luna 9	(USSR)	31 Jan 66	A-2-e	3,490 (1,583)	First successful soft lunar landing at 7°8'N x 64°33'W. Returned TV panoramas and radiation data over four days. 220lb (100kg) capsule
Cosmos 111	(USSR)	1 Mar 66	A-2-e	3,530 (1,600)*	Lunar orbit attempt. Earth orbit only
Luna 10	(USSR)	31 Mar 66	A-2-e	3,490 (1,583)	First successful lunar orbit. 540lb (245kg) satellite returned data from 217 x 632 miles (350 x 1,017km). 178·3min, 71°32' orbit over 56-day life
Surveyor 1	(USA)	30 May 66	Atlas-Centaur	2,194 (995)	Soft-landing at 2°27'S x 43°13'W. Returned 11,237 TV pictures and engineering data over six weeks
Explorer 33	(USA)	1 Jul 66	Thrust-Aug Delta	205 (93)	Lunar orbit attempt. Achieved 9,880 x 270,300 mile (15,900 x 435,000km) Earth orbit. Returned particle and field data
Lunar Orbiter 1	(USA)	10 Aug 66	Atlas-Agena	850 (385)	Lunar orbit 25 x 1,159 miles (40 x 1,865km). 12°12'. Returned 211 TV pictures of photographs of surface
Luna 11	(USSR)	24 Aug 66	A-2-e	3,615 (1,640)	Lunar orbit, 99 x 746 miles (159 x 1,200km). 178min, 27°
Surveyor 2	(USA)	20 Sep 66	Atlas-Centaur	2,200 (1,000)	Soft-landing attempt. Crashed south-east of crater Copernicus
Luna 12	(USSR)	22 Oct 66	A-2-e	3,585 (1,625)*	Lunar orbit, 62 x 1,081 miles (100 x 1,740km), 205min, 15°. Returned TV pictures of surface
Centaur 5	(USA)	26 Oct 66	Atlas-Centaur	1,600 (726)	High Earth orbit with Surveyor mass model. Centaur restart development flight
Lunar Orbiter 2	(USA)	6 Nov 66	Atlas-Agena	860 (390)	Lunar orbit 25 x 1,146 miles (40 x 1,845km). 11°48'. Returned 184 TV pictures of photographs of potential Apollo landing sites
Note: Actual Soviet spacecraft weights are those quoted by *Tass*, the official Soviet News Agency. All others are estimates and are indicated by an asterisk (*).					

Surveyor Descent Profile

1 Cruise attitude.
2 Manoeuvre 30 minutes before touch-downs aligns retro-rocket.
3 Altitude marking radar (which ejects from retro-rocket nozzle) ignites main retro. Lander is stabilised by vernier motors from 52 miles (83·7km) altitude; velocity 5,900 mph (9,495km/h).
4 Retro-rocket burns out and separates: from 37,000ft (11,728m) descent is controlled by vernier retro motors.
5 Vernier motors cut off at 14ft (4·27m) from Moon's surface; velocity 3·5mph (5·6km/h).
6 Spacecraft lands at 8mph (12·9km/h) on shock absorbing footpads.

Technical Data
Surveyor 3
Height: 10ft (3·05m).
Width across landing legs: 14ft (4·27m).
Weight: 2,283lb (1,035kg).
Weight on surface: 625lb (283kg).

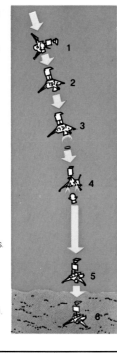

man and his lander vehicle. Apollo 12 astronauts later landed within a quarter of a mile of Surveyor 3, and retrieved parts from it for studies of the effects of long exposure to the lunar environment.

Surveyor 4 was lost half-way through retro fire when all transmissions abruptly ceased. Starting with Surveyor 5, the series also carried an alpha scattering experiment. Soil irradiated by a curium[252] source in the instrument provided the first measure of lunar soil composition.

Surveyor 6, after a thorough site survey, was re-launched from the Moon using its vernier engines for a short hop some 8ft (2·5m) away for more studies.

Unlike previous missions designed to sample potential equatorial Apollo landing sites, Surveyor 7 was sent to a point just outside the rim of the crater Tycho in the southern lunar highlands. When its alpha backscatter probe initially failed to deploy, the soil scoop was used to nudge it downward to the surface. Surveyor 7 returned over 21,000 pictures including some showing two

laser beams emitted from stations on the night side of Earth.

Surveyor examined the lunar surface in regions representative of Apollo landing sites, and found them to have sufficient bearing strength to support an Apollo Lunar Module. Its survey TV cameras had shown a minimum of surface debris which might impede a manned landing; information vital to the Apollo programme.

Survey from Orbit

The last remaining phase of preparation for Apollo was a site survey: a detailed look from above at the equatorial region of the Moon. Five Lunar Orbiter spacecraft were prepared for this role, each fitted with a photographic system to conduct the survey. The series ran concurrently with Surveyor to aid in site selection for them as well.

Once safely on their way to the Moon, the Lunar Orbiters used their propulsion systems to conduct midcourse corrections and later lunar orbit insertion burns. The initial orbits were typically 125 x 1,150 miles (200 x 146)

LUNAR MISSION UNMANNED SPACECRAFT

NAME		DATE	BOOSTER	WEIGHT lb (kg)	MISSION
Luna 13	(USSR)	21 Dec 66	A-2-e	3,570 (1,620)	Soft-landing at 18°52'N x 62°3'W. Returned TV panoramas and radiation data. Tested soil
Lunar Orbiter 3	(USA)	5 Feb 67	Atlas-Agena	849 (385)	Lunar orbit, 25 x 1,150 miles (40 x 1,850km), 21°. Returned 182 TV pictures of photographs of surface
Cosmos 146	(USSR)	10 Mar 67	D-1-e	11,060 (5,017)	Zond attempt. Earth orbit only
Cosmos 154	(USSR)	8 Apr 67	D-1-e	12,300 (5,600)*	Zond attempt. Earth orbit only
Surveyor 3	(USA)	17 Apr 67	Atlas-Centaur	2,283 (1,035)	Soft-landing at 2°56'S x 23°20'W. Returned 6,315 TV pictures and engineering data. Surface weight 625lb (283kg)
Lunar Orbiter 4	(USA)	4 May 67	Atlas-Agena	860 (390)	Lunar orbit 1,680 x 3,749 miles (2,704 x 6,033km), 85°. Returned 163 TV pictures of photographs of surface
Surveyor 4	(USA)	14 Jul 67	Atlas-Centaur	2,291 (1,039)	Soft-landing attempt. Crashed at 0°26'N x 1°20'W
Explorer 35	(USA)	19 Jul 67	Thrust-Aug Delta	229 (104)	Lunar orbit, 500 x 4,600 miles (804 x 7,400km), 147°. Returned particle and fields data
Lunar Orbiter 5	(USA)	1 Aug 67	Atlas-Agena	860 (390)	Lunar orbit, 122 x 3,737 miles (196 x 6,014km), 85°. Returned 213 TV pictures of photographs of surface
Surveyor 5	(USA)	8 Sep 67	Atlas-Centaur	2,216 (1,005)	Soft-landing at 1°25'N x 22°15'E. Returned 18,006 TV pictures. First chemical analysis of soil
Surveyor 6	(USA)	7 Nov 67	Atlas-Centaur	2,223 (1,008)	Soft-landing at 0°25'N x 1°20'W. Returned 30,065 TV pictures and chemical analysis data
Zond	(USSR)	22 Nov 67	D-1-e	11,465 (5,200)*	Zond attempt. Failed to achieve Earth orbit
Surveyor 7	(USA)	7 Jan 68	Atlas-Centaur	2,293 (1,040)	Soft-landing at 40°53'S x 11°26'W near rim of crater Tycho. Returned 21,274 TV pictures and chemical analysis data from lunar highlands
Zond 4	(USSR)	2 Mar 68	D-1-e	12,300 (5,600)*	Zond mission check-out. Solar orbit
Luna 14	(USSR)	7 Apr 68	A-2-e	3,561 (1,615)*	Lunar orbit. 100 x 540 miles (160 x 870km), 160min, 42°.
Zond	(USSR)	22 Apr 68	D-1-e	12,300 (5,600)*	Zond attempt. Failed to reach Earth orbit
Zond 5	(USSR)	14 Sep 68	D-1-e	12,300 (5,600)*	Circumlunar fly-by. Return to Indian Ocean
Zond 6	(USSR)	10 Nov 68	D-1-e	12,300 (5,600)*	Circumlunar fly-by. "Skip" return to Soviet Union
Zond	(USSR)	5 Jan 69*	D-1-e	12,300 (5,600)*	Zond attempt. Failed to achieve Earth orbit
Luna	(USSR)	15 Apr 69	D-1-e	12,300 (5,600)*	Soil sample-return attempt or rover attempt. Failed to reach Earth orbit
Luna	(USSR)	12 Jun 69	D-1-e	12,300 (5,600)*	Soil sample-return attempt or rover attempt. Failed to reach Earth orbit
Luna 15	(USSR)	13 Jul 69	D-1-e	12,570 (5,700)	Soil sample-return attempt or rover attempt. Failed to achieve soft lunar landing
Zond 7	(USSR)	7 Aug 69	D-1-e	12,300 (5,600)*	Circumlunar fly-by. "Skip" return to Soviet Union
Cosmos 300	(USSR)	23 Sep 69	D-1-e	12,300 (5,600)*	Soil sample-return attempt or rover attempt. Failed to leave Earth orbit
Cosmos 305	(USSR)	22 Oct 69	D-1-e	12,300 (5,600)*	Soil sample-return attempt or rover attempt. Possible successful trans-lunar injection only
Luna	(USSR)	19 Feb 70*	D-1-e	12,300 (5,600)*	Soil sample-return attempt or rover attempt. Failed to achieve Earth orbit
Luna 16	(USSR)	12 Sep 70	D-1-e	12,620 (5,725) 4,145 (1,880)†	First successful automatic lunar soil sample return. Sample from *mare* region at 0°41'S x 56°18'E †Dry lander only
Zond 8	(USSR)	20 Oct 70	D-1-e	12,300 (5,600)*	Circumlunar fly-by. Return to Indian Ocean
Luna 17	(USSR)	10 Nov 70	D-1-e	12,300 (5,600)*	Lunokhod 1 Rover = 1,667lb (756kg); empty descent stage 2,381lb (1,080kg). Total surface payload 4,084lb (1,836kg). First successful automatic lunar rover, 38° 18'N x 35°W.
Apollo 15 P & F Sub-Satellite	(USA)	26 Jul 71	Saturn V	79 (36)	Particle and fields Sub-Satellite released from Apollo 15
Luna 18	(USSR)	2 Sep 71	D-1-e	12,125 (5,500)*	Soil sample-return attempt. Crashed at 3°34'N x 56°30'E
Luna 19	(USSR)	28 Sep 71	D-1-e	12,300 (5,600)*	Lunar orbit. Initially 87 mile (140km) circular; 48 x 239 miles (77 x 385km), 131min, 40° after manoeuvring
Luna 20	(USSR)	14 Feb 72	D-1-e	12,300 (5,600)*	Automatic soil sample-return from lunar highlands at 3°32'N x 56°33'E
Apollo 16 P & F Sub-Satellite	(USA)	16 Apr 72	Saturn V	79 (36)	Particle and fields Sub-Satellite released from Apollo 16
Luna 21	(USSR)	8 Jan 73	D-1-e	12,300 (5,600)*	Lunokhod 2 Rover 1,852lb (840kg); 25°54'N x 30°30'E
Explorer 49	(USA)	10 Jun 73	Thrust-Aug Delta	723 (328)	Radio Astronomy Explorer placed in lunar orbit
Luna 22	(USSR)	29 May 74	D-1-e	12,300 (5,600)*	Lunar orbit. Conducted extensive manoeuvring
Luna 23	(USSR)	28 Oct 74	D-1-e	12,570 (5,700)	Deep soil sample return attempt. Damaged on landing at 12°41'N x 62°18'E
Luna	(USSR)	13 Oct 75*	D-1-e	12,300 (5,600)*	Deep soil sample return attempt. Failed to achieve Earth orbit
Luna 24	(USSR)	9 Aug 76	D-1-e	11,698 (5,306)	Deep soil sample return from 12°45'N x 62°12'E

Note: Actual Soviet spacecraft weights are those quoted by *Tass*, the official Soviet News Agency. All others are estimates and are indicated by an asterisk (*).

Probes to the Moon

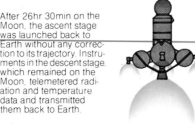

Lunar Operations

After Luna 16 had been manoeuvred in lunar orbit, an Earth command put it into a descent trajectory by firing the main descent engine. When the craft was within 65·6ft (20m) of the surface, this was switched off and two vernier engines com-

pleted the touchdown. Ground controllers sent the command which lowered the drilling rig to the surface. After drilling had been completed, the rig was raised and the hollow drill containing the sample deposited in the spherical capsule at the top of the descent stage.

After 26hr 30min on the Moon, the ascent stage was launched back to Earth without any correction to its trajectory. Instruments in the descent stage, which remained on the Moon, telemetered radiation and temperature data and transmitted them back to Earth.

When the Americans were landing on the Moon, the USSR undertook a bold series of experiments in which remote-controlled robots were launched to explore the Moon "at less cost and without risk to human life". The first was Luna 15 which, having been placed into orbit round the Moon, crashed on the Sea of Crises while attempting to land on 21 July 1969.

The Russians had to wait until the following year to achieve their first success when the soil-sampler Luna 16 soft-landed on the Sea of Fertility, drilled into the soil, and returned a small sample of lunar material to Earth for analysis. The next to fly was Luna 17 which, to the great surprise of Western scientists, landed a remote-controlled roving vehicle on the Sea of Rains. The 8-wheeled rover, called

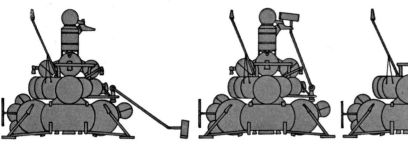

Luna 16 Soil Sampler

1 Return capsule for lunar samples.
2 Attachment strap of return capsule.
3 Antenna on ascent stage.
4 Instrument compartment for ascent stage.
5 Propellant tanks of ascent stage.
6 Telephotometer.
7 Instrument compartment of descent stage.
8 Drilling mechanism rod.
9 Drilling device.
10 Rocket engines of descent stage (one main, two vernier) concealed in this view.
11 Landing legs.
12 Footpad.
13 Propellant tanks of descent stage.
14 Small rocket motors for in-flight control.
15 Rocket engine of ascent stage (concealed behind instrument compartment).
16 Omni-directional antenna on descent stage.

First successful two-way lunar soil-sampling unmanned spacecraft. Landed Sea of Fertility (0°41'S, 56°18'E), 20 September 1970. The automatic drilling rig had a reach of 2·95ft (0·9m)' and was designed to extract 100gr of rock and soil to a depth of 13·8in (35cm). On atmosphere re-entry, inflatable "sausage" balloons deployed the parachute, whip antennas and metallic "needles" to assist location by radar. An onboard radio beacon allowed recovery aircraft and helicopters to home in on its signals.

Technical Data

Height: c13ft (3·96m).
Width across landing legs: 13ft (3·96m).
Weight: 4,145lb (1,880kg).

Other robot samplers: Luna 18 — crashed Sea of Fertility Sept 1971; no sample recovery. Luna 20 landed in lunar highlands between Sea of Fertility and Sea of Crises February 1972, returned soil samples. Luna 23, suffered landing damage southern region Sea of Crises November 1974; no sample recovery. Luna 24, landed SE region Sea of Crises, returning soil sample from depth of about 6·56ft (2·0m).

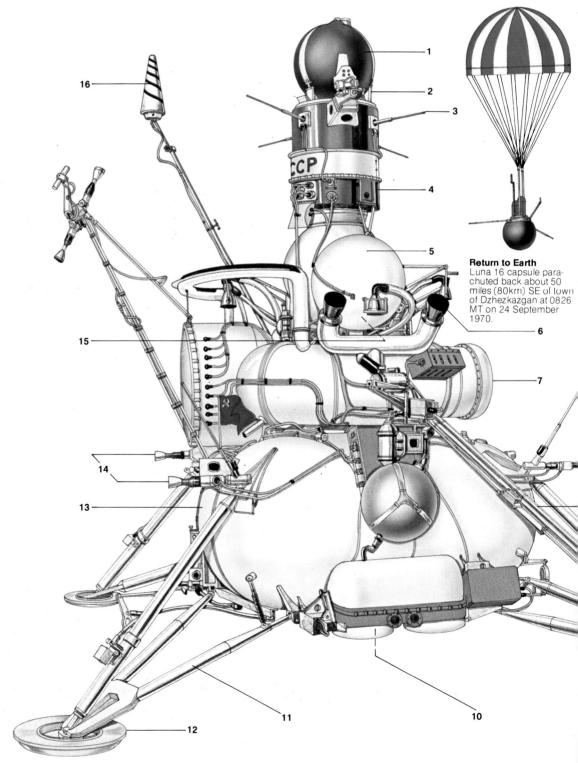

Return to Earth

Luna 16 capsule parachuted back about 50 miles (80km) SE of town of Dzhezkazgan at 0826 MT on 24 September 1970.

Lunokhod 1, which was controlled by a TV/radio link from the Soviet Union, travelled a total distance of 34,588ft (10,542m) in 10½ months, sending TV images and testing the properties of the lunar soil at various stopping points.

More robot expeditions were to follow, not all of them successful. Luna 18—a soil-return sampler—crashed near the edge of the Sea of Fertility in September 1971. The following February Luna 20 landed in a mountainous region between the Sea of Fertility and the Sea of Crises, returning a sample to Earth. In January 1973 came another rover—Lunokhod 2—which was disembarked from Luna 21 within the Le Monnier crater on the eastern edge of the Sea of Serenity. During its four-month life it roamed some 121,390ft (37,000m), obeying every command of its controllers.

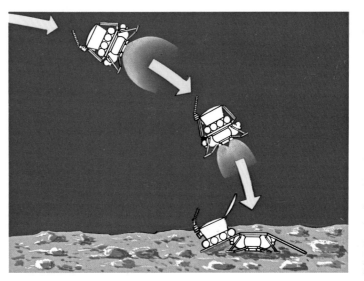

Luna 17 and 21: Braking and Soft Landing

The main braking engine operates to reduce speed under control of radar altimeter and velocity meter. The main engine shuts off; descent continues under braking thrust of small vernier engines. The spacecraft soft-lands; the vernier engines are switched off. Ramps extend and Lunokhod moves from landing platform onto the lunar surface under radio control from Soviet Earth station. The Soviet technique of landing on the Moon was similar to that adopted by the United States in the Apollo programme. Following manoeuvres in lunar orbit, the craft was put into a descent trajectory aligned with the pre-selected landing site.

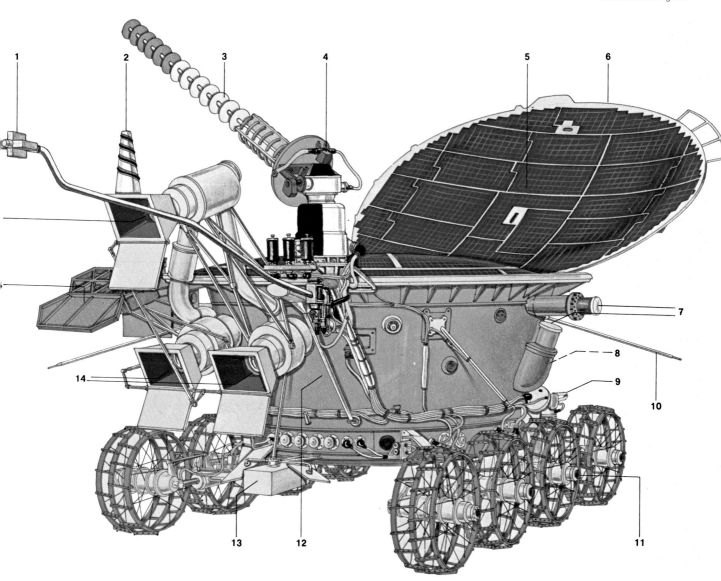

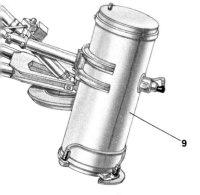

Lunokhod 2 (Luna 21)
1 Magnetometer.
2 Omni-directional antenna.
3 Narrow-beam directional antenna.
4 Antenna pointing mechanism.
5 Solar cells (generate electricity from sunlight to recharge chemical batteries).
6 Hinged lid (closed during transit and when "parked" during the lunar night).
7 Horizontal and vertical scan panoramic cameras.

8 Nuclear heater with reflector shield; also 9th wheel for distance measurement (obscured at rear.)
9 Soil probe (retracted).
10 Telescopic antenna.
11 Wheel unit.
12 Pressurised compartment.
13 Rifma-M chemical soil analyser (X-ray spectrometer) in retracted position.
14 Stereoscopic pair of television cameras with lens hoods and dust covers.
15 French-built laser reflector.

16 Television camera with lens hood and dust cover.

Luna 21 soft-landed inside Le Monnier crater near the eastern rim of the Sea of Serenity at 0135 Moscow Time on 16 January 1973. The first period of lunar exploration began on 17-18 January when Lunokhod 2 moved off from the landing site in a south-easterly direction over basalt lava, negotiating craters and boulders. Panoramic pictures received on Earth clearly

showed the surrounding scene, including mountains bordering the Sea of Serenity.

Technical Data
Dimension over four wheels: 87in (221cm).
Wheel track: 63in (160cm).
Wheel diameter: 20in (51cm).
Weight: 1,852lb (840kg) at launch, about 220lb (100kg) heavier than Lunokhod 1 which operated on the Sea of Rains for 10½ months from 17 November 1970.

1,850km). After several days of tracking, the perilune was lowered to about 31 miles (50km) in preparation for the photographic survey. Each spacecraft carried about 262ft (80m) of film with about 210 frames. An onboard chemical process developed the film after it was exposed so the negative could be scanned and the image transmitted back to Earth once every 40 minutes.

Problems with Lunar Orbiter 1's high-resolution camera resulted in photographic image blurring, making them unusable. The medium-resolution camera functioned normally, so that 75 per cent of the mission was completed: some 16,025 sq miles (41,500 sq km) of potential Apollo landing sites, 140,000 sq miles (360,000 sq km) of other near-side features, and 2,007,917 sq miles (5,200,000 sq km) of the far side were photographed.

Lunar Orbiter 2 used 184 of its frames to shoot 13 candidate Apollo sites, the remainder being used for a mixture of far-side coverage and additional near-side shots.

Lunar Orbiter 3 returned 182 frames before a film advance motor failed. These included site confirmation (rather than site search) pictures of ten potential Apollo sites plus one showing Surveyor 1, as well as 600,000 sq miles (1,550,000 sq km) of the near side and 251,000 sq miles (650,000 sq km) of the lunar far side. This completed the primary objective of the Surveyor and Apollo site surveys.

As a result, Lunar Orbiters 4 and 5 were placed in near-polar orbits to conduct a photo survey of the remaining portions of the Moon, and to look at non-equatorial sites for a later cancelled Apollo follow-on series. Film fogging on Lunar Orbiter 4 meant that only 163 frames were returned, while all 213 from Lunar Orbiter 5 were sent. These provided coverage of approximately 99 per cent of the lunar surface.

The Lunar Orbiters also collected micrometeoroid and radiation environment data, and tracking their orbits provided a detailed map of the lunar gravitational field.

One additional radiation monitoring spacecraft was placed in lunar orbit: Explorer 35. Explorer 35 confirmed the near-total absence of a magnetic field, and revealed no evidence of radiation belts or an ionosphere. This meant that, unlike Earth, there was nothing to impede the solar wind from striking the surface of the Moon at full strength.

The Later Probes

The last of the American lunar probes launched to support Apollo requirements was Surveyor 7 in January 1968. Eighteen months then remained before the launch of the first Apollo landing attempt. The Soviet pace picked up at about that time, giving all indications that a Russian vehicle, rather than American, might make the first manned lunar landing. In the spring of 1968 the mysterious Zond 4 was launched on a trajectory that eventually sent it into solar orbit. Six months later Zond 5 made a circumnavigation flight around the Moon before returning to Earth for a splashdown and recovery in the Indian Ocean. Two months later Zond 6, repeating this feat but with a skip re-entry, landed in the Soviet Union. It was later learned that these were modified versions of the Soyuz three-man

spacecraft, carrying not men but biological specimens. An anticipated launch with one or more cosmonauts aboard in late 1968 never materialised, possibly because of the success of the Christmas 1968 lunar orbit mission of Apollo 8. Two more missions were conducted, but Zond 7 and 8 were essentially repeats of the Zond 6 flight, and came after the landing of Apollo 11.

After the successful landing on the Moon of Apollo 11, Soviet officals denied that they had been planning a manned lunar landing programme. Instead, they would be continuing their lunar studies with unmanned vehicles in the Luna series.

These new, heavier Luna spacecraft again featured a standardised design that could be fitted with a specialised payload.

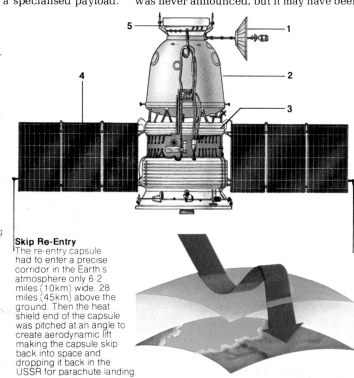

Above: *Part of the Moon's hidden side taken by Lunar Orbiter 3. This and other spacecraft of the series helped both to map the Moon and to select areas on the near side on which to land Apollo.*

Left: *A Lunar Orbiter emerges from the 50ft (15·2m) high space environment chamber at the Boeing Space Center in February 1966. Careful testing of equipment was essential.*

The base consisted of four spherical propellant tanks for the 1·1 mile/sec (1·8km/sec) lunar orbit to surface velocity-change requirement, plus four more cylindrical strap-on tanks for the 0·62 miles/sec (1·0km/sec) lunar orbit injection burn and any in-orbit manoeuvring.

The series, which continues to this day, is divided into three categories: soil sample return, rovers, and orbiters. Luna 15 was the first successful launch of the series, coming just three days before the launch of Apollo 11. After a four-day flight it entered lunar orbit where it remained for several more days making minor orbit adjustments. A landing attempt, after 52 orbits, failed when it crashed on the surface. Its mission was never announced, but it may have been

Zond Circumlunar Spacecraft
1 High-gain antenna.
2 Re-entry module similar to that of Soyuz spacecraft.
3 Service module with manoeuvre engine and attitude control system.
4 Extensible solar panels. Drawing shows the view from the underside.
5 Instrument package.

This spacecraft was described by the Soviets as "an automatic station" for perfecting the technology for distant space flights. In fact the station was based on a modification of the early manned Soyuz spacecraft omitting the orbital module. In 1968, Zond 5 flew around the Moon on a free-return trajectory with small live passengers tortoises and other biological specimens which it brought safely back to Earth. Zonds 5 and 8 splashed down in the Indian Ocean. Zonds 6 and 7 made an aerodynamic skip which enabled them to land in the USSR.

Skip Re-Entry
The re-entry capsule had to enter a precise corridor in the Earth's atmosphere only 6·2 miles (10km) wide. 28 miles (45km) above the ground. Then the heat shield end of the capsule was pitched at an angle to create aerodynamic lift making the capsule skip back into space and dropping it back in the USSR for parachute landing.

a rover intended to remain active on the surface long after the astronauts had left, or a soil-sample retriever intended to beat Apollo 11 back to Earth.

Luna 16, some 15 months later, did successfully conduct the first automatic soil-sample return mission. Once safely on the Moon, a special drill assembly on a long arm was lowered to the surface. There a hollow rotary/percussion drill bored 1ft (0·35m) into the surface, filling the drill in the process. The arm and drill assembly was then raised back up to the ascent stage of the craft, and the drill transferred to a re-entry capsule for the trip home. Unfortunately about half of the core sample spilled out as it was being raised so only 0·22lb (0·1kg) of *maria* soil was returned. Luna 20, a similar mission, experienced the same problem and only returned 0·11lb (0·05kg) of highland soil. The six Apollo manned missions, by comparison, returned approximately 838lb (380kg) of rock and soil samples. The drill assembly was extensively modified after that and with Luna 24, penetration to a depth of nearly 6·56ft (2m) was accomplished. Here, the hollow drill had an inner flexible liner which filled much like stuffing a sausage as the boring progressed. When the drilling was complete, the filled liner (0·3in diameter x 63in length/8mm x 1,600mm) was withdrawn and coiled like a rope on a winch. It was then transferred to and sealed in the re-entry capsule. The drilling assembly, now minus its core sample, was then swung clear of the upper part of the spacecraft, and the ascent stage engine fired for a vertical climb and burn-out at 1·7 miles/sec (2·7km/sec). The sample site had been carefully selected, so that when the ascent stage cleared the Moon's gravitational field, it was falling straight towards Earth, eliminating the need for a midcourse correction firing. In time the Luna ascent stage may be improved to allow sampling at locations other than just 56°E near the equator. The re-entry capsule was recovered three days later and its 0·37lb (0·17kg) core sample removed for analysis.

Luna 17 was the first of the lunar rover missions. After a successful descent, ramps were lowered on the soft-lander to permit its 8-wheel rover, called Lunokhod 1, to descend to the surface. Lunokhod 1 was one of the most successful of the Soviet lunar probes, travelling more than 6·5 miles (10·5km) over a period of ten months. During the day, a protective thermal lid was folded back, exposing two banks of solar cells to generate electrical power. During the two-week lunar night the lid would cover the top of the rover and circulated air, warmed by a nuclear heater, would keep the interior warm. The Lunokhod was fitted with a set of TV cameras, two on Lunokhod 1 and three on Lunokhod 2, to allow its five operators back on Earth to decide where to steer it. Speed was not important; the human crew of Apollo 15 travelled 40 miles (64·5km) in three days on their rover, an unfair comparison. The Lunokhod would be stopped periodically to allow another set of TV cameras on the side to transmit a full 360° panorama of its current location. Testing the soil was also conducted, the vehicle measuring bearing strength with a penetrometer and chemical composition with an X-ray spectrometer. A 14-element retro-reflector mirror allowed precise laser ranging of the Earth-Moon separation to within an accuracy of 15in (40cm).

Lunokhod 2 was placed on the Moon by the Luna 21 spacecraft, inside the 34 mile (55km) diameter Le Monnier crater. This was an old crater whose floor had receded and later flooded with lava, leaving only part of the exposed rim. It therefore contained both *maria* and highland features. The rover's route of travel took it first south across the crater floor to the transition region, and then east to a long fault similar to Hadley Rille explored by the crew of Apollo 15. Lunokhod 2 travelled 23 miles (37km) during its four-month life.

The Lunokhod/Luna structure minus the wheels has been used for at least one orbital mission. Luna 19 was placed in an 87-mile (140km) circular lunar orbit which was later reduced to 84 x 79 miles (135km x 127km). From there it returned pictures of a region 30°S to 60°S and 20°E to 30°E, and sampled the radiation and micrometeoroid environment. Tracking of its orbit over the first two months of its life was sufficient to define the asymmetry of the northern and southern hemispheres of the Moon.

Luna 22 conducted rather extensive manoeuvring in lunar orbit during its life of some 18 months. Like Luna 19, it returned pictures but none has been published from either probe. A measure of gamma radiation from the surface was also made in an effort to make a broad chemical composition survey. Tracking of its orbit helped to give some measure and extent of gravitational anomalies due to mascons. These are local concentrations of denser material which exert a slightly stronger gravitational pull as a spacecraft passes overhead slightly distorting its orbit in the process.

One additional American craft was placed in lunar orbit, but not to study the Moon. Explorer 49, the Radio Astronomy Explorer, was fitted with four 755ft (230m) long antennas, which when fully extended gave the appearance of a giant X. From lunar orbit it monitored celestial radio sources, free of any background noise from Earth. Locations of emitters could be fixed by noting the time when they disappeared and reappeared from behind the Moon.

The Moon continues silently to circle the Earth today as it has for thousands of millions of years. Scattered over its surface at nearly three dozen locations are evidence of the presence of man; either his machines or (in the case of six Apollo landing missions) the footprints of 12 astronauts. The information returned by them has answered many basic questions about the Moon, but probably generated far more questions in the process. In time man and more machines will return to the Moon, perhaps for the erection of permanent bases which will have been made possible by the knowledge we have gained from the lunar probes launched over the last decades.

Above: *This impressive shot of Earth was taken by Russia's Zond 7 spacecraft less than a month after America's Apollo 11 mission. The unmanned craft made a flight around the Moon and returned to the USSR.*

Right: *Soviet co-ordinating and computing centre for the automatic roving vehicle Lunokhod 1. Information received included data on the robot's performance, internal systems, and research results.*

Probes to the Planets

Many years ago, Konstantin Tsiolkovsky expressed his conviction that Man's ultimate destiny lay among the stars. In time, Man will set foot on other planets, but for now, the exploration of worlds other than Earth can be conducted only by machines, deep space probes that return the data that we need to further our knowledge of the Universe.

Sending a probe to the planets requires precise timing and accuracy. An understanding of a few basic principles of astronautics is in order better to appreciate this.

It can be shown that for a given booster, the heaviest possible payload that can be sent to another planet is one that travels in an elliptical solar orbit that just touches Earth's orbit at departure and that of its destination planet at arrival. If the probe is any heavier than this maximum, its transfer orbit will be too slow to reach its target planet. Conversely, it can be made lighter than the maximum allowable to reach its target planet sooner, but at the expense of valuable payload weight. This minimum velocity/maximum payload transfer path, which would take a probe roughly half way around the Sun, is called a Hohmann Transfer Orbit. Near-optimum such orbits have been used for all planetary missions to date. Since each planet travels at a different velocity about the Sun, their positions relative to one another are constantly changing. Planetary missions must be timed so that after leaving Earth, a probe will meet its destination planet half way around the Sun from where it started. The time during which a launch satisfying this condition can be made is referred to as a Launch Window, and is typically several weeks in duration. In recent years several spacecraft have been sent to more distant planets using a gravitational boost during a fly-by of a closer planet. For example, we can see this principle in operation in the use of Venus to reach Mercury, and the use of Jupiter to reach Saturn and then Saturn to reach Uranus.

Probes Around the Sun

The first of the deep-space probes was not aimed at a particular planet, but was intended rather to sample the fields and particles of the interplanetary medium, free of the Earth's influence. The Earth's magnetic field shields life from the solar wind; a very faint constant outward stream of ionised atomic particles from the Sun's atmosphere which passes the Earth on the average at some 250 miles/sec (400km/sec).

Pioneer 5, the first interplanetary probe, was launched on 11 March 1960 into an elliptical 0·8AU x 1·0AU solar orbit, just inside Earth's circular 1·0AU orbit (1AU = one Astronomical Unit, the distance of the Earth from the Sun). The final transmission from Pioneer 5 was detected at a distance of some 22·68 million miles (36·5 million kilometres), 55 times the previous record.

The Pioneer series was resumed in 1965 to continue studies of interplanetary space from widely separated locations near Earth's orbit. Five spacecraft were successfully launched into paths around the Sun, both inside and outside Earth's orbit. Each Pioneer was planned to have a six-month life, but in all cases that was extended because of the quality of data being returned. Data from the Pioneers showed that the solar wind was like the pattern from a lawn water-sprinkler; a spiral pattern due to the Sun's 27-day period of rotation. Along with other high Earth orbit satellites they also found that the

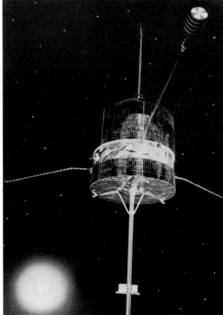

Above: *Pioneer 6 which passed within about 77 million miles (124 million km) of the Sun in 1966. It carried six experiments to study interplanetary magnetic fields, the solar wind and cosmic rays.*

Right: *The swirling acid clouds of Venus show clearly in this computer-enhanced mosaic of images obtained by Mariner 10. The planet appears blue instead of whitish-yellow because of the filters used.*

Earth's magnetic field is compressed by the solar wind on the side facing the Sun, and that it is stretched out to at least 3·1 million miles (five million kilometres) in the other direction, waving like a flag in a breeze.

In 1974 the first of a pair of West German probes was launched to conduct studies at a distance of only 0·2AU to 0·3AU from the Sun. At closest approach, Helios 1 and 2 (launched in 1976) were exposed to the full fury of the Sun's glare, 25 times the intensity at Earth. This is the closest approach any man-made object has ever made to the Sun, only half the distance of Mercury, the closest planet. The Ulysses probe will rely on a Jupiter fly-by gravity assist to send it into a highly inclined orbit that will pass directly over the poles of the Sun in the mid 1990s. And finally, Starprobe, planned for a launch after the turn of the century, could pass within 2 million miles (3 million km) of the Sun, travelling pole to pole in just 14 hours where it would be exposed to 3,200 times the intensity of solar radiation here on Earth.

Hohmann Transfer Orbit
This diagram illustrates the ideal geometry for a 145 day flight from Earth (green ring) to Venus (blue ring) and a 260 day flight to Mars (orange ring) using the most economical flight path: the Hohmann transfer orbit. The relative positions of the planets at the beginning of the missions are shown by the green globes. Relative positions at arrival are indicated in blue (Venus/Earth) and orange (Mars/Earth).

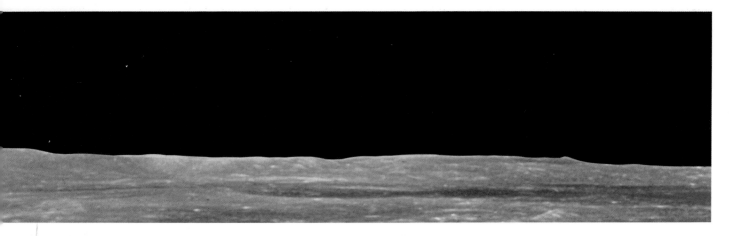

Fly-by of Venus

The cloud-covered planet Venus is one of the brightest objects in the night sky and it became one of the first targets for planetary probe attempts. As explained earlier, planetary probes are launched into long elliptical transfer orbits that touch Earth's orbit at departure and that of their destination planet at arrival. If a probe is to climb higher than Earth's orbit its velocity relative to the Sun must be increased. Conversely, if it is to fall closer to the Sun than Earth, it must be slowed down. For flights to Venus or Mars the velocity change to be added or subtracted from Earth's 18·6 miles/sec (30km/sec) is typically 2·2 miles/sec (3·5km/sec), once free of the force exerted by the Earth's gravitational field.

The first opportunity to launch a planetary probe came in late 1960, when the Soviet Union had completed the construction of the first of its A-2-e boosters. Soviet Premier Krushchev used the opportunity of the pending launches to conduct a fist-pounding tirade at the United Nations Assembly in New York. He later returned to Russia without any space spectaculars having been conducted during his tour. It was eventually learned that two Mars launch attempts had been made in the first two weeks of October, neither achieving Earth orbit.

The next available planetary window was for Venus, early in 1961. Two more Soviet attempts were made at that time; Sputnik 7, which remained in Earth orbit when its escape stage failed to fire, and Venera 1, which was successfully injected into a solar orbit. Unfortunately, radio contact with it was lost before a planned Venus fly-by.

Autumn 1962 saw both Venus and Mars planetary windows. The Soviet Union launched two Venus and three Mars attempts between August and November of that year. Only the second Mars probe, Mars 1 was successfully injected into a solar orbit. Radio contact with it was lost before a fly-by of Mars could be conducted.

The United States also used the 1962 Venus opportunity to launch a pair of Mariner spacecraft. The Mariner 1 Atlas-Agena booster had to be destroyed by range safety action when it began to veer off course. It was later determined that the cause of the deviation had been a simple hyphen that had been omitted from one of the launch-vehicle guidance-data editing equations. A month later Mariner 2 was successfully launched on a trajectory that took it to a planned 21,640 mile (34,830km) fly-by of Venus on 14 December 1962. Mariner 2 found no appreciable magnetic field or radiation belts. A pair of heat-sensing radiometers that scanned the disc of Venus as the probe swept by produced data that showed the surface to be dry and scorching hot, a fairly even 425°C over the entire planet. The surface atmospheric pressure had to be at least 20 times sea-level pressure on Earth (ie 20 atmospheres).

Two additional Mariner probes were sent on fly-by missions past Venus: Mariner 5 in 1967 and Mariner 10 in 1973. Mariner 5 flew within 2,500 miles (4,000km) of Venus, providing additional atmospheric data, including proof of atmospheric super-refractivity. Mariner 10 returned the first TV pictures of Venus. Global coverage in the ultraviolet region of the spectrum starting 3 hours after closest approach and continuing for the next eight days provided a motion picture of the flow and turbulence of the upper atmosphere of Venus.

Venus Atmosphere Probes

Mariner 5 was accompanied in flight by the Soviet Venera 4, launched just two days before it. Since Venera 1 in 1961, the Soviets had launched probes in every Venus window: three in 1962, two in 1963/64, and three again in 1965. Two of the 1965 probes, Venera 2 and 3 (a TV fly-by and an atmosphere penetrator), both fell silent just before Venus encounter. Venera 4, the only successful launch of a pair in the 1967 window, was aimed directly at Venus. At 28,000 miles (45,000km) from the planet it released a 39·4in (1m) diameter spherical capsule that survived an entry deceleration of up to 300g's. A parachute system then permitted a slow descent through the atmosphere that lasted 94 minutes. Soviet announcements that the probe's final transmission was from the surface had later to be revised when American investigators working with Mariner 5 S-band occultation data showed that the reported 271°C and 17 to 20 atmospheres of pressure corresponded to an altitude of 15·5 miles (25km). Chemical sensors in the capsule showed that the atmosphere was made up almost entirely of carbon dioxide.

Right: *Mariner 5 which was sent on a mission to Venus in 1967. It passed within 2,500 miles (4,000km) on 19 October. Weight 540lb (245kg). Span over solar panels 18ft (5·48m); height 9·5ft (2·89m).*

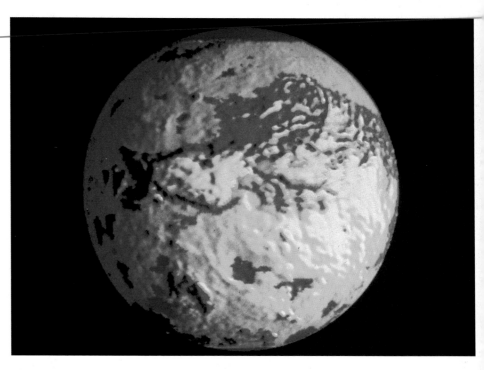

Above: *Global view of Venus stripped of its perpetual cloud cover by the radar altimeter of Pioneer Orbiter. This photograph produced from radar data shows the highland area Aphrodite. Lower elevations are yellow in this false colour representation. The point of observation is over the equator at 90° East longitude. Artificial lighting has been used to highlight the surface relief.*

Several more Soviet penetrator missions were conducted. Venera 5 and 6, launched during the 1969 Venus window, were fitted with smaller parachutes for a faster descent to reach the surface before being destroyed by heat, but they too failed before touchdown, probably crushed by atmospheric pressure.

Venera 7, one of two attempts in the 1970 Venus window, finally survived to reach the surface, reporting back a pressure of 90 ± 15 atmospheres at 475°C. This is equivalent to the pressure at a depth of about half a mile in the ocean on Earth, and temperatures

hot enough to melt lead and zinc. Venera 8, one of two attempts in the 1972 window also reached the surface, but for the first time on the day side. Light-level and soil-density data were also returned.

Detailed Studies of Venus

The Soviet Union continued its exploration of Venus in 1975 with two heavy spacecraft Venera 9 and 10. Two days before encounter, each detached a lander probe, allowing it to continue on to a shallow entry path into the atmosphere of Venus. Each spacecraft then performed a deflection manoeuvre to pass within 1,000 miles (1,600km) of the surface. At minimum approach, each used an on-board propulsion system to insert itself into a two-day, highly elliptical orbit of Venus. Probe entry then took place over the day side of the planet, in a region not visible from Earth at that time. All probe data were recorded by the orbiting spacecraft for later relay back to Earth. The Venera 9 and 10 orbiters became the first spacecraft to orbit the

planet Venus. In addition to the probe data, they relayed back sensor data of their own; particle and fields data in near-Venus space, as well as thermal, visual and spectroscope characteristics of the upper atmosphere.

The highlight of each mission, however, was the entry probe results. Each probe was housed in a heat-shield covered, 7·8ft (2·4m) diameter sphere that protected it down to a speed of 820ft/sec (250m/sec), at 40·4 miles (65km). Parachutes were then used down to 31 miles (50km), at which point they too were cast off, and only a large disc at the top of the probe retained for final braking. After a 75 minutes descent, the Venera 9 probe set down at a 90-atmosphere, 485°C landing site, where it transmitted 53 more minutes of data before succumbing to the heat. The Venera 10 probe provided 65 minutes of surface data. For the first time the probes were fitted with TV cameras, and they sent back the first-ever views of the planet's surface. In spite of the dense atmosphere and thick cloud cover, each single panorama showed its landing site to be as bright as a cloudy day here on Earth, with features up to 330ft (100m) away clearly visible. The landing sites were like stony deserts lacking both sand or dust, covered by rocks up to 33ft (10m) across.

The Venera 11 and 12 probes, launched in the 1978 Venus launch window, were essentially repeats of these missions. In addition to a set of sensors similar to those on previous craft, each carried instrumentation to monitor the equivalent of thunderstorms. Venera 11 counted an average of some 25 strikes per second; Venera 12 a total of nearly 1,000. One loud clap reverberated for

Left: *Engineering replica of the Venera 4 spacecraft which parachuted an instrument capsule through the atmosphere of Venus in 1967. The 39·4in (1m) diameter capsule marked CCCP is attached by metal straps.*

Below: *Full size exhibition model of Venera 11/12 which landed on Venus in 1978. The spacecraft resembled the earlier Venera 9 and 10 which obtained TV pictures from the fiercely hot surface.*

Venera 4 Descent
1 845lb (383kg) descent capsule separates.
2 Atmosphere entry.
3 Drogue parachute deploys.
4 Main parachute deploys; transmitter switches on.
5 Radio altimeter measures altitude.
6 Lands.

After penetrating the atmosphere of Venus, drogue and main parachutes opened. Parachutes' fabric was able to withstand 450°C temperatures. Data transmitted to Earth over 94 minutes, during which the capsule descended to within 15·5 miles (25km) of the surface, indicated temperatures ranging from 40° to 280°C and pressures from 1 to 15-22 atmospheres. It is believed that transmissions ceased some distance above the surface because the lid of the instrument compartment caved in under atmospheric pressure.

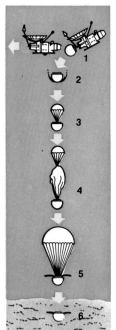

Venera 9 Descent
1 Venera orbital station on impact trajectory. Instrument compartment pre-cooled to −10°C before separation.
2 Mothercraft is course-corrected for entry into orbit around Venus.
3 Capsule enters Venus' atmosphere at 6·6 miles/sec (10·7km/sec), altitude 77·7 miles (125km). Temperatures up to 12,000°C.
4 Hemispherical covers of research station separate. Velocity 820ft/sec (250m/sec).
5 Drogue parachute deploys.
6 Three main parachutes deploy 40·4 miles (65km).
7 Parachutes jettison at 31 miles (50km). Descent controlled by aerodynamic drag brake.
8 Landing. Shock absorbing landing ring deforms at touchdown. Impact velocity 19·7 to 26·2ft/sec (6 to 8m/sec). TV camera covers eject; density meter hinges onto surface. Cameras and instruments switched on.

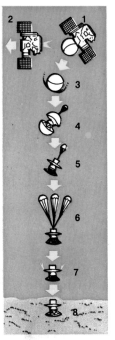

Above: *Pioneer-Venus Orbiter being prepared for the multi-million mile journey to Venus. It was launched on 20 May 1978. The Pioneer-Venus multi-probe spacecraft (behind) followed on 8 August.*

15 minutes. There is little water in the atmosphere, but a high sulphuric acid content may have played a role in producing these electrical discharges.

Nineteen seventy-eight marked a veritable invasion of Venus, for the two Russian Veneras were accompanied by two American probes, one of which released four separate landers. Pioneer-Venus 1 arrived first, entering an orbit around the planet to conduct a detailed study of near-Venus space and to probe by radar its hidden surface. The Pioneer-Venus 2 craft followed close behind, releasing four cone-shaped probes some three weeks before encounter. All five craft entered the atmosphere of Venus on schedule. The drum-shaped bus (carrier spacecraft) that had carried the four probes was destroyed, as planned, but not before it had transmitted back data on upper-atmosphere density and composition from a region not sampled by the probes nor reached by the orbiter. The probes had diverged in their independent cruise phase, so that by the time they reached the atmosphere of Venus they were widely separated. Each probe was intended to send back data right up to the point of impact. One probe survived impact and continued transmitting an additional 67 minutes of data. This information showed the presence of fine surface dust that took 15 minutes to settle after impact. The atmosphere was found to be 97 per cent carbon dioxide, 1-3 per cent nitrogen and 0.1-0.4 per cent water vapour.

The orbiter's radar slowly mapped out surface features from above, revealing giant plateaus, huge canyons, and many old impact craters. Overall, however, Venus was found to be smoother and more perfectly spherical than Earth, with more than half of its surface features within 0.3 miles (0.5km) of the average planet radius. The orbiter's infra-red radiometer probed the atmosphere and found it to be stratified into five generalized regions: clear up to 19 miles

(31km), haze up to 30 miles (48km), the main cloud cover blanket up to 43 miles (70km), followed by another region of haze up to 56 miles (90km), and finally an ionosphere that extends out to 620 miles (1,000km). Winds aloft were measured at speeds indicating that they completely circle the planet in just 4 days. The mechanism that drives these winds is still not well understood, since Venus rotates so very slowly (243 Earth days for one day on Venus). Pioneer-Venus Orbiter will return data right up to the point when it enters the atmosphere of Venus in 1992.

The Soviets continued their exploration of Venus with two more probes in 1981: Venera 13 and 14. Lander probes released by the fly-by buses provided greater detail of the structure and composition of the cloud blanket during descent. Once on the surface, higher resolution TV cameras, fitted with special filters produced the first colour images of the surface of Venus. Mechanical and chemical properties of the soil were also measured, showing it to be similar to basaltic granite found on Earth.

Venera 15 and 16, launched in 1983, were of a different design. The basic bus or central core of the spacecraft was lengthened to accommodate more propellant, and the spherical lander probes from previous missions were replaced with a folding synthetic aperture radar antenna. Each was put into a highly elliptical, 24 hour, near-polar orbit around Venus. During the low altitude portion of each orbit, the onboard radar mapped out successive swaths of surface area with a resolution of 0.6 to 1.2 miles (1 to 2km). This was considerably better than the 45 mile (75km) resolution of the earlier Pioneer-Venus Orbiter. Mosaics of the images show impact craters or volcanos, and everything from low hills to mountain ranges, and random ridges and valleys indicating that Venus was several thousand million years old.

The next two Soviet Venus probes were a major departure from previous missions in that they were truly international projects, with many of the instruments provided by socialist and western countries. Vega 1 and 2

were launched in 1984 carrying lander probes intended to explore the surface of Venus again. After the release of these probes, the two buses performed small manoeuvres designed to send them on their way to fly through Halley's Comet in 1986.

The Vega 1 and 2 lander probes each released French balloon instruments above the night side of the surface, where they drifted for 6,200 miles (10,000km) over the next two days, providing direct sampling of the sulphuric acid cloud blanket that completely encircles the planet. Vertical measurements showed the presence of wind vortices more powerful than would be found in hurricanes here on Earth. Each lander was fitted with a drill mechanism to collect a soil sample and analyze its elemental composition inside the probe. Little information was released about the Vega 1 probe, because its drilling sequence started while it was still 10 miles (16km) above the surface. The Vega 2 probe data showed that it had landed in a soft sandy region with soil similar to that found in the lunar highlands. The balloons were designed to travel from night to day, so the landers had to set down at night. As a result, no cameras for surface images were provided.

Detailed surface mapping is scheduled to resume when the NASA Magellan spacecraft achieves a near-polar Venus orbit in 1990. Its S-band synthetic aperture radar will be able to achieve a ground resolution of 820ft (250m) over approximately 70 per cent of the surface. That should be sufficient to resolve the number of questions about the evolution of the surface that cannot be determined with the coarser resolution of Pioneer and Venera data.

Mars Fly-by and Orbit

The United States chose the 1964 launch window as its first opportunity to send a pair of Mariner spacecraft to Mars. The Mariner 3 spacecraft was lost when a new, previously untested aerodynamic shroud that covered the spacecraft during ascent through the atmosphere, failed to separate. A new shroud was quickly fabricated and three weeks later Mariner 4 was success-

Mariner 9
1 Low-gain antenna.
2 Manoeuvre engine.
3 Propellant tank (2).
4 Canopus sensor.
5 Propulsion pressurisation tank.
6 Temperature control louvres.
7 Infra-red interferometer spectrometer.
8 Narrow angle TV camera.
9 Ultra-violet spectrometer.
10 Wide-angle TV camera.
11 Infra-red radiometer.
12 High-gain antenna.
13 Acquisition Sun sensors (4).
14 Cruise Sun sensor.
15 Medium-gain antenna.
16 Solar panel (4).

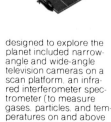

Mariner 9, the first artificial satellite of Mars, swung into orbit on 13 November 1971 after successfully completing a braking manoeuvre. The initial orbit ranged between 868 x 11,135 miles (1,397 x 17,916km) inclined at 64·3° to the equator. Instruments designed to explore the planet included narrow-angle and wide-angle television cameras on a scan platform, an infra-red interferometer spectrometer (to measure gases, particles, and temperatures on and above the surface), an ultra-violet spectrometer (to identify gases in the upper atmosphere), and an infra-red radiometer (to measure surface temperatures). At the time of the spacecraft's arrival, a dust storm hid many features of the planet. When the dust cleared its cameras made startling disclosures – an equatorial canyon bigger than Earth's Grand Canyon, volcanoes, and features that resembled dried-out river beds.

fully launched into a solar orbit. On 14 July 1965 it swept past Mars at a distance of 6,000 miles (9,600km) revealing the absence of both radiation belts and magnetic field. Radio signals received from the Mariner as it passed behind Mars (radio occultation) provided a measure of the propagation characteristics of Mars' ionosphere and an atmospheric density profile. From this data it was established that the surface air pressure was less than 1 per cent of that at sea-level on Earth; equivalent to the Earth's atmosphere at 19-22 miles (30-35km) altitude. The Mariner also sent back 21 pictures of the surface; pictures that for the first time showed craters similar to those on the Moon.

The Soviet Zond 2 probe launched two days after Mariner 4 experienced a power drop early in its mission and passed within 930 miles (1,500km) of Mars without returning any data.

Two more, heavier Mariner spacecraft were flown past Mars during the 1969 launch window passing the planet respectively at 2,120 miles (3,412km) and 2,190 miles (3,524km). Mariner 6 returned 75 pictures of th e surface; Mariner 7,126.

The orbit of Mars around the Sun is slightly more elliptical than Earth's. This means that the distance that a spacecraft has to climb to meet the orbit of Mars varies over the years. In 1971 that distance was almost at a minimum, so that an Atlas-Centaur could send a 2,273lb (1,031kg) probe to Mars then, as opposed to only 911lb (413kg) in the 1969 window. NASA engineers took this opportunity to use most of that weight increase for a large propulsion system capable of placing a spacecraft in orbit around Mars.

Two United States Mariner spacecraft

Left: Atlas-Agena blasts off from Launch Complex-12 at Cape Canaveral on 28 November 1964 carrying the Mars probe Mariner 4. Seven months later Mariner swept past the planet at a distance of 6,000 miles (9,600km), and its single TV camera returned 21 pictures that for the first time revealed surface craters.

were launched in that window. Mariner 8 was lost during launch, but Mariner 9 was successfully inserted into a 14 hour orbit around Mars. It was the first spacecraft to orbit another planet. It was hoped that the Mariner could immediately start its survey, but the entire planet was engulfed in a giant dust storm that obscured all the surface for the next two months. Once the dust had cleared and the survey finally began, the TV pictures transmitted back to Earth revealed Mars to be a truly remarkable world. A huge rift valley stretching one-fifth of the way around the planet was discovered, 2,300 miles (3,700km) long, 155 miles (250km) at the widest, and 4 miles (7km) deep. Several dormant volcanoes were found, the biggest being Nix Olympica (Snow of Olympus); measuring 340 miles (550km) across its base. No liquid water has been found, but several of the surface features appeared to show the results of extensive water erosion. In all, Mariner 9 sent back over 7,000 TV pictures from its orbit around Mars. While it was waiting for the dust storm to clear, it took pictures of both the tiny moons of Mars, Phobos and Deimos. Phobos was shown to look somewhat like a potato, with one side that always faces Mars. Deimos, the other moon, was later shown to be smoother and more spherical.

Soviet Mars Landers

Mariner 9 was accompanied in flight by two heavy Soviet spacecraft, Mars 2 and Mars 3. As each craft approached Mars, a probe was separated and a small solid-propellant engine fired to deflect its course towards the atmosphere of Mars. After surviving impact, it was planned that a set of protective covers on each probe much like Luna 9, would open to permit the start of surface studies.

Mars 2 and 3 arrived at the planet Mars at the height of the 1971 dust storm, the biggest ever recorded by astronomers using Earth-based telescopes. The release of the probes could not be postponed since the primary propellant supply could not put the whole spacecraft into orbit. The probes had to be separated before their carrier space-

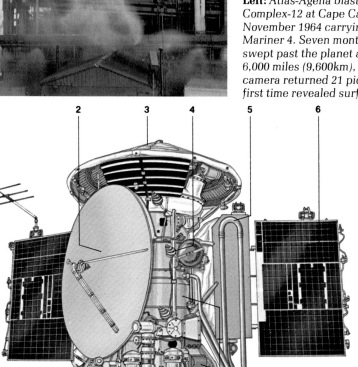

Mars 3
1 Antenna for French-supplied "Stereo" experiment.
2 High-gain parabolic antenna.
3 Descent capsule with "coolie-hat" heat shield.
4 Low-gain antenna.
5 Thermal radiator.
6 Extensible solar panels.
7 Propellant tanks.
8 Sensors for automatic navigation system.
9 Optical sensors.
10 Course-correction and braking engine.
11 Instrument compartment.

The descent capsule contained an automatic research station which erected itself automatically by opening petal-like panels which set it upright (similar to the technique used by Luna 9 on the Moon). The capsule landed on 2 December 1971 in the southern hemisphere of Mars between Electris and Phaethontis but stopped transmitting after only 20 seconds.

Mars 3 Descent
1 Descent capsule separates from orbital station (subsequently braked into orbit around Mars).
2 Path of capsule deflected to ensure landing on Mars.
3 Enters thin Martian atmosphere protected by "coolie-hat" heat shield.
4 Drogue parachute deployed by rocket, pulling out main parachute; heat shield jettisons.
5 Retro-rocket ignites; rocket deflects parachute.
6 Instrument capsule drops onto Martian surface; covers open; instruments deploy.

The Mars 3 landing capsule contained instruments for measuring atmospheric pressure and temperature and wind velocity. A mass-spectrometer was expected to determine chemical composition of the atmosphere. Also, there was apparatus for determining the chemical composition and mechanical properties of soil.

Above: *Viking 2 Lander on the Martian desert at Utopia Planitia. The rocks are typical of those found as volcanic basalts associated with thin lava fields on Earth. The colour is probably due to oxidation in the iron-rich soil, and the fine reddish dust is distributed globally on the surface and in the atmosphere.*

Right: *Sunset on Mars. To obtain this remarkable picture, the camera of the Viking 1 Lander began scanning the scene from the left about 4 minutes after the Sun had dipped below the horizon, continuing for 10 minutes. The line of the horizon is sharp and 5° above it the sky colour grades from blue to red.*

craft were inserted into orbit to reduce the total weight. The Mars 2 probe did not return any data. The Mars 3 probe did successfully land on the surface, but fell silent only 20 seconds after the start of a TV scan. What little was returned contained no distinguishable features. In the meantime the remaining portions of both spacecraft were successfully placed in highly elliptical orbits around Mars, from where they took a limited set of photographs and sampled the near-Mars environment.

The Soviet Union launched another set of spacecraft in the 1973 Mars launch window, one that was not as favourable as the 1971 window. This meant that each spacecraft could carry either propellant for orbit insertion or a re-entry probe, but not both. Mars 4 and 5 were just orbiters, while Mars 6 and 7 carried entry probes to be cast off as they flew past Mars. Mars 4's engine failed at encounter, causing it to continue on into solar orbit. Mars 5 did successfully achieve orbit and later returned data and pictures. Mars 7 arrived ahead of Mars 6, but its entry probe missed the atmosphere of Mars and entered a solar orbit. Mars 6 did successfully enter the atmosphere of Mars, but fell silent just before touchdown. It did return data for 150 seconds during descent, which helped to refine the air density profile and composition. Data from its atmosphere-sampling mass spectrometer indicated difficulty was encountered when the equipment was trying to pump itself empty, meaning it was working against a large quantity of inert gas. Soviet scientists later announced that this was interpreted to be a possibly significant argon atmospheric constituent.

Life on Mars?

The United States chose the 1975 launch window to begin the search for the presence of life on Mars. After achieving a highly elliptical orbit around Mars, Viking 1 began a TV survey of its candidate landing sites. A detailed examination of the primary site showed it to be unacceptable, so 16 days of orbital manoeuvring and survey work was required to evaluate alternate sites.

After a landing site at Chryse Planitia was finally approved, a lander vehicle was separated from the orbiter and its retro-rocket fired to send it down into the atmosphere. A heat shield, followed by a parachute and finally terminal landing rockets safely reduced the Viking Lander's descent speed to a soft Mars landing on 20 July 1976. Viking Lander 2 set down several weeks later at Utopia Planitia to begin a coordinated set of surface studies.

Once on the surface, panoramic scans of the landing sites showed them to be rock-strewn deserts with a rusty brown cast. The sky was almost pink in colour, due to a high concentration of dust in the air. The air itself was found to comprise 95 per cent carbon dioxide, 2·7 per cent nitrogen, plus traces of argon, oxygen and water vapour.

Pictures of the landing site did not show any evidence of plant life, and a gas-chromatograph used to determine soil composition was unable to detect any complex organic molecules. It was not designed for that purpose and its sensitivity level would fail to detect as many as a million bacteria per cubic centimetre. Its analysis of the soil showed it to be composed of: silicon 15-20 per cent, iron 14 per cent, plus traces of

calcium, aluminium, sulphur, titanium, magnesium, caesium and potassium.

The primary tests for life however were left to three experiments on each lander that would try to incubate living soil organisms with simulated sunlight, water, and nutrients.

Each experiment was run several times with significant variations, for example with or without simulated sunlight, surface soil or soil from under a rock shielded from the Sun's ultraviolet rays, raw soil or soil that was first sterilized at 175°C for hours.

The results were puzzling. Raw soil with simulated sunlight and water released some carbon dioxide, but even more oxygen. Without light, or if sterilized first, there was little change. The release of gases could be halted if the temperature was over 120°C. Since no organic compounds were detected in the soil (within the range of instrument sensitivity), the best conclusion that could be drawn was that the observed reactions were probably chemical due to a strong oxidiser in the soil such as hydrogen peroxide. However, since none of the sets of results could be exactly duplicated in a laboratory, there is still the remote possibility of some primitive, but exotic form of life on Mars.

Prelude to Men on Mars

Mankind will surely walk on the surface of Mars someday. Before that can happen, however, there is a great deal more that must be learned about that planet. As a result, unmanned probes will continue to fly to Mars over the next decade or more. The Soviets resumed their Mars exploration programme with the launch of two Phobos probes in 1988, designed to explore near

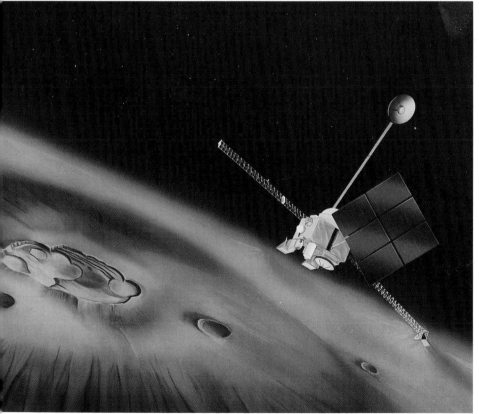

Above: *The US probe Mars Observer is scheduled to go into orbit around the planet in 1993. Its high resolution onboard camera system will be able to map surface features as small as just 5ft (1·5m) in size. Spectrometers will also conduct a mineral composition survey.*

Mars space and its inner moon Phobos in particular. The moon Phobos is a small irregular object measuring 12×14×17 miles (19×22×27km), orbiting just 5,860 miles (9,377km) from the centre of Mars. It keeps one face always pointing at Mars as it takes a mere 7hr 39min to complete one orbit.

Both spacecraft were successfully launched out of Earth orbit in July 1988. Unfortunately, an error in an uplink instruction command rendered Phobos 1 inoperable shortly thereafter, but Phobos 2 continued on to achieve an elliptical orbit around Mars in 1989. In-orbit manoeuvring over the next few months brought it into a rendezvous orbit with the moon Phobos, for a slow fly-by at less than 330ft (100m) lasting nearly half an hour. During that flyby, two lander probes were to be released to provide a direct measure of the chemical and physical properties of the moon. Approximately two weeks before the flyby, Phobos 2 was commanded to change from an Earth orientation to point in another direction for a data-gathering session, as it had done many times before during the mission. At the end of that session, it was programmed to return to an Earth orientation to resume communications. However, radio contact was never re-established, and Phobos 2 was declared lost, just short of its goal. A tremendous amount of data had been obtained up to that point that would take years to analyse. However, since the primary mission for both spacecraft was not achieved, plans for follow-on missions had to be reassessed.

The United States is planning to resume its Mars exploration programme with the Mars Observer, scheduled to achieve Mars orbit in August 1993. From a near-polar elliptical orbit it will scan the surface below over the next two Martian years (687 Earth days per year). A mineral composition survey will be conducted using a gamma-ray, and a visual and infra-red spectrometer with

Viking Orbiter

1 S-band low-gain antenna
2 Stray light sensor.
3 Orbiter propulsion engine, 300lb (136kg) thrust, gimbal-mounted.
4 Fuel tank (monomethyl-hydrazine).
5 Pressurant tank (helium).
6 Oxidiser tank (N_2O_4).
7 Relay antenna.
8 S- and X-band high-gain antenna.
9 Sun gate detector and cruise Sun sensor.
10 Infra-red thermal mapper.
11 Visual imaging camera.
12 Mars atmospheric water detector.
13 Orbiter "bus".
14 Thermal control louvres.
15 Attitude control thrusters (CO_2).
16 Solar panel (4), generates electricity from sunlight.
17 Canopus tracker.

Technical Data
Orbiter body: an octagonal ring 18in (45·7cm) high with alternate 55in (139·7cm) and 20in (50·8cm) sides. Weight, with propellants: 5,125lb (2,324kg). Prime contractor: Jet Propulsion Laboratory.

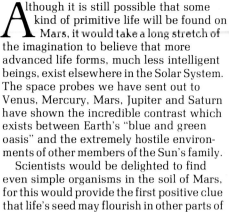
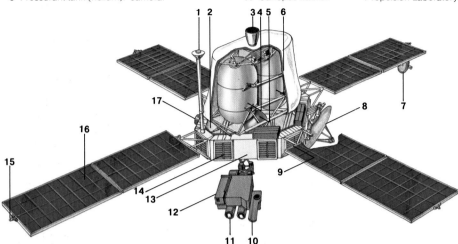

Viking Lander: Descent Profile

1 Separation from orbiting mothercraft.
2 Deorbit orientation.
3 Deorbit burn (8 engines, hydrazine monopropellant).
4 Coast (data relay to Orbiter for onward transmission to Earth).
5 Entry into Martian atmosphere at 800,000ft (243,840m). Aeroshell separates. Descent speed at this point is 560mph (900km/h).
6 Parachute deploys at 19,000ft (5,791m).
7 Parachute jettisons: terminal descent begins at 4,600ft (1,402m). Descent speed drops from about 145mph (233km/h) to 6mph (9·6km/h) under rocket braking.
8 Soft-landing. Foot pad sensors shut down engines.

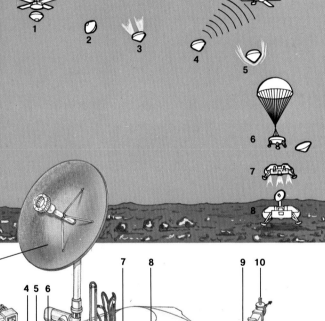

Although it is still possible that some kind of primitive life will be found on Mars, it would take a long stretch of the imagination to believe that more advanced life forms, much less intelligent beings, exist elsewhere in the Solar System. The space probes we have sent out to Venus, Mercury, Mars, Jupiter and Saturn have shown the incredible contrast which exists between Earth's "blue and green oasis" and the extremely hostile environments of other members of the Sun's family.

Scientists would be delighted to find even simple organisms in the soil of Mars, for this would provide the first positive clue that life's seed may flourish in other parts of the Universe. In 1976 the United States landed two Viking spacecraft on the Martian deserts. The first touched down on Chryse Planitia on 20 July, the second on Utopia Planitia on 3 September.

While the Viking mothercraft made observations from orbit, each Lander's onboard computer was programmed (by JPL controllers) to test the soil for signs of life. A mechanical arm scooped up samples and transferred them to an automatic biological laboratory inside the Lander for analysis. Although strong chemical reactions were obtained, there was no certain proof that the soil contained microbes.

In the meantime, the United States had begun to investigate the giant gas planet Jupiter which received its first robot visitors, Pioneers 10 and 11, on 4 December 1973 and 5 December 1974 respectively; Pioneer 11 went on to achieve a close encounter with Saturn on 1 September 1979.

These spacecraft (both of which returned much scientific data) were pathfinders for larger Voyager spacecraft which probed Jupiter, Saturn, Uranus and Neptune, and several of their moons with such spectacular and exciting results between 1979 and 1989.

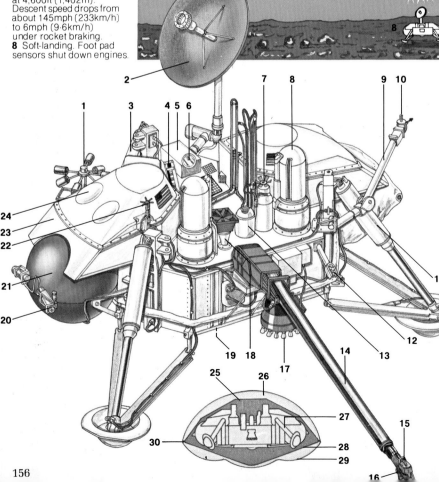

Viking Lander

1 Ultra-high frequency antenna (relay).
2 S-band high-gain antenna (direct).
3 Seismometer.
4 Magnet and camera test target.
5 Radar altimeter electronics No 2.
6 Magnifying mirror.
7 Gas chromatograph mass spectrometer processor.
8 Television camera (2).
9 Meteorology boom assembly.
10 Meteorology sensors.
11 Landing shock absorber.
12 Magnet cleaning brush.
13 Biology processor.
14 Surface sampler boom.
15 Sampler head.
16 Magnets.
17 Terminal descent engine (1 of 3) — 18 nozzles each, hydrazine mono-propellant, throttleable between 62 and 638lb (28·1 and 289·4kg).
18 X-ray fluorescence funnel.
19 Radar antenna and Terminal Descent Landing Radar (underside of Lander structure).
20 Roll engine (4), hydrazine monopropellant, 8·7lb (3·94kg) thrust.
21 Terminal descent propellant tank (2).
22 S-band low gain antenna.
23 Radioisotope Thermoelectric Generator wind cover (2).
24 RTG power source (2) inside cover.

Encapsulated Viking Lander
25 Aeroshell cover.
26 Bioshield cap.
27 Lander, legs in stowed position.
28 Aeroshell heatshield.
29 Bioshield base.
30 Separation point.

The Lander biology unit in 1ft³ (0·028m³) of space, contained: 3 automated chemical labs, a computer, tiny ovens, counters for radioactive tracers, filters, sun lamp, gas chromatograph to identify chemicals, 40 thermostats, 22,000 transistors, 18,000 other electronic parts, and 43 miniature valves.

Technical Data
The Lander body is a hollow six-sided box 18·2in (46·2cm) deep enclosed by cover plates, top and bottom. The six sides are 43in (109·2cm) and 22in (55·9cm) alternately. Height, from footpads to top of S-band antenna: 7ft (2·13m).

Encounter with Jupiter—1

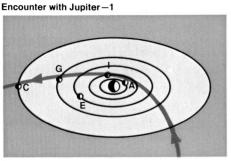

Encounter with Jupiter—2

Encounter with Saturn—1

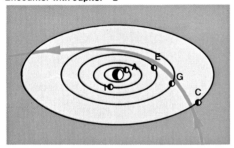

Encounter with Saturn—2

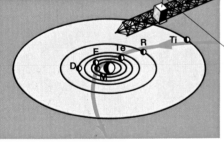

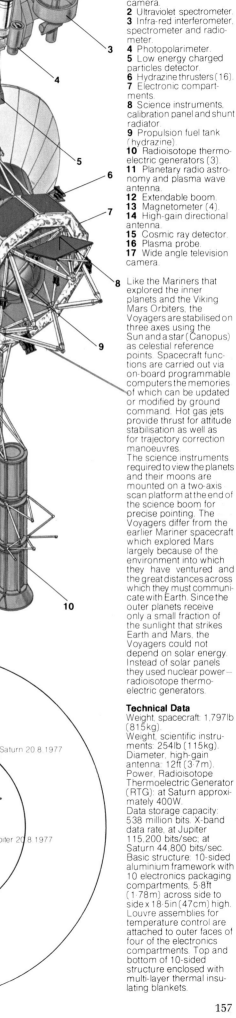

Voyager Spacecraft
1 Narrow angle television camera.
2 Ultraviolet spectrometer.
3 Infra-red interferometer, spectrometer and radiometer.
4 Photopolarimeter.
5 Low energy charged particles detector.
6 Hydrazine thrusters (16).
7 Electronic compartments.
8 Science instruments, calibration panel and shunt radiator.
9 Propulsion fuel tank (hydrazine).
10 Radioisotope thermoelectric generators (3).
11 Planetary radio astronomy and plasma wave antenna.
12 Extendable boom.
13 Magnetometer (4).
14 High-gain directional antenna.
15 Cosmic ray detector.
16 Plasma probe.
17 Wide angle television camera.

Like the Mariners that explored the inner planets and the Viking Mars Orbiters, the Voyagers are stabilised on three axes using the Sun and a star (Canopus) as celestial reference points. Spacecraft functions are carried out via on-board programmable computers the memories of which can be updated or modified by ground command. Hot gas jets provide thrust for attitude stabilisation as well as for trajectory correction manoeuvres.

The science instruments required to view the planets and their moons are mounted on a two-axis scan platform at the end of the science boom for precise pointing. The Voyagers differ from the earlier Mariner spacecraft which explored Mars largely because of the environment into which they have ventured and the great distances across which they must communicate with Earth. Since the outer planets receive only a small fraction of the sunlight that strikes Earth and Mars, the Voyagers could not depend on solar energy. Instead of solar panels they used nuclear power— radioisotope thermoelectric generators.

Encounter with Jupiter—1
Voyager 1 allowed scientists to study in detail Jupiter's Great Red Spot, banded clouds and intense belts of radiation previously explored by the Pioneer probes. Its unique flight path permitted study at close range of five of Jupiter's moons. Each is shown at its closest point to the trajectory. Voyager 1 passed within 177,720 miles (286,000km) of the giant planet on 5 March 1979.

Encounter with Jupiter—2
Voyager 2 passed within 399,560 miles (643,000km) of the planet on 9 July 1979, on a more cautious trajectory that avoided much of Jupiter's intense radiation. The spacecraft encountered the moons on its approach path. Jovian moons on Voyagers' tracks:
A — Amalthea; **C** — Callisto;
E — Europa; **I** — Io;
G — Ganymede.

Encounter with Saturn—1
Voyager 1 passed about 77,000 miles (124,200km) below Saturn's south pole on 12 November 1980. Wide-angle and narrow-angle cameras, polarimetric, ultraviolet and

infra-red instruments scanned the planet and its rings. Saturn's moons were also scanned.

Encounter with Saturn—2
Voyager 2 passed within 63,000 miles (101,385km) of the cloud tops of Saturn on 25 August 1981 making a detailed examination of the complex ring system. Discovered narrow ring in the Encke division; and some six new moons making total of 23. Spacecraft was gravitationally diverted to Uranus which it should reach in 1986.
Saturnian moons on Voyagers' tracks:
D — Dione; **E** — Enceladus;
M — Mimas; **R** — Rhea;
Ti — Titan; **Te** — Tethys.

Voyager Flight Paths
Voyager 1 (red).
1 Earth launch 5 September 1977.*
2 Jupiter fly-by 5 March 1979.
3 Saturn fly-by 12 November 1980.

Voyager 2 (green).
1 Earth launch 20 August 1977.
2 Jupiter fly-by 9 July 1979.
3 Saturn fly-by 25 August 1981.
4 Uranus fly-by 30 January 1986.

*Voyager 1, launched second, overtook Voyager 2 while en route to Jupiter.

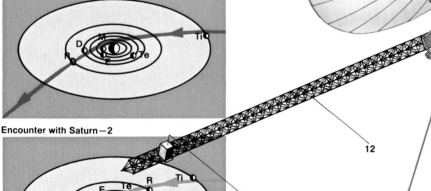

Technical Data
Weight, spacecraft: 1,797lb (815kg).
Weight, scientific instruments: 254lb (115kg).
Diameter, high-gain antenna: 12ft (3·7m).
Power, Radioisotope Thermoelectric Generator (RTG): at Saturn approximately 400W.
Data storage capacity: 538 million bits. X-band data rate, at Jupiter 115,200 bits/sec; at Saturn 44,800 bits/sec.
Basic structure: 10-sided aluminium framework with 10 electronics packaging compartments, 5·8ft (1·78m) across side to side x 18·5in (47cm) high. Louvre assemblies for temperature control are attached to outer faces of four of the electronics compartments. Top and bottom of 10-sided structure enclosed with multi-layer thermal insulating blankets.

Above: *Mariner 10 undergoes a pre-launch check at the Boeing Space Center, Kent, Washington, where it was manufactured for NASA. The two tiltable solar panels are deployed and extensive thermal shielding is evident. Mariner 10 made a gravity-swing past Venus in February 1974 to reach Mercury in March of that year.*

Right: *A photomosaic of the surface of Mercury composed of eighteen pictures taken at 62-second intervals by Mariner 10's two TV cameras. The pictures were taken when Mariner was about six hours away from its close encounter with the planet on 29 March 1974. The largest craters are 124 miles (200km) across.*

Mariner 10

1 Low-gain antenna.
2 Airglow ultraviolet spectrometer.
3 Television camera (2).
4 Scan platform.
5 Charged particle telescope.
6 Occultation ultraviolet spectrometer.
7 Cruise Sun sensor.
8 Magnetometer.
9 Sunshade.
10 Acquisition Sun sensor.
11 Reaction control jets (roll and yaw).
12 Plasma science experiment.
13 Infra-red radiometer.
14 Thermal control blanket.
15 Heat shield.
16 High-gain antenna (motor-driven).
17 Canopus tracker.
18 Tiltable solar array.
19 X-band radio transmitter (hidden behind Canopus tracker).

Mercury Trajectory (right)

Conceived as a double planet probe, Mariner 10—launched November 1973—flew past Venus in early February 1974. Accelerated by Venus' gravitational field, Mariner 10 then flew on to encounter Mercury for the first time in late March, skimming the planet at a distance of only 437 miles (703km). Mariner 10 then went into a tight orbit about the Sun. This was designed to cross Mercury's path so as to allow further encounters, and these took place in September 1974 and March 1975.

Technical Data

Basic bus: 54·5in (1·3m) across diagonals, 18in (0·46m) deep.
Solar panels: 106in (2·7m) long, 38in (0·97m) wide; total area 54·9 sq ft (5·1m²); output 455W (at Mercury).
Total weight c1,110lb (503kg).
Science package: 170lb (77kg).
Design: Boeing Aerospace Company.

Mariner 10, launched on 3 November 1973, was an extremely successful space probe designed to investigate and report on the physical characteristics of the two innermost planets, Mercury and Venus. For the first time in a major space venture, the gravity-assist technique was used, the pull of Venus being harnessed to provide enough energy for the craft to continue on to its smaller neighbour. The planets' relative alignment was crucial to the outcome of the mission, and hence the programme had to be rigidly scheduled.

a ground resolution of just 325ft (100m). An onboard camera system, with a ground resolution of 5ft (1·5m) will map the surface in sufficient detail to locate earlier Viking and Soviet Mars lander probes.

If the Soviets choose not to repeat the Phobos missions, the Mars Observer may be joined in Mars orbit in the late 1990s by two Soviet spacecraft with camera systems to conduct similar surveys. After achieving Mars orbit, each will release a large re-entry capsule into the atmosphere below. Each capsule will deliver a French designed balloon payload that will inflate and deploy right after re-entry. These instrumented payloads will consist of an upper helium balloon and a lower balloon with an open base. Attached to them will be an instrument drag rope, looking like a tail of tin cans. During the Martian nights, the instrument tail will rest on the surface, conducting various experiments and studies. During the day, atmospheric carbon dioxide in the black lower balloon will warm and expand, inflating it to increase the overall buoyancy. When fully inflated, the balloons will rise to an altitude of 5 miles (8km) where they will travel as much as 300 miles (500km) before sundown. Then they will cool and settle back to the surface at night to start the cycle over again. Sections of the tails will be released to compensate for loss of buoyancy as the missions progress. Smaller probes may be released from either the orbiter or the balloon to send back meteorological and seismic data from different points over the planet. Data returned from these separate spacecraft sections will provide valuable information for planning of missions that will follow.

A pair of small Soviet rover vehicles may be delivered to the surface of Mars in 1997, where they could travel up to 62 miles (100km) over the next three years. Mars soil samples could be collected by Soviet

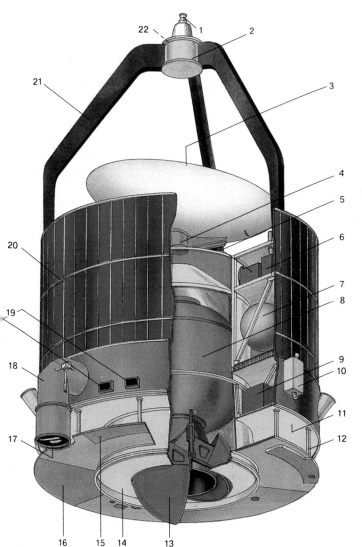

Giotto
1 Low-gain cardioid antenna.
2 S-band and X-band feed.
3 High-gain dish antenna.
4 Despin mechanism.
5 Travelling-wave-tube amplifier.
6 Optical probe experiment.
7 Hydrazine tank.
8 Mage-1S kick motor.
9 Experiment box.
10 Attitude control thrusters.
11 Rear shield (13·5mm thick Kevlar-49/polyurethane foam sandwich).
12 GRP strut.
13 Nozzle closure shells.
14 Inner bumper shield.
15 Dust impact detector (DID) system sensor (3+1 on rear shield).
16 Outer bumper shield (1mm thick aluminium alloy sheet).
17 Multicolour camera telescope (modified Ritchey-Chrétien).
18 Camera telescope baffle.
19 Experiment sensors.
20 Solar cell array.
21 Hollow carbon-fibre tripod.
22 Magnetometer sensor (hidden in this view).

The Giotto probe was launched by Ariane on 2 July 1985 for a rendezvous some eight months later with Halley's Comet. The spin-stabilized spacecraft carried ten scientific instruments to study the comet: a camera; neutral mass, ion mass and dust mass spectrometers; a dust impact detector system; two plasma analyzers; a magnetometer; an energetic particles experiment; and an optical probe.

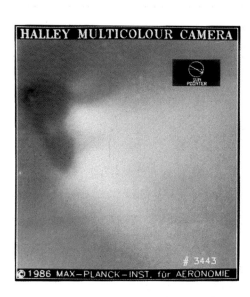

HALLEY MULTICOLOUR CAMERA

SUN POINTER

3443

© 1986 MAX-PLANCK-INST. für AERONOMIE

Above: *Giotto returned this image of Halley's Comet on 14 March 1986 from a distance of about 11,200 miles (18,000km). The comet's solid nucleus is the dark area visible in the top left of the picture.*

missions in either 1999 or 2001 for return to Earth. These could finally help resolve the questions of the specific chemistry that produced the puzzling results in 1976 when the American Viking spacecraft made their initial searches for life.

By the turn of the century, sufficient information will have been gained about detailed Martian topography and the availability of important minerals and chemicals to make planning for possible manned expeditions to Mars possible. The moon Phobos may well serve as an outpost before descent to the surface. Building materials and supplies derived from the Martian surface will make a permanent base there possible. Therefore, by the second or third decade into the 21st century, there may well be men and women from Earth walking on the surface of Mars.

Mercury

The United States has expanded its exploration of the Solar System outwards beyond Mars and inwards from Venus. The first Mercury mission was Mariner 10, a dual planet probe launched first toward Venus in 1973. As it passed by Venus its trajectory was dramatically altered: slowing it down and deflecting it inwards towards the Sun. On 29 March 1974 the spacecraft reached its primary objective, Mercury, passing within 430 miles (690km) of the planet's night side. That fly-by distance had been carefully chosen to ensure that Mariner 10 would meet Mercury at least once more. The propellant supply was sufficient to

permit course refinements and attitude control for a total of three Mercury encounters, each about six months apart. During each fly-by extensive surface studies were conducted. Mercury was found to have a faint trace atmosphere of argon, neon and helium, one trillionth that of Earth's. Surface temperatures were found to range from 510°C to −210°C. A magnetic field of 1 per cent that of the strength of Earth's was found, and the planet's mass was measured to be 6 per cent that of Earth. This means Mercury has a huge Earth-like iron core some 1,000miles (1,600km) in diameter just below its surface. Pictures of the surface itself showed it to be heavily cratered like the Moon, but unlike the Moon it has scarps or cliffs which run for hundreds of kilometres across its face, sometimes slicing through older features. These may be the equivalent of wrinkles formed by surface compression when the core shrank as it cooled thousands of millions of years ago.

Comets

1986 marked the year of the return of Halley's Comet. Japan, the Soviet Union, and the European Space Agency (ESA) all planned missions to benefit from this once in a lifetime opportunity. Funding constraints prevented the United States from participating. However, studies showed that the International Sun-Earth Explorer-3 (ISEE-3) spacecraft launched in 1978 into a halo orbit between the Earth and the Sun still possessed enough propellant to conduct an alternate comet fly-by mission. Starting in

1982, it was manoeuvred back into an orbit around Earth, and then commanded through a series of five lunar fly-bys that gradually built up its velocity for an escape trajectory. Once free of the Earth's gravitational field, it was renamed the International Comet Explorer (ICE) and given course adjustments that sent it within 4,910 miles (7,900km) of the nucleus of the short period comet Giacobini-Zinner on 11 September 1985. Its 20 minute passage through the coma was mankind's first direct contact with a comet.

This encounter was followed just six months later by a retinue of five spacecraft that each conducted separate fly-bys of and through Halley's Comet in March 1986. The Japanese Sakigake and Suisei probes made passages through the shock wave well in front of the comet. The Vega 1 and 2 probes, after casting off lander probes at the planet Venus, made penetrations into the coma within 5,600 miles (9,000km) of the nucleus. Finally the ESA Giotto spacecraft plunged to within 375 miles (600km) of the nucleus, sustaining so many impacts in the process that it is probably coated with as much as 20lb (12kg) of comet material.

What the probes found was a strange object indeed. Foggy images of the peanut shaped nucleus showed it to be extremely dark, measuring 5 x 5 x 10 miles (8 x 8 x 16km), with a period of rotation of approximately 53 to 56 hours. Most of the surface was inactive, probably covered with a thin crust of dark carbon-based and other materials. Cracks in that crust, representing about 10 per cent of the total surface area, produced seven jets that spewed forth as much as 20 metric tonnes of comet material per second. This consisted of about 80 per cent water, 10 per cent carbon monoxide, plus traces of carbon dioxide, methane, ammonia, and hypocyanic acid. About 3 metric tonnes of dust was also being generated per second. That was a miniscule amount compared to the overall nucleus mass of approximately 100 thousand million metric tonnes. These findings confirmed earlier theories that comets were essentially giant flying "dirty snowballs".

Above: *Engineering mockup of Pioneer 10. The 9ft (2·74m) diameter antenna dish is surmounted by a medium-gain horn antenna. Two Radioisotope Thermic Generators and a magnetometer are mounted on extensible booms.*

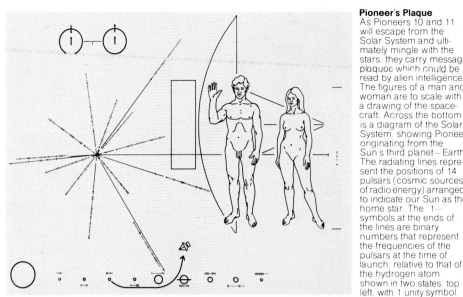

Pioneer's Plaque
As Pioneers 10 and 11 will escape from the Solar System and ultimately mingle with the stars, they carry message plaques which could be read by alien intelligence. The figures of a man and woman are to scale with a drawing of the spacecraft. Across the bottom is a diagram of the Solar System, showing Pioneer originating from the Sun's third planet — Earth. The radiating lines represent the positions of 14 pulsars (cosmic sources of radio energy) arranged to indicate our Sun as the home star. The '1—' symbols at the ends of the lines are binary numbers that represent the frequencies of the pulsars at the time of launch, relative to that of the hydrogen atom shown in two states, top left, with 1 unity symbol.

The Other Planets

Exploration of the outer planets of the Solar System began in 1972 with the launch of Pioneer 10. Missions of this sort require long travel times into regions where the Sun's light is too weak to generate solar power needed to energise the spacecraft systems. The solution was to design the spacecraft around a large dish antenna and to power it with nuclear thermoelectric generators. Attitude-control propellant expenditure is kept to a minimum by spin-stabilising the craft at 5rpm, with the spin and antenna axis kept pointed at Earth.

Pioneer 10 was aimed at Jupiter, a trip that required 21 months and nearly 600 million miles (one thousand million kilometres) of travel. About 180 days into the mission it entered the asteroid belt between Mars and Jupiter, but passed through unscathed. The Jupiter encounter phase lasted two months with the closest approach 81,000 miles (130,300km) occuring on 3 December 1973 (US time). As it swept past the largest of all planets, Pioneer 10 returned over 300 medium-resolution pictures of Jupiter and its satellites. The gravitational field of Jupiter then whipped it into a trajectory that would carry it past the orbit of Pluto by 1987, to become the first man-made object to leave the Solar System. In eight million years it will reach a point in space where Aldebaran is today.

Pioneer 11 launched a year later flew 26,680 miles (42,940km) past Jupiter in December 1974 and received the same swingby kick to its trajectory. This time, however, the impulse sent the craft into a huge arc, 100 million miles (160 million kilometres) above the plane of the Solar System to an encounter with Saturn.

Pioneer 10 and 11 provided the first close-up pictures of Jupiter and sampled the full strength of its lethal radiation fields. They found its trapped radiation belts to be 10,000 times more intense than Earth's Van

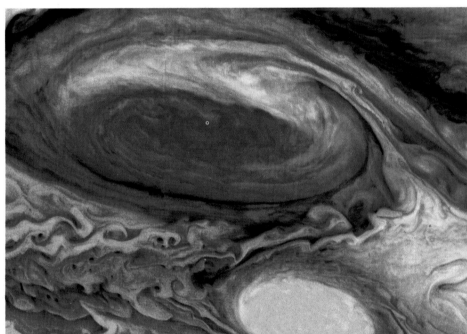

Above: *Jupiter's Great Red Spot and its turbulent surroundings are shown in exaggerated colour which tends to emphasise red and blue. Large enough to swallow several Earths, it is a tremendous atmospheric storm that rotates counter-clockwise every six days. At the bottom is one of three oval cloud systems which formed nearly 40 years ago.*

Right: *Voyager 1 took this photograph of Jupiter on 1 February 1979 from a distance of 20 million miles (32·7 million km). The Great Red Spot has been observed by astronomers for hundreds of years but never in this fantastic detail. Other discoveries included auroras and lightning in Jupiter's atmosphere, new moons and a thin ring around the planet.*

Allen belts, and its pulsating magnetic field, which can extend outward to the orbit of Saturn, to be generated by a large ring current plus many smaller eddies deep below the planet's surface.

Pioneer 11 went on to pass within 21,000 miles (34,000km) of Saturn's main outer ring system on 1 September 1979, returning valuable composition information on the ring system that extends nearly 62,140 miles (100,000km) out from the planet.

Both Pioneers were aptly named, for they were intended to pave the way for heavier spacecraft that would follow, spacecraft whose design would depend on the severity of the micrometeoroid environment and the strength of planetary radiation fields.

The Pioneers returned images of the

cloud cover of Jupiter and Saturn by relying on the spacecraft spin to scan individual pictures: an effective but slow process. Far better and clearer pictures were to come with the Jupiter fly-by missions of Voyager 1 and 2 in 1979. Imaging started 80 days before encounter and by ten days before closest approach they were better than any returned from Pioneer. Voyager 1 passed within 177,720 miles (286,000km) of Jupiter and Voyager 2 within 400,000 miles (643,000km), providing truly incredible views of the cloud cover below. Jupiter's atmosphere was shown to be a turbulent, ever-changing mass of reds, oranges, yellows, browns, and even blues. Individual bands would narrow or widen, merge or come apart as they interfered and mixed with one

Right: *An enormous volcanic explosion on the Jovian moon Io captured by Voyager 1 from a distance of about 304,000 miles (490,000km). In this computer-enhanced photograph solid material is being thrown up 100 miles (161km) at about 1,200mph (1,930km/h). At least eight active volcanoes were observed on Io.*

another. Individual vortices would overtake one another, sometimes reversing their rotational direction only to be deflected in another direction. The Great Red Spot, the only permanent feature on the planet's face, displayed a rather static, though granular centre, surrounded by a counterclockwise rotating cloud mass.

The camera systems were also trained on Jupiter's four water-ice and rock, planet-

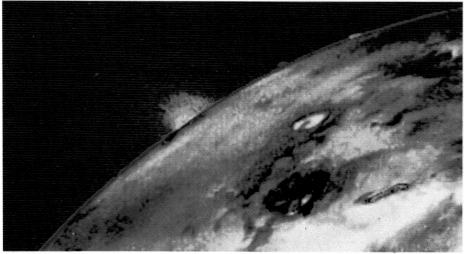

sized moons, revealing each to be unique and distinctly different from the others: Callisto, with an impact feature surrounded by eight to ten concentric frozen ripple-like rings extending across 620 miles (1,000km); Europa, orange hued and featureless except for huge ray-like cracks running for many hundreds of kilometres in random directions across its surface; Ganymede, a blue and brown ice world with strange bright white patches; and Io. Io was known to be different, orbiting within a highly ionised sulphur plasma torus and "attached" to Jupiter via a 400,000-volt, 1 million-ampere electromagnetic flux tube that continually bombards it with high-energy particles. Voyager showed Io to be a young waterless world totally devoid of craters, but possessing at least eight highly active volcanoes. Its smooth face was covered with yellow and reddish blotches with patches of white plus pock-marks of deep black. The magnitude of

the volcanic activity indicates that it resurfaces itself in as little as a million years.

As Voyager 1 was drawing away from Jupiter, a long time exposure revealed for the first time the presence of a faint ring system whose outer edge was some 35,500 miles (57,000km) above the clouds. A thorough analysis of the images revealed the existence of four previously unknown moons, bringing to 16 the number orbiting Jupiter.

The Jupiter fly-bys propelled each Voyager towards their next destination, the planet Saturn, for a closer look at its system of rings and moons. As each swept by Saturn in November 1980 and August 1981, they found a planet whose cloud cover was more subdued than Jupiter. Saturn possesses bands like Jupiter, but absent are the vivid colours, turbulence and any large spots. But unlike Jupiter, Saturn possesses a magnificent system of rings that can be clearly

seen from Earth. As the spacecraft drew closer to Saturn, what appeared at a distance to be three broad rings could soon be seen to be made up of hundreds of individual narrow ringlets of water ice debris. Four more rings were eventually discovered, bringing to seven the total number for Saturn. One of these, the new F-ring, was made up of three intertwining, or braided ringlets, the braiding being caused by the gravitational effects of two tiny shepherd moons just inside and outside the ring. Another inner, tiny moon produced the sharp outer edge of the A-ring. Other tiny moons were found at positions 60 degrees ahead of and behind larger moons: two co-orbital with the moon Tethys, one with the moon Dione, and two more in a co-orbit of their own.

Saturn is now known to possess no fewer than 22 moons ranging in size from a few miles to over 3,000 miles (over 5000km).

PLANETARY SPACECRAFT					
NAME		**DATE**	**BOOSTER**	**WEIGHT** lb (kg)	**MISSION**
Pioneer 5	(USA)	11 Mar 60	Thor-Able	95 (43)	First deep-space probe, returned data from a distance of 22·7 million miles (36·5 million kilometres)
Mars	(USSR)	10 Oct 60	A-2-e	1,410 (640)*	Mars probe, failed to achieve Earth orbit
Mars	(USSR)	14 Oct 60	A-2-e	1,410 (640)*	Mars probe, failed to achieve Earth orbit
Sputnik 7	(USSR)	4 Feb 61	A-2-e	1,410 (640)*	Venus probe, failed to leave Earth orbit
Venera 1	(USSR)	12 Feb 61	A-2-e	1,419 (644)	Passed within 62,000 miles (100,000km) of Venus but failed before encounter
Mariner 1	(USA)	22 Jul 62	Atlas-Agena	445 (202)	Venus probe, failed to achieve Earth orbit
Venera	(USSR)	25 Aug 62	A-2-e	1,960 (890)*	Venus probe, failed to leave Earth orbit
Mariner 2	(USA)	27 Aug 62	Atlas-Agena	447 (202·7)	First successful fly-by of Venus. Found heavy atmosphere and hot surface. No magnetic field
Venera	(USSR)	1 Sep 62	A-2-e	1,960 (890)*	Venus probe, failed to leave Earth orbit
Venera	(USSR)	12 Sept 62	A-2-e	1,960 (890)*	Venus probe, failed to leave Earth orbit
Mars	(USSR)	24 Oct 62	A-2-e	1,960 (890)*	Mars probe, failed to leave Earth orbit
Mars I	(USSR)	1 Nov 62	A-2-e	1,970 (893)	Mars probe, passed within 120,000 miles (193,000km) of Mars but failed before encounter and before mid-course correction
Mars	(USSR)	4 Nov 62	A-2-e	1,960 (890)*	Mars probe, failed to leave Earth orbit
Cosmos 21	(USSR)	11 Nov 63	A-2-e	1,960 (890)*	Venus probe, failed to leave Earth orbit
Cosmos 27	(USSR)	27 Mar 64	A-2-e	1,960 (890)*	Venus probe, failed to leave Earth orbit
Zond 1	(USSR)	2 Apr 64	A-2-e	1,960 (890)*	Venus probe, passed within 62,000 miles (100,000km) of Venus, but failed before encounter
Mariner 3	(USA)	5 Nov 64	Atlas-Agena	575 (261)	Mars probe, failed to achieve Earth orbit
Mariner 4	(USA)	28 Nov 64	Atlas-Agena	575 (261)	First successful fly-by of Mars. 21 pictures returned. Found cratered surface, no canals or flowing water. Mostly CO_2 atmosphere, 1 per cent of Earth's sea-level pressure
Zond 2	(USSR)	30 Nov 64	A-2-e	1,960 (890)*	Mars probe, passed within 930 miles (1,500km) of Mars but failed before encounter
Venera 2	(USSR)	12 Nov 65	A-2-e	2,123 (963)	Venus fly-by, probe failed at encounter
Venera 3	(USSR)	16 Nov 65	A-2-e	2,120 (960)	First Venus atmosphere entry, failed to return any data
Cosmos 96	(USSR)	23 Nov 65	A-2-e	2,120 (960)*	Venus probe, failed to leave Earth orbit
Pioneer 6	(USA)	16 Dec 65	Thrust-Aug Delta	135 (61)	Solar probe orbiting Sun inside Earth's orbit
Pioneer 7	(USA)	17 Aug 66	Thrust-Aug Delta	135 (61)	Solar probe orbiting Sun outside Earth's orbit
Venera 4	(USSR)	12 Jun 67	A-2-e	2,439 (1,106)	First successful Venus atmosphere entry. Returned data to within 15·5 miles (25km) of surface. Entry probe 845lb (383kg)
Mariner 5	(USA)	14 Jun 67	Atlas-Agena	540 (245)	Venus probe fly-by, 2,500 miles (4,000km) from planet
Cosmos 167	(USSR)	17 Jun 67	A-2-e	2,425 (1,100)*	Venus probe, failed to leave Earth orbit
Pioneer 8	(USA)	13 Dec 67	Thrust-Aug Delta	145 (66)	Solar probe orbiting Sun outside Earth's orbit
Pioneer 9	(USA)	8 Nov 68	Thrust-Aug Delta	148 (67)	Solar probe orbiting Sun inside Earth's orbit
Venera 5	(USSR)	5 Jan 69	A-2-e	2,490 (1,130)	Venus atmosphere entry probe, 893lb (405kg). Crushed during descent
Venera 6	(USSR)	10 Jan 69	A-2-e	2,490 (1,130)	Venus atmosphere entry probe, 893lb (405kg). Crushed during descent
Mariner 6	(USA)	24 Feb 69	Atlas-Centaur	911 (413)	Mars fly-by probe, returned data and 75 pictures
Mariner 7	(USA)	27 Mar 69	Atlas-Centaur	911 (413)	Mars fly-by probe, returned data and 126 pictures
Mars	(USSR)	27 Mar 69	D-1-e	7,035 (3,190)	Mars probe, failed to reach Earth orbit
Pioneer E	(USA)	27 Aug 69	Thrust-Aug Delta	148 (67)	Solar probe, failed to achieve Earth orbit
Venera 7	(USSR)	17 Aug 70	A-2-e	2,600 (1,180)	Venus atmosphere entry probe, 1,091lb (495kg). First successfully to survive to surface
Cosmos 359	(USSR)	22 Aug 70	A-2-e	2,600 (1,180)*	Venus probe, failed to leave Earth orbit
Mariner 8	(USA)	8 May 71	Atlas-Centaur	2,273 (1,031)	Mars probe, failed to achieve Earth orbit
Cosmos 419	(USSR)	10 May 71	D-1-e	10,250 (4,650)*	Mars probe, failed to leave Earth orbit
Mars 2	(USSR)	19 May 71	D-1-e	10,253 (4,650)	Mars probe. Returned data from orbit but lander failed to return any data
Mars 3	(USSR)	28 May 71	D-1-e	10,253 (4,650)	Mars probe. Returned data from orbit but lander failed after reaching surface. Entry probe 1,400lb (635kg); surface payload 992lb (450kg).
Mariner 9	(USA)	30 May 71	Atlas-Centaur	2,270 (1,030)	First successful Mars orbiter. Returned over 7,000 pictures of surface and moons
Pioneer 10	(USA)	3 Mar 72	Atlas-Centaur	570 (258)	First successful fly-by of Jupiter
Venera 8	(USSR)	27 Mar 72	A-2-e	2,602 (1,180)	Venus atmosphere entry probe, 1,090lb (495kg). Returned air and surface data from day side
Cosmos 482	(USSR)	31 Mar 72	A-2-e	2,600 (1,180)*	Venus probe, failed to leave Earth orbit
Pioneer 11	(USA)	6 Apr 73	Atlas-Centaur	571 (259)	Jupiter probe. First successful fly-by of Saturn providing detailed view of ring structure

Note: Actual Soviet spacecraft weights are those quoted by *Tass*, the official Soviet News Agency. All others are estimates and are indicated by an asterisk (*).

Images of the six larger moons showed them to be scarred with impact craters: one on Mimas was nearly one third the diameter of that moon. A 2,500 mile (4,000km) fly-by of the largest moon, Titan, revealed its thick, opaque, orange atmosphere to be made up of nitrogen and methane, with a base pressure 1·6 times that of Earth at sea level.

Left: *A spectacular montage of Voyager 1 and 2 images obtained during their encounters with Saturn. The satellites shown are (clockwise from upper right) Titan, Iapetus, Tethys, Mimas, Enceladus, Dione, and Rhea. Hyperion and Phoebe are not shown, nor are the thirteen smaller satellites that were discovered by the Voyagers during their fly-bys. The biggest of Saturn's moons is Titan which, with a diameter of 3,194 miles (5,140km), is larger than the planet Mercury. It possesses an extremely dense atmosphere.*

PLANETARY SPACECRAFT

NAME		DATE	BOOSTER	WEIGHT lb (kg)	MISSION
Mars 4	(USSR)	21 Jul 73	D-1-e	8,710 (3,950)*	Mars probe failed to achieve orbit. Returned fly-by data
Mars 5	(USSR)	25 Jul 73	D-1-e	8,710 (3,950)*	Returned data from Mars orbit
Mars 6	(USSR)	5 Aug 73	D-1-e	8,710 (3,950)*	Mars fly-by. Lander returned 150sec of data during descent
Mars 7	(USSR)	9 Aug 73	D-1-e	8,710 (3,950)*	Mars fly-by. Lander probe failed to enter Mars atmosphere
Mariner 10	(USA)	3 Nov 73	Atlas-Centaur	1,109 (503)	First TV pictures of Venus during fly-by. Three fly-by encounters with Mercury
Helios 1	(Germany)	10 Dec 74	Titan III/Centaur	816 (370)	Solar probe orbiting within 0·3 AU of Sun
Venera 9	(USSR)	8 Jun 75	D-1-e	10,884 (4,936)	Venus lander. Returned data and first TV pictures from surface. Orbiter returned data. Entry sphere 3,440lb (1,560kg); surface payload 1,455lb (660kg).
Venera 10	(USSR)	14 Jun 75	D-1-e	11,098 (5,033)	Venus lander returned data and pictures from surface. Orbiter returned data. Entry sphere 3,440lb (1,560kg); surface payload 1,455lb (660kg).
Viking 1	(USA)	20 Aug 75	Titan III/Centaur	7,497 (3,400)	Mars orbiter returned pictures and data. First successful Mars landing. Returned pictures and data. Orbiter 5,125lb (2,224kg). Lander surface weight 1,270lb (576kg)
Viking 2	(USA)	9 Sep 75	Titan III/Centaur	7,497 (3,400)	Mars orbiter returned pictures and data. Mars lander returned pictures and data. Orbiter 5,125lb (2,224kg). Lander surface weight 1,270lb (576kg)
Helios 2	(Germany)	15 Jan 76	Titan III/Centaur	830 (376)	Solar probe orbiting within 0·29 AU of Sun.
Voyager 2	(USA)	20 Aug 77	Titan III/Centaur	1,797 (815)	Fly-by probe of Jupiter, Saturn, Uranus, Neptune. Returned pictures and data
Voyager 1	(USA)	5 Sep 77	Titan III/Centaur	1,797 (815)	Fly-by probe of Jupiter, Saturn. Returned pictures and data. Discovered volcanoes on Io; Jupiter ring; new Saturn moons and ring structure.
Pioneer-Venus 1	(USA)	20 May 78	Atlas-Centaur	1,283 (582)	Venus orbiter, returned pictures and data
Pioneer-Venus 2	(USA)	8 Aug 78	Atlas-Centaur	1,993 (904)	Venus bus, released four entry probes before encounter. Returned data from surface
ICE	(USA)	12 Aug 78	Delta	478 (217)	Originally launched as International Sun-Earth Explorer 3 (ISEE-3). Transfer to escape trajectory and renamed International Comet Explorer. First ever comet fly-by on 2 Sep 85 of Giacobini-Zinner Comet.
Venera 11	(USSR)	9 Sep 78	D-1-e	9,812 (4,450)	Venus fly-by probe, returned data. Lander returned atmosphere and surface data, descent payload 3,528 (1,600).
Venera 12	(USSR)	14 Sep 78	D-1-e	9,837 (4,461)	Venus fly-by probe, returned data. Lander returned atmosphere and surface data, descent payload 3,554 (1,612).
Venera 13	(USSR)	30 Oct 81	D-1-e	9,620 (4,363)	Venus fly-by probe, first colour pictures of surface. Conducted first soil analysis at landing site, descent payload 3,627 (1,645).
Venera 14	(USSR)	4 Nov 81	D-1-e	9,620 (4,363)	Venus fly-by probe, returned colour pictures of landing site and conducted analysis of soil, descent payload 3,627 (1,645).
Venera 15	(USSR)	2 Jun 83	D-1-e	11,574 (5,250)	Venus orbiter. Radar surface mapper.
Venera 16	(USSR)	7 Jun 83	D-1-e	11,819 (5,360)	Venus orbiter. Radar surface mapper.
Vega 1	(USSR)	15 Dec 84	D-1-e	10,850 (4,920)*	Venus lander and French atmosphere balloon probe. Halley's Comet fly-by 6 Mar 86.
Vega 2	(USSR	21 Dec 84	D-1-e	10,850 (4,920)*	Venus lander and French atmosphere balloon probe. Halley's Comet fly-by 9 Mar 86.
Sakigake	(Japan)	7 Jan 85	Mu-3SII	304·5 (138·1)	First Japanese deep space probe. Distant Halley's Comet fly-by 11 Mar 86.
Giotto	(ESA)	2 Jul 85	Ariane 1 (V14)	1,265 (573·7)	First close encounter with a comet. Halley's Comet fly-by 14 Mar 86.
Suisei	(Japan)	18 Aug 85	Mu-3SII	307·6 (139·5)	Japanese deep space probe. Distant Halley's Comet fly-by 11 Mar 86.
Phobos 1	(USSR)	7 Jul 87	D-1-e	13,715 (6,220)*	Mars probe failed due to telemetry message error.
Phobos 2	(USSR)	11 Jul 87	D-1-e	13,715 (6,220)*	Mars orbiter, contact lost before planned fly-by of the moon Phobos.
Magellan	(USA)	4 May 89	Shuttle/IUS	7,662 (3,475)	Venus orbiter, surface radar mapper.
Galileo	(USA)	Oct 89	Shuttle/IUS	5,883 (2,668)	Jupiter orbiter, atmosphere probe.
Ulysses	(US/ESA)	Oct 90	Shuttle/IUS/PAM-S	818 (371)	Jupiter gravity assist International Solar Polar Mission (ISPM).
Mars Observer	(USA)	Sep 92	Shuttle-TOS	4,630 (2,100)	Mars orbiter. Detailed surface mineral and topography survey. Relay for Mars 94.
—	(Japan)	94	—	—	Venus orbiter.
CRAF	(USA)	Oct 94	Titan IV/Centaur G	—	Comet rendezvous/Asteroid fly-by.
Mars 94	(USSR)	Oct 94	D-1-e	13,780 (6,250)*	Mars survey orbiters with atmospheric balloon probes.
Corona	(USSR)	95	—	—	Jupiter fly-by gravity assist for close solar fly-by.
Vesta	(Fr/ESA/USSR)	Feb 96	D-1-e	4,400 (2,000)	Twin probes launched by a single booster; missions to 7 asteroids and 2 comets.
Cassini	(USA/ESA)	Apr 96	Titan IV/Centaur G	3,815 (1,730)	Saturn orbiter (USA), Titan atmosphere probe (ESA).
Mars 98	(USSR)	98	D-1-e	13,780 (6,250)*	Mars surface rover missions.
—	(USSR)	99	—	—	Jupiter/Saturn atmospheric probes, Titan lander.
CNSR	(USA/ESA)	9 Nov 00	Titan IV/Centaur G	—	Comet nucleus sample return mission.
Mars 02	(USSR)	02	—	—	Mars surface sample return missions.
TAU	(USA)	05	—	—	Deep space probe out to one Thousand AU.
Starprobe	(USA)	—	—	—	Jupiter gravity assist probe to the Sun at 2 million miles (3 million km).

Arrival at Uranus

The Saturn encounter made it possible to boost Voyager 2 into a trajectory for a fly-by of the planet Uranus in 1986. When it arrived, Voyager 2 found Uranus to be an almost featureless cloud-covered world with its axis of rotation tilted at 95 degrees. Its south pole, currently pointed at the Sun was as warm as its darkened north pole. Its magnetic axis is at 55 degrees to the axis of rotation, so its magnetosphere appears like a giant helix, spiralling away from the Sun. Imagery revealed 10 new moons (15 total) and two new complete rings (11 total) plus evidence of more partial rings. The larger moons exhibited features indicating a violent past, Miranda being unlike anything ever seen before. It may have fragmented at least a dozen times in the past, before solidifying into its present state which exhibits a strange giant square flow pattern.

Once past Uranus, Voyager 2 sped on to an encounter with the planet Neptune in 1989. Imagery showed more cloud features than Uranus, a faint set of partial rings, and more tiny moons (see Diary). The trajectory had been aimed to skim over Neptune's north pole and then on to within 25,000 miles (40,000km) of the giant moon Triton 5 hours later. That fly-by was the last and final for the Voyager series. Voyager 1, after its Saturn encounter, is now climbing up out of the Solar System at a 35 degree angle. Voyager 2 is heading in a different direction, descending away at a 48 degree angle. It will pass within 0·8 light years of the star Sirius in about 358,000 years time. Both should be detectable until about the year 2016 when they will be at a distance of more than 100 AU. It is hoped that sometime before then they should have passed through the heliopause: the region where the influence of the Sun's solar wind gives way to the background of our Milky Way galaxy.

The NASA Galileo spacecraft, launched in 1989, will reach Jupiter in 1995, after fly-bys of Venus, Earth twice, and two asteroids. After releasing a Jupiter re-entry probe, it will enter a Jupiter orbit and weave its way among the various moons over its two year mission life. A similar mission, the joint NASA/ESA Cassini spacecraft, to be launched in 1996, will reach Saturn in 2002. Prior to arrival, an ESA Huygens probe will be released to descend into the atmosphere of the moon Titan. The orbiter will then spend the next 4 years studying Saturn's system of rings and moons.

Still more exotic spacecraft, now in the planning stage, may use multiple gravity assist fly-bys eventually to explore all of the planets and their moons in the Solar System, as well as a variety of asteroids and comets of all sizes and shapes. These machines will provide a greater understanding of our fascinating little corner of the Universe, and pave the way to the stars.

Right: *An artist's impression of the Galileo probe on its approach to Jupiter. Scheduled for launch in late 1989, Galileo consists of an orbiter and an atmospheric probe which will separate from the mother craft and penetrate Jupiter's turbulent atmosphere, relaying data to Earth as it descends. The orbiter will study both the planet and its major moons.*

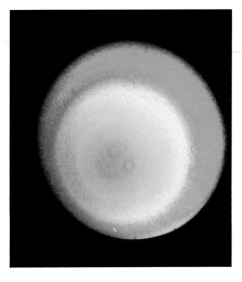

Above: *A false colour Voyager 2 image of Uranus' polar region. The lighter bands surrounding the dark polar hood are thought to be areas of smog so arranged by zonal motions in the upper atmosphere.*

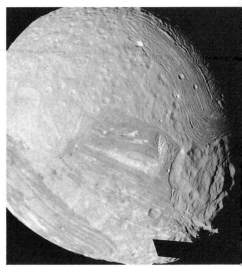

Above: *Miranda was the strangest of the moons of Uranus imaged by Voyager. It is a bizarre hybrid of geological forms, and may actually have fragmented on numerous occasions in its past history.*

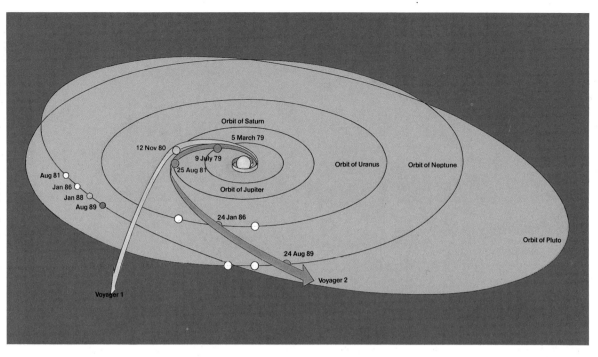

Voyager Flight Paths

The trajectories of the two Voyager spacecraft, as planned by JPL analysts, are charted in this diagram. Close encounters are colour-coded to flight paths. Following its encounter with Saturn on 12 November 1980, Voyager 1 passed the orbits of Uranus, Pluto (then inside Neptune's orbit) and Neptune between 1984 and 1990, at a steep angle. It will then move steadily out of the Solar System, although it is not directed towards any particular star. Voyager 2 had been accelerated by its encounter with Saturn on 25 August 1981, and made its closest approach to Uranus on 24 January 1986. Its final destination in the Solar System was Neptune, which it flew by on 24 August 1989. Although it will be closing in on Pluto's orbit in January 1990. Pluto itself will be too far away for a close encounter. No Pluto probes are planned.

The Uranus Encounter

In early 1986, Voyager 2 flew through the Uranus system. It passed within 66,500 miles (107,000km) of the planet's centre on 24 January 1986 outside the orbit of the satellite Miranda and just inside the orbit of Ariel. The "encounter sequence" depicted here began 8 hours before closest approach and ended 8 hours after it. During this latter period, there were a number of occultations when Uranus and its rings interposed between Voyager and the Earth and Sun. Voyager 2 began passing behind the rings about 90 minutes after close approach, and behind the planet some 2 hours after closest approach. The diagram is colour-coded to show the successive phases of ring-Sun and Uranus-Sun occultation, and Uranus-Earth, ring-Earth occultation. During the occultation sequence, the spacecraft beamed radio signals through the rings and the atmosphere of Uranus. Distortion of these waves on reaching the DSN antennas on Earth provided clues to the detailed ring structure and density of the atmosphere. While Voyager 2 was behind the planet itself, its signals were blocked, and controllers on Earth were unable to make contact with the craft. Voyager was also unable to "see" the Sun, an essential reference for spacecraft attitude control (which keeps its radio antenna pointing directly towards Earth)-and so control had to be maintained gyroscopically. During the encounter at least 10 new moons were discovered, the largest being about 100 miles (170km) across; others perhaps 25-30 miles (40-50km). Two new rings were found, one narrow, one broad, making the total 11. Some moons and rings had very dark material, possibly radiation-blackened methane ice.

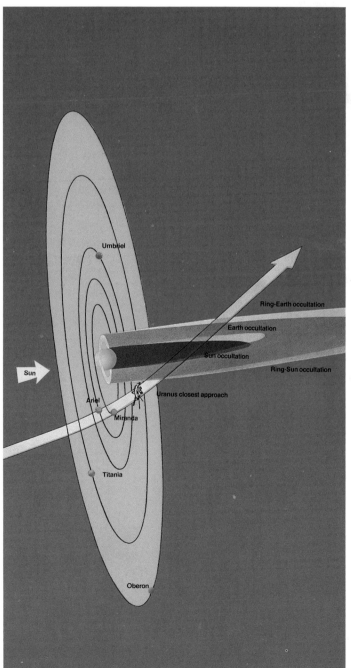

Man on the Moon

The Apollo-Lunar programme of 1969-72 sent nine expeditions to the Moon. Six succeeded in landing a total of 12 astronauts on the near side from Oceanus Procellarum in the west to the Taurus Mountains in the east. Two earlier flights were confined to reconnaissance in lunar orbit and one landing mission was cancelled because an oxygen tank exploded in the Apollo service module two days out from Earth: The crippled vessel, Apollo 13, flew around the Moon and returned safely.

Although they may be viewed as an ad hoc effort motivated by competition with the Soviet Union, the Apollo lunar expeditions can also be regarded as a first step in human expansion into the Solar System. Like earlier voyages of discovery, they were not part of a systematic plan of exploration. Manned lunar exploration was discontinued with the sixth landing (Apollo 17) in December 1972.

The decision to go to the Moon was a political one. Its main purpose was to restore in the eyes of the world American technological primacy which had been eroded by the Soviet Union's early lead in space flight. In his State of the Union message to Congress on 25 May 1961 President Kennedy announced the decision by declaring,

"I believe this nation should commit itself to achieving the goal, before this decade is out, of landing a man on the Moon and returning him safely to Earth."

The declaration had the effect of galvanising a slowly moving space effort in the

> **"We have brought back rocks, and I think it's a fair trade. For just as the Rosetta Stone revealed the language of ancient Egypt, so may these rocks unlock the mystery of the origin of the Moon, and indeed even of our Earth and Solar System."**
>
> Michael Collins,
> CM Pilot, Apollo 11
> *Before a joint session of Congress, 16 September 1969*

United States and of mobilising public and Congressional support for it. The US space programme had been lagging conspicuously behind the Russian one which had launched the first satellite, Sputnik 1, 4 October 1957, and the first manned orbital flight (Yuri Gagarin in Vostok 1) 12 April 1961.

Compared with this feat, the sub-orbital flight of Lt-Cdr Alan B. Shepard in Mercury-Redstone on 5 May 1961 seemed an anticlimax. Three weeks later, President Kennedy's call for the lunar landing precipitated the United States into a race to be first on the Moon and challenged American industry to win it.

Although the Soviet space establishment later denied any intention of landing men on the Moon, a belief that it would attempt either a manned landing or circumlunar flight persisted among NASA officials. It was not finally dismissed until December 1968 when Apollo 8 reached lunar orbit on Christmas Eve and flew ten revolutions of the Moon before returning to Earth.

The Russian space lead increased during 1961 with the 17½ orbit flight of Gherman Titov in Vostok 2, beginning on 6 August. The United States achieved manned orbital flight on 20 February 1962 when Major John H. Glenn flew three revolutions in Mercury-Atlas 6 (*Friendship 7*).

Mercury missions then spun around the planet in a precise order, with a second three-orbit mission by Lt-Cdr M. Scott Carpenter in Mercury-Atlas 7 (*Aurora 7*) on 24 May 1962; a six-orbit flight by Lt-Cdr Walter M. Schirra in Mercury-Atlas 8 (*Sigma 7*) on 3 October 1962, and a 22-orbit flight by Air Force Capt L. Gordon Cooper in Mercury-Atlas 9 (*Faith 7*) on 15 May 1963.

When it was inaugurated in 1958, Project Mercury was an open-ended programme. In the context of the lunar-landing project it

Man on the Moon: A remarkable British Forecast

Although it was American technology that made the Moon-landing possible, the exploit was international in the sense that scientists and engineers in many lands contributed to the basic theory. The British Interplanetary Society, for example, had set guidelines for lunar exploration 30 years before in a technical study remarkable for its grasp of key principles.

The story begins in 1937 when few people considered a flight to the Moon could be more than fantasy. The BIS, which had been founded four years earlier, wished to know how the breakthrough could be achieved — specifically, how three men could be landed on the Moon and returned safely to Earth.

Their task was formidable. At that time there was no rocket industry and large rocket engines had yet to be developed. What little experience Britain had, took the form of small solid-fuel rockets being developed for military purposes. After investigating more powerful propellants, the group produced its first sketches. They showed a rocket of unprecedented size — 100ft (30·5m) tall

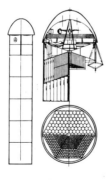

BIS Lunar Spaceship, 1939 the cylindrical launch vehicle has in its nose a pressure cabin, double-walled to give good thermal insulation and to minimise risk of meteorite damage, with contour couches for a crew of three. Its 2,490 solid-fuel rocket motors are in honeycomb configuration.

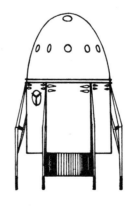

R.A. Smith's drawing shows the BIS spaceship of 1939 in lunar landing configuration. Braking rocket motors provide support thrust during landing, and extensible legs absorb the landing shock. Fine control was to be achieved by using liquid-fuel thrusters.

by 20ft (6·09m) diameter and weighing about 1,000 tonnes. Its propulsion system consisted of 2,490 solid-fuel rocket motors arranged as a honeycomb in steps or banks.

In the nose was a pressure cabin, not unlike the command module of Apollo. Built up layer by layer beneath it were clusters of rockets so arranged that as the spent motors in the first stage dropped off the next layer fired, and so on, until the vehicle escaped the Earth's gravity pull at nearly 25,000mph (40,232km/h).

After the craft had been turned over in flight by steam jets, more rocket layers were assumed to be used in braking against the Moon's pull; similar jet controls were proposed for making course corrections and manoeuvring prior to landing.

The really important feature of the BIS design — as subsequently adopted for Apollo — was to have the craft make a vertical touchdown on landing legs while retro-rockets killed its speed of descent a few feet above the lunar surface. It thus arrived in an upright position and could be re-launched by the remaining rocket clusters from the leg-supports, in effect from a built-in launch pad.

Society members even proposed the use of inertial instruments for navigation. Such devices

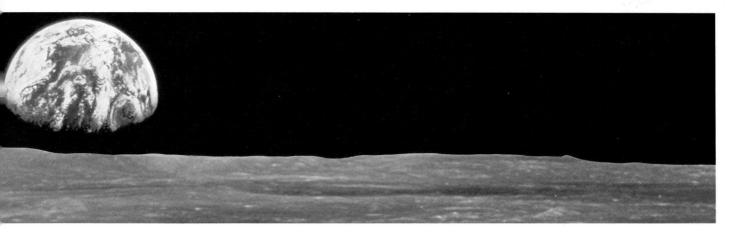

became the first stage of a vehicle-development programme designed to put men on the surface of the Moon.

The second stage was a more advanced vehicle called Gemini carrying two crewmen. About double the weight of Mercury, the 8,360lb (3,791kg) Gemini spacecraft consisted of two modules. An adapter module in the rear contained a propulsion system that enabled the crew to manoeuvre the vehicle in space, while a re-entry module forward contained the crew compartment and parachute landing system. Just before re-entry, the capsule separated from the adapter. Some aerodynamic lift at supersonic speed, coupled with the capsule's offset centre of gravity, enabled the crew to adjust the descent path by about 200 miles (322km).

Ten Gemini missions were flown between 23 March 1965 and 11 November 1966, and astronauts learned how to perform extra-vehicular activity (EVA), execute rendezvous manoeuvres, dock with another vehicle (an Agena rocket) in orbit, and perform limited scientific experiments. An endurance of 14 days in orbit was achieved by Major Frank Borman and Lt-Cdr James A. Lovell aboard Gemini 7 between 4 and 18 December 1965. The flight demonstrated that a trained crew could endure zero gravity without ill-effects long enough for a lunar trip.

As an intermediate step from Mercury to Apollo, Gemini provided a training programme for the manoeuvres which had to be performed in order to execute the lunar

Above: *With a first stage thrust of 1·3 million lb (0·58 million kg), the first Saturn space vehicle is launched on test from Cape Canaveral, 1006 EST, 27 October 1961. This verification of the aerodynamic and structural design of the entire vehicle was totally successful. The flight lasted some 8 minutes 4 seconds.*

orbit rendezvous method of landing on the Moon, a concept attributed to NASA researcher John Houbolt. This method was adopted by NASA in July 1962 after two others—direct ascent from the Earth and Earth orbit rendezvous—were rejected.

In terms of energy expenditure, lunar orbit rendezvous (LOR) was the most economical system. It called for ascent via Earth parking orbit to lunar orbit. From there, two astronauts would land in a lunar module (LM) while a third remained in orbit aboard the Apollo command and service modules (CSM). At the conclusion of surface activity, the explorers would return to lunar orbit in the LM ascent stage. They would make rendezvous and dock with the Apollo for the return to Earth.

A calculation of the weight to be lifted to the Moon, about 110,000lb (49,887kg), showed that LOR was within the lifting capability of the Saturn V launcher. In 1962 the Saturn family of rockets was well along in development at NASA's Marshall Space Flight Center, Huntsville, Alabama.

The Saturns were descendants of the German A-4 and were developed by the same team under Wernher von Braun that had built the war rockets at Peenemünde during World War 2. Working for the Army Ballistic Missile Agency at the Redstone Arsenal and at the Marshall Center, von Braun and the war-time associates who had emigrated with him to the United States developed the Jupiter C and Redstone

have since reached a high state of perfection for submarines, aircraft and missiles as well as spacecraft. A lightweight chemical battery was suggested to run electrical equipment.

As the effect of weightlessness on the crew was unknown, the BIS spaceship was designed to revolve about its major axis to induce artificial gravity by centrifugal force. To provide a stationary view of the heavens from within the ship, the Society invented an optical device—a "Coelostat"—which must rank as the first instrument ever designed for use in a spaceship. A working model was demonstrated at the Science Museum, London, during 1939.

Nor were other human factors overlooked. The astronauts reclined on contour couches and a double-walled cabin minimised the risk of puncture by meteoroids and also ensured good thermal protection. A jettisonable heat-shield protected the cabin from air friction during the rocket's ascent from Earth, while the return assumed that the capsule would gradually reduce its speed in elliptical orbit around the Earth by "grazing" the outer layers of the atmosphere. When speed was sufficiently reduced the separated capsule would land by parachute.

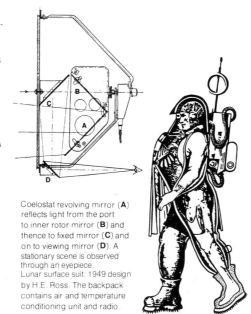

Coelostat revolving mirror (**A**) reflects light from the port to inner rotor mirror (**B**) and thence to fixed mirror (**C**) and on to viewing mirror (**D**). A stationary scene is observed through an eyepiece. Lunar surface suit: 1949 design by H.E. Ross. The backpack contains air and temperature conditioning unit and radio.

Each astronaut was to have a spacesuit; there would be a spare for emergency use and a repair kit. The suits were visualised as being made of thin but tough rubber and leather, with a roomy headpiece and a backpack oxygen supply. For exploration on the shadow side of the Moon it was proposed that the suits should be electrically heated. Cabin air, supplied in much the same way as in a modern spacecraft, was to have excess carbon dioxide and water vapour from the astronauts' breath removed by chemical filters.

Sanitation was no problem. Human wastes would be placed in a small airlock. When the inside door was closed and the outside door mechanically opened, air remaining in the lock would "drive it away from the ship".

Food was chosen for energy-yield rather than protein content. Bread and butter, cheese, porridge, chocolate and sweet cocoa were to be staple items. But to avoid monotony there would be small quantities of raisins, ham, honey and salmon. Water was to be the spartan basis of all beverages. A small supply of coffee would be taken for strictly practical purposes in the pre-computer age—"as a stimulant for navigators falling asleep over their interminable calculations."

launchers. Jupiter C (Juno I) orbited the first American satellite, Explorer 1; Redstone launched the first two Mercury craft.

First of the Saturn family, the Saturn I was successful on its first launch, 27 October 1961. None of the Saturn launch vehicles ever failed. First-stage thrust was increased from 1·3 to 1·5 million pounds (0·58 million to 0·68 million kg) from the Saturn I to the Saturn IB and to 7·5 million pounds (3·4 million kg) in the Saturn V, the Moon rocket.

Development of hydrogen-oxygen propellant engines in the 1960s provided high-energy upper stages for the Saturn. The S-IVB, with its 225,000lb (102,040kg) thrust J-2 hydrogen-oxygen engine, became the second stage of the Saturn IB and the third stage of the Saturn V. The second stage of the Saturn V was the S-II, with five J-2 engines creating a million pounds of thrust.

The smaller Saturn IB with the S-IVB second stage proved its capability of launching a Block I Apollo in a test on 5 July 1966 by lifting a 58,500lb (26,531kg) payload into a 117-mile (188km) orbit. The more powerful Saturn V was required to lift the heavier lunar mission payload which included the Lunar Module.

The First Saturn V

On 9 November 1967 one of the most memorable technological feats of the space age was staged at the Kennedy Space Center. The Saturn V, with all three stages "live" and a 45,000lb (20,408kg) Apollo spacecraft on top, was launched "all up" for the first time. Its un-muffled roar rattled nearby structures like an earthquake. At the press site, three miles away, the roof of the Columbia Broadcasting System's television booth collapsed. The sound volume was compared to the explosion of Krakatoa, a volcano in the Sunda Strait, in 1883. The air-pressure wave generated by first-stage engines was detected by the instruments at the Lamont-Doherty Geological Observatory, Palisades, NY, 1,100 miles (1,770km) away.

All three stages performed nominally. The S-IVB stage with Apollo attached was thrust into a 115-mile (185km) orbit. The stage's powerful engine then re-started to propel itself and the Apollo to 10,696 miles (17,210km) altitude. Apollo separated and fired its own engine to increase its altitude to 11,232 miles (18,072km). A second firing of the spacecraft engine accelerated its plunge toward the atmosphere to simulate its re-entry at lunar return velocity.

With the outcome of this test, recorded as Apollo 4, the Apollo-Saturn transportation system demonstrated that it was capable of reaching the Moon. Sound-suppression devices modified the thunder of the Saturn V first stage after that.

In the autumn of 1961 North American Aviation won the contract to develop the Apollo spacecraft system. Like Gemini, Apollo consisted of two sections: a conical command module where the crew rode, and a cylindrical service module containing the main engine, fuel-cell batteries and the environmental control system. As in Mercury and Gemini spacecraft, the cabin atmosphere in Apollo was oxygen at 5 pounds pressure per square inch (0·35kg/sq cm).

The lunar mission version of the Apollo command and service module (Block II) was 34ft (10·4m) long and weighed 67,000lb (30,385kg). At its conical base, the command module was 12·8ft (3·9m) in diameter, tapering to the recovery section where the parachute landing system was stored. A docking tunnel and probe at the apex of the cone provided the means of docking with the lunar module, which ferried two of the crew between lunar orbit and the surface. The service module was 24·3ft (7·4m) long and 12·8ft (3·9m) in diameter. It was jettisoned before re-entry into Earth's atmosphere. An ablative heat shield protected the command module from the heat of re-entry at lunar return speed.

A Block I Apollo, designed for Earth orbital flight only, was launched by a Saturn IB on a 5,500-mile (8,850km) suborbital flight down the Atlantic Missile Range on 26 February 1966. It made a satisfactory parachute splashdown in the South Atlantic. Except for a pressure drop in the engine, which was fired, shut down and restarted, the Apollo Directorate was satisfied with the vehicle's performance.

The first manned orbital test of the spacecraft was planned for 1967 when tragedy struck the programme and delayed it a year. A sudden fire ignited plastics in the cabin of Apollo 1 while it was mounted on the Saturn IB launcher on the pad on 27 January 1967. The flight crew that was testing its systems

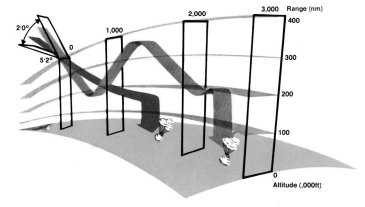

Re-entry and Landing
Service module is jettisoned before entering Earth's atmosphere. Pitch control jets turn command module so heat shield orientates to withstand heating up to 2.742°C. "Skipping" by module's aerodynamic lift, commander manoeuvres within 26 mile (42km) wide re-entry corridor. Drag-braking reduces speed to around sonic velocity at 30,000ft (9,144m). Drogue parachutes deploy at 25,000ft (7,620m). From 15,000ft (4,572m), huge ringsail parachutes lower module gently into sea.

Below: *F-1 engine on test at NASA Rocket Engine Test Site, Edwards, Calif. Kerosene and liquid oxygen are the propellants. Tons of water cascade over the flame deflector producing great clouds of steam.*

Right: *Apollo/Saturn V is launched "all up" for the first time, Kennedy Space Center, 9 November 1967. Launch vehicle and Apollo 4 proved out their flight compatibility in this unmanned Earth-orbiting mission.*

was suffocated by dense smoke from burning plastic before the hatch could be opened.

Dead were Col Virgil I. (Gus) Grissom, veteran of Mercury and Gemini flights; Lt-Col Edward H. White II, the first American to perform extra-vehicular activity or EVA (Gemini 4); and Lt-Cdr Roger B. Chaffee, who was preparing for his first flight.

The subsequent investigation attributed the cause of the fire to an electrical spark, caused by faulty wiring. The spark ignited plastics which had been assumed to be relatively fire resistant. However, although they resisted fire in a normal oxygen-nitrogen atmosphere, they burned readily in the pure oxygen atmosphere which had been introduced into the cabin to simulate flight conditions.

After a successful test of an unmanned Apollo-Saturn V system, NASA launched the first manned flight of the spacecraft, Apollo 7, on 11 October 1968. A successful although occasionally argumentative mission lasting 11 days in Earth orbit was flown by Navy Capt Walter M. Schirra, Air Force Major Donn F. Eisele, and Walter Cunningham, civilian test pilot. Crewmen protested that they were overburdened with experiments during the mission.

Indications that the Soviet Union was prepared to launch one or two cosmonauts on a

Above: *Apollo 9 command/service modules and lunar module are hard-docked in Earth orbit as CSM pilot David Scott, standing in the open hatch of Gumdrop, is photographed from LM Spider by Russell Schweickart.*

Below: *In a simulated landing mission, Apollo 10 LM Snoopy approaches within 47,000ft (14,325m) of the Moon's surface, without entering final descent trajectory. On the lunar horizon, the Earth rises.*

circumlunar flight were perceived during this period by NASA officials and other American space observers. Two unmanned Soyuz-type vehicles designated Zond 5 and Zond 6 were launched in September and November 1968 respectively around the Moon. Zond 5 landed in the Indian Ocean and Zond 6 in the USSR.

In early autumn 1968 it became apparent to observers that NASA intended to send the next Apollo test flight—Apollo 8—to the Moon. The mission was launched on 21 December with Col Frank Borman, Capt James Lovell and Lt-Col William A. Anders aboard. There was some concern at the Mission Control Center, Houston, when Borman became ill after the spacecraft passed through the Van Allen radiation belts and cleared the magnetosphere. However, he quickly recovered.

Falling into the predominant gravitational field of the Moon, Apollo 8 approached to within 70 miles (112·6km) of the surface early on 24 December. Its engine was then fired in the direction of travel to insert it into a 69 mile (111km) orbit.

The crew flew ten revolutions of the Moon on Christmas Eve and members took turns reading extracts of the Book of Genesis over the radio. In the control room at the Manned Spacecraft Center, Houston, controllers anxiously awaited a signal that the Apollo engine had fired behind the Moon to return the crew to Earth.

At last the signal came and Apollo headed home. At 10,357 miles (16,664km) above the Earth, the command module was separated from the service module and re-entered the atmosphere at 24,243 miles an hour (39,010km/hr). It splashed down in the Pacific on 27 December about 5,000 yards (4,575m) from the recovery ship, the USS *Yorktown* after a flight of 147 hours.

Apollo 9, 3-13 March 1969, was flown by Col James A. McDivitt, Col David R. Scott, and Russell L. Schweickart to rehearse rendezvous and docking manoeuvres with

Below: *Some 60 miles (97km) above the far side of the Moon, Apollo 10 CSM Charlie Brown, manned by John Young, gleams in the sunlight as it drifts a few yards from the lunar module manned by Cernan and Stafford.*

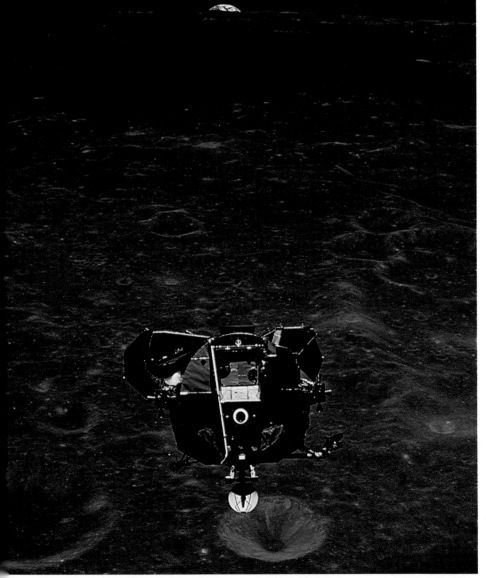

the lunar module in Earth orbit. The LM was then flown in lunar orbit on Apollo 10 (18-20 May) for the dress rehearsal of a Moon landing. Col Thomas P. Stafford and Navy Cdr Eugene A. Cernan piloted the LM to within 50,000ft (15,240m) of the surface on 22 May while Cdr John W. Young remained in lunar orbit in the Apollo CSM. After separating from the LM descent stage, Stafford and Cernan manoeuvred the LM ascent stage back to the Apollo and docked. The ascent stage was then cast off and the crew returned to Earth.

With the conclusion of that mission, NASA announced that the first attempt to land men on the Moon would be launched no earlier than 16 July 1969 on Apollo 11.

The Lunar Module

Developed to implement the 1962 lunar orbit rendezvous decision, the lunar module (at first known as the lunar excursion module or Bug) was a two-stage, self-sufficient spacecraft built by Grumman. It was carried to the Moon attached to the command module docking port, with its powerful descent stage engine pointing forward. In this configuration, the LM descent engine could be fired as a back-up propulsion system to boost the Apollo-LM combination out of lunar orbit in the event the Apollo engine failed before the landing sequence. Apollo 8 did not carry the LM, however, because a flight module was not ready at the time the mission was flown. Consequently, the safety of that mission depended entirely on the Apollo engine once the vehicle was in lunar orbit.

The LM stood 22·92ft (6·98m) high on four cantilevered landing legs which looked insect-like while retracted during flight. Each of the four legs ended in a dish-shaped pod which Grumman had designed to support the 33,000lb (14,965kg) vehicle (Earth weight) on a variety of surfaces. One leg was equipped with a ladder.

The landing legs were attached to the descent stage which carried a rocket engine throttleable from 1,050 to 10,000 pounds (476 to 4,535kg) of thrust. On the Moon, the descent stage served as a launching platform for the ascent stage, which consisted of a pressurised cabin, guidance and navigation

systems, including radar altimeter and computor, and a throttleable rocket engine. While it was docked with Apollo, the crew entered or left it through a tunnel. On the Moon, crewmen depressurised the cabin, opened the hatch and climbed out on to a small "porch" in their bulky moon suits, clambered down the descent stage ladder and jumped to the ground.

When the crew completed outside surface activities, they climbed back into the ascent stage, hoisted samples aboard with line and pulley, closed the hatch, re-pressurised the cabin and lifted off the descent stage by firing the ascent engine. The ascent was timed to minimise rendezvous manoeuvres. Docking became routine.

When development of the LM began in 1962, the nature of the lunar surface was unknown and the question of whether it would support the weight of the ferry vehicle was disputed by scientists. Telescopic observation from Earth could not

Below: *One month before their historic mission, the Apollo 11 crew—Michael Collins, command module pilot; Neil Armstrong, commander; Edwin Aldrin, lunar module pilot—pose before an LM mock-up.*

Below: *History in the making at 0932 EDT on 16 July 1969, as the Apollo 11 Saturn V rises on a column of flame from Pad 39A, Kennedy Space Center, on the way to the first manned landing on the Moon.*

Evolution of the Lunar Module

On the occasion of the 10th anniversary of the historic first Moon landing, the Apollo 11 command module pilot Michael Collins paid this handsome tribute to the British Interplanetary Society: "Since its foundation in 1933, your Society has steadfastly held to its aim of manned interplanetary flight. In your pre-War studies of lunar spacecraft were embodied many design concepts which eventually were used to take us to the Moon. I am sure that most of these enthusiasts never expected to see their project realised within their lifetimes..."

A NASA history[2] noted that space-agency planners had tended to overlook the part that rendezvous might play (except as it related to space-stations) until a short paper was presented by William H. Michael in May 1960:

"Michael was part of a small group in the Theoretical Mechanics Division at Langley Research Center that had been working on trajectories for lunar and planetary missions ... Michael's contribution was a brief calculation of the amount of

A drawing made by R.A. Smith in 1947 represents a re-evaluation of the BIS lunar spaceship concept in terms of liquid-propellant technology. The leg-supported base is to act as a launch platform for lift-off from the Moon. Similar techniques were later employed in building the Apollo Lunar Module.

NASA's Moon-landing vehicle concept, 1961-1962: in the early years of the Apollo programme, NASA made investigation of both tail-first and horizontal lunar-landing techniques. The latter are illustrated below. (Left) The vehicle makes a horizontal jet-support braking approach, touching down on

skis and a tail-bumper. (Right) For take-off, the landing vehicle serves as a launcher for the Apollo return spacecraft. It will be seen that the lunar module in these illustrations differs considerably from that advocated earlier by the BIS, whose concepts finally proved to be most influential.

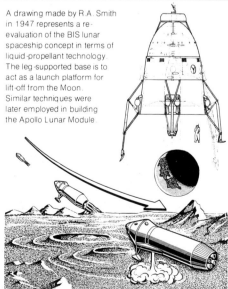

resolve lunar surface details smaller than a kilometre in size. As a result, speculation arose about a wide range of surface conditions, from deep dust in which a craft might founder to a fairy castle crust which might give way under landing impact to allow the LM to fall into a crevasse.

After failing in several attempts to hit the Moon with early Pioneer probes, the United States embarked on Project Ranger. It was designed to obtain by television close-up pictures of the surface during lunar impact trajectories. Ranger 7 came down successfully on 31 July 1964 and sent back 4,306 photographs. They showed a heavily cratered surface, smaller craters nestled within larger ones, down to features a few inches in diameter.

Rangers 8 and 9 in February and March 1965 were also successful, sending back a total of nearly 13,000 pictures. A second reconnaissance programme called Surveyor called for landing a vehicle softly on the surface to make soil bearing tests, chemical analyses of the soil and take photographs.

After months of technical delays during which the Soviet Union soft-landed its 220lb (100kg) Luna 9 in Oceanus Procellarum on 3 February 1966, Surveyor 1, with an Earth weight of 594lb (269kg), landed in another region of Procellarum on 2 June 1966. It sent back over 11,000 pictures and showed that the soil was firm enough to support a spacecraft. In fact, close-up shots showed that the surface soil appeared to have the consistency of a freshly ploughed field.

Four more Surveyors were landed. Three carried chemical analysers that showed the *maria* basins to consist of basaltic rock, similar to terrestrial basalt, which appeared to have hardened from a magma that had flowed in the molten state out of the lunar interior. From this it was deduced that the Moon had been partially or wholly melted, either by the energy of its accretion or by the decay of radioactive elements deep within it. The chemical analysis showed that the most abundant elements on the surface were oxygen and silicon.

Between 1966 and 1968, while Surveyor was in operation, NASA launched five camera spacecraft into lunar orbit to photograph the surface. The Lunar Orbiters returned enough data to enable scientists to construct a photo map of large areas of the Moon, from which Apollo landing sites could be selected.

The prime site was designated on the basaltic surface of Mare Tranquillitatis (Sea of Tranquillity) in the east-central lunar lowlands. Neil Armstrong and Col Edwin E. Aldrin landed there in the lunar module *Eagle* on 20 July 1969 at 4:17:43 pm Eastern Daylight Time (20:17:43 Greenwich Mean Time) and radioed:

Houston, Tranquillity Base here. The Eagle has landed.

Armstrong descended the ladder to the crumbly soil and announced:
"That's one small step for man, one giant leap for mankind."

The article "a" was missing in the live voice transmission and in the official transcript. It was later inserted in the record to amend the message to "one small step for a man." The step Armstrong referred to was a

Below: *Neil Armstrong's camera records Edwin Aldrin's descent to the Moon, as Apollo 11's lunar module pilot jumps the small gap between the base of* Eagle's *ladder and the lunar surface, 21 July 1969.*

Below: *Mirrored in Aldrin's helmet visor are Armstrong,* Eagle, *and part of the scientific package. With his spacesuit and equipment, Aldrin would weigh 360lb (163kg) on Earth: on the Moon, only 60lb (27kg).*

weight that might be saved in a lunar-landing mission by parking the return propulsion and part of the spacecraft in lunar orbit. The idea hit John C. Houbolt like revealed truth:

'I can still remember the "back of the envelope" type of calculations I made to check that the scheme resulted in a very substantial saving in Earth boost requirements. Almost spontaneously, it became clear that lunar-orbit rendezvous offered a chain reaction simplification on all back efforts: development, testing, manufacturing, erection, count-down, flight operations, etc.... All would be simplified. The thought stuck in my mind, "This is fantastic. If there is any idea we have to push, it is this one!" I vowed to dedicate myself to the task.'

And dedicate himself he did. Houbolt and a band of disciples embarked on a crusade to convert the rest of NASA to the truth that lunar orbit rendezvous was the quickest and cheapest road to the Moon."

In mid-1962, thoroughly convinced that lunar orbit rendezvous (LOR) was the best method of effecting a lunar landing, Grumman launched a

Evolution of the Lunar Module. By the time NASA announced the Apollo programme, the landing craft (at first called the lunar excursion module, then the lunar module) had the basic configuration advocated by the BIS more than 20 years earlier. Stages in its evolution are shown below: (top left) 1962; (top right) 1963; (bottom left) 1965; and (bottom right) the 1969 vehicle which was used in the Apollo 11 moon landing.

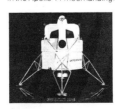

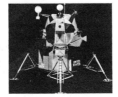

feasibility study. NASA then asked for proposals involving use of the LOR concept and the lunar excursion module. Grumman submitted its proposals in September 1962, nominating RCA as principal subcontractor. NASA Administrator James E. Webb emphasised at the time that only since July had NASA committed itself to "lunar orbit rendezvous" using the advanced Saturn booster. More than a million man-hours had gone into studies of how to get men to the Moon and back.

When NASA finally announced the Apollo project, the landing craft had reverted to the basic configuration advocated by the BIS over 20 years before. It was described as a lunar excursion module (later the word 'excursion' was to be dropped). A press communiqué stated that "LEM will look something like the cab of a two-man helicopter measuring 10 feet in diameter and standing about 15 feet tall on its skid-type legs." In fact, the final vehicle was much larger. Stages in the evolution of the design are shown left.

The final configuration of the Lunar Module (LM) stood c.23ft (7m) tall and measured 31ft (9·4m) with legs extended.

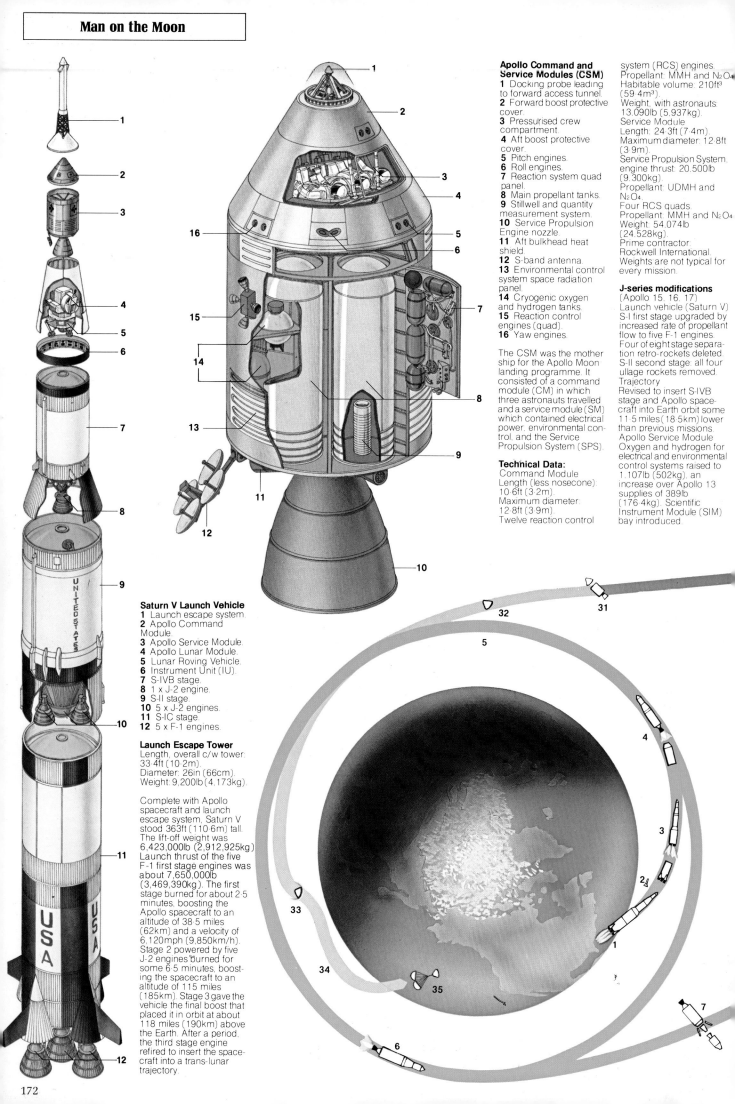

Apollo Command and Service Modules (CSM)

1 Docking probe leading to forward access tunnel.
2 Forward boost protective cover.
3 Pressurised crew compartment.
4 Aft boost protective cover.
5 Pitch engines.
6 Roll engines.
7 Reaction system quad panel.
8 Main propellant tanks.
9 Stillwell and quantity measurement system.
10 Service Propulsion Engine nozzle.
11 Aft bulkhead heat shield.
12 S-band antenna.
13 Environmental control system space radiation panel.
14 Cryogenic oxygen and hydrogen tanks.
15 Reaction control engines (quad).
16 Yaw engines.

The CSM was the mother ship for the Apollo Moon landing programme. It consisted of a command module (CM) in which three astronauts travelled and a service module (SM) which contained electrical power, environmental control, and the Service Propulsion System (SPS).

Technical Data:
Command Module
Length (less nosecone):
10·6ft (3·2m).
Maximum diameter:
12·8ft (3·9m).
Twelve reaction control system (RCS) engines.
Propellant: MMH and N₂O₄.
Habitable volume: 210ft³ (59·4m³).
Weight, with astronauts:
13,090lb (5,937kg).
Service Module
Length: 24·3ft (7·4m).
Maximum diameter: 12·8ft (3·9m).
Service Propulsion System,
engine thrust: 20,500lb (9,300kg).
Propellant: UDMH and N₂O₄.
Four RCS quads.
Propellant: MMH and N₂O₄.
Weight: 54,074lb (24,528kg).
Prime contractor:
Rockwell International.
Weights are not typical for every mission.

J-series modifications
(Apollo 15, 16, 17)
Launch vehicle (Saturn V)
S-I first stage upgraded by increased rate of propellant flow to five F-1 engines.
Four of eight stage separation retro-rockets deleted.
S-II second stage: all four ullage rockets removed.
Trajectory
Revised to insert S-IVB stage and Apollo spacecraft into Earth orbit some 11·5 miles (18·5km) lower than previous missions.
Apollo Service Module
Oxygen and hydrogen for electrical and environmental control systems raised to 1,107lb (502kg), an increase over Apollo 13 supplies of 389lb (176·4kg). Scientific Instrument Module (SIM) bay introduced.

Saturn V Launch Vehicle
1 Launch escape system.
2 Apollo Command Module.
3 Apollo Service Module.
4 Apollo Lunar Module.
5 Lunar Roving Vehicle.
6 Instrument Unit (IU).
7 S-IVB stage.
8 1 x J-2 engine.
9 S-II stage.
10 5 x J-2 engines.
11 S-IC stage.
12 5 x F-1 engines.

Launch Escape Tower
Length, overall c/w tower:
33·4ft (10·2m).
Diameter: 26in (66cm).
Weight: 9,200lb (4,173kg).

Complete with Apollo spacecraft and launch escape system, Saturn V stood 363ft (110·6m) tall. The lift-off weight was 6,423,000lb (2,912,925kg). Launch thrust of the five F-1 first stage engines was about 7,650,000lb (3,469,390kg). The first stage burned for about 2·5 minutes, boosting the Apollo spacecraft to an altitude of 38·5 miles (62km) and a velocity of 6,120mph (9,850km/h). Stage 2 powered by five J-2 engines burned for some 6·5 minutes, boosting the spacecraft to an altitude of 115 miles (185km). Stage 3 gave the vehicle the final boost that placed it in orbit at about 118 miles (190km) above the Earth. After a period, the third stage engine refired to insert the spacecraft into a trans-lunar trajectory.

It is still too early to assess the full significance of the Apollo Moon landings. Did they represent a blind alley of technological advance never to be repeated, or were they the beginning of a bold new era in which mankind eventually will colonise the Solar System?

After the last mission—Apollo 17—returned, Dr Bevan M. French, Programme Chief of the NASA Extra-terrestrials Research Program, summed up:

"Between 1969 and 1972, supported by thousands of scientists and engineers back on Earth, 12 astronauts explored the surface of the Moon. Protected against the airlessness and the killing heat of the lunar environment, they stayed on the Moon for days and some of them travelled for miles across its surface in Lunar Rovers. They made scientific observations and set up instruments to probe the interior of the Moon. They collected hundreds of pounds of lunar rock and soil, thus beginning the first attempt to decipher the origin and geological history of another world from actual samples of the crust.... But here on Earth, scientists are only now beginning to understand the immense treasure of new knowledge returned by the Apollo astronauts."

These pages illustrate the vehicles that had to be specially designed to achieve the lunar landings.

LM Descent Trajectory
Landing on the lunar surface relied on the use of radar to gauge height above the surface and regulate engine thrust. The procedure was as follows:
1 At the end of the braking phase, altitude was 10,000ft (3,048m) and thrust 6,000lb (2,721kg).
2 Coming into visible range of the landing site, altitude was 9,680ft (2,950m) and thrust 5,600lb (2,540kg).

3 As the landing phase began, altitude was about 3,000ft (914m).
4 Descending to 500ft (152·3m) thrust was 2,800lb (1,270kg) and vertical velocity 27ft/sec (8·2m/sec).
5 Dropping in, vertical velocity fell from 27 to 3ft/sec (8·2 to 0·91m/sec).
6 Vertical velocity prior to touchdown was about 3·5ft/sec (1·06m/sec). Distance between **2** and **6** was 6 miles (9·6km).

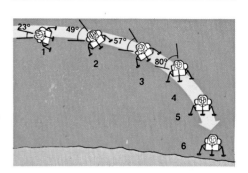

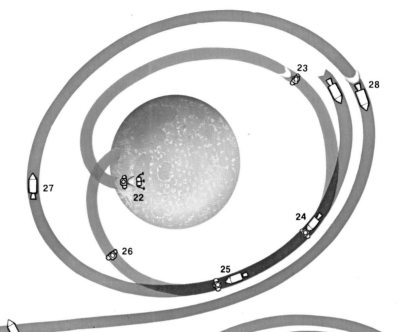

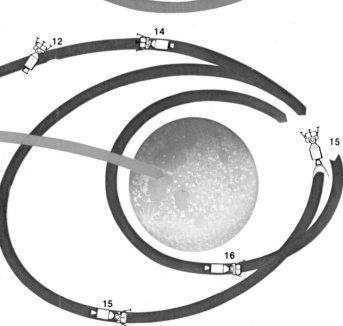

Apollo 17 Flight Profile
1 Lift-off of Saturn V with Apollo spacecraft.
2 Escape tower jettison.
3 S-IC first stage separation; second stage ignition.
4 S-II second stage separation; third stage ignition. S-IVB stage insertion into low Earth orbit.
5 Earth parking orbit.
6 Trans-lunar insertion (S-IVB second burn).
7 CSM separation.
8 CSM transposition.
9 CSM docks with LM.
10 CSM/LM separation.
11 CSM/LM mid-course correction.
12 CSM second mid-course correction (if necessary).

13 S-IVB deflected onto lunar impact course.
14 Final mid-course correction.
15 Lunar orbit insertion. First two orbits, 58·7 x 196·8 miles (94·4 x 316·6km).
16 CSM/LM descent orbit insertion 67·9 x 17·2 miles (109·2 x 27·7km); two astronauts transfer to LM.
17 LM/CSM separation on orbit 12.
18 LM retro-fire.
19 LM lands.
20 CSM orbit circularisation.
21 CSM orbit operations 62·5 x 80·9 miles (100·5 x 130·2km).
22 LM ascent stage lift-off.

23 Rendezvous with CSM.
24 Docking with CSM; astronauts re-united.
25 LM ascent stage jettisoned.
26 LM ascent stage on collision course with Moon.
27 Ejection of sub-satellite.
28 Trans-Earth insertion.
29 Mid-course correction.
30 Mid-course correction (if necessary).
31 Final mid-course correction followed by CM/SM separation.
32 Orient CM for re-entry.
33 400,000ft (121,920km) altitude penetration.
34 Communications blackout.
35 Splashdown.

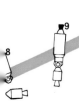

To effect control of the combined command/service modules, the Honeywell stabilization and control subsystem (SCS) directed the firing of reaction jet thrusters installed in four clusters or 'quads' equally spaced around the perimeter of the service module, or positioned the service propulsion engine properly (by swivelling or gimballing it to the correct angle) before it was fired. Some of the key functions performed by the Honeywell SCS and lunar equipment during Apollo missions were: link up with the Lunar Module (after the S-IVB stage of the launch vehicle had inserted the CSM into a trans-lunar trajectory); mid-course corrections en-route to the Moon; lunar orbit insertion; descent of the Lunar Module and subsequent ascent and re-docking with the CSM; trans-Earth injection; execution of mid-course corrections during the return flight, and orientation of the command module for re-entry into the Earth's atmosphere after it had separated from the service module.

Apollo Lunar Module (LM)
1 LM/CM docking hatch.
2 Docking hatch (entrance to pressurised cabin).
3 VHF antennas (2).
4 Reaction-control oxidiser (N_2O_4).
5 Relay box.
6 Water tank.
7 Reaction-control pressurant (helium).
8 Reaction-control fuel (Aerozine 50).
9 Ascent fuel tank (Aerozine 50).
10 Reaction-control thrusters.
11 Radioisotope thermal generator.
12 Primary shock absorber strut.
13 Foot pad.
14 Secondary shock absorber strut.
15 Descent fuel tank (Aerozine 50, port and starboard).
16 Descent engine, 10,000lb (4,535kg) thrust approximately, throttleable.
17 Descent oxidiser tank (N_2O_4, fore and aft).
18 S-band erectable antenna (lunar surface).
19 Descent structure.
20 Ladder.
21 Thermal insulation.
22 Ingress/egress platform and rails.
23 Ascent engine, 3,500lb (1,587kg) thrust in vac.
24 Portable Life Support System.
25 Exhaust deflectors.
26 Cabin air recirculation fan.
27 Tracking light.
28 LM pilot's console.
29 S-band in-flight antenna.
30 Rendezvous radar.
31 S-band steerable antenna.

The odd shape of this spacecraft was dictated by the fact that it operated only in airless space; it did not have to be streamlined in any way. Two flight stations, at which the astronauts stood with harness restraints, had display panels, armrests, controls and landing aids, two front windows, and an overhead docking window. The landing gear struts, released explosively, were extended by springs. The main struts were filled with

Lunar Lift-Off
The Lunar Module operated as a unit until the time of leaving the Moon, when the ascent stage (which contained the crew) functioned as a separate spacecraft for rendezvous and docking with the CM. This section had a docking port for linking up with the command ship and crew transfer.

crushable aluminium honeycomb for absorbing compressive loads. Foot pads 37in (95cm) in diameter provided support for the vehicle on the lunar surface. All except the forward one were fitted with 68in (170cm) long sensing probes which upon contact with the lunar surface signalled the crew to shut down the ascent engine.

Technical Data
Height: 22·92ft (6·98m). Width, diagonally across landing legs: 31ft (9·5m). Habitable volume: 160ft³ (4·5m³). Launch weight (Apollo 11): 33,205lb (15,059kg) (cf Apollo 17: 36,244lb, 16,440kg). The cylindrical crew compartment had a diameter of 7·83ft (2·35m) and was 3·5ft (1·07m) deep.

J-Series Modifications
Descent stage: increased supplies of oxygen and water; extended electrical life, Quad 1 re-arranged to permit stowage of folded Lunar Rover Vehicle (LRV). Quad 4 — new 111lb (50kg) water tank, waste container and additional oxygen pressure tank and gaseous oxygen module replaces Modularised Equipment Stowage Assembly (MESA). A re-designed MESA is fitted outside Quad 4, includes tool pallet, sample containers, batteries for personnel life support systems, and cosmic ray detector. Four descent engine propellant tanks lengthened by 3·4in (8·6cm) providing 1,150lb (521·5kg) extra fuel and oxidant. Descent engine burned for longer period; combustion chamber modified to reduce erosion: expansion skirt modified. Ascent stage: New stowage for re-designed pressure suits of greater flexibility which had increased supplies of oxygen, water and electricity for extended EVAs. Plumbing added to waste container in descent stage.

It took 400 years of trial and error, from Leonardo to the Wright Brothers, to bring about the first flying machine. But difficult as these steps were, nature allowed one advantage — there was air to provide lift and a medium for stability and control. The spaceship enjoys no such privilege. It operates in a medium in which air is no longer available (except when leaving or entering the Earth's atmosphere) and total reliance must be placed on rocket thrust for all the delicate manoeuvres necessary to navigate.

The problems were further compounded in the case of the Apollo Lunar Module which had to land two men safely on the Moon using helicopter-like skills in the approach and touchdown. In view of these difficulties, one might have expected the lunar landings to have been almost touch and go missions in which astronauts made brief forays to the lunar surface. The record shows, however, that by the final mission the amount of time the astronauts could spend outside their spacecraft had increased by a factor of ten.

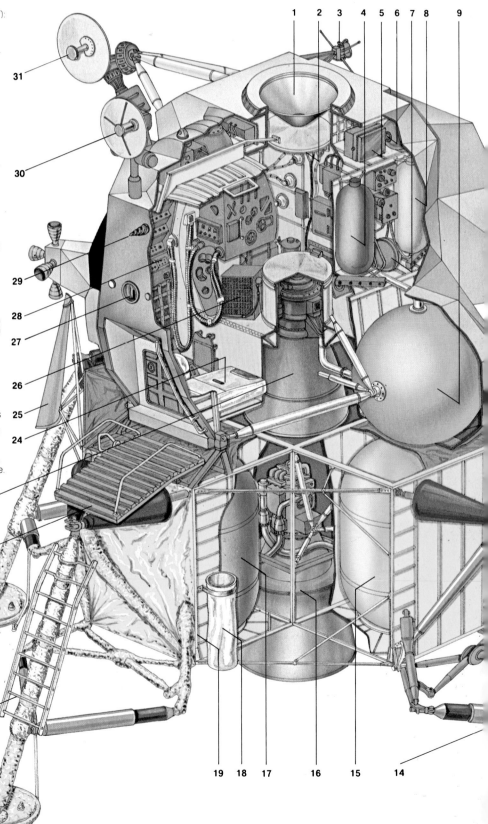

Apollo Extravehicular Mobility Unit (EMU)

1 Lunar extravehicular visor.
2 Backpack control box.
3 Water circulation from PLSS.
4 Penlight pocket.
5 Oxygen inlet and outlet to PLSS.
6 Communication, ventilation and liquid cooling umbilicals.
7 Utility pocket.
8 Lunar overshoe.
9 Integrated thermal micrometeoroid garment.
10 Urine transfer connector, biomedical injection, dosimeter access flap and donning lanyard pocket.
11 Extravehicular glove.
12 Chest cover.
13 Connector cover, rolled back to show detail.
14 Oxygen from purge system.
15 Sunglasses pocket.
16 Communications.
17 Oxygen purge system actuator.
18 Portable Life Support System (PLSS).
19 Oxygen purge system.

The EMU is a closed-circuit pressure vessel that envelops the astronaut. The environment inside the suit consists of 100% oxygen. The complete article includes liquid cooling garment, pressure garment assembly; integrated thermal micrometeoroid garment.

Portable Life Support System (PLSS)

1 Oxygen purge system.
2 High pressure oxygen subsystem (provides storage for emergencies).
3 Low pressure oxygen subsystem. (Provides emergency oxygen to the suit for breathing, ventilation and suit pressurisation.)
4 Radio.
5 Electrical junction box.
6 Feed water loop (for thermal control).
7 Oxygen ventilating circuit.
8 Liquid transport loop (for body cooling).
9 Primary oxygen subsystem.
10 Oxygen and water recharge fittings.

The backpack supplied oxygen at 3·7lb/in² (0·26kg/cm²) and water to the cooling garment worn next to the skin. Return oxygen was cleansed of solid and gas contaminants by a liquid hydroxide and activated charcoal canister. Installed in the PLSS also were communications and telemetry equipment, displays and controls, and a power supply. On top of the PLSS was mounted the Oxygen Purge System (OPS) which provided a reserve supply of gaseous oxygen.

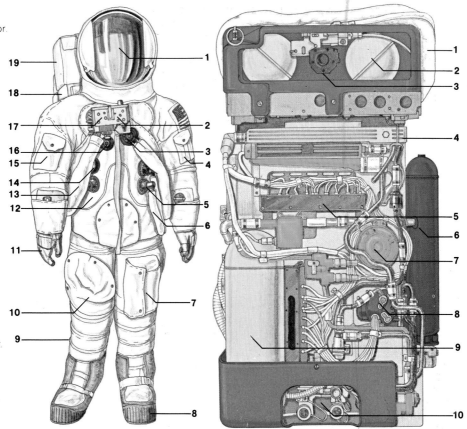

Lunar Roving Vehicle (LRV)

1 High-gain antenna.
2 Television camera.
3 Low-gain antenna.
4 Display console.
5 16mm camera pack.
6 Hand controller.
7 Sample collection bags.
8 Science and crew equipment storage.
9 Wire-mesh wheels.
10 Underseat stowage.
11 Dust guards.
12 Lunar communications relay unit.

The LRV greatly extended the area of the lunar surface which could be explored by astronauts of the Apollo 15, 16 and 17 missions. Deceptive in appearance it looked like a simple "dune buggy" but in fact was a specialised space vehicle designed to operate in conditions of vacuum, wide extremes of temperature and over difficult terrain. To keep weight to a minimum the electrically powered vehicle was built largely of aluminium. Its specially woven wire wheels were made of coated piano-wire. The LRV folded for stowage in the descent stage of the Lunar Module in a quadrant to the right of the ladder down which the astronauts descended to the Moon's surface. The chassis was hinged in three places and the four wheels were pivoted nearly flat against the folded chassis occupying only 30ft³ (0·85m³).

Technical Data

Length: 10·2ft (3·1m).
Width to centre of wheels: 6ft (1·82m).
Wheel base: 7·5ft (2·3m).
Wheel diameter: 32in (81·3cm).
Ground clearance: 14in (35·5cm).
Turning radius: 10ft (3·05m).
Maximum speed: 8·7mph (14km/h).
Power supply: two 36-volt primary silver-zinc batteries.
Traction drive: four ¼hp DC series wound motors (one each wheel).
Earth weight: 462lb (209·5kg).
Moon weight: 77lb (35kg).
Total loaded weight: 1,600lb (725·6kg).

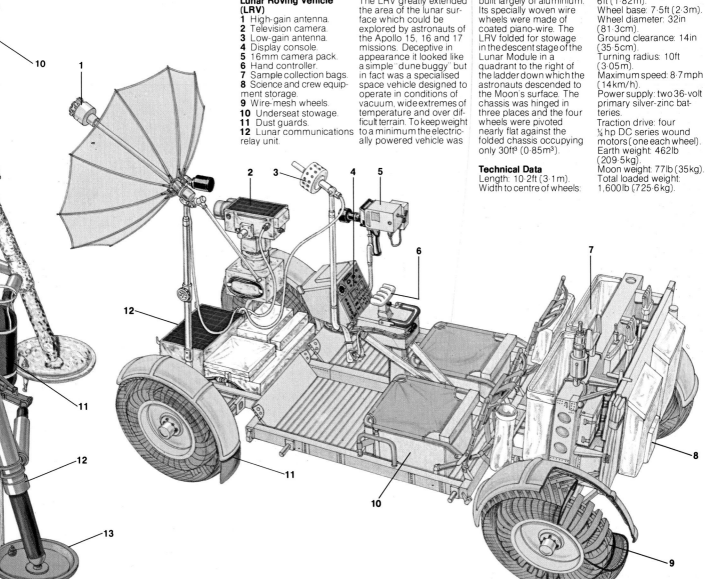

short gap between the ladder and the ground which required him to jump down.

Armstrong and Aldrin spoke to President Nixon via spacecraft radio when he called them from the White House.

They erected the United States flag (a special stiff one on a wire frame because there was no breeze to display it), set up a laser reflector, a seismometer to detect moonquakes, and a sheet of aluminium foil to trap particles of the solar wind. They took photographs of the rocks and landscape, and they collected 48·5lb (22kg) of soil and rock samples to be examined at the Lunar Receiving Laboratory at Houston. First out of the LM and last in, Armstrong spent 2hr 31min on the Moon. On the sixth lunar landing in December 1972, crew time outside the LM was extended to 22hr 5min. The traverse range on the surface also increased from about 100m on foot during Apollo 11 to a total of 21·7miles (35km) in an electric car on Apollo 17.

With Apollo 11, the race to the Moon ended. The Soviet Union announced it would restrict manned space operations to Earth orbit. More intensive scientific investigation of the Moon began with Apollo 12 (14-24 November 1969). Navy commanders Charles Conrad and Alan L. Bean landed in the LM *Intrepid* on 18 November in Oceanus Procellarum (Ocean of Storms) near the equator. Cdr Richard F. Gordon cruised overhead in lunar orbit in the CSM *Yankee Clipper*.

ALSEP

Conrad and Bean made two extra-vehicular sorties. They set up an array of instruments which had been designed for an Apollo Lunar Scientific Experiments Package (ALSEP). In addition to the solar-wind collector, which was exposed for a short time and then rolled up to be taken home for analysis, the ALSEP included a seismometer,

Lunar Landing Sites

This projection shows the landing sites of Apollo missions. Apollo 11 (16-24 July 1969) landed in the Sea of Tranquillity; Apollo 12 (14-24 Nov 1969) in the Ocean of Storms; and Apollo 14 (31 Jan- 9 Feb 1971) at the Fra Mauro formation – the planned target of the aborted Apollo 13 mission. Landing sites for the later missions were not targeted so closely to the equator. They were chosen primarily to expand knowledge of the Moon's highland areas and its crust; and compromises had to be made between this intent and the limitations imposed by availability of high-quality imagery for planning, ideal distribution of geophysical instruments, landing safety, and the capability of the Apollo/Saturn propulsion system. Thus, Apollo 15 (26 July-7 Aug 1971) landed in the Hadley Apennines; Apollo 16 (16-27 April 1972) in the Descartes highlands; and Apollo 17 (7-19 Dec 1972) made a landing in the Taurus Littrow valley.

magnetometer, solar-wind spectrometer, suprathermal ion detector and cold cathode gauge (see also page 165).

These instruments reacted to moonquakes, magnetic fields, solar wind particles and gases at the surface. Their data were radioed to Earth from a central transmitter. Most of them continued operating long after the crew departed.

During their second sortie, Conrad and Bean walked to Surveyor 3, which they found covered with tan-coloured dust. It had been standing for two years and seven months on the Moon, but except for dust film, it showed little evidence of degradation. They collected 74·7lb (33·9kg) of rocks.

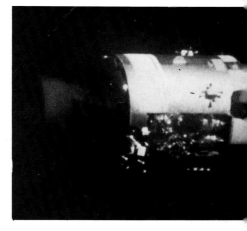

Below: *Once in a blue Moon . . . ! Shrouded in haze, an Apollo 12 astronaut works in the Ocean of Storms, where the Lunar Module* Intrepid *landed only 600ft (183m) away from the Surveyor 3 probe of 1967.*

Below: *Thirty-one months after its lunar landing, Surveyor 3 is photographed by an astronaut from Apollo 12 LM (background). The lunar explorers retrieved the probe's TV camera and other parts.*

Above: *Photographed from the combined CM/LM, the LM now the Apollo 13 "life-boat", the jettisoned service module displays the damage caused when an exploding oxygen tank blew out the side panel.*

MET Tool Rack
1 Staff-mounted 16mm camera.
2 35-bag dispenser.
3 Scoop.
4 Hammer.
5 Gnomon.
6 Penetrometer.
7 Tongs.
8 Colour chart and traverse map.

Some of the tools carried in the rack on the Modularized Equipment Transporter (MET) the two-wheeled hand-cart used by the Apollo 14 astronauts to transport equipment and samples.

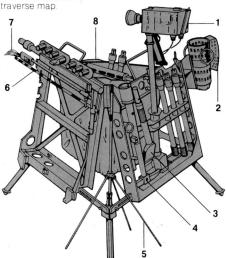

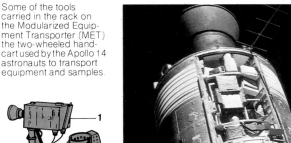

Above: *Sensors peer from the Scientific Instrument Module bay (SIMbay) of Apollo 15 CSM* Endeavour. *The eight instruments carried in this section included broad-scale remote sensors, cameras and spectrometers.*

Next up was Apollo 13, headed for the Fra Mauro formation. Two days after it was launched on 11 April 1970, an oxygen tank of the electrical power supply exploded in the Service Module. Mission control at Houston ordered the crew to cancel the landing plan and return to Earth after rounding the Moon. Lovell, Fred. W. Haise and John L. Swigert would have faced the harrowing prospect of slow suffocation had it not been for the reserves of oxygen in the Lunar Module. They fired its engine to accelerate the crippled CSM *Odyssey* around the Moon and hasten the return to Earth. By using the LM, *Aquarius*, as a "lifeboat", they were able to return safely on 17 April after

casting it off and separating in the landing capsule for re-entry and splashdown.

In Apollo 14 (31 January-9 February 1971), Shepard and Cdr Edgar D. Mitchell landed in the Fra Mauro region and spent nine hours outside the LM *Antares* collecting 98lb (44·5kg) of rocks. They set up the ALSEP and a laser mirror, while Major Stuart A. Roosa remained in orbit in the CSM *Kitty Hawk*. Television camera transmission from the landing site showed some of the activity to watchers on Earth, including Shepard's feat of driving a golf ball one-handed across the Moon's surface.

This mission introduced a wheeled vehicle into the American lunar programme in the

form of a rickshaw-like cart pulled by the astronauts. The wheeled vehicle concept was greatly advanced on Apollo 15 which carried a four-wheeled, battery-powered "jeep"—the lunar rover.

Apollo 15 was targeted to the Hadley Apennine Mountains. Flown between '26 July and 7 August 1971, its crew produced a wealth of data on the ground and also from orbit. Scott and Lt-Col James B. Irwin landed at the foot of the Lunar Apennines in the LM *Falcon* while Major Alfred M. Worden circled overhead in the CSM *Endeavour*.

Driving the Rover, Scott and Irwin explored the mountain slopes for a total of 18hr 36min, collecting some 173lb (78·6kg) of soil and rock samples. They explored a deep gorge called the Hadley Rille but found its sides too steep to investigate on foot without mountain climbing equipment.

Apollo 15, for the first time, carried eight scientific experiments in a section of the Service Module called the SIMbay. The instruments included mapping and panoramic cameras and spectrometers. As the spacecraft swung round the Moon, two of the latter, mounted on the ends of telescopic booms over 20ft (6·1m) long, probed the composition of surface material, the interaction of solar X-rays and particle emissions.

Worden was assigned to make extensive photographic maps of the ground track. From the SIMbay a 31in (0·79m) sub-satellite was deployed into orbit. Equipped with a transponder so that its flight-path could be tracked from Earth, the sub-satellite was an experiment to measure concentrations of mass (mascons) in the Moon.

Below: *Apollo 15 astronaut James Irwin salutes the US flag planted in the lunar dust of the Hadley Apennines. In the background is LM* Falcon *with (right) the Lunar Roving Vehicle, a battery-powered "jeep".*

On the ground, after driving 7·6 miles in the Rover, Scott and Irwin set up the ALSEP instruments and a laser reflector, the third in a triangle of landing sites. The purpose of the reflectors was to enable astronomers to refine the Earth-Moon distance by timing the round trip of a laser beam sent from Earth. Measurements would reveal whether the Moon is receding from the Earth.

It was the task of astronaut Worden to spacewalk after the Apollo CSM had departed for home to retrieve from the SIMbay exposed film and other scientific data.

The Final Voyages

Having sampled the lunar *maria* (basaltic basins) and a mountain system, NASA sent Apollo 16 (16-27 April 1972) to the Descartes highlands, a part of the light coloured *terrae* of the Moon where soil and rock composition were believed to be quite different from that of darker lowlands. Young and Charles M. Duke landed in the LM *Orion*, while Lt-Cdr Thomas K. Mattingly II orbited the Moon in the CSM *Casper*. Young and Duke spent a total of 20hr 14min outside the LM and collected 210lb (95·2kg) of rocks. During three sorties they covered 16·8 miles (27km) in the rover.

Near the landing site Young and Duke set up an ultra-violet camera on a tripod for astronomical observations, took deep core rock samples by means of a drill, attempted to set up detectors to measure heat flow from the lunar interior (but accidentally damaged the instrument), and arrayed passive and active seismic instrumentation.

The magnetometer experiment yielded information that they were in a magnetised region of the Moon, a finding that suggested an ancient magnetic field. Young picked up an object resembling a glass prism, the remnant of an old heating event.

A heat-flow experiment was successfully installed in the Littrow Valley in the Taurus Mountain region on Apollo 17 (7-19 December 1972) by Cernan and Harrison H. Schmitt. They landed in the LM *Challenger*, spent 22hr 5min outside, setting up experiments and collecting 243lb (110kg) of soil and rocks. Upstairs, Lt-Cdr Ronald E. Evans circled the Moon in the CSM *America*.

Schmitt, a geologist, was the only professional scientist sent to the Moon. He influenced the selection of the Taurus-Littrow site because he believed evidence of volcanic activity would be found there. He and Cernan picked up orange glass which at first was thought to have a volcanic origin, but which later analysis did not confirm.

Once more, the lunar explorers roamed about in their electric car, the third one to be used on the Moon. In addition to the ALSEP instruments, they carried two gravity meters, one to measure gravitational changes at various points in the landing area and the other to attempt to detect gravity waves propagated through the Universe.

Apollo 17 was the final lunar mission. The six landings resulted in the collection of 847·2lb (384·2kg) of soil and rock samples. Of numerous discoveries made in the programme, two major ones were widely accepted. The first was that the Moon is sterile. No form of indigenous life was found there. After Apollo 14, a 21-day quarantine requirement for returned lunar

Above: *The colour TV camera mounted on Apollo 16's Lunar Rover Vehicle recorded and transmitted to Earth this lunar leap by LM commander John Young during the first of three EVAs in the Descartes highlands.*

Below: *The gnomon (foreground) deployed by Charles Duke from Apollo 16's LRV facilitates the calibration of pictures by providing a vertical-seeking rod of known length, a colour chart, and a shadow.*

mission crews was dropped. The second major finding was that the Moon, like the Earth, has been through several periods of internal heating. It has a crust, which is quite thick relative to the Moon's radius, a mantle and a core, which some investigators suggest is iron sulphide.

Although in some ways chemically similar to Earth, the Moon was found to be quite dissimilar in others, enough to support strong arguments refuting the theory that it was torn from the Earth during the formation of the planets.

Consistent with the lack of evidence that life ever existed in any form on the Moon, is an apparent total lack of water, at least on or near the surface. A suggestion that water may exist as ice or permafrost beneath the surface or in hydrated minerals was indicated in studies that followed from the Apollo 17 orange glass findings.

The record of the rocks and fines (dirt) has shown clearly that the Moon is as old as the Earth, approximately 4,500 million years old. Whether the Moon accreted hot or cold remains in dispute. However the preponderant view holds that the Moon underwent differentiation, as a result of heating, during its first 1,500 million years. Its surface features were sculpted by planetoid and meteoroid bombardment which appears to have reached a climax 3,900 million years ago. Erosion, once believed to be non-existent on the Moon, was found to occur from the impact of the solar wind.

The question of the origin of the Moon, which scientists once believed lunar exploration would resolve, remains as controversial as ever. Two theories are considered by most of the lunar investigators and experimenters on the Apollo programme. One holds that the Moon was captured after being formed somewhere else in the Solar System. Another maintains that the Moon was formed in the general vicinity of the Earth, possibly as part of a double-planet system. The idea of Sir George H. Darwin (1845-1912) that the Moon broke away from the Earth was not supported by the chemical evidence of Surveyor and Apollo.

Any theory of the origin of the Moon has to explain the difference in density between it and the Earth. The Moon's average density is 3·36gm/cu cm; the Earth's is 5·5. Element abundances differ considerably. Although Moon rocks and Earth rocks contain the same chemical elements, it was found that their proportions were different. Moon rocks, for example, contain more calcium, aluminium and titanium than do average Earth samples. Elements with high melting points, such as hafnium and zirconium,

Below: *The LRV's TV camera, remotely controlled from Mission Control Center, Houston, Texas, makes it possible for Earth viewers to watch lift-off from the Moon of Apollo 16 LM Orion ascent stage.*

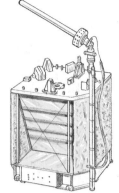
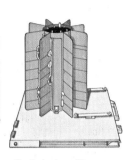

ALSEP Central Station
Apart from serving as a junction-box for the cables linking the generator and the scientific equipment, Central Station is a telemetry transmitter carrying a gimbal-mounted, helical S-band antenna. This must be carefully aimed Earthward in order to maintain radio communication for the transmission of experiment data and to receive instrument adjustment commands. Each ALSEP on the Moon can send about 9 million instrument readings a day.

Radio Isotope Thermoelectric Nuclear Generator
SNAP (System of Nuclear Auxiliary Power)-27 generator, fuelled by a plutonium capsule, is the powerhouse of ALSEP. The temperature difference between the fuel capsule, centrally housed in a vertical position, and the finned outer housing is converted into electrical power by 442 lead telluride thermocouples. Starting at about 74W, and slowly diminishing, output to Central Station will continue for several years.

Suprathermal Ion Detector Experiment (SIDE)
SIDE measures the Moon's ionosphere, sampling the energy and mass of the positive ions that result from the ionisation of gases near the lunar surface by the solar wind or ultra-violet radiation. Its three wide-range look angles permit study of the directional characteristics of ion flow on both sides of the Earth's magnetospheric tail. Also housed in SIDE are the electronics for the Cold Cathode Gauge Experiment (CCGE).

Solar Wind Spectrometer
In this experiment, a plasma spectrometer uses seven Faraday-cup sensors to measure the velocity and direction of protons, electrons and alpha-particles in the solar wind as they arrive at the Moon, and the inter-action of these particles with the lunar surface. Because the Moon, unlike the Earth, is not protected from the solar-wind plasma by a magnetic shield, the instrument can detect subtle variations in the wind's intensity and direction.

Below: *To further scientific experiments, self-contained Apollo Lunar Surface Experiments Package (ALSEP) stations were included in the Apollo 12, 14, 15, 16 and 17 missions. Here, an ALSEP is deployed.*

Lunar Surface Magnetometer
Measures the three orthogonal components of the Moon's magnetic field and the interaction of the solar wind with the magnetic field around the Moon. Periodically, the fluxgate sensors at the boom ends flip over mechanically to check the calibration. By using data from this experiment in conjunction with free-space magnetic data from the Explorer 35 satellite, scientists have estimated rock temperatures deep in the lunar interior.

Passive Lunar Seismic Experiment
Uses four extremely sensitive seismometers to measure lunar surface vibrations, free oscillations and tidal variations in surface tilt. Three long-period seismometers measure wave motions with periods between 0·5-250sec; the short-period seismometer measures vertical motions with periods between 0·05-20 sec. The thermal shroud isolates the sensor and an area 5ft (1·5m) in diameter from day/night temperature extremes.

appear to be more plentiful on the Moon than on Earth. But elements with low melting points, such as sodium and potassium, are less abundant on the Moon. As a result, some investigators have speculated that the Moon accreted in a higher temperature environment than did the Earth. This may explain the absence of water and other volatiles in the lunar samples.

The abundance of aluminium and titanium has suggested to space planners that the

Moon may become an important source of those critical metals. But the present consensus is that industrial operations on the Moon are unlikely in the foreseeable future unless water in some form is found there, possibly at the unexplored polar regions. The prospects of developing a mining colony on the Moon are discussed in Chapter 17.

Each of the Apollo landing missions contributed elements of a scientific scenario about the evolution of the Moon. In many respects, it paralleled the theory of the evolution of the Earth and other terrestrial planets.

Limited seismic data indicated that the crust is 37 to 40 miles (60 to 65km) thick on the near side, that is two to three times the average thickness of the Earth's continental crust. On the far side of the Moon the crust may be thicker—up to 93 miles (150km). Below the crust, the mantle extends for 621 miles (1,000km) and below that is the core.

The upper mantle, about 124 miles (200km) thick, consists of iron-rich silicates. Below, the rock type is similar to that of a common

type of meteorite (chondrite). The lower mantle appears to be molten. The fluid portion is distorted by tidal pull of the Earth and this effect produces barely detectable moonquakes. There is also seismic evidence for a molten core.

A popular view that emerged from the series of lunar science conferences where the results of the Apollo missions were reviewed held that the Moon was formed in a high temperature region of the solar nebula. Volatile elements existed there as vapour; consequently, the Moon is deficient in these elements.

Accretion continued during the Moon's first 500 million years and the surface was heavily bombarded. Huge planetoids crashing on the Moon gouged out the maria basins. Heated by the decay of radio-active elements, the crust and upper mantle melted and the lava poured into the basins to form their basaltic floors. These eventually became covered by a layer of crushed rock and dust called the "regolith" or surface soil. In terms of structure, the Moon is considered a partly

Deployment of Lunar Roving Vehicle (LRV)

The electric-powered 'moon-jeep' is stowed in a nose-down, floorpan-out position in the LM descent stage, from which it can be deployed by an astronaut paying out two nylon tapes. Torsion-bar springs and latches make assembly semi-automatic.
1 The LRV is swung out from its storage bay.
2 The rear part of the chassis unfolds and locks, and the rear wheels unfold.

3 The front chassis and wheels snap out on to the lunar surface.
4 The astronaut lowers the rear of the LRV to the lunar surface; he must now unfold the seats and footrests. The LRV weighs 462lb (209·5kg) on Earth—only 77lb (35kg) on the Moon. The vehicle's power comes from two 36-volt silver-zinc batteries driving an independent 0·25hp motor in each wheel, giving a maximum speed on the level of 8·7 mph (14km/h).

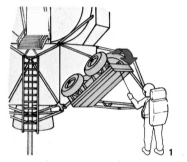
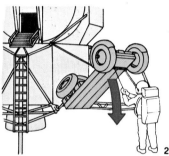
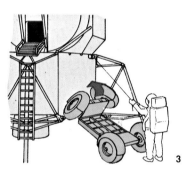
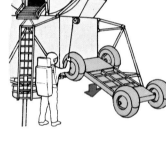

Left: *Apollo 17 LM pilot Harrison Schmitt collects lunar samples. With Eugene Cernan, Schmitt recorded the programme's longest surface stay-time, 74hr 59min 38sec, and longest total EVA, 22hr 5min 6sec.*

Below: *Schmitt, a qualified geologist, collects samples with a lunar rake. Long-handled tools like the rake, scoop and spring-loaded tongs, enabled astronauts to collect small rocks without undue bending.*

evolved planet where tectonic (planet-shaping) processes that still continue on the Earth stopped millions of years ago.

Since Apollo 17, 125 scientific teams around the world have continued to examine lunar rocks and fines and instrument data. About 12 per cent of the samples returned were distributed to laboratories outside NASA as of 1979.

During the Apollo period it was the view of several geologist investigators that a complete geological survey of the Moon would be required to resolve some of the questions about its origin and evolution. This, it was surmised, would involve extensive surface operations, at least as large as those mounted in Antarctica during the International Geophysical Year (1957-58) and immediately thereafter, and if conducted at a lower level of effort, might take as long as a century.

Apart from unmanned reconnaissance, there are no present plans (1980) by the United States to resume a programme of manned exploration of the Moon.

Above: *Photomicrograph of a thin section of a lunar sample (number 70017)—described as a loose rock-vesicular, porphyritic, coarse-grained basalt—brought back by Apollo 17 from the Taurus-Littrow site.*

REFERENCES

1 Charles D. Benson and William Barnaby Faherty, *Moonport—A History of Apollo Launch Facilities and Operations*, NASA SP-4204.
2 Barton C. Hacker and James M. Grimwood, *On the Shoulders of Titans—A History of Project Gemini*, NASA SP-4203.
3 John L. Sloop, *Liquid Hydrogen as a Propulsion Fuel, 1945-1959*, NASA SP-4404.
4 Kenneth Gatland, *Manned Spacecraft*, Blandford Press, London, 1967.
5 *Journal of the British Interplanetary Society*, London, 1939.
6 R. C. Parkinson, *High Road to the Moon*, British Interplanetary Society, London, 1980.
7 R. S. Lewis, *Appointment on the Moon*, Viking Press, New York, 1969.
8 R. S. Lewis, *Voyages of Apollo*, New York Times Book Co. New York, 1974.
9 Edgar N. Cortright (Ed), *Apollo Expeditions to the Moon*, NASA SP-350.

Below: *Ronald Evans makes a spacewalk to retrieve film cassettes as Apollo 17 returns to Earth. He receives oxygen from the spacecraft through the umbilical hose—but note emergency supply on his back.*

The First Space Stations

America's Skylab space station was born in that period of enthusiasm for manned spaceflight which accompanied the so-called Race to the Moon in the 1960s. NASA was anticipating an era when space exploration would blossom as a Number One priority supported by large fiscal budgets. Serious consideration was given to the design of large space stations which were expected to lead to a research base on the Moon—even flights to Mars by nuclear-powered manned spaceships.

Two major events were to change this enthusiasm. One was the immense success of the Apollo programme in landing men on the Moon, which satisfied the national demand to counter Soviet advances achieved with Sputnik and Vostok which, at the time, had rocked America to its foundations. The second was the growing demands of the Vietnam War and the drain of that effort on the US economy. Skylab and the Space Shuttle were sole survivors of the post-Apollo programme; the former was expected to give the United States basic experience in the use of a large orbital laboratory which could be developed at minimum cost, making use of existing Apollo hardware.

The Russians, for their part, had always looked upon space stations as part of the basic philosophy of cosmonautics. Mr Brezhnev has himself emphasised that

"Soviet science considers the creation of orbital stations with changing crews as the highway of man into space."

Key steps in this direction were Soyuz-type spacecraft which could be docked together automatically, with or without the participation of cosmonauts on board. The early emphasis given by Soviet designers to the automatic control of spacecraft in docking manoeuvres has paid immense dividends enabling Salyut space stations, far smaller than America's Skylab, to be re-supplied by manned and unmanned ferries allowing cosmonauts to remain in space for much longer periods.

Skylab

Skylab was built from the S-IVB stage of a Saturn V Moon rocket, its hydrogen tank being converted at the factory into spacious two-storey accommodation for a three-man crew. The bottom section contained a ward room, sleep compartments and a zero-g washroom/toilet or "waste compartment"; above was the spacious workshop in which the astronauts could "swim" under weightless conditions. The total internal volume of Skylab with Apollo Command and Service Modules docked was, in fact, about 11,700 cu

---

> ## "The Earth is the cradle of reason, but one cannot live in the cradle for ever."
> Konstantin E. Tsiolkovsky

---

ft (331·5 cu m)—approximately the same as a small two-bedroom house.

Water, food and clothing sufficient for all nine astronauts of the three planned Skylab missions were stowed in special containers before launch. Water was in tanks in the upper section, food in compartments and freezers in the upper section and wardroom. The astronauts breathed a mixture of oxygen and nitrogen at a pressure of 5lb/sq in (0·35kg/sq cm) and a thermal control and ventilation system was designed to maintain a nominal temperature of 21·1°C (70°F). Attached to the outside of the station were large solar "wings", retracted during the launch phase, while covering the workshop area was a thin aluminium shield which sprang out on links for protection against micrometeoroids and excessive solar heat.

Forward of the workshop was the Instrument Unit, the Airlock Module and Multiple

---

Docking Adapter which enabled Apollo spacecraft to dock with the station and transfer their crews; and mounted at the top was a major scientific instrument for observing the Sun called the Apollo Telescope Mount (ATM).

The big space station was launched, unmanned, by a two-stage Saturn V from the Kennedy Space Center on 14 May 1973. At first all seemed to be going well and it was only after the station had arrived in orbit some 270 miles (435km) above the Earth that Mission Control began to realise that something was seriously wrong. Sixty-three seconds into the flight part of the meteoroid shield had been torn off by air pressure and this had carried away one of the station's two solar wings. Although the ATM had hinged out and locked into position, deploying its own four "wings", the station was seriously underpowered electrically and was liable to heat up under the glare of the Sun.

Skylab had the largest solar cell panels ever devised for a space vehicle. The arrays,

Below: *Skylab space station is launched by a two-stage Saturn V from Launch Complex-39A at the Kennedy Space Center on 14 May 1973. Just a minute after this picture was taken Skylab had sustained serious damage.*

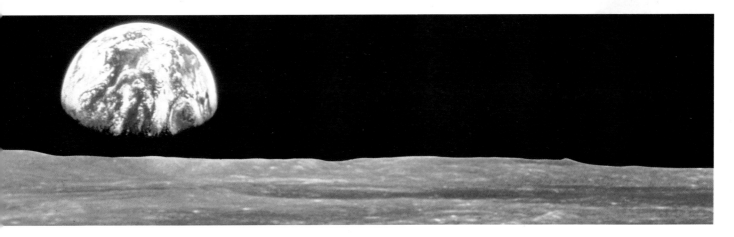

with almost 7,858 sq ft (730 sq m) of surface area, were each designed to provide 10,500W of power at 55°C (131°F) while in the sunlit portion of the orbit. Some of this was diverted to battery chargers which kept nickel-cadmium batteries at full charge and ready for use while the station was in the Earth's shadow. A power-conditioning system was designed to regulate Skylab's voltage to a nominal level of 4,000W of power at 28 volts direct current.

Without the protective shield, temperatures inside the station began to rise; and while others worked on the problem of salvage, Mission Control had the task of keeping the station in an attitude which would minimise heating while keeping the ATM's solar panels at an angle at which they could generate sufficient electrical power to run internal equipment. NASA and company technicians worked round the clock to devise various tools and sunshades which astronauts could take into orbit to attempt repairs.

Skylab 2

On 25 May—just 11 days after the mishap to Skylab—Charles Conrad, Dr Joseph Kerwin and Paul Weitz lifted off in their Apollo command and service module (CSM). After achieving rendezvous with the station 7½ hours later, they made a fly-around 186

Below: *Skylab with Earth's clouds in the background and a distant star, photographed by the first crew to visit the station during their final fly-around inspection. The makeshift "sunshade" is clearly visible on the side of the workshop.*

Above: *The various elements of Skylab underwent the most rigorous testing before they were assembled for flight. Here tests are carried out on the Apollo Telescope Mount control and display panel in the Multiple Docking Adapter.*

Skylab was America's first manned space station. Astronauts in Mercury, Gemini and Apollo had lived in cramped quarters, been fed foods which on the whole were bland and uninteresting and missed the small luxuries they enjoyed on Earth. For the first time, Skylab offered some of the more common creature comforts. There was 13,000ft³ (368m³) of space in which to move around and work. Privacy was possible. There was water for occasional showers and other needs of personal hygiene. On previous space missions, astronauts ate mainly pastes, concentrates and liquids out of plastic bags. On Skylab there was some 2,000lb (907kg) of food stored in 11 food stowage containers and five food freezers. The nutriment was packaged mainly in metal cans with pull-off tops and was a mixture of frozen, de-hydrated and dry foods to allow more varied menus. There were facilities for heating or chilling meals within the crew quarters. Clothing for Skylab crewmen was stored in "28-day clothing modules" located in lockers in the crew quarters. Nothing was washed in the space station. When an astronaut changed his clothes, he disposed of used garments in a "garbage can" — the empty tank beneath the floor of the living quarters. There were 60 changes of jackets, shorts

and slacks, 30 constant-wear garments, 15 pairs of boots and gloves, and 210 pairs of underpants. Extra garments were kept in "contingency modules". The big luxury was the toilet-cum-washroom or "waste management compartment". Lockers here stored some 55 bars of soap, 210lb (95·2kg) of towels and about 18,000 urine and fecal bags, While this washroom served the needs of crewmen, it was really a medical laboratory, allowing study of the astronauts' mineral and body fluids balance. Medical experiments carried out aboard Skylab, involving the use of special apparatus, increased knowledge of man himself and his relationship to his earthly environment and adaptability to space flight. Primarily, scientists were interested in identifying the precise mechanisms that change the chemistry of the human body when Earth's gravity is absent. They were also anxious to study human re-adaptation to normal gravity conditions after the return to Earth. Other objectives of the Skylab missions were to evaluate techniques designed to gather information on Earth's resources; a major investigation of the Sun using Skylab's solar telescopes; and experiments with industrial processes which may be enhanced by the unique micro-gravity/vacuum environment which is experienced on a space station.

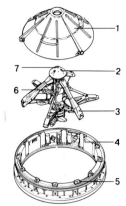

Docking Unit (CSM)
1 Drogue assembly (MDA).
2 Capture latches.
3 Probe assembly (CSM).
4 Docking ring (CM).
5 Latch assemblies.
6 Self-locking extension latch
7 Capture latch release handle (MDA side).

Docking of the CSM with Skylab was achieved by manoeuvring close enough to the MDA so that the probe of the CM engaged a drogue on the MDA. When the probe came into contact with the drogue, it was guided into the socket at the bottom of the drogue and held by latches.

Skylab
1 Solar shield.
2 Apollo telescope sensors.
3 Battery and regulator module.
4 "Pantograph" extension linkage.
5 ATM solar panels.
6 Antenna boom.
7 Orbital workshop solar array.
8 Nitrogen tank.
9 Oxygen tanks.
10 Water tanks.
11 Stowage lockers.
12 Waste management compartment.
13 Wardroom and galley.
14 Sleep compartment.
15 Shower cabinet.
16 Rotating litter chair.
17 Control console.
18 Workshop floor grids.
19 Exercise bicycle (velo-ergometer).

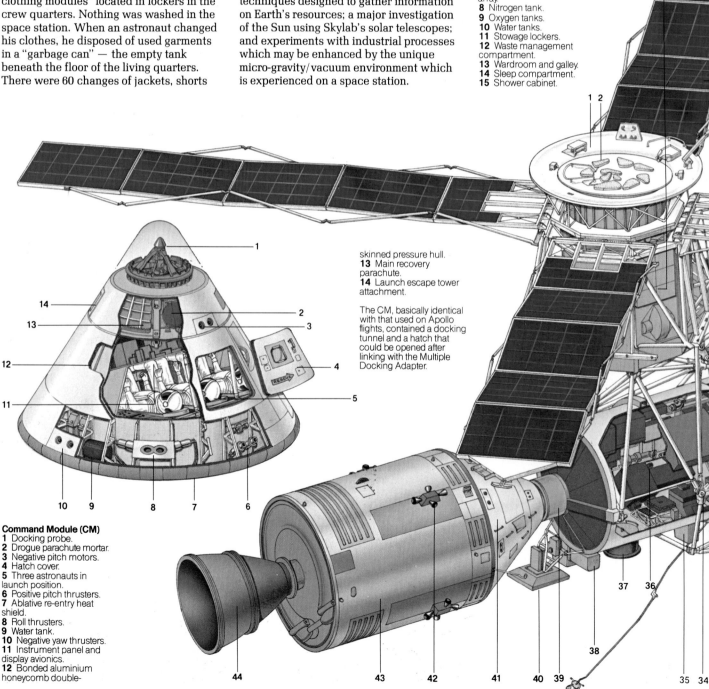

skinned pressure hull.
13 Main recovery parachute.
14 Launch escape tower attachment.

The CM, basically identical with that used on Apollo flights, contained a docking tunnel and a hatch that could be opened after linking with the Multiple Docking Adapter.

Command Module (CM)
1 Docking probe.
2 Drogue parachute mortar.
3 Negative pitch motors.
4 Hatch cover.
5 Three astronauts in launch position.
6 Positive pitch thrusters.
7 Ablative re-entry heat shield.
8 Roll thrusters.
9 Water tank.
10 Negative yaw thrusters.
11 Instrument panel and display avionics.
12 Bonded aluminium honeycomb double-

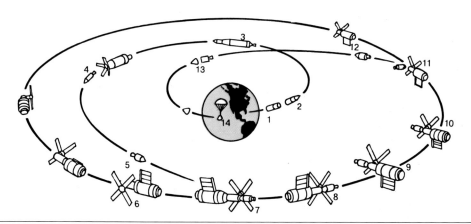

Skylab: Docking Profile
1 Launch of third crew from Cape Canaveral, Florida LC-39B..
2 S-IB stage separates.
3 S-IVB boost to 93 x 138 miles (150 x 222km) orbit.
4 CSM/S-IV separation.
5 CSM rendezvous manoeuvres to 270 miles (434km).
6 Skylab orients to Z-axis local vertical for CSM rendezvous: docking lights and ranging system on.
7 Skylab orients to solar inertial attitude. CSM docks with Skylab.
8 Combined vehicles orient to Z-axis local

vertical attitude for Earth resources experiments.
9 Orient to solar inertial attitude: complete 84-day mission.
10 Skylab prepared for closedown and storage. Crew transfer to CSM.
11 CSM undocks.
12 CSM retro-thrust starts return to Earth.
13 CM/SM separate.
14 CM re-enters atmosphere. Parachutes deploy; splashdown in Pacific.
At the end of the mission the astronauts prepared the Skylab cluster for unmanned operation transferred to the CSM and separated from the station.

20 Lower body negative pressure experiment.
21 Waste tank separation screens.
22 Attitude control nitrogen bottles.
23 Refrigeration system radiator.
24 Solar array. (Skylab is shown here in its original design configuration. In fact this panel was torn off by air pressure during the launch phase.
25 Solar panel deployment boom.
26 Micrometeoroid shield (also torn off during launch phase).
27 Cabin atmosphere distribution ducts.

28 Orbital workshop hatch.
29 Discone antennas.
30 Docking hatch.
31 Battery box.
32 Multiple Docking Adapter.
33 Microwave radiometer/ scatterometer.
34 Apollo Telescope Mount (ATM) support struts.
35 Multispectral scanner.
36 Multiple Docking Adapter workshop.
37 Radial docking port.
38 Infra-red spectrometer.
39 Axial docking hatch.
40 L-band antenna.
41 Command Module.
42 Vernier control motors.

43 Service Module.
44 Propulsion engine nozzle.

Principal Scientific Experiments:

Primary work station for conducting the solar experiments of the Apollo Telescope Mount (ATM) was in the Multiple Docking Adapter (MDA). Through a television system, the astronauts were able to see images of the Sun recorded by the telescopes. The control and display panels for the Earth resources experiments were also located in the MDA. A special airlock in

the wall of the orbital workshop allowed the crew to perform special "outside" experiments. For example a camera equipped with calcium fluoride transmission optics to pass ultra-violet light was aimed at stars in the Milky Way. Knowledge of the Earth's upper atmosphere air glow measurements were gained from UV photography from two positions inside the Workshop. One camera position was at the wardroom window. Medical apparatus installed in Skylab included equipment for monitoring an astronaut's cardiovascular

system. A slight suction applied to the lower half of the man's body placed a stress on the heart and blood vessels. Responses to this before, during and after the flight provided information on cardiovascular accommodation during long-duration space flight. In another test using a revolving litter chair (which could be adjusted to a horizontal position) the effects of weightlessness and sub-gravity conditions on astronaut perception, motion sensitivity, orientation and balance were investigated. This helped to determine

the need for artifical gravity in future space missions. Because astronauts had experienced problems due to sleep disturbance on previous space flights, sleep quality and quantity were also measured so that remedies might be found by space doctors. The wardroom had about 100ft² (9·29m²) of area with an eating table, compartments and freezers for food storage, and a window 18in (45·7cm) in diameter. The waste management compartment — containing toilet and washing facilities — was 30ft² (2·79m²).

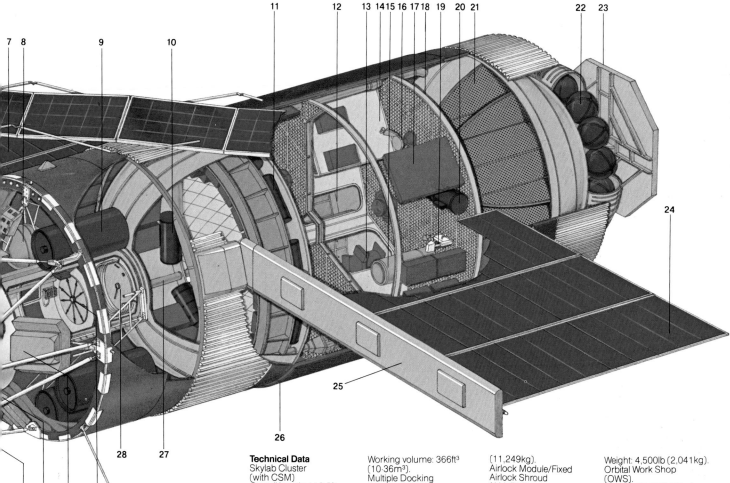

Technical Data

Skylab Cluster (with CSM)
Overall length: 118·5ft (36·1m).
Conditioned work volume 11,700ft³ (331·5m³).
Command/Service Module (CSM).
Length: 34·3ft (10·4m).
Diameter: 12·8ft (3·9m).
Weight: 29,500lb (13,381kg)

Working volume: 366ft³ (10·36m³).
Multiple Docking Adapter (MDA).
Length: 17·3ft (5·67m).
Diameter: 10ft (3·05m).
Weight: 13,600lb (6,169kg).
Working volume: 1,140ft³ (32·28m³).
Apollo Telescope Mount (ATM).
Length: 13·3ft (4·05m).
Weight: 24,800lb

(11,249kg).
Airlock Module/Fixed Airlock Shroud (AM/FAS).
Length: 17·6ft (5·36m).
Diameter: 10ft (3·05m).
Weight: 49,200lb (22,317kg).
Working volume: 613ft³ (17·4m³).
Instrument Unit (IU).
Length: 3ft (0·91m).
Diameter: 21·6ft (6·58m).

Weight: 4,500lb (2,041kg).
Orbital Work Shop (OWS).
Length: 48·1ft (14·7m).
Diameter: 21·6ft (6·58m).
Weight: 76,000lb (34,473kg).*
Working volume: 9,550ft³ (270·4m³).

*This figure includes one solar "wing" and the Orbital Work Shop meteoroid shield.

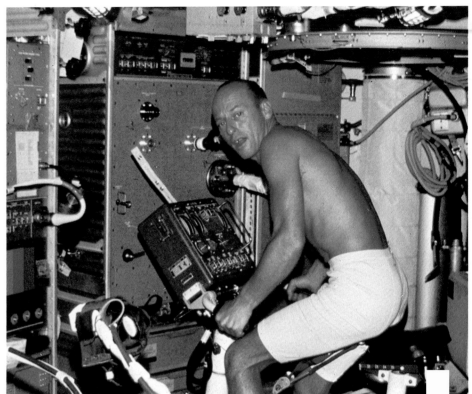

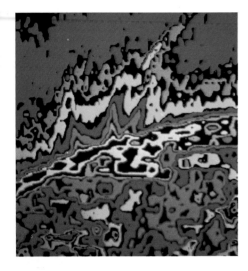

Above: *Solar prominences photographed by Skylab astronauts using the Solar Telescope. Interpretation of the rich store of Skylab ultraviolet data was facilitated by computerised colour enhancement of the original black and white image, highlighting subtle but important brightness differences. Colour enhancement of solar data was among the new techniques of data reduction brought into use by Skylab scientists.*

inspection and confirmed that one solar wing was missing and the other stuck fast by a piece of metal from the meteoroid shield.

With the astronauts wearing EVA suits Conrad manoeuvred round Skylab as close as he dared while Weitz stood in the hatchway with toggle cutters fixed to a long pole, his legs firmly held by Kerwin. Despite heroic efforts the panel would not move.

There were further frustrations. Repeated attempts to dock with the station proved abortive. So the astronauts had to don their spacesuits again and look for the reason by removing the special probe from the docking tunnel. They found the remedy by fitting a by-pass lead to switches of the docking mechanism. After fixing the problem, the astronauts spent their first night aboard the Apollo ferry craft. The next day they cautiously entered the station wearing breathing masks in case the overheated metals and plastics inside were giving off toxic fumes. But conditions were tolerable, and one of their first acts was to deploy a parasol-like sunshade through an experiment airlock in the side of the workshop, which helped bring the temperature down. As the sleeping compartments were too hot the men slept initially in the Multiple Docking Adapter, which retained its thermal shield. It was even possible to begin a limited programme of experiments.

Then, on 7 June, after careful preparations Conrad and Kerwin made a 3½ hour spacewalk to free the solar "wing". At first Conrad tried to cut away the torn piece of metal securing the beam of the solar panels with the toggle cutters attached to a 25ft (7·6m) pole, but to no avail. He was forced to crawl along the outside of the station and guide the cutters at close quarters. Kerwin, from his position on top of the workshop, then was able to operate them with a lanyard.

Having attached a 30ft (9·1m) rope to the beam, Conrad retreated to a safe distance and stood up with it over his shoulder to

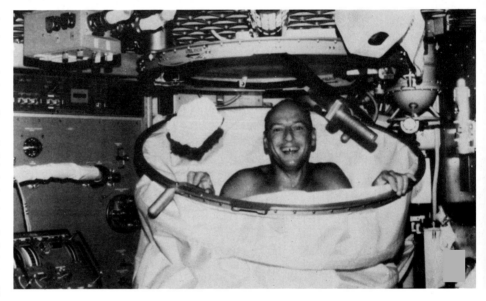

Top: *Charles "Pete" Conrad works out on the bicycle ergometer in the Orbital Workshop crew quarters of Skylab as it orbits the Earth in the early summer of 1973. While the astronaut "toned up his muscles" his heart rate, pulse and respiration could be automatically measured.*

gain leverage. The beam swung open deploying the panels—and the two men were almost separated from the station by the reaction. After completing a few more necessary tasks outside, the elated EVA team re-entered the station to find the workshop's eight internal batteries being recharged by the solar panel they had deployed.

With the additional power available the astronauts were able to get back to the original flight plan. They observed the Sun through Skylab's telescopes for 82 hours, retrieved film canisters from the ATM, and photographed more than four million square miles (10,355,500 sq km) of the Earth's surface. More biomedical experiments were

Above: *Conrad prepares to take a shower in Skylab's "deployable tub". When bathing the astronaut had to close the lid to prevent shimmering water globules floating all over the space station in the weightless environment. Used water was drawn off by a vacuum head on a hose.*

made than were listed in the programme, giving encouragement to the aim of keeping space crews at work for long periods. The astronauts returned to Earth on 22 June 1973 after a mission lasting 28 days.

Skylab 3

Skylab 3 astronauts—Alan Bean, Owen Garriott and Jack Lousma—lifted off from Cape Canaveral on 28 July 1973, made a textbook rendezvous with the space station and docked, only to find a new problem. Two of four vernier control engines on the Apollo ferry were leaking fuel, a circumstance which might have prevented a safe return to Earth. NASA immediately put in

Above: *Jack R. Lousma, Skylab 3 pilot, who participated with Owen K. Garriott, Skylab 3 science pilot, in the successful spacewalk to deploy the twin-pole sunshade to protect the damaged space station from overheating in the glare of the Sun. The Earth is reflected in Lousma's helmet visor.*

MAJOR SKYLAB ASTRONOMICAL EXPERIMENTS	
EXP	**OBJECTIVE**
Hα	Examination of hydrogen alpha emission near the Sun's surface during solar flare activity, the primary mode of classifying flare size
S009	Cosmic ray flux measurement
S019	UV line spectra of young, hot stars and galaxies
S020	UV and X-ray solar photography for highly ionised atoms
S052	Analysis of solar corona between 1·5 and 6 solar radii
S054	X-ray spectrography of solar flares and active regions
S055	Chromospheric and coronal extreme UV photography
S056	X-ray emissions of lower solar corona
S073	Gegenshein and zodiacal light intensity and polarisation
S082A	Study of inner corona structure via spectroheliography
S082B	Spectrographs of coronal and chromospheric transition region
S149	Mass, speed, and chemical composition of interplanetary dust
S150	Faint X-ray source survey
S183	UV stellar spectrography
S201	Comet Kohoutek structure

hand contingency plans to fly a Skylab rescue mission, if this became necessary. For the first time in any space programme, a craft similar to the one in which astronauts commuted to and from space could act as a rescue vehicle. Two astronauts could fly the modified Apollo CSM to Skylab and bring back the three crewmen.

The recovery mission, scheduled to be flown on 5 September by Vance Brand and Dr Don Lind, in fact never took place as the leak turned out to be less serious than at first appeared.

In the meantime experiments aboard Skylab continued in the field of biology, space medicine, solar physics, astrophysics, Earth observation, and technology. On 7 August astronauts space-walked to fix a twin-pole sunshade over the sunshield erected by the previous crew, which gave more permanent protection. They also replaced film in the ATM. Later, two of the men were to go outside again to install electrical connections for the control of a gyro package which they

had brought with them. This rectified a fault which had developed in the station's attitude-control system. Once again the full flight programme was fulfilled. The second boarding party splashed down on 25 September after spending 59 days in space.

Skylab 4

The third and final Skylab mission which left Cape Canaveral on 16 November 1973 was to break all records. The astronauts, Gerald Carr, Dr Edward Gibson and William Pogue, spent more time on major medical experiments than their predecessors. They performed more physical exercises on the station's monitored bicycle velo-ergometer and got used to running on the spot, using a portable treadmill they brought with them. Despite spending more time in space than any previous space crew—84 days—the men were in better physical shape after they returned to Earth and also readjusted more quickly to normal gravity conditions. They actually grew taller by an inch or more but shrank back to their normal heights after their return. This was put down to the stretching of the vertebrae of the spinal column under weightless conditions and the shifting of body fluids from the lower to the upper extremities.

During the mission the men of Skylab 4 observed and photographed the comet Kohoutek as it rounded the Sun. They described it as looking "yellow and orange, just like a flame—but mostly yellow". Like their predecessors they spent many fruitful hours observing the Earth—the "Blue Planet" because blue is its predominant colour—to determine the best instruments for routine survey. In all the astronauts obtained 40,286 film frames giving a wealth of information related to agriculture, forestry, ecology, geology, geography, meteorology, hydrology and oceanography.

Another significant event was the observation of a medium-size solar flare by one of the astronauts who spent long hours at the ATM solar observatory console. This was the first occasion that a flare had been recorded from beginning to end with powerful space-borne instruments, and scientists were able to study in greater detail the processes taking place when a flare suddenly bursts from the Sun. It is then that the puzzling energy transfer from magnetic field into thermal (heat) energy takes place. Unlocking the secret of this energy transfer may offer a way to obtain inexpensive energy on Earth. Altogether the Skylab 4 astronauts obtained some 75,000 telescopic images of the Sun in the X-ray, ultraviolet and visible portions of the spectrum, making a total of 182,842 for the whole programme.

It was the Sun that at length frustrated plans to prevent the station from making an uncontrolled descent into the atmosphere. After the last astronaut team left in 1974 Skylab had been expected to keep circling the Earth into the early 1980s and plans were made to have a Space Shuttle crew fly up and rendezvous with it. The spaceplane was to have released from its cargo bay a small robot device called a Teleoperator Retrieval System (TRS) which had its own propulsion system, docking probe and TV control system. An astronaut aboard the Shuttle would then manoeuvre the TRS by remote control and dock it with the station. The docked robot would then have been commanded to ignite its main engine in order to manoeuvre Skylab back into a safe orbit or, by retro-fire, to dump it harmlessly over the Pacific Ocean.

As it turned out, however, the early estimates of Skylab's lifetime in orbit were wide of the mark and all hopes of a salvage operation had to be abandoned. Sunspot activity, on the increase in 1978-79, caused expansion of the Earth's atmosphere which, combined with problems in maintaining a low-drag attitude of the orbiting laboratory, made it certain that the end would come much sooner. In April 1979 Northern American

Waste Management
The collection of the body wastes of the Skylab astronauts posed particular problems for NASA planners because they had to be stored as samples for analysis back on Earth. This was accomplished by the collector module. For defecation and urination, the crewman used it in a seated position facing the floor secured by a lap belt. Standing urination was also possible with the use of foot restraints. It contained one fecal bag for each defecation and three urine drawers (one per crewman) for chilled urine storage. A blower unit provided suction to draw in the body waste. The airflow was filtered before recirculation. The fecal bag was replaced after each use and its contents weighed and then vacuum-dried in waste processors for on-board storage for eventual return to Earth. The urine drawers were used for collecting, storing for 24 hours, measuring and sampling the urine. Each drawer had a refrigeration subsystem to cool the urine and the unit that separated it from the cabin air through centrifugal action. The urine freezer below the waste processor units provided interim low-temperature storage for its return to Earth and subsequent analysis in 120ml urine containers.

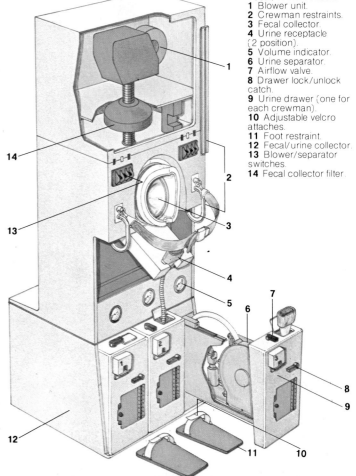

Fecal/Urine Collector
1 Blower unit.
2 Crewman restraints.
3 Fecal collector.
4 Urine receptacle (2 position).
5 Volume indicator.
6 Urine separator.
7 Airflow valve.
8 Drawer lock/unlock catch.
9 Urine drawer (one for each crewman).
10 Adjustable velcro attaches.
11 Foot restraint.
12 Fecal/urine collector.
13 Blower/separator switches.
14 Fecal collector filter.

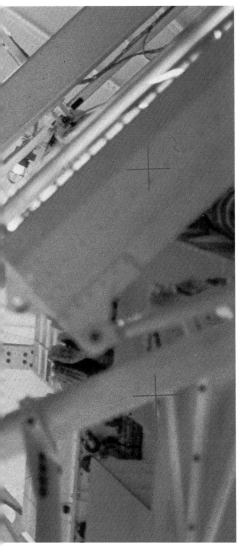

Above: *Skylab 4 astronauts Pogue and Carr load bags of waste into the "trash airlock" of the Orbital Workshop. Pogue is preparing to jump onto the airlock hatch cover to force another bag further down. A third bag floats in the zero-g environment.*

Left: *Owen K. Garriott space walks to the Apollo Telescope Mount (ATM). He has just deployed the Skylab Particle Collection Experiment S149 on one of the ATM solar panels. Object of the experiment was to collect material from interplanetary dust.*

Skylab Vertical Sleep Station
1 Stowage position for sleep restraint.
2 Sleep restraint frame.
3 Crew preference kit.
4 Sleep restraint.
5 Privacy partition.
6 Triangle shoes (to fix to floor grid).
7 Trash container.
8 Trash bags.
9 Clothing storage.

For crewmen operating under the stress of a long duration mission, sound sleep periods were essential. As there is neither "up" nor "down" in space, it was possible to sleep in a vertical position without discomfort. Each crewman was provided with an individual compartment for privacy and isolation from light and noise. It contained a sleep restraint, storage space and a removable overhead light baffle. The sleep restraint kept the men warm and could accommodate various sleep positions. Its frame was strapped to the floor and ceiling for rigidity. Access was gained to it through the hole in the neck. Openings for the astronaut's arms were also provided. The total unit was replaced every 14 days, but individual items like the headrest and blankets could be substituted more frequently at the discretion of the individual crew member.

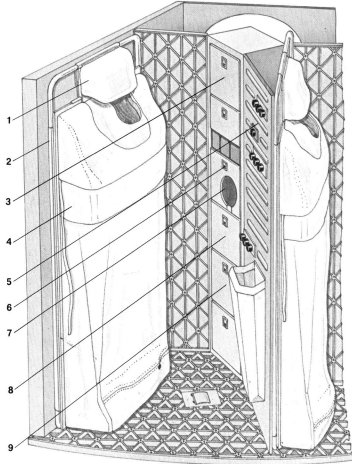

Air Defense Command (the US organisation which is responsible for monitoring all spacecraft and satellites in orbit) predicted that the station would re-enter the atmosphere between 11 June and 1 July.

Although more than 70 per cent of Skylab's path was over the sea, debris could fall anywhere between about 50°N and 50°S. Should any debris fall on foreign soil, the United States offered any assistance that might be necessary. John F. Yardley, NASA's Associated Administrator for Space Transportation Systems, gave the orbiting mass of Skylab as 157,000lb (71,202kg) and thought it possible that 40,000lb-50,000lb (18,140kg-22,675kg) might survive re-entry.

Once the atmosphere took its grip, the station was expected to tumble and disintegrate, much of it burning up by friction with the air. The re-entry path was estimated to cover some 4,000 miles (6,436km) and as much as 50 miles (80km) on each side of the orbital track. Estimates of the number of pieces that might survive ranged from 400 to 500, from small fragments to pieces weighing several hundred pounds. Most of them were expected to be big pieces of alloy "skin".

Skylab Re-Entry

Skylab made its final plunge on 11 July 1979. Earlier NASA had managed to place the station in a high-drag attitude, travelling side-on to the direction of motion so as to hasten its demise. When, however, it became apparent that it might fall on North America a decision was made to reduce drag by having nitrogen thrusters aboard start a tumbling motion. The command sent at 0245 Houston time (0745 BST) was expected to extend the station's life by about 30 minutes so that it would descend over the South Atlantic or southern Indian Ocean.

Much of the debris did, in fact, fall into the Indian Ocean but incandescent pieces were seen crossing the Australian coast at Esperance and passing close to Balladonia, some 100 miles (161km) inland. Many fragments were eventually picked up in the Australian outback and a large cylindrical piece 6ft (1·8m) long and 3ft (0·9m) wide, weighing half a ton, was found on farmland near Rawlinna, some 550 miles (885km) east of Perth. Happily, there was neither injury to persons nor damage to property. Skylab had completed its 34,981st orbit.

NASA found that Skylab did not experience re-entry heating quite as high as had been predicted. Disintegration began at an altitude about ten miles (16km) lower than had been expected, resulting in a "footprint" or area of debris distribution such smaller than anticipated: about 40 miles (64km) wide and 2,400 miles (3,862km) long. Several months after the event residents of thinly-populated Western Australia continued to find and report pieces of the station. A Perth writer on a "Skylab safari" found a large piece of aluminium weighing 180lb (82kg) near Balladonia. Most likely it was a door from the film vault in the Skylab workshop. Another significant "find" was a pair of titanium spheres which held nitrogen. They were found near Rawlinna, in the area where two large oxygen tanks were found earlier. The debris footprint appeared to end at about 26°S and 131°E, about 500 miles (804·5km) northeast of Rawlinna.

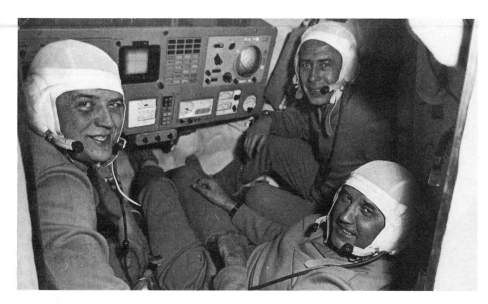

Salyut Space Stations

The Soviet space station programme began in the late 1960s with preliminary experiments to develop rendezvous and docking techniques with Soyuz-type spacecraft. Soviet designers apparently were already looking to the large Type G rocket as a means of challenging America to the Moon and launching a big modular station into Earth-orbit, serving many scientific and economic tasks. However, the severe technical problems encountered with this booster meant that these plans had to be deferred.

It was soon apparent, however, that an intermediate programme had been prepared based on the Type D launcher which appeared to be the counterpart of the USAF's Manned Orbiting Laboratory (MOL), abandoned in 1969. The existence of this project was revealed on 19 April 1971 when Salyut 1 station arrived in orbit. On 23 April the Soyuz 10 ferry took off from Baikonur with cosmonauts Vladimir Shatalov, Alexei Yeliseyev and Nikolai Rukavishnikov with the object of testing a new docking system. However, although they succeeded in docking with the station, they

Above: Cosmonauts G. Dobrovolsky, V. Patsayev and V. Volkov during training for their Soyuz 11 space mission in 1971. After a successful occupation of the Salyut 1 space station, they died in a decompression accident aboard their Soyuz ferry.

did not transfer inside and two days later were back on the ground.

After this brief visit, Salyut 1 continued to orbit the Earth for one and a half months, unmanned but under the supervision of the Soviet mission control centre. Then, on 6 June, Soyuz 11 ascended with a fresh crew—Georgi Dobrovolksy, Vladislav Volkov and Viktor Patsayev. After the necessary approach manoeuvres had been made under automatic control, the crew executed the final docking from a distance of 328ft (100m). The action of docking automatically linked the craft electrically and hydraulically, and after equalising pressures and opening the hatch the cosmonauts were able to transfer into the station. The all-important docking unit was essentially new. It not only provided more rigid "tightening" of the two spacecraft after docking, but there was a more effective

hermetic seal. The docking unit on the station's axis led into a short cylinder of about 6·56ft (2m) diameter. Next along was a cylinder of about 9·5ft (2·9m) diameter, widening into a further section of about 13·6ft (4·15m) diameter. A rear section of some 7·2ft (2·2m) diameter contained rocket motors fed from propellant tanks having the shape of a hemisphere and cone.

Dr Konstantin Feoktistov, the spacecraft designer and cosmonaut, described the layout. Going aboard Salyut, he said, *"Cosmonauts first enter an interconnecting tunnel, where part of the astrophysical apparatus and several control panels are installed. This leads to a hatch in the working compartment. Inside is a small platform at which two cosmonauts are seated facing the hatch. In front of them are a number of control and instrument panels, at their sides command and signal equipment of the type used in Soyuz. Nearby is a cosmonaut's position for research into the parameters of the plasma around the ship, a porthole and two more work positions. To the left and right of the work positions are basic systems of the station, air-regulation units and filters and beyond these are more station equipment and bio-medical research apparatus."*

The overall length of the station, with the Soyuz ferry docked, was about 65ft (20m). Total weight of the Salyut 1/Soyuz complex exceeded 55,125lb (25 tonnes).

Feoktistov particularly stressed the importance of perfecting instruments for astrophysical research, and research in the interests of the national economy.

"We have a big station with many tonnes of apparatus including telescopes, spectrometers, electrophotometers and television devices. During the lifetime of the station, it may be established that man does not have to go into space to carry out many of the experiments, but research methods can be determined only by man."

Early Space Station Concepts

It is remarkable how many of the space developments anticipated today had their origins in the minds of the early astronautical pioneers. The space station idea, for example, pre-dates practical methods for landing men on the Moon and was considered by K.E. Tsiolkovsky, Yu V. Kondratyuk and F.A. Tsander in Russia and their European contemporaries Hermann Oberth, Walter Hohmann, Guido von Pirquet, and "Hermann Noordung". Noordung was in fact the pen name of an Austrian named Potočnic, a captain of the reserve and a graduate engineer. Little of this man's background is known but he must rank as one of the greatest of the astronautical pioneers.

The idea took root largely because calculations suggested that chemically fuelled rockets might lack the energy to embark on flights to the Moon and planets. The space station was seen as a means of overcoming this deficiency by providing a kind of stepping-stone refuelling base in Earth-orbit for such missions.

Tsiolkovsky even went as far as to suggest a large cylindrical space station which spun on its longitudinal axis to simulate gravity by centrifugal force. Occupants of the station therefore would have their feet firmly planted on the inner

walls of the station on which they would be free to walk. Moreover, according to Tsiolkovsky, they would walk among plants growing in a kind of "cosmic greenhouse" to which light would be admitted, providing food and oxygen. These ideas have something in common with the giant spinning space habitats examined by Prof Gerard K. O'Neill (Chapter 20).

Another early contributor to orbital theory was Dr Walter Hohmann, the city architect of Essen-on-the-Ruhr. His book, "Die Erreichbarkeit der Himmelskörper" (The Attainability of the Celestial Bodies), dealt with the problems of conservation of energy in departure trajectories from Earth, return to Earth, and transfer orbits to other planets.

Guido von Pirquet—the son of Baron Peter Pirquet, an Austrian diplomat and landowner—wrote no classic book like other great pioneers, but he published many papers and articles on the various techniques of space flight. Perhaps his greatest contribution was the emphasis he placed on the space station as a springboard for true interplanetary voyages. He advocated refuelling the spaceship from a space station in a stable orbit near the Earth before proceeding further with a flight to the Moon. Although other writers described similar schemes, von Pirquet developed

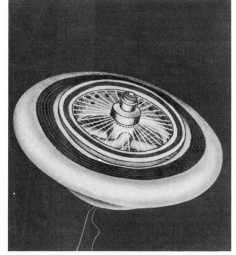

An artist's impression (above) of the 164ft (50m) wheel-shaped Noordung space station. The living quarters wheel was meant to spin on its axis to create artificial gravity by centrifugal effect.

The design, published in 1928, has been the inspiration of many space station concepts of more recent times including large space colonies such as are discussed in Chapter 20.

To test the ability of men to work in space for long periods, Russia developed a series of Salyut space stations. The design of Salyut 1 was based on four cylinders of different diameters. At the forward end was a docking port and transfer compartment which the crews of visiting Soyuz spacecraft entered after they had docked. Two pairs of wing-like solar panels opened fore and aft once the vehicle had arrived in orbit. The station had an overall length of about 47·3ft (14·4m) and from the front end, the cylinders had diameters of about 6·56ft (2m); 9·5ft (2·9m); 13·6ft (4·15m) and 7·2ft (2·2m). The last cylinder contained the manoeuvre engine. This view shows Soyuz 11 docked with the station. The large conical telescope housing has been removed from the cut-away of the interior.

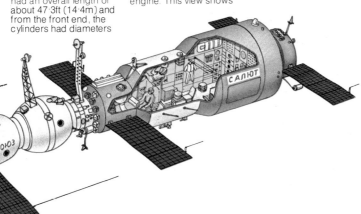

Stations of this type, Feoktistov added, would be invaluable in helping to solve many terrestrial problems including forecasting agricultural harvests and prospecting for minerals. Already some astronomical studies could be carried out and this part of the programme would be expanded in the future to include other parts of the spectrum.

Aboard Salyut 1 was an "Orion" astrophysical observatory, described as a complex and highly accurate optical-electronic system. One telescope and spectrograph were mounted outside the pressurised working area and another telescope was inside. The cosmonaut observer simply pointed the instruments towards a selected star using a "sighting tube". The telescope then locked onto the star while photographs were taken. Spectrograms were obtained of the bright star Alpha Lyrae in two different ultraviolet regions of the spectrum.

Experiments in plant growth were also made aboard Salyut 1, continuing research studies already made in lone Soyuz spacecraft. Biologists wished to know how plants, which might be used to supply oxygen and food aboard future space stations, would stand up to long periods of weightlessness, and plant species were chosen to produce specific results. Crepis (hawk's beard) was a good subject for genetic studies; flax had a tissue structure which might prove to be unnecessarily strong in weightless conditions. Kale could be eaten as a salad and it was important to know about any changes in the nutritional value of plants that might take place under space conditions. The cosmonauts also studied the fading of radio signals (due to high-frequency electron resonance on transmitting antennas), and continued their observations of the Earth and the meteorological phenomena above it.

Having completed their pioneer experiments, the three men separated from the station in their Soyuz 11 ferry. It was after retro-fire that disaster struck. When the orbital module separated, a pressure-equalising valve in the command module opened, releasing air from the cabin. The capsule made a perfect landing beneath its recovery parachute, which opened automatically, but when rescue teams arrived and opened the hatch the cosmonauts were dead. This tragic episode in the history of the Soviet space programme showed that there were still great risks associated with space flight. Making the Soyuz safe could not happen overnight and so, 175 days after it was launched, mission control commanded a retro-burn which caused the Salyut 1 station to re-enter the atmosphere harmlessly over the Pacific.

Salyut 2

Another setback to the Soviet space programme occurred after Salyut 2 was launched on 3 April 1973. Within 24 hours tracking stations of North American Air Defense Command detected several metallic fragments which seemed to have come from the separated carrier rocket. Despite reassuring statements from the Russian side that the space station itself was operating normally, by 25 April it was obvious that the unmanned Salyut 2 was breaking up.

What seemed to be another attempt to launch a space station occurred on 11 May 1973, when Western tracking stations identified another large cylindrical object in a precariously low orbit. The Russians called it Cosmos 557. After 11 days it burned up in the atmosphere.

In the meantime, the Soviet design team had been working to remedy the problem with the Soyuz ferry and Soyuz 12 took cosmonauts Lt-Col Vasily Lazarev and Oleg Makarov into orbit on 27 September 1973. The Soyuz craft had been greatly modified to improve safety. The third seat was replaced by additional life-support equipment. It was now obligatory for crews to wear pressure suits during launch, docking and return, doffing them only when they had achieved the relative security of orbital flight. The other major change was the removal from the spacecraft of the solar "wings". Henceforth, Soyuz ferries would depend for electrical power on internal chemical batteries, which limited their independent flight to about two and a half days. However, after linking up with a space station they could re-charge by drawing power from that vehicle's large solar panels.

---

it most fully, demonstrating the large savings in vehicle size (and initial thrust) which it theoretically made possible.

The Austrian pioneer also made proposals which anticipated the use of "space tugs" for ferry purposes between orbits. One of his schemes described a three-unit system in which an "inner station" circled the planet at 472 miles (760km) just above the upper limits of the atmosphere and an "outer station" circled at 3,100 miles (5,000km). He then set a third unit, called the "Transit Station", to orbit between them but not actually to intersect their orbits. It was assumed that men or cargo could transfer between them during a close pass.

It was left to "Hermann Noordung" to put the space station into engineering perspective. In 1928 he published a book, "Das Problem der Befahrung des Weltraums", in which he proposed quite detailed systems. Noordung saw the space station as consisting of three units—a wheel-shaped structure containing living quarters, a bowl-shaped power-house, and a cylindrical observatory. The living quarters wheel had an overall diameter of 164ft (50m)—the inhabited part being 98ft (30m) across—and the unit was to spin around the central axis to provide the occupants with artificial gravity.

The Smith/Ross space station concept of 1948 emphasised the importance of solar energy for power supply in the shape of a 200ft (61m) solar mirror designed to run 8 turbo-electric generators. Behind the mirror were living quarters, laboratories and workshops for a crew of 24 engineers and scientists. On the axis of the station were large astronomical telescopes to be used for stellar observation.

Solar power was to be obtained by two large concave mirrors, one bowl-shaped and the other in the form of a circular trough. These mirrors were to focus sunlight onto ducts containing nitrogen which would drive turbines coupled to d.c. generators with storage batteries to cater for periods when the station was in shadow.

Noordung proposed that the occupants of the station would breathe a standard oxygen-nitrogen atmosphere topped up by oxygen transported from the Earth. The tyre-like living quarters were to be divided into separate rooms with laboratories, workshops, a dark room, a kitchen, a bathroom and laundry. Airtight bulkheads, he suggested, would lessen the risk of complete disaster in the event of serious damage to the structure.

After World War 2 these ideas were recognised by the British Interplanetary Society and Harry Ross and R.A. Smith began to examine the assembly of large space structures from pre-fabricated parts. They envisaged the use of winged cargo rockets and made a complete study of a space station embodying wheel-shaped living quarters 100ft (30·5m) in diameter supporting a 200ft (61m) parabolic mirror. The mirror was meant to collect the equivalent of some 3,900kW of solar energy, of which a maximum of nearly 1,000kW might be usable in a turbo-generator.

In the meantime a long-duration two-man spacecraft, Soyuz 13, made an independent flight between 18-26 December 1973, packed with instruments of the kind destined for later Salyut space-stations. They included an Orion 2 telescope, an Oasis 2 closed-cycle biological experiment, and cameras for Earth observations.

Salyut 3

Six months later, on 25 June 1974, came the launch of Salyut 3 with the stated object of "continuing bio-medical studies of men in space, obtaining data for the solution of economic tasks, and testing improved design features and equipment aboard the station."

On 3 July Soyuz 14 was launched in pursuit with cosmonauts Col Pavel Popovich and Lt-Col Yuri Artyukin. They made an uneventful docking and went aboard. It was clear that the Soviets now had a space-station of greatly modified design. Instead of having two sets of solar panels opening like wings fore and aft, three solar panels were grouped in the centrebody.

Space officials again stressed improvements made in the cosmonauts' routine of physical exercises. The station contained a moving-belt running track and a cosmonaut using it wore a special sweatshirt with elastic cords which placed a load on bones and muscles as he ran on the spot. The living quarters also contained a wide variety of nourishing food and drink which could be heated on a stove. There was also a radio, a tape recorder and a small library of books.

Four "aerial cameras" (of the type used in aircraft) were installed in the floor and roof, and a large instrument, described as a solar telescope, was installed in a conical housing. The operator stood on a platform at the base of the instrument, directing the telescope by means of a small control panel. An RSS-2 spectrograph was used to investigate aerosol particles in the Earth's atmosphere, and further experiments were made in culturing bacteria and in recycling water. The cosmonauts also made a full check of new engineering systems embodied in Salyut 3.

The crew returned from their mission on 19 July, leaving the station to operate automatically with some systems shut down. Its orbit could be modified by ground control by operation of the propulsion system, preventing its decay under the influence of air drag.

As it turned out, the station was to remain unoccupied longer than had been anticipated because the next ferry, Soyuz 15, developed a control fault and was unable to dock. On 26 September Moscow announced that Salyut 3 had completed its work programme, a data capsule having been recovered in the Soviet Union three days earlier. However, in a final series of control experiments the station's "aerodynamic characteristics in low orbit" were checked in conjunction with on-board navigational aids. It was then made known that the station had been orientated on the Earth for five months so that a TV system could be used "in the interests of the national economy", recording data on natural resources.

There were no further ferry missions and Salyut 3 was commanded to re-enter the atmosphere over the Pacific on 24 January 1975. Some aspects of this mission suggested to Western observers that part of the research

Above: *Pavel Popovich, Soyuz 14 commander (right) and flight engineer Yuri Artyukhin during a training session at the Gagarin Cosmonauts' Training Centre before their successful flight to Salyut 3.*

programme concerned the testing and refinement of military equipment, e.g. the low orbit placing emphasis on reconnaissance photography, the release of a data capsule, and the fact that the crew members were both military personnel.

Salyut 4

Meanwhile, Salyut 4 had been launched on 26 December 1974. On 11 January 1975 Soyuz 17 cosmonauts Lt-Col Alexei Gubarev and Georgi Grechko flew in pursuit to achieve a smooth docking. This mission fell more clearly into the "civilian" category. The station had a higher orbit, the second crew-member was a civilian, and the scientific investigations were more varied. Another significant test included an apparatus for condensing water from the cabin atmosphere. The cosmonauts were able to use the recycled water for food preparation, drinking and personal hygiene.

The cosmonauts returned to Earth on 9 February 1975, leaving the station in the automatic mode of operation. As it happened

Below: *Pyotr Klimuk and Vitaly Sevastyanov, crew of Soyuz 18B, finish a training session in an engineering mock-up of the Salyut 4 space station. Note the uncluttered interior of the training module.*

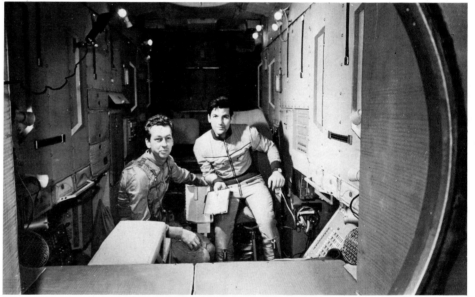

Salyut 4
Salyut 4 differed from Salyut 1 in having three large rotatable solar panels indexed at 90° on the 9·5ft (2·9m) diameter work compartment. The panels were mounted on bearings and turned to face the Sun. This increased the station's supply of electricity and allowed visiting Soyuz spacecraft to re-charge their own chemical batteries. Thus Soyuz ferries were able to dispense with solar panels of their own for the short flight to the space station although failure to dock meant a quick return to Earth. In all cases the docked Soyuz (in this drawing Soyuz 17) was considered to be an integral part of the station because of the extra space provided by the orbital module.

this period was longer than expected because of a launch mishap to Soyuz 18A carrying Lt-Col Vasily Lazarev and Oleg Makarov. After a normal take-off from Baikonur, the upper stage of the SL-4 rocket burned for only about 4 seconds. The malfunction set in chain an automatic abort sequence, and the men made a forced landing on the outskirts of the Siberian town of Gorno-Altaisk near the Chinese/Mongolian border.

The replacement launch by Soyuz 18B on 24 May 1975 took Lt-Col Pyotr Klimuk and Vitaly Sevastyanov to the station. Their research programme was largely a continuation of the previous mission. The cosmonauts used the X-ray telescope to study the constellations Scorpio, Virgo and Cygnus; more experiments were made with fruit-flies and flour beetles. Regular observations were made of agricultural patterns and forests, and tests were made of a new navigational system, Kaskade, which orientated the space station with great precision for Earth-resources photography. This highly successful mission lasted 63 days, the crew landing on 26 July 1975.

By now control techniques for spacecraft developed within the Cosmos programme were preparing the way for the re-supply of space stations by automatic vehicles. Soyuz 20, launched unmanned on 17 November 1975, docked with Salyut 4 in a prolonged test of linked systems. Although there was no attempt to transfer fuel, it was a vital step towards the Progress cargo ships which were later to make their appearance.

Few details of the payload were given other than that Soyuz 20 carried tortoises and other biological specimens, and returned to Earth on 16 February 1976. This significant experiment resembled the manned mission flown unsuccessfully with Soyuz 15, when the docking system failed.

Salyut 5

After the launch of Salyut 5 on 22 June 1976, the next spacecraft to dock with a Russian space station was Soyuz 21 containing another all-military crew: Col Boris Volynov and Lt-Col Vitaly Zholobov. Launched on 6 July 1976, the mission was described as concerning tasks of an applied nature. They included the smelting of molten metals—bismuth, lead, tin and cadmium—and a crystal-growth experiment.

Using a hand-held spectrometer, the men studied aerosol industrial pollution in the Earth's atmosphere. Study was also made of a pregnant guppy-fish in an aquarium. One particularly noteworthy experiment concerned the transfer of propellants in space without the use of pumps, and demonstrating a method by which liquid in a sphere could be transferred into an empty container above it by the action of surface tension.

The crew observed the solar corona and took more Earth-resources photographs relating to minerals, environmental damage due to mud streams in mountainous areas, and the sites of hydro-electric power-stations. The cosmonauts used a set of spectrometers to study ultraviolet radiation from the Sun, and also measured small changes in ozone and water-vapour content in the Earth's upper atmosphere.

One of the important new systems carried aboard Salyut 5 was the Delta automatic navi-

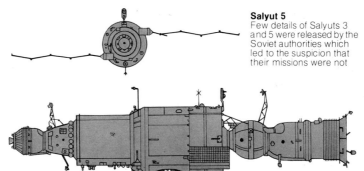

Salyut 5
Few details of Salyuts 3 and 5 were released by the Soviet authorities which led to the suspicion that their missions were not entirely scientific. The fact that they pursued low orbits was perhaps an indication that they were testing reconnaissance and surveillance equipment. This drawing, researched by Charles P Vick, is provisional. It assumes that Salyut 5 had an aft docking port like Salyut 6 with facilities for returning a data capsule at the forward end. An extra panel was added to each solar wing.

Above: *Commander of Soyuz 22 V.F. Bykovsky with flight engineer V.V. Aksyonov at the Gagarin Training Centre. Their mission principally involved them in photographing the Soviet Union and GDR.*

gator. This allowed the cosmonauts to determine their position in space using a radio-altimeter to measure height, and optical instruments to measure the setting and rising of the Sun. From these basic parameters, a computer calculated the time to complete one revolution, gave the period when the spacecraft was within range of ground-stations, and indicated the time the engine had to operate when making manoeuvres. The computer provided a print-out of essential information every half-revolution of the globe.

Once again, much emphasis was placed on the cultivation of algae and higher plants in a "cosmic garden". Green peas began to sprout within a week of planting. Other biological specimens aboard were bacterial cultures, fruit-flies, samples of hamster tissue, and fertilised frog-spawn.

Western analysts wondered if the mission also served to assess the ability to obtain detailed information from space during military actions. At the time, extensive military manoeuvres were taking place in Siberia involving land, sea and air forces.

The cosmonauts landed in darkness on 24 August at 21.33hr (Moscow time) some 124 miles (200km) south-west of Kokchetav in Kazakhstan.

Soyuz 22, flown by Col Valery Bykovsky and Vladimir Aksyonov, was not intended to dock with a Salyut station though its experiments were related to space-station activity. It carried a multi-spectral camera built by the famous optical company Karl Zeiss Jena of East Germany on an eight-day mission during which parts of the Soviet Union and East Germany were photographed "in the interests of the national economy".

The next Salyut-mission spacecraft, Soyuz 23, left the launch-pad on 14 October 1976 but failed to dock with Salyut 5 due to a fault in the rendezvous approach equipment. Forced to make an early return, it landed in darkness during a snowstorm in Lake Tengiz some 121 miles (195km) south-west of Tselinograd. The crew—Lt-Col Vyacheslav Zudov and Lt-Col Valery Rozhdestvensky—were retrieved by frogmen dropped by helicopter. Although cosmonauts normally return to solid ground, braked by retro-rockets, training for water recoveries has been routine to cater for an emergency descent into the ocean or, as happened in this case, into one of Russia's inland seas.

The replacement crew, Lt-Col Yuri Glazkov and Viktor Gorbatko, took off on 7 February 1977 in Soyuz 24. After a successful docking they continued the work of their predecessors in Earth observation, study of the atmosphere, technical experiments including crystal growth, plant growth and experiments with fish and other subjects. Before they left the cosmonauts made a complete change of the station's atmosphere.

Salyut 6

These missions were to set the stage for Russia's most ambitious set of space-station visits, beginning with the launch of Salyut 6 on 29 September 1977.

Soyuz 25 crewed by Lt-Col Vladimir Kovalenok and Valery Ryumin ascended from Baikonur on 9 October, but ran into trouble when it approached the station under automatic control from a distance of 394ft (120m). An official communiqué stated that the link-up was called off "because of a

196

The First Space Stations

By the early 1980s the Soviet Union had begun to establish a long lead in the duration of manned space flight, using a series of Salyut space stations. The early 18·5 tonne stations were visited by Soyuz ferries which docked at the forward end to transfer their crews. With the appearance of Salyut 6 in September 1977, the programme became more ambitious. The new station had docking ports fore and aft and the propulsion system was re-arranged to permit refuelling by manned Progress cargo ships which docked on the aft airlock. The robot ships also brought fresh supplies of air, food, water and other consumables, as well as new scientific equipment. Unlike America's Skylab,

Salyut had a re-startable rocket engine which could be used to manoeuvre it into a higher orbit in order to offset the effect of air drag and position it ready for the next visit of a ferry ship. When Salyut's engine could not be used (as when, for example, one of the station's tanks had to be drained during the mission), it was possible to use the engines of a visiting ferry craft to adjust the orbit. Regular re-supply missions by Progress ships enabled Soviet cosmonauts to establish new duration records. It was also possible to embark on a series of highly successful international space flights within the Intercosmos programme, in which Soviet cosmonauts flew with foreign colleagues.

Salyuts 1 and 4 compared
When Salyut 1 (left) was introduced in 1971, the station had two sets of solar arrays which extended like wings fore and aft. In 1974, Salyut 4 (below) revealed a new distribution of solar panels in which three arrays — two horizonal, one vertical — were centrally disposed on the station. Only one docking port was provided for visiting Soyuz ferries on both these vehicles. Ferry craft docking with Salyut 4 dispensed with solar panels being able to recharge internal chemical batteries from the space station's own solar power supply.

Salyut 6 Space Station
1 Soyuz instrument module.
2 Soyuz descent module.
3 Rendezvous antenna.
4 Soyuz orbital module.
5 Docking interface.
6 External TV camera mounting.
7 Docking hatch.
8 External thermal control panels.
9 EVA handrails.
10 TV camera.
11 Instrument panel.
12 Control system.
13 Solar panel rotary drive.
14 Cosmonauts' seats.
15 Water storage.
16 Electronics racks.
17 Bicycle exercise machine (velo-ergometer).
18 Steerable solar array.
19 Sleep restraint.
20 Refuse ejection airlock.
21 Food lockers.
22 Dust filter.
23 Sanitary facilities.
24 Propulsion engine and attitude thrusters control group.
25 EVA handrail.
26 Attitude control thrusters.
27 Rendezvous antenna.
28 Aft hatches.
29 Fuel, food, water and oxygen supplies.
30 Propulsion system.
31 Progress service module.
32 Visual docking target.
33 Progress/Salyut docking systems.
34 Main propulsion engine.
35 Attitude control thrusters.
36 Propellant tank.
37 Water storage.
38 Refuse containers.
39 EVA handrails.
40 BST 1M submillimeter telescope and instrument module with cryogenic cooling unit (top left) and 12 x optical sight (right of conical housing).
41 Launch shroud.

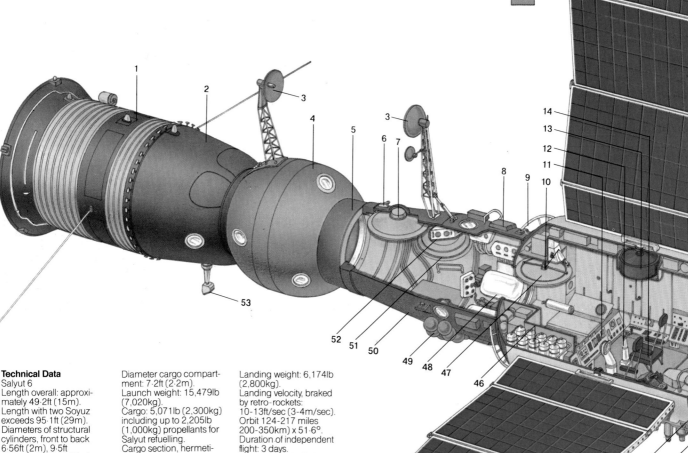

Technical Data
Salyut 6
Length overall: approximately 49·2ft (15m).
Length with two Soyuz exceeds 95·1ft (29m).
Diameters of structural cylinders, front to back 6·56ft (2m), 9·5ft (2·9m), 13·6ft (4·15m).
Weight, without ferry attachments: 41,674lb (18,900kg). Weight, scientific equipment: 3,307lb (1,500kg).
Docking ports: 1 fore 1 aft.
Solar cell panels: three each of 215·3ft² (20m²).
Thrust manoeuvre engine 661lb (300kg).

Progress
Length, docking probe to base: 26ft (7·94m).
Length, face of docking assembly to base: 22·9ft (6·98m). Maximum diameter, base: 8·92ft (2·72m).

Diameter cargo compartment: 7·2ft (2·2m).
Launch weight: 15,479lb (7,020kg).
Cargo: 5,071lb (2,300kg) including up to 2,205lb (1,000kg) propellants for Salyut refuelling.
Cargo section, hermetically sealed, volume: 233ft³ (6·6m³): 1 atm pressure: 3-30°C temp.
Duration of joint flight with orbital station: up to 30 days.
Orbit: 124-217 miles (200-350km) x 51·6°.
Approach to docking controlled by 14 x 22lb (10kg) and 8 x 2·2lb (1kg) jets.

Soyuz
Length: 26ft (7·94m).
Maximum diameter: 8·92ft (2·72m).
Internal volume, descent module: 134·2ft³ (3·8m³).
Launch weight: 14,994lb (6,800kg).

Landing weight: 6,174lb (2,800kg).
Landing velocity, braked by retro-rockets: 10-13ft/sec (3-4m/sec).
Orbit 124-217 miles 200-350km) x 51·6°.
Duration of independent flight: 3 days.
Duration of joint flight with orbital station: 90 days.

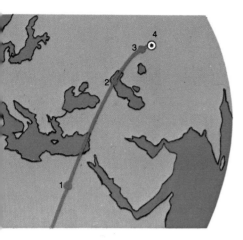

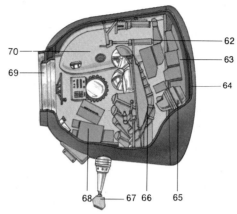

Soyuz Landing Profile
1 Entry into atmosphere.
2 RF blackout begins.
3 RF blackout ends.
4 Landing area.

The Soviet Union normally recovers its manned spacecraft in an area just north of Baikonur in the Republic of Kazakhstan. Returning from an orbit inclined at 51·6° to the equator, the re-entry module makes its approach over North Africa, the eastern end of the Black Sea and the western end of the Caspian. The capsule is tracked by radar and an on-board radio beacon directs recovery forces.

Soyuz Descent Module
The Soyuz descent module is hermetically sealed and is supplied with a normal oxygen-nitrogen atmosphere at sea-level pressure. The capsule has two windows on its sides and another window fitted with a sighting device. The shell of the compartment is covered with heat shielding material on the outside and thermal insulation and decorative materials on the inside. The capsule lands by parachute, the landing shock being minimised by retrorockets which ignite a few feet above the ground. The crew wear pressure-suits during re-entry.

attachment.
42 Close-loop running track.
43 MKF-6M multispectral camera.
44 Zero-gravity weighing machine.
45 Vacuum cylinder.
46 Oxygen cylinders.
47 Docking tunnel hatch.
48 Space suit stowage.
49 Compressed air bottles.
50 Docking tunnel.
51 EVA hatch.
52 Airlock controls.
53 Optical sighting system.
54 Soyuz docking probe.
55 Orbital module.
56 Rendezvous antenna.
57 Command module/ re-entry module.
58 Attitude thrusters.
59 Service module.
60 Propulsion system.
61 Optical sighting system.
62 Couch support.
63 Electronics racks.
64 Thermal insulation.
65 Waste management system.
66 Cosmonauts' couches.
67 Optical sighting system.
68 Instrument panels.
69 Docking hatch.
70 Main parachute.

Salyut 6 served the Soviet Union superbly for over 3 years, and Soviet faith in the pursuit of a manned space station programme was underlined by the Soyuz T-3 flight in late November 1980. This was the first three man mission since the ill-fated Soyuz 11 flight in which the crew died during re-entry. In the T-3, the crewmen were able to wear pressure suits. The cosmonauts Lt-Col Leonid Kizim (commander), Oleg Makarov (flight engineer) and Gennady Strekalov (research cosmonaut) docked with Salyut 6 on 28 November with the express intention of carrying out extensive repair work. Their tasks included repairing a complex hydraulic system; incorporating pumps in Salyut's fluid-based temperature control system which involved managing liquids in zero-g; programming a timing device in the control system; and replacing telemetry components.

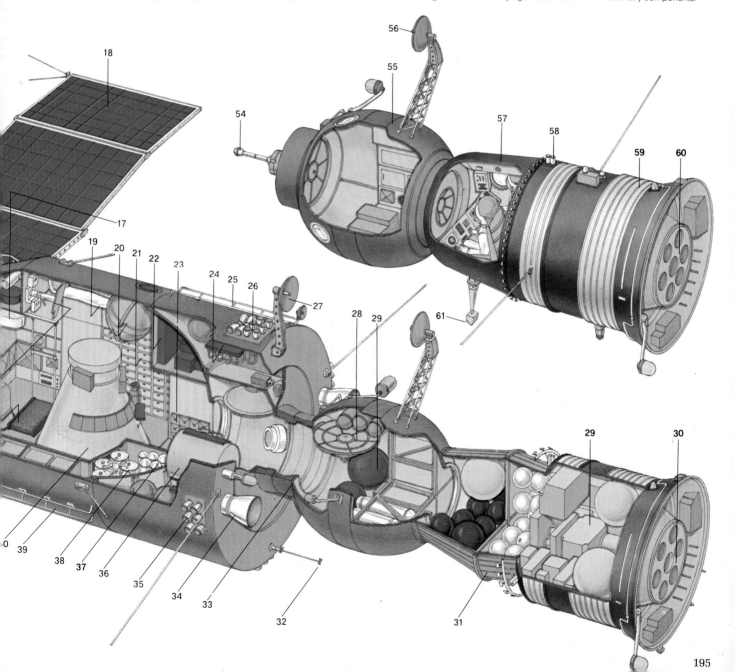

deviation from the planned procedure for the docking". The crew landed in a cornfield some 115 miles (185km) north-west of Tselingrad on 11 October.

It was not until the docking of Soyuz 26 on 11 December 1977 that it was confirmed that Salyut 6 had docking ports fore and aft. This time the crew—Lt-Col Yuri Romanenko and Georgi Grechko—ignored the forward port which appeared to have given trouble during the previous mission, and docked at the back of the station. After equalising atmospheres and opening the transfer hatch the men entered the station. One of their first tasks was to check and investigate the forward docking assembly.

On 20 December Grechko made a spacewalk to inspect possible external damage but found "not even a scratch". This time the research programme included

"The study of physical processes and phenomena in outer space; exploitation of the Earth's surface and atmosphere in the interests of the national economy, bio-medical investigations, technical experiments, and the testing of on-board systems and instruments."

The second docking port, introduced for the first time, would allow "two ferry craft to dock with a station, which is important for replacing crews, carrying out rescue operations and delivering foodstuffs and equipment." Other design changes included use of water regeneration as a standard feature of the life-support system: on Salyut 4 it had been purely experimental. Its main function was to supply the crew with drinking water. There was also a portable closet made of polythene in which a cosmonaut could enjoy a shower without the risk that water would escape into the station's living quarters.

When Lt-Col Vladimir Dzhanibekov and Oleg Makarov docked their Soyuz 27 spacecraft with the Salyut 6/Soyuz 26 complex on 11 January, they completed the world's first link-up of three spacecraft. No particular difficulties were experienced and after completing a number of on-board experiments with the resident crew, they returned to Earth in Soyuz 26 five days later.

The Progress Ferry

On 20 January 1978 an A-2 rocket rose from the Baikonur cosmodrome bearing within its nose shroud the first of a new breed of unmanned ferry ships, Progress 1. Progress had the task of docking automatically with Salyut stations to keep them supplied with provisions. This new craft, which corrects its own course by braking and accelerating, depends on radio guidance working in conjunction with the station it is about to meet. Data on the operation of on-board systems transmitted to Earth are processed and signals are sent to cause the craft to make appropriate manoeuvres. If necessary the crew aboard the space-station can participate in the docking routine.

Above: *Col Alexei Gubarev and Capt Vladimir Remek (Czechoslovakia) who flew in Soyuz 28. Remek was the first of a series of cosmonauts from the Socialist countries to visit the Salyut 6 station.*

Progress 1, which took two days to dock with Salyut 6, was about 26ft (7·9m) long and had a diameter of 7·2ft (2·2m) across the cargo section. It weighed 15,479lb (7,020kg) of which 5,071lb (2,300kg) was cargo including 2,205lb (1,000kg) of fuel. As the spacecraft was wholly expendable, it was no longer necessary to penalise it with a descent module bearing a heavy ablative heat shield, and this section was modified to provide a structural framework for containers which were attached to quick-release locks. The compartment was hermetically sealed to allow cosmonauts to work inside and transfer cargo into Salyut.

In a second compartment were four propellant tanks and several others containing compressed air and nitrogen for tank-pressurisation. Among items transferred into the station were air-purification filters, carbon dioxide absorber units and fans, drinking water and fruit juices, fresh supplies of films and scientific apparatus. There were also new gravity suits, gymsuits, equipment for technological experiments, safety belts for the seats and extra life-support equipment, a new television

Docking Manoeuvres
1 Soyuz and Salyut 6 at the beginning of docking procedures. Soyuz uses its IGLA system to acquire the station.
2 Salyut orientates itself on Soyuz to align IGLA antennas. Soyuz fires its main engine to adjust its orbit and approaches Salyut.
3 Soyuz makes a transposition manoeuvre and uses its main engine to reduce speed.

4 Soyuz executes a final transposition and approaches Salyut gently using low-thrust motors, guided in to eventual docking by radio commands.

The use of computerised systems in the new 3-man Soyuz-T emphasises the significance the Soviets attach to automatic flight control, which may lead to the assembly of large structures in Earth orbit.

Left: *Unmanned Progress cargo ship approaches to dock with Salyut 6. For the first time a station could be refuelled in Earth orbit and kept routinely supplied with air, water and food.*

receiver for news reports, and replacement batteries for the "stellar globe".

Although Progress docked with the station in such a way that the main fuel lines were connected, getting the fluids aboard was not an easy procedure. Before pumping could begin it was necessary for the crew to purge the tanks of nitrogen and check that the fuel lines were properly sealed. On the second day pumping tests were made, and on the third and fourth days the transfer was made. Then, after checking the sealing of the appropriate tanks and pipes, the oxidiser was pumped on board. Finally, the cosmonauts had to "blow off" the pipelines so that when Progress separated, fuel and oxidiser did not contaminate the station.

Before Progress 1 was finally cast off, it demonstrated another necessary function of space station activity. It was used as a space-tug to push the station into a higher orbit, its engine being ignited for a precomputed time under command from Earth. Such techniques will make it possible for space-tugs to assemble space stations much bigger than the present Salyut-Soyuz combinations, declared Dr Igor Konstantinovich, deputy head of flight ballistics. They could also transfer modules of space stations for assembly or bring individual spacecraft to space-based repair shops. Progress 1, having been loaded with waste material from Salyut 6, was made to re-enter over the Pacific.

It was now time for the first of the Intercosmos cosmonauts to fly to the station with a Soviet commander. The flight time of these missions was 7 to 8 days. Most of the experiments they performed concerned materials processing, Earth observation and bio-medical checks. Soyuz 28 brought Col Alexei Gubarev and Captain Vladimir Remek, a Czechoslovakian, to the station.

Refuelling of Salyut stations by Progress cargo ships was to become the key to breaking the 84-day endurance record set by American astronauts in the much larger Skylab. When Soyuz 29 cosmonauts Col Vladimir Kovalenok and Alexander Ivanchenkov returned from Salyut 6 on 2 November 1978, they had spent nearly 140 days in space without any apparent damage to

biomedical research and the task of obtaining data of value to the national economy. Once again emphasis was placed on the velo-ergometer and records made of heart-function and the tone of blood vessels generally. Blood samples were taken at regular intervals for later examination on Earth. Scientific experiments included use of a 9·8in (25cm) solar telescope and two Filin X-ray telescopes used to observe the Crab nebula in the constellation Taurus and a supernova in Vela.

Another pair of cosmonauts, Lt-Col Vladimir Lyakhov and Valery Ryumin (who reached Salyut 6 in Soyuz 32 on 26 February 1979), were to set new records. Altogether this mission lasted 175 days 36 minutes, more than twice the duration of the longest American manned space flight. They returned to Earth in Soyuz 34 which had been launched unmanned.

On board the station the cosmonauts carried out repairs and maintenance, including work on the power unit, and replaced certain systems and equipment with new components flown to them in Progress freighters. They also conducted more refuelling operations. They observed and photographed the Earth's surface during long periods of the flight and carried out more than 50 micro-gravity experiments to obtain "monocrystals of semi-conductor materials, metallic alloys and compounds...". A number of experiments were also made into the application of metallic coatings under microgravity and space vacuum "by methods of evaporation and subsequent condensation".

The astronauts also succeeded in assembling and deploying from the back end of the space station the KPT-10 radio-telescope with a 32·8ft (10m) erectable dish antenna. The KPT-10 had been delivered to Salyut 6 in kit form by Progress 7 and assembled by the crew inside the station. Despite this extra payload the automatic ferry still served to refuel the station and transfer additional air supplies. Its engine was also used to propel the complex into a higher orbit, 248 x 255 miles (399 x 411km).

After the radio-telescope had been assembled and checked out in the station, Progress 7 was undocked. The instrument then was released into space while a TV camera aboard the Progress craft allowed Soviet ground controllers to observe and control its movement and the erection of its antenna. Unfortunately, the antenna was caught up on a projection on the station and had to be cut free by a cosmonaut.

The Soviet news agency *Tass* noted that the KPT-10 was intended to operate in conjunction with a new 229·7ft (70m) ground-based radio-telescope at the long-range space communications centre in the Crimea. It had been arranged that the cosmonauts should prepare the radio-telescope for experiments every other day while specialists at mission control analysed results. The first experiments included the mapping of radio emissions from the Milky Way. The Sun's radio emissions were also studied, and some work was carried out on the Earth's land and water surfaces.

But most exciting of all, from the astronomical point of view, was the ability to use ground-based and space-based telescopes in combination as an interferometer. The distance between the two instruments could

Above: *Col Vladimir Kovalenok and Alexander Ivanchenkov—the Soyuz 29 cosmonauts—who remained in orbit for nearly 140 days in 1978, are seen here at work during their mission to Salyut 6.*

Left: *Col Valery Bykovsky, who flew on the Soyuz 31 mission with Sigmund Jaehn, the East German cosmonaut, the third such international flight. He is delivering film cassettes for the MFK-6M.*

their health. They had lost some of their muscle mass, but this was quickly regained.

Col Pyotr Klimuk and Major Miroslaw Hermaszewski, the first Polish cosmonaut, docked their Soyuz 30 ferry with the Salyut 6/Soyuz 29 combination in June 1978. Between July 7 and August 4 a second Progress supply flight was made to replenish Salyut 6 expendables. On 27 August 1978 the first East German—Lt-Col Sigmund Jaehn—boarded the space station with Col Valery Bykovsky in Soyuz 31.

As flight-times grew, the cosmonauts found that living in space and re-adaptation

to normal gravity after a mission became easier with the aid of special equipment, like the station's stationary bicycle velo-ergometer, the closed-loop running track and their Chibis suits.

To use the track it was necessary to wear a special training suit to which were attached elastic cords which placed a load of some 110lb (50kg) on the body, holding the cosmonaut down. (The device was first tested aboard Soyuz 9 in 1970.) The Chibis suits were also important as they created negative pressure in the lower part of the body which stopped the blood "pooling" in the upper body and placed more work on the cardiovascular system.

Soviet officials emphasised that space operations were now settling down to a routine, with work being concentrated on the testing of a station of improved design.

Space Station Refuelling

Salyut 6 represented a major departure from the earlier civilian space stations, with engines moved outboard to enable a second docking port to be accommodated at the rear end. The propulsion system was designed with the capability of orbital refuelling firmly in mind.

Whereas previous Salyut stations had main engines fuelled by nitric acid and kerosene, with hydrogen peroxide for cold-gas attitude control thrusters, the new system employing nitrogen tetroxide and UDMH for all engines not only improved performance but also greatly simplified in-flight operations.

In Salyut 6 were three fuel tanks and three oxidant tanks with the fluids contained within flexible bladders. Nitrogen stored at 200

atmospheres pressure was fed via a reduction valve into the space between the inner wall and the bladder, exerting a pressure of 20 atmospheres to force the liquid through to the engines. In the Progress supply craft were two fuel and two oxidiser tanks, each containing 2,205lb (1,000kg) of transferable propellant under pressure from nitrogen bottles. This procedure filled four of the six tanks aboard Salyut, the other two being kept in reserve.

As the main tanks of Salyut were almost empty when refuelling began, the 20 atm pressure had to be reduced to allow liquids to flow in from the tanks of the cargo ship. This was achieved by a compressor powered by a 1kW motor which pumped the gas back into the storage bottles. The motor operated from a power converter drawing power from Salyut's solar panels.

vary from 248 to 6,214 miles (400km to 10,000km) during synchronous experiments forming a "radio-bridge" which equalled the capability of a radio-telescope roughly the size of the Earth's diameter.

Extra television cameras—two black-and-white and one colour inside and outside the station—gave full coverage to the various research activities. The cameras were of the kind used aboard Soyuz 19 during the Apollo-Soyuz Test Project (ASTP). These facilities were further improved during the visit of one of the automatic cargo ships, Progress 5, which brought a TV set to permit two-way transmissions. Now it was possible to beam up to the space crew images of texts, "blue-prints" and engineering instructions from video tapes. The cosmonauts could also receive entertainment programmes from Moscow during off-duty periods and enjoy face-to-face contact with their families.

In a further attempt to ease the physiological problems of weightlessness during this protracted flight new types of Penguin suits were delivered to the crew by Progress 7. Unlike previous suits, which placed stress on the muscles only when the wearer was actively moving around the station, the new ones were effective even when the wearer was at rest in the station.

The next international cosmonaut was the Bulgarian Air Force Major Georgi Ivanov flying with Nikolai Rukavishnikov in Soyuz 33, but their opportunity to board the station was frustrated by a malfunction. As they closed with the Salyut 6/Soyuz 32 complex, their propulsion unit "failed to align the ship correctly" and they were forced to return. They landed in darkness after a flight lasting 1 day 23 hours. Because of this failure the usual exchange of ferry on the station could not be achieved and since the original Soyuz 32 had exceeded its safe lifetime in orbit, Soyuz 34 was sent up unmanned on 6 June 1979 to dock with the station automatically. It was subsequently used to return the long-stay cosmonauts Lyakhov and Ryumin.

The record-breaking partnership of Lyakhov and Ryumin finally came to an end on 19 August 1979 when their command module made a perfect landing some 105 miles (170km) south-east of Dzhezkazgan. They had been in flight for a total of 175 days 36 minutes, more than double the duration achieved by American astronauts. After taking a few days to re-adapt to normal Earth gravity, they were apparently none the worse for their experience. Salyut 6 continued to orbit the Earth unmanned for the next four months until mission control was ready for an important new experiment.

An Improved Ferry

On 16 December 1979 the Soviets launched a much improved spacecraft, Soyuz-T, which three days later docked with Salyut 6 under automatic control. The ship, being tested unmanned, was very much like the former

Right: Soyuz 33 cosmonauts Nikolai Rukavishnikov and the Bulgarian Georgi Ivanov familiarise themselves with docking procedures at the Gagarin Cosmonauts' Training Centre. In the event their Salyut 6 docking mission failed, and they were forced to return to Earth.

Soyuz craft in its outward appearance, but many changes had been made to its internal arrangements. For one thing certain parts of the ship's life-support, flight-control and Earth-landing systems had been changed. Spacecraft designer Dr Konstantin Feoktistov described it as having a kind of robot intelligence:

> "The on-board digital computer system which does the manoeuvring and controls the spacecraft systems also transmits processed data to Earth."

When a docking is under way, for example, the ship's computer puts up on a visual display unit at the mission control centre comprehensive information on the working of all its main systems. The data were also displayed on a screen on board the ship. A new powerplant was also tested. Whereas earlier Soyuz craft had various engines for correcting, docking and positioning, with separate fuel systems and also different propellants, now they had a common system similar to that of Salyut 6 itself.

Finally, the introduction of micro-electronics had made it possible to reduce the weight of systems for life-support, thermal-control and radio communications. This had restored the ability of a Soyuz to fly three cosmonauts in a compact cabin. In short, Soyuz-T incorporated the manned transport features of the basic Soyuz with the cargo-carrying abilities of the Progress unmanned transports.

The skills of the flight operators and the increasing reliability of the spacecraft were emphasised anew when Soyuz 35 crewed by Lt-Col Leonid Popov and Valery Ryumin docked with Salyut 6 on 10 April 1980. Ryumin, who had only returned from a record 175 days space mission the previous

Above: *Col Leonid Popov, commander of Soyuz 35, with Valery Ryumin who set a new space endurance record of 184 days 20 hours 12 minutes on 11 October 1980. In the background: a Salyut 6 mock-up.*

August, had volunteered to go up again in place of Valentin Lebedev who had injured his knee in a trampoline accident during pre-flight training. This remarkable switch in personnel, by-passing the normal cosmonaut back-up procedure, gave the Soviet medical team the opportunity to continue extensive medical checks on a man whose total time in space, in three missions, exceeded 361 days. Again high on the list of experiments performed on the mission were

Above: *Arnaldo Tamayo Mendez — the first Cuban in space — with Yuri Romanenko, the commander of the Soyuz 38 craft. Continued Salyut activity led to the establishment of a larger station.*

smelting experiments in the Splav and Krystall furnaces and Earth observations.

The programme continued with the launch of Valery Kubasov and Captain Bertalan Farkas — the first Hungarian cosmonaut — who docked their Soyuz 36 ferry with the Salyut 6/Soyuz 35 combination on 28 May 1980. They returned in Soyuz 35.

On 5 June 1980 Lt-Col Yuri V. Malyshev and Vladimir V. Aksyonov ascended in Soyuz T-2, the first manned Soyuz T, and the following day joined the resident cosmonauts aboard the Salyut 6/Soyuz 36 complex. The docking was achieved on the aft airlock under manual control after the automatic docking system had brought the ship within 590ft (180m) of the station (Soyuz 36 had previously been re-docked on Salyut's forward airlock). It was explained that the cosmonauts tested

"*Various mechanisms and new on-board systems; before starting a manoeuvre the computer asks the crew's permission and only then does it proceed . . . electronic devices can now change the orbit and orient the ship to any given star speedily and with lower fuel consumption.*"

Malyshev and Aksyonov returned to Earth in the T-2 re-entry module on 9 June. They were followed into space by Col Viktor Gorbatko and Lt-Col Pham Tuan, a Vietnamese air force pilot, who were launched in Soyuz 37 on 23 July 1980. They spent seven days in the space station, returning to Earth in the Soyuz 36 capsule on 31 July, leaving their spacecraft as a fresh return vehicle for Popov and Ryumin.

Next in line was the Cuban cosmonaut Arnaldo Tamayo Mendez — the first Latin American in space — who took off with Col Yuri Romanenko in Soyuz 38 on 18 September 1980. This, the seventh international space crew, joined Popov and Ryumin aboard Salyut 6/Soyuz 37 for a seven-day mission which included some 15 experiments pre-

pared jointly by Soviet and Cuban specialists and some begun by previous cosmonaut researchers. These included the study of sucrose crystallisation in weightlessness, intra-cellular processes of rapid-growth yeasts and bio-medical research related to study of human brain functions, blood circulation, cosmonauts' eye function and other aspects of space flight conditioning. The men returned in the Soyuz 38 capsule after a flight lasting 7 days 20 hours 43 minutes.

As no Progress supply craft had visited the station since Progress 10 in July 1980, the cosmonauts on board had been forced to dump containers of waste from a small airlock chamber. (Normally such waste is incinerated with the discarded Progress vehicle). Western tracking stations reported that several small objects — the waste canisters — began to appear in the orbit of Salyut 6 during the middle of August.

It was not until Romanenko and Mendez had departed that another cargo ship — Progress 11 — joined the station. Popov and Ryumin guided the ship to a safe docking on 30 September.

The long-stay cosmonauts then began to prepare for their own departure in the Soyuz 37 ferry, leaving the station in ship-shape order. They landed on 11 October some 112 miles (180km) from Dzhezkazgan to a rapturous welcome from the recovery teams. Not only had Popov and Ryumin set a new endurance record of 184 days 20 hours 12 minutes, but Ryumin, having completed his third space flight, had spent a total of nearly one year in orbit. It was by any reckoning an event to celebrate.

On 18 November 1980 Salyut 6 was manoeuvred into a higher orbit by Progress 11.

After Salyut 6 had finished its useful period of cosmonaut occupation, a large space vehicle, Cosmos 1267, was docked to it automatically on 19 June 1981. Dr Konstantin Feoktistov, the spacecraft designer, described this as a key step in the assembly of a large orbiting operations centre. For several months Soviet mission control conducted temperature and pressure checks

Below: *Krystall furnace used aboard Salyut 6 for the preparation of semi-conductor crystals. Another furnace, Splav, was used in smelting experiments.*

to confirm compatibility of the two elements.

Another member of the design team, Viktor Sergeyev, pointed out that Cosmos 1267 also performed as a "space tug" using its engine to move the attached space station into higher orbit to offset the effects of air drag. The tug acted like a "robot navigator" ensuring the best possible working conditions, e.g. for a submillimetre telescope which required highly accurate pointing.

Salyut 7

Salyut 6 had spent some five years in orbit roughly two of them with people on board. Salyut 7, launched on 19 April 1982, would greatly expand the opportunities for long-stay cosmonauts. Differences included a strengthened docking unit at the forward end, two additional rendezvous antennae and a porthole with a new protective cover. There was also a major instrument for X-ray astronomy.

It fell to A.N. Berezovoi and V.V. Lebedev in Soyuz T-5 to open up the station on 14 May, testing on-board equipment and ensuring that it responded to control. Many technical and scientific experiments were performed including the release from an airlock of an amateur radio satellite. A spacewalk enabled them to attach instruments to the exterior of Salyut 7 and assess the performance of mechanical joints which could be used in future assembly work. This epic mission, lasting from 13 May to 10 December 1982, set a new duration record of 211 days 8 hours 5 minutes.

Progress 13, which had docked on 25 May 1982, brought 1,455lb (660kg) propellant, 63·8 gallons (290 litres) water, 1,973lb (895kg) scientific equipment including furnaces Kristall and Magma-F: also the electrophotometer EFO-1.

Between 24 June and 2 July Berezovoi and Lebedev had been joined by the Soyuz T-6 cosmonauts V.A. Dzhanibekov, A.S. Ivanchenkov and the Frenchman Jean-Loup Chrétien carrying out medical, biological and "space factory" experiments. From 19-27 August it had been the turn of Soyuz T-7 which brought L.I. Popov, A.A. Serebrov and Svetlana Savitskava (the second woman in space).

By the time Berezovoi and Lebedev returned to Earth on 10 December, four unmanned Progress freighters (Progress 13,

MAJOR SALYUT ASTRONOMICAL EXPERIMENTS	
EXP	**OBJECTIVE**
Anna 3	Gamma ray telescope to detect 100 MeV gamma rays
BST-1M	Infra-red telescope for investigation of galactic centre and interstellar clouds
FEK-7	Search for Dirac monopoles, antinuclei, and trans-uranium nuclei in primary cosmic rays
Filin-2	Spectra of new and established X-ray sources; background radiation in the 1A-60A range
ITS-K	Planetary and galactic infra-red spectrometry
KDS-3	Solar radiation in the 760A-1,060A range
KRT-10	Ten metre diameter radio telescope for exploration of deep space radio emissions
Orion 1	Stellar spectrography in the 2,000A-3,000A range
OST-1	Solar telescope for solar radiation in the 800A-1,300A range
RT-4	Fluctuating X-ray sources in the 44A-60A range
Silya 4	Mass, charge, and energy of interplanetary particles
Yelena	Examination of the intensity and direction of gamma ray fluxes in the vicinity of Salyut for use in the designing of future large space-borne gamma ray telescopes.

14, 15 and 16) had visited Salyut 7 in order to replenish supplies.

On 2 March 1983 another large "tug", Cosmos 1443, ascended from the Baikonur cosmodrome. After spending eight days in free-flight while on-board systems were checked, it docked automatically with the space station (then unmanned) delivering two containerised solar panels for later installation to one of the main solar arrays. Sergeyev says the "tug" literally took over control of the station, performing more than 100 dynamic operations including orbit correction. It undocked on 14 August 1983, and ejected a capsule for recovery on 23 August.

The men who were meant to install the solar panels, V.G. Titov, G.M. Strekalov and A.A. Serebrov followed in Soyuz T-8 on 20 April but, possibly because of a damaged antenna, ran into trouble during the rendezvous phase and docking was not achieved. Two days later they were back on the ground.

The next mission flown between 27 June and 23 November put Soyuz T-9 cosmonauts V.A. Lyakhov and A.P. Alexandrov aboard the station. They conducted a full range of medical, biological and technical experiments and during EVAs on 1 and 3 November succeeded in attaching the two supplementary panels to Salyut's main upper solar array.

The men who had trained to do this, Titov and Strekalov, had again been frustrated on 26 September in dramatic fashion. As they were in the last stage of countdown in Soyuz T-10-1 at Baikonur, fire broke out on the pad and they were forced to use the spacecraft emergency escape system before the rocket exploded. As debris burned on the launch apron, they landed safely within the confines of the cosmodrome.

In-Orbit Repairs

It was not until 8 February 1984 that the Soviets were ready again and this time it was the turn of Soyuz T-10 cosmonauts L.D. Kizim, V.A. Solovyov and O.Y. Atkov, a qualified doctor. It turned out to be one of the most ambitious missions ever attempted in space, aided by tools and materials delivered by three Progress freighters. The trouble had started during Salyut 7's refuelling by Progress 17 which caused one of the propellant lines to become depressurised. In successive EVAs, Kizim and Solovyov had to work their way to the back of the station, first on 23 April with a folded ladder, tools and materials. On 26 April they succeeded in fitting a bypass pipeline and valve. Third and fourth spacewalks were made on 29 April and 3 May; two extra solar panels were installed during the fifth on 18 May.

A final EVA took place on 8 August when Kizim and Solovyov again moved to the propulsion unit to close off a section of pipeline; before re-entering the station they removed a sample from a solar panel for post-flight examination. Although the engine would never again be used to manoeuvre the station, the attitude control thrusters were operating and re-fuelling could again take place from freighters.

India's turn to reach Salyut 7 had come on 3 April 1984 when Rakesh Sharma took his seat in Soyuz T-11 alongside Y.V. Malyshev and G.M. Strekalov. Their researches aboard

the station included detailed examination of the Indian sub-continent related to agriculture, forestry, soil condition and water resources. Mineral surveys were also made.

On 17 July 1984 Soyuz T-12 took Svetlana Savitskaya back to the station with V.A. Dzhanibekov and I.P. Volk. The high point was a 3hr 55min EVA by Dzhanibekov and Savitskaya using a multi-purpose welding tool. They returned on 29 July.

After another session of scientific and technical experiments, during which close attention was paid to the cosmonauts' cardio-vascular systems and water and salt exchange, Kizim, Solovyov and Atkov returned in the T-11 capsule on 2 October having set a new endurance record of 236 days 22 hours 50 minutes.

By the end of the year cosmonaut teams were preparing for still more ambitious exploits. Then, on February 1985 came news of another setback. Mission control had lost

Above: *On Soyuz T-12 Savitskaya became not only the first woman to be launched for a second time, but also the first to complete a spacewalk.*

radio contact with Salyut 7 which had been orbiting unmanned for the past four months.

A Rescue Mission

Vladimir Dzhanibekov and Viktor Savinykh in Soyuz T-13 eventually set out on a repair mission on 6 June. They first flew around the station, which was tumbling slowly in space with its solar arrays non-aligned with the Sun, but reported no obvious sign of damage. So the rendezvous sequence was started and with the help of a new laser range-finder they succeeded in docking under manual control. As it was possible that the station was filled with toxic fumes, the men donned gas masks before opening the airlock's hatches, passing cautiously into

The Soyuz-T/Salyut 7/ Cosmos 1443 Orbital Complex
1 Cosmos re-entry module with retro-rocket pack.
2 Propulsion system nozzle (another underneath the module).
3 Propellant tanks outside the module.
4 Fixed solar panels covering propellant tanks.
5 Flared section, to interface with the Proton launch vehicle third stage.

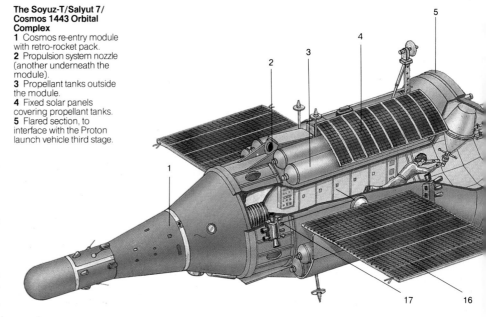

the dark interior by the light of torches. To their relief they found no evidence of electric fire damage. "I took off my mask and breathed," said Dzhanibekov. "To my surprise, the air was fresh — but the station was freezing cold."

After consulting mission control using the radio equipment in their own spacecraft, the men began repairs.

"We cut a cable and connected a circuit which enabled us to switch one storage battery into a solar panel. When we saw the voltage rising, we started to charge from it one battery after another. But every 40 minutes we had to move back into our ferry to keep warm."

By 11 June they had succeeded in stabilising the station; the solar arrays were realigned. Lights came on in the work module, life-support systems were restored and the station was warming up and becoming habitable. Efforts to restore communications also succeeded and on 13 June the TV link came back on and the station once more responded to commands.

Operations were assisted by Progress 24 which docked on 23 June bringing new parts and equipment requested by the repairmen, plus two more solar panels. On 16 July the unmanned freighter Cosmos 1669 went up with more supplies. This was not the heavy Cosmos but a spacecraft of Progress type fitted with solar panels. Its contents included scientific apparatus for studying the generation of high energy particles in the Earth's radiation belt — the Mariya experiment. Cosmos 1669 was detached

from the station on 28 August and re-entered the atmosphere over the Pacific.

Dzhanibekov and Savinykh spacewalked on 2 August to fix the two supplementary solar panels to the station's third solar array. This EVA lasted about 5 hours and before re-entering the airlock, they retrieved a micro-meteoroid detector and various materials samples which had been exposed to the space environment.

Soyuz T-14 took V.V. Vasyutin, G.M. Grechko and A.A. Volkov to Salyut 7 on 18 September. Dzhanibekov and Grechko returned to Earth in the Soyuz T-13 capsule on 26 September leaving the others at work.

The next day came the launch of Cosmos 1686 which docked with Salyut's forward port on 2 October. This large freighter carried five tonnes of cargo including one tonne of scientific apparatus, various assemblies and parts, gas regenerators and food. It could be used as a research lab or "hothouse" — also as a "space tug". However, the experimental programme had to be curtailed when Vasyutin fell ill and the decision was taken to recall the crew. They landed in the Soyuz T-14 capsule on 21 November.

Space Station Mir

In the meantime, preparations were under way at the Baikonur cosmodrome for the launch of the new space station, Mir (Peace) which ascended on the nose of a D-1 booster on 19 February 1986 (20 February Moscow Time). Based on Salyut technology, the station had no fewer than six docking ports with improved crew accommodation.

Much of the scientific equipment found in Salyut stations was absent. Cosmonauts now enjoyed separate compartments with table, chair and intercom. Life-support and ventilation systems were improved and water was regenerated from atmospheric moisture.

At the front end was a spherical multiple docking unit with five docking ports, one axial for visiting spacecraft and four disposed radially at 90° to each other for the future attachment of lab modules. At the rear of the

Above: *Repaired and revitalised, the Salyut 7/Soyuz T-14 complex is photographed by the departing Soyuz T-13 crew on 25 September 1985.*

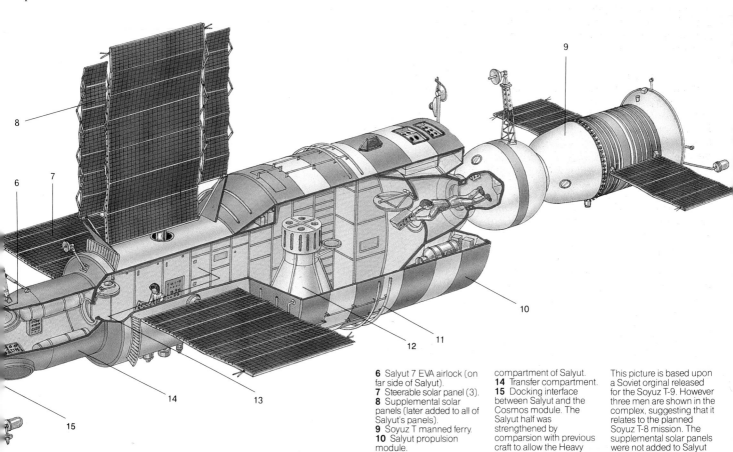

6 Salyut 7 EVA airlock (on far side of Salyut).
7 Steerable solar panel (3).
8 Supplemental solar panels (later added to all of Salyut's panels).
9 Soyuz T manned ferry.
10 Salyut propulsion module.
11 Handrails on the outside of the large work compartment — added to aid EVA work.
12 Shroud covering the X-ray detection equipment.
13 Small work

compartment of Salyut.
14 Transfer compartment.
15 Docking interface between Salyut and the Cosmos module. The Salyut half was strengthened by comparsion with previous craft to allow the Heavy Cosmos to dock safely.
16 Steerable solar panels (2).
17 Main Heavy Cosmos work module, based upon the smaller diameter Salyut work compartment.

This picture is based upon a Soviet orginal released for the Soyuz T-9. However three men are shown in the complex, suggesting that it relates to the planned Soyuz T-8 mission. The supplemental solar panels were not added to Salyut until after Cosmos 1443 had separated from the station, although this work probably was scheduled for the Soyuz T-8 visit while Cosmos was still docked with Salyut.

station was another port for the docking of a fifth lab module and visiting spacecraft including freighters.

The opportunity to open up the Mir station for human occupation fell to T-15 cosmonauts L.D. Kizim and V.A. Solovyov in March 1986 who initially spent much of their time adjusting technical equipment and testing a new space-to-ground radio/video link using the Luch communications satellite.

One more impressive demonstration of Soviet mastery of space technique was to follow on 5-6 May when the two men made space history by transferring from one orbiting space station to another. After docking with the unmanned Salyut 7/Cosmos 1686 complex, they completed a series of experiments which included making two EVAs testing the erection of a lattice and pin-jointed structure of the type to be used in future space construction work.

On 21 May 1986 an unmanned Soyuz TM ascended from Baikonur to dock with the unmanned Mir-Progress 26 complex. This was the key test of an improved ferry (intended to be manned) which embodied several new systems: approach and docking; radio communications; a combined propulsion unit for manoeuvres and orientation, and a lighter and stronger recovery parachute. Mutual search, rendezvous and docking with Mir was carried out by automatic systems aboard both vehicles. A new system "Kurs" (Course) allowed the TM ship to manoeuvre for docking while the Mir expended nil propellant. Communications

could now be made via the geostationary satellite Luch.

Before separating on 29 May, Soyuz TM used its combined propulsion unit to adjust the orbit of the Mir complex. Its descent capsule was stated to have landed in the "designated area of the Soviet Union".

Meanwhile, having spent 50 days aboard Salyut 7-Cosmos 1686, Kizim and Solovyov returned to Mir on 26 June. Altogether it was a most remarkable demonstration of human dexterity in space. From both stations they continued Earth observations, astrophysical studies and medical research. They returned to Earth on 16 July bringing with them equipment salvaged from the older station.

Between 17-23 August ground controllers used the engine of Cosmos 1686 to boost the Salyut 7 station complex into a higher, "parking" orbit of 294 x 306 miles (474 x 492km). One day, say the Soviets, space shuttles may be launched to recover the separate elements.

Soyuz TM-2

On 5 February 1987 Soyuz TM-2 took off carrying Y.V. Romanenko and A.I. Leveykin. It docked with the Mir-Progress 27 complex two days later using the new "Kurs" automatic system. After adjusting on-board systems, they re-activated Mir's radio and TV communications link and continued the experiments programme. Regular re-supply missions continued and among the cargo of Progress 28, which docked on 5 March, was the Korund (Corundum) "semi-industrial"

plant used to grow crystals under micro-g. Together with the Splav (Alloy) and Kristall (Crystal) equipment, the cosmonauts were able to start pilot production of metals, alloys and semi-conductors.

A main task of the TM-2 cosmonauts was to receive the station's first lab module Kvant (Quantum) which was to dock automatically with the assistance of an attached service module or "tug" on 9 April. This was not without difficulty, however, because unknown to crew and ground controllers, a "foreign object" was lodged in the docking receptor causing Romanenko and Laveykin to make an unscheduled EVA. The object turned out to be a piece of plastic material which the cosmonauts were able to remove. After they had re-entered the space station, hard-docking was finally achieved on 11 April. After the tug had been cast off on 13 April, a second Kvant docking port was exposed which enabled the docking of Soyuz and Progress ferries.

There followed a number of significant steps in space station operation and re-supply which set Mir-Kvant apart from its predecessors. Kvant, an astrophysics module, allowed the station to operate as an astronomical platform. Aboard were the Roentgen X-ray observatory designed by teams from the USSR, Britain, the Netherlands, West Germany and ESA; also the Glasar UV telescope designed jointly by Soviet and Swiss scientists. Kvant's telescopes were first to record X-ray emissions from the supernova in the Large Magellanic Cloud.

Mir Space Station
1 Soyuz TM craft (to bring crew to the station).
2 Interlock.
3 Axial docking port.
4 Approach and rendezvous system (Igla) antenna.
5 EVA handrails.
6 Work module hatch cover.
7 Connection for possible auxiliary solar array.

8 Mir work module.
9 Solar panels, probably made of gallium arsenide (span, 29·73m; generating 9-10kW).
10 Rendezvous antenna.
11 Telemetry antenna.
12 Individual sleeping compartment.
13 Approach and rendezvous system (Igla) antenna.
14 Transfer module.

15 Luch relay satellite communications antenna (11/14GHz).
16 Toilet and washing area.
17 Aft docking port, primarily for Progress re-supply ferry craft.
18 Main engine.

19 Docking target.
20 Docking hatch.
21 Transfer module.
22 Treadmill exerciser.

23 Attitude control thrusters (32).
24 Propellant tanks.
25 Work and dining table.
26 Exercise bicycle (velo-ergometer).
27 Station control consoles, provide access to the eight control computers.
28 Observation window.
29 Multiple docking adapter, one aft docking port and four axial ports.
30 Axial docking port.
31 Socket for attachment of remote manipulator arm on docking modules.
32 EVA handrails.
33 Observation window.

Fundamental to Mir's design is the multiple docking adapter, which permits four modules to be docked axially to it. Each experiment module first docks on the aft port; a remote manipulator arm then attaches to a socket on the Mir hub, and after checkout, the arm then swings round the socket through 90° and re-docks the module on one of the vacant side docking ports.

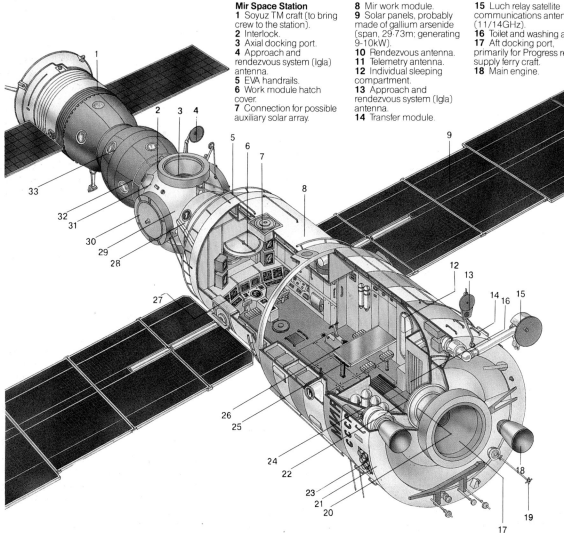

Romanenko and Leveykin spacewalked on 12 and 16 June to emplace two supplementary solar panels on Mir's third solar array.

On 22 July Soyuz TM-3 ascended with A.S. Viktorenko, A.P. Alexandrov and the Syrian M.A. Faris. Part of their task was to map the Syrian Republic and study water, mineral and oil resources. Leveykin, the resident Mir flight engineer, in the meantime was found to have irregular heart rhythm when taking physical exercise, and he returned with Viktorenko and Faris on 30 July. Three more Progress freighters arrived — on 5 August, 26 September and 23 November — building up supplies. The last carried astrophysical equipment and a new solar-powered beam furnace for the study of crystal growth under micro-g.

Another launching came on 21 December when Soyuz TM-4 entered space with V.G. Titov, M.K. Manarov and A.S. Levchenko to reach the station two days later. On 29 December 1987, Romanenko returned with Alexandrov and Levchenko setting a new endurance record of 326 days 11 hours 8 minutes.

Operations in 1988-89

The New Year opened with the launch of three more Progress freighters. Titov and Manarov spacewalked on 26 February to modify Mir's third solar array. Then came the Soyuz TM-5 mission between 7-17 June 1988 with A.Y. Solovyov, V.P. Savinykh and the Bulgarian A.P. Alexandrov. Experiments aboard Mir-Kvant included space physics, biology and medicine, remote sensing and materials processing.

On 30 June Titov and Manarov spacewalked outside again in a vain attempt to repair an X-ray telescope in the Kvant module (They eventually succeeded during a second EVA on 20 October).

Between 29 August-7 September came the TM-6 mission which brought to the station V.A. Lyakhov, V. Polyakov and the Afghan Abdol Ahad Mohmand. The research programme Shamshad concentrated on photographic and spectral examination of Afghanistan in the search for water, oil and gas.

On 26 November international ventures continued with Soyuz TM-7 taking up A. Volkov, Sergei Krikalev and the Frenchman Jean-Loup Chrétien. The highlight was a spacewalk from Mir-Kvant by Volkov and the Frenchman whose main task was to install on a platform a self-erecting lattice structure of carbon fibre tubes. After carrying out other technical experiments, including the test of the deployment mechanism of an experimental solar panel, Armedeus, the men returned inside and the experimental lattice was rejected overboard. The mission ended on 21 December when Chrétien landed with Titov and Manarov who had been in space a full year.

By 14 February 1989 Volkov and Krikalev had worked in orbit 2·5 months and Poliakov 170 days. Their work included operating the Glasar telescope checking UV sources in the constellations Augiga, Gemini and Monoceros. Supporting these activities were the usual Progress freighters replacing expendables and bringing new tools and equipment. Progress 40 arrived on 12 February and there was also news of a new development — a Progress freighter with a re-entry capsule

Above and right: *Leonid Kizim at work aboard the Mir core station. The above picture is looking towards the multiple docking adapter, while the picture at right looks towards the aft docking port.*

for returning film and experiment samples to Earth. Soyuz, too, would be further improved to provide extra crew comfort.

In three years the Mir cosmonauts had completed nine EVAs totalling over 37 hours and in addition to astronomical observations, materials processing and medical experiments, had carried out some 5,000 photographic sessions mostly related to planet Earth. Progress freighters had delivered more than 40 tonnes of supplies.

Problems with Mir

It was after this busy period that the programme began to fall short of its objectives. The two 20 tonne "building block" modules which were expected to be launched to Mir for attachment to the multiple docking unit failed to meet the deadline and the three cosmonauts still aboard in April 1989 were told to prepare the station for a period of unmanned operation. To complicate matters, there had been reports of Mir's storage batteries failing to hold their full charge from the solar arrays. The intended launch of Soyuz TM-8 on 19 April with Alexander Viktorenko and Alexander Balandin was called off.

Progress 41, which had docked with the station on 18 March, had brought up replacement supplies and before being cast off its engine was used to boost the station complex into a higher "parking" orbit. When finally undocked on 21 April, it ran out of fuel during retro-burn and spent over four days in independent flight before destroying itself in the atmosphere.

Meanwhile, cosmonauts Volkov, Krikalev and Polyakov had been busy "mothballing" some of the station's on-board systems. They reported that a number of power generation items "which had exceeded their warranty" had been replaced. The trio landed safely in the descent module of Soyuz TM-7 north-east of Dzhezkazgan on 27 April. Information continued to be received from essential systems including the Kvant telescopes.

It would now be necessary to train cosmonauts to fly a re-activation mission later in 1989 and to send up more Progress freighters. Only then would it be possible to contemplate launching the two "building

block" modules. The aim was to position them on the station's multiple docking adapter at right angles to the axis to maintain the station's symmetry.

The first module was stated to have a total mass of some 45,000lb (20·6 tonnes); maximum length 41ft (12·5m); diameter 13·45ft (4·1m). Module "D" (*Doosnashcheniye*, meaning additional or service equipment), had an enlarged EVA airlock with a 3·28ft (1m) diameter hatch and all facilities for working outside the station including a manned manoeuvring unit (MMU) to improve mobility during EVAs.

Other features of the "D" module are a large-capacity computer; 32 orientation thrusters; six "gyrodynes" to enhance stabilisation of the Mir complex with 1 arc minute precision; new solar panels; a water electrolytic decomposition unit for oxygen supply and a shower compartment. Extra supplies of water, fuel and food were also on the rosta.

It was also suggested that platforms could be attached to the outside for the mounting of telescopes and other scientific equipment which could be pointed at celestial targets or objects on Earth without having to orientate the station itself.

Module "T" (*Teknologicheskaya*) was described as a "mini-factory" in which to start pilot production of semi-conductor monocrystals for the electronics industry and drugs for medical practice. It was suggested that some 220lb (100kg) of ultra-pure crystals could be produced per year. This module is expected to begin operation in late 1990 or early 1991.

According to the original schedule, two more "building blocks" were to arrive in 1991: Module "O" (*Optizont*) dedicated to remote sensing of ground and ocean, and a fourth for biological and medical research. There was talk of incorporating a 5-tonne "greenhouse" with "a small zoo and garden".

The five attachments (Kvant included) would bring the stations's total mass to about 286,600lb (130 tonnes). However for the immediate future, cosmonaut missions would last no longer than six months. Later it was stated, "their duration would be increased to a year and a half".

Handshake in Orbit

One of the great milestones in manned spaceflight, and an event that evoked world-wide acclaim, was the July 1975 link-up of a Soviet and an American spacecraft in Earth orbit, a fraternisation the mass media were quick to dub "Handshake In Orbit". This history-making mission was welcomed throughout the world as symbolising both the extension of *detente* to outer space and the potential of international efforts in space exploration.

ASTP Origins

Although, after basically similar initial space programmes, the Soviet Union and the United States embarked upon national space projects with distinctly different goals and priorities, there was a certain measure of co-operation between the space scientists of the two countries from the outset. The first formal agreement on such co-operation was concluded by the USSR Academy of Sciences and the US National Aeronautics and Space Administration in June 1962, less than five years after Sputnik had ushered in the Space Age.

This and other early bilateral agreements led to a direct communications link between the world meteorological centres founded in Moscow and Washington, to joint experiments in communicating via outer space by means of the Echo 2 passive communications satellite, to joint work on a treatise entitled *Foundations of Space Biology and*

"Then the TV screen showed movement at the far end of the passageway and the face and body of the Soyuz crew commander appeared.... He stretched his arm forward through the passageway where his hand was clasped by that of the American crew commander."

Walter Froehlich
Apollo Soyuz

Below: The five men who flew in the joint US/USSR Apollo-Soyuz Test Project in 1975. The two commanders were Thomas P. Stafford, standing left, and Alexei A. Leonov, standing right. The others were Donald K. Slayton and Vance D. Brand, seated left, and Valery N. Kubasov.

Medicine, and to exchanges of data concerning the Earth's magnetism. But on the whole Soviet-American co-operative efforts in the latter half of the 1960s remained limited and fell far short of what might have been expected of two major space powers, which had by then developed their respective third-generation spacecraft for manned flight — Soyuz and Apollo.

It was only with the further expansion of international co-operation in space and, especially, with the improvement of Soviet-American relations that the Apollo-Soyuz Test Project (ASTP) became possible.

In the course of a series of exchanges that began in 1969, Soviet and American space officials and experts identified the problem of manned flight safety as a potentially fruitful area for joint efforts, and formulated the idea of designing a compatible docking system to improve safety measures by making possible mutual rescue in space. Because of incompatible docking systems, Soviet and American spacecraft could not dock in an emergency; a compatible docking system would remove this obstacle to rescue operations in space.

Joint working groups were, accordingly, set up in October 1970, each responsible for a specific aspect of the effort to develop new docking facilities. They considered such problems as radio and visual systems needed for rendezvous and docking, differences in the communications and environmental control systems used by the spacecraft of the two countries, the basic functions and design of the proposed docking system, the costs involved, and the possibility of testing the new docking system.

The project was finalised at the USSR-US summit meeting in May 1972 in a five-year "Agreement on Co-operation in the Exploration and Use of Outer Space for Peaceful Purposes", which formally endorsed

"Projects for developing compatible rendezvous and docking systems of Soviet and United States manned spacecraft and stations in order to enhance the safety of manned flights in space and provide the opportunity for conducting joint scientific experiments in the future."

The Agreement scheduled a joint flight for 1975, stipulating that it should involve

"the docking of a Soviet Soyuz-type spacecraft and a United States Apollo-type spacecraft with visits of astronauts in each other's spacecraft."

Dr Konstantin Bushuyev and Dr Glynn Lunney were named ASTP Technical Directors for the Soviet and US sides respectively.

Compatibility Problems

The very first meetings of the Soviet and American experts revealed that ASTP hinged on problems of compatibility, which could be grouped under five general headings.

Firstly there was the problem of making the ranging and rendezvous facilities of the two spacecraft mutually acceptable. Although the Soyuz and Apollo systems developed for these purposes were based on the same principles, differences in their characteristics and *modus operandi* made them quite incompatible. Both craft, for example, employed radio methods for rendezvous, but the frequencies used, the methods of data acquisition, and the parameters measured were completely different. The Soyuz facilities, in addition to measuring the distance between two approaching craft, could monitor their centre-of-mass line, be

Below: *Charles Harrington, an American aerospace expert, examines a flight model of the ASTP docking system at the Space Research Institute of the USSR Academy of Sciences during an exchange visit.*

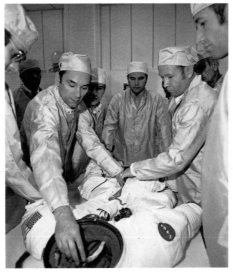

Above: *A Soviet interpreter (left) points out a feature of an Apollo spacesuit to Valery Kubasov (third from left) and Alexei Leonov (second from right) during a visit to the Kennedy Space Center in February 1975.*

used for mutual radio tracking, and issue signals for angular control. The Apollo facilities, on the other hand, served for ranging only—all the other parameters necessary for rendezvous were determined visually. Furthermore, whereas Apollo rendezvous procedures were based on manual control only, Soyuz had facilities for both manual and automatic rendezvous and docking. (Such facilities had made possible the Cosmos 186 and Cosmos 188 automatic docking as far back as 1967 and have since enabled Progress unmanned cargo ferries to dock with Salyut orbital stations.) The optical characteristics of the Soyuz surface were likewise out of keeping with the requirements of Apollo's optical equipment. Since the July 1975 deadline (finalised in October 1972) ruled out any possibility of jointly developing a unified system meeting all the requirements of compatibility, the working group charged with this problem decided to adopt the Apollo rendezvous system.

This decision was prompted mainly by the consideration that Apollo—designed for the flight to the Moon and therefore having the bigger fuel supply—would be the active partner in the rendezvous and docking procedure. Accordingly, Soyuz was fitted with a transponder, a passive transmitter-receiver that responds automatically to the proper interrogation. Then there were the difficulties of making the optical characteristics of the Soyuz surface conform to Apollo optical system requirements. Changing the traditional Soyuz colour to a milky white, and thus completely altering its surface light reflection and absorption characteristics, would have disturbed temperature conditions aboard the craft. A compromise was therefore reached, and Soyuz became part white and part green. An appropriate optical model tested in both countries confirmed the suitability of this colour scheme. The Apollo crew were, in fact, able to spot Soyuz from a distance of several hundred kilometres. Soyuz was also fitted with white flashing beacons for use in the Earth's shadow and with orientation lights for the final phase of rendezvous. Two docking targets completed this part of its equipment.

The second compatibility problem concerned the actual docking units; that is all the parts that had directly to interface during docking. Both spacecraft had previously used a pin-and-cone docking assembly, whereby the active craft is fitted with a pin ("probe" in US terminology), which slides into the cone ("drogue") of the passive craft once the two craft have been manoeuvred together. Latches complete the

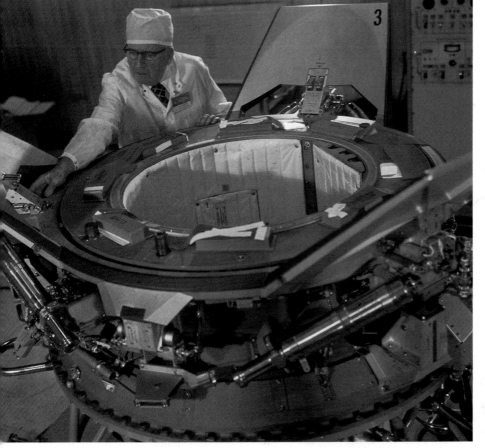

mating process, assuring a rigid and pressure-tight seal. Although operating on the same principle, the Soyuz and Apollo docking assemblies had different dimensions, latches, rigidising mechanisms, etc, and this precluded any possibility of mating the two assemblies. The working group concerned with the docking assembly problem therefore had to tackle the task of developing an entirely new docking unit. Two basic requirements were formulated: the new system would have to be androgynous—such as to enable any craft to operate in either the active or the passive mode, and it would have to rely upon peripheral action—have no centrally located parts, thus leaving a free passageway between the coupled spacecraft. The working groups, which held ten meetings in each country, adopted a ring-and-petal design proposed by the Soviet engineers, headed by Vladimir Syromyatnikov. To avoid changing the basic Apollo design, which would have required costly reverification tests, the Americans developed an adapter element called the Docking Module. This new piece of space hardware could dock with the Apollo Command Module at one end by means of a probe-and-drogue docking unit and with Soyuz at the other end by means of the newly developed unit. The Soviet and American docking assemblies actually differed substantially—for example, in shock-attenuation and guide-ring systems—but they conformed to certain agreed-upon requirements, which assured their compatibility and made the Soyuz-Apollo docking possible. After numerous ground tests involving mock-ups of the docking system, the Soviet docking assembly was tested in flight aboard Soyuz 16, with a special ring simulating the Apollo docking assembly. The test was entirely successful.

The third group of compatibility problems concerned the means of communication and flight control. Although not as formidable as the problems discussed above, it related to such important factors as communication between the two spacecraft in flight, co-or-

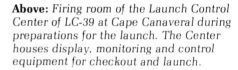

Above: *Firing room of the Launch Control Center of LC-39 at Cape Canaveral during preparations for the launch. The Center houses display, monitoring and control equipment for checkout and launch.*

dination between each craft and the ground control complex supervising the flight of the other craft, and co-ordination between the two ground control complexes. The problems involved were solved by installing additional radio equipment on board both spacecraft, standardising the frequencies to be used, and providing the two craft with wire communication facilities for use during their flight when docked. All communication systems were subjected to laboratory testing in both countries, after which they were tested, early in 1975, aboard Apollo at the Kennedy Space Center in Florida and aboard Soyuz at the Baikonur Cosmodrome.

The fourth group of problems concerned the compatibility of the life-support systems and transfer facilities. Here again the appropriate working group was confronted with sizeable problems. When Soyuz and Apollo had been conceived a decade earlier, the two spacecraft development teams had followed their own, independent engineering philosophies. The Soviet engineers chose for Soyuz an atmosphere which was lower than that on Earth: a mixture of 19-32 per cent oxygen and 66-78 per cent nitrogen at a pressure of 490-520mm of mercury. For Apollo, the Americans chose an atmosphere of pure oxygen at a pressure of only 280mm of mercury, about one-third the atmospheric pressure at the surface of the Earth. A direct transfer of crew members from the Soyuz atmosphere to the low-pressure oxygen atmosphere of Apollo would therefore cause the "bends", a condition experienced by deep-sea divers when they surface too quickly and nitrogen gas bubbles form in their body fluids. Only patience and a mutual willingness to compromise enabled the working group faced with such baffling environmental problems to cope with them. First and foremost agreement was reached on an American proposal to include an airlock in the docking module. To eliminate the need for a lengthy adaptation period inside the airlock for crew members passing

Below: *The scene at the Soviet Mission Control centre during a training exercise. On the screen are represented the ground tracks of the ASTP spacecraft. Right of the screen is an image of the docked craft.*

Above: *An A-2 rocket blasts off from the Baikonur cosmodrome in a Soyuz 16 dress rehearsal for the ASTP mission on 2 December 1974. Aboard was the Soviet back-up team, A. Filipchenko and N. Rukavishnikov.*

This diagram shows the method of equalising the spacecraft atmospheres to allow crew transfer. Apollo had a pure oxygen atmosphere at 280mm Hg. Soyuz oxygen/nitrogen at 520mm Hg.
1 Astronauts and cosmonauts prior to transfer: hatches closed.
2 Hatch 2 opened. Apollo commander and docking pilot enter the DM.
3 Hatch 2 closed. O_2 and N_2 enters Tunnel 2.
4 DM atmosphere adjusts slowly to oxygen/nitrogen at 490mm Hg.
5 Hatch 4 opened. Tunnel 2 pressure equalised with Soyuz.
6 DM and Soyuz pressures are equalised. The Apollo astronauts open Hatch 3 and enter Soyuz for the historic greeting. In the case of a Russian transfer, reverse procedures applied.

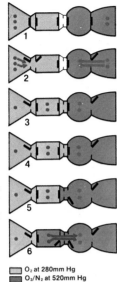

☐ O_2 at 280mm Hg
☐ O_2/N_2 at 520mm Hg
☐ O_2/N_2 at 490mm Hg
● Apollo astronaut
● Soyuz cosmonaut

Above: *The Saturn IB ASTP vehicle is taken from the Vehicle Assembly Building to LC-39B on the giant crawler. The long white cylinder at the top of the service tower is a lightning conductor.*

from Soyuz to Apollo, the Soviet engineers agreed to reduce the atmospheric pressure aboard Soyuz by about one-third for the duration of the link-up. This was not an easy decision, since it required altering a number of systems, introducing additional equipment, and verifying the safety and reliability of the operation of the onboard equipment at a higher partial oxygen pressure. But the smaller difference in pressures enabled the Americans to simplify and reduce the cost of the docking module, since crew members would not be required to spend long periods in the airlock. It would also make enough time available to enable all crew members to take part in the exchange of visits.

Finally, a fifth group of problems concerned organisational and methodological compatibility. It covered a wide range of matters from the principles of joint flight control and provisions for various contingency situations to standardisation of terminology and overcoming the language barrier. A major problem this working group had to contend with was the selection of what are known as "launch windows": the periods of time during which a launch would allow mission objectives to be met, and which would satisfy all requirements and constraints. For example, the Soyuz launch window had to be chosen so that at least eight minutes before the retro-rocket firing for descent the craft would be passing over the sunlit side of the Earth, the cosmonauts thus being able to operate the orientation system manually. In the case of Apollo, the launch window had to ensure that it would be daylight in the splash-down area for the descent vehicle rescue. Here again the problem was solved by a compromise whereby the somewhat modified demands of both sides could be met.

Cosmonauts and Astronauts

The Soyuz prime crew was headed by Colonel Alexei Leonov of the Soviet Air Force, who had been the first man to "walk in space" during the Voskhod 2 flight in 1965. A graduate of the Zhukovsky Air Force Academy with a passion for painting, he had been awarded the title of Hero of the Soviet Union after his previous spaceflight.

The prime crew flight engineer was

Valery Kubasov, who had conducted the first space welding experiment during the Soyuz 6 flight in 1969. Likewise a Hero of the Soviet Union, Kubasov was a graduate of the Moscow Aviation Institute and had a scientific degree.

The Apollo prime crew was commanded by Brig-Gen Thomas Stafford of the US Air Force, a veteran of three spaceflights, including the Apollo 10 moonflight in 1969. The US Naval Academy had conferred a Bachelor of Science degree on Stafford, and he was the recipient of three NASA Service Medals.

Donald Slayton, the Apollo docking module pilot, and Vance Brand, the Apollo command module pilot, had made no previous spaceflights, although both had been with the astronaut corps for many years.

With the back-up crews, a total of eight cosmonauts and nine astronauts received extensive training in all aspects of the joint flight. In the course of the training, Soviet personnel familiarised the US astronauts with the Soyuz craft in exercises at the Gagarin Cosmonaut Training Centre just outside Moscow, and Soviet crewmen practised in an Apollo training device at the Johnson Space Center in Houston, Texas.

Joint training built up fine teamwork between the Soviet and American crews, and also between the ASTP Flight Directors, Alexei Eliseyev and Peter Frank.

The Flight

The joint flight got off to a fine start with a Soyuz launching at 1220 GMT on 15 July 1975 that was right on time (the error not exceeding 5 milliseconds) and was in every respect flawless.

In a novel departure from Soviet tradition, the launching was televised live, and more than 100 million people in the USSR alone 210

Left: *The green Soyuz 19 spacecraft contrasts strongly against a black sky with heavily cloud-covered Earth below. The picture was taken through the rendezvous window of the Apollo spacecraft.*

Below: *Apollo from Soyuz. On the nose of the American spacecraft is the Docking Module (DM) which was attached during a transposition manoeuvre with the final stage of the Saturn IB launch vehicle.*

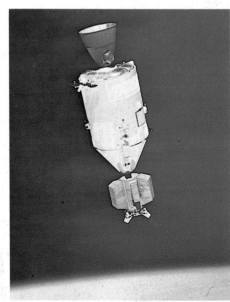

ASTP Spacecraft in Docked Configuration
1 Apollo Service Module (SM) with bell-shaped engine nozzle. Contained propellants, fuel cells, oxygen and other supplies and equipment.
2 Reaction control quad.
3 Pitch control thrusters.
4 Apollo Command Module (CM) with accommodation for three cosmonauts. Cabin atmosphere pure oxygen at 5lb/in² (0·35kg/cm²).
5 Control consoles.
6 Docking Module (DM) which cosmonauts/astronauts entered to acclimatise to different atmospheres before entering the other ship.
7 Apollo VHF antennas (frequency 121·75MHz).
8 Docking target.
9 Guide (1 of 3).
10 VHF antenna.
11 Soyuz Orbital Module used by crow for work and rest.
12 Soyuz Descent Module (DM) with accommodation for two cosmonauts. Normal cabin atmosphere oxygen/nitrogen at about 14·7lb/in² (1kg/cm²), reduced during period of docking to 10lb/in² (0·7kg/cm²).
13 Soft-docking and orientation jets, thrust
22lb (10kg), total 14.
14 Flashing beacon.
15 Solar sensor.
16 Soyuz Instrument Module (IM).
17 Approach and orientation thrusters.
18 Orientation jets, 5·5lb (2·5kg) thrust, total 12.
19 Manoeuvre engine, 661·5lb (300kg) thrust.
20 Thermal control system radiator.
21 Rendezvous antenna.
22 Extensible solar panels, span 27·5ft (8·37m).
23 Telemetry antenna.
24 Orientation jets, thrust 55lb (25kg), total of 12.
25 Infra-red orientation.
26 Flashing beacon.
27 Antenna ring.
28 Sighting device for optical orientation.
29 TV antenna (1 of 2).
30 TV camera and orientation light (red).
31 Apollo VHF antenna.
frequency 121·75MHz.
32 Oxygen pressure bottle.
33 Nitrogen pressure bottle.
34 Soyuz docking target.
35 CSM docking ring.
36 Astronaut's couch.
37 Yaw thrusters.
38 High-gain antennas (for communications with ground via satellite ATS-6, frequencies 2256MHz out, 2077·4MHz in).

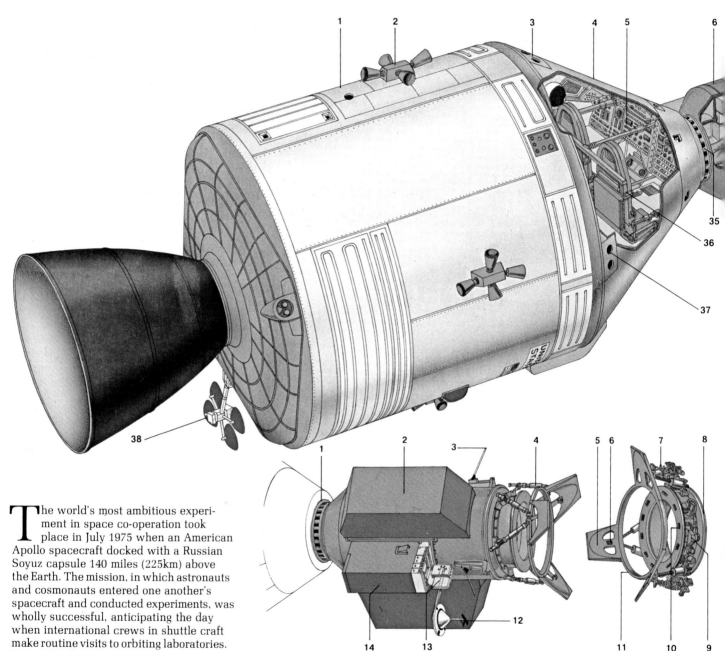

The world's most ambitious experiment in space co-operation took place in July 1975 when an American Apollo spacecraft docked with a Russian Soyuz capsule 140 miles (225km) above the Earth. The mission, in which astronauts and cosmonauts entered one another's spacecraft and conducted experiments, was wholly successful, anticipating the day when international crews in shuttle craft make routine visits to orbiting laboratories. To join Apollo and Soyuz (which had different pressures) it was necessary for the Americans to take into orbit a Docking Module jointly developed by American and Russian engineers. Future American spacecraft will have the same nitrogen-oxygen atmosphere as Soviet spacecraft to ease the problem of crew transfer between two docked vehicles. One of the major objectives of the mission was the performance of a series of micro-gravity, astronomy, medical and Earth observation experiments, which the Soviet Union has further pursued in its Salyut 6 programme. Such experiments can be seen as the necessary steps towards the establishment of a full scale factory in space.

Docking Module
1 CSM docking ring.
2 O₂ and N₂ tank cover (1 of 2).
3 VHF-FM antenna (1 of 3).
4 Attenuators.
5 Guide (1 of 3).
6 Capture latch (1 of 3).
7 Attenuator (1 of 6).
8 Tunnel interface.
9 Cable retract system motors and gearbox.
10 Structural latches.
11 Guide ring (extended).
12 Soyuz docking target.
13 Multiple operation door.
14 UV spectrometer.

Making Apollo and Soyuz compatible for the space docking involved many
modifications. In particular a Docking Module had to be introduced between the two craft in which cosmonauts and astronauts could acclimatise to cabin atmospheres of different composition and pressures to avoid the "bends" familiar to deep sea divers ascending too rapidly from the ocean depths.

Technical Data
Length of cylindrical chamber: 10·3ft (3·15m).
Maximum diameter: 4·7ft (1·42m).
Total weight with experiments, stowage, fluids and docking system: 7,390lb (5.907kg).

Mission Profile
1 Soyuz 19 launched from Baikonur at 1520 MT, 15 July 1975.
2 Central core of launch vehicle separates: spacecraft injected into orbit.
3 Soyuz assumes docking attitude.
4 Awaits arrival of Apollo.
5 Apollo is launched by Saturn IB from Kennedy Space Center at 1550 Washington time (2250 Moscow time).
6 First stage of launcher separates: second stage ignites.
7 Apollo CSM separates, exposing docking module in nose of 2nd stage.
8 Spacecraft through 180°.
9 Docks with ASTP
module, pulling it free.
10 Manoeuvres for rendezvous.
11 Prepares to dock.
12 US and Soviet spacecraft are joined for crew transfers and joint experiments.
13 Spacecraft separate.
14 Soyuz retro-fire.
15 Service and orbital modules separate.
16 Command module lands in USSR.
17 Apollo continues in orbit.
18 Jettisons ASTP docking module: retrofires.
19 SM jettisons.
20 Command module splashes down in Pacific 270 miles (432km) west of Hawaii.

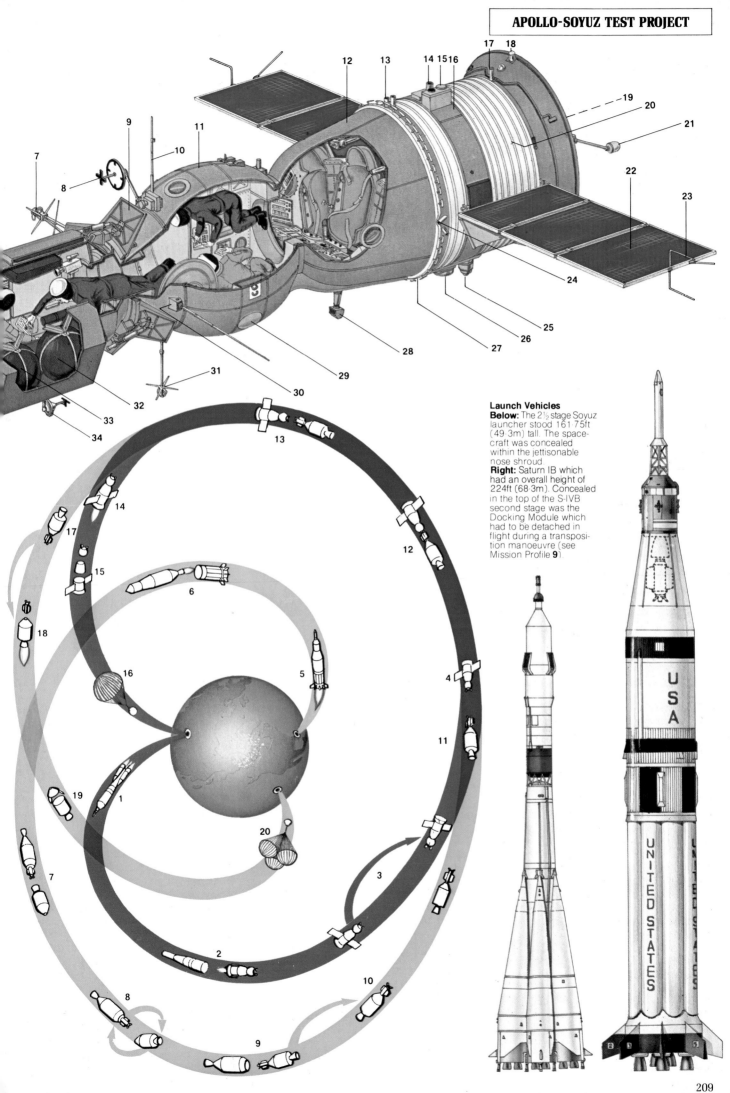

Launch Vehicles
Below: The 2½ stage Soyuz launcher stood 161·75ft (49·3m) tall. The spacecraft was concealed within the jettisonable nose shroud.
Right: Saturn IB which had an overall height of 224ft (68·3m). Concealed in the top of the S-IVB second stage was the Docking Module which had to be detached in flight during a transposition manoeuvre (see Mission Profile **9**).

watched the rocket, gushing orange flame and smoke, rise with a thunderous roar and streak off in a north-easterly direction. Among those who watched the launch at the Baikonur Cosmodrome were the US Ambassador to the USSR Walter Stoessel and NASA Assistant Deputy Administrator W. Shapley.

Exactly 530 seconds after the launch the Mission Control Centre announced that the final-stage engine had been cut and that the command had gone out for the third-stage separation. Soyuz 19 was in orbit.

During the fourth and 17th circuits of the globe, Leonov circularised the craft's orbit at 140 miles (225km). These manoeuvres were highly successful: the maximum deviation of the resulting orbit from that specified in the ASTP joint documents was 820ft (250m) as against a permissible margin of 4,921ft (1,500m), while the time of the craft's arrival at a given point of the orbit differed from the rated time by 7·5 seconds as against a permissible margin of 90 seconds.

Meanwhile, 7 hours 30 minutes after the Soyuz launch, a Saturn IB rocket had carried Apollo into a 92·5 x 103·8 mile (149 x 167km) orbit with the same 51·8° inclination as that of the Soyuz orbit. An hour after Apollo orbit insertion the astronauts began a transposition and docking procedure to extract the docking module from the launch vehicle. They then carried out an evasive manoeuvre to avoid recontact with the launch vehicle and a series of phasing manoeuvres in preparation for the docking.

Minor problems that had arisen in both craft had been dealt with effectively and could in no way affect the results of the mission. The astronauts had run into trouble at one stage with their probe-and-drogue arrangement in the tunnel leading to the docking module. But this was a problem they had encountered before, during one of the moonflights, and it was soon solved. The trouble aboard Soyuz concerned the TV cameras and likewise had no lasting effect on the course of the mission. Subsequent problems aboard Apollo—a difficulty in operating the urine disposal system, a bubble of inert gas in one fuel line, and a mosquito that had hitched a ride into space—were of even less consequence.

The actual docking in orbit—51 hours 49 minutes after the Soyuz launch—was probably the most dramatic episode of the flight. It went off without a hitch and was, in fact, completed several minutes ahead of schedule. This was the crucial part of ASTP; the testing, in real spaceflight conditions, of the principles embodied in the new, compatible docking system was successful.

Another highlight of the flight was the transfer of crews, a vital element in ASTP's demonstration of a potential rescue-in-space capability. The crew transfers were in shirtsleeves, but the absence of evening dress in no way detracted from the momentous nature of the occasion. Millions of TV viewers around the world were thrilled to see the commanders of the Soviet and American spacecraft Leonov and Stafford hug each other in space.

It was during this first meeting that the Soviet leader Leonid Brezhnev sent a message to the docked spacecraft, wishing both crews a successful mission, and the United States President Gerald Ford spoke to the

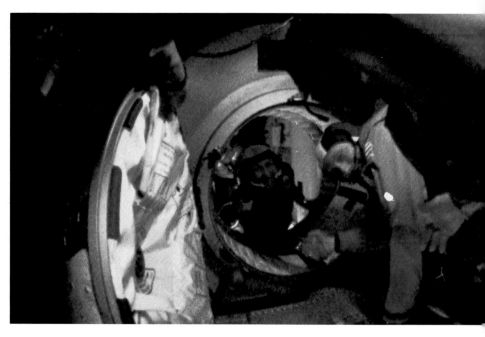

Above: *A photograph for the history books. Astronaut Stafford grasps the hand of Leonov through the tunnel of the docking module which links Apollo and Soyuz. "Glad to see you", said the smiling Russian in English.*

Above: *Valery Kubasov adds his name to the official joint certificate of the ASTP flight, as Americans and Russians orbit the Earth together. It had already been signed by Stafford, Slayton and Leonov.*

crews. The crew commanders exchanged national flags, and the Soyuz commander presented to the Apollo commander a United Nations flag.

The emotional first rendezvous was followed ten hours later by a second meeting and subsequently two further unions. All four crew transfers went off very smoothly without technical hitches. The spacemen conducted joint TV programmes and performed physical exercises together. They carried out some science demonstrations from space, and replied to questions from newsmen at the Soviet and American ASTP Press Centres.

The spirit of camaraderie at these meetings in orbit was also well illustrated by the informal exchanges between the crew members, all of whom, after the training sessions, were on friendly terms and were quite

fluent in each other's language. At one point during a joint meal aboard Soyuz, Leonov confirmed his reputation of loving practical jokes by producing a large toothpaste tube—such as the cosmonauts use for food and beverages—with the name of a popular Soviet brand of vodka on it. This, however, turned out to contain nothing but borsch!

The first undocking of the two craft was followed by a second docking, in which the roles were reversed and Soyuz was the active partner. The success of this second docking completed the verification of the androgynous docking system.

Soyuz descended from orbit and landed safely in Soviet Kazakhstan after a six-day flight. Apollo splashed down in the Atlantic three and a half days later. A malfunction during the Apollo descent caused noxious nitrogen tetroxide gas to penetrate the cabin and all but marred the successful conclusion of the flight.

Scientific Experiments

The 32 scientific experiments performed during the flight included five joint projects, all of which yielded valuable data.

In one of the experiments, the artificial solar eclipse, the Apollo craft (following the first undocking) served as an occulting disc over the Sun, while the Soyuz crew conducted observations and took pictures of the solar corona (this beautiful phenomenon cannot be observed unless the Sun's direct rays are somehow suppressed). Both cosmonauts reported beautiful coronas in the course of the experiment, although some technical difficulties created complications in carrying it out.

Another joint experiment was designated "Zone-Forming Fungi—Biorhythm", the double name referring to the biological object used in the experiment and to its main purpose. This was to study how exposure to outer space affects the rhythms of cellular activity in a living organism. The object chosen for the experiment was the *Actinomyces Levoris Kras* fungus, which rhythmically forms ring-shaped zones of sporogeneous mycelium visible to the eye.

A microbiological exchange experiment was concerned with the effects of space-

Above: *Thomas Stafford and Donald Slayton drink a toast from borsch containers over which vodka labels have been pasted. The absence of alcohol in orbit did nothing to dampen the spirit of cameraderie.*

flight upon the human immunisation system. It was conducted by analysing the quantity and types of microbes at various locations in both spacecraft, and by comparisons of skin swabs taken before, during, and after the mission from both crews. ASTP provided a unique opportunity for such tests, since the two crews came from widely divergent geographical locations and, hence, ideal initial conditions.

The ultraviolet absorption experiment was designed to measure the concentrations of atomic oxygen and nitrogen in the Earth's upper atmosphere. This was done by flashing light beams from Apollo to a Soyuz retro-reflector and back to a optical absorption spectrometer on the American spacecraft. The experiment, which was conducted after the final undocking of the two craft, failed to produce a satisfactory result the first time. However, consultations between the crews and with the Mission Control Centres helped to accomplish it successfully in the end.

Finally, the multi-purpose electric-furnace experiments demonstrated the feasibility of using the weightless space environment for studying crystallisation, convection, and miscibility processes, and their possible future applications in space. These experiments have since been continued and carried further aboard Salyut orbital stations under the Soviet national space programme.

During the stages of separated flight, the Soyuz cosmonauts carried out experiments in microbe growth, the embryonic development of fish, genetics, and astrophysics, while the Apollo astronauts did work in astrophysics, the study of the Earth and its atmosphere from space, biomedical and technological research.

ASTP Results

The Soviet-American link-up in orbit was acclaimed all over the world as both a landmark in space exploration and an important contribution to improving Soviet-

Below: *Leonov and Kubasov autograph the side of the Soyuz 19 descent capsule after landing north-east of Arkalyk in Kazakhstan on 21 July 1975. Soviet space programme officials and newsmen look on.*

Below: *The Apollo command module begins to move into an upright position as the astronauts inside inflate flotation bags. The spacecraft splashed down safely west of Hawaii after a textbook flight.*

American relations and the entire international climate. The Soviet leader Leonid Brezhnev, in a message to President Ford, expressed the hope that the joint flight would serve as the foundation for possible subsequent work in this field, and President Ford voiced the conviction that the example of the Apollo and Soyuz crews would be followed by others, and that this would contribute to science and international understanding.

The United Nations Secretary-General Kurt Waldheim welcomed the flight as a milestone in human history, an achievement made possible by close co-operation between the two countries.

Following their flight, the cosmonauts and astronauts, with their families, were given a rapturous welcome when they toured both countries.

ASTP and the equipment jointly developed for it, tested so successfully in the Soyuz-Apollo flight, could prove invaluable in future joint flight by spacecraft and stations of various countries, and in the rescue of spacecraft in difficulties.

In May 1977, when their previous space co-operation agreement expired, the Soviet Union and the United States concluded a new five-year agreement on joint activities. In it the two major space powers pledged
"To make the results of scientific research gained from the exploration and use of outer space for peaceful purposes available for the benefit of the peoples of the two countries and of all the peoples of the world."
Article 3 of the new agreement specifically calls for further co-operation in manned spaceflight
"Including the use of compatible docking and rendezvous systems derived from those developed during the experimental flight of Soyuz and Apollo spacecraft in July 1975."
Undoubtedly, the success of further co-operative efforts in this field will depend in no small measure on the general climate of USSR-US relations.

REFERENCES

1 Walter Froehlich, *Apollo Soyuz*, National Aeronautics and Space Administration, EP-109.
2 Edward Clinton Ezell and Linda Neuman Ezell. *The Partnership — A History of the Apollo-Soyuz Test Project*, NASA SP-4209.

The Space Shuttle

The advent of the reusable Space Shuttle Transportation System (SSTS) in the United States marks Part 2 of the space age. Freed from the urgency of international competition which influenced the development of the expensive Apollo-Saturn transportation system, the Shuttle is a product of a cost-benefit approach to space operations.

About the size of a DC-9 commercial airliner, the Shuttle is essentially a rocket-boosted aircraft embodying rather special technology. The system includes not only the vehicle itself but two solid-rocket boosters and a large propellant tank.

The Shuttle is launched vertically, its own liquid-fuel rocket engines firing in concert with the solid rocket boosters (SRBs). The boosters are dropped off at altitude and recovered for re-use. The space plane, called the Orbiter, continues to orbital altitude, where its propellant tank is jettisoned as the engines shut down. The tank is not recovered, the only unit of the system that is expendable.

In orbit, the vehicle is flown as a spacecraft by means of its orbital manoeuvring system (OMS) engines mounted on the aft fuselage under the delta wing. Its attitude in orbit is controlled by small thrusters.

It re-enters the atmosphere by firing its OMS rockets against the direction of flight and descends as a glider, travelling about one-fifth of the way around the planet to land horizontally on a three-mile (5km) long runway at the Kennedy Space Center.

As a glider in the atmosphere during descent, the Orbiter is the heaviest ever built, weighing 150,000lb (68,027kg). It has been designed to lift payloads weighing up to 65,000lb (29,478kg) in its 60ft (18·3m) cargo bay.

This capability enables it to carry the European Space Agency's Spacelab, a manned orbital workshop with open pallets for scientific instruments. NASA wanted the Shuttle to replace all current expendable launch vehicles (Atlas-Centaur, Delta, Titan IIIC and Titan III-Centaur) except Scout.

The Shuttle's long-range function is to serve as a transport for the development of manufacturing and large-scale commercial operations in space and the construction of a permanent space station.

Early Concepts

The concept of a rocket-boosted glider is nearly as old as that of flying machines, and its earliest expression appeared in Germany in the 1920s (see Chapter 1). A rocket craze had invaded European technical

> ## "We are entering the Shuttle era, which can bring the benefits of space back to Earth. Our challenge is to seize this opportunity and make it a reality."
>
> Senator Adlai E. Stevenson
> *On the occasion of the 10th anniversary of the first Apollo Moon landing*

Above: *The Space Shuttle Columbia stands poised for its maiden flight into space on Pad-A Launch Complex-39 at Kennedy Space Center, 9 April 1981. Note that the rotating service structure has been retracted ready for lift-off.*

societies in that period, fostering romantic notions of interplanetary travel. It was stimulated and given some credence by the widely published rocket experiments of Robert Goddard in the United States and the projections of Konstantin Tsiolkovsky in Russia and Hermann Oberth in Germany.

As a result of the Versailles Treaty, artillery and military aviation development was banned in Germany. The Army Board of

Launch Azimuths
Shuttle flights may be launched from both Kennedy Space Center, Fla., and Vandenberg AFB, Calif. From KSC (red track) payloads will be launched into equatorial orbits of 28·5° to 57° inclination; from VAFB (blue track) into polar orbits of 56° to 104° inclination. Azimuths are restricted to preclude a released tank or booster impacting on land, and also are affected by the Earth's rotation. An azimuth due east from KSC, assisted by the easterly rotation, permits a payload up to 65,000lb (29,478kg). The most westerly azimuth from VAFB permits a payload of only 32,000lb (14,512kg).

Ordnance became interested in the potential of rocket experiments by private individuals and societies.

In 1928, the racing enthusiast Max Valier experimented with a rocket motor to propel a small Opel car. In the same year another experimenter, Friedrich Stamer, flew three-quarters of a mile in a small glider which was propelled by an elastic rope and two small rockets.

In August 1929 a Junkers 33 seaplane conducted a rocket-assisted take-off at Dessau, Germany, while during the following September Fritz von Opel, the car magnate, flew a rocket-propelled glider for about 0·95 miles (1·52km) near Frankfurt-am-Main. The glider was accelerated to a speed of 95mph (153km/h) and remained in the air for 75 seconds. The propulsion system consisted of 16 solid-fuel rockets.

The mid-1930s found the rocket-experimenter, young Wernher von Braun, investigating the feasibility of aircraft rocket propulsion. As the Army Board of Ordnance, under Professor-General Karl Becker, took over rocket engine development for a ballistic missile, two rocket-powered aircraft were tested. One was the Heinkel 176, the world's first rocket-powered aeroplane designed for sustained flight.

As the more reliable, throttleable and more economic jet engine became the

standard propulsion system for aircraft, rocket-engine development was centred on missiles. Beyond the operational V-2 (A-4), the von Braun group had drawn preliminary plans for a two-stage rocket capable of crossing the Atlantic. The first stage was designated as the A-10 and the second, the A-9, was equipped with wings to extend its range. The A-9 was designed to reach New York, carrying a ton of high-explosive.

Although the transatlantic rocket was never built, the idea represented an early version of a rocket-boosted, winged vehicle. A more sophisticated and ambitious development was proposed between 1938-42 by Eugen Sänger, a Viennese engineer, and his assistant, Irene Bredt, a mathematician, whom he later married. They drafted a mathematical model of a 92ft (28m) bomber with a wing-span of 49·2ft (15m) and a gross weight of 100 tonnes including fuel, bomb load and pilot.

This vehicle was to be boosted initially by a rocket-propelled sled on tracks. Its own rocket engines would then lift it to an altitude of over 100 miles (161km) and accelerate it ultimately to a speed of 3·73 miles/sec (6km/sec).

It was theorised that the vehicle would glide back into the atmosphere at such a shallow angle that it would skip out, like a flat stone skidded over the surface of a pond. Again, it would descend; again, it would skip, each time at a lower altitude. At the fifth skip, it would have covered 7,643 miles (12,297km) from the launch site and by the ninth, 9,818 miles (15,797km).

At 24·8 miles (40km) altitude the vehicle would settle down to a continuous, descending glide. It would land at a speed of 90mph (145km/h) half-way around the world from the launch site. During one of its numerous dips, it would drop a 660lb (300kg) bomb.

The Sänger-Bredt vehicle became known as the "antipodal bomber". However, by increasing the thrust of powered flight, it could do even better—it could go entirely

Top left: *Just after 7 am EST, 12 April 1981: Space Transportation System-1 rises majestically on a column of flame carrying John Young and Robert Crippen towards space. Shock diamonds can be seen in the exhaust from the Orbiter's main engines.*

Left: *The historic moment on 14 April when Columbia gently touched down on Runway 23 at Dryden Flight Research Center, Edwards AFB. The split rudder is deployed as a speed brake; touchdown speed was an estimated 216mph (348km/h).*

The Space Shuttle

The Space Shuttle is designed to carry into orbit up to seven people. Two of these are the mission commander and pilot; the others are technical and scientific personnel known respectively as **mission specialists** and **payload specialists**.

Flying to and from space aboard the Shuttle Orbiter does not impose as great a strain on the flight crew as previous space missions. Acceleration during lift-off is limited to about 3g (three Earth gravities) and re-entry forces are normally less than 1·5g. For this reason engineers and scientists in good health—men and women—can travel with only a minimum of pre-flight training. They do not have to be experienced jet pilots like the regular astronauts. They will, of course, have undergone a full course of training in spacecraft procedures including simulation (in aircraft and water tanks) of "weightless" conditions. Initially, Orbiters remained in orbit for up to 10 days. Later, missions of 30 days' duration were anticipated.

When the spaceplane returns to Earth it has the capability of manoeuvring left or right of its entry path about 994 miles (1,600km). It touches down like a normal aircraft but without engine power at about 210mph (335 km/h).

Crew Cabin Arrangement

At launch and re-entry:
A Three extra seats (replacing sleep station) for space rescue missions.
B Airlock.
C Side hatch.
D Passenger seats (3).
1 Pilot.
2 Mission specialist.
3 Payload specialist.
4 Commander.

In orbit:
A Table.
B Horizontal sleep station.
C Vertical sleep station.
D Waste management compartment and hygiene facility.
E Side hatch.
F Galley.
G Stowage under table.
1 Pilot's seat.
2 Mission specialist at mission station.
3 On-orbit pilot.
4 Payload handlers at payload station.
5 Commander.

The Orbiter cabin is designed as a combined working, living and storage area. Seating for four crewmen is provided on the flight deck; the mid-deck has provision for 3 more crewmen. Beneath this is an equipment and stowage bay reached through an airlock.

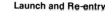
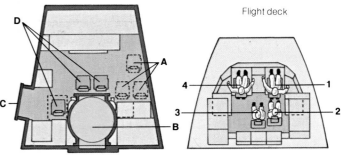

Launch and Re-entry

Mid-deck · Flight deck

In Orbit

Mid-deck · Flight deck

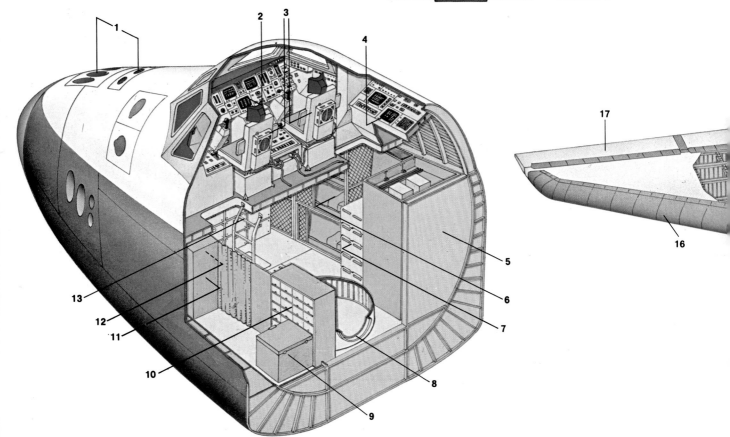

Crew Accommodation
1 Forward control thrusters.
2 Flight deck controls and displays.
3 Seats for commander (left) and pilot (right).
4 Mission station (controls and displays).
5 Avionics bay.
6 Sleep station.
7 Modular lockers.
8 Airlock base.
9 Waste management compartment (schematic: details on page 220.)
10 Avionics and stowage bay.
11 Personal hygiene station.
12 Galley with refrigerated food store, oven, eating trays, drinks, water and hand towels.
13 Access to flight deck.

Not illustrated are three passenger seats (sleep station can be exchanged for three additional seats for space rescue). Despite its reassuring aeroplane-like appearance, there is nothing ordinary about the Shuttle Orbiter. Everything about it is new from the powerful rocket engines in the tail to the external, reusable insulation that prevents the craft from being consumed by air friction when it re-enters the atmosphere at 17,600 mph (28,320km/h).

The task before its designers was to produce a spacecraft which would be reusable. When the project was approved by former President Nixon in 1972, it was estimated that the cost of putting one pound (0·45kg) into orbit could fall from around $1,000 to $100. This degree of optimism was not fulfilled in actual operation. Much depended on containing weight growth in Shuttle development (initially four vehicles were on order) and the frequency with which the Solid Rocket Boosters could be re-used. It also remained to be seen how durable the Orbiter would be in regular operation. The initial target was 100 flights with minimum refurbishment.

Technical Data (initial design, total system)
Overall length 184·2ft (56·1m).
Height: 76·6ft (23·34m).
Gross lift-off weight: 4,500,000lb (2,040,816kg).
Payload: Mission 1: 65,000lb (29,478kg) assuming orbital insertion 115 miles (185km) due east of Kennedy Space Center.
Mission 2: 25,000lb (11,340kg) assuming orbital insertion 310 miles (500km) from KSC at 55° to Equator.
Mission 3: 32,000lb (14,512kg) assuming orbital insertion 115 miles (185km) from Vandenberg AFB into near polar orbit.

Technical Data (Orbiter)
Length: 122·2ft (37·24m).
Height: 56·67ft (17·27m).
Wingspan: 78·06ft (23·79m).
Weight, landing, with payload: 188,000lb (84,260kg).
Payload: unmanned spacecraft to fully equipped scientific labs.

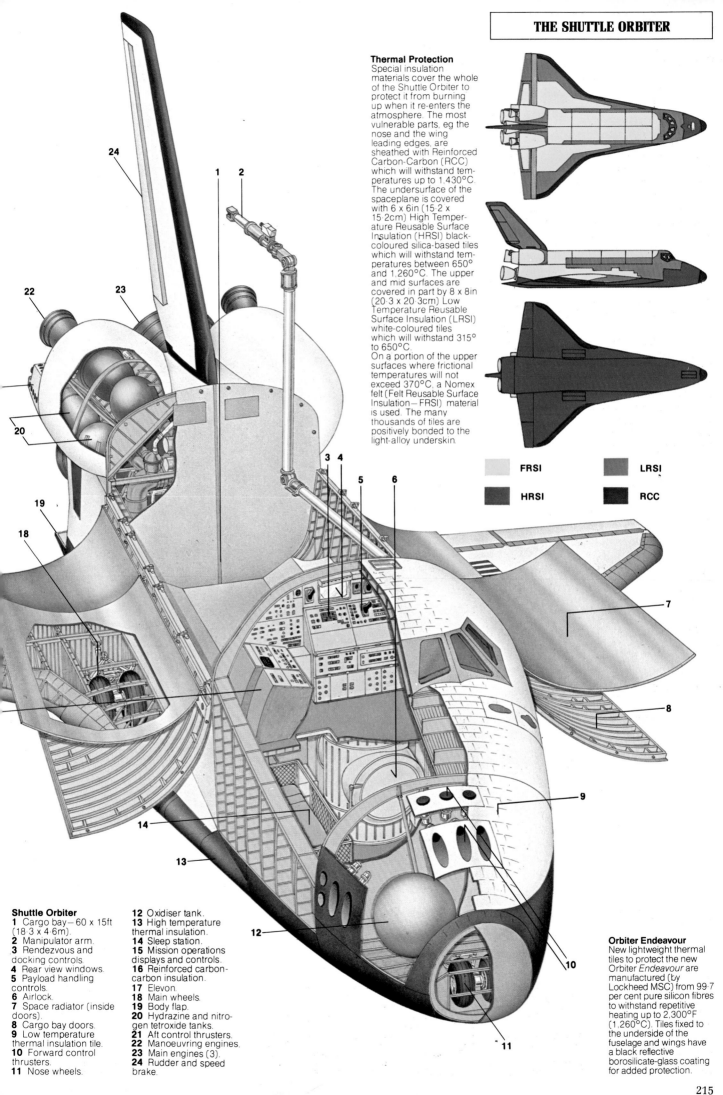

Thermal Protection

Special insulation materials cover the whole of the Shuttle Orbiter to protect it from burning up when it re-enters the atmosphere. The most vulnerable parts, eg the nose and the wing leading edges, are sheathed with Reinforced Carbon-Carbon (RCC) which will withstand temperatures up to 1,430°C. The undersurface of the spaceplane is covered with 6 x 6in (15·2 x 15·2cm) High Temperature Reusable Surface Insulation (HRSI) black-coloured silica-based tiles which will withstand temperatures between 650° and 1,260°C. The upper and mid surfaces are covered in part by 8 x 8in (20·3 x 20·3cm) Low Temperature Reusable Surface Insulation (LRSI) white-coloured tiles which will withstand 315° to 650°C.

On a portion of the upper surfaces where frictional temperatures will not exceed 370°C, a Nomex felt (Felt Reusable Surface Insulation—FRSI) material is used. The many thousands of tiles are positively bonded to the light-alloy underskin.

▢ FRSI		▨ LRSI	
▨ HRSI		■ RCC	

Shuttle Orbiter

1 Cargo bay—60 x 15ft (18·3 x 4·6m).
2 Manipulator arm.
3 Rendezvous and docking controls.
4 Rear view windows.
5 Payload handling controls.
6 Airlock.
7 Space radiator (inside doors).
8 Cargo bay doors.
9 Low temperature thermal insulation tile.
10 Forward control thrusters.
11 Nose wheels.
12 Oxidiser tank.
13 High temperature thermal insulation.
14 Sleep station.
15 Mission operations displays and controls.
16 Reinforced carbon-carbon insulation.
17 Elevon.
18 Main wheels.
19 Body flap.
20 Hydrazine and nitrogen tetroxide tanks.
21 Aft control thrusters.
22 Manoeuvring engines.
23 Main engines (3).
24 Rudder and speed brake.

Orbiter Endeavour

New lightweight thermal tiles to protect the new Orbiter *Endeavour* are manufactured (by Lockheed MSC) from 99·7 per cent pure silicon fibres to withstand repetitive heating up to 2,300°F (1,260°C). Tiles fixed to the underside of the fuselage and wings have a black reflective borosilicate-glass coating for added protection.

215

The Space Shuttle

At the Kennedy Space Center, Shuttles are to employ the same two launch complexes—LC-39A and 39B—that Apollo astronauts used when starting their journeys to the Moon. In their new role, they are much modified. For example, whereas the launch tower for the Apollo-Saturn rocket was on a mobile launch platform, the tower for the Shuttle is fixed at each pad. The Space Shuttle arrives mounted vertically on the mobile launch platform on the back of the "giant crawler" which places the complete unit over the blast pit. The space-plane itself is mounted on the side of a huge External Tank, strapped to which are two Solid Rocket Boosters. The vehicle is supported on the launch platform by four attachments on the SRBs. At the base of the platform are box-like fuelling stations for LO_2 and LH_2 which are pumped aboard the External Tank in the last hours before flight. The first Orbiters were *Columbia, Challenger, Discovery* and *Atlantis*. In 1992 *Endeavour* replaces *Challenger* which was lost in the Shuttle accident.

Flight Profile
Preparation of a Space Shuttle at the Kennedy Space Center begins in the Vehicle Assembly Building (VAB), **A**, with the assembly of the Solid Rocket Boosters (SRBs) on the mobile launch platform. Next the External Tank (ET) is assembled, **B**, followed by the Orbiter itself, **C**. The assembled vehicle is moved to the launch complex on the giant crawler, **D**. After final checkout and fuelling, the Shuttle is ready for flight. **E**: Blast off under thrust of Orbiter's three main engines and two SRBs. **F**: SRBs separate at an altitude of about 28 miles (45km) some 25.6 miles (41km) downrange 2 minutes after launch. The main engines cut off; External Tank separates, **G**, just before orbital insertion at 68 miles (109km) altitude approximately 8 minutes after launch. **H**: Orbiter is propelled into orbit by manoeuvre engines: final altitude varies according to mission. Orbital operations, **I**, — lasting 7 to 30 days, 115 to 690 miles (185 to 1,110km) altitude. **J**: Orbiter is turned to backward angle for OMS retro-fire. **K**: Retro-fire. **L**: Orbiter changes attitude to take brunt of frictional heating — wing leading edges and nose cap heat to 1,430 deg C (2,606 deg F). **M**: Terminal phase of re-entry. **N**: Glide approach to airstrip, landing at 213-226mph (343-364km/h). **O**: Systems are made safe before, **P**, removal to maintenance and checkout building. In the meantime, the SRBs, **Q**, will have been recovered after parachuting into the sea, **R**, and will be refurbished, **S**. Later, having been re-filled with solid propellant, they will assemble again on the mobile platform ready for another flight. Special facilities were built at Vandenberg AFB. California for Space Shuttle operations beginning in the mid 1980s. They were mainly to enable the U.S. Air Force to launch military satellites into near-polar orbits including large reconnaissance satellites. KSC and Vandenberg both have an airstrip for Shuttle recovery. Emergency landing strips are available at other centres. They would be used in a crisis when prompt deceleration from orbit would leave the craft out of range of its home base in the USA. After the Challenger accident in 1986 and before it could be used for launching Shuttles into polar orbits, the Vandenberg facility was "mothballed". This frustrated plans to service, repair and retrieve satellites in high-inclination orbits. Edwards AFB had already become the main recovery centre for Shuttles launched from the East Coast after limitations of the landing strip at Cape Canaveral were recognised. The Orbiter is returned to the KSC on a modified Boeing 747.

Solid Rocket Booster (SRB)
1 Drogue parachute.
2 Four separation motors of 21,680lb (9,832kg) thrust each.
3 Main parachute pack.
4 Solid rocket booster/ external tank thrust attachment.
5 Segmented motor, propellant mixture comprising an aluminium perchlorate powder (oxidiser), aluminium powder (fuel), iron oxide (catalyst) and a polymer (a binder that holds the mixture together and also acts as a fuel). Each SRB's propellant grain is shaped to reduce the thrust of the booster approximately 33% 55 seconds after lift-off to prevent overstressing the vehicle during the period of maximum dynamic pressure. The material resembles the hard rubber of a typewriter eraser.
6 Four separation motors of 22,000lb (9,977kg) thrust each.
7 Nozzle and thrust vector control system.
8 Aft skirt and launch support.
9 Solid rocket booster/ external tank attachment ring, aft avionics, tank thrust attachment and sway braces.
10 Separation avionics, operational flight instrumentation, recovery avionics, and range safety system.
11 Forward skirt.
12 Nose fairing.

Technical Data:
Length: 149.16ft (45.5m).
Diameter: 12.14ft (3.7m).
Thrust, sea level: 2,650,000lb (1,201,815kg).
Approximate gross weight: 1,293,246lb (586,506kg).
Prime contractor: Thiokol Chemical Corporation.
Two of these large motors, recoverable by parachute, fire in parallel with the SSMEs of the Orbiter to lift the Shuttle from the pad into vertical flight.

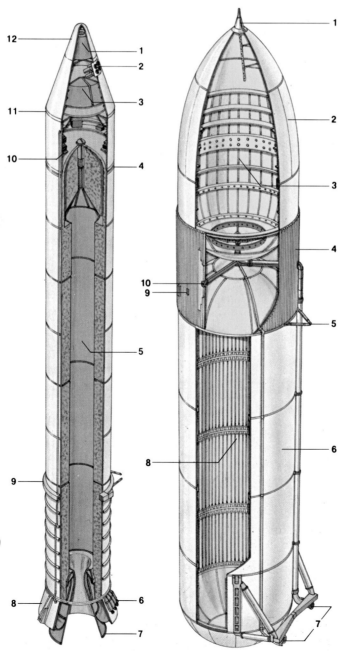

External Tank (ET)
1 LO_2 tank vent valve and fairing.
2 LO_2 tank.
3 LO_2 slosh baffles.
4 Inter-tank section.
5 Orbiter forward attachment.
6 LH_2 tank.
7 Propellant feed, pressurisation lines and electrical umbilicals.
8 Internal stringers.
9 Inter-tank umbilical plate.
10 SRB forward attachment.

The external tank contains the propellants for the Space Shuttle's main engines. Spray-on foam insulation is applied over the forward portion of the oxygen tank, the inter-tank, and the sides of the hydrogen tank. This is required to reduce ice or frost formation on the tank during launch and to minimise heat leaks into the tank which cause boiling of the liquid propellants. An ablative material—a substance that chars away—is applied to the External Tank bulges and projections to protect them from aerodynamic heating during flight through the atmosphere. Tank level sensors provide information for propellant loading and shutdown signals to the Space Shuttle Main Engine at low propellant levels.

Technical Data:
Length: 154.2ft (47m).
Diameter: 27.56ft (8.38m).
Gross lift-off weight: 1,638,873lb (743,253kg).
Inert weight: 73,874lb (33,503kg).
LO_2 nominal: 1,332,000lb (604,082kg).
LO_2 usable: 139,623gal (528,473lit).
LH_2 nominal: 224,000lb (101,587kg).
LH_2 usable: 378,378gal (1,432,161lit).
All weights approximate.
Prime contractor: Martin Marietta Aerospace.

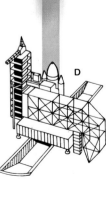

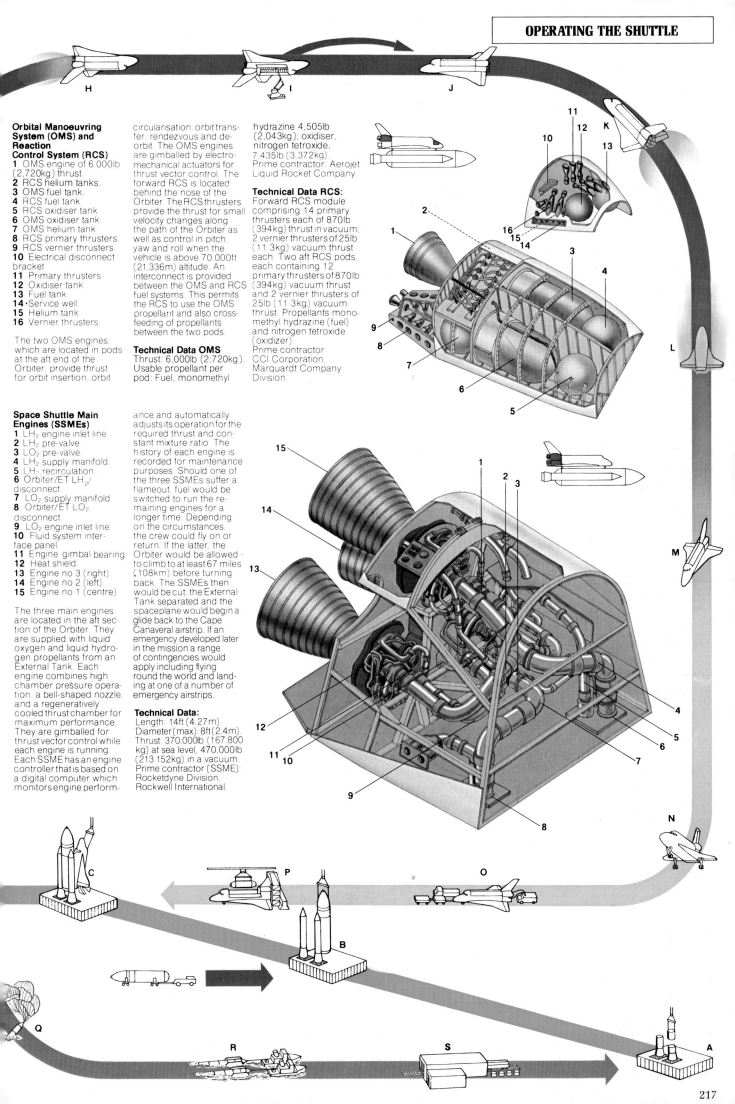

Orbital Manoeuvring System (OMS) and Reaction Control System (RCS)

1 OMS engine of 6,000lb (2,720kg) thrust.
2 RCS helium tanks.
3 OMS fuel tank.
4 RCS fuel tank.
5 RCS oxidiser tank.
6 OMS oxidiser tank.
7 OMS helium tank.
8 RCS primary thrusters.
9 RCS vernier thrusters.
10 Electrical disconnect bracket.
11 Primary thrusters.
12 Oxidiser tank.
13 Fuel tank.
14 Service well.
15 Helium tank.
16 Vernier thrusters.

The two OMS engines, which are located in pods at the aft end of the Orbiter, provide thrust for orbit insertion, orbit circularisation, orbit transfer, rendezvous and de-orbit. The OMS engines are gimballed by electro-mechanical actuators for thrust vector control. The forward RCS is located behind the nose of the Orbiter. The RCS thrusters provide the thrust for small velocity changes along the path of the Orbiter as well as control in pitch, yaw and roll when the vehicle is above 70,000ft (21,336m) altitude. An interconnect is provided between the OMS and RCS fuel systems. This permits the RCS to use the OMS propellant and also cross-feeding of propellants between the two pods.

Technical Data OMS

Thrust: 6,000lb (2,720kg). Usable propellant per pod: Fuel, monomethyl hydrazine 4,505lb (2,043kg); oxidiser, nitrogen tetroxide, 7,435lb (3,372kg). Prime contractor: Aerojet Liquid Rocket Company.

Technical Data RCS:

Forward RCS module comprising 14 primary thrusters each of 870lb (394kg) thrust in vacuum; 2 vernier thrusters of 25lb (11·3kg) vacuum thrust each. Two aft RCS pods, each containing 12 primary thrusters of 870lb (394kg) vacuum thrust and 2 vernier thrusters of 25lb (11·3kg) vacuum thrust. Propellants mono-methyl hydrazine (fuel) and nitrogen tetroxide (oxidizer). Prime contractor: CCI Corporation, Marquardt Company Division.

Space Shuttle Main Engines (SSMEs)

1 LH_2 engine inlet line.
2 LH_2 pre-valve.
3 LO_2 pre-valve.
4 LH_2 supply manifold.
5 LH_2 recirculation.
6 Orbiter/ET LH_2/ disconnect.
7 LO_2 supply manifold.
8 Orbiter/ET LO_2 disconnect.
9 LO_2 engine inlet line.
10 Fluid system interface panel.
11 Engine gimbal bearing.
12 Heat shield.
13 Engine no 3 (right).
14 Engine no 2 (left).
15 Engine no 1 (centre).

The three main engines are located in the aft section of the Orbiter. They are supplied with liquid oxygen and liquid hydrogen propellants from an External Tank. Each engine combines high chamber pressure operation, a bell-shaped nozzle, and a regeneratively cooled thrust chamber for maximum performance. They are gimballed for thrust vector control while each engine is running. Each SSME has an engine controller that is based on a digital computer which monitors engine perform-ance and automatically adjusts its operation for the required thrust and constant mixture ratio. The history of each engine is recorded for maintenance purposes. Should one of the three SSMEs suffer a flameout, fuel would be switched to run the re-maining engines for a longer time. Depending on the circumstances, the crew could fly on or return. If the latter, the Orbiter would be allowed to climb to at least 67 miles (108km) before turning back. The SSMEs then would be cut, the External Tank separated and the spaceplane would begin a glide back to the Cape Canaveral airstrip. If an emergency developed later in the mission a range of contingencies would apply including flying round the world and land-ing at one of a number of emergency airstrips.

Technical Data:

Length: 14ft (4.27m). Diameter (max): 8ft (2.4m). Thrust: 370,000lb (167,800 kg) at sea level, 470,000lb (213,152kg) in a vacuum. Prime contractor (SSME): Rocketdyne Division, Rockwell International.

around the world and land at the launch site, thus becoming an orbital bomber. A variation of this concept, in which a rocket-boosted glider plunged into the atmosphere on a trans-oceanic glide, was suggested in 1949 by Chien Hsueh-Sen at the California Institute of Technology. This approach was proposed as an idea for an intercontinental passenger rocket.

Although seized by the Allies after V-E Day, the Sänger-Bredt report was never implemented, but the Chien Hsueh-Sen variation became ancestral to a US Air Force project called Dyna Soar, an acronym for Dynamic Ascent and Soaring Flight. Later known as the X-20, Dyna Soar was a 35ft (10·7m) glider with a small, delta wing, a flat lower surface, twin vertical wing-tip fins and a rounded nose. It was to be boosted into orbit by a Titan III rocket, re-enter the atmosphere with a retro-rocket manoeuvre, and glide to a horizontal landing.

Begun in 1958, Dyna Soar was cancelled in 1963 as being unnecessary because of NASA's manned spacecraft programme. Although essentially a hypersonic glider, it became a prototype for later wingless aircraft experiments using so-called lifting bodies which have their place, also, in the evolution of the Shuttle.

The lifting-body fuselage was shaped to provide lift without wings. The omission or reduction of wing surface on a glider designed for re-entry was considered necessary to reduce frictional heating at hypersonic (ie much higher than supersonic) velocities.

Preliminary Shuttle design was influenced also by another ancestral concept proposal by Walter Dornberger and Krafft Ehricke. It was an intercontinental passenger transport consisting of two delta-winged airplanes boosted by rocket engines. The first stage, the larger of the two, was to be powered by five rocket engines and the second stage, accommodating the passengers, by three.

130 seconds after launch the stages would separate. The booster would be flown back to a landing site by its crew while the second stage continued on its journey. The second stage was to reach a maximum velocity of 8,450mph (13,596km/h) and a peak altitude of 27·5miles (44·2km). It would zoom across the Atlantic in 75 minutes.

The same basic concept was incorporated in the early design of a fully reusable Shuttle in 1969-70, but that design was altered to the earlier, rocket-boosted glider concept by federal budget constraint.

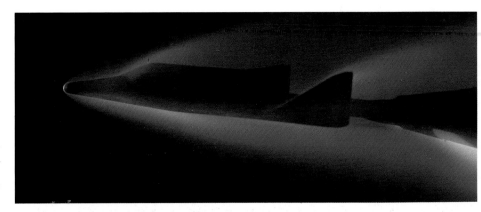

Top: *A model of the US Air Force's X-20 Dyna Soar (for "dynamic soaring") is tested in a hypersonic tunnel. This attempt at a reusable "space glider" which would utilise inherent aerodynamic qualities to glide back to base was cancelled in 1963.*

Above: *Rocket-powered vehicles used in the joint USAF/NASA Lifting Body Flight Research Program during the 1960s. Left to right: X-24A; M2F3; HL-10. Such wingless or reduced-wing craft provided valuable data for development of the Shuttle.*

Above: *X-24B, last of the lifting bodies to fly, in 1975, touches down. Compare this aircraft's long, pointed nose—designed to improve low-speed stability—with the blunt noses of the earlier vehicles shown above.*

Lifting Bodies

NASA and the US Air Force pushed along lifting-body research during the 1960s in an effort to find the optimum design for a rocket-powered aerospace plane. The Air Force launched its research with START (Spacecraft Technology and Advanced Re-entry Test) in 1961. In an advanced phase called PRIME (Precision Recovery Including Manoeuvring Re-entry), the Martin-Marietta Company built the experimental SV-5D which flew three successful tests. A

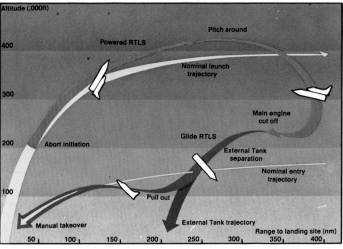

Shuttle Abort Profile
An ascent emergency during first 262 sec of flight makes orbit insertion impossible or unwise and necessitates return to launch site. Propellant is dissipated as Shuttle continues powered flight on abort trajectory (orange) until some 400 miles (644km) downrange at 400,000ft (121,920m) altitude. Then a powered manoeuvre points Shuttle back up-range and slows velocity. Main engine cut-off is followed by separation of External Tank. Orbiter has descended below nominal re-entry path and must pull-out to minimise dynamic pressure and maximise range potential to reach recovery runway.

Above: These jet- and rocket-powered aircraft of the 1940s and 50s provided experience in high-altitude flight at supersonic speeds and had a crucial influence on the Orbiter's design. In the centre is the Douglas X-3; at lower left, the Bell X-1A, flown at 1,650mph (2,655km/h). Continuing clockwise: the turbojet Douglas D-558-I "Skystreak"; Convair XF-92A; Bell X-5, with variable sweep-back wings; Douglas D-558-II "Skyrocket"; and the Northrop X-4.

aircraft, the D-558-I or Skystreak. It was a jet-engine alternative to the rocket plane.

The X-1 was air-dropped from a B-29 bomber, but the D-558-I was designed to take off from the ground. A later version, the D-558-II, was equipped with rocket engines and air-dropped from a B-29.

On 14 October 1947 Charles (Chuck) Yeager, a World War 2 fighter pilot in the European theatre, was taken aloft in the needle-nosed Bell X-1 under a B-29 to an altitude of 37,000ft (11,277m). The X-1 was dropped over Rogers Dry Lake, in the Mojave Desert in California. It was the first manned aircraft to exceed Mach 1, the speed of sound. (Thirty years later, the Space Shuttle-Orbiter *Enterprise* completed its test glides on that same lake runway after being released from a Boeing 747.)

The follow-on rocket plane, the X-2, was designed to go higher and faster than the X-1. It tested a new nickel stainless-steel alloy (monel-K) for heat resistance. On 7 September 1956 Capt Iven C. Kincheloe drove the X-2 to 126,000ft (35,403m). The "X" series of experiment vehicles included the X-1A, the X-1E, the X-3, the X-4, the X-5 and XF-92A.

The next long step in rocket aircraft was the X-15, three of which were built by North American Aviation. It made its first free flight in 1959 after being released from under the wing of a B-52 bomber. By June

Above: Shortly before the end of a ten-year programme (1959-68) during which it set a speed record of Mach 6·7 (7,274km/h), the North American X-15 rocket plane is poised for launch from a B-52.

more advanced phase of START was a piloted vehicle, the X-24, designed to be launched from a converted B-52 bomber at 45,000ft (13,715m). The X-24A (1969-71) flew at 1,000mph (1,609km/h) and reached 71,000ft (21,640m). Later, the same craft was converted to a delta configuration.

NASA's programme began with the Northrop Company's M2F1 lifting body in 1963 and continued through the M2F2 in 1966-67 and another lifting body design, the HL-10, which had a cockpit in the nose. Both

vehicles were designed for rocket power.

Although lifting-body designs were considered for the Shuttle-Orbiter, they were set aside in favour of the delta wing which provided greater cross-range capability. The re-entry heating problem was solved by the development of ceramic and carbon-carbon heat-shielding for the leading edges, and for the nose of the Orbiter.

Gathering Experience

In the United States, the concept of rocket powered aircraft was first realised in the X-1, manufactured by the Bell Aircraft Company for the Army Air Corps, later the Air Force. Concurrently, the Navy Bureau of Aeronautics contracted with the Douglas Aircraft Company for a turbojet, transonic

Above: Attitude control thrusters were fitted in the nose and wing tips of the X-15, as it was designed to fly at altitudes at which control by rudder, elevators and ailerons would be impossible.

1962 it had reached 250,000ft (76,196m) altitude and by August 1963, 354,000ft (107,894m). It reached a speed of Mach 6·7 before the programme ended in October 1968 on the 199th flight.

A major contribution of the X-series of rocket planes to the Shuttle was experience in high-altitude flight at supersonic speed. The performance of the X-15 at high mach numbers has been deemed predictive of the Orbiter's performance. The X-vehicles had a crucial influence on the Orbiter's design.

The MOL Project

Although manned spaceflight was pre-empted by NASA, the US Air Force resumed its effort to establish a manned space programme with a project called Gemini-B/MOL (Manned Orbiting Laboratory). Gemini was the two-seater spacecraft developed for and flown by NASA in the mid-1960s in preparation for the Apollo lunar missions. It was boosted into orbit by a Titan II launcher.

The Air Force project proposed modifying the Gemini spacecraft and launching it with a Titan II as a shuttle for the MOL vehicle which would be launched separately.

NASA experimented with the feasibility of a land recovery of Gemini by means of a paraglider wing instead of using the Mercury-style parachute descent into the sea. The wing, initially developed by Francis M. Rogallo of NASA's Langley Research Center, would be deployed from a canister after re-entry. A long series of tests failed to yield encouraging results, however, and the scheme was dropped. (Hang-gliding enthusiasts, however, adapted the Rogallo wing as the basis of their activities.) Gemini craft descended by parachute into the sea, as did the later Apollo vehicles.

The Air Force considered the paraglider wing for Gemini-B/MOL, but abandoned it when NASA did. Although the Gemini-B/MOL project looked promising, it was shelved by the Air Force in 1969 for lack of urgency and funding, as the X-20 had been. It also seemed to some critics to be redundant in view of NASA's upcoming Skylab.

Although the Gemini-B/MOL scheme was not carried any further by the United States, the concept was developed by the Soviet Union with the Salyut space station and the Soyuz spacecraft. This programme continues as the main Soviet manned space effort.

The inability of the Air Force to bring to fruition two manned space flight programmes after a considerable amount of research and development reflected a general attitude in Washington that manned space activity should remain a civilian enterprise. In Mercury, Gemini and Apollo, civilian direction prevailed and all the flights were strictly non-military in character and objectives.

With the advent of the Shuttle, however, the Air Force entered a limited partnership with NASA in the use of the vehicle, and about one-third of all projected Shuttle missions will be military ones. The arrangement by which military and civilian agencies would share transport facilities to and from space appeared early in 1969 when President Nixon appointed a NASA Space Task Group and Department of Defense chiefs to plan a post-Apollo programme. Although the lunar landings were just ahead, it was already apparent to planners that the Apollo-Saturn system based on expendable launchers and vehicles was too costly to be continued after the lunar-landing objective was achieved.

The Task Group concluded that the only reasonable way to run a manned space programme was to develop a reusable transport system. Vehicles that could fly up to 100 missions before complete overhaul could cut the cost of space operations by several orders of magnitude. As one NASA official suggested, the expense of orbiting a payload might be reduced from $1,000 a pound to $20 a pound with a fully reusable system.

Left: *The original NASA Space Shuttle concept of 1968. Large-capacity, V-shaped drop tanks (not shown), forming the nose and sides of the vehicle at lift-off, were to be jettisoned on the way to orbit.*

Right: *Before settling on a final design for the present Space Shuttle, a full review was made of all possible booster systems. This one retains the concept of a winged booster, but in a simpler form.*

Below: *NASA concept of 1970. At an altitude of c50 miles (80km) the Orbiter fires its engines and separates from the booster, which returns to Earth. Later designs adopted a delta-wing configuration.*

Looking into the 21st century, the Space Task Group proposed a space transportation system of interplanetary scope. It would consist of a ground-to-orbit Shuttle; a chemically fuelled, reusable tug to move payloads about in space once they were delivered by the Shuttle; a nuclear-powered transfer stage that could move payloads, including manned vehicles, between lunar and planetary orbits; landing modules for shuttling passengers and cargoes from orbit to lunar and planetary surfaces and the establishment of large, permanent space stations in Earth and lunar orbits.

By combining several elements of this system, interplanetary voyages could be made. The Task Group recommended that a manned mission to Mars be one of the goals of the new system, some time in the 1980s. Fiscal constraints restricted subsequent implementation of this ambitious programme to the Shuttle which, as a result of technical problems, did not make its first orbital flight test until early 1981.

Planning The Shuttle

In April 1969 a Space Shuttle Task Group was formed at NASA. In Phase A, the con-

Waste Management
1 Contoured urinal on flexible hose (may be used in standing or seated position).
2 Seat.
3 Hinged slinger tines.
4 Tissues.
5 Motor (operational speed: 1500rpm).
6 Ballast airflow.
7 Debris filter.
8 Faeces (accelerated onto commode walls).
9 Gate valve.

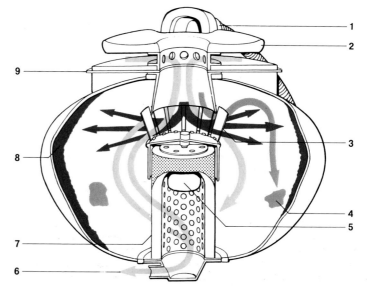

The waste management system collects and processes liquids (urine, washing water, sweat, lung vapour, liquid from galley and EMU) and solid waste (faeces, vomit and tissues) in zero gravity. Solids are collected in the commode illustrated; they are drawn in by airflow. Pulling the gate valve control activates the slinger motor causing the hinged tines to rotate and so unfold. These shred the faeces and deposit it thinly on the commode walls. Tissues move over the slinger and settle at the bottom. The air passes through filters to fan separators. If a slower motor speed is selected, the tines do not unfold, so allowing a faecal/vomit bag to enter the storage area unobstructed. Storage capacity for vacuum-dried faeces and tissues equals 210 crew-member days, an average usage resulting in 0.27lb (0.12kg) of faecal and paper waste. It may be use up to 4 times an hour.

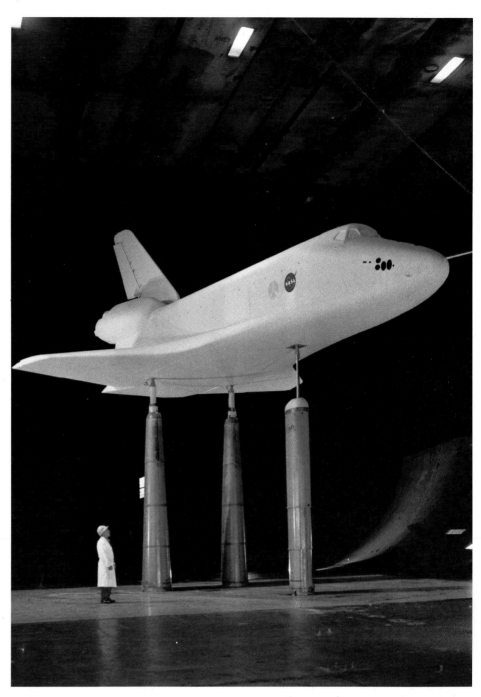

Above: *When the Orbiter encounters the upper atmosphere on re-entry, friction will subject it to searing heat of around 1,260°C in the hottest spots—the nose and the leading edges of the wings. These critical areas are protected up to 1,430°C by reinforced carbon-carbon material.*

Above: *A ⅓ scale model of the Space Shuttle Orbiter in Ames Research Center's 40 x 80ft (12·2 x 24·4m) wind tunnel. The object of these experiments was to confirm the Orbiter's aerodynamic qualities at low speeds, including the glide approach to the recovery runway and landing.*

ceptual stage of developing the project, it was concluded that the system should consist of two rocket-powered aircraft: a Booster and an Orbiter. The Orbiter was to be capable of operating in a 300-mile (483km) orbit and of returning to land horizontally on a runway like a conventional aircraft.

Both stages, coupled together, would be launched vertically, propelled by throttleable, high-performance, oxygen-hydrogen engines. At altitude, the two would be separated. The Booster crew would fly back to base while the Orbiter craft would continue powered flight into orbit, where it would function as a spacecraft.

The Orbiter payload maximum was 25,000lb (11,338kg) carried in an aft cargo bay. Forward, pressurised cabin compartments would accommodate 12 passengers and two crewmen.

The Phase A plan was studied by a dozen aerospace companies. Following a preliminary review in August 1969 NASA held a symposium on shuttle design at the Smithsonian Museum of Natural History auditorium in Washington on 16-17 October 1969, where 30 papers were presented on vehicle configuration, engine design and related technology. In addition to major American aerospace firms and government laboratories, British, French and West German aerospace interests were represented.

Although straight wing and lifting-body designs were considered, a delta-wing con-

figuration was adopted for the Orbiter (as well as for the Booster) for greater stability and cross-range. The Orbiter as well as the Booster vehicle would carry turbojet engines for manoeuvring in the atmosphere.

Early in 1970 NASA released an artist's impression of its new, winged spaceship, as it appeared from the preliminary Phase B study. Both stages were large, the Booster about the size of the Boeing 747 Jumbo jet and the Orbiter comparable with a Boeing 707 transport. Their size was dictated by internal propellant tanks for the rocket engines as well as tanks for the turbojet engines.

In all respects, this preliminary Phase B shuttle was fully reusable, but although it promised a minimal cost per flight it had the highest development cost of all designs considered. Studies had shown that operating costs were inversely proportional to development costs using expendable hardware.

Because national budget policy restricted development cost of the Shuttle to about $5,150 million, expendable hardware substitutions had to be made to save the project. NASA considered several compromises. One was an expendable, external propellant tank. With this concession, a smaller Orbiter was feasible. Further development cost-reduction could be achieved by eliminating the fly-back Booster vehicle and substituting booster rockets, and solid-propellant boosters were cheaper than those employing liquid fuels.

When these compromises were adopted at the end of 1971 to enable the programme to fit the Procrustean bed of the Office of Management and Budget, the US Government's budget monitor, the Shuttle Transportation System emerged in final Phase B studies as a rocket-boosted glider. For a while, the Orbiter retained its turbojet engines (at great penalty to payload) to give it a "go around" capability to ensure safe landing. Eventually, these engines came off, along with a crew launch escape system.

There were gains as well as losses as a result of these design changes. The cargo lifting capability of the Shuttle was more than doubled, reaching 65,000lb (29,478kg) at launch. Return cargo weight maximum increased to 32,000lb (14,512kg).

With the increase in launch and return cargo weight, it became feasible to fly a fully equipped space laboratory in the Orbiter's 60ft (18·3m) cargo bay. Thus the way was opened for Europe's Spacelab to become the Shuttle's largest and most important payload.

The Shuttle System

The three-element Shuttle consisting of Orbiter, rocket boosters and a disposable propellant-tank was approved by President Nixon on 5 January 1972. A debate whether liquid or solid propellant boosters would be preferable was settled on 15 March 1972 in favour of twin, solid-propellant rocket motors that would be recovered at sea after being jettisoned at altitude and reused. NASA envisaged a programme of 570 Shuttle flights in the 1980s and 1990s. The Space Division of North American Rockwell Corporation (now Rockwell International) was selected as prime contractor for the Orbiter at an estimated cost of $2,600 million over six years. A separate main engine contract had been awarded earlier to Rocketdyne, a Rockwell subsidiary. Chosen to build the solid rocket booster were Thiokol Chemical Corporation for the engines; McDonnell Douglas Astronautics, structures; and United Space Boosters for checkout, assembly, launch and refurbishment. Martin Marietta received the contract to build the huge external propellant tank.

As approved finally for development, the Space Shuttle Transportation System was pictured as an aircraft-like vehicle 122·2ft (37·24m) long with a delta-shaped wing 78·06ft (23·79m) across, a cargo bay 60ft (18·3m) long and 15ft (4·57m) wide and a tall, vertical fin and rudder with movable flaps to serve as speed-brakes.

The Orbiter is dwarfed by the SRBs 149·16ft (45·46m) tall and 12·14ft (3·7m) in diameter and by the 154·2ft (47m) external tank which is 27·56ft (8·38m) in diameter. The SRBs are mounted on each side of the tank, flanking the Orbiter in vertical launch position. Auxiliary solid rockets can be added or strapped on to provide additional boost for extra-heavy payloads.

Above: *Static firing tests are made of the Space Shuttle Solid Rocket Booster in February 1979. During this two-minute firing, thrust level reached a peak of around 2,900,000lb (1,315,193kg).*

Above right: *Forward Reaction Control System is installed in Columbia, December 1979. RCS modules—one forward, with 16 small thrusters; two aft, each with 14 thrusters—provide attitude control.*

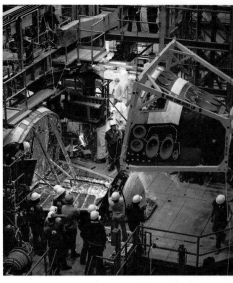

Right: *The flight article of the Remote Manipulator System arm, which is used to deploy articles from the Orbiter's cargo bay, lies on an air bearing floor at the SPAR facility, Toronto, Canada.*

With the indefinite postponement of the space station, the space tug and other elements of the Space Task Group's 1969 blueprint, the Shuttle was being developed as an all-purpose transport with no place in particular to go. It had been thought of primarily as a means of ferrying personnel and supplies to a space station; since no space station had been provided, nor was funded, the Shuttle's job had to be redefined.

NASA spokesmen lost no time in justifying the system as a partially reusable replacement for NASA's stable of major launch vehicles, all expendable. But inasmuch as the Shuttle is confined to orbits ranging from 115 to 690 miles (185km to 1,110km), it cannot accomplish all the work of the Atlas-Centaur, Delta or Titan III expendable launchers because it cannot reach synchronous orbit at 22,300 miles (35,880km) altitude. To emplace communications, meteorological or scientific satellites in such an orbit, an upper stage is needed.

In the Space Task Group prospectus, that task was allocated to the chemical-powered space tug. But its development was not authorised. Consequently, several alternatives were being studied. The Department of Defense expected to use an Inertial Upper Stage (IUS) for military missions requiring synchronous or very high orbits.

NASA commenced, then halted, development of a radio-controlled stage called the teleoperator retrieval system (TRS), originally designed to be docked with Skylab as a booster on its second orbital test flight. The TRS was postponed when Shuttle development delays ruled out any possibility of reaching Skylab soon enough to boost it to a safe orbit or control its plunge.

Several aerospace firms agreed with NASA to manufacture spinning solid-fuel upper stages (SSUSs) as a commercial venture for specific payload missions. All of these upper-stage devices would be carried into low Earth orbit with their satellite payloads in

Above: *Roll-out ceremony marks delivery to NASA by Martin Marietta of the first external fuel tank for the Shuttle, 9 September 1977. The giant tank will hold up to 440,000 Imperial gallons (2,000,000lit) of propellant.*

Above: *In the Vehicle Assembly Building, Orbiter Enterprise is about to be lowered for mating with the external fuel tank and its two solid rocket boosters, before transportation to the launch pad, May 1979.*

Below: *The Inertial Upper Stage booster incorporates two solid-fuel rocket motors, an interstage structure and an avionics module. It may place loads of up to about 5,000lb (2,270kg) in geostationary orbit.*

the Shuttle cargo bay, from which they would be deployed by a manipulator arm operated by remote-control from the cabin. They differ from the reusable space tug in that they are expendable and thus would be more costly to use over the years.

Spacelab

Beyond its function as a space truck, replacing expendable launchers, the Shuttle was projected by NASA and industry planners as a means of establishing industrial operations in space. Experiments on Apollo lunar flights, the 1975 Apollo-Soyuz Test Project and on Skylab had shown that the zero-gravity conditions in space provided an advantageous industrial environment for

precision manufacturing. Among the processes that could benefit were growth of high-purity crystals for electronic components, the creation of superior strength metal alloys and the manufacture of purer pharmaceuticals, such as vaccines.

The industrial potential suggested by Apollo and Skylab experiments could hardly be realised without a workshop. Budget limitation did not allow NASA to develop such a facility. NASA turned to Western Europe where, as a result of NASA proposals, a consortium of ten nations agreed to develop a laboratory complex—Spacelab.

Spacelab was designed to fit into the Orbiter cargo bay and meet weight limitations. Initially, it would be captive, but later could become a free-flyer and remain in orbit between Shuttle flights.

A Memorandum of Understanding was signed on 14 August 1973 by NASA and the European Space Agency (ESA) representing the consortium. It provided for the development of Spacelab at an initial cost of 340 million ESA accounting units—about $500 million at that time.

Spacelab is a two-element system. One element is a pressurised, cylindrical workshop or module. The other is open pallets on which arrays of scientific instruments can be mounted.

The pressurised module consists of two segments, each 8·85ft (2·7m) long and 13·32ft (4·06m) in diameter. One segment, the core, contains life-support equipment, data-processing apparatus and some working space. The other is a complete laboratory-workshop. Flown together, the two segments make up a laboratory module 22·6ft (6·9m) long with end domes attached. The core segment can be flown separately.

Below: *Technicians work on prototype equipment in the laboratory module of ESA's Spacelab. In space, three scientists are able to work in the pressurised laboratory in "shirt-sleeve" conditions.*

Above: *Spacelab's segmented pallets, seen here, form an open "porch" for the orbiting laboratory, exposing large instruments directly to space and accommodating experiments controlled from the laboratory module, Orbiter flight deck, or the ground.*

The pallets are also constructed in segments 9·5ft (2·9m) long. Up to five can be fitted in the cargo bay and combinations of modules and pallets can be flown. Spacelab I, the first Shuttle and Spacelab mission, carried a workshop module and one pallet segment. Although planned for the second half of 1982, first flight was eventually achieved in November 1983 because of delays in developing the Shuttle. Spacelab flights typically carry six crew: commander, pilot, two mission specialists with astronaut training, and two payload specialists who are scientists with limited astronaut training.

ESA members initially contributing to Spacelab were Austria, Belgium, Denmark, France, West Germany, Italy, Netherlands, Spain, Switzerland and the United Kingdom. The West German firm of VFW-Fokker/ERNO, Bremen, was selected as prime contractor, Germany having put up the greatest share of the money. Programme management was centralised in the European Space Research and Technology Centre (ESTEC) at Noordwijk, Netherlands.

On early Shuttle and Spacelab missions, mission specialists were scientist-astronauts who had been members of the astronaut corps for years. A new crop of Shuttle astronauts commenced training in 1978. Thirty-five, including six women, were selected from among 8,000 applicants. They eventually replaced older astronauts as pilots and mission specialists. The re-selection procedure continues.

Enterprise and Columbia

Testing of the first Orbiter, dubbed *Enterprise* at the behest of fans of the science-fiction television series *Star Trek*, began at NASA's Dryden Flight Research Center at Edwards AFB in February 1977.

The tests were designed to assess the Orbiter's systems and flight characteristics in the lower atmosphere. The series began with taxi tests. The Orbiter was mounted, piggy-back, atop a Boeing 747 jet transport.

Next, a sequence of unmanned then manned captive flight tests was conducted, with the Orbiter firmly attached to the 747 through take-off and landing. The action of the Orbiter's aerodynamic controls—elevons on the wings, body flap on the fuselage and speed brakes on the higher rudder—were carefully checked.

Manned free-flight tests began on 12 August 1977, when astronauts Fred W. Haise and C. Gordon Fullerton flew the 75-ton glider around a U-shaped course to a flawless landing after it had separated from the 747 at 22,800ft (6,950m). Haise and Fullerton said the quick responses of the Orbiter surprised them. It handled like a fighter aircraft.

Four more free-flight tests confirmed the

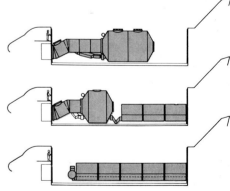

Flight Configurations
Typical Spacelab flight configurations in cargo bay. **(Top)** Extended pressurised module, 17·6ft (5·4m) long, connected to Orbiter's crew compartment by 15ft (4·6m) flexible tunnel, occupies more than half of 60ft (18·3m) long bay. Large instruments or antennas may be housed in vacant area. **(Centre)** Basic pressurised module, some 8·85ft (2·7m) long, and flexible tunnel in first half of bay. Module connected by power lines to three pallet segments constituting a 29·25ft (8·9m) platform to accommodate equipment and experiments. **(Bottom)** Without a module, bay holds up to five joined pallets, supporting close on 12,000lb (5,443kg) of equipment and experiments. Note circular "igloo" at head of line of pallets: a pressurised, temperature-controlled housing for essential services for the experiments, such as computers and a power distribution box.

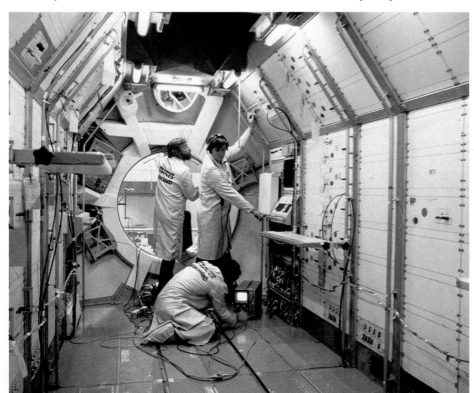

findings of the first—the Orbiter performed as wind tunnel tests predicted in the lower atmosphere. How it would handle in the high atmosphere at hypersonic velocity only an orbital test-flight would tell. The approach and landing tests at Edwards ended on 26 October 1977.

Orbiter *Enterprise* was then flown atop its 747 carrier to the Marshall Space Flight Center, Huntsville, Alabama for eight months of structural vibration test. Pronounced structurally flight-worthy, the vehicle was ferried by the 747 to the Kennedy Space Center on 10 April 1979, where it was fated to serve as a test bed for later models.

On 1 May 1979, *Enterprise* was rolled out of the vehicle assembly building mated to the external tank and solid rocket boosters on a mobile launch platform. Weighing more than 11 million pounds, the assembled Shuttle and platform were carried three and a half miles (5·6km) to Pad A of Launch Complex-39 on a 2,700-ton, diesel-electric transporter. The ponderous vehicle, developed to

Above: *Enterprise separates from its Boeing 747 carrier for Approach and Landing Test, 12 October 1977. Note support assemblies atop the 747's fuselage and the 200ft² (18·6m²) vertical fins added to its tail assembly to improve directional stability.*

carry the fully assembled Saturn-Apollo rockets to the pad, was adapted for the Shuttle—as were the two launching pads themselves.

Enterprise was deposited on the pad in launch position. There it remained for thousands of sightseers to admire—a squat, broad-winged, fat-bodied bird nesting amid the tall propellant tank and rocket boosters. The transport exercise was carried out to test clearances, especially in the remodelled Vehicle Assembly Building (VAB), for the later transfer of the *Columbia*—Orbiter 102 —which was launched on the first orbital flight test of the Shuttle in April 1981.

Columbia arrived on 24 March 1979 aboard the 747 ferry from California. It had been

Below: *In December 1977, ESA presents candidates for the job of payload specialist on the first Spacelab mission. Left to right: Franco Malerba (Italy); Ulf Merbold (West Germany); Wubbo Ockels (Netherlands); Claude Nicollier (Switzerland).*

Spacelab
1 Instrument pointing system (eg telescope).
2 Barium canisters.
3 Boom extension system (eg supporting magneto-meters for geological survey of Earth).
4 Electron accelerator.
5 Lidar system (radar probing of little-known regions of the atmosphere between 22-74 miles [35-120km] above Earth).
6 Instrument pallets 9·5ft (2·9m) long x 13·32ft (4·06m) wide.
7 Deployable units.
8 Transmitter/coupler system.
9 Controls, displays and data processing.
10 Access tunnel.
11 Pressurised laboratory twin segment illustrated: each segment 8·85ft

(2·7m) long x 13·32ft (4·06m) diameter.
12 Optical window and scientific airlock.

Spacelab is a separate contribution to the NASA Space Transportation

System programme by the European Space Agency. Weight, max. 25,005lb (11,340kg) including experiments. Represented here is an Atmospheric and Space Physics payload.

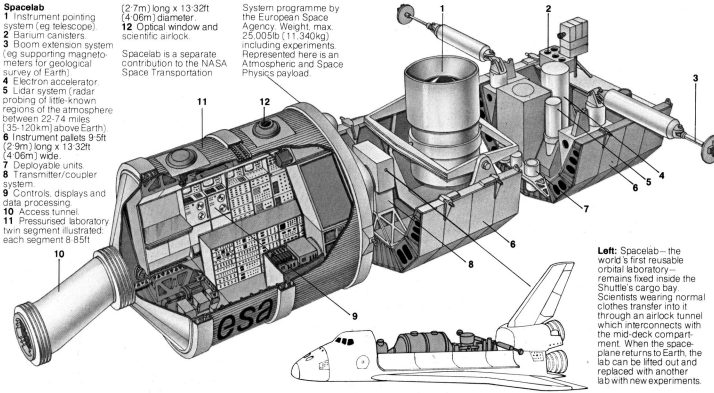

Left: *Spacelab—the world's first reusable orbital laboratory— remains fixed inside the Shuttle's cargo bay. Scientists wearing normal clothes transfer into it through an airlock tunnel which interconnects with the mid-deck compartment. When the space-plane returns to Earth, the lab can be lifted out and replaced with another lab with new experiments.*

rolled into the newly completed Orbiter processing facility to be prepared for launch. The main preparatory tasks were installation of the three rocket engines in the tail and completion of installing the thermal protection system, which had been partially done at the factory.

The thermal protection system (heat shielding) consists mainly of 30,922 individually shaped silica fibre tiles, roughly 6in (15·2cm) and 8in (20·3cm) square, glued on the upper and lower surfaces. The nose cap and wing leading edges, subjected to higher temperatures, are shielded by carbon-carbon. Felt Nomex insulation is applied to protect the cargo-bay doors, lower aft fuselage and upper aft wing areas. Each tile is specially contoured to match the exact shape of the Orbiter. After they were attached to strain isolator pads on *Columbia*'s light alloy skin, they were pull-tested to see if the bonding was up to strength. The tiles that failed this test had to be replaced with tiles which had undergone a densification process which increased the strength of the bonded surface by a factor of two to four. The surface glued to a Nomex felt isolator attached to the Orbiter's light-alloy skin was treated with a silica ammonia slurry, then baked twice for 24 hours. About 4,500 tiles underwent this densification process.

The densified tiles when bonded with Room Temperature Vulcaniser (RTV) to the isolator pad, explained Rockwell, "literally can't be pulled off". However, the process of testing the tiles added months to *Columbia*'s already extended schedule.

The three hydrogen-oxygen rocket engines, rated at 470,000lb (213,152kg) of thrust in vacuum, were previously the pacing items for the Shuttle. Difficulties in their development had caused nearly two years' delay in the launch schedule. Designed to run at the highest chamber pressure and specific impulse of any system known to NASA, the engines are throttleable between 50 and 109 per cent of their rated thrust.

In building a more powerful rocket engine, Rocketdyne had encountered many of the problems of developing a new one, although the technology was 15 years old. Engine problems and delays have escalated costs

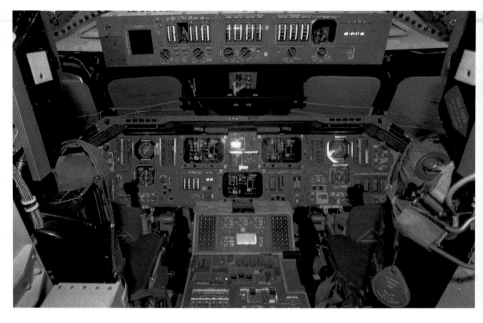

Above: *Columbia's flight deck. Commander's seat left, separated by flight computer and navigation aids console from pilot's seat. Rotational hand controllers to fly the vehicle are in front of each seat. Cathode ray tubes display computer information.*

Below: *Some of the Orbiter's thermal protective tiles are wired to onboard sensors which measure temperatures and pressures during the mission. Here, a technician prepares a cavity for bonding of an instrumented tile on Columbia.*

and delayed the entire proposed Shuttle-Spacelab timetable.

When it was authorised in 1972, the Shuttle was scheduled to make its first manned orbital test flight (FMOF) in March 1978. A series of engine and heat shield problems dogged the programme, but in early 1981 NASA was able to confirm a launch date of 10 April. However, at T-20 minutes on that day a 40-millisecond "time skew" between the four primary computers and the backup prevented communication between the systems and caused yet another launch delay. The problem was swiftly diagnosed and overcome, and at 7.00.03.98am EST on 12 April *Columbia* rose from Launch Complex-39A at KSC riding a combined thrust of nearly 6·5 million lb (2·95 million kg) generated by the three main engines and two SRBs. The booster and External Tank sep-

Main Engine
1 Low pressure fuel turbopump.
2 High pressure fuel turbopump.
3 Main fuel valve.
4 Coolant control valve.
5 Nozzle tubes.
6 Main combustion chamber.
7 Preburner valve.
8 Preburner.
9 Hot gas manifold.
10 Main injector.
11 Low pressure oxidiser turbopump.
12 High pressure oxidiser turbopump.
13 Main oxidiser valve.
14 Preburner valve.
15 Preburner.

The flow of liquid hydrogen (fuel) and liquid oxygen (oxidiser) from the Shuttle's External Tank is restrained by prevalves located in the Orbiter above the low pressure turbopumps. Before firing, prevalves are opened and propellants flow through low pressure and high pressure turbopumps to

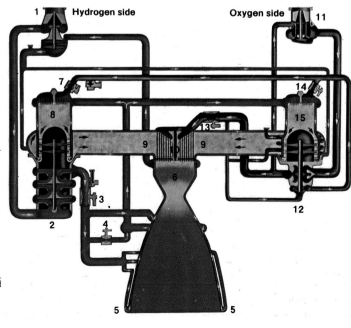

the main propellant valves. On the liquid oxygen side, the system fills to preburner valves. Cryogenic propellants are held in ducts long enough to chill the engine and attain liquid condition in their respective systems. In start sequence, hydrogen and oxygen sides act near-simultaneously.

Hydrogen side: Main fuel valve opens and allows hydrogen to flow into coolant loop, through nozzle tubes, and through channels in main combustion chamber. Part of coolant loop flow is diverted by coolant control valve for combustion and cooling of preburner walls; another part, warmed to near-ambient conditions, is tapped off at main combustion chamber and routed back to drive turbine of low pressure turbopump.

Oxygen side: Main oxidiser valve opens and liquid

oxygen flows through two turbo-pumps to the main injector and, through preburner valves, to the preburners. Oxygen tapped off downstream of high pressure oxidiser turbopump goes to drive turbine of low pressure pump.

Combustion: Initiated by spark igniters in domes of preburners and in main chamber. Operating at mixture ratios less than one part oxygen to hydrogen, the preburners produce hydrogen-rich steam which drives the two high pressure pump turbines before entering the hot gas manifold. There, it is transferred from the turbines to the main injector and mixed with additional liquid oxygen from the high pressure oxidiser turbopump for combustion. The combustion process is completed at a mixture ratio of six parts of oxygen to one part hydrogen.

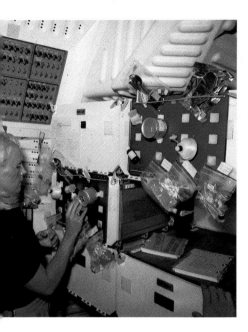

Above: *Scientist-astronaut Rhea Seddon, at work in a mock-up of the Shuttle's galley, uses Velcro and springs to attach articles to food trays. The first US woman in space was Sally Ride, who flew on STS-7, a Challenger mission, in June 1983.*

arations went without a hitch—(the SRBs being recovered in good condition about 151 miles [243km] downrange)—and the OMS functioned smoothly to place the Orbiter in a 150 miles (241.3km) circular orbit.

Columbia commander John W. Young and pilot Capt Robert L. Crippen were enthusiastic about the spacecraft's orbital performance, and the only serious flaw in the programme was the discovery after the deployment of the payload bay doors and radiators that portions of the tiles on the rear OMS pods were missing. Nevertheless, after careful scrutiny NASA officials were confident that the gaps were not in critical areas likely to experience very high temperatures during the re-entry phase. In the event their confidence was justified as *Columbia* made a safe re-entry on 14 April, flying from Mach 25 orbital velocity through a 5,064 mile (8,148km) glide to a perfect touchdown on Runway 23, Rogers Dry Lake, Edwards AFB, California just 54 hours 22 minutes after lift-off.

The first four flights of *Columbia* were research and development missions flown by two-man crews. Air Force style ejection seats were provided on the flight deck and then removed after the Shuttle was declared operational at the conclusion of the fourth flight, STS-4, in 1982.

Following STS-1, the test flights were STS-2, 12-14 November 1981 with Joseph H. Engle, commander, and Richard H. Truly, pilot; STS-3, 22-30 March 1982 with Jack R. Lousma, commander, and Charles G. Fullerton, pilot; and STS-4 27 June-4 July 1982 with Thomas K. Mattingly, commander, and Henry W. Hartsfield, pilot.

Three more Orbiters were added to the Space Shuttle Transportation System: *Challenger* in 1983, *Discovery* in 1984 and *Atlantis* in 1985. From 12 April 1981 to 28 January 1986, the Shuttle flew 24 consecutive successful missions: two in 1981, three in 1982, four in 1983, five in 1984, nine in 1985

Above: *Designed by Martin Marietta to assist Shuttle astronauts in EVAs, the Manned Manoeuvring Unit (MMU) weighs some 240lb (109kg) and utilises 1·5lb (0·68kg) thrusters, fed from dual tanks of* nitrogen gas at the rear, for movement and auto-stabilisation system. The hand controls comprise (left hand) translation control for direction of flight; (right hand) translation control for roll/pitch/yaw.

and one in 1986. Approximately 73·2 seconds after lift-off on the 25th Shuttle mission, 28 January 1986, the external propellant tank exploded as the result of a hot gas leak from a solid rocket motor field joint and destroyed the Orbiter *Challenger*. The crew of seven perished when their cabin, emerging intact from the explosion, fell into the Atlantic Ocean. As they broke away from the tank propulsively, the SRBs were detonated by the Air Force range safety officer.

The three remaining Orbiters in the Shuttle fleet, were grounded for 32 months while the field joints connecting the motor segments, the nozzle joints and the nozzles were redesigned and tested. Shuttle flight was resumed on 29 September 1988 with the launch of *Discovery* on Mission 26.

Following the investigation of the Challenger accident by a Presidential Commission, the NASA administrative command was reorganized. A former administrator, James C. Fletcher, who had headed the agency during the Nixon administration, was recalled. Congress authorized immediate construction of a billion dollar replacement Orbiter.

New goals and objectives for the national space programme were drafted at NASA headquarters in a report by astronaut Sally K. Ride. Astronauts were moved into NASA management. Truly was appointed associate administrator for space flight, and Crippen was named his deputy for the Shuttle.

The basic role of the Shuttle, as defined in 1972, was changed from that of a satellite

Above: *Orbiters are transported atop a modified Boeing 747. Here Challenger is seen returning to Kennedy Space Center.*

Right: *A beautiful study of Challenger in orbit during Mission STS-7 taken by a remote camera on the SPAS-1 satellite.*

carrier replacing expendable rockets to that of a transport restricted to payloads of national, international or scientific importance. Under a new space policy announced by President Reagan, private enterprise was encouraged to develop satellite launching services.

On the Shuttle's 24 missions prior to the *Challenger* accident, the National Space Transportation System had delivered 28 non-military satellites to orbit, 24 of them commercial communications satellites. Three were scientific satellites and one was the first of two Tracking and Data Relay Satellites for NASA's advanced space-to-ground communications system. The European Space Agency's Spacelab was carried on four Shuttle missions.

All Shuttle flights were launched to the east from the Kennedy Space Center on the Atlantic coast of central Florida at an inclination of 28·5° to the equator, except for one Spacelab mission that flew at 57° inclination. On 24 flights, five landings were made at the Kennedy Space Centre landing facility, 18 at Edwards Air Force Base, California, in the Mojave Desert, and one at White Sands, New Mexico.

Extravehicular activities (EVAs) became extensive as a Remote Manipulator System (Canadarm), developed by Canada, was installed in the Orbiter cargo bay. It is operated like a crane from a console in the mid-deck and can grasp large objects, such as satellites, lift them over the side or retrieve them from space. The Canadarm also provides a moveable platform for astronauts working in the bay.

The range of astronaut activity was increased by the addition of the Manned Manoeuvring Unit (MMU). Strapped into it the astronaut can fly, Peter Pan style, around the cargo bay and beyond it, into space, without a tether. With these devices, astronauts were able to retrieve four disabled satellites, repair two and retrieve two more for refurbishment and re-launch.

Mission Log

STS-5 *Columbia*, 11-16 November 1982. On this first operational mission, *Columbia* deployed two commercial communications satellites, Anik C-3 for Telesat Canada and SBS-C for Satellite Business Systems. Vance D. Brand commanded the four man crew with Robert F. Overmyer, pilot and two mission specialists, Drs Joseph P. Allen and William B. Lenoir. The flight carried a long term processing experiment, the Monodisperse Latex Reactor. It produced tiny latex beads used in medicine to carry medication and radioactive isotopes to malignant tumours in the body.

STS-6 *Challenger*, 4-9 April 1983. This was the first flight of *Challenger*. It carried a four man crew: Paul J. Weitz, commander; Karol J. Bobko, pilot; and mission specialists Donald H. Peterson and Dr Story Musgrave, physician. The first of two Tracking and Data Relay Satellites (TDRS) was deployed. Peterson and Musgrave performed the first spacewalk in the cargo bay for 4hr, 17mins.

STS-7 *Challenger* 18-24 June 1983. *Challenger's* second flight carried the first American woman into space, Dr Sally K. Ride, mission specialist. Robert Crippen commanded the crew of five with Frederick Hauck, pilot and Dr John M. Fabian and Dr Norman Thagard, physician, mission

specialists. The specialists operated the Canadarm to deploy an instrumented spacecraft, the Shuttle Pallet Satellite (SPAS), over the side and retrieve it. They also deployed two commercial communications satellites, Anik C-2 for Canada and Palapa B-1 for Indonesia. The flight was planned to conclude with the first Shuttle landing on the Kennedy Space Center's 15,000ft (4,572m) runway but bad weather in Florida forced it to land at Edwards Air Force Base, California.

STS-8 *Challenger*, 30 August-5 September 1983. Richard Truly commanded the mission, the first to be launched and landed at night. The pilot was Daniel C.Brandenstein. Dale A. Gardner, Dr Guion S. Bluford, Jr and Dr William Thornton, physician, were the mission specialists. The crew deployed Insat 1B for India, tested the Canadarm with large payloads, observed the reaction to microgravity of a half dozen caged rats and re-tested a biology experiment, this time with live human cells — the Continuous Flow Electrophoresis System, which was a Johnson & Johnson/McDonnell Douglas Astronautics joint development. It separates blood cells and other biological materials by their surface electrical charge as they flow through an electrical field.

STS-9 *Columbia*, 28 November-8 December 1983. Flown for the first time, Spacelab filled

Above: *Sally Ride was the first US woman in space. She returned to orbit aboard STS 41-G in October 1984.*

Below: *STS-8 was the first Shuttle mission to be launched at night. It also landed at night after a six day flight.*

the cargo bay. The pressurized cylinder was 23ft (7m) long and 13ft (4m) in diameter and was equipped like a small space station. The mission lasted 10 days, the longest of the Shuttle programme. The first European to fly in the Shuttle was Dr Ulf Merbold of West Germany, payload specialist. John Young was commander and Brewster H. Shaw, pilot. Own Garriott and Dr Robert Parker were mission specialists and Dr Byron K. Lichtenberg, Massachusetts Institute of Technology, was the American payload specialist. Spacelab carried 72 investi-

gations in atmospheric physics, Earth observations, space plasma physics, solar physics and astronomy.

STS 41-B *Challenger*, 3-11 February 1984. On mission 10, NASA changed the flight designation code to include the fiscal year (4), the launch site (the Kennedy Space Center was No 1) and mission sequence in alphabetical terms. STS-9 had been 41-A. Vance D. Brand was commander and Robert L. Gibson, pilot. Bruce McCandless II, Dr Ronald E. McNair and Robert L. Stewart were mission specialists. They deployed two commercial communications satellites, Westar 6 for Western Union and Palapa B-2. The Payload Assist Modules (PAMs) failed to boost the satellites into geosynchronous transfer orbits. They remained stranded in orbits too low to make them useful. McCandless and Stewart tested the Manned Manoeuvring Units which fitted on their backs like heavy packs with armrests and seats. McCandless flew up to 320ft (97·5m) from the Orbiter under the thrust of the MMU's gas jets. He thus became the first human to fly free in space. At 0717 Eastern Standard Time 11 February 1984, Brand executed the first Shuttle landing at the Kennedy Space Center. It ended a busy mission of 7 days, 23 hours duration.

STS 41-C *Challenger*, 6-13 April 1984. A 288 mile (463km) orbit was reached by direct ascent for the first time in the Shuttle programme, without boost from the Orbital Manoeuvring System engines. These were fired only to circularise the orbit. A satellite was repaired for the first time. It was the important Solar Maximum Mission spacecraft, orbited in 1980. Dr George D. Nelson, Dr

James D. van Hoften and Terry J. Hart, mission specialists, retrieved it with the Canadarm, replaced malfunctioning electronic parts and returned it to orbit. They also deployed the 30ft (9·1m) Long Duration Exposure Facility, a cylinder 14ft (4·3m) in diameter weighing 21,300lb (9,662kg). It carried 57 experiments including 12 million tomato seeds. The seeds were to be planted after a year's exposure to microgravity and cosmic rays by school children who would be asked to report any mutations. However, the Long Duration Exposure Facility was not recovered as planned and was still in orbit in 1989. Robert Crippen commanded the mission and Francis R. Scobee was pilot.

STS 41-D *Discovery*, 30 August-5 September 1984. The first flight of *Discovery* was commanded by Henry W. Hartsfield with Michael L. Coats, pilot. Dr Judith A. Resnik, Dr Steven A. Hawley and Richard M. Mullane were mission specialists. A payload specialist was added to the crew for the first time to operate the Continuous Flow Electrophoresis Experiment. He was Charles D. Walker of McDonnell Douglas Astronautics. From a small package, a 105ft (32m) tall solar cell array was erected by Resnik to demonstrate a compact means of supplying additional electrical power. Three commercial communications satellites were deployed for the first time: Leasat 2, SBS 4 and Telstar 3-C (AT&T). *Discovery* carried a 47,000lb (21,300kg) payload, the heaviest of the programme.

Below: *Another remarkable "first" as Bruce McCandless flies his MMU without a tether up to 320ft (97·5m) away from Challenger.*

Above: *A dramatic view of* Discovery *surging off Pad 39A as the DoD mission STS 51-C gets underway on 24 January 1985.*

Left: *Sherwood Spring, standing on the end of the RMS arm, checks the joints of the ACCESS tower which was erected while* Atlantis 61-B *was in orbit in 1985.*

STS 41-G *Challenger*, 5-13 October 1984. Robert Crippen commanded a crew of seven, the largest thus far with Jon A. McBride, pilot; Sally Ride, Dr Kathryn D. Sullivan and David C. Leestma, mission specialists, and Paul Scully-Power, a US Navy oceanographer, and Marc Garneau, a Canadian scientist, payload specialists. The mission carried sensors to measure the amount of pollution escaping from the atmosphere into space. With the Canadarm, the specialists deployed NASA's Earth Radiation Budget Satellite. Sullivan became the first woman to walk in space when she and Leestma spent 3·5 hours in the cargo bay testing an orbital refuelling system for satellites. A Shuttle Imaging Radar system was activated to photograph ground targets, but image quality was reduced by antenna pointing difficulties. A highly successful Shuttle Imaging Radar camera had been flown in 1981 on STS-2. It penetrated below the surface of the Sahara to depict ancient river courses. The mission landed at the Kennedy Space Center.

STS 51-A *Discovery*, 8-16 November 1984. The mission lasted 7 days, 23 hours and was manned by a crew of five: Frederick Hauck, commander; David M. Walker, pilot; Joseph Allen, Dr Anna L. Fisher, a physician, and Dale Gardner, mission specialists. Two satellites were deployed, Anik 2 and Syncom IV-1. Working in the cargo bay with the Canadarm and their MMUs, Allen and Gardner retrieved Palapa B-2 and Westar 6 and stowed them in the cargo bay to be

refurbished at the factory. The mission landed at Kennedy.

STS 51-C *Discovery*, 24-27 January, 1985. This was a classified Defense Department mission which deployed a new generation Sigint 5 satellite designed to monitor military and diplomatic communications. Thomas Mattingly was commander, Loren J. Shriver, pilot; James F. Buchli and Ellison S. Onizuka, mission specialists, and Gary E. Payton, US Air Force, payload specialist. The mission landed at Kennedy.

STS 51-D *Discovery*, 12-19 April 1985. US Senator E. J. "Jake" Garn (R-Utah), an experienced jet aircraft pilot, flew on this mission as a payload specialist, the first American public official to fly in space. Karol Bobko was commander, Donald E. Williams, pilot, Dr Margaret Rhea Seddon, S. David Griggs and Dr Jeffrey A. Hoffman, mission specialists, and Charles Walker, payload specialist. Because a tyre blew out during landing at Kennedy, NASA directed all future flights to land at Edwards. Two satellites, Anik C and Syncom IV-3 were deployed.

STS 51-B *Challenger*, 29 April-6 May 1985. Spacelab again was flown to conduct experiments in life sciences, materials processing, fluid mechanics, astronomy and atmospheric physics. The crew was Robert Overmyer, commander; Frederick D. Gregory, pilot; Drs Don L. Lind, Norman Thagard and William Thornton, mission specialists, and Lodewijk van den Berg of EG&G Energy Management, Inc. and Taylor G. Wang, Jet

Propulsion Laboratory, payload specialists.

STS 51-G *Discovery*, 17-24 June 1985. The crew of this mission were: Daniel Brandenstein, commander; John O. Creighton, pilot; Dr Shannon W. Lucid, Steven R. Nagel and John M. Fabian, mission specialists; Patrick Baudry, France, and Prince Salman Al-Saud, Saudi Arabia, payload specialists. Three satellites were deployed: Arabsat 1B, Morelos 1 and Telstar 3-D. A free flying retrievable astronomy experiment, Spartan 1, and an experimental Strategic Defense Initiative tracking device were also deployed.

STS 51-F *Challenger*, 29 July-6 August 1985. Spacelab 2 was flown in a configuration consisting of three open pallets and an "igloo", a pressurised cylinder with subsystems necessary to operate pallet experiments, and an instrument pointing system for solar physics and astronomy observations. The crew were C. Gordon Fullerton, commander; Roy D. Bridges, pilot; Dr Anthony W. England, Dr Karl G. Henize and Story Musgrave, mission specialists; Loren W. Acton, Lockheed Corp. and John-David Bartoe, were payload specialists.

STS 51-I *Discovery*, 27 August-3 September 1985. The crew for this mission comprised Joe H. Engle, commander; Richard O. Covey, pilot; James van Hoften, John Lounge and Dr William F. Fisher, physician, mission specialists. Fisher and van Hoften retrieved and repaired a disabled communications satellite, Syncom IV-3, and deployed three more: Syncom IV-4, Aussat 1 and ASC (American Satellite Co)-1.

STS 51-J *Atlantis*, 3-7 October 1985. On its maiden flight, *Atlantis* carried a second classified Department of Defense payload, two DSCS-3 communications satellites. The crew was Karol Bobko, commander; Ronald J. Grabe, pilot; David Hilmers and Robert Stewart, mission specialists, and William Pailes, Air Force, payload specialist.

STS 61-A *Challenger*, 30 October-6 November 1985. The flight carried Spacelab D with 75 experiments connected with materials processing, crystal growth, cell functions, fluids and human adaptation to microgravity. Henry Hartsfield commanded the crew of eight with Steven Nagel, pilot; Bonnie J. Dunbar, James Buchli and Guion Bluford, mission specialists and three European payload specialists, Ernst Messerschmid and Reinhard Furrer, West Germany and Wubbo Ockels, Netherlands.

STS 61-B *Atlantis*, 26 November-3 December 1985. Crew: Brewster H. Shaw, commander; Bryan D. O'Connor, pilot; Mary L. Cleave, Sherwood C. Spring and Jerry L. Ross, mission specialists; Rudolfo Neri Vela, Mexico, and Charles Walker, payload specialist. The main event was a demonstration by Ross and Spring of two methods of assembling large structures in orbit, such as elements of a space station. The work required two extravehicular activity sessions lasting more than 12 hours. Three communications satellites were deployed: Morelos B, Satcom K-2 for the American Communications Co, and Aussat 2.

STS 61-C *Columbia*, 12-18 January 1986. The second US elected official to fly on the Shuttle, US Representative Bill Nelson (D-Florida), was aboard as a payload specialist. Robert L. Gibson was commander, Charles F. Bolden, Jr., pilot; Steven A. Hawley, Franklin Chang-Diaz and George Nelson were mission specialists and Robert Cenker, RCA Astro-Electronics Co, the other payload specialist. The main payload was an RCA Satcom K-1 satellite which was deployed successfully. Mission Control told Gibson to land at Kennedy to make up time lost in launch delays, but the landing was waved off three times by bad weather and *Columbia* was diverted to Edwards.

STS 51-L *Challenger*. The 25th mission of the Shuttle was launched at 1138 28 January 1986 and destroyed 1 minute 13 seconds later. Those who perished were Francis R. Scobee, commander; Michael J. Smith, pilot; Judith A. Resnik, Ellison Onizuka and Ronald E. McNair, mission specialists, and S. Christa McAuliffe, teacher, and Gregory B. Jarvis, Hughes Aircraft Co, payload specialists.

The explosion was caused by a combustion gas leak through the right solid rocket motor aft field joint, the NASA Data and Design Analysis Task Force reported. The leak was caused by the failure of the pressure seal in the field joint due to faulty design, according to the Presidential Commission report. The hot gas weakened and/or penetrated the hydrogen tank in the External Tank, initiating structural break-up, the Task Force report stated.

At 73·124 seconds, it added, the hydrogen tank failed and then the oxygen tank failed. At 73·191 seconds, the report went on, a flash was seen between the tank and the Orbiter, followed by total vehicle structural

Above: *US Representative Bill Nelson getting to grips with a grapefruit in Columbia's mid-deck during STS 61-C. He was aboard as a payload specialist.*

Below: Challenger *is destroyed in the explosion that occurred just 73 seconds after STS 51-L lift-off on 28 January 1986. All seven crew members were lost.*

break-up explosion at 73·213 seconds.

On 13 June 1986, President Reagan directed NASA to implement Commission recommendations for a redesigned solid rocket motor. The field joint metal parts, internal case insulation and seals were redesigned and a heating system that would protect the seals from the effects of low temperatures in winter was added.

The major change in the field joint was the addition of a capture feature that would prevent the deflection between the tang and clevis O-ring sealing surfaces caused by motor pressure, especially at ignition, and

by structural loads (bending) by high winds. Deflection allowed hot gases to by-pass the O-ring seals and it was known for months that this process eroded them.

The case-to-nozzle joint which had shown instances of O-ring erosion in flight also was redesigned and the internal joints of the nozzle were redesigned and strengthened. NASA reported that detailed inspection of the Mission 26 *Discovery* Solid Rocket Boosters (the first to fly after the accident) showed no evidence of O-ring seal leakage or erosion after the booster cases were recovered from the sea on 30 September 1988.

Return to Orbit

The investigation into the *Challenger* disaster and the subsequent requalification of the elements of Shuttle system that are critical to its safety grounded the fleet for nearly three years. It was only in September 1988 that NASA felt ready to commit an Orbiter to flight. The crew assigned to this mission were Frederick H. Hauck, commander; Richard O. Covey, pilot; John H. Lounge, David C. Hilmers, and George D. Nelson, mission specialists.

STS-26 *Discovery*, 29 September-3 October 1988. *Discovery*'s five man crew deployed a second Tracking and Data Relay Satellite (TDRS 3) to replace TDRS 2 that was lost in the *Challenger* accident. TDRS 3 was stationed in geosynchronous orbit over the Pacific Ocean at 171° west longitude south of Hawaii.

STS-27 *Atlantis*, 2-6 December 1988. The next Shuttle flight of the post-*Challenger* period was flown by *Atlantis*. The mission was secret, its military payload is believed to have been a Lacrosse radar imaging reconnaissance satellite. On this launch, as well as the *Discovery* launch, the Solid Rocket Boosters performed nominally and were recovered for re-use. The crew on this occasion were Robert L. Gibson, commander; Guy S. Gardner, pilot, Jerry L. Ross, William M. Shepherd and Mike Mullane, mission specialists.

STS-29 *Discovery*, 13-18 March 1989. *Discovery* next flew Mission 29 (ahead of STS-28 in sequence) and deployed a third Tracking and Data Relay Satellite (TDRS 4). It was stationed over the Atlantic Ocean at 41° west longitude off Brazil. TDRS 4 replaced TDRS 1 which had been damaged at launch in 1983 and had sustained electronic degradation from cosmic ray particles. Still partially operating, TDRS 1 was shifted to 79° west longitude south of Florida as a spare. The crew were Michael Coats, commander; John Blake, pilot; James Buchli, Robert Springer and James Bagian, mission specialists.

After six years of development, the TDRS network was completed in the first quarter of 1989. It was designed to supplant NASA's global array of ground stations by relaying data between the shuttle, the *Freedom* Space Station and major scientific satellites in Earth Orbit and a single ground station at White Sands, New Mexico. The network provides continuous communication over 85 per cent of an orbit. A zone of exclusion which blacks out 15 per cent of the orbit exists over the Indian Ocean opposite the ground station at White Sands.

STS-30 *Atlantis*, 4-8 May 1989. The first planetary observatory to be deployed from the Shuttle was the Magellan radar imaging spacecraft. The crew for this mission were David Walker, commander; Ronald Grabe, pilot; Norman Thagard, Mary Cleave and Mark Lee, mission specialists. Magellan was carried into low Earth orbit by *Atlantis*, deployed over the eastern Pacific Ocean and boosted by a two-stage Inertial Upper Stage launcher into a 15 months voyage to Venus. It is scheduled to encounter Venus on 10 August 1990 and enter a polar orbit with a periapsis of 155 miles (249km) and apoapsis of 4,977 miles (8,009km). It will acquire high resolution images of the entire surface of

Venus by means of the spacecraft's Synthetic Aperture Radar system. The initial radar image data would be collected over a cycle of 243 (Earth) days, the period of the planet's axial rotation, when Magellan is at periapsis in its 3hr 9min orbit. The data would then be transmitted to Earth when Magellan is at apoapsis. About 70 to 90 per cent of the surface area was to be imaged during the first 243 day cycle and the balance of the surface area in an extension of the mission.

Above: *The first Shuttle flight after the Challenger disaster was STS-26, launched on 29 September 1988. Here its TDRS 3 satellite cargo is seen nosing out of Discovery's payload bay.*

Below: *STS-27 astronaut Mike Mullane is pictured on the flight deck of Atlantis; above him is the overhead window through which we glimpse clouds. Note cameras, binoculars and (floating) spectacles.*

Above: *STS-29's External Tank is seen falling back towards Earth after ET separation. The burn scar on the left of the tank was caused by the SRB separation motor firing earlier in the flight.*

Orbiter Endeavour

In the meantime, a new Orbiter had been ordered from Rockwell International to replace *Challenger*. On 10 May 1989, President Bush announced the name, *Endeavour*, which followed the results of a national competition among elementary and secondary schools. Two student groups, one from Mississippi, the other from Georgia, submitted the same name which had to correspond with a sea-faring vessel used in research and exploration. *Endeavour* was the first ship commanded by James Cook, the British explorer, navigator and astronomer. In 1768, on *Endeavour's* first voyage, Cook observed the transit of the planet Venus.

The new *Endeavour* was expected to be completed in 1991, with the maiden flight taking place in March/April 1992. Its first assignment would be to deploy Europe's retrievable platform Eureca.

Advanced Booster

In 1989 Lockheed-Aerojet won the contract to build the Advanced Solid Rocket Motor (ASRM) which was to replace the original Thiokol SRBs. They would enable the Shuttle to reach its original design objective of placing 65,000lb (29,484kg) payloads into near Earth orbit. The first Shuttle flight with these boosters was expected in 1994. Featuring more energetic solid propellant and lighter steel casings 3·94in (10cm) wider than the original SRBs, the new boosters stand 126ft (38·4m) tall. They have three

segments (instead of the SRB's four) with welded factory joints plus field joint which seals when pressurised. The design allows thrust to be adjusted as the Shuttle attains maximum dynamic stress after launch, eliminating the need to throttle the Orbiter's main engines.

How these major projects will work out in practice remains to be seen. With Congress keeping a close reign on federal budgets in Fiscal Year 1990, NASA was finding great difficulty in financing the space station *Freedom* and other programmes were expected to be stretched out or even face cancellation.

Design Review Post-Challenger

Apart from redesign of the field joints of the Solid Rocket Booster (SRB), the extensive review of the Space Shuttle following the *Challenger* disaster required some 220 modifications to the Orbiter. These included changes to the Orbital Manoeuvring System (OMS) to cure a leak problem; improvements

Above: *The replacement Orbiter is to be known as Endeavour; it should be completed in 1991. Here workers at Rockwell's Downey facility braze fluid lines in the upper forward fuselage section.*

to fuel cell power units to prevent freezing of associated pipelines; improvements to the main propulsion unit disconnect valve; stiffening of axles of main landing gear and brakes' improvement; Thermal Protection System (TPS): new design to prevent damage to wing elevon cove region, and replacement of TPS tiles between nose cap and nose wheel door with new carbon panel; changes to reaction control thrusters with facility for automatic shutdown in the event of failure; provision of emergency escape system in gliding flight, side hatch jettisoned by explosive bolts, installation of telescopic pole for astronaut parachute escape. Some 30 changes were made to the Space Shuttle Main Engine (SSME) to improve safety, reliability and operating life.

The drawings show how improvements in the Solid Rocket Motor field joints were made after the 51-L accident. The major change in the motor case is the new tang capture feature which limits the deflection between tang and clevis O-ring sealing surfaces caused by motor pressure and structural loads. A third O-ring is also included in the capture feature, while the internal case insulation has been modified to be sealed with a pressure-actuated flap called a J-seal, rather than with putty as was previously the case. Longer mating pins with a reconfigured retainer band have been added, while an external heater maintains the joint and O-rings at a minimum temperature of 75°F to avoid the degradation of O-ring performance caused by low temperatures.

Original Field Joint

Redesigned Field Joint

SRB Field Joint Comparision
(Similarities)
1 Tang.
2 Primary O-ring.
3 Leak check port.
4 Secondary O-ring.
5 Pins.
6 Clevis.
(Redesign improvements)
7 Vent port.
8 V₂ filler.
9 Capture feature tang.
10 Capture feature O-ring.
11 Joint heater.
12 J-slit in insulation.
13 Pressure-sensitive adhesive.
14 Custom shims.
15 Longer pins.
16 New pin retainer band.

Our Future In Space

The shuttlecraft lines up with the docking bay in the double-wheel space station, and, as the "Blue Danube" waltz plays in the background, the two dance a celestial ballet until rendezvous is completed.

The 1967 movie—*2001: a space odyssey*—from which this scene comes envisaged an optimistic future in space that did not seem far-fetched. Paradoxically today, just a decade away from the end of the century, this dream seems farther away than ever. But the near future remains no less exciting. Our questions about space have been sharpened, and the probes and explorers which have gone before us have shown how truly fascinating the Solar System and Galaxy are.

Even before the *Challenger* disaster in 1986 it was apparent that the US space programme had a great deal of energy but no real direction. In 1985 Congress formed a National Commission on Space (NCOS) and charged it with charting a future. Its report, *Pioneering the Space Frontier*, was issued a few months after the *Challenger* accident. Unfortunately it was too much a "wish list", and it was poorly received. NASA formed its own "tiger team", chaired by Astronaut Sally Ride, to develop a set of credible goals and objectives.

The Ride Commission's report, *Leadership and America's Future in Space*, spoke what would have been heresy only a few years before: "The United States has clearly lost leadership in these two areas (planetary and manned flight), and is in danger of being surpassed in many others during the next several years."

"To energize discussion of long-range goals and strategies," the Commission selected "four bold initiatives" for further study: Mission to Planet Earth, Exploration of the Solar System, Outpost on the Moon, and Humans to Mars. The latter two have stirred public debate and interest, and have led to the first important result of the Ride Commission's efforts, a new office of Exploration (also called "Code Z" for its organizational mail code).

Space Station

The first stepping stone in that exploration, as recognized many years ago, is the Space Station, a permanent research facility and a transportation node. It is to be known

"For I dipt into the future, far as human eye could see, Saw the Vision of the world, and all the wonder that would be; Saw the heavens fill with commerce, argosies of magic sails, Pilots of the purple twilight, dropping down with costly bales."

Alfred, Lord Tennyson
Locksley Hall

as "Freedom". In January 1984 President Reagan, in his State of the Union address, committed the United States to the Space Station. The "Twin Keel" configuration selected at that time had two spines that would support science instruments at the "Sky" and "Earth" ends of the station. Unfortunately, the cost of the station grew, and the $8 billion ($8,000 million) figure NASA had been touting for some time had never been realistic. The total price for the new baseline would be $30 billion! The Reagan White House decided to develop the station in two phases instead, deferring the twin keels, their science instruments, and an advanced solar power system. The first phase would build only a horizontal boom—still 509ft (155m) wide and 208ft (63m) tall—and four modules, plus conventional solar cell arrays.

The current plans call for the Space Station to be assembled over the course of three years using some 20 or so launches of the manned Space Shuttle as the exclusive launch vehicle. Its orbit will range from 207 to 288 miles (334 to 463km) at 28·5° inclination. First element launch (FEL)

Right: *An artist's impression of Space Station "Freedom" released by Rockwell International, one of the major contractors. "Freedom" is a cornerstone of US space planning for the 1990s.*

will be in 1995. After six launches the laboratory will be attached and man-tended operations will be possible. Astronaut crews will work aboard the station but live aboard the Shuttle in case of an emergency. The habitat module will not be added until the twelfth launch, at which time four astronauts will make up the initial permanent crew. Another four will be added later. An important portion of the Space Station system will be unmanned platforms carrying instruments to study the Earth and heavens.

The manned base comprises two major areas, the module raft and the solar power arrays, joined by a truss assembly of 16·4ft (5m) cubes. Holding the station together is graphite epoxy tubing, a stable, lightweight, rigid material.

The module raft includes the US laboratory and habitat modules, the ESA Columbus lab module, and the Japanese Experiment Module (JEM), plus four resource nodes, two airlocks, and a logistics module. The US "lab and hab" modules will be 14ft (4·3m) wide and 45ft (13·7m) long. Although a number of unusual designs were analyzed, an "Earth normal" interior design was selected to make assembly and training easier and to give crews an easy reference frame while in space. The "ceiling" and "floor" racks house life support systems, and emergency supplies. Systems that the astronauts will routinely use are located in racks along the sides of the aisle. To keep the station as flexible as possible, each 42in (107cm) wide rack has the same basic design and attaches to identical utilities.

The four resource nodes will enclose various control stations and cupolas so the crew can observe traffic in the area, and Shuttle docking mechanisms. The nodes also serve as bumpers for manmade orbital debris, nuts, bolts, even paint flaked off satellites by endless day-night cycles. As further protection, NASA is planning an Advanced Crew Return Capability (also called Crew Emergency Rescue Vehicle) that would bring five or six astronauts back at a time. Candidate designs include a new Apollo-type capsule, a small lifting body, or an enlarged capsule like those used by spy satellites for film magazines.

The airlocks will allow two astronauts to don spacesuits with the assistance of other crewmen, and then exit to work around the exterior of the station. One airlock will be outfitted as a hyperbaric airlock to raise air pressure to 2 or 3 atmospheres in case of a decompression accident involving an EVA crewman. The spacesuits will be "zero-prebreath" hardsuits that operate at 8 psi

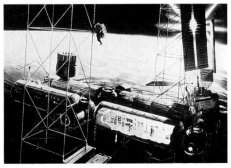

Above: *ESA's contribution to "Freedom" includes the creation of a pressurized lab module with facilities for microgravity experiments as part of the Columbus project.*

(0·56kg/cm²) vs. 4·3 psi (0·30kg/cm²) and thus do not require that the crewman breathe pure oxygen for some time before EVA.

Because crew time is valuable outside as well as inside, two automated EVA servants will be available. The first and largest of these is the Mobile Servicing System (MSS), a cousin of the Remote Manipulator System now aboard the Space Shuttle. The MSS will have two robot arms, one to handle cargoes and the other to support astronauts. These will be mounted on a trolley platform that will roll back and forth on the station structure. It will be one of the first elements launched and will assist in positioning other elements as they are delivered. The MSS will include a special purpose dextrous manipulator capable of handling a number of tools. The advanced Flight Telerobotic Servicer (FTS), a man-sized robot which can be attached to the larger RMS or to a Manned Manoeuvring Unit for independent flight around the station, will help assemble and maintain the station, either under direct astronaut control or using programmed sequences. A similar Intravehicular Activity (IVA) robot will help with routine work in the lab modules so the crew can spend time doing experiments rather than rummaging through drawers.

An equally important adjunct to man will be automated systems within the station. Robots, by definition, have arms; automation means systems that operate without direct human supervision. This will be an essential feature of the Space Station if the astronauts are to have time to perform experiments and not become bogged down with simple housekeeping chores. Skylab, which was about as complex as a single module for the Space Station, required a full time ground crew of 17 to balance power supplies and loads. As computer science progresses,

artificial intelligence will be added so that the onboard computers will be able to learn from their decisions and operate spacecraft systems with greater skill.

Contemporary with the US Freedom Space Station will be the Soviet Mir 2 space complex to be launched by Energiya no sooner than 1994. This will have a mass of some 200 tonnes. Docked to it will be 100 tonne lab modules. The Soviet space shuttle will fly in attendance; also possibly Europe's Hermes spaceplane.

Space Station Sciences

Although the US Space Station was once touted as useful to all space science disciplines, it will (in its first version) be of greatest use to the materials and life sciences.

Materials processing in space takes advantage of microgravity; true zero gravity is not possible since gravity extends to infinity (although its effects diminish greatly with distance). Objects in orbit experience free fall since they fall almost together. "Almost" is inserted as a qualifier because each object is in a slightly different orbit and

Above: *A Soviet artist's impression of a possible configuration for the next generation modular Mir 2 space station to be launched during the 1990s.*

thus will move at a slightly different rate around the planet. Even objects physically attached to a larger one (like components of a satellite), are distant from the centre of mass and thus will pull ahead or behind. This causes low-level accelerations ranging from a few millionths to a few thousandths of a gravity; hence the term microgravity is applied.

This loss of weight becomes useful to materials science in forming new substances. Virtually all substances go through a fluid phase (liquid or gas) as they take shape. Two or more components may be mixed as fluids then solidifed, or a solid may be turned to a fluid then condensed as a new solid. Or, one may wish to separate diverse components of a fluid. In any case, buoyancy may cause unwanted movement of the components. Heat used in a process will expand a fluid and cause it to rise (and the cold portion to sink). Convective flows can be frozen as strain lines and dislocations. Molecular forces may cause immiscible materials (like oil and water) to segregate quickly. Materials being separated may rise or sink more rapidly that the buffer that carries them. Weight of a new material may deform its shape just enough to cause defects that alter its properties. Or contact with the container walls can cause additional strain lines.

Processing materials in the free fall of space seemed to promise an end to a whole range of production problems. As a Microgravity Materials Science Assessment Task Force noted

> "during the late 1970s, the credibility of the program suffered. In an effort to demonstrate the program's potential commercial payoff, advocates sometimes promoted unrealistic near-term rewards."

McDonnell Douglas and Rockwell International both postulated industries that would yield billions of dollars, predicated on easy, cheap access to space which was, in fact, becoming restrictive even before *Challenger*. A 1988 report on *Industrial Applications of the Microgravity Environment* by the National Research Council recommended that

> "NASA focus its current microgravity program on basic materials science, processing research, and in-space processing technology, rather than on manufacturing."

Greater payoffs were likely to come from research using micro-g to understand and improve processes that take place in 1-g, this and other reports have concluded. It is in this spirit that the NASA microgravity sciences programme continues.

Soviet Experiments

The Soviets, for their part, make no secret of their belief that new alloys and composites will be made in space; also ultra-pure semi-conductor crystals for the electronics industry. Glavkosmos, the Soviet space agency, makes available to foreign customers electric furnaces and other equipment aboard the Mir space station and unmanned satellites.

Microgravity research, says Professor L. Leskov, has "moved us into a yet unexplored field of colloidal chemistry". By 1995 he anticipates

> "pieces of semi-conductor materials weighing as much as 77lb (35kg) for use in super-high-speed and very large integrated circuits. Such circuits could find application in laser and infra-red devices and in photo-cells for solar panels. Medical practice in particular awaits sensitive IR imagers."

Above: *Boeing Aerospace artwork showing how the Freedom laboratory module may look in orbit. The astronaut on the left is working in a commercial processing area; at the centre is a general work station.*

For the manufacture of semi-conductors, says Mikhail Chernyshov, the Soviet Union offers the use of, for example, the Zona and Splav rocket-borne electric furnaces. The output of the ingots they make is dozens of times that which can be produced on Earth.

Ultra-pure biological and medical preparations can be produced by the Kashtan electrophoresis plant. In 1987 two biologically active and costly substances — thymosin and interferon — were prepared in a Cosmos satellite. Preparations of the interferon type are used in the treatment of viral and tumour diseases. It could well be that some of the answers to cancer and Aids will be found in space.

France and West Germany lead European research in the general field of materials processing, having secured places aboard United States, Soviet and Chinese recoverable satellites. Austria, West Germany, Italy, Britain and others are lining up astronaut candidates to work in the Mir space station.

However, as far as is known, the only "made in space" products to be sold by the late '80s were latex microspheres manufactured aboard the US Shuttle. Formed by reaction of styrene in a solvent, latex microspheres are used as calibration markers for electron microscopes, pharmaceuticals, and other applications.

The most famous MPS venture was the Continuous Flow Electrophoresis System (CFES) developed by McDonnell Douglas Astronautics Co. This was to become a space-based pharmaceutical-refining system that would produce proteins, cells, and other products which could only be refined at exorbitant costs on Earth. In space, with buoyancy effects eliminated, scientists hoped they could refine certain products at much higher rates and purities than was possible hitherto. Indeed, some early results indicated that could be the case, but the new field of genetic engineering overtook the promises made for CFES and by the late 1980s the principal product (erythropoietin, a clot dissolving protein) was being made on the ground. While the CFES venture failed to produce the industry that was desired, it succeeded from a scientific standpoint. The science was unpredictable, NASA said of its own calibration tests, and that is the best kind, because it leads to discovery. In this case experiments in space helped unmask a phenomenon that previously had hampered electrophoretic separation since its development in 1937.

The growth of protein crystals has been one of the outstanding surprises in the field of microgravity materials science. "Shining" x-rays through mineral crystals produces a pattern which can unveil the structure of the crystal. Much of our knowledge of heavy, complex proteins is derived from this same technique, but one must first grow a crystal of the candidate material. For many proteins this is almost impossible because their fragility and weight destroys or alters the crystal as it grows.

Based on promising results from Spacelab 1, 3M Corp. and the University of Alabama in Birmingham embarked on separate programmes to grow organic materials in space. Since then experiments have been developed and flown aboard the USSR's Salyut and Mir space stations and a Chinese satellite. After a difficult period of learning how to handle protein crystal growth in space, the programme resumed with vigour on the first post-*Challenger* Shuttle flight in 1988.

To learn from these successes and trials, a Microgravity and Materials Processing Facility (MMPF) is planned for the US-International Space Station. Candidate facilities include: a Modular Multizone Furnace Facility, a Modular Containerless Processing Facility, an Advanced Protein Crystal Growth Facility, a Biotechnology Facility, a Fluid Physics/Dynamics Facility, and a Modular Combustion Facility.

Life Sciences

Life sciences is the other microgravity field which is being developed with great interest. There are two fundamental aspects here: occupational health (the long-term effects on the human body and its function) and variable-g biology (using gravity as a variable that allows other effects to be studied). Organisms do not react to weightlessness in quite the same way as materials (insofar as we yet know). But there are receptors that sense changes in accelerations and alter the body's response. Elastic blood vessels in the legs shove fluids to the upper body, causing shifts in electrolyte balances as fluid is eliminated. Stress on bones diminishes, turning off the portion of the metabolism that constantly rebuilds it. Muscles are used less and atrophy. Immune systems become less responsive.

Although the Soviet Union has set a series of duration records lasting up to one year.

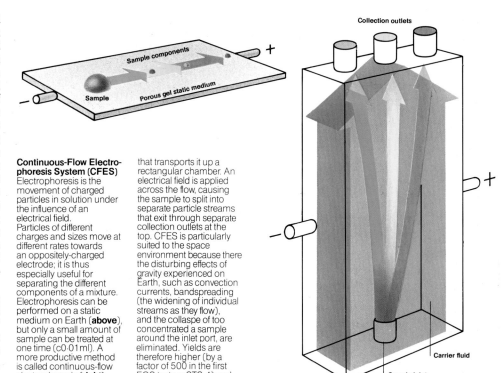

Continuous-Flow Electrophoresis System (CFES)
Electrophoresis is the movement of charged particles in solution under the influence of an electrical field.
Particles of different charges and sizes move at different rates towards an oppositely-charged electrode; it is thus especially useful for separating the different components of a mixture. Electrophoresis can be performed on a static medium on Earth (**above**), but only a small amount of sample can be treated at one time (c0·01ml). A more productive method is called continuous-flow electrophoresis (**right**). Here a sample is continuously injected into a flowing buffer solution that transports it up a rectangular chamber. An electrical field is applied across the flow, causing the sample to split into separate particle streams that exit through separate collection outlets at the top. CFES is particularly suited to the space environment because there the disturbing effects of gravity experienced on Earth, such as convection currents, bandspreading (the widening of individual streams as they flow), and the collaspe of too concentrated a sample around the inlet port, are eliminated. Yields are therefore higher (by a factor of 500 in the first EOS test on STS-4) and the product purity greater. A CFES payload specialist flew on STS 41-D.

much remains to be learned. The Extended Duration Crew Operations Project aboard Space Station Freedom will develop countermeasures to allow space crews to stay aboard the Station for six months at a time (current tours of duty are to last three months, the duration set by Skylab).

Life science facilities aboard the Space Station will be similar to those of terrestrial laboratories with adaptations for handling in micro-g (such as always keeping fluids enclosed, weighing items by their inertia against a spring, and wearing restraints while exercising). Glove boxes and special cages will protect crewmembers from exposure to organisms that might multiply in a closed environment. A key piece of life sciences equipment will be a 6ft (1·8m) centrifuge. First and foremost the centrifuge will hold control specimens at 1-g so that the effects of space radiation, launch, etc, can be factored out of analyses of micro-g specimens. Second, the centrifuge will allow specimens to be cycled between g levels to study space adaptation syndrome (space sickness) which occurs largely at the onset of weightlessness. The centrifuge can also expose specimens to partial-g levels to determine at what point a body starts to adapt or deteriorate.

Experiments outside the station will require support similar to what is offered on Spacelab pallets, but for longer duration. Two early candidates would collect shards from planets and stars. A Cosmic Dust Collection Facility would capture tiny grains of dust from comets, micrometeors, and other flotsam believed left over from the creation of the Solar System. Astromag would use a superconducting magnet as the focusing coil to capture the heaviest and most energetic particles believed created in the death throes of stars.

ESA's portion of the Space Station programme, dubbed Columbus, parallels the US effort at a smaller scale. What Americans will call the Columbus module is, for ESA, the Attached Pressure Module of the Columbus programme. The other major components are the Man-Tended Free Flyer (MTFF) and the Polar Platform (PPF). The Franco-ESA Hermes vehicle, although not a formal part of the programme, will complement it by providing on-orbit servicing (and it has been suggested as the crew rescue system). The APM and MTFF are derived from the Spacelab module and share some features. Both will use racks interchangeable with those aboard the US station. While the APM will be manned and operated continually, the MTFF (launched by an Ariane 5) will house automated and remote-controlled experiments in materials and life science and technology development. It will be visited periodically by Hermes or brought to the US station for replacement of samples or regular maintenance. The PPF, also launched by an Ariane 4 or 5, will be unmanned and carry the ESA portion of the Earth Observing System instrument complement (see Chapter 8). The Japanese Experiment Module (JEM) will comprise a pressurized module, an exposed facility and an experiment logistic module for the supply, storage and transport of samples and materials.

Future Transportation

Following the *Challenger* disaster and the final realization of how tight a bottleneck space launching is, US studies looked at alternate heavy-lift launch vehicles for the 1990s and beyond.

To reduce the cost of space transportation and the risk of being grounded, in 1987 the Air Force started an Advanced Launch System (ALS) programme. Strategic Defense Initiative ("Star Wars") payloads were a major driver in the studies, but requirements for heavy NASA payloads also were included. The problem, as the Air Force programme director noted, was not the launching of heavy payloads per se — the Shuttle places more than 200,000 pounds in orbit with each launch (although most of that is the reusable Orbiter) — but trying to slash the cost of launching payloads from $3,000 to $300 per pound. At the outset the seven contractors were told to use a "clean sheet of paper" in their analyses.

Emerging as a lead contender among the several designs examined in Phase I was a stage-and-a-half vehicle similar to the Atlas and Space Shuttle: a liquid hydrogen/oxygen core stage burns from lift-off through orbital insertion, and is assisted for the first few minutes by a booster stage.

A key factor in reducing launch costs was a minimum of interface and support for payloads: the ALS vehicle would be designed to put the payload in Earth orbit and little else. Trade studies will determine whether simple, robust, throwaway systems with ample design margins are better than highly-reliable, reusable systems, and how much redundancy is affordable. Manufacturing techniques also are being examined with an eye towards increasing automation (which also increases reliability while decreasing labour costs). Contractors have also been told to "spend weight to save money", a cultural change for engineers who have been squeezing the last gram or second of performance out of systems for decades.

About the same time NASA started studying Shuttle derivatives that could be developed quickly and with little impact on the manned Shuttle system. The concept, called Shuttle C (for cargo) will replace the Shuttle Orbiter with an unmanned, throw-away cargo vehicle capable of carrying 170,000lb (77,100kg) of payload, more than triple the 55,000lb (25,000kg) allowed for the current Shuttle. Payloads could also be 82ft (25m) long, half again longer than the 50ft (15·2m) normally allowed in the Shuttle's 60ft (18·3m) bay. The design will make use of existing Shuttle systems, such as a boattail and engines identical to the Orbiter. Although the system would be disposable, the increased payload mass would make Shuttle C competitive with the existing Shuttle's costs. Shuttle C could carry completely outfitted Space Station modules and other equipment that would take three or more conventional Shuttle launches to orbit. Using Shuttle C as an adjunct to the manned Shuttle could cut Space Station assembly time down from 36 to 19 months, and greatly reduce crew risks.

Shuttle C has also been promoted as a start for the evolution of Shuttle II, a 21st century replacement for the current Shuttle. A first step could be development of Liquid Rocket Boosters which would be easier to manufacture and recycle than solids. These would evolve into a flyback booster that would also reduce the size of the external tank by assuming more of the burden of placing the Shuttle in orbit. The Orbiter itself would undergo major changes, such as the addition of a crew escape module.

An alternative, of course, is an "all new" vehicle. It would be markedly different from the Shuttle by using active controls on the aerodynamic surfaces, composite structures, lightweight, durable heatshields, and other advanced technologies only now becoming available. Because the Space Station would be available and Spacelab-style missions

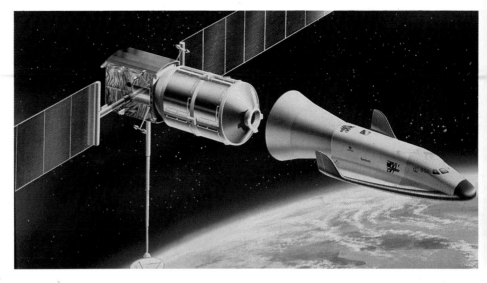

would be in lesser demand, payloads would be carried in an easily detached pod on the back and the mission length remain brief. Studies are starting only now and could lead to a first flight in 2005 as the current Shuttle approaches retirement.

Aerospace Planes

The most attractive concept dates back to the 1940s when Eugen Sänger proposed an antipodal bomber that would skip across the upper layers of the atmosphere at hypersonic speeds as it travelled to its target. Suddenly, his dream seems on the point of fulfilment. Across the globe government agencies and aerospace firms are pouring large quantities of money into an assortment of aerospace plane projects, vehicles that would be able to take off like a jetliner, dash into space, then return to Earth as a jetliner.

The US programme, called the National Aero-Space Plane, was initiated by President Reagan in 1986. He talked of a flying "Orient Express" that might carry passengers and cargo from New York to Tokyo in a few hours. Unfortunately the resulting programme, jointly managed by NASA and the military, has become highly classified and little is known about the X-30 test aircraft that is to fly in the 1990s. The NASA/Air Force plan for the NASP calls for two X-30 demonstrator vehicles to start flying in 1994-95 and to achieve orbital flight by 2000.

Developing the NASP has challenged all

Above: *Hermes will be the crew transportation and service vehicle for ESA's future in-orbit operations. It is seen here approaching the Columbus Free Flying Laboratory for docking.*

areas of technology, including advanced computation fluid dynamics. This complex field uses super computers to simulate the flow of gases at pressures and speeds beyond those which can easily be simulated or sampled. It is applied to the flow of exhaust gases inside rocket engines and to the flow of air over airframes moving at Mach 25. A key challenge to the designers is to design an airframe that houses scramjet engines or rocket engines plus hydrogen fuel tanks inside a slender, flyable body. The principal approach favours a blended body (similar to lifting bodies of the 1960s) where the wings and fuselage are an integrated whole.

In operation the NASP, the British HOTOL (which takes off from a launch trolley) and other similar concepts, will undergo a countdown at its launch facility, start its

Below: *A McDonnell Douglas concept of the National Aero-Space Plane during orbital operations. The NASP programme is seen as having both military and civil applications. The X-30 experimental vehicle is scheduled to fly in the mid-1990s and achieve orbit by the year 2000.*

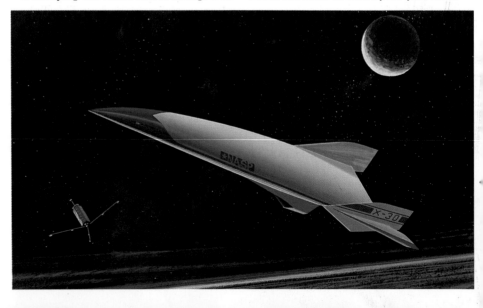

Above: *West Germany's hopes for a hypersonic space plane are pinned on MBB's Sänger project. This two stage vehicle will be lifted to LEO by an airbreathing, hydrogen-powered propulsion system.*

engines, then roll out and lift off somewhat like a jet fighter. It then climbs and goes supersonic after reaching altitude (since there is no sense in burning off precious fuel while the atmosphere is thick), then accelerates to Mach 25 in the upper atmosphere and aims itself into a suborbital trajectory. Once in space, small onboard rockets fire for orbital insertion and re-entry. Re-entry and landing will be similar to that of current space shuttles (the only vehicles which are, briefly, hypersonic), but, unlike the shuttle, powered flight will be resumed at some point.

West Germany and Japan are studying similar concepts. Germany's Sänger vehicle, under study by Messerschmitt-Boelkow-Blohm, is a two-stage vehicle using a Mach 7 hypersonic transport to carry the orbital vehicle to altitude. The orbital vehicle could be a manned spacecraft or unmanned cargo carrier. Japan's objective is a single-stage-to-orbit vehicle by the year 2006. That nation is pursuing a Mach 7, 2-man research aircraft and an unmanned, limited-duty spaceplane that would pave the way for a true aerospace plane. In addition to their utility as space launchers, such vehicles are also expected to have a strong impact on the transoceanic passenger trade.

Soviet Visions

With Energiya Soviet dreams are soaring to the level of near-fantasy. One idea is to put into orbit an optical telescope having a mirror diameter of nearly 33ft (10m). Whereas NASA's Hubble Space Telescope (mirror diameter 7·87ft, 2·4m) will penetrate up to 14 billion light years, an observatory with a 33ft (10m) mirror would theoretically enlarge observation of the visible Universe 40 times over.

Could this enable us to determine the size and mass of the Universe, asked the late Yuri Bochkov? In a closed Universe each galaxy is bound to be observed in two mutually opposite directions — from the "face" side and from the "rear" side. In the first case the light emitted by the galaxy directly towards us arrives over the shortest path; in the

second, it will start in the opposite direction but, having taken the longer route, will also reach us. We perceive a double image.

We therefore have a breathtaking opportunity, Bochkov said.

"We determine the distances of galaxies from the magnitude of the red shift in their spectra. The sum of distances to the two diametrically opposed galaxies, which happen to be one and the same object, is the sum of two arcs constituting a totally closed pathway."

Having estimated the "curvature" of space, we should be able to determine not merely the dimensions of the Universe but also its mass and density.

Another exciting possibility, according to Nikolai Kardashev, deputy director of the Space Research Institute, is the creation of a space-based radiometer. If it were possible to assemble in space two or more sufficiently large antennae and place them hundreds of millions of kilometres apart (e.g. one in Earth orbit and another somewhere near Jupiter), a network of radio telescopes would have a resolution of several millionths of a second of arc. One second of arc is an angle at which a human hair is visible from a distance of 164ft (50m).

This would mean that astronomers could study the motions of other galaxies and accurately measure distances at which incredibly remote objects are located — they too would be able to measure the curvature of our time continuum.

Kardashev also spoke of the value of Energiya rockets in setting up a lunar observatory in the 21st century. First, it would be necessary to build an orbital station intermediate between Earth and Moon so that lunar operations could be broken down into easy stages. When the time comes, it may be more expedient to launch expeditions to Mars from an intermediate platform or from the Moon itself, saving energy.

Another group of Soviet scientists, led by Nikolai Lidorenko, is designing large erectable space mirrors which, deployed in orbit, would provide spot-beam illumination of areas of the Earth below, bathing cities and towns in artificial "moon-glow" and possibly limiting the onset of frost in agricultural fields.

A small experimental version has a mass

of 441lb (200kg) and a reflecting area of 1,184ft² (110m²).

They also contemplate building space mirrors for huge solar power stations fixed on flat structures which direct powerful energy beams towards Earth-based receivers using laser or microwave frequencies. The researchers say the "head block" of an orbital platform having a useful capacity of 100,000 to 500,000kW could be drawn up today!

This is reminiscent of the schemes proposed in 1968 by America's Dr Peter E. Glaser of Arthur D. Little Company. The idea depends on establishing a huge array of solar cells to intercept the maximum amount of sunlight to generate electricity by the process known as photovoltaic conversion. Smaller plants could be utilised to support industrial production in space.

Solar power stations in geostationary orbit would be massively expensive to establish and maintain, and many scientists who have studied them conclude that the better investment for our future energy requirements, probably lies in solving the problems of nuclear fusion, deriving fuel from sea water. If new superconductors can be made to work at room temperatures — a possibility raised by the development of superconducting ceramics — smaller electromagnets could be made capable of maintaining the powerful magnetic fields necessary to contain gas plasmas of millions of degrees. Superconductors, which normally require temperatures near absolute zero, have the property of conducting energy without loss.

Whereas superconducting ceramics could revolutionise electrical and electronic technology on Earth, say A.T. Lawton and Penny Wright of the British Interplanetary Society, they would have even greater potential on the Moon. Superconducting ceramics could be made from lunar rocks with the cooling necessary for their operation being derived from the wide temperature variations of the lunar surface. Power grids, electromagnetic launchers and several allied items would be feasible — all cooled by natural lunar refrigeration.

Below: *Peter Glaser's dream of solar power stations in orbit envisages beaming energy to Earth in the form of microwaves which would be converted into electricity.*

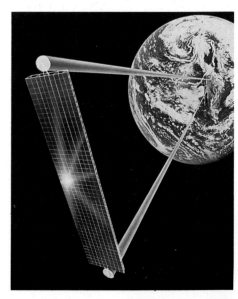

Our Future In Space

When Dr Peter Glaser first proposed the concept of the Satellite Solar Power Station (SSPS) in 1968, energy was cheap and plentiful. The idea of building immense structures in space for the purpose of tapping the raw energy of sunlight and beaming energy to Earth was regarded with much scepticism.

Times have changed a little since then. The energy crisis which followed the Arab-Israeli War in 1973 and increasing pressure by oil-rich nations to raise prices have resulted in consideration being given to a range of future energy options.

Detailed studies made by NASA and the Department of Energy in conjunction with industry suggest that the SSPS could be within the bounds of feasibility by the year 2000; though much depends on the ability to reduce drastically the cost of delivering large payloads to geostationary orbit.

The drawings presented here depict the kind of operation that would be necessary to build a photovoltaic power system capable of relaying substantial amounts of energy to Earth in the form of microwaves.

By any reckoning it would be a gigantic enterprise. Proposed methods of building the Solar Power Stations range from constructing them directly in geostationary orbit to assembling large sections in low Earth orbit and transferring these to this high orbit.

Two construction bases are envisaged. The base in low Earth orbit (LEO) will construct and service the large orbit transfer vehicles which employ electric propulsion. The function of the LEO is to transfer heavy payloads received from heavy lift launch vehicles (HLLVs) to the electric orbit transfer vehicles (OTVs). It would also serve as a base for transferring crew from Shuttles to personnel orbit transfer vehicles (POTVs).

The first task, therefore, is to establish a large space factory in low Earth orbit equipped with rows of automated Beam Builders. Grumman Aerospace pointed out that the factory must be big enough to accommodate astro-workers, maintenance shops, construction control depots, refuelling facilities and a Shuttle-docking terminal.

SSPS Antenna Structure
Major problems must be solved in building light-weight framework of this type because under solar illumination thermal expansion can deform it. Boeing has studied:

Tetrahedral Truss
Maximum efficiency; no tension members; non-square sub-arrays; access difficult.

A-Frame
Good access; square sub-arrays; poor stiffness efficiency; uses tension members; secondary structure is part of primary structure. Represents an attempt to design the antenna structure for ease of maintenance and repair.

Pentahedral Truss
Good access; good efficiency; no tension members; square sub-arrays. Appears to offer a good compromise. Maintains good access with high efficiency, eliminates tension members and allows square sub-arrays.

Rectenna
The rectifying antenna (rectenna) on the ground must capture microwave energy from the Solar Power Satellite at the highest possible efficiency. This one has an elliptical format 8 miles (13km) long and 6 miles (9·5km) wide. The microwave intensity ranges from up to 25 milliwatts per square centimetre at the centre to 1mW/cm² at the periphery. Rectification of received energy to direct current (DC) is accomplished by circuit elements built into the rectenna. Such structures — since they will block out most of the microwave energy — should allow the ground beneath to be cultivated.

SSPS Dimensions
Manhattan compared to scale with ground-based rectenna (left) and Satellite Solar Power Station. The latter is 13·3 miles (21·3km) long and 3·32 miles (5·3km) wide.

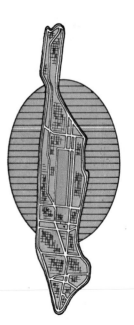
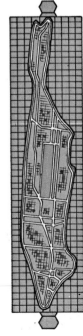

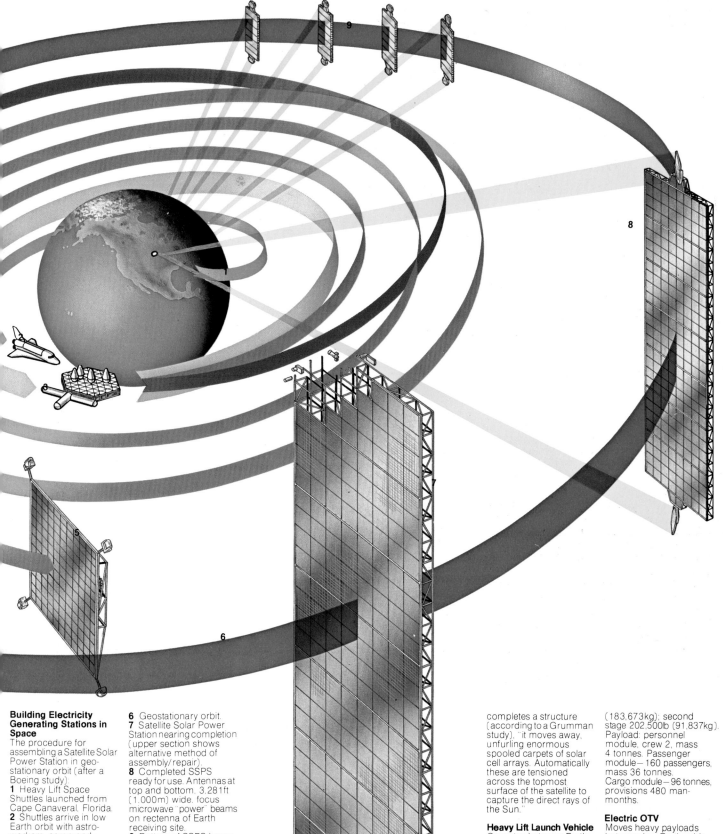

Building Electricity Generating Stations in Space

The procedure for assembling a Satellite Solar Power Station in geostationary orbit (after a Boeing study):
1 Heavy Lift Space Shuttles launched from Cape Canaveral, Florida.
2 Shuttles arrive in low Earth orbit with astro-workers, cargo and supplies.
3 Space Platform with accommodation for astro-workers, propellant storage, "beam builders" and other factory equipment.
4 Personnel Orbit Transfer Vehicle (POTV) makes fast transit to geostationary orbit. Carries astro-workers, tools and equipment.
5 Electric-powered Orbit Transfer Vehicle (OTV) slowly expands orbit to reach geostationary orbit after about 140 days. Brings sections of SSPS for final assembly.

6 Geostationary orbit.
7 Satellite Solar Power Station nearing completion (upper section shows alternative method of assembly/repair).
8 Completed SSPS ready for use. Antennas at top and bottom, 3,281ft (1,000m) wide, focus microwave "power" beams on rectenna of Earth receiving site.
9 Battery of SSPS beaming microwave energy to "third-world" countries.

A favoured method of construction proceeds from the establishment in low Earth orbit (LEO) of a space factory equipped with rows of automated Beam Builders. The first task is to build the large OTVs necessary to transfer completed sections of the SSPS to geostationary orbit for final assembly. Lightweight truss members could be made of graphite and epoxy composite to limit temperature stresses in high orbit. As the factory

completes a structure (according to a Grumman study), "it moves away, unfurling enormous spooled carpets of solar cell arrays. Automatically these are tensioned across the topmost surface of the satellite to capture the direct rays of the Sun."

Heavy Lift Launch Vehicle
Operates between Earth base and low Earth orbit. Fully reusable flyback vehicle, two stages. Propellants: booster LO_2/LCH_4; orbiter LO_2/LH_2.
Launch weight: 11,000 tonnes.
Payload net/gross: 384/420 tonnes.
Cost per flight: $14 million (1979 prices).

POTV
This delivers astro-workers and cargo to assembly base in geostationary orbit. Two-stages, reusable. Propellants: LO_2/LH_2.
Thrust: booster 405,000lb

(183,673kg); second stage 202,500lb (91,837kg). Payload: personnel module, crew 2, mass 4 tonnes. Passenger module— 160 passengers, mass 36 tonnes. Cargo module— 96 tonnes, provisions 480 man-months.

Electric OTV
Moves heavy payloads between low Earth orbit and geostationary orbit. This huge vehicle 3,425 x 4,954ft (1,044 x 1,510m) across employs low thrust solar electric propulsion and takes 180 days to move 4,000 tonnes of payload up, 40 days to move 200 tonnes down. Initial power: 296Mw. Photovoltaic array area: 0·58 miles² (1·5km²). Electric thrust: 753lb (341kg). Empty mass: 1,462 tonnes. Propellants: argon, for electric thrusters; LO_2/LH_2 for supplementary rocket motors used during eclipse periods and for high-torque manoeuvres.

241

Spaceships to Mars

Visiting, if not colonizing the planets is, of course, the grand dream of space flight. And in the 1988 National Space Policy, NASA was instructed "to expand human presence and activity beyond Earth orbit into the Solar System." Exactly how and where man will soar cannot be known for several years. As predictions about Moon Bases and solar power satellites have shown, this is an "iffy" business at best. In its first annual report in late 1988, Code Z (NASA's Office of Exploration) outlined three "Pathways to Human Exploration" that could take man to the planets. Which of these is selected will only become known as studies progress.

The three Pathways are called **human expeditions, science outpost,** and **evolutionary expansion.** Significantly, each uses the Space Station as the starting point:

> "As a base to gain long-duration operations experience, to conduct life sciences research, and to function as a testbed to demonstrate technology, Space Station Freedom's contributions to human exploration of the Solar System will be monumental."

Further, it can serve as a transportation depot where propellants, upper stages, and payloads are stored until the full vehicle is ready for assembly.

Four cases within the three Pathways were studied by Code Z in 1988: human expeditions to Phobos and to Mars, a lunar observatory, and a lunar outpost leading to early Mars evolution. While each is technically feasible — and the expeditions to Mars places humans on the Red Planet at the earliest opportunity — the study showed that the required mass that would have to be inserted in Earth orbit was phenomenal, up to 1,800 metric tonnes a year if one goes directly to Mars. Beyond the sheer mass there is the problem of the number of launches required, from 10 to 20 a year. The peaks for the other three cases are much lower, less than 500 tons, at three to five launches a year. Although it may delay the ultimate goal, an evolutionary approach might be the wisest.

Before the first humans embark to Mars a number of robotic servants will help pave the way. The USSR's Phobos mission was intended to sample the composition of Phobos, but contact with both Phobos probes was unfortunately lost before the mission had been achieved. The NASA Mars Observer mission (scheduled for launch in 1992) should provide a comprehensive survey of the planet from orbit. Following that, a Mars Aeronomy Observer will

> "Then, through the vast and gloomy dark, There moves what seems a fiery spark, A lonely spark with silvery rays Piercing the coal-black night."
>
> Edward Lear
> *The Dong with a Luminous Nose*

monitor the weather, climate and atmospheric chemistry. The next major step will be a Mars rover/sampler to survey the surface first hand and send specimens back for analysis on Earth.

Return to the Moon

Some of the new technology anticipated by the Soviets for Mars exploration will be tested on and around the Moon. The programme begins in 1992 with the launch of a Soviet orbiter which will overfly the Moon's polar regions.

There are places at the Moon's poles where sunlight never penetrates. One such area, studied by Robert L. Staehle and Richard Dowling of the World Space Foundation in South Pasadena, California, is a small crater at the north pole on the rim of Peary. Its floor and those of smaller nearby craters are never illuminated and so may act as "cold traps" for water and other volatile ices, as pointed out by Watson, Murray and Brown in 1961. Staehle points out that while there is not a shred of evidence to suggest that ice or permafrost exists in such places, it would be wise to find out.

The discovery of water ice and other workable volatiles would transform the Moon as a trans-shipment base to other planets. Approximately seven times less propulsive energy is necessary to lift something off the face of the Moon into low Earth orbit, and the availability of high performance propellants on the Moon could reduce the tonnage needed to be launched from Earth by factors of five to 10. Ultimately, the Moon could become the supply base from which space factories draw raw materials using electromagnetic launchers on the lunar surface.

Staehle had campaigned for a gamma-ray spectrometer left over from the Apollo programme to be incorporated in a future lunar orbiter. Although gamma rays do not penetrate well through rock, and water ice below more than a metre of rock would not be detected, a radar sonde (also used on Apollo) routinely makes soundings at several frequencies to greater depths to map terrestrial glaciers. Down-looking radar, he reminds us, does not show a signal uniquely diagnostic of ice but it does indicate discontinuities between layers of different materials such as rock and ice.

A combination of gamma ray spectrometer and radar sounder would be virtually certain to detect ice if it exists in the shadowed craters if useful quantities exist near enough to the surface.

The Soviets anticipate a new-generation of moon rovers (Lunokhods) with a larger radius of action. The late Professor Boris Petrov spoke of the desirability of having a

Below: *Mars, the Red Planet, is the next major goal in Man's exploration of the Solar System. A number of robot probes, comprising orbiters, rovers, atmosphere and soil samplers and the like, are due to visit the planet in the next decade, and both the Soviet Union and the USA have outlined plans then to send human crews to establish a base on the planet's surface.*

way-station in lunar orbit which could be visited periodically by cosmonauts flying out from the space stations in Earth orbit.

At a Soviet-French meeting on space research held in Moscow in December 1988, Professor Yuri Surkov — after reviewing past US and Soviet achievement on the Moon — said it was time to begin thinking of practical applications of Earth's natural satellite. However, before we could think of setting up a base there, it was necessary to get close-up pictures of the surface over larger areas than had already been surveyed, including of course the polar regions.

Luna '92 makes use of the "bus" structure of the Mars-Phobos automatic station and its principal systems. Its camera will have a resolution of a few metres; gamma and X-ray spectrometers will analyse the chemical composition of rock and soil. There will also be an infra-red spectrometer to study mineral composition and a magnetometer to probe for magnetic fields.

In the opinion of Professor Surkov, the Moon's importance is bound to grow. It holds the greatest scientific interest as a vestige of the early history of the Solar System. Telescopes to observe remote objects in the Universe could be installed there. Eventually, it will become a source of raw materials, since low gravitation facilitates greatly the extraction of minerals. He agreed that the Moon could also serve as a "proving ground" for space technology, and as a trans-shipment base for distant space expeditions.

At a Moscow meeting in April 1987 the USSR and the United States agreed to resume cooperation in space research in keeping with Summit accords. At a subsequent meeting, held in Washington 3-10 November that year, the two sides exchanged information on contemporary national programmes until the year 2000 and mapped out areas of possible cooperation.

It is interesting to review this meeting through the eyes of Lenin Prize Winner Yuri Surkov, Professor of the Geochemistry and Analytic Chemistry Institute of the USSR Academy of Sciences.

"An American orbiter will soon (1992) head for Mars to become its satellite. It will be followed by Soviet platforms with balloons, penetrators and roving vehicles. The taking of Martian rock samples to Earth, expected around the turn of the century, will be an epoch-making event. The USA and the USSR are chosing rock-sampling areas on Mars and the possibility of installing equipment in each others' spacecraft."

Confirmation of Soviet plans came from Vyacheslav Kovtunenko, a corresponding member of the Academy of Sciences (scientific supervisor of the Babakin Research and Testing Centre) in December 1988. Mars, he said, is to be studied in 1994 by an orbiter and by a lander with penetrators which will be "anchored to its surface". The same mission will carry a Franco-Soviet instrumented helium balloon 82ft (25m) in diameter, volume 176,572ft^3 (5,000m^3). The gondola has a mass of 33lb (15kg) and the guide rope 22lb (10kg). The balloon is designed to ascend 2·5 miles (4km) during the Martian day and to descend to the surface at night to examine local conditions. Its objectives are to conduct surface photography, chemical analysis and electro-magnetic sounding of soil, and atmospheric study.

If all goes to plan, in 1996 a Soviet orbiter will drop a rover on the Red Planet and in 1998 or 2000 a sample return mission will lift off from Mars. Kovtunenko explained,

"We had to abandon plans for a Mars rover in 1994, because of the need to make sure that the rover would make a safe landing on the planet's boulder-strewn surface. To select a suitable landing site, we need television images of Mars that show surface detail down to several metres."

In August 1989, Soviet scientists revealed that technical problems would eliminate the 1994 orbiter/lander mission.

The Soviet probes that eventually fly to Mars will have a mass of around 14,300lb (6,500kg), instrumentation aboard the orbiter accounting for some 440lb (200kg) of the total. The mass of the orbiter will be about 1,102lb (500kg) including 440lb (200kg) of instruments. The rover will carry a radio locator to facilitate the future sample return mission.

Placing a rover on the surface of Mars would probably be a logistical feat similar to the Viking landings in 1976, enhanced by terminal guidance to ensure landing on the desired spot free from boulders. As such techniques develop, the rovers themselves would use robot vision and artificial intelligence. NASA/industry studies suggest that stereo TV cameras on an articulated head will allow the scene to be inspected from various heights. Floodlights and laser rangefinders will eliminate dependence on natural lighting which can trick the eye. Because of the time involved in getting a signal from Mars to Earth and back — plus human decision time in the middle — the Mars rover would have to decide some things for itself or the shortest treks would take months. It also seems likely that it will have an articulated design so that in case it miscalculates and starts to drive off the edge of a crater, one end will have enough traction to back up.

Like the Apollo astronauts on the Lunar Rover, early forays from its lander will be limited. The rover will travel a few kilometres to collect samples from different sites. Multi-spectral scanners will help it pick a variety of interesting minerals rather than merely filling a grab bag. Robot arms will select different tools for scraping, chipping, digging, handling, tagging, and stowing samples. A small chemistry lab may be built into the rover to allow basic analysis of the 246▷

Below: *Two astronauts explore the surface of Phobos while Mars looms behind. NASA believes that landing on Phobos would be simpler than attempting a manned mission to land directly on Mars itself.*

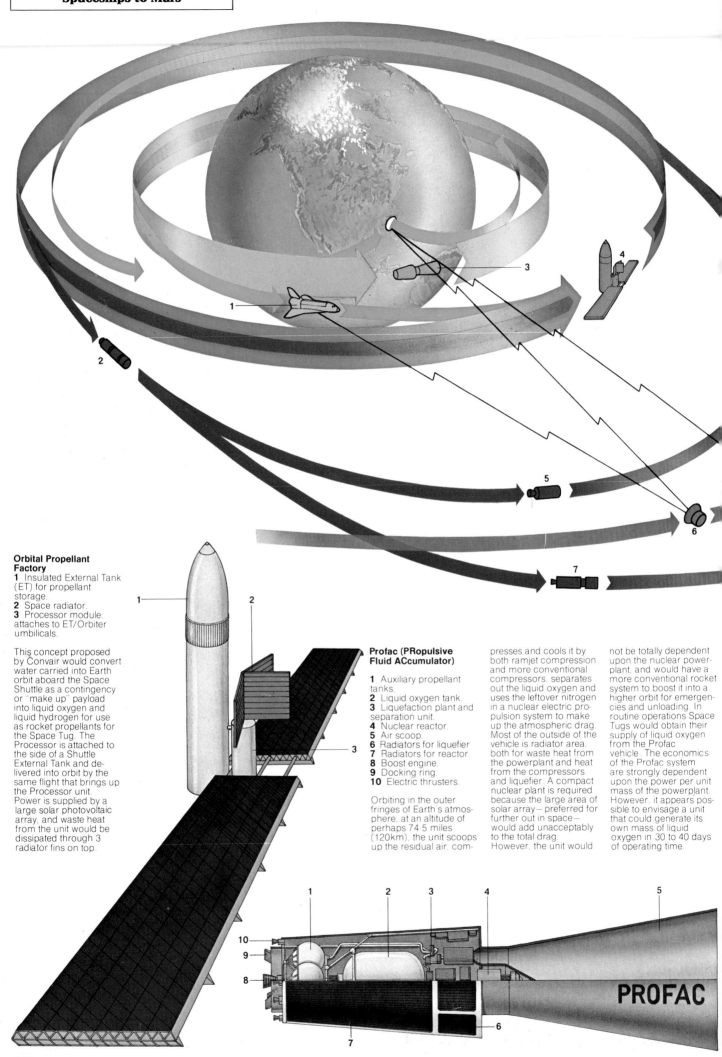

Orbital Propellant Factory

1 Insulated External Tank (ET) for propellant storage.
2 Space radiator.
3 Processor module: attaches to ET/Orbiter umbilicals.

This concept proposed by Convair would convert water carried into Earth orbit aboard the Space Shuttle as a contingency or "make up" payload into liquid oxygen and liquid hydrogen for use as rocket propellants for the Space Tug. The Processor is attached to the side of a Shuttle External Tank and delivered into orbit by the same flight that brings up the Processor unit. Power is supplied by a large solar photovoltaic array, and waste heat from the unit would be dissipated through 3 radiator fins on top.

Profac (PRopulsive Fluid ACcumulator)

1 Auxiliary propellant tanks.
2 Liquid oxygen tank.
3 Liquefaction plant and separation unit.
4 Nuclear reactor.
5 Air scoop.
6 Radiators for liquefier.
7 Radiators for reactor.
8 Boost engine.
9 Docking ring.
10 Electric thrusters.

Orbiting in the outer fringes of Earth's atmosphere, at an altitude of perhaps 74.5 miles (120km), the unit scoops up the residual air, com-presses and cools it by both ramjet compression and more conventional compressors, separates out the liquid oxygen and uses the leftover nitrogen in a nuclear electric propulsion system to make up the atmospheric drag. Most of the outside of the vehicle is radiator area, both for waste heat from the powerplant and heat from the compressors and liquefier. A compact nuclear plant is required because the large area of solar array — preferred for further out in space — would add unacceptably to the total drag. However, the unit would not be totally dependent upon the nuclear power-plant, and would have a more conventional rocket system to boost it into a higher orbit for emergencies and unloading. In routine operations Space Tugs would obtain their supply of liquid oxygen from the Profac vehicle. The economics of the Profac system are strongly dependent upon the power per unit mass of the powerplant. However, it appears possible to envisage a unit that could generate its own mass of liquid oxygen in 30 to 40 days of operating time.

Space Transportation System for a Lunar Base
1 Space Shuttle.
2 Two-stage Tug launch.
3 Profac
4 Orbital propellant factory.
5 Boost Tug return orbit.
6 Tracking and Data Relay Satellite (TDRS) in Clarke orbit.
7 Space Tug.
8 Libration Point communications satellite.
9 Lunar orbit station.
10 Lunar surface oxygen plant.
11 Halo orbit communications satellite.

The drawing shows how an efficient and economic Earth-Moon transportation system may develop from existing technology by the end of this century. By the year 2000 NASA confidently expects Shuttles to be lifting a constant stream of supplies into orbit, both for experimental purposes and to support orbital industries. (Similar developments can be expected from the Soviet Union). Some of these activities will take place close to the Earth, in the Shuttle orbit, but others will require an upper stage "booster" for the Shuttle, to lift its cargo into higher orbits, and in due course to carry people there and return them safely to the waiting

Shuttle orbiter. The same upper stage vehicle, originally named by NASA the "Space Tug", can be used to support operations on the Moon. Like the Shuttle, these Tugs will have to be designed to be reusable and versatile, carrying either cargo or crew. At first the Tugs will be recovered after each mission and returned to Earth, but later they will be refuelled in orbit and permanently based in space. To launch a payload into orbit about the Moon a Shuttle will ascend into low Earth orbit carrying two Space Tugs in tandem within its hold, together with the payload module. The first Tug boosts the assembly into a highly elliptical orbit about the Earth and then separates to return to the low Earth orbit and rendezvous with the Shuttle under its own power. The second Tug proceeds onwards to orbit about the Moon and still have enough fuel to return the empty Tug to the Shuttle orbiting the Earth. Landing on the Moon is accomplished by the use of a third Tug, modified with landing legs and a landing radar but otherwise identical to the Tugs operating between Earth orbit and lunar orbit.

Fuel costs are an im-

portant factor in the overall cost of shipping cargo to the Moon. For every ton delivered to the surface of the Moon, four or five tons of propellant have to be shipped into Earth orbit. Two systems for reducing cost of fuel in orbit are illustrated: an orbital propellant processor taking contingency payload from the Shuttle in the form of water and converting it into oxygen and hydrogen, and a Profac air scoop operating at the fringes of Earth's atmosphere to ingest oxygen. By far the most economical scheme, however, appears to be the generation of liquid oxygen on the Moon by extracting it from rock.

Communications also play an important role in reducing support costs on Earth. The Shuttle will operate with a Tracking and Data Relay Satellite (TDRS) in Clarke orbit, supplanting the worldwide communications network required for Apollo. Lunar operations may call for a similar satellite in a "halo orbit" behind the Moon, providing support for all "farside" operations. A communications satellite would also be stationed at a Lagrange point between the Earth and the Moon to provide the radio link for nearside bases.

The colonisation of the Moon lacks exact parallels in our history. North America and Australia were colonised by agrarian societies and offered immediate benefits in the values of the times. The Moon, in its turn, will be colonised by a "post industrial", high-technology society in which gold and land are no longer primary values. In our age nearer parallels are to be found in the outposts founded in Antarctica and the Alaskan North Slope, but the Lunar Colony will demand from its inception a higher degree of self-sufficiency than either of these.

Setting up a permanent manned base on the Moon will be critically dependent upon the development of efficient, economic transport systems between Earth and Moon. As with Apollo, future operations will use lunar orbit rendezvous techniques. In this scenario, cargo, equipment and astronauts are delivered into orbit about the Moon by a two-stage launch from Earth orbit, and from there ferried to the surface by a separate vehicle operating only between the Moon's surface and lunar orbit. At first it will probably be achieved through two sequential launches. Later it may be more economic to develop a fuel dump in orbit around the Moon to provide a regular refuelling station.

* Mission profile devised by Dr R.C. Parkinson.

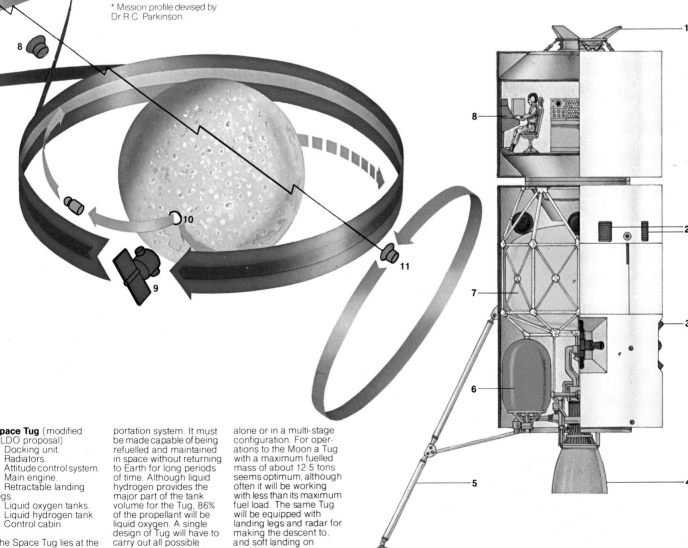

Space Tug (modified ELDO proposal)
1 Docking unit.
2 Radiators.
3 Attitude control system.
4 Main engine.
5 Retractable landing legs.
6 Liquid oxygen tanks.
7 Liquid hydrogen tank.
8 Control cabin.

The Space Tug lies at the heart of the lunar trans-

portation system. It must be made capable of being refuelled and maintained in space without returning to Earth for long periods of time. Although liquid hydrogen provides the major part of the tank volume for the Tug, 86% of the propellant will be liquid oxygen. A single design of Tug will have to carry out all possible missions, either working

alone or in a multi-stage configuration. For operations to the Moon a Tug with a maximum fuelled mass of about 12·5 tons seems optimum, although often it will be working with less than its maximum fuel load. The same Tug will be equipped with landing legs and radar for making the descent to, and soft landing on the Moon's surface.

samples. At the end of each foray the rover will return to the lander and deposit a select few samples in a canister for the return trip to Earth.

When the canister is filled, the lander's upper stages will lift off from Mars to rendezvous and dock with the mother spacecraft that inserted it in Mars orbit. Another stage will then fire it back to Earth where it will use the atmosphere as a brake, going into orbit to await pickup by the Space Shuttle or the Orbital Manoeuvring Vehicle, perhaps for a period of initial quarantine and study at the Space Station.

The rover, meanwhile, would start an extended tour of Mars. Along the way it might emplace remote stations for seismology and weather networks, and gather still more samples in addition to sending back countless pictures of the surface. Its ultimate destination would be a landing site for either a subsequent Mars rover, or a human expedition.

Man on Mars

The long-term aims of the Soviet Union in manned space flight were outlined by Leonid I. Brezhnev as long ago as 1969. He stated that his country was:

"About to produce long-lived orbital stations and laboratories — the decisive means for the extensive conquest of outer space. Soviet science regards the establishment of orbital stations with replaceable crews as man's main highway into space. They will become 'cosmodromes' in orbit, launching pads for flights to other planets. There will appear large research laboratories for the study of space technology and biology, medicine and geophysics, astronomy and astrophysics."

Later Academician Boris Petrov, a former director of the Intercosmos programme, amplified these remarks saying that "final adjustments will be made to spaceship systems" on orbital space platforms:

"There will be training sessions and cosmonauts will be able to acclimatise to space conditions and participate in the assembly and checkout of interplanetary ships."

The project appeared to be closely related to the development of a Soviet Space Shuttle for ferrying cosmonauts to and from space-stations and a "kosmobuksir" (space tug) for bringing separately launched modules of space vehicles together in orbit. Part of this programme has already been developed in the Salyut and Mir orbital laboratories launched by Proton D rockets. Larger space-stations are expected to be assembled from modular components put into Earth orbit by the Energiya booster. This is the path to the construction of space factories and stations equipped with multiple, perhaps interchangeable, laboratories.

This was broadly the course that NASA had charted for the post-Apollo programme of the late 1960s before the demands of the Vietnam War and other national considerations cut space spending and ended the Apollo programme in its prime.

At such orbital workshops the large spaceships which can be sent to explore Mars and other planets could be put

Above: *The Energiya/VKK combination will be integral elements in Soviet plans to land men on Mars. Here Buran is seen mated to Energiya in the assembly building.*

together and fitted out. The Soviet rocket engine designer, V.P. Glushko, regarded spaceships with mixed propulsion systems as offering the greatest promise. A combination of chemically fuelled, nuclear and electric rocket engines, he said,

"would enable us to cover huge interplanetary distances at very high velocities and reduce the travel time from years to months."

The endeavour to develop biological closed systems of life-support for space stations and spaceships may not be unrelated to an eventual Mars mission, while the ability to keep cosmonauts in space for one year as was done with Mir in 1988 is possibly another indication of Soviet determination to press forward in this direction.

The Abandoned Option

The idea of sending an expedition to Mars is not new. It was part of a long-term space programme produced by President Nixon's space task group in the heady days of enthusiasm for manned space exploration which led to the first triumphant Moon landing. Archaeologists of the future may well puzzle over a derelict site in Nevada called Jackass Flats and surrounded by barren mountains, for it was there that NASA and the US Atomic Energy Commission set up the Nuclear Rocket Development Station (NRDS) and ran a series of tests, which were

REACTOR AND ENGINE SYSTEM TESTS	
NAME	**DATE**
Kiwi-B4D (one power test)	May 1964
Kiwi-B4E (two power tests)	Aug 1964-Sep 1964
NRX-A2 (two power tests)	Sep 1964-Oct 1964
Kiwi-TNT	Jan 1965
NRX-A3 (three power tests)	Apr 1965-May 1965
Phoebus-1A (one power test)	Jun 1965
NRX/EST (ten starts)	Dec 1965-Mar 1966
NRX-A5 (two power tests)	Jun 1966
Phoebus-1B (one power test)	Feb 1967
Phoebus-2 (cold flow tests)	Jul 1967-Aug 1967
NRX-A6 (one power test)*	Dec 1967
XECF (cold flow tests)	Feb 1968-Apr 1968
Phoebus-2A (three power tests)	Jun 1968-Jul 1968
Pewee-1 (two power tests)	Nov 1968-Dec 1968
XE (28 starts)	Dec 1968-Aug 1969
Note: *Operated 60 minutes at full power (1100MW)	

expected to lead to the first flight-ready nuclear rocket engines.

The principle is simple. Instead of burning liquid hydrogen with liquid oxygen in a conventional rocket, the nuclear engine has a carbon-moderated uranium reactor which operates at white heat. It contains channels through which the hydrogen is pumped at high pressure and flashed into a powerful propelling jet. No oxygen is required. The attraction of this technique (although the engine is much heavier and more expensive) is that the reactor, acting as a heat exchanger, raises the temperature of the hydrogen to the extent that its energy per unit weight of propellant is increased by nearly 70 per cent.

It was in May 1961 — at the time he established the Apollo Moon-landing programme — that President Kennedy recommended development of nuclear rocket propulsion technology. This led to the NERVA project and NASA and the AEC awarded a contract to the industrial team of Aerojet-General Corporation and Westinghouse Electric Corporation for the development of a NERVA engine of 55,000lb (25,943kg) thrust. NERVA stands for Nuclear Engine for Rocket Vehicle Application.

A NASA spokesman later explained:

"A NERVA-propelled nuclear stage could provide transportation of automated spacecraft for exploration of the surfaces to Mars, Venus, Mercury, some of the moons of Jupiter and certain asteroids. The return of samples to the Earth will be possible in some cases."

For the fully-fledged manned expedition to Mars, a larger NERVA engine of 200,000lb (90,703kg) thrust was envisaged. The thrust could be far smaller than the big chemical rockets which lifted Apollo spacecraft because they would begin their mission from Earth orbit. To achieve the necessary performance for interplanetary travel, the designers evolved a "building block"

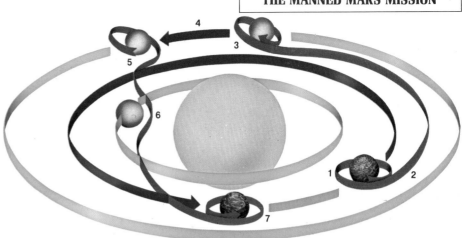

THE MANNED MARS MISSION

When the Moon Race with the Soviet Union was at its height in 1969, President Nixon's space task group laid plans for a bold new assault on the Space Frontier—a Manned Mission to Mars. The project depended on the use of NERVA thermodynamic nuclear rocket engines for which preliminary tests were already underway in the Nevada desert. The scheme involved assembling in Earth orbit two identical spaceships (for safety reasons), each carrying six astronauts. According to one option, the joint expedition would have set out in November 1981, land on Mars in August 1982 and return in August 1983.

NERVA

1 Base of liquid hydrogen tank.
2 Spherical pressurisation bottles.
3 Structural supports.
4 Radiation shield.
5 Reflector surrounding reactor core.
6 Carbon-moderated nuclear reactor (has channels through which LH₂ flows at high pressure).
7 Nozzle coolant pipe.
8 Nozzle.
9 Nozzle extension.
10 Reactor efflux to turbine.
11 Pressure shell.
12 Control drum.
13 Turbine exhaust (used for attitude control and thrust augmentation).
14 Ring of control-drum actuators.

NERVA Diagram

1 From LH₂ tank.
2 Pump.
3 Turbine.
4 Turbopump exhaust.
5 Nozzle coolant pipe (carries entire hydrogen flow).
6 Exhaust nozzle.
7 3% of reactor efflux.
8 Radiation shield.
9 Turbine power control valve.

The thermodynamic nuclear rocket scores over the conventional bi-propellant engine because the LH₂ can be heated (without being oxidised) to a much higher temperature, with consequent increase in thrust.

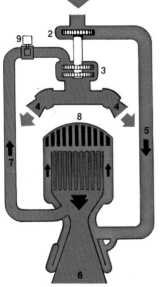

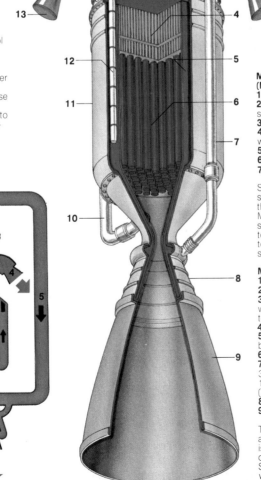

Mars Mission Profile

1 Two expedition ships assembled in Earth-orbit.
2 Inserted into near-Hohmann trajectory to Mars 12 November 1981.
3 Ships inserted into 24-hr elliptical orbit round Mars 9 August 1982.
4 Period of Mars exploration, including deployment of unmanned probes and landing excursions by three men from each ship.
5 Depart from Mars orbit 28 October 1982.

6 Venus swing-by 28 February 1983, brakes speed and deflects path for fast return to Earth. Probes released into atmosphere of Venus.
7 Insertion into Earth orbit 14 August 1983. Crews transfer to space shuttles for return to Earth's surface.

Dates are those used in the original study for round trip lasting 640 Earth-days.

Mars Excursion Module (MEM)

1 Docking port.
2 Control cabin (ascent stage).
3 Access to descent stage.
4 Command station within main consoles.
5 Laboratory.
6 Mars Roving Vehicle.
7 Ascent stage propulsion.

Separates from mother ship orbiting Mars with three-man crew; enters Martian atmosphere and soft-lands for a stay of up to one month. Crew return to mother ship in ascent stage.

Mars Spaceship

1 Stowage for probes.
2 Mars Excursion Module
3 Crew accommodation with central tunnel leading to MEM.
4 Two-stage NERVA core.
5 Strap-on NERVA boosters.
6 NERVA 2 engine.
7 LH₂ tank, diameter 33ft (10m), capacity 100,000-350,000lb (45,350-158,730kg).
8 Clustering attachments.
9 Docking port.

The Mars ship was to be assembled from standardised propulsion modules compatible with the Saturn V launcher. This was one of several options.

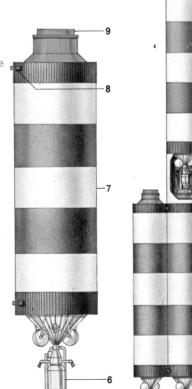

technology in which separate Nerva Propulsion Modules could be clustered together to meet different requirements.

For safety reasons it was proposed to build the Mars expedition around two ships of identical design. A crew of six would travel in each vehicle in quarters not unlike those envisaged for long-life space-stations. Leaving Earth-orbit on 12 November 1981 (according to one plan) they would be docked together nose-to-nose immediately their strap-on Nerva boosters had separated. These boosters would supply the only propulsion to put the vehicle on course to Mars, the core engines and fuel being reserved for later operations. Towards the end of the transfer path to Mars, the ships would separate in readiness for the braking manoeuvres which would allow them to swing into orbit around the planet.

The first stage of exploration would involve observations from orbit and the release of automatic probes to make independent soundings at proposed landing sites. When the results had been analysed, landing parties would descend in Apollo-like capsules while their parent ships continued to make scientific studies of the surface and atmosphere. To help them explore their surroundings, the landing parties would take with them electric-powered roving vehicles with laboratory facilities for making on-the-spot analyses of rock and soil samples. They would be limited to a stay time of about 30 days on the surface of Mars.

However, the return flight could not begin immediately the landing parties had rejoined their motherships. It would be necessary to wait a full 80 days from the time of arrival — while three planets, Mars, Venus and Earth — moved into the correct positions in their respective orbits. Should one of the ships become unserviceable, the full 12-person expedition could be accommodated in one vehicle. At the appointed time the engines would be re-started to put the re-docked vehicles on a return swing around the Sun. The trajectory would take them close to Venus so that its gravitational field provided a braking action, diverting the ships onto a path which intersected Earth in its orbit. After a round-trip lasting 640 days, the two ships (separated once more) swing into Earth orbit on 14 August 1983. The exploration teams would transfer to space shuttles and fly home.

Von Braun, who played a leading part in designing the mission, proposed that the big interplanetary ships should be parked in Earth-orbit so that after necessary servicing they could be refuelled with hydrogen and used for further missions. Even the discarded strap-on boosters, he believed, could be re-directed back into orbit for re-use.

End of a Dream

Several factors combined to eliminate the project from serious consideration. First, the high cost of a venture which in 1969 appeared to stretch technology to the limits. Second, the impact of the Vietnam War on the United States' economy, and third, the advance of robot exploration techniques which promised to yield basic data on Mars for a fraction of the cost. And fourth, the challenge of the Soviet Union to be first in space had faded. (Had Russians been first to

Above: *A nuclear rocket system ready for testing at the NRDS, Jackass Flats, Nevada, in 1966. This experiment was part of the ill-fated NERVA project.*

land on the Moon, it could have been a different story).

As a result, the NERVA Project, on which hundreds of millions of dollars had been spent, was terminated. It was probably a wise decision. The ground rules established by Tsiolkovsky — that the exploration of the Solar System should proceed from an orbital platform in Earth-orbit — seem basic to a venture of this kind.

Even better results were anticipated with nuclear-electric drive. Instead of using reactor heat to expand large amounts of hydrogen fuel through a nozzle, the nuclear reactor operates in a closed cycle, using its thermal energy to produce large amounts of electrical energy. As Glushko points out, electrical rockets require only small amounts of propellants. In the ion rocket, for example, the working gas is ionised — and electro-statically expelled. The ions have very small mass but very high velocities.

Whereas the thermodynamic nuclear rocket might develop some 200,000lb (90,703kg) to 250,000lb (113,379kg) thrust for a maximum of 40 minutes at the start of a flight to Mars, a large nuclear-electric system might produce as little as 20lb (9.07kg) thrust, but this could be maintained over very long periods. Assuming that nuclear-generators of suitable power-weight ratio are available, it should be possible to achieve much higher terminal velocities than with either chemical or nuclear rockets.

New Soviet Plans

Chief designer of the Energiya rocket, Boris Gubanov, believes that apart from its purely scientific importance, robot exploration of Mars and its satellites paves the way to Mars settlements. Energiya can lift payloads greater than 100 tonnes. "This gives us grounds to believe that it will be able to launch a multi-tonne manned spaceship towards Mars."

In December 1988 Oleg Borisov of the Soviet Academy of Sciences outlined a Soviet plan (presumably one of many) for landing men on Mars between 2005 and 2010. This would depend on two spaceships powered by nuclear-electric engines being assembled in Earth orbit after eight Energiya

launchings. Each would be powered by 80-tonne nuclear-electric engines located 328ft (100m) behind the 10 tonne crew compartment. After going into orbit around Mars, two cosmonauts plus roving vehicles descend to the surface in 60 tonne landing modules. After a set period the exploration party returns in ascent modules to re-dock with the orbiting "mother". The second spaceship is for supply and/or rescue.

If the Soviets are serious about applying nuclear-electric propulsion to an early Mars' mission considerable progress must have taken place in ground laboratories which must lead to a thorough regime of space testing. Small-scale tests of electric propulsion were made by NASA under the SERT programme (see Space Diary entry 4 February 1970). Apart from the huge technical problems involved in a practical nuclear-electric engine suitable for interplanetary flight, such development would inevitably raise international concern on the grounds of launch safety and possible environmental damage. Most schemes today rely on the use of high-energy chemical propellants.

In the Spring of 1989 the State Commission had included Mars exploration among five major technical research programmes to be pursued by the USSR. "Flight Mars" was stated to include development of a detailed engineering model of the Red Planet and study of "the technical potential of a manned expedition in 2015-17", somewhat later than previous estimates. Moreover, it would be considered viable only "if scientific knowledge of the USSR, USA and other developed countries were pooled."

The other research objectives were described as "Human Genome" (Genome: a full set of chromosomes with their associated genes); "Safe EAS"; "Artificial Intelligence" and "Automobile 2000".

An Evolutionary Approach

Let us consider an evolutionary approach: an expedition to Phobos followed by development on that tiny moon of a scientific base. Phobos is attractive from several standpoints. The energy to reach it is modest, only slightly more than going to the Moon because Phobos' gravity is minimal and it is in a high orbit around Mars. Landing would be more like rendezvous with a huge space station because of the planetoid's low gravity. Phobos (and its smaller cousin, Deimos) probably is a captured asteroid, a leftover from the creation of the Solar System and thus worth investigation in its own right. It would also serve as a base to leave instruments for remote Mars observations since the rock is in a synchronous orbit (like our Moon) always keeping one face to the planet.

A mission to Phobos would use the "split/sprint" approach popularized by the Ride Commission. An unmanned vessel is launched first with exploration gear and the crew's return stage. After a nine-month journey it is inserted in Mars orbit. A month after that the four-man crew embarks on their own nine-month journey to Mars (some options use a higher-energy stage to get there in a few months, hence the "sprint" terminology). One advantage of this approach is that the two ships needed for the trip can be prepared in sequence rather than both at once, thus reducing costs and launch requirements.

The crewship will rendezvous with the cargo ship in Mars orbit, and a two-man crew flies an excursion vehicle to the surface of Phobos. The crew will then spend almost three weeks collecting samples and emplacing science instruments. After 20 days they return to the main ship where the other two astronauts have been surveying Mars and remotely controlling rovers on the surface and refuelling from the cargo ship. After 30 days orbiting Mars, the crew blasts off for Earth, now four months away.

This seems a simple mission, but only in comparison to a landing on Mars itself. There are several technical challenges, including the maintenance of crew health in a micro-g environment for 14 months (two months longer than the 1988 Mir crew stayed in space), transferring large quantities of propellant in micro-g, and high-reliability systems that require minimal maintenance.

Below: *In this NASA study, astronauts explore the Valles Marineris canyons on Mars. This scenario envisages sending manned craft directly to the planet.*

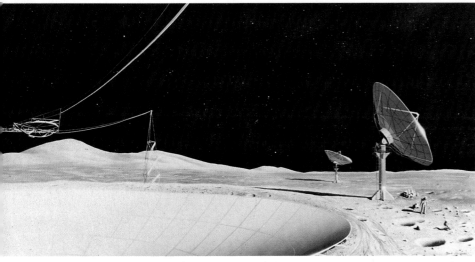

Above: *NASA views the establishment of a base on the Moon as building "a bridge between worlds". This artist's impression is of a lunar far side observatory.*

Below: *An evolutionary approach to landing on Mars calls for the creation first of an outpost on the Moon. This artwork depicts a possible lunar oxygen production plant.*

Bridge Between Worlds

Meanwhile, Man will have returned to the Moon, "a keystone for [planetary] science". An initial step might be a lunar observatory on the far side, isolated from the radio noise and light pollution of Earth (although half the month would find it exposed to the Sun's output). There, it will be possible to build immense radio telescopes out of flimsy structures that need withstand only 1/6th gravity and no winds. The year 2004 might see two landings on the far side, a cargo vehicle and a crew vehicle carrying four astronauts. They would spend two weeks setting up the radio telescopes, emplacing geophysics instruments in the neighbourhood, and gathering rock and soil samples. A pressurized rover would allow them to travel up to 6·2 miles (10km) away from the lander. A similar pair of missions could revisit and expand the site in 2005. The flights would take place only once a year afterwards further to explore the Moon or to maintain the observatory. Because the missions are short, no permanent habitation is set up — the crew lives in the landers — but robot vehicles will be needed to keep the facility active in the crew's absence.

Lessons from these missions would directly support expansion to Mars. Indeed, the National Commission on Space called the Moon a "bridge between worlds". One of its most important assets is oxygen. Since it is not free (the low gravity cannot retain an atmosphere) it has to be liberated from rocks which are metal oxides. Hydrogen might be available — in water ice trapped in shaded areas of the poles — but this is not a certainty. However, helium-3, an ideal fuel for fusion reactors, is available.

A permanently staffed facility would be established, requiring the transport of large quantities of equipment to the surface of the Moon. A split/sprint transport scheme could be used with crews taking a fast trip aboard high-energy chemical stages, the cargo having arrived before them aboard high-efficiency nuclear-electric shuttles. The landing parties would establish base camps first, scout the detailed geologic structure, and set up solar collectors and other equipment to "crack" lunar soil and rocks to yield oxygen. The slag itself could be useful in building foundations and other large structures for base expansion rather than continuing to bring materials from Earth. Towards the year 2010 enough experience will have been gained, and the output of the lunar mines will be great enough, that the mission to Mars can be attempted.

Again the split/sprint approach would be used with the cargo and exploration equipment being sent ahead by an unmanned vehicle. Among its cargoes would be a plant for producing both liquid hydrogen and oxygen from Phobos if its chemistry matches expectations. After robotic vehicles have emplaced these systems around Mars, the crew transport will be sent (unmanned) to the Moon for refuelling, followed by manning and departure.

The journey to Mars will take about eight months. The stay time at Mars can range from 60 days to two years, depending on exact mission plans. From facilities that this crew develops on the surface a base will grow enabling extended exploration of Mars.

Deep Space Habitat

Another ingenious scheme for Mars flight evolved during a joint workshop conference in 1987 co-sponsored by the World Space Foundation, the American Astronautical Society, NASA-JPL, Los Alamos National Laboratory, NASA-Ames Research Center, Johnson Space Center, MSFC and the Planetary Society. The object was to define the facilities required in Earth orbit to prepare for and assemble spacecraft for a sustained presence on Mars beginning with the first expedition.

Assisted by support facilities of Space Station Freedom, the project begins with the assembly of a rotating "Gravistation" in Earth orbit to verify habitability under Mars-level gravity (38 per cent of Earth's).

The expedition itself depends on assembling three almost identical spaceships alongside Freedom which, when fuelled and equipped, leave individually but dock together in flight to create a spinning Deep Space Habitat which eventually swings past Mars, dropping off crew. Most supplies would be carried on slower cargo vehicles sent ahead of the expedition.

Not only does the spinning complex ensure Mars-level gravitation in the crew compartments throughout most of the journey but it affords maximum security for the 15 crew with adequate redundancy of operating systems. Slung under the rotating arms are Mars Landers — shaped lifting bodies — each protected by "coolie hat" heat shield for entry into the thin Martian atmosphere. The Habitat's design is such that each Mars shuttle is surrounded by propellant tanks and structural elements, thus affording the travellers "storm shelters" for protection against radiation from major solar flares.

Several days before reaching Mars, the Habitat is de-spun using its thrusters. At the appropriate time the landing vehicles are

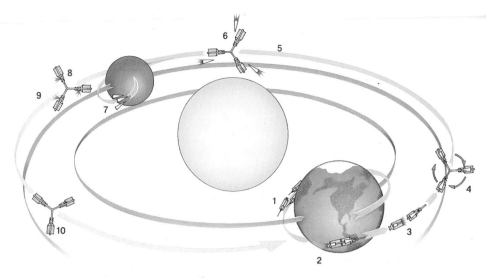

slipped from their berths with their respective crews to brake their fall into the thin atmosphere protected by the heat shields, finally to break free and glide down to a precision landing with the aid of parachutes and retro-rockets.

First priority for the exploration teams is to set up an economy base with plant for the manufacture of propellant. Using heat and electricity, atmospheric carbon dioxide is compressed, then electrolised to split it into carbon monoxide and oxygen, the propellants used in the landing vehicles' engines for ascent to orbit on the next trip.

Meanwhile, the Habitat, now without a crew, is course-corrected and sent on a return swing back to Earth where it arrives some 20 to 30 months later, the separate spaceships undocking to re-enter Earth orbit.

When the ships have been serviced and refuelled, they can be sent back to Mars

Deep Space Habitat
1 Three Interplanetary Vehicles (IPVs) are assembled in low Earth orbit.
2 IPVs launched towards Mars.
3 Vehicle staging.
4 Three IPVs dock and spin-up to form Deep Space Habitat. The Habitat spins at 3rpm to induce Mars-level gravity. Each IPV is manned by five crew; the expedition thus comprises 15 people.
5 Habitat despun.
6 Mars lander shuttles deployed two days before Mars encounter.
7 Aerocapture and landing on Mars by shuttles.

8 Periapsis burn ends.
9 Habitat respun.
10 Unmanned Habitat on Earth return trajectory. On reaching Earth orbit, it will be occupied by replacement crews.

This mission scenario grew out of a conference that was held in 1987 and attended by many of the USA's most important space institutions and study groups. As envisaged here, the crews would travel to Mars in a rotating "Gravistation" in which they would experience artificial Mars-level gravity. Mars shuttles and propellants are slung underneath.

Below: *Shortly after departure for Mars, the crucial docking manoeuvre between the three IPVs is underway. Once linked the IPVs become the Deep Space Habitat. All artist's impressions are by Carter Emmart.*

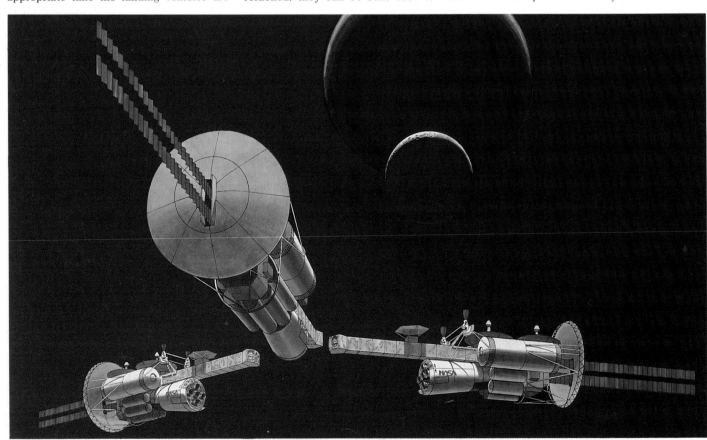

with replacement crews. Opportunities to launch occur every 26 months, an interval dictated by the relative orbits of Earth and Mars. The second mission drops off another crew in landers and as before swings past the planet. At about the time of the Habitat's closest approach, return crews waiting in Mars orbit fire up the engines of their aerospace vehicles which, within a day or two, will catch up with the unmanned Habitat and transfer into it. After the spaceships that comprise the Habitat separate to re-enter Earth orbit at the end of the loop, the same procedures apply as the first except that the aerospace vehicles used on Mars serve to recover the crews.

Three sets of Habitats and landers are required to send an expeditionary force to Mars at each successive launch opportunity. The first returns just prior to the departure of the third, allowing time for refurbishment.

International Collaboration?

There is no denying that colossal sums of money and major industrial support will be involved in setting up such ambitious projects. What, then, are the chances of the major powers proceeding to a Lunar Base and flights to Mars in cooperation?

It has been suggested that such a commitment would help maintain peaceful

Below: *The Mars lander shuttles are deployed from each of the arms of the Habitat in preparation for the actual descent to the planet's surface.*

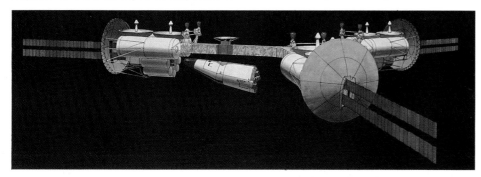

Above: *Braked by parachutes and retro-rockets, landers touch down on Mars. After landing, the vehicles are winched to the horizontal to begin surface operations.*

Below: *Equipment is deployed to establish a Mars base. A priority would be the creation of a plant to manufacture propellant for the return to orbit.*

relations; once started neither side would wish to pull out. Much will depend on realistic space budgets likely to be enforced in and beyond the Gorbachev era. The Soviets, more accustomed to planning in the long term with fewer political distractions than their counterparts in the West, seem more stable in this respect but even so there is always the possibility that a future international crisis could lead to one side "pulling the plug". The way in which budgets are administered in the West, with regular government changes and policy shifts, introduce great uncertainties when it comes to maintaining long-term funding on the scale envisaged. Economic distractions on the home front may also play a greater role in Soviet space planning in the future.

Few of the ventures we have discussed can be accomplished with existing technology. Robotic explorations of the Moon and Mars will be essential to scout the most promising sites for exploitation. The Path-finder Technology Program, started by the United States in 1987, may be expected to split technologies across a broad spectrum, including the SP-100 nuclear reactor programme which will provide multi-kilowatt or megawatt electrical capabilities in space. A similar life sciences research effort will use Space Station Freedom and other vehicles to expand human capabilities in space. An offshoot of this will be development of artificial gravity systems since it now appears that there are strict limits to human adaptability in space. This, in turn, will place new constraints on the design of spacecraft.

High-efficiency chemical and nuclear-electric stages must be developed for orbit-to-orbit transportation. Equally important, aerobraking must be developed as a means to slow spacecraft when they return from deep space (the Space Shuttle uses aerobraking, but at much lower speeds than interplanetary probes). This can reduce the mass of planetary expeditions by as much as 50 per cent.

In the style of explorers of the last centuries, NASA now sees this effort as affecting mankind as a whole:

"As more and more nations join together to explore space — the territory that cannot be claimed by any one nation — perhaps the narrow and artificial boundaries that exist on Earth will no longer matter. Major breakthroughs in science and technology will become possible, as the great minds and varying perspectives of many cultures combine to address the questions that face humanity in the future. Nations of the world may lay aside their differences and form alliances, not for defeating a common enemy, but for achieving a common goal . . ."
"This is our vision: humanity expanding its presence and activity beyond Earth orbit and into the Solar System, fulfilling mankind's aspirations to explore, to discover, to understand, and to apply what we have learned for the betterment of life on Earth and in space."

The Soviets express similar sentiments. We can only wait and see.

Space Diary

Few events in our history have been more impressive or significant for mankind than the dawn of space exploration. Strange new worlds swim into the view of our robot spacecraft ranging deep within the Solar System and we are becoming more aware of the chemistry that brought the mystery of life to our part of the Galaxy thousands of millions of years ago.

Today that evolved life has left footprints on the Moon and—always assuming our civilisation survives—may spread its influence among the stars.

Though we have no positive evidence that other civilisations exist outside our tiny global island, the quest will be one of the most fascinating of all the exciting explorations that await us. And now that the new instruments of astronomy routinely operate in space, our eyes are being opened to the wonders of the Universe as never before. Along the way we can look forward to learning more about our world—the one planet in a sea of apparent sterility that burgeons with life and which, through satellite observation, we are beginning to understand more fully.

Remembering those days at the start of the space era, when many scientists questioned the value of going into space, it is astonishing how rapidly the results have been transformed into useful techno-logy. One has only to think of the revolution that has taken place in telecommunications, navigation, meteorology and Earth-observation to recognise the dividend — and we are only just beginning. Barely 30 years after Gagarin, cells of human life in the form of small space stations swing round the Earth in regular orbits.

We must not forget that such incredible progress in our time owes much to imaginative people down the ages. All science and technology must start in the imagination, though sometimes an idea must wait years, even centuries, to strike root. And yet progress is influenced not only by the will of inventors and "dreamers" but by the political and economic environ-ment into which ideas are born. The Napoleonic Wars of the early 19th Century were the spur to big improvements in gunpowder rockets. The rise of Hitler in the 20th led to the major breakthrough in large liquid fuel rockets, and in the early years after World War II Stalin's determination to challenge the United States put the intercontinental ballistic missile into the forefront of technology. Krushchev's bid

to use rockets and Sputniks as instruments of world power and influence led directly to Kennedy's challenge to land men on the Moon. To achieve that signal goal many technical disciplines had to come together at the same time—not just rocketry and spacecraft engineering but radar and vastly superior radio communications, computers and much more.

The object of this "Space Diary" is to illustrate the step-by-step evolution that has gone to build our present Space Age. Expressing technical evolution in this way has many advantages. In the slow, often painful struggle to get new ideas accepted, we find many fundamental concepts being re-invented over the years and people working in isolation, often in different countries, totally unaware of work that has gone before. Johannes Winkler, for example, launched his HW-I liquid fuel rocket in Dessau, Germany, in 1931 fully believing that he had been first to succeed in this fundamental goal. It was not until 1936 that he heard that the American Robert H. Goddard had flown the world's first liquid fuel rocket at Auburn, Massachusetts, five years before him.

Coming more up to date we have the records of that truly remarkable era—the First Golden Age of Astronautics—that spans the period between the first Sputnik and the Apollo Moon landings.

The second era, now underway, involves the routine use of manned space stations for many practical purposes and the birth of a new age of flight in the reusable Shuttles of the USA and USSR.

In these pages we list some of the key steps of this rapid development including every manned flight that has taken place between Vostok 1 and the Shuttle. The dated entries help to put signi-ficant technical ideas and achievements into per-spective. There are many questions. Who were the principal inspirers of astronautics? Who were first to turn theory into practice? What are the ideas which, even today, look far into the future?

In preparing this unique record, acknowledgement must be given to several pioneers who were freely consulted. They include Hermann Oberth, Rolf Engel, Arthur Rudolph and the late Wernher von Braun—all truly "men of the first hour".

Kenneth W. Gatland
Ewell, Surrey, 1989

360 BC

Hollow model of a pigeon suspended by a string over a flame is made to move by steam issuing from small exhaust ports (described by Aulus Gellius in *Noctes Atticae*, "Attic Nights").

c. AD 62

Hero (or Heron), a Greek resident of Alexandria, invents the "Aeolipile", a hollow sphere with canted nozzles which spins on pivots by the reaction of steam jets. One of the supports on which the sphere rotates is hollow to admit steam generated in a "boiler" supported over a fire.

c. 850

Chinese use some form of gunpowder in making fireworks to celebrate religious festivals.

1232

Chinese repel Mongols besieging the town of Kai-fung-fu with "arrows of flaming fire". (If these are true rockets, as seems likely, the Chinese must have discovered how to distil organic saltpetre to increase rate of burning.)

Early Chinese solid-fuel fire-arrows.

1242

Roger Bacon, an English Franciscan monk, produces secret formula for "gunpowder": saltpetre 41·2; charcoal 29·4; sulphur 29·4. He also distils saltpetre — the oxygen-producing ingredient — to achieve faster rate of burning. The formula is concealed in an anagram written in Latin which (freely translated) reads: "... but of saltpetre take 7 parts, 5 of young hazel twigs, and 5 of sulphur; and so thou wilt call up thunder and destruction, if thou know the art".

1280

In *The Book of Fighting on Horseback and with War Engines,* the Syrian military historian al-Hasan al-Rammah gives instructions for making gunpowder and rockets which he describes as "Chinese arrows".

1379

Gunpowder rockets used in the siege of Chioggia, near Venice, Italy.

1680

Peter the Great establishes the first Rocket Works in Moscow (later transferred to St. Petersburg) to make signal illuminating rockets for the Russian Army.

1687

Sir Isaac Newton enumerates Laws of Motion; eg, in his third law he states that: "for every action there is an equal and opposite reaction" (principle of the rocket).

1770s

Capt Thomas Desaguliers examines rockets brought from India to Royal Laboratory, Woolwich, England, but fails to reproduce reported range or accuracy. (Some will not even lift from their stands.)

1780s

Indian ruler Hyder Ali, Prince of Mysore, employs iron-cased rockets with 8-10ft (2·4-3·0m) balancing sticks against troops of the East India Company. Weighing 6-12lb (2·7-5·4kg), they travel up to 1·5 miles (2·4km).

1789

Innes Munroe publishes *A Narrative of the Military Operations on the Coromandel Coast*. Describes an incident in 1761, when an Indian rocket corps of 1,200 men led by Hyder Ali of Mysore defeated British in the Battle of Panipat. Rockets volleyed at enemy cavalry 2,000 at a time travelled over half a mile (0·8km).

1792

Troops of Hyder Ali's son, Tippu Sultan (who enlarges rocket corps from 1,200 to 5,000 men and supplies them with larger rockets) use rockets against British in Third Mysore War. Tippu Sultan defeats British several times between 1782 and his death in battle at Seringapatam in 1799.

1804-05

Colonel William Congreve (later knighted) requests large rockets to be made at Woolwich to his specification. Because rockets have no recoil, he believes that they may be launched from ships as well as from land. Within one year he produces a 24lb (10·9kg) rocket with a range of 2,000yds (1,830m). He then produces 32lb (14·5kg) iron-cased rockets: length of casing 42in (107cm) x 4in (10cm) diameter; charge of 7lb (3·17kg); detachable balancing stick 15ft (4·6m) long. He develops a faster-burning powder to increase range.

Congreve tests rockets at Woolwich Arsenal, increasing range and accuracy. By 1805 he has demonstrated that a 6lb (2·7kg) rocket can travel about 6,000ft (1,830m) — approximately

Sir William Congreve (by J. Lonsdale).

twice as far as Indian rockets. (A 6lb rocket refers to the weight of a lead ball loaded into the cylindrical motor case; not the weight of the fuelled rocket.)

1806

October 8 First use of Congreve rockets during the Napoleonic Wars, when 18 rocket boats with sail and oarsmen attack Boulogne harbour. The iron-cased rockets are 32-pounders (14·5kg), 3·5ft (1·06m) long x 4in (10·1cm) diameter, to which are attached 15ft (4·6m) balancing sticks. Range is about 3,000yds (2,743m). Many of the rockets overshoot the French invasion fleet, setting fire to parts of the town.

1807

September 2-7 Congreve rockets are launched against Copenhagen, setting fire to large parts of the town. Blunt warheads discharge carbine balls; pointed heads have holes through which an incendiary mixture squeezes out after impaling wooden ships and buildings.

Congreve rockets from Copenhagen.

1813

A Treatise on the Motion of Rockets by William Moore, published by the Royal Military Academy, Woolwich, includes a mathematical description of the trajectories of rockets, including the motion of the rocket both in air and vacuum according to Newton's Third Law of Motion.

1814

September 13-14 British use Congreve rockets in the attack on Fort McHenry, Baltimore, inspiring Francis Scott Key to compose *The Star-Spangled Banner* which includes the phrase "... the rocket's red glare"

1828-29

Solid-fuel rockets designed by Alexander D. Zasyadko (1779-1837) are used in the Russo-Turkish War.

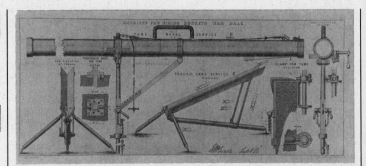

Launcher for William Hale rockets.

1840s

William Hale, an Englishman, produces spin-stabilised rockets by placing three curved metal vanes in the rocket exhaust. Employed by US forces in the Mexican War (1846-48), in the Crimean War (1853-56), in Hungary, Italy, Prussia, and during the American Civil War (1861-65).

1853-56

Some Russian ships are armed with rockets during the Crimean War.

1857

September 17 Konstantin Eduardovich Tsiolkovsky — who becomes the Father of Cosmonautics in the USSR — is born in the village of Izhevskoye, Spassky Uyezd, Ryazan Gubernia. (Died, Kaluga, 19 September 1935).

1865

Jules Verne, in his novel *De la Terre à la Lune* ("From the Earth to the Moon"), puts his passengers into a huge aluminium bullet fired towards the Moon from a giant cannon buried in Florida soil. Although the "space cannon" is impossible, the choice of Florida as the launch site is oddly prophetic of the actual Apollo Moon shots at Cape Canaveral, 100 years later.

The weightless environment of space as pictured in Jules Verne's novel, "De la Terre à la Lune".

Achille Eyraud (France), in his novel *Voyage à Venus*, makes first serious suggestion of the reaction principle as a means of space travel.

1869-70

A story published in *Atlantic Monthly*, "The Brick Moon" by Edward Everett Hale, contains first known proposal for a habitable Earth satellite of 200ft (60·9m) diameter. Hale considers weather, communication and navigation aspects.

1879

Jules Verne, in his novel *Les ang cents millions de la Begum*, suggests launching Earth satellites by means of rockets fired from a huge cannon.

1881

Nikolai Ivanovich Kibalchich (1853-1881), a Russian revolutionary sentenced to death by the Tsar, sketches a design for a man-carrying rocket platform stabilised by tilting the rocket motor in a gimbal frame. He proposes feeding gunpowder cartridges successively into a blast chamber. (The same steering principle is used in modern rockets.)

1882

October 5 Robert Hutchings Goddard — who becomes the Father of Astronautics in the United States — is born at Worcester, Massachusetts. (Died, Baltimore, 10 August 1945).

1883

Konstantin E. Tsiolkovsky, in *Outer Space*, develops the theory of reaction propulsion, arguing that a rocket will work in the vacuum of space.

1890

Hermann Ganswindt (Germany) proposes a reaction-powered spaceship fuelled with steel cartridges charged with dynamite.

1894

June 25 Hermann Julius Oberth, who became the Father of German Rocketry, is born in Sibiu on the northern slopes of the Transylvanian Alps.

1897

Kurt Lasswitz publishes science-fiction novel *Auf Zwei Planeten* ("On Two Planets"). Years later, Willy Ley applies the term "Repulsor", from the space rockets in this book, to the rockets for the VfR (Verein für Raumschiffahrt).

1898

H.G. Wells, in his novel *War of the Worlds,* describes a Martian invasion of Earth in which the invaders are eventually vanquished by terrestrial diseases.

1901

H.G. Wells, in his novel *The First Men in the Moon* "invents" an anti-gravity material, Cavorite, to transport his spaceship to the Moon.

1903

Tsiolkovsky, in treatise on space travel, advocates use of liquid propellants and establishes principles of spaceship design. First treatise is entitled: *Exploration of the Universe with Rocket-Propelled Vehicles;* supplements appear in 1911, 1912 and 1914.

Tsiolkovsky describes cylindrical spin-stabilised space habitat with artificial gravity and a "space greenhouse" with a closed ecological system in "The Rocket Into Cosmic Space", *Science Survey,* Moscow, 1903.

Konstantin Tsiolkovsky at work in the study of his home in Kaluga, which is now a national museum.

1909

Professor Robert H. Goddard (1882-1945) begins study of liquid-propellant rockets, concluding that liquid oxygen and liquid hydrogen would be an excellent combination.

A 1916 picture of Robert H. Goddard holding a circular vacuum tube.

1917

January 5 Goddard receives grant of $5,000 from Smithsonian Institution for work on rockets to probe the upper atmosphere.

1918

Goddard postulates nuclear-propelled "ark" carrying civilisation from a dying Solar System towards another star. Manuscript ("The Ultimate Migration", dated 14 January 1918) is sealed into an envelope for posterity and is not published (*The Goddard Biblio Log*, Friends of the Goddard Library) until 11 November 1972.

November 7 Goddard demonstrates tube-launched solid-propellant rockets (forerunners of "Bazooka") at Aberdeen, Maryland.

1919

Goddard publishes monograph, *A Method of Attaining Extreme Altitude,* containing basic mathematics of rocketry. One section entitled "Calculation of Minimum Mass Required to Raise One Pound to an 'Infinite Altitude'" is Goddard's carefully-worded reference to space flight, at this time a subject considered to lack the dignity of serious scientific enquiry. He outlines a scheme by which a rocket, with rapid-fire solid-propellant feed, might be made to impact the shadow side of the Moon with a charge of flash powder to announce its arrival. (Smithsonian Miscellaneous Collections, Vol 71, No 2).

1921

Soviets establish state-laboratory for research on solid-propellant rockets. Founder: N.I. Tikhomirov (1860-1930).

Fridrikh Tsander aged 26. He later developed the concept of solar sailing.

Fridrikh A. Tsander suggests a composite "aerospace" vehicle which takes off with propellers like an aeroplane; at altitude, liquid-fuel rocket engines are started and metallic parts of the vehicle no longer useful for flight are fed to a furnace to be used as fuel.

1923

H. Oberth's classic work, *Die Rakete zu den Planetenräumen,* is published.

November 1 Goddard operates small rocket motor burning liquid oxygen and gasoline fed by pumps, on a test stand.

1924

In book *Cosmic Rocket Trains,* Tsiolkovsky considers multi-staged rockets in which the lower stage returns to Earth after expending its propellants.

Tsiolkovsky, in an article "The Spaceship", proposes use of the atmosphere as a braking medium for vehicles returning from outer space. (Others reaching the same conclusion are Fridrikh A. Tsander in his article "Flight to Other Planets" and Yu V. Kon-

dratyuk, who shows that a properly designed aerofoil could result in large savings of propellant on re-entry.

1925

Walter Hohmann in his book *Die Erreichbarkeit der Himmelskörper* ("The Attainability of Celestial Bodies") defines principles of rocket motion in space.

1926

March 16 Goddard achieves world's first flight of liquid-propellant rocket at Auburn, Massachusetts (page 11).

1927

July 5 A group of German rocket enthusiasts, inspired by Oberth, form Verein für Raumschiffahrt. (Society for Space Travel). Meeting takes place in the parlour of an alehouse, the "Goldenen Zepter" (Golden Sceptre), Schmiedebrücke 22, Breslau. Principals: Johannes Winkler, Max Valier, Rudolf Nebel.

Max Valier proposes rocket aircraft developed from Junkers G.23.

1928

Dr Frank von Hoeff proposes 30-tonne rocket-powered lifting-body capable of taking off from water like a hydroplane. Upper stage is assumed to have orbital capability.

Capt Potocnik (pseudonym "Hermann Noordung") postulates three-element space station in Earth orbit: "Wohnrad" (living wheel), "Maschinenhaus" (machine station) and "Observatorium" (observatory). The "Wohnrad" assumes diameter of 98ft (30m).

Professor Hermann Oberth is contracted by UFA film company to build liquid-propellant rocket for launching on the day of the première of Fritz Lang film, *Frau im Mond* ("Woman on the Moon"). Assistants are: A.B. Scherschevsky (author of *Die Rakete für Fahrt und Flug,* or "The Rocket for Transport and Flight"), and Ing Rudolf Nebel (then employed as an advertising engineer with Siemens und Hulske, Berlin). Together they build and test a rocket chamber designed by Scherschevsky, fuelled with gasoline and liquid oxygen, fitted with *Spaltduese* ("slit nozzle") designed by Oberth. Although the chamber is inefficient ("burning like a blowtorch"), with the *Spaltduese* they achieve a thrust of 5·5lb (2·5kg). Oberth aims at

Hermann Oberth, aged 34, on the set of the UFA Fritz Lang film "Frau im Mond".

a rocket intended to reach an altitude of at least 62 miles (100km), but later this is reduced to 12·4 miles (20km). Propellants are to be either methane or alcohol with LO₂. Proposed launch site is to be the island of Horst on the Baltic coast. After experiencing difficulties with leaking tanks and pipework — and problems with getting the liquid oxygen into the tank — the rocket is set up in Horst and promptly explodes. The project is abandoned.

February 1 Robert Esnault-Pelterie and André Hirsch, a French banker, establish the REP-Hirsch International Astronautics Prize of 5,000 Fr to be awarded annually for the best original scientific work, either theoretical or experimental, that will advance the state-of-the-art in space travel or related sciences. (First recipient is Hermann Oberth for second edition of his book *Wege zur Raumschiffahrt*, "The Roads to Space Travel", 1929.)

June 11 Sailplane *Ente* (Duck) flies from Wasserkuppe Mountain, Germany, powered by two Sander solid-propellant rockets. After catapult launch, it flies more than three-quarters of a mile (1·2km) in about 60 seconds. Pilot: Fritz Stamer.

1928-32

Nikolai A. Rynin publishes nine-volume encyclopedia *Interplanetary Communications*, covering myths and legends of space travel, science fiction (Verne and Wells), methods for communicating with other worlds, rocket history, mathematics of propulsion, long-range artillery, aircraft, international rocket pioneers (including the work of Tsiolkovsky, Goddard, Esnault-Pelterie), astronavigation, and information on the Moon and planets. Extensive bibliography.

1929

Group for development of electric and liquid-propellant rocket engines is formed within Gas Dynamics Laboratory (GDL) under V.P. Glushko. Location: Admiralty building and St John Ravelin of the Peter and Paul Fortress, Leningrad.

J.D. Bernal (*The World, the Flesh and the Devil*, Methuen & Co, London) and Olaf Stapledon (*Star Maker*, K. Paul, Trench, Trubner & Co, London) describe concepts of artificial planets and self-contained worlds.

Yuri V. Kondratyuk publishes his best-known work, *The Conquest of Interplanetary Space*. Contains first known statement of orbital technique for landing on planetary bodies: "The entire vehicle need not land; its velocity need only be reduced so that it moves uniformly in a circle as near as possible to the body on which the landing is to be made. Then the machine part (*landing module. Ed*) separates from it, carrying the amount of active agent (*propellant*) necessary for landing and subsequently rejoining the remainder of the vehicle".

Kondratyuk proposes a lifting surface to brake the speed of a spacecraft returning to Earth from outer space. The craft, having entered the atmosphere, performs braking ellipses, slowly shedding speed by aerodynamic drag, and finally descends as a glider. Alternatively, the craft makes a direct descent through the atmosphere (like the Space Shuttle).

July 17 Goddard launches a "weather rocket" with a barometer, thermometer and camera. Instruments are recovered by parachute.

September 30 Fritz von Opel flies a rocket glider at Rebstock, near Frankfurt, powered by 16 solid-propellant rockets, each of 50lb (22·7kg) thrust. There is no catapult. The glider reaches 95mph (153km/h), is air-

Von Opel just before his flight; with him are Stamer (left) and F. Tsander.

borne for about 75 seconds, and travels nearly 5,000ft (1,525m).

November 23 Col Charles A. Lindbergh visits Goddard and subsequently arranges a grant of $50,000 from Guggenheim Fund for the Promotion of Aeronautics to support Goddard's work with rockets.

1930

Glushko designs USSR's first liquid-propellant rocket engine, the ORM-1.

Esnault-Pelterie, French rocket pioneer, publishes his major work *L'Astronautique*, ranging from consideration of sounding rockets to projects for interplanetary travel and including extensive mathematical treatment of rocket performance and trajectories. Work is an expansion of lectures to the French Astronomical Society (1927) and a book *L'Exploration par Fusées de la Très Haute et la Possibilité des Voyages Interplanétaires* (1928).

April 4 American Interplanetary Society is founded by G. Edward Pendray, David Lasser and others at apartment of Mr and Mrs Pendray, 450 West 22nd Street, New York City. Four years later (6 April 1934) name is changed to American Rocket Society (incorporated within Institute of

American Rocket Society Rocket 1.

Aeronautics and Astronautics, formed by merger of Institute of the Aerospace Sciences [IAS] and ARS, 1 February 1963).

May 17 Max Valier is killed by exploding steel-cased rocket motor, fuelled by kerosene/water mixture and liquid oxygen, at Heylandt factory in Berlin-Britz. Motor is being static tested for demonstration in rocket car Rak 7.

Valier in a liquid-fuelled rocket car.

July 23 Oberth's *Kegelduese* is static tested at the *Chemisch-Technische Reichanstalt* (see page 13).

October 19 Gottlob Espenlaub flies rocket glider at Düsseldorf, powered by Sander solid-propellant rockets, reaching 55·9mph (90km/h).

Gottlob Espenlaub's rocket glider takes to the air near Düsseldorf.

December 30 Goddard launches 11ft (3·3m) long liquid-propellant rocket at Roswell, New Mexico, which achieves altitude of 2,000ft (609m) and speed of 500mph (805km/h). Propellants liquid oxygen/gasoline, gas-pressure feed.

1931

Esnault-Pelterie starts development of rocket engine employing liquid oxygen/hydrocarbon for static testing.

Dr Eugen Sänger begins series of rocket-motor experiments at University of Vienna. Test motor has a spherical jacketed combustion chamber of approximately 2in (5·08cm) diameter with 10in (25·4cm) long nozzle. Light fuel oil is circulated through jacket before being injected into chamber for combustion with liquid oxygen. High combustion pressure of 30 to 50 atm obtained by Bosch injector of type used in contemporary Diesel engines. Average thrust 55lb (25kg); burning times up to 15 minutes.

January Klaus Riedel and Rudolf Nebel design a new combustion chamber after an idea of Guido von Pirquet. A cylinder of aluminium is spun into two hemispheres and fitted with an entry section for a conventional nozzle, the parts being welded together. The chamber is provided with a water-jacket for cooling and propellants are fed by upstream injection (as formerly proposed by Winkler). According to Engel, the motor is 10 times lighter than the *Kegelduese* and for the same propellant consumption gives 2·2lb (1kg) more thrust. A series of these motors is built, each having a dry weight of just 8·75oz (250g).

February Austrian engineer Friedrich Schmiedle establishes first officially-recognised rocket mail service. His solid-fuel rockets project mail for a distance of some 2 miles (3·2km) over mountainous country between the Austrian towns of Schöckel and Radegund. A parachute is automatically released after the rocket has ceased firing.

February 21 Johannes Winkler launches his HW-I (Hückel-Winkler) rocket, fuelled with methane and liquid oxygen, at Breslau. It hops 6·56ft (2m) into the air, turns over and falls back to the ground.

March 14 Winkler re-launches HW-I rocket fitted with stabilising fins. It climbs 295ft (90m), turning horizontally, and lands some 656ft (200m) from the point of departure. (This is the first known liquid-propellant rocket to fly in Europe).

April Klaus Riedel enlarges dimensions of aluminium rocket motor to give thrust of 70·5lb (32kg).

April 11 Rocket car of Heylandt/Valier team makes test run under thrust of improved liquid-propellant motor built by chief engineer Alfons Pietsch. New and more efficient propellant injector is designed by Arthur Rudolph. Motor weighing 30·7lb (18kg) is capable of producing up to 350lb (160kg) thrust for a few minutes. Another test run is made on 3 May.

April 15 Near Osnabrück, Reinhold Tiling demonstrates 6ft (1·82m) solid-propellant rocket of aluminium construction, with folding wings which open out for recovery.

R. Tiling with his folding-wing rocket.

Johannes Winkler with the HW-II on test at the Raketenflugplatz, Berlin.

May Johannes Winkler begins design of HW-II rocket.

May 10 First (unintentional) flight of liquid fuel rocket by VfR. A water-cooled Mirak III, developed by Riedel, "broke loose from its test stand and went up 60ft (18·3m)".

May 14 Same VfR rocket which made unscheduled flight on May 10, now re-named Repulsor 1, ascends 200ft (61m). It is a so-called "two-stick Repulsor", named from the fuel/nitrogen tank layout beneath the motor in the head.

June 9 Goddard patents design for rocket-propelled aircraft.

July-August Constantin Generales, an American medical student, and Wernher von Braun conduct in Zürich first known experiment in "space-medicine". They build a primitive centrifuge in which they place a number of mice to determine the effects of high rates of acceleration. Generales then dissects the mice to obtain physiological data.

August VfR launches a Repulsor rocket to an altitude of 3,300ft (1,006m), recovered by parachute.

September 20 *Gesellschaft für Raketenforschung* (Society for Rocket Research) is founded in Hanover by Albert Püllenberg and Albert Löw.

September 29 Goddard launches 9·94ft (3·03m) by 12in (30·5cm) rocket. Flight lasts 9·6 seconds, reaching 180ft (59m).

Goddard and assistants placing the October test rocket in the tower.

October 13 Goddard rocket with simplified combustion chamber climbs more than 1,700ft (518m). Length 7·75ft (2·36m) by 12in (30·5cm) diameter.

November 13 *Gruppa Isutcheniya Reaktivnovo Dvisheniya* ("Group for the Study of Reaction Propulsion") is formed in Leningrad under auspices of the Osoaviakhim (LenGird).

November 18 "Group for the Study of Reaction Propulsion" is formed in Moscow under auspices of Central Council of the Osoaviakhim (MosGird). Principal: F.A. Tsander.

1931-32

Glushko makes 100 static firings of series ORM rocket engines.

1932

Tsander publishes his book, *Problems of Flight by Jet Propulsion.*

Rolf Engel (with support from Hugo A. Hückel) forms rocket group within

the *Verein Deutscher Ingenieure* (Society of German Engineers)—a voluntary labour service for young engineers during the depression. Group is formed in Dessau, where a large number of engineers from the Junkers company are unemployed. Participants include Heinz Springer, Werner Preuss and (later) Werner Brügel. Activities end with arrest of Engel and Springer by Gestapo on grounds of "negligent high treason" (ie, communicating information about German rocket activities to enthusiasts abroad).

Spring Officials of Ordnance Department of the Reichswehr visit *Raketenflugplatz*, near Berlin: Col Prof Karl Becker, Chief of Ballistics and Ammunition; Major von Horstig, ammunition specialist; and Capt Dr Walter Dornberger, in charge of powder rockets for the German Army.

April 19 Goddard launches gyro-controlled liquid-oxygen/petrol rocket. Nitrogen gas pressure feeds propellants to thrust chamber and operates bellows working coupled air/exhaust control vanes.

July Klaus Riedel, Rudolf Nebel and Wernher von Braun stage rocket demonstration for Ordnance Department at Army Proving Grounds at Kummersdorf, about 60 miles (96·5km) south of Berlin. Mirak II, which reaches altitude of about 200ft (60·9m), crashes before parachute can open.

September Goddard resumes full-time teaching at Clark University, allowing him to make experiments in the laboratory under grant from Smithsonian Institution.

October 6 HW-II rocket built by Johannes Winkler, Rolf Engel, Hans Bermüller and Heinz Springer explodes on launch stand because of a malfunction of the liquid oxygen and liquid methane control valves (page 15).

Left to right: Hans Bermüller, Johannes Winkler, Rolf Engel, Heinz Springer and two unidentified journalists.

November 1 Wernher von Braun becomes civilian employee of the German Army at Kummersdorf, under Dornberger, charged with the development of liquid-propellant rockets.

General Walter R. Dornberger.

November 12 First liquid-fuel rocket built by American Interplanetary Society produces 60lb (27kg) of thrust for 20-30 seconds during static test, Stockton, New Jersey. Damaged and never flown. Basis of design: German "two-stick" Repulsor.

December 21 At Kummersdorf-West a 20in (50·8cm) liquid-oxygen/ethyl-alcohol rocket motor explodes on static test. Participants: Walter Dornberger, Walter Riedel, Heinrich Grünow and Wernher von Braun.

1933

Goddard receives grant from Daniel and Florence Guggenheim Foundation making possible further improvement of rocket components: welding techniques for light metals, pumps, thrust chambers, insulators, etc.

January At Kummersdorf, von Braun bench-tests a small, water-cooled rocket motor which develops a thrust of 308lb (140kg) for 60 seconds.

Von Braun, at Kummersdorf, makes plans for "A"-series of experimental rockets. A-1 rocket has regeneratively-cooled liquid-oxygen/alcohol motor of 661lb (300kg) thrust. Explodes on test stand within 0·5 second. Development abandoned.

May 14 American Interplanetary Society's Rocket No 2 ascends about 250ft (76m) from Great Kills, Staten Island, New York; then liquid oxygen tank bursts due to a stuck valve.

August 17 USSR launches world's first hybrid (solid/liquid propellant) rocket GIRD 09, from the Nakhabino Polygon, near Moscow. Propellants: liquid oxygen and gasoline and colophony, a dark-coloured resin obtained from turpentine. Rocket attains an altitude of about 1,312ft (400m), although motor burns through. Designed by M.K. Tikhonravov and built by a group which includes S.P. Korolev. Length 7·9ft (2·4m); launch weight 41·9lb (19kg); average thrust 66·1lb (30kg).

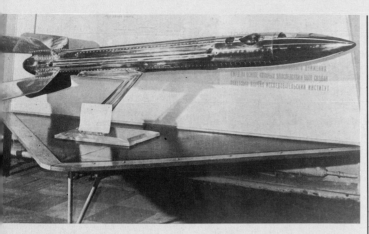

A model of the Tikhonravov-designed GIRD O9, the first Soviet liquid/solid fuel rocket to fly.

October Rocket engines OR-2 and OR-10 designed by Tsander are static tested.

Soviet liquid-propellant rocket engines ORM-50 and ORM-52 designed by Glushko (GDL) are static tested.

October 10 Reinhold Tiling, his laboratory assistant Miss Angelika Buddenböhmer, and Friedrich Kuhr, are fatally injured by an explosion while compressing some 40lb (18kg) of black powder into fuel pellets for rockets.

October 13 British Interplanetary Society is founded in Liverpool by P.E. Cleator. Because Explosives Act of 1875 precludes the development and testing of rockets on unlicensed premises, Society concentrates on theoretical studies in astronautics.

October 31 Soviets establish Reaction Propulsion Institute (RNII) on the basis of GDL and MosGird. Glushko's GDL group for the development of electric and liquid-propellant rocket engines continues as a department of RNII.

November 25 First Soviet fully liquid-propellant rocket, GIRD X, attains altitude of nearly 262ft (80m). Engine OR-2 designed by F.A. Tsander employs liquid oxygen and petrol. Overall length 7·2ft (2·2m); weight less than 66·1lb (30kg); thrust 154lb (70kg).

1934

Arthur Rudolph, one of Valier's assistants, joins the Kummersdorf group.

June 5 William G. Swan reaches altitude of 200ft (61m) in his "Steel Pier Rocket Plane" in Atlantic City, New Jersey, USA.

William Swan in his glider which was propelled by 12 powder rockets.

September 9 Successful flight test of fourth liquid-fuel rocket built by American Rocket Society, from Marine Park, Staten Island, New York, achieves distance of 1,338ft (407m), splashing into New York Bay. Has single-thrust chamber with four canted nozzles. (Originally tested 10 June 1943, but did not fly because fuel ports too small.)

December Two A-2 rockets, "Max" and "Moritz", launched by von Braun group from island of Borkum, North Sea, attain altitudes of about 1·5 miles (2·4km).

1934-35

Goddard begins testing A-series of rockets, employing pressure-feed and stabilised by gyro-controlled exhaust vanes, at Roswell, New Mexico.

1935

Glushko and G.E. Langemak publish their book, *Rockets, Their Design and Applications.*

March 8 Goddard flies liquid oxygen/gasoline rocket with pendulum stabiliser, reaching speed of more than 700mph (1,126km/h) and landing about 9,000ft (2,743m) from launch tower.

March 28 Goddard launches 14·8ft (4·51m) rocket which reaches 4,800ft (1,463m) altitude, travelling 13,000ft (3,962m) at average speed of 550mph (885km/h). Rocket corrected its path by action of gyro on vanes in the exhaust.

Summer Rocket motor installed in Heinkel He-112 is static-tested by Kummersdorf group (which now comprises some 80 people). Von Braun's group receives 5 million marks from Luftwaffe and 6 million marks from the Army (before this the annual budget did not exceed 80,000 marks!).

1935-36

Goddard begins new series of experiments in which the aim is to develop a more powerful liquid oxygen/gasoline rocket motor of 10in (25·4cm) diameter.

1936

Soviets launch "Aviavnito" sounding rocket to an altitude of 3·5 miles (5·6km). Length 10ft (3·05m), weight 213lb (96·6kg).

Glushko publishes *Liquid Propellants for Reaction Engines*, based on his course of lectures at Zhukovsky Air Force Academy.

February GALCIT Rocket Research Project is initiated at California Institute of Technology by Dr Frank J. Malina, J.W. Parsons and E.S. Forman. It pioneers work on hypergolic (self-igniting) propellants. Rocket experiments are made in the Arroyo Seco, north of Pasadena (now the site of the Jet Propulsion Laboratory). First application, in 1940, is JATO (jet-assisted take-off) for aircraft; later the Corporal and Sergeant missiles for the US Army, and the WAC-Corporal (first successful US sounding rocket) launched by a German A-4 in "Bumper Project".

T. von Karman, whose laboratory was used by GALCIT pioneers.

November 7 Goddard launches four-chamber liquid-propellant L-7 rocket, which climbs 200ft (61m), at Roswell, N.M.

1936-37

Rocket motor built by Esnault-Pelterie develops a thrust of 275lb (125kg) for 60 seconds.

1937

Dr Walter Thiel takes over von Braun's rocket facility at Kummersdorf "to study and perfect liquid propellant rocket motors".

February Walter H_2O_2 rocket engine assists take-off of Heinkel He-72 Kadett in experiment sponsored by German Air Ministry.

April Rocket engine of 2,200lb (1,000kg) thrust, fuelled by alcohol and liquid oxygen, installed in Heinkel He 112, is flight tested. (Static trials began in the summer of 1935.)

April Wernher von Braun's group moves into newly-constructed rocket research establishment at Peenemünde on the Baltic coast of Germany. More workers from Raketenflugplatz co-opted: Klaus Riedel, Hans Hueter, Kurt Heinish and Helmuth Zoike.

May 9 H.F. Pierce (American Rocket Society) launches a liquid-fuel rocket to about 250ft (76m) altitude at Old Ferris Point, Bronx, New York.

May 19 Goddard flies rocket with excellent automatic stabilisation.

July 28 Goddard flies 18·5ft (5·64m) by 9in (22·8cm) diameter rocket with movable tailpiece steering, wire-bound tanks, barograph payload. Reaches altitude of 2,055ft (626m), but parachute opens prematurely.

August 27 First Soviet gas-generator GG-1, designed by Glushko, completes bench tests.

A map showing Peenemünde and Greifswalder Oie island (top right).

Autumn Three A-3 rockets are launched from Greifswalder Oie. Much improved design has three-axis gyro control system operating exhaust vanes for control at low speeds. Also, liquid nitrogen pressurisation system, vaporiser, alcohol and oxygen valves, and two-stage propellant flow which largely eliminates ignition explosions. On first launch parachute opens prematurely after five seconds and rocket crashes into the sea. On second and third launches parachutes are omitted, but rockets still go out of control (page 16).

1937-38

Soviet ORM-65 rocket engine completes 30 ground tests in RP-318-1 glider designed by S.P. Korolev. Propellants: nitric acid/kerosene; thrust: 110 to 386lb (50 to 175kg); multi-start capability. Specific impulse 210-215.

1938-1942

Dr Eugen Sänger and Dr Irene Bredt conduct research into development of "antipodal rocket bomber" at Research

Model of the antipodal bomber and typical skip trajectory.

Institute for the Technique of Rocket Flight, Trauon, near Hanover, Germany. Overall length 91·8ft (28m); wing span 49·2ft (15m); launch weight 100 tonnes; maximum velocity 13,596mph (21,880km/h); maximum range 14,596 miles (23,490km). Launch method: captive rocket booster riding a monorail track 1·8 miles (2·9km) long; launch velocity Mach 1·5. After climbing at 30° under rocket power aircraft is intended to follow a ballistic trajectory of 100 miles (161km) apogee, followed by a series of aerodynamic "skips" in the upper atmosphere. Project abandoned 1942.

1938

April 20 Goddard rocket with barograph reaches 4,215ft (1,285m) altitude, landing 6,950ft (2,121m) from tower. Motor operated for 25·3 seconds.

Summer Successful launchings of A-5 rockets are made without guidance system at Greifswalder Oie.

An aerodynamic-test A-5 model before dropping from an He 111E. A-5s were successfully launched in 1938.

December 10 American Rocket Society tests 90lb (41kg) thrust regeneratively-cooled liquid-fuel rocket motor designed by James H. Wyld. (An improved Wyld motor subsequently [1941-42] becomes the basis for a US Navy contract to develop rocket-assisted take-off units for seaplanes).

1938-39

Goddard concentrates on development of small high-speed centrifugal pumps.

1939

British Interplanetary Society concludes two-year engineering study of technique for landing men on the Moon.

Glushko's rocket group separates from RNII to become independent design group of Moscow-based aero-engine factory.

June 20-July 3 Heinkel He-176, first rocket-plane employing liquid propellants, is test-flown at Peenemünde by Erich Warsitz. It is powered by a Walter engine of 1,100lb (500kg) thrust and has a pressurised cockpit which can be separated from the fuselage and recovered by parachute.

Autumn First A-5 with new gyro-control system operating exhaust vanes is launched from Greifswalder Oie—and recovered by parachute. (Approximately 25 of these test rockets—forerunners of the A-4—are launched over the next two years, some of them several times. Programme tests three different guidance systems. At first launchings are vertical, reaching

altitudes of 8 miles (12·9km); then inclined. Radio guide beams are also tested.)

1940

February 28 Russian rocket glider RP-318-1 designed by S.P. Korolev flies under power from modified ORM-65 rocket engine burning nitric acid/kerosene. Thrust is variable from 110 to 386lb (50 to 175kg); top speed 124mph (200km/h). Pilot: Vladimir P. Fyodorov. Tow aircraft: P-5.

June DFS 194, powered by 600lb (272kg) thrust Walter rocket engine, is test-flown by Heini Dittmar.

August 9 Goddard makes first rocket flight with propellant pumps at Roswell, N.M. Rocket attains 300ft (91·4m) altitude at velocity of only 10 to 15mph (16 to 24km/h).

1941

January 6 Goddard motor on static test develops highest thrust to date: 985lb (447kg).

September Goddard group begins work under contract from US Navy Bureau of Aeronautics and US Army Air Corps.

September 10 First glide test of Russian BI-1 rocket fighter designed by A. Ya Bereznyak and A.M. Isayev, from military airfield near Sverdlovsk. Tow aircraft: twin-engined bomber.

October 2 Me 163 rocket-powered interceptor, based on Lippisch tailless concept, attains 624mph (1,004km/h) during early test flight.

Pre-flight test of Me 163 propellant feed system. C-Stoff is being vented.

December 18 American pioneer rocket company—Reaction Motors, Incorporated—is formed by leading members of the American Rocket Society: James H. Wyld, Lovell Lawrence, John Shesta and Hugh F. Pierce. Subsequently produces engines

for various applications, eg, Bell X-1, X-15 research aircraft, Viking sounding rocket.

1942

March 19 American pioneer rocket company—Aerojet Corporation—is officially incorporated in California. (An outgrowth of the GALCIT Rocket Research Project begun by Dr Frank J. Malina and under the direction of Dr Theodore von Karman, California Institute of Technology).

May 15 Rocket interceptor BI-1 making low-level run under power flies into the ground, killing the pilot G. Ya Bakhchivandzhi. Aircraft is powered by RNII's D-1-A-1100 liquid-propellant rocket engine.

July Goddard group moves to Naval Engineering Experimental Station, Annapolis, Maryland. (Developments to July 1945 include liquid-propellant take-off unit for flying boats; also, variable-thrust rocket motors).

October 3 First successful A-4 rocket is launched at Peenemünde. It travels a distance of 118 miles (190km), reaching a maximum altitude of 53 miles (85km).

1943

First flight of Soviet RD-1 engine installed in tail of Pe-2R aircraft.

May-June Germans make operational test launchings of V-2 rockets at Blizna, Poland.

August 17-18 Six hundred RAF bombers raid Peenemünde rocket establishment causing some 800 casualties, about half being Soviet prisoners of war. Dr Walter Thiel, currently in charge of the A-4 power plant, is killed.

RAF photograph of Peenemünde used to plan the 600-bomber raid.

1944

Two versions of RD-1 engine are put into production by State Defence Committee (GKO). In 1944-45 flight

trials are made in Pe-2, La-7, Yak-3 and Su-6 aircraft.

Soviet design bureau (OKB) is established under A.M. Isayev to design cryogenic liquid-propellant rocket engines.

Spring Disused underground oil depôt south of Harz Mountains, Germany, converted into underground assembly plant—the so-called Mittelwerke—produces 300 V-2 rockets per month (later increasing to 900!).

The Mittelwerke plant; here a US soldier inspects a captured V-2 rocket.

June 22 California Institute of Technology receives US Army Ordnance contract for research and development of long-range rockets.

September 7 First V-2 rocket with one-tonne amatol explosive warhead is launched against London in retaliation for Allied air attacks on Germany. Civil Defence records show that about 4,320 V-2s are launched between 6 September 1944 and 27 March 1945, of which about 1,120 are directed against London and its suburbs, killing 2,511 people and seriously injuring nearly 6,000.

One of a mobile battery of three V-2s ready for launch in September 1944.

1945

Soviet GDL-OKB under V.P. Glushko begins development of high-thrust liquid-propellant rocket engines.

February Bachem Ba 349, first vertically-launched rocket interceptor, crashes on first and only manned test flight, killing the pilot. At 492ft (150m) cockpit cover carrying pilot's headrest flies off; the plane turns on its back, climbs inverted to 4,921ft (1,500m) at 15 degrees to the horizontal, and then dives into the ground. Powerplant: Ba 349A-HWK 109-509; Ba 349B—HWK 109-509D with cruise chamber.

Arthur C. Clarke (right) and F.C. Durant with a model of the Sänger bomber.

May Arthur C. Clarke, in memorandum placed before British Interplanetary Society, advocates geostationary (24hr) orbit for global telecommunications by satellite.

May 2 General Dornberger, Dr Wernher von Braun and other Peenemünde personnel, having fled westward in a convoy of vehicles, surrender to US 7th Army.

May 5 German rocket establishment at Peenemünde, on island of Usedom, and the port of Swinemünde, are taken by Second White Russian Army under General Konstantin K. Rokossovsky. Installations have been largely destroyed by retreating Germans.

Von Braun (centre) at White Sands.

September 20 Wernher von Braun and other leading German rocket engineers arrive in United States under "Project Paperclip".

October First group of German rocket engineers arrives at White Sands Proving Ground, New Mexico.

1945-46

GDL-OKB makes flight trials of RD-100 rocket engine for long-range ballistic missile (Soviet version of the German V-2) and a geophysical rocket (1RA-E).

1946

Soviet occupation forces reorganise V-2 rocket production in Germany. Ex-Peenemünde engineer Helmut Gröttrup is put in charge of Germans working at Zentralwerke in Niedersachswerfen. Instead of launching V-2s, they are static-tested at Lehesten under Soviet rocket engineer V.P. Glushko.

Work begins in United States on intercontinental ballistic missile programme (Project MX-774).

April 16-September 19 1952 Sixty-four V-2s—including six two-stage "Bumper" rockets—are launched from White Sands, N.M. Two "Bumper" rockets are launched from the Long Range Proving Ground, Florida (now USAF Eastern Test Range and Kennedy Space Center). One V-2 is launched from an US aircraft carrier.

June 28 V-2 rocket instrumented by Naval Research Laboratory (NRL) for upper air research reaches altitude of 67 miles (108km).

July-August Soviet rocket engineer S.P. Korolev designs "stretched V-2", lengthening propellant tanks by about 9ft (2·74m) and increasing engine thrust from 55,116 to 70,540lb (25,000 to 32,000kg), using two turbopumps in tandem.

August 18 Soviet Air Force flypast at Tushino, Moscow, includes demonstration of RD-1X3 rocket engine in S.A. Lavochkin's 120R aircraft.

September 28 Dr Frank Malina and Prof Summerfield of JPL (Caltec) give results of theoretical study on "The Problem of Escape from Earth by Rocket" at 6th International Congress for Applied Mechanics (Paris) (*J. Inst. Aero Sc.*, Vol 14, No 8), setting out requirements for multi-stage rockets capable of achieving escape velocity. Contains the suggestion that instrument could measure cosmic radiation. (Malina was responsible for developing at JPL the WAC-Corporal sounding rocket which, at Summerfield's suggestion, is launched as second stage from a German A-4 rocket in 1949.)

October 28 German rocket engineers recruited by USSR arrive in Moscow. They are divided into two groups: one (including Helmut Gröttrup) is established in Moscow suburb, near Datschen (Nii-88); the other, on the island of Gorodomlya in Lake Seliger, some 150 miles (241km) northwest of Moscow.

November 29 Academician M.V. Keldysh appointed chief of RNII.

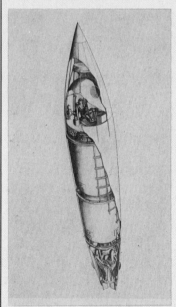

R.A.Smith's original drawing of the BIS man-carrying rocket proposal.

December 23 Study group of British Interplanetary Society (R.A. Smith and H.E. Ross) submits re-design of German V-2 as a man-carrying rocket with a separable pressurised cabin to give a man experience of space flight, including periods of weightlessness (*JBIS*, May 1948). Although proposal submitted to (then) Ministry of Supply is not adopted, the work is fully vindicated in the US Mercury-Redstone project, in which US astronauts (Shepard and Grissom) are exposed to short periods when they experience zero-g in 1961.

1947

GDL-OKB designs RD-101 engine for V-2-A medium-range missile and geophysical sounding rocket.

May 22 Corporal E surface-to-surface missile, launched at White Sands, New Mexico, is first to employ radar system of ground control.

June 20 "Bumper Project" for development of two-stage launcher based on German V-2 rocket and modified WAC-Corporal is initiated by US Army Ordnance.

Autumn German groups in USSR under Helmut Gröttrup design R.10 rocket of conical configuration: length 46·5ft (14·1m); maximum diameter 5·3ft (1·6m); launch weight 40,490lb (18,366kg); empty weight 4,235lb (1,921kg). Engine: improved A-4 type employing LO₂/ethyl alcohol; thrust 70,400lb (31,993kg). Propellant tanks of very thin steel are to be pressurised, forming integral part of structure. Warhead—with ablative wood covering—designed to separate after propulsion ends. Guidance: beam-riding. Design range 570 miles (917km). Although the R.10 is not produced as such, it undoubtedly plays a part in formulating ideas for Soviet missiles of the 1950s, developed under S.P. Korolev.

September 6 V-2 rocket is launched from aircraft carrier USS *Midway*.

This V-2 was the first large rocket to be launched from the deck of a ship.

October 14 Bell X-1 rocket-powered research aircraft, powered by four-chamber 6,000lb (2,722kg) thrust Reaction Motors RMI engine, makes first manned supersonic flight in history. Pilot: Charles E. Yeager. Launch aircraft: modified B-29.

October 30 Soviets begin launch tests of V-2 type missiles near the village of Kapustin Yar, some 75 miles (121km), east of Stalingrad (now Volgograd). First missile flies almost due east for nearly 175 miles (281km), landing "not too far from the target". Another V-2, launched the next day, goes out

of control and crashes from a height of about 500ft (152m). Present are Sergei Korolev and Helmut Gröttrup.

1948

Winter-Spring German rocket group in Moscow (Nii 88) merges with existing group at Gorodomlya, where Soviets continue to use personnel as consultants on various problems of rocket engineering. Work includes study of an R.12 multi-stage rocket to launch a 2,200lb (998kg) warhead to a distance of 1,500 miles (2,413km).

December 29 US Secretary of Defense James V. Forrestal reveals the existance of an "Earth Satellite Vehicle Programme". Studies undertaken within the framework of the RAND Corporation include such companies as Douglas, North American Aviation and Aerojet-General. The studies look towards military applications which would involve considerable engineering effort and heavy expenditure. RAND, for example, recommend a 500lb (227kg) satellite launched by a three-stage liquid oxygen/alcohol rocket; launch weight 233,669lb (105,992kg). Launch vehicle estimated to cost (1948 prices) $150 million. 'A later project recommends a liquid oxygen/liquid-hydrogen multistage rocket of 82,000lb (37,195kg) estimated to cost some $82 million. US Navy advocates a single-stage LO₂/LH₂ rocket, launch weight 101,000lb (45,805kg), named HATV (High Altitude Test Vehicle). Responding to this study are North American Aviation, Bureau of Aeronautics, Glenn L. Martin and Aerojet-General. The idea is that the entire vehicle will become the satellite, telemetering back data from instruments contained in the nose. None of these proposals is, in fact, taken up.

1948-49

Two Britons, Dr L.R. Shepherd, a Harwell physicist, and A.V. Cleaver, a leading British rocket engineer, examine feasibility of applying nuclear energy to rocket propulsion in classic series of papers published by the British Interplanetary Society. (*JBIS*, September, November 1948; January and March 1949).

1948-51

British Interplanetary Society advocates reducing scale and cost of engineering to achieve early experience of orbital flight with instrumented satellite, in series of studies, culminating in paper "Minimum Satellite Vehicles" by K.W. Gatland, A.M. Kunesch and A.E. Dixon, given at 2nd IAF Congress in London (*JBIS*, November 1951). Calculated that a three-stage rocket with "balloon tanks" and liquid oxygen/hydrazine propellants, with launch weight of about 16 tonnes, could orbit radar-reflecting inflatable balloon and single cosmic ray experiment. Conclusions are taken into account in early planning (1952) of Project Orbiter by Office of Naval Research, Washington, D.C., which leads to first US satellite Explorer 1 (see page 27).

1949

Dr Chien Hsueh-Sen, a member of the California Institute of Technology, proposes a boost-glide hypersonic aircraft of 3,107 miles (5,000km) range. (See also entry 1972 November).

A V-2/WAC-Corporal lifts off from the White Sands Proving Ground, N.M.

February 24 Two stage V-2/WAC-Corporal rocket launched from White Sands, N.M., attains record altitude of 244 miles (393km). American WAC-Corporal —designed and developed under direction of Dr Frank J. Malina at JPL —is propelled by an RFNA/aniline rocket engine with gas pressure feed producing 1,500lb (680kg) thrust for 45 seconds.

April German group at Gorodomlya prepares design study of R.14 rocket to launch a 6,600lb (2,994kg) warhead a distance of 1,800 miles (2,897km). Characteristics: single stage; balloon tanks of pressurised stainless steel or aluminium alloy; length 77·6ft (23·6m); diameter 9ft (2·74m); launch weight 156,200lb (70,852kg); dry weight 15,400lb (6,985kg); propellants LO₂/ethyl alcohol; thrust 220,000lb (99,792kg). Engine test stand of this thrust value established near Zagorsk, about 36 miles (58km) northeast of Moscow.

1949-1952

Systematic research into the effects of space flight on living organisms begins at Kapustin Yar. Dogs are rocketed to altitudes of some 60 miles (96·5km) within recoverable nose-cones of Pobeda rockets.

1950

May 11 Viking 4 sounding rocket is launched to record altitude of 106 miles (170km) from research ship USS *Norton Sound*, a converted sea-plane tender. Maximum velocity 5,160ft/sec (1,573m/sec). Location: near Christmas Island, Pacific Ocean. Object: to determine relationship between Earth's magnetic field and cosmic rays.

September 30-October 2 First International Astronautical Congress in Paris leads to formation of International Astronautical Federation (IAF) in London one year later. Principals: Gesellschaft für Weltraumforschung (GfW), West Germany; Groupement Astronautique, France; British Interplanetary Society.

November Arthur C. Clarke suggests possibility of mining the Moon and launching lunar material into space by electromagnetic catapult. ("Electromagnetic Launching as a Major Contribution to Space-Flight", *JBIS*, November 1950).

1951

March 21-November 28 1953 German rocket engineers taken to work in Soviet Union are repatriated to Germany in stages, beginning with lower-grade technicians and ending with senior design engineers, including Helmut Gröttrup and family. Among last to leave are rocket guidance specialists.

August Viking 7 sounding rocket achieves record altitude for single-stage rockets of 135 miles (217km) and speed of 4,100mph (6,597km/h).

The record-breaking Viking leaving the launch platform at White Sands.

The original Bell concept of the two-stage Project Bomi rocket aircraft.

1951-1955

Dr Walter Dornberger —former commandant at Peenemünde —and Dr Krafft A. Ehricke undertake design at Bell Aircraft Corporation of two-stage winged rocket aircraft under Project Bomi (Bomber Missile). Sub-orbital and orbital versions are envisaged, taking off vertically from a launch pad. Studies by USAF at Wright-Patterson Air Force Base. Project abandoned 1955.

1952

March Dr Wernher von Braun proposes a spinning wheel-shaped space station of 250ft (76·2m) diameter orbiting 1,062 miles (1,730km) above the Earth. ("Crossing the Last Frontier", *Colliers*, 22 March 1952).

May US Air Force announces that mammals—two monkeys ("Pat" and "Mike") and two mice— have been recovered alive and unharmed after being launched in an Aerobee sounding rocket to an altitude of some 200,000ft (60,960m) from Holloman AFB. The animals were subjected to a brief acceleration of about 15g, lasting less than one second, and to a force of 3-4g lasting 45 seconds. Animal

compartments were in nosecone of Aerobee which descended by parachute. Total programme includes three Aerobee launchings: 18 April 1951: monkey killed on impact; 20 September 1951: monkey and 11 mice recovered; 21 May 1952: two monkeys and two mice recovered. Conclusion: "Weightlessness does not appear to affect the animals' heart rates, blood pressure or respiration systems."

July Dr L.R. Shepherd considers "Noah's Ark" starship—a nuclear-powered million-tonne colony shaped like an oblate spheroid. ("Interstellar Flight", *JBIS*, July 1952).

1953

August 31 Douglas D-558-II, powered by 6,000lb (2,722kg) thrust engine, attains unofficial world's altitude record of about 15 miles (24·1km). Pilot: Lt-Col Marion E. Carl.

November 20 D-558-II flies at 1,325mph (2,132km/h), nearly twice the speed of sound. Pilot: A. Scott Crossfield.

December 12 Bell X-1A sets new unofficial speed record of more than 1,600mph (2,575km/h).

The Bell X-1 supersonic aircraft from which the X-1A developed.

1954

GDL-OKB begins development of RD-107 and RD-108 rocket engines for central core and strap-on boosters of first Soviet ICBM. Propellants: liquid oxygen/kerosene.

Design bureau under S.A. Kosberg begins work on aircraft rocket engine using monopropellant (isopropyl-nitrate).

1955

United States initiates research into nuclear rocket propulsion under Project Rover, a joint activity of the US Atomic Energy Commission and the US Air Force. Research is centred on graphite reactor design at Los Alamos Scientific Laboratory (LASL), concentrating on materials. Project, which initially examines the possibilities of nuclear rockets for military purposes, is switched in 1957 to a programme of nuclear rockets for space propulsion at LASL alone.

May 26 Soviets launch two dogs in geophysical rocket from Kapustin Yar (Volgograd cosmodrome). Seven similar sub-orbital experiments are flown over next two years.

May 31 Construction of the Baikonur cosmodrome begins on the steppes of Kazakhstan. Massive deployment of construction machinery is made to build launch facilities for the R.7 ICBM, preparation and test buildings, control station, highways and dormitory areas with heat and water supply. First stage of work is completed by April 1957. Nearby is site of Zvezdograd (Star City)—now Leninsk—adjoining the old town of Tyuratam.

July 15 President Eisenhower announces decision to launch a small scientific satellite based on Office of Naval Research (ONR) Project Orbiter and modified Jupiter-C launch vehicle. Later, it is decided to base America's first satellite attempt on a "civilian" launcher under Project Vanguard.

September 9 US Secretary of the Navy gives Naval Research Laboratory (NRL) authority to proceed with Project Vanguard satellite launcher for International Geophysical Year (IGY).

The third US Navy Vanguard test vehicle leaves Launch Complex-18 Pad-A at Cape Canaveral.

Autumn US Department of Defense assigns development of intermediate range ballistic missile, 1,500-mile (2,414km) range to Redstone group at Huntsville, Alabama.

1956

GDL-OKB begins development of RD-214 rocket engine for first stage of SS-4 Sandal MRBM. Propellants: nitric acid/kerosene. Thrust 74 tonnes; chamber pressure 45 atm (abs); specific impulse 264. Sandal is adapted as first stage of small Cosmos satellite launcher (B-1) introduced in 1962.

February 1 US Army Ballistic Missile Agency (ABMA) activated under Maj-Gen John B. Medaris to develop Jupiter IRBM.

July 23 Bell X-2, powered by Curtiss-Wright rocket engine of 15,000lb (6,804kg) thrust, sets unofficial world's speed record of 1,900mph (3,058km/h).

The Bell X-2 before its flight that broke the world's speed record.

September Darell Romick describes cylindrical Space Colony 0·6 miles (1km) long by 980ft (300m) diameter, with hemispherical ends and with 1,640ft (500m) rotating disc at one end, to be inhabited by 20,000 people. ("Manned Earth—Satellite Terminal Evolving from Earth-to-Orbit Ferry Rockets [METEOR]", IAF Congress, Rome, Italy, September 1956).

September 7 Bell X-2 sets new unofficial world's altitude record for manned aircraft exceeding 126,000ft (38,403m).

September 20 Three-stage Jupiter-C launched from Cape Canaveral on sub-orbital trajectory carries an 86·5lb (39·2kg) payload to an altitude of 680 miles (1,094km) and a downrange distance of more than 2,980 miles (4,800km). (At this stage the United States is approaching the ability to launch a small satellite into Earth orbit, but Project Orbiter has been halted by a political decision in favour of Project Vanguard. This is a decision that the Eisenhower administration lives to regret, since history now records that the world's first artificial satellite was launched by the Soviet Union.)

September 27 Bell X-2 sets new unofficial world's speed record for manned aircraft of 2,100mph (3,380km/h). Flight ends tragically when aircraft goes out of control and crashes, killing pilot Capt Milburn G. Apt.

1957

August First Soviet intercontinental ballistic missile, the R.7 (NATO codename Sapwood), is launched on test from newly-built launch centre north of Tyuratam in Kazakhstan. (Launch centre is later developed as Baikonur cosmodrome.)

An exploded view of Sputnik 1.

October 4 Soviets launch world's first artificial satellite, Sputnik 1, by R.7 ICBM from Baikonur cosmodrome.

A Soviet drawing of Laika with Sputniks 1, 2 and 3 in the background.

November 3 Soviets launch Sputnik 2, containing the dog Laika, by modified R.7 ICBM.

December 6 First US attempt to launch an artificial satellite, by Vanguard three-stage rocket, fails on launch pad at Cape Canaveral. Rocket develops insufficient thrust, topples over and explodes in flames.

1958

GDL-OKB begins design development of RD-219 rocket engine for second stage application. Thrust 90 tonnes; chamber pressure 75 atm (abs); specific impulse 293. Propellants: nitric acid/dimethylhydrazine. Flight tests 1961.

January 31 First US artificial satellite, Explorer 1, is launched from Cape Canaveral by Juno I. Instrumented by Dr James A. Van Allen, its major discovery is that the Earth is girdled by radiation belts.

Final preparations at Cape Canaveral for the "UE" Juno I/Explorer 1 launch.

March Richard L. Garwin publishes first technical discussion on possibility of using solar radiation pressure to propel a "solar sail" spaceship (*Jet Propulsion*, JARS, March 1958). Concept appears to have originated in the early 1920s with Konstantin Tsiolkovsky and F.A. Tsander. First mention in the USA of solar sail idea was made by Carl A. Wiley (pen name Russell Saunders) in *Astounding Science Fiction,* May 1951.

October 1 National Aeronautics and Space Administration (NASA) is formally inaugurated. Administrator: Dr T. Keith Glennan; Deputy Administrator: Dr Hugh L. Dryden.

October 7 NASA formally approves Project Mercury "to send a man into orbit, investigate his capabilities and reactions in space and return him safely to Earth".

December 12 Nosecone containing squirrel monkey "Old Reliable" is lost at sea following launch of a Jupiter IRBM from Cape Canaveral, Florida.

December 18 US launches into Earth-orbit Project Score (Atlas), which broadcasts human voice from space for first time: a recorded Christmas message from President Eisenhower.

1959

January 2 Soviets launch Lunik (Luna) 1 which misses Moon by 3,100 miles (5,000km) and goes into orbit around the Sun.

April 2 Seven astronauts are selected for Project Mercury: Captains L. Gordon Cooper, Jr, Virgil I. Grissom and Donald K. Slayton, USAF; Lt M. Scott Carpenter, Lt-Cmdrs Alan B. Shepard, Jr, and Walter M. Schirra, Jr, USN; Lt-Col John H. Glenn, Jr, USMC.

May 28 Monkeys "Able" and "Baker" recovered after flight in Jupiter nosecone launched from Cape Canaveral. "Able" later dies during an operation to remove bio-electrodes; "Baker" survives to take up residence at Alabama Space and Rocket Center, Huntsville, Alabama.

September 12 Soviets launch Lunik (Luna) 2, which becomes first man-made object to impact the Moon.

Lunik 2 probe on display in Moscow.

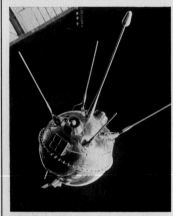

October 4 Soviets launch Lunik (Luna) 3, which circumnavigates the Moon to photograph the far side, returning images to Earth by television.

December 4 Monkeynaut "Sam" recovered in Mercury capsule abort test after launch on Little Joe LJ-2 from Wallops Island, Virginia. On 31 January 1960, "Miss Sam" makes a similar flight in Little Joe LJ-1B.

1960

April 1 First meteorological satellite, Tiros 1, is launched by United States. Drum-shaped; 22in x 42in (0·56m x 1·07m) diameter; 283lb (128kg) weight.

RCA technicians make their final pre-launch check of Tiros 1.

April 13 First experimental navigation satellite, Transit 1B, is launched by United States. Spherical; 3ft (0·91m) diameter; 267lb (121kg) weight.

May 24 First experimental infra-red surveillance satellite, Midas 2, is launched by United States. Cone-cylinder 23ft (7m) long x 5ft (1·5m) diameter; 5,070lb (2,300kg) weight.

August 12 NASA launches Echo 1, the first experimental passive communications satellite. Satellite has the form of a balloon of aluminized Mylar plastic which inflates to a diameter of 100ft (30·5m) in space. It is successfully used to reflect radio waves from ground-based transmitters to receiving Earth stations separated by thousands of miles; e.g., Holmdel, New Jersey, USA—Jodrell Bank, Cheshire, England. LC Cape Canaveral. LV Delta. D 24 May 1968. A 135ft (41·1m) diameter balloon satellite, Echo 2, is launched 25 January 1964, made of thicker material.

Echo 1 during an inflation test.

August 18 US Air Force launches Discoverer 14 from Vandenberg Air Force Base into orbit of 115 x 500 miles (186 x 805km) x 79·65°. Releases re-entry capsule, first to be air-snatched by aircraft (C-119). A similar capsule, from Discoverer 13, parachuted into the sea, 11 August 1960.

August 19-20 Sputnik 5 is launched from Baikonur cosmodrome with two dog-passengers, Strelka and Belka. First recovery of living creatures from orbital flight. Vostok prototype. LC Baikonur. LV A-1. FT 1·1 days.

Final check-out of Courier comsat.

October 4 US Army launches active repeater communications satellite, Courier 1B, which records signals from Earth stations and re-transmits them on command.

October 10-14 Two Soviet space rockets "failed in flight" on 10 and 14 October, according to NASA. Believed to be concerned in attempts to launch unmanned spacecraft to Mars while Premier Nikita Khrushchev is attending UN in New York. One source refers to a major accident at the Baikonur cosmodrome.

October 13 Three mice, "Amy", "Sally" and "Moe", make successful sub-orbital flight into space in RVX-2A nosecone of Atlas D ICBM launched from Cape Canaveral. They endure some 20 minutes of weightlessness.

December 1 Soviets launch two dogs, "Pchelka" and "Mushka", in Sputnik 6 (Vostok prototype). After circling the Earth for nearly 24 hours, ground control sends the command for retrofire, but spacecraft is seemingly misaligned: the re-entry trajectory is too steep and the capsule (and dog passengers) burns up in the Earth's atmosphere. LC Baikonur. LV A-1. FT 1 day.

December 19 First Mercury-Redstone flight vehicle (MR-1A) is launched on sub-orbital flight from Cape Canaveral. Unmanned capsule ascends 130 miles (209km) and splashes 235 miles (378km) downrange.

1961

GDL-OKB begins design development of RD-253 topping cycle rocket engine for first stage of Proton launch vehicle. Flight tests begin 1965. (Engines of upper stages developed by Kosberg-OKB.)

Work begins on the Spaceport at Merritt Island, Cape Canaveral, Florida, subsequently the John F. Kennedy Space Center.

January 31 A 137lb (62kg) chimpanzee, "Ham", is recovered after sub-orbital flight in Mercury capsule

Ham in the couch designed for MR-2.

launched by Redstone MR-2 from Cape Canaveral. Height of achieved trajectory is 155 miles (249km); downrange distance 420 miles (676km). Flight is meant to achieve 115 miles (185km) altitude and 290 miles (467km) range, but thrust of booster is "higher than expected".

March 24 Professor Carl Sagan proposes scheme to make Venus habitable by injecting colonies of algae into atmosphere to reduce CO_2 concentration. ("The Planet Venus", *Science*, Vol 133, 24 March 1961, pp. 849-858).

25 March Last trial launching of Vostok-type spacecraft, making one Earth revolution, before first manned space flight. Includes a dummy cosmonaut and dog, "Zvesdochka". Similar test (with "dog Chernushka") 9 March 1961 also succeeded. LC Baikonur. LV A-1. FT 0·1 day.

April 12 Soviet Union launches first man into space. Lt Yuri Gagarin in Vostok 1 completes one circuit of the Earth in a flight lasting 108 minutes. Orbit ranges between 113 x 204 miles (181 x 327km) x 65° to equator. Total distance travelled is 25,400 miles (40,868km). LC Baikonur. LV A-1. LT 0907 MT. R near village of Smelovaka, Ternov District, near Saratov.

Yuri Gagarin in the hour of triumph.

April 20 Harold Graham, 27-year-old engineer, makes first free-flight with Bell Aerosystems rocket belt. Flight lasts 13 seconds and covers distance of 112ft (34·1m). On a later flight Graham flies up and over a 30ft (9·1m) hill with a slope of about 60°, maintaining a parallel course about 3 to 4ft (0·98 to 1·31m) from the ground.

May President Kennedy recommends development of nuclear rocket propulsion technology; this leads to the NERVA Project and the award of a contract to the industrial team of Aerojet-General and Western Electric for the development for flight testing of a NERVA engine based on the LASL Kiwi-B reactor. The contract then specifies a NERVA engine of 55,000lb (24,948kg) thrust (1,100 MW) and a specific impulse of 760. (NERVA is the acronym of Nuclear Engine for Rocket Vehicle Application.)

May 5 NASA launches Cdr Alan B. Shepard, Jr, in Mercury 3 spacecraft *Freedom 7* on sub-orbital flight lasting 15min 22sec. Maximum altitude 116 miles (186km); distance travelled 297 miles (478km). Astronaut demon-

Alan Shepard goes aloft in MR-3.

strates ability to achieve manual control of spacecraft under weightlessness. LC Cape Canaveral. LV Modified Redstone. LT 0934 EST. R Atlantic, USS *Champlain*.

May 25 President Kennedy, at a joint session of Congress, declares national space objective: "I believe that this nation should commit itself to achieving the goal, before this decade is out, of landing a man on the Moon and returning him safely to Earth...."

July 21 NASA launches Lt-Col Virgil I. Grissom in Mercury 4 spacecraft *Liberty Bell 7* on sub-orbital flight lasting 15min 37sec. Maximum altitude 118 miles (190km); distance travelled 303 miles (487km). Mission successful but spacecraft sinks; astronaut recovered. LC Cape Canaveral. LV Modified Redstone. LT 0720 EST. R Atlantic, USS *Randolph*.

Grissom's capsule wallows during the unsuccessful recovery attempt.

August 6-7 Major Gherman Titov in Vostok 2 completes 17 Earth revolutions in flight lasting 25hr 18min. Distance travelled 436,656 miles (703,150km). LC Baikonur. LV A-1, LT 1130 MT. R Saratov region, about 450 miles (724km) SE of Moscow.

October 27 First launch of Saturn 1 (Block 1) vehicle demonstrating validity of clustered engines. Launches dummy upper stages on sub-orbital trajectory, reaching 98 miles (157·5km) apogee, 246 miles (396·3km) downrange.

November 10 Monkey "Goliath" dies when Atlas E launched from Cape Canaveral is destroyed in flight by range safety officer. Experiment is 'Small Primate Unrestrained Test' (Spurt).

November 15 First known poem to be sent into space is inscribed on an instrument panel of the satellite Traac launched from Cape Canaveral. Called "Space Prober", it is by Prof Thomas G. Bergin, Professor of Romance Languages, Yale University:
"From Time's obscure beginning, the Olympians
Have, moved by pity, anger, sometimes mirth,
Poured an abundant store of missiles down
On the resigned, defenceless sons of Earth.
Hailstones and chiding thunderclaps of Jove,
Remote directives from the constellations,
Aye, the celestials have swooped down themselves,
Grim bent on miracles or incarnations.
Earth and her offspring patiently endured,
(Having no choice) and as the years rolled by
In trial and toil prepared their counter-stroke—
And now 'tis man who dares assault the sky.
Fear not, Immortals, we forgive your faults,
And as we come to claim our promised place
Aim only to repay the good you gave
And warm with human love the chill of space."
Traac—which achieves an orbit of 585 by 695 miles (941 by 1,119km) has a lifetime of some 800 years.

November 29 NASA launches Mercury 5 capsule with chimpanzee passenger "Enos". Spacecraft is commanded down after two orbits because of development of abnormal roll rate. Chimp recovered in good condition. LC Cape Canaveral. LV Atlas D. FT 3·3hr.

December 20 Rhesus monkey "Skatback" is launched in Atlas F ICBM from Cape Canaveral.

1962

February 20 Lt-Col John H. Glenn becomes first American to orbit the Earth in space. His Mercury 6 capsule *Friendship 7* completes three Earth revolutions in flight lasting 4hr 55min 23sec. Retro-rocket pack retained during re-entry when false signal indicates possibility of loose heat shield. Safe recovery. LC Cape Canaveral. LV Atlas D. LT 0947 EST. R Atlantic, USS *Noa*, about 210 miles (338km) NW of San Juan, Puerto Rico.

John Glenn sits next to the capsule in which he made three Earth orbits.

May 24 Lt-Cdr M. Scott Carpenter in Mercury 7 spacecraft *Aurora 7* completes three revolutions of the Earth in flight lasting 4hr 56min 5sec. LC Cape Canaveral. LV Atlas D. LT 0845 EDT. R Atlantic, USS *Pierce*, about 125 miles (201km) NE of Puerto Rico.

June 27 North American X-15, powered by Reaction Motors engine of 50,000lb (22,680kg) thrust, flies at 4,105mph (6,605km/h). Pilot: Joseph A. Walker, NASA. Launch aircraft: modified B-52.

July 10 NASA launches Telstar 1, first privately-financed communications satellite (by American Telephone & Telegraph Company) into elliptical orbit; this enables Earth stations tracking the satellite to transmit live television between North America and Europe. Periods of communication limited to about 20 minutes when Telstar is above the horizon of communicating terminals. Serviceable until February 1963. Weight 170lb (77kg); diameter 34·5 in (87·6cm). Orbit 592 x 3,500 miles (952 x 5,632km) x 44·79°. Telstar 2 is launched 7 May 1963 into higher orbit to reduce exposure to damaging radiation in the Van Allen belt.

Telstar 1: pre-flight check-out.

August 11-15 Major Andrian G. Nikolayev in Vostok 3 completes 64 revolutions of the Earth in flight lasting 94hr 22min. First television from a manned spacecraft. Distance travelled 1,639,190 miles (2,639,600km). LC Baikonur. LV A-1. LT 1130 MT. R S of Karaganda (48°02'N, 75°45'E).

August 12-15 Lt-Col Pavel R. Popovich in Vostok 4 completes 48 Earth revolutions in flight lasting 70hr 57min. First dual flight with another manned spacecraft, passing within some 4 miles (6·5km) of Vostok 3. Distance travelled 1,230,230 miles (1,981,050km). LC Baikonur. LV A-1. LT 1102 MT. R S of Karaganda (48°10'N, 71°51'E).

August 27 NASA launches Mariner 2 spacecraft to achieve flyby of Venus on 14 December 1962. Finds heavy atmosphere, mostly carbon dioxide, 100 times the pressure of Earth's; surface temperature exceeding 800°F (426·7°C); no magnetic field.

Preparations for the Mariner 2 launch.

October 3 Cdr Walter M. Schirra, Jr, in Mercury 8 spacecraft *Sigma 7* completes six Earth revolutions in flight lasting 9hr 13min 11sec. Distance travelled 153,900 miles (247,625km). Lands 4·5 miles (7·2km) from recovery ship. LC Cape Canaveral. LV Atlas D. LT 0815 EDT. R Pacific, USS *Kearsarge*, about 295 miles (475km) NE of Midway Island.

November 1 Soviets launch Mars 1 spacecraft from Baikonur. Expected to pass within 620-6,700 miles (998-10,780km) of Mars on 19 June, 1963, but communications lost 21 March 1963. Carries photo-TV system for photographing surface of Mars; instruments for discovering organic compounds on planet's surface, and spectrometer; magnetometer for cosmic rays and radiation belt investigations, etc. LC Baikonur. LV A-2-e. Weight spacecraft: 1,970lb (893·5kg).

December 13 Relay 1, NASA prototype for an operational communications satellite, is launched into an orbit of 821 x 4,622 miles (1,322 x 7,439km) inclined at 47·49° to the equator to test transmission of television, telephone, facsimile and digital data. Size 2·66ft (0·81m) long x 2·43ft (0·74m) diameter. Weight 172lb (78kg).

1963

Dandridge Cole suggests Space Colony habitat made from hollowed-out asteroid of ellipsoidal form, some 18·6 miles (30km) long, with landscaped interior, rotating about its major axis to create artificial gravity. Mirrors reflect sunlight inside to give impression of daylight. Similar concept proposed to achieve migration to the stars.

May 15-16 Major L. Gordon Cooper, Jr, in Mercury capsule *Faith 7*, completes 22 Earth revolutions in flight lasting 34hr 19min 49secs. Distance travelled 583,469 miles (938,801km). LC KSC (Cape Canaveral). LV Atlas D. LT 0904 EDT. R Pacific, USS *Kearsarge*, about 80 miles (129km) SE of Midway Island.

June 14-19 Lt-Col Valery F. Bykovsky in Vostok 5 completes 81 Earth revolutions in flight lasting 119hr 6min. Passes within 3·1 miles (5km) of Vostok 6. Travels more than 2,050,620 miles (3,300,000km). LC Baikonur. LV A-1. LT 1459 MT. R about 337 miles (540km) NW of Karaganda on latitude 53°.

June 16-19 Junior Lieutenant Valentina V. Tereshkova, first woman in space, completes 48 Earth revolutions in Vostok 6 in flight lasting 70hr 50min. Travels about 1,242,800 miles (2,000,000km). LC Baikonur. LV A-1. LT 1230 MT. R 390 miles (627km) NE of Karaganda on latitude 53°.

Valentina Tereshkova receives the BIS gold medal from Dr. L. R. Shepherd.

August 22 North American X-15 reaches altitude of 67 miles (108km). Pilot: Joseph A. Walker, NASA. Under NASA ruling pilot qualifies as an astronaut, having exceeded altitude of 50 miles (80·5km).

September 25 Col Yuri Gagarin, speaking at Paris Congress of the International Astronautical Federation (IAF), states: "Techniques being developed in my country involve the assembly of components of spacecraft in Earth-orbit and the introduction of propellant." The technique is being adopted "because it was not possible to launch vehicles of several scores of tons directly to the Moon".

October Nikita Krushchev talks of watching the Americans reach the Moon: "We will see how they fly there, and how they land there ... and, most important, how they take off and return".

October 4 On sixth anniversary of Sputnik 1, Col Yuri Gagarin writes: "It

may, of course, be too bold of me to conclude that interplanetary travel will be a fact within a few years. Preparations for these flights will call for a still greater effort including many more flights into Earth-orbit...." When these experiments are completed, "we shall be able to assemble spacecraft of any size in flight and the refuelling problem, which is so important for protracted space travel, will also be solved".

Secretary of the Air Force Eugene M. Zuckert in front of an X-20 mock-up.

December 10 US Air Force's X-20 Dyna-Soar project is abandoned. Project began in late 1950s with Boeing as prime contractor; aimed at developing a one-man space-glider capable of orbiting Earth and returning to land on a runway. Booster: Titan III.

December 13 Soviets launch first experimental meteorological satellite, Cosmos 23. Orbit 149 x 381 miles (240 x 613km) x 49°

1964

July 28 NASA launches Ranger 7 on mission to obtain close-up pictures of lunar surface down to impact. Hits Moon 31 July after 65·6hr flight, Sea of Clouds 8·5°S, 19·5°W. Returns 4,306 photographs.

August 19 NASA launches Syncom 3 communications satellite into geostationary orbit above International Date Line. Broadcasts opening ceremonies Tokyo Olympics. Preliminary experiments: Syncom 1 (14 February 1963, radio failed); Syncom 2 (26 July 1963). LC Cape Canaveral. LV Thrust Augmented Delta.

October 12-13 Col Vladimir M. Komarov, Dr (of Sc) Konstantin P. Feoktistov and Dr (of Medicine) Boris G. Yegorov in Voskhod 1 complete 16 Earth revolutions in flight lasting 24hr 17min 3sec. First three-man crew in space; Feoktistov, spacecraft designer, and Yegorov, medical doctor, specialists gaining first-hand experience of space flight. Distance travelled 415,936 miles (669,241km). LC Baikonur. LV A-2. LT 0730.1 MT. R about 194 miles (312km) NE of Kustanai.

November 28 NASA launches Mariner 4 spacecraft to achieve flyby of Mars on 14 July 1965. Twenty-one close-up pictures reveal cratered surface from distance of about 6,000 miles (9,656km). No evidence of "artificial canals" or flowing water. Atmospheric density about one-hundredth that of Earth, mostly carbon dioxide.

1965

February 16 NASA launches Pegasus 1, first Saturn launch vehicle with operational payload (meteoroid detector); first TV from orbiting satellite. Separation of "boilerplate" Apollo CSM from S-4 stage.

March 18-19 Col Pavel I. Belyayev and Lt-Col Alexei A. Leonov in Voskhod 2 complete 17 Earth revolutions in flight lasting 26hr 2min 17sec. Leonov performs world's first spacewalk lasting 10 minutes; total time outside pressurised cabin (including time in extensible airlock) 23min 41sec. Distance travelled 445,420 miles (716,680km). Faulty sensor in attitude control system enforces extra Earth orbit, with manual control of re-entry by Belyayev. LC Baikonur. LV A-2. LT 1000 MT. R near Perm, Urals, some 746 miles (1,200km) NE of Moscow.

Leonov during man's first spacewalk.

March 23 Lt-Col Virgil I. Grissom and Lt-Cdr John W. Young in Gemini 3 complete three Earth revolutions in flight lasting 4hr 53min. First US two-man space mission; first spacecraft to manoeuvre from one orbit to another. LC Cape Canaveral. LV Titan II. LT 0924 EST. R USS *Intrepid*, Atlantic, off Grand Turk Island.

April 6 First geostationary commercial communications satellite, Early Bird (Intelsat 1), is launched from Cape Canaveral.

Testing Early Bird at Hughes.

April 23 Soviets launch Molniya 1A communications satellite into 12-hr elliptical orbit inclined at 65° to equator for relay of telephone and TV services within USSR.

June 3-7 Capt James A. McDivitt and Capt Edward H. White, II, in Gemini 4 complete 62 Earth revolutions in flight lasting 97hr 56min 31sec. White spacewalks for 21 minutes; manoeuvres in space with gas-gun. First EVA by US astronaut; first extensive manoeuvre of spacecraft by pilot. Distance travelled 1,609,700 miles (2,590,000km). LC Cape Canaveral. LV Titan II. LT 1015.59 EST. R USS *Wasp*, Atlantic, 390 miles (628km) E of Cape Canaveral.

Gemini 4: Ed White's spacewalk.

July 16 Soviets launch 12·2 tonne Proton 1 automatic space laboratory to study the primary particles of high-and-low energy cosmic rays. Heaviest Soviet payload to date. First use of new heavy launch vehicle. Proton 2 (2 November 1965) and Proton 3 (6 July 1966) similar. LC Baikonur. LV D-1. FT 86·86 days.

August 21-29 Major L. Gordon Cooper, Jr, and Lt Charles Conrad, Jr, in Gemini 5, complete 120 Earth revolutions in flight lasting 190hr 55min 14sec. Demonstrate man's ability to function in space environment for long period. Use fuel cells for electrical power supply; evaluate guidance and navigation system for future rendezvous missions. LC KSC (Cape Canaveral). LV Titan II. LT 0900 EST. R USS *Champlain*, Atlantic, 335 miles (539km) SW of Bermuda.

December 4-18 Major Frank Borman and Lt-Cdr James A. Lovell, Jr, in Gemini 7, complete 206 Earth revolutions in flight lasting 330hr 35min 17sec. World's longest manned space flight to date. Provide rendezvous target for Gemini 6. Distance travelled 5,716,900 miles (9,198,492km). LC KSC (Cape Canaveral). LV Titan II. LT 1230.03 EST. R USS *Wasp*, Atlantic, about 700 miles (1,727km) SW of Bermuda; splashdown is 6·4 miles (10·3km) from target.

Geminis 6 and 7 rendezvous in orbit.

December 15-16 Cdr Walter M. Schirra, Jr, and Capt Thomas P. Stafford, in Gemini 6, complete 16 Earth revolutions in flight lasting 25hr 51min 43sec. Mission includes rendezvous and station-keeping with Gemini 7, closing to within about one foot (30cm) of that vehicle. LC Cape Canaveral. LV Titan II. LT 0837.26 EST. R USS *Wasp*, Atlantic, 630 miles (1,014km) SW of Bermuda.

1966

January 31 Soviets launch Luna 9 to the Moon; lands 3 February, Ocean of Storms, west of craters Reiner and Marius. First mechanical object to land in working condition; sends panoramic pictures by television.

Model of Luna 9 with "petals" open.

March 16 Neil A. Armstrong (C) and Capt David R. Scott in Gemini 8 complete 6½ Earth revolutions in flight lasting 10hr 41min 26sec. Achieve first docking between a manned spacecraft and an unmanned space vehicle—Gemini Agena Target Vehicle (GATV)—but experiment ends prematurely when a thruster in Gemini malfunctions, causing the combined spacecraft to spin. After separating the spacecraft the astronauts make a safe return to Earth. (In subsequent Apollo programme, Armstrong becomes commander of Apollo 11 and "the first man to walk on the Moon" (see 1969 July 16-24). LC KSC (Cape Canaveral). LV Titan II. LT 1141.02 EST. R USS *Mason*, Pacific, 690 miles (1,110km) SE of Okinawa; splashdown is 1·1 miles (1·8km) from planned target in secondary recovery area.

March 31 Soviets launch Luna 10, which becomes first artificial satellite of the Moon on 3 April.

May 30 NASA launches Surveyor 1, which soft-lands 1 June, after 63hr 36min flight, just north of crater Flamsteed, Ocean of Storms, 2°27'S, 43°13'W. Sends 11,237 pictures by television.

June 3-6 Capt Thomas P. Stafford and Lt Eugene A. Cernan in Gemini 9 complete 45 Earth revolutions in flight lasting 72hr 20min 50sec. Achieve

rendezvous with Augmented Target Docking Adapter (ATDA), but docking frustrated because nose shroud of ATDA has failed to jettison. Cernan carries out 2hr 8min of EVA, unrelated to ATDA. Distance travelled 1,255,630 miles (2,020,308km). LC KSC (Cape Canaveral). LV Titan II. LT 0839.33 EST. R USS *Wasp*, Atlantic, some 345 miles (555km) E of Bermuda; splashdown 0·38 miles (0·61km) from target.

Cernan (left) and Stafford emerge from Gemini 9 aboard the recovery ship.

July 18-21 Lt-Cdr John W. Young and Capt Michael Collins in Gemini 10 complete 43 Earth revolutions in flight lasting 70hr 46min 39sec. First use of target vehicle—Agena—as source of propulsion after docking, setting new altitude record for manned spacecraft of 474 miles (763km). Also rendezvous with Gemini 8 target vehicle. Collins' stand-up EVA 49 minutes; EVA to retrieve experiment from Agena 8min 39sec. LC KSC (Cape Canaveral). LV Titan II. LT 1720.26 EST. R USS *Guadalcanal*, Atlantic, some 529 miles (851km) due E of Cape Canaveral.

10 August NASA launches Lunar Orbiter 1 which swings into orbit round the Moon on 14 August after 92hr 1min flight. Photographs about 2 million sq miles (5·18 million sq km), including 16,000 sq miles (41,440 sq km) over primary Apollo landing sites.

Gordon astride the nose of Gemini 11.

September 12-15 Lt Charles Conrad, Jr, and Lt-Cdr Richard F. Gordon, Jr, in Gemini 11, complete 44 Earth revolutions in flight lasting 71hr 17min 08sec. Achieve first-revolution rendezvous and docking with Agena target; use Agena propulsion to achieve record altitude of 850 miles (1,368km). During EVA, Gordon fastens Agena-anchored tether to Gemini docking bar, and spacecraft later make two Earth revolutions in tethered configuration. Gordon EVA time 2hr 43min. LC KSC (Cape Canaveral). LV Titan II. LT 0942.26 EST. R Atlantic, 701 miles (1,128km) E of Miami.

Astronauts Lovell and Aldrin (waving) are recovered from their Gemini 12.

November 11-15 Lt-Cdr James A. Lovell, Jr, and Major Edwin E. Aldrin, Jr, in Gemini 12, complete 59 Earth revolutions in flight lasting 94hr 34min 31sec. Docks with Agena target on third revolution. Aldrin works outside spacecraft, including standup EVAs, for record 5hr 30min. First solar eclipse photo from space. Distance travelled 1,628,510 miles (2,620,272km). LC KSC (Cape Canaveral). LV Titan II. LT 1546.33 EST. R USS *Wasp*, Atlantic.

December 21 Soviets launch Luna 13 to Moon; lands Ocean of Storms (18°52'N, 62°3'W) on 24 December. 360° panoramic camera reveals surface objects down to 0·38 to 0·50in (1·5 to 2·0mm) across. Also carries soil density meter and gamma ray density meter on extensible "flop out" arms.

1967

James E. Webb, NASA Administrator, tells House Space Committee in Washington that Soviet Union is developing a launch vehicle which may have a thrust exceeding 10 million lb (4·5 million kg); it could appear "during 1968 or shortly thereafter".

January 27 Crew of first manned Apollo mission, Lt-Col Virgil I. Grissom, Lt-Col Edward H. White, II, and Lt-Cdr Roger Chaffee, die when fire breaks out in their command module during a launch pad rehearsal at KSC. Capsule had been installed on unfuelled Saturn 1B.

Vladimir Komarov's widow at his tomb.

April 23-24 Col Vladimir M. Komarov, making first manned test flight in new spacecraft Soyuz 1, is killed when parachute lines of re-entry module become entangled after returning from orbit. Believed that one of solar panels on spacecraft did not deploy, de-stabilising spacecraft and impeding attitude control. Flight time 26hr 45min; number of Earth revolutions 18. LC Baikonur. LV A-2. LT 0335 MT. R crashed outskirts of Orenburg.

June 14 NASA launches Mariner 5 to achieve flyby of Venus 19 October 1967. Confirms and refines Mariner 2 findings. Finds that exosphere of Venus is made up of hydrogen, as is that of Earth. Detects Venerian ionosphere.

October 30 Cosmos 186 and 188 achieve first automatic rendezvous and docking during 49th Earth revolution of Cosmos 186. TV camera shows act of docking. Spacecraft fly together, linked mechanically and electrically, for 3·5hr. Both craft separate Soyuz-type capsules for recovery 31 October and 2 November 1967 respectively.

November 9 First Saturn V flight, unmanned, from Kennedy Space Center, sending Apollo 4 into Earth-orbit for test of spacecraft re-entry module.

1968

Dr Peter E. Glaser originates concept of Satellite Solar Power Station beaming energy to Earth by microwave. ("Power from the Sun, Its Future", *Science*, Vol 162, 1968).

March 27 Col Yuri Gagarin, first man in space, and flying instructor Col Vladimir Seryogin die in aircraft accident during routine flight in two-seat MiG-15 from airfield adjoining Star Town cosmonauts' training centre. The MiG takes off at 1019 MT; it is said to have crashed some 30 miles (48·3km) E of Moscow at 1031.

April 4 Second Saturn V flight, unmanned, sending Apollo 6 into Earth orbit. Despite propulsion difficulties in second and third stages, Apollo spacecraft are tested satisfactorily.

June 28 Early Bird (Intelsat 1) in geostationary (Clarke) orbit achieves third anniversary in commercial service, more than doubling original life expectancy, including 220hr of received and transmitted television.

September 14 Soviets launch Zond 5 on first circumlunar flight, returning to the Indian Ocean (32°38′S, 65°33′E). Flies within 1,212 miles (1,950km) of lunar surface. Carries tortoises, wine flies, mealworms, bacteria, plants and seeds; broadcasts tape-recorded voice giving simulated instrument values. Objective: "to perfect systems and units for trajectory manoeuvring and return to Earth".

October 11-22 Capt Walter M. Schirra, Jr, Major Donn F. Eisele and R. Walter Cunningham (C), in Apollo 7 command and service modules, complete 163 Earth revolutions in flight lasting 260hr 9min 03sec. First manned mission of Apollo programme, demonstrating ability of spacecraft, crew and manned space flight network to conduct Earth orbital mission; live TV broadcast from

The crewmen of Apollo 7 stand on the prime recovery carrier USS Essex.

space. LC Cape Canaveral. LV Saturn ID. LT 0711 EDT. R USS *Essex*, Atlantic.

October 26-30 Col Georgi Beregovoi in Soyuz 3 completes 61 Earth revolutions in flight lasting 94hr 51min. Beregovoi, at 47, is oldest man in space to date. Manoeuvres near unmanned Soyuz 2 in test of spacecraft modified after Soyuz 1 accident. Automatic systems are used in radar search phase, bringing the two craft within 656ft (200m) of each other. Final approach to Soyuz 2 "target" is under manual control, but (apparently) there is no attempt to dock. A second rendezvous manoeuvre is made after the ships have drawn apart 351 miles (565km). LC Baikonur. LV A-2. LT 1134 MT. R "in pre-set area of Karaganda".

November 10 Soviets launch Zond 6 on circumlunar flight, returning to Soviet Union by aerodynamic "skip" in Earth's atmosphere. Flies within 1,503 miles (2,418km) of lunar surface. Carries automatic camera, biological specimens, nuclear emulsions, micrometeoroid detectors. LC Baikonur. LV D-1-e.

November 16 Soviets launch 17-tonne Proton 4 automatic space laboratory, with 12·5 tonnes of scientific apparatus. Object: to study "the nature of cosmic rays of high and ultra-high energies and their interaction with atomic nuclei". LC Baikonur. LV D-1.

November 30 First attempt by European Launcher Development Organisation (ELDO) fails to orbit a test satellite by Europa I (F7) from Woomera, Australia. Electrical interference in German (Astris II) third stage operates the self-destruct system on separation.

First launch of the ELDO Europa I rocket from the Woomera range.

Searchlights illuminate the Saturn V/ Apollo 8 stack before launch from LC-39 Pad-A at Cape Canaveral.

December 21-27 NASA launches Apollo 8 (CSM only) on world's first manned flight to vicinity of the Moon. Col Frank Borman (Cdr), Capt James A. Lovell, Jr (CMP) and Lt Col William Anders (LMP) orbit the Moon 10 times in 20hr 6min, coming within 70 miles (112·6km) of lunar surface, televising scenes to Earth. Total flight time of two-way mission—launch to splashdown—is 147hr 0min 42sec. LC Cape Canaveral. LV Saturn V. LT 0751 EST R USS *Yorktown*, Pacific.

1969

Professor Gerard K. O'Neill begins study of Space Colonies at Princeton University.

Breakfast is served aboard Soyuz 4.

January 14-17 Col Vladimir A. Shatalov in Soyuz 4 completes 48 Earth revolutions in flight lasting 71hr 14min. Achieves first docking between two manned spacecraft. After joining up with Soyuz 5, two cosmonauts, Yeliseyev and Khrunov, spacewalk to Soyuz 4 to join Shatalov for the return flight. Spacecraft separate after 4hr 35min. LC Baikonur. LV A-2. LT 1039 MT. R about 25 miles (40km) NW of Karaganda.

January 15-18 Col Boris Volynov, Aleksei S. Yeliseyev (C) and Col Yevgeny Khrunov in Soyuz 5 participate in major docking experiment with Soyuz 4. Volynov returns alone after his two companions transfer to other craft by EVA lasting about 1 hour. Flight time 72hr 46min; number of Earth revolutions, 49. LC Baikonur. LV A-2. LT 1014 MT. R about 124 miles (200km) SW of Kustanai.

February 24 NASA launches Mariner 6 to achieve flyby of Mars 31 July 1969. Together with Mariner 7 (launched 27 March 1969; fly-by 5 August 1969) takes some 200 close-up pictures that show smooth, cratered and chaotic surfaces. Confirms and refines atmospheric data. Flies within 2,000 miles (3,218km) of planet.

March 3-13 NASA launches Apollo 9 into Earth orbit in first flight of complete spacecraft (CSM/LM). Col James A. McDivitt (cdr); Col David R. Scott (CMP) and Russell L. Schweickart (LMP) (C) complete 151 Earth revolutions in flight lasting 241hr 00min 54sec. Crew evaluate Lunar Module for first time in space, qualifying total system for lunar flight. Achieve first docking of CSM with LM. First crew transfer from CSM/LM through interior docking tunnel. EVA from LM, by Schweickart, lasts 37min. LC KSC. LV Saturn V. LT 1100 EST. R USS *Guadalcanal*, about 1,000 miles (1,609km) E of Cape Canaveral.

March 20 Test firings of NASA/AEC NERVA-XE experimental nuclear rocket engine in a vertical stand begin at Nuclear Rocket Development Station, Jackass Flats, Nevada. This is non-flying prototype of 75,000lb (39,019kg) thrust engine intended for flight-testing in late 1970s.

May 18-26 NASA launches Apollo 10 in full dress rehearsal of Moon landing. Col Thomas P. Stafford (cdr), Cdr John W. Young (CMP) and Cdr Eugene A. Cernan (LMP) demonstrate Lunar Module *Snoopy* rendezvous and docking with CSM *Charlie Brown* in lunar orbit, confirming all aspects of lunar landing procedures except actual descent. Stafford and Cernan fly separated LM to within 9·4 miles (15km) of lunar surface. Number of Moon revolutions by CSM, 31, taking 61hr 34min; 4 revolutions by undocked LM. Total flight time of mission 192hr 03min 23secs. LC KSC. LV Saturn V. LT 1249 EST. R USS *Princeton,* Pacific.

June NERVA experimental rocket engine is run under close to full power 50,000lb (22,680kg) for the first time under simulated altitude conditions. In all, 15 rocket reactors are tested, the last of which, the XE, is started up 28 times. In the course of three tests, a specific impulse of 825 is demonstrated for extended durations in a flight-size reactor. A range of thrust levels, including the NERVA thrust of 75,000lb (34,019kg), is demonstrated The ability to stop and restart at will is also demonstrated. Despite its success, the project is terminated in the early 1970s.

July 3 Prototype of Soviet super-booster (Type G-1) catches fire and explodes seconds after it had been launched from Baikonur cosmodrome (earlier failure 21 February 1969).

July 13 Soviets launch Luna 15 automatic Moon probe into lunar orbit, as US attempts first landing by manned spacecraft on Sea of Tranquillity. After manoeuvring in lunar orbit, probe crashes in Sea of Crises (about 17°N, 60°E) some two hours before Apollo 11 astronauts lift-off on return flight.

July 16-24 NASA launches Apollo 11 on first manned lunar landing mission. Astronauts Neil A. Armstrong (C) (cdr); Lt-Col Michael Collins (CMP) and Col Edwin E. Aldrin, Jr (LMP) fulfil the goal set by President Kennedy on 25 May 1961 of landing a man on the Moon within the decade. After separating from CSM *Columbia* in lunar orbit, Armstrong and Aldrin in LM *Eagle* land on Sea of Tranquillity at 1617.43 EDT, 20 July. Armstrong puts his left foot on the Moon at 2056 EDT. Aldrin follows him down some 15 minutes later. Together they deploy US flag and scientific instruments, collect 48·5lb (22kg) of rock and soil samples. Total EVA time, hatch open to hatch close, is 2hr 31min 40sec. Total stay time on Moon is 21hr 36min 21sec. Number of CSM Moon revolutions 30 in 59·5hr. Total flight time of mission 195hr 18min 35sec. LC KSC. LV Saturn V. LT 0932 EDT. R USS *Hornet*, Pacific, SW of Hawaii.

President Nixon welcomes the Apollo 11 crew (inside the quarantine facility).

August 7-14 Soviets launch Zond 7 from Earth-parking orbit on free-return circumlunar trajectory. Equipment includes "a high precision astro-orientation system"; on-board computer controls all phases of flight. Craft has "special protection against radiation". Closest approach to Moon 1,243 miles (2,000km). Re-entry module makes aerodynamic skip in Earth's atmosphere to land in Soviet Union. LC Baikonur. LV D-1-e. R "in predetermined area S of Kustanai".

September 18 President Nixon's space task force advocates manned expedition to Mars "before end of century". One option, recommended by Vice-President Spiro Agnew, chairman of task force, calls for Mars expedition in 1986, with peak expenditure in early 1980s of some $8,000 million a year. More immediately, report calls for ".... very heavy emphasis on proceeding with scientific applications .... Earth satellites for geology, the atmosphere, oceans .... Earth resources .... applying space technology directly to people on Earth".

October 11-16 Col Georgi Shonin and Valery Kubasov (C) in Soyuz 6 complete 75 Earth revolutions in flight lasting 118hr 42min. Participate in non-docking group flight with Soyuz 7 and Soyuz 8. During the mission Kubasov conducts the first welding and smelting experiments in space using automatic "Vulkan" unit, located in orbital module, designed by Academician Boris Paton. LC Baikonur. LV A-2. LT 1410 MT. R about 112 miles (180km) NW of Karaganda.

October 12-17 Col Anatoly Filipchenko, Vladislav Volkov (C) and Col Viktor Gorbatko in Soyuz 7 complete 75 orbits in flight lasting 118hr 41min. Participate in group flight with Soyuz 6 and Soyuz 8. LC Baikonur. LV A-2. LT 1345 MT. R about 96 miles (155km) NW of Karaganda.

October 13-18 Col Vladimir A. Shatalov and Aleksei S. Yeliseyev (C) in Soyuz 8 complete 75 Earth revolutions in flight lasting 118hr 41min. Participate as "flagship" in non-docking group flight with Soyuz 6 and Soyuz 7. Craft change orbits several times in 31 distinct manoeuvres, approaching each other and separating. Target vehicle is Soyuz 7, which other craft approach within "several hundred metres, using manual controls and on-board automatic navigation devices". LC Baikonur. LV A-2. LT 1329 MT. R about 90 miles (145km) N of Karaganda.

Alan Bean examining the Surveyor 3 probe. Note LM in the background.

November 14-24 NASA launches Apollo 12 on second manned lunar landing mission. Astronauts Cdr Charles Conrad, Jr (cdr); Cdr Richard F. Gordon, Jr (CMP); Cdr Alan L. Bean (LMP). After separating from CSM *Yankee Clipper* in lunar orbit, Conrad and Bean in LM *Intrepid* make "pin-point" landing in Ocean of Storms within walking distance of Surveyor 3 space probe (which landed April 1967). In two EVAs of 3hr 56min and 3hr 49min respectively, astronauts set out ALSEP, collect 74·7lb (33·9kg) lunar samples, and remove TV camera and other parts from Surveyor for examination on Earth. Total stay time on Moon 31hr 31min. Number of CSM Moon orbits, 45 in 88hr 56min. Total flight time of mission 244hr 36min 25sec. LC KSC. LV Saturn V. LT 1122 EST. R USS *Hornet*, Pacific.

1970

February 4 NASA launches Space Electric Rocket Test (SERT) 2 from WTR by Thrust Augmented Thor Agena D. Agena carries two electron ion bombardment engines to test ion engine operation in Earth orbit. Each engine derives thrust by ionising vaporised mercury propellant; the resultant electrically-accelerated and neutralised ion flow produces thrusts of about 0·07oz (2gm). By 17 May

1970 its continuous thrust has raised the spacecraft nearly 29 miles (46km), from an original near-circular orbit of 620 miles (998km).

February 11 Japan becomes fourth nation, after USSR, USA and France, to launch an artificial satellite: *Ohsumi* by Lambda 4S-5 from Kagoshima Space Centre.

Ohsumi: Japan's first satellite.

April 11-17 NASA launches Apollo 13 in attempt to land astronauts on Fra Mauro. Astronauts Lt-Cdr James A. Lovell, Jr (cdr); John W. Swigert, Jr (C) (CMP) and Fred W. Haise, Jr (C) (LMP). Mission is aborted after explosion of fuel cells' oxygen tank in Service Module of *Odyssey* CSM some 205,000 miles (329,845km) from Earth, approaching the Moon. Astronauts are successfully recovered after enforced circumnavigation of Moon, using LM *Aquarius* oxygen and power until just before re-entry into Earth's atmosphere. Flight lasts 142hr 54min 41sec. LC KSC. LV Saturn V. LT 1413 EST. R USS *Iwo Jima*, Pacific.

Apollo 13's makeshift air purifier.

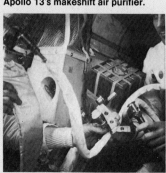

April 24 People's Republic of China becomes fifth nation—after USSR, USA, France and Japan—to launch an artificial satellite by independent effort. Launched from Shuang-ch'eng-tzu, Inner Mongolia, the 382·5lb (173kg) satellite broadcasts the music of "Tungfanghung" (The East is Red). Believed first attempt failed 1 November 1969. LC Shuang-ch'eng-tzu. LV Long March 1 (based on CSS-2 IRBM).

June 1-19 Col Andrian G. Nikolayev and Vitali Sevastyanov (C) in Soyuz 9 complete 268 Earth revolutions in flight lasting 424hr 59min. They set new duration record for manned space flight, exceeding time spent in space by US Gemini 7 astronauts in 1965. LC Baikonur. LV A-2. LT 2200 MT. R about 47 miles (75km) W of Karaganda.

The record-breaking Soyuz 9 cosmonauts, Nikolayev and Sevastyanov.

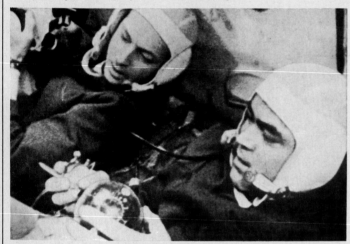

June 12 Third attempt by ELDO to orbit a test-satellite from Woomera fails when Italian-built satellite shroud of Europa I (F9) fails to jettison (because an electrical plug is forced out of contact by trapped air pressure behind it, in *vacuo*); also because of imperfect thrust programming of German third stage. Payload impacts in the Caribbean after traversing North Pole.

August 17 Soviets launch Venera 7 spacecraft from Baikonur. Achieves first confirmed landing on Venus, 15 December 1970, following parachute descent; faint signals received indicate atmospheric pressure 90±15 atm, surface temperature 475±20°C.

A-2-e/Venera 7 lifts off from Baikonur.

September 12 Soviets launch Luna 16, first successful unmanned Moon-craft capable of returning soil samples to Earth. Lands Sea of Fertility (0°41'S, 56°18'E) 20 September. Drilling device obtains ·22lb (100g) of soil and rock fragments to depth of 13·8in (35cm) and places sample into return capsule. Injected into trans-Earth trajectory 21 September, capsule soft-lands by parachute 3 days later at 0826 MT, about 50 miles (80km) SE of Dzhezkazgan, Kazakhstan.

October 20-27 Soviets launch Zond 8 from Earth parking orbit on free-return circumlunar trajectory passing within 695 miles (1,118km) of Moon. Vehicle tested "a possible variant of the return of a spacecraft into the atmosphere from the direction of the Northern Hemisphere". LC Baikonur. LV D-1-e. R "in preset area of the Indian Ocean 453 miles (730km) SE of Chagos archipelago".

November Dr George Low, acting NASA Administrator, tells Congress that programme to develop a large Soviet launch vehicle is still moving forward, despite setbacks.

November 10 Soviets launch Luna 17 with first remote-controlled Moon rover, Lunokhod 1. Lands Sea of Rains (38°18'N, 35°W) 17 November. Steered via a TV/radio link from control station in USSR, vehicle travels total distance of 34,588ft (10,542m). Sends more than 200 panoramic pictures; more than 20,000 others. Physical and mechanical properties of lunar soil studied at more than 500 points; chemical composition analysed at 25 points. Laser retroreflector experiments from Earth. Active research programme ends 4 October 1971. LC Baikonur. LV D-1-e. LT 1744 MT.

Lunokhod 1 automated Moon rover.

December 12 Explorer 42 is launched into equatorial orbit from San Marco platform off the coast of Kenya by an Italian crew. First American satellite to be sent aloft by people of another country.

1971

January 31-February 9 NASA launches Apollo 14 on fourth lunar landing mission. Astronauts Alan B. Shepard, Jr (cdr); Major Stuart A. Roosa (CMP); Lt-Cdr Edgar D.

Mitchell unloading tools from the MET.

Mitchell (LMP). After separating from CSM *Kitty Hawk* in lunar orbit, Shepard and Mitchell in LM *Antares* land in hilly upland region north of Fra Mauro crater. During two EVAs lasting 4hr 48min and 4hr 35min respectively, they set out second ALSEP and collect 98lb (44·5kg) of lunar samples, using small handcart for first time to transport them. Total stay time on Moon 33hr 31min. Number of CSM Moon revolutions, 34 in 66hr 39min. Total mission flight time 216hr 01min 57sec. LC KSC. LV Saturn V. LT 1603 EST. R USS *New Orleans*, Pacific, some 780 miles (1,255km), S of Samoa.

April 23-25 Col Vladimir A. Shatalov, Alexei S. Yeliseyev and Nikolai Rukavishnikov (C) in Soyuz 10 complete 32 Earth orbits in flight lasting 47hr 46min. Spacecraft docks for 5½hr with Salyut 1 (launched 19 April) but cosmonauts do not board. LC Baikonur. LV A-2. LT 0254 MT. R about 74 miles (120km) NW of Karaganda.

May 19 Soviets launch Mars 2—first new-generation 5-tonne spacecraft. Ejects landing capsule on final approach to Mars, 27 November 1971, which crash-lands. Mothercraft swings into 857 x 15,535 miles (1,380 x 25,000km) orbit; sends TV pictures and data. Orbiter has photo-TV system, IR radiometer, UV spectrometer, etc. Weight spacecraft: 10,253lb (4,650kg). LC Baikonur. LV D-1-e.

May 28 Soviets launch Mars 3 spacecraft. Ejects capsule on final approach to Mars, which lands (45°S, 158°W) 2 December 1971 at height of a dust storm. Transmissions cease as it begins to send TV picture. Mothercraft sends data from orbit. Objectives as Mars 2. Weight spacecraft: 10,253lb (4,650kg). LC Baikonur. LV D-1-e.

June 6-29 Lt-Col Georgi Dobrovolsky, Vladislav Volkov (C) and Viktor Patsayev (C) in Soyuz 11 dock with Salyut 1 for about 22 days to conduct engineering proving trials and experiments in biology and space-medicine. Described as "first manned orbiting scientific laboratory". Crew die while returning to Earth when a pressure equalisation valve opens at the time of separating the orbital module, releasing air from the command module. The CM lands automatically after a flight lasting 570hr 22min. Cosmonauts are the second, third and fourth Russians to die during a space flight. LC Baikonur. LVA-2. LT 0725 MT.

June 24 Second prototype of Soviet super-booster (Type G-1) explodes at 7·4 miles (12km) altitude.

July 26-August 7 NASA launches Apollo 15 on fifth lunar landing mission. Astronauts Col David R. Scott (cdr), Lt-Col James B. Irwin (LMP) and Major Alfred M. Worden (CMP). After separating from CSM *Endeavour* in lunar orbit, Scott and Irwin in LM *Falcon* land in Hadley-

Apennine region near Apennine Mountains. Three EVAs lasting 6hr 34min, 7hr 12min and 4hr 50min respectively, astronauts deploy third ALSEP and collect 173lb (78·6kg) of rock and soil samples. Mission is first of "J" series, doubling stay time on Moon using Lunar Roving Vehicle (LRV) and improved spacesuits which give greater mobility and stay time. LRV travels total of 17·3 miles (27·9km). Lunar surface stay time 66hr 55min. First live TV coverage of LM ascent stage lift-off from Moon. Number of CSM Moon revolutions, 74. Small sub-satellite left in lunar orbit for first time. Worden trans-Earth EVA 38min. Total mission flight time 295hr 11min

Scott leading out Worden and Irwin.

53sec. LC KSC. LV Saturn V. LT 0934 EDT. R USS *Okinawa*, Pacific, N of Honolulu.

October 28 Britain becomes sixth nation, after USSR, USA, France, Japan and China, to launch a satellite by independent effort, placing 145lb (66kg) Prospero (X-3) technology satellite into orbit of 334 x 990 miles (537 x 1,593km) x 82°. LC Woomera, Australia. LV Black Arrow (R.3). LT 0409 GMT.

Prospero undergoes vibration testing.

November 5 First (and only) attempt by ELDO to orbit a test satellite from French Equatorial range at Kourou, Guiana, South America, by Europa II (F11), fails because of stoppage of guidance computer (subsequently traced to electrical interference in German third stage). Violent manoeuvres just before first stage separation cause vehicle to break up. Main debris fall into Atlantic about 253 miles (407km) downrange.

1972

January 5 President Nixon announces approval to develop NASA Space Shuttle: "an entirely new type of space transportation system designed to help transform the space frontier of the 1970s into familiar territory easily accessible for human endeavour in the 1980s and 1990s" (see Chapter 15). Shuttle will ferry four people and freight to and from orbiting space stations. Development over six years, followed by test flights estimated to cost $5,500 million. Choice of booster to be made known later (see March 15).

February 14-25 After manoeuvring in lunar orbit, Luna 20 softlands on NE edge of Sea of Fertility (3°32'N, 56°33'E). Automatic drilling device obtains core sample of lunar material, transferring this to return capsule. Injected into trans-Earth trajectory by rocket stage, capsule soft-lands by parachute in blizzard some 25 miles (40km) NW of Dzhezkazgan, Kazakhstan. LC Baikonur. LV D-1-e.

March 3 NASA launches Pioneer 10 on 21-month fly-by mission to Jupiter. Will become first man-made object to escape from Solar System. LC KSC. LV Atlas-Centaur-TE-M-364-4.

Final adjustments are made to Pioneer 10 at its California assembly plant.

March 15 NASA announces that Space Shuttle orbiter will have solid-propellant boosters in parallel-stage configuration. Overall development cost reduced from estimated $5,500 million to $5,150 million, with some increase in estimated cost per mission. Horizontal test flights to begin 1976; manned orbital flight tests 1978. Payload 65,000lb (29,500kg) into 100 n. mile (185km) due east orbit.

March 29 United States, Soviet Union and United Kingdom sign in Washington convention on international liability for damage caused by space objects. (The three nations are depository states for the treaty, to which many other nations later add signatures.) The convention complements two earlier treaties governing Man's space activities: the Outer Space Treaty of 1967 and the Astronaut Rescue Agreement of 1968.

April 16-27 NASA launches Apollo 16 on sixth lunar landing mission. Astronauts Capt John W. Young (cdr), Cdr Thomas K. Mattingly, II (CMP) and Col Charles M. Duke, Jr (LMP). After separating from CSM *Casper* in lunar orbit, Young and Duke in LM *Orion* land in Descartes highlands region, 18,000ft (5,486m) higher than

Young deploys the Apollo 16 ALSEP.

Apollo 15 site. In three EVAs lasting 7hr 11min, 7hr 23min and 5hr 40min respectively, they deploy fourth ALSEP, set up first lunar astronomical observatory, and collect 210-213lb (95·2-96·6kg) of rock and soil samples. This is second "J" series mission, including LRV, which travels total of 16·8 miles (27km). Total stay time on Moon 71hr 2min. Number of CSM Moon revolutions, 64. Releases sub-satellite in lunar orbit. Mattingly trans-Earth EVA 84min. Total mission flight time 265hr 51min 05sec. LC KSC. LV Saturn V. LT 1254 EST. R USS *Ticonderoga*, Pacific.

May 24 President Nixon and Premier Kosygin in Moscow sign agreement providing for cooperation in the exploration of outer space for peaceful purposes and the docking in space in 1975 of a US and a Soviet spacecraft (see Chapter 14).

May 26 NASA announces retirement of Dr Wernher von Braun, Deputy Associate Administrator for Planning, effective 1 July 1972.

Wernher von Braun poses before an ATS-6 satellite—his last NASA project.

July 23 NASA launches first Earth Resources Technology Satellite (ERTS-1)—later re-named Landsat 1 —from Western Test Range, California.

November Dr Chien Hsueh-Sen, a pioneer member of the American rocket team at the California Institute of Technology, who returned to China in 1955 during the Un-American activities campaign of the late Senator

Joseph McCarthy, returns on a visit to United States as Director of the Dynamics Research Institute, Academy of Sciences, People's Republic of China. He has played a leading role in establishing China's missile and space programmes.

November 10 NASA launches Anik 1 (Telesat A), first of a series of geo-stationary communications satellites to provide transmission of TV, telephone and data services throughout Canada.

November 24 (?) Third prototype of Soviet super-booster (Type G-1) explodes at 24·8 miles (40km) altitude.

December 7-19 NASA launches Apollo 17 on seventh and last lunar landing mission of series. Astronauts Capt Eugene A. Cernan (cdr), Lt-Cdr Ronald E. Evans (CMP) and Dr Harrison H. Schmitt (C) (LMP). After separating from CSM *America* in lunar orbit, Cernan and Schmitt land in LM *Challenger* land in Taurus-Littrow region. In three EVAs lasting 7hr 12min, 7hr 37min and 7hr 16min respectively, they deploy fifth ALSEP and collect 243lb (110kg) of rock and soil samples. This is third "J" series mission, including astronauts' LRV which travels total of

Schmitt aboard the Apollo 17 LRV.

21·7 miles (35km). Total stay time on Moon 74hr 59min 38sec. Number of CSM Moon revolutions, 75. Released sub-satellite in lunar orbit. Evans trans-Earth EVA 66min. Total mission flight time 301hr 51min 59sec. LC KSC. LV Saturn V. LT 0033 EST. R USS *Ticonderoga*, Pacific.

1973

January 16 After manoeuvring in lunar orbit, Luna 21 softlands inside Le Monnier crater near eastern rim of Sea of Serenity at 0135 MT. Discharges remote-controlled Lunokhod 2 from ramp at 0414 MT.

April 3 Soviets launch Salyut 2 orbital laboratory which develops fault, spins and breaks up. Orbit: 128 x 154 miles (207 x 248km) x 51·56°. Telemetry 19·944 MHz. Lifetime 55 days. May carry some military research equipment.

April 6 NASA launches Pioneer 11 on fly-by mission to Jupiter (December 1974) and Saturn (September 1979)

May 11 Soviets launch structure resembling Salyut space laboratory (called Cosmos 557) which fails upon orbital insertion. Orbit 133 x 151 miles (214 x 243km) x 51·59°. Lifetime 11 days.

May 14 NASA launches Skylab 1 space station into Earth orbit from KSC by two-stage Saturn V. Station is damaged by air pressure during ascent, which rips away meteoroid shield of orbital workshop and one solar "wing", leaving other solar "wing" in closed position, trapped by piece of torn metal. Astronaut teams (Skylabs 2, 3 and 4) carry out repairs and conduct full range of experiments. Station decays from orbit 11 July 1979.

Skylab in orbit; note missing solar panel and emergency solar shield.

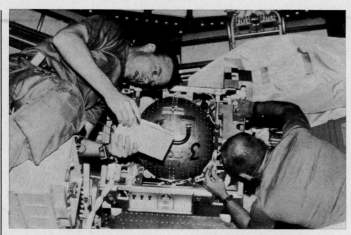

Conrad and Kerwin with the Astronaut Maneuvering Unit Experiment.

May 25-June 22 NASA launches Skylab 2 ferry with astronauts Capt Charles Conrad, Jr, Dr Joseph Kerwin (C) and Capt Paul J. Weitz. Their spacecraft is modified Apollo CSM. After some difficulty they dock with, and board, Skylab 1, erect sun shield and release stuck solar "wing" during EVA. Astronauts obtain data on 46 of 55 planned experiments; perform three spacewalks totalling 5hr 41min. Number of Earth revolutions 404. Total flight time 672hr 49min 49sec. LC KSC. LV Saturn IB. LT 1400 BST. R USS *Ticonderoga*.

July 21 Soviets launch Mars 4 spacecraft. Passes Mars at a distance of 1,367 miles (2,200km), 10 February 1974, when braking engine fails to place it into orbit; takes pictures. LC Baikonur. LV D-1-e.

July 25 Soviets launch Mars 5 spacecraft. On 12 February 1974 it swings into orbit around Mars ranging between 1,093 and 20,195 miles (1,760 and 32,500km), inclined at 35° to equator. LC Baikonur. LV D-1-e.

July 28-September 25 NASA launches Skylab 3 ferry with astronauts Capt Alan L. Bean, Major Jack R. Lousma and Dr Owen K. Garriott. En route to dock with Skylab 1 space station an attitude control thruster on their Apollo CSM ferry begins leaking; on 2 August (while docked with station) a second thruster develops leaks. At KSC an Apollo rescue ship is prepared, but the problem proves less serious than feared and the men are allowed to complete the mission and use their own Apollo CSM for return. Number of Earth revolutions 858. Three EVAs totalling 13hr 44min; new sunshield deployed, rate gyros replaced. Total flight time 1427hr 09min 04sec. LC KSC. LV Saturn IB. LT 1208 BST R USS *New Orleans*.

Slayton reviews flight plan during Skylab 3 pre-launch suiting activities.

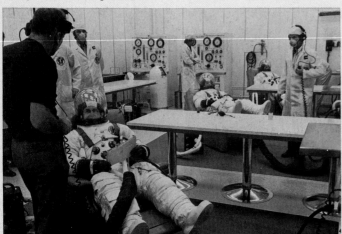

August 1 X-24B lifting body with NASA pilot John Manke makes first flight, unpowered, from B-52 "mother" at 40,000ft (12,192m), landing after 4min 11·5sec at Edwards Air Force Base, California.

Martin Marietta X-24B (foreground).

August 5 Soviets launch Mars 6 spacecraft. On 12 March 1974, it ejects a capsule which parachutes through atmosphere of Mars, obtaining scientific data, but stops transmitting just before it lands (24°S, 25°W). Mothercraft continues in heliocentric orbit. LC Baikonur. LV D-1-e.

August 9 Soviets launch Mars 7 spacecraft. On 9 March 1974 it ejects a capsule which misses Mars by 808 miles (1,300km). Mothercraft continues in heliocentric orbit. LC Baikonur. LV D-1-e.

September 27-29 Lt-Col Vasily Lazarev and Oleg Makarov (C) in Soyuz 12, test modification of basic spacecraft for ferry missions to Salyut orbital laboratories. In this configuration extensible solar panels are replaced entirely by chemical batteries. Flight lasts 47hr 16min. First manned test flight following Soyuz 11 disaster, in which third crewman is replaced by a life-support system allowing a two-man crew to wear spacesuits for added protection during launch, docking and undocking, and the separation of spacecraft modules before re-entry. The suits are removed during orbital operations. LC Baikonur. LV A-2. LT 1518 MT. R some 248 miles (400km) SW of Karaganda.

November 3 NASA launches Mariner 10 by Atlas-Centaur from KSC on double-planet mission to Venus (5 February 1974) and Mercury (29 March 1974). Spacecraft makes two further working encounters with Mercury from heliocentric orbit. Obtains first pictures of Mercury's heavily cratered surface; detects magnetic field.

November 16-February 8 1974 NASA launches Skylab 4 ferry with astronauts Lt-Col Gerald P. Carr, Dr Edward G. Gibson (C) and Lt-Col William R. Pogue. Final Skylab 1 visit. Replenishes coolant supplies, repairs antenna, observes Comet Kohoutek. Four EVAs totalling 22hr 21min. Sets record for EVA duration of 7hr 1min. Number of Earth revolutions 1214. Total flight time, 2017hr 15min 32sec. LC Cape Canaveral. LV Saturn IB.

LT 0901 EST. R USS *New Orleans*, Pacific, about 175 miles (281km) SW of San Diego.

December 18-26 Major Pyotr Klimuk and Valentin Lebedev (C) in Soyuz 13 complete 128 Earth revolutions in flight lasting 188hr 55min. Conduct experiments in biology, Earth resources observation and astrophysics. Spacecraft has extensible solar panels for electrical power supply. LC Baikonur. LV A-2. LT 1455 MT. R about 124 miles (200km) SW of Karaganda.

May 30 NASA launches Applications Technology Satellite ATS-6 to pioneer educational satellite transmission by satellite from geostationary orbit. After

Technicians check out ATS-6's umbrella antenna which unfurls in orbit.

a year of operation above a position near the Galapagos Islands, serving the United States, the satellite is moved to a position above East Africa, providing educational programmes to some 5,000 Indian villages. The satellite is returned to its original location in 1976, for continuing experiments in the USA. It is subsequently moved out of geostationary orbit by firing onboard rocket motors to avoid interference with other satellites in this congested orbit. LC Cape Canaveral. LV Titan IIIC. Lifetime indefinite.

June 25 Soviets launch Salyut 3 into orbit of 133 x 157 miles (213 x 253km) x 51·58°. Telemetry frequencies 19·944 MHz; 143·625 MHz. Capsule ejected and recovered 23 September 1974. Orbit after manoeuvres 159 x 181 miles (256 x 292km). Lifetime in orbit 214 days. Some military experiments. Related missions: Soyuz 14 and 15.

July 3-19 Col Pavel Popovich and Lt-Col Yuri Artyukhin in Soyuz 14 dock with Salyut 3 orbital laboratory for 353hr 33min. LC Baikonur. LV A-2. LT N.A. (orbital insertion 2151 MT).

August 26-28 Lt-Col Gennady Sarafanov and Col Lev Demin in Soyuz 15 fail to dock with Salyut 3 orbital laboratory on 27 August because of fault in automatic control system. Flight lasts 48hr 12min. LC Baikonur. LV A-2. LT 2258 MT. R about 30 miles (48km) SW of Tselinograd.

September 23 A recoverable module containing "materials of research and experiments" is separated from unmanned Salyut 3. "The engines were started at a set time and the module began its descent to Earth landing in the predetermined area of the USSR."

December 2-8 Col Anatoly Filipchenko and Nikolai Rukavishnikov (C) in Soyuz 16 conduct flight tests of spacecraft modified for forthcoming ASTP mission. Craft has extensible solar panels for electrical power supply. Cosmonauts test docking system and reduction of cabin pressurisation (see page 192). Flight lasts 5days 22hr 24min. LC Baikonur. LV A-2. LT 1240 MT. R 1104 MT.

December 26 Soviets launch Salyut 4 into orbit of 131 x 156 miles (212 x 251km) x 51·57°. Telemetry frequencies 15·008 MHz; 922·75 MHz. Orbit after manoeuvres 208 x 216 miles (336 x 349km). Lifetime 770 days. Related missions: Soyuz 17, Soyuz anomaly, Soyuz 18B, Soyuz 20.

January 11-February 9 Lt-Col Alexei Gubarev and Georgi Grechko (C) in Soyuz 17 dock with Salyut 4 orbital laboratory for extensive series of experiments. Total flight time is 29days 13hr 20min. LC Baikonur.

LV A-2. LT 0043 MT. R 68 miles (110km) NE of Tselinograd, Kazakhstan, 1403 MT.

April 5 Lt-Col Vasily Lazarev and Oleg Makarov (C) in Soyuz 18A fail to reach orbit because of launch vehicle upper stage malfunction. They are recovered safely in Western Siberia near Gorno-Altaisk inside their command module. The craft had been intended to dock with the Salyut 4 orbital laboratory. LC Baikonur. LV A-2. LT N.A.

May 24-July 26 Lt-Col Pyotr Klimuk and Vitaly Sevastyanov (C) in Soyuz 18B dock with Salyut 4 orbital laboratory for extensive series of experiments. Total flight time is 1511hr 20min. LC Baikonur. LV A-2. LT 1758 MT. R about 35 miles (56km) NE of Arkalyk.

The Soyuz 18B cosmonauts in training.

June 8 Soviets launch Venera 9 spacecraft from Baikonur. Releases landing capsule being going into orbit around Venus 22 October 1975. Capsule, which transmits from surface for 53 minutes, sends first TV picture of surface conditions: confirms pressure 90 atm, temperature 485°C. Position 30°N, 293° long.

June 14 Soviets launch Venera 10 spacecraft from Baikonur. Releases landing capsule before going into orbit around Venus 25 October 1975. Capsule, which transmits from surface for 65 minutes, sends second TV picture of surface conditions: surface pressure 92 atm, temperature 465°C. Position 15°N, 295° long.

July 15-21 Col Alexei Leonov and Valery Kubasov (C) in Soyuz 19 participate with US Apollo 18 CSM/DM in Apollo-Soyuz Test Project (see Chapter 14). Number of Earth revolutions 96. Total flight time 142hr 30min. LC Baikonur. LV A-2. LT 1520 MT, 0820 EDT. R 54 miles (87km) NE of Arkalyk, Kazakhstan.

July 15-24 Brig-Gen Thomas P. Stafford, Vance D. Brand (C) and Donald K. Slayton (C) in Apollo 18 participate with Soviet cosmonauts in

ASTP crewmen are interviewed at the Gagarin Cosmonauts Training Centre.

Apollo-Soyuz Test Project (ASTP). (Slayton, at 51, oldest man in space). They dock with Soyuz 19 flown by Col. Alexei Leonov and Valery Kubasov at 1209 EDT on 17 July, remaining together (including undocking and redocking exercise 19 July) for about two days (Chapter 14). Number of Earth revolutions 138. Total flight time (Apollo 18) 217hr 28min. LC KSC. LV Saturn IB. LT 1550 EDT. R USS *New Orleans,* Pacific, about 270 miles (434km) W of Hawaii.

July 26 People's Republic of China launches China 3 heavy (two-tonne) military satellite into low Earth orbit. Similar launchings on 26 November 1975 (China 4; returns capsule to earth); 16 December 1975 (China 5); 7 December 1976 (China 7; returns capsule to earth); 26 January 1978 (China 8; returns capsule to earth). LC Shuang-ch'eng-tzu. LV FB-1, also known as CSL-2.

August 20 NASA launches Viking 1 spacecraft to Mars; inserted into orbit 19 June 1976, releases Lander which soft-lands *Chryse Planitia* (22·46°N, 48·01°W), 20 July 1976. Transmits pictures from Martian surface, examines soil in automatic laboratory, obtains "met" data. Mothercraft observes from orbit.

Viking 1's picture of Mars' channels in the Chryse Planitia region suggests massive floods long ago.

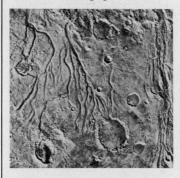

September 9 NASA launches Viking 2 spacecraft to Mars; inserted into orbit 7 August 1976, soft-lands *Utopia Planitia* (47·97°N, 25·67°W) 3 September 1976. Transmits pictures from Martian surface, examines soil in automatic laboratory. Mothercraft observes from orbit.

November 17-February 16 1976 Soviets launch unmanned Soyuz 20 which docks with Salyut 4 automatically in space station re-supply rehearsal. After separating from station 16 February 1976, re-entry module is recovered "in pre-set area of USSR".

1976

February 10 Pioneer 10 crosses the orbit of Saturn on its way out of the Solar System.

March 17 NASA announces four crews for early flights of the Space Shuttle from Kennedy Space Center: Capt John W. Young; Cdr Robert L. Crippen; Col Joe H. Engle; Cdr Richard H. Truly; Fred W. Haise, Jr (C); Lt-Col Jack Lousma; Vance D. Brand (C); Lt-Col Charles G. Fullerton.

June 22 Soviets launch Salyut 5 into orbit of 129 x 144 miles (208 x 233km) x 51·6°. Telemetry frequency 19·944 MHz. Orbit after manoeuvres 133 x 159 miles (214 x 257km). Some military experiments. Returns two re-entry capsules to USSR. Lifetime 412 days. Related missions Soyuz 21, Soyuz 23, Soyuz 24.

July 6-August 24 Col Boris Volynov and Lt-Col Vitaly Zholobov in Soyuz 21 dock with Salyut 5 on 7 July. Cosmonauts perform extensive series of experiments (page 185). Total flight time 49days 6hr 24min. LC Baikonur. LV A-2. LT 1509 MT. R about 124 miles (200km) SW of Kokchetav, Kazakhstan.

August 17 Indonesia—celebrating 31st year of independence—becomes first nation in Southeast Asia to operate its own telecommunications system, via Hughes-Palapa satellite located 83°E longitude over Indian Ocean. Launched by NASA on 8 July, geostationary satellite provides telephone, television, radio, telegraph and data services to populated areas on some 5,000 of the nation's 13,000 islands, which extend more than 3,100 miles (5,000km).

Palapa 2 undergoing weight tests.

August 18 Luna 24, after manoeuvring in lunar orbit, soft-lands in south-eastern region of Sea of Crises (12°45'N, 62°12'E). Returns core sample from depth of some 6·5ft (2m); landing 22 August, 124 miles (200km) SE of Surgat, Kazakhstan.

September 15-23 Col Valery F. Bykovsky and Vladimir Aksyonov (C) in Soyuz 22 complete 127 Earth revo-

lutions in independent flight lasting 7days 21hr 54mins. Spacecraft, which embodies extensible solar "wings" for electrical power supply, carries MKF-6 multi-spectral camera made by Carl Zeiss Jena, GDR. LC Baikonur. LV A-2. LT 1248 MT. R about 93 miles (150km) NW of Tselinograd.

October 14-16 Lt-Col Vyacheslav Zudov and Lt-Col Valery Rozhdestvensky in Soyuz 23 fail to dock with Salyut 5 because of a fault in spacecraft's automatic control system. Flight lasts 48hr 6min. Re-entry capsule, blown off course by a snow storm, in darkness and at sub-zero temperature splashes into Lake Tengiz some 121 miles (195km) SW of Tselinograd, Kazakhstan. Cosmonauts rescued by helicopter and boats. First occasion that a Soviet space crew has come down on water. LC Baikonur. LV A-2. LT 2040 MT.

November 24 Reported in Washington that China has begun trials of CSS-X-4 full-range ICBM; estimated range 6,835 miles (11,000km).

December 15 Soviets launch double re-entry test payload Cosmos 881/882, both returning same day to Soviet recovery area. Orbits: C.881—124 x 150 miles (201 x 242km) x 51·6°; C.882—118 x 132 miles (191 x 231km) x 51·6°. Similar test missions: Cosmos 997/998 and Cosmos 1100/1101. Probably related to future manned space programme.

1977

February 7-25 Col Viktor Gorbatko and Lt-Col Yuri Glazkov in Soyuz 24 dock with Salyut 5 orbital laboratory. Test and replace units aboard station, including some parts of onboard computer. Continue research programme: photograph Earth; study crystal growth; soldering experiments and casting of metal spheres; also biological and bio-medical experiments. Flight lasts 17days 16hr 08min. LC Baikonur. LV A-2. LT 1912 MT. R about 23 miles (37km) NE of Arkalyk, Kazakhstan.

July 17-2 February 1978 Soviets launch Cosmos 929—a large unmanned space vehicle—into 51·6° inclination orbit; it performs several power manoeuvres over a period of months. Possible test of a new propulsion system for space station or space tug.

August 12 Space Shuttle Orbiter *Enterprise* with astronauts Fred W. Haise, Jr (C) and Lt-Col Charles G. Fullerton makes first free flight from Boeing 747 "mother" after release at 22,800ft (6,950m) above NASA's Dryden Flight Research Center, Edwards, California. Flight test includes practice flare about 20 seconds after separation at 19,700ft (6,004m) before making two left turns

Enterprise and Boeing 747 take off for first free flight, Edwards, California.

to line up with dry lake runway. Final approach from 8 miles (13km) range at 9° glide angle, landing gear being deployed at 180ft (55m), about 20 seconds before touchdown at just under 200kt (407km/h). Flight lasts 5min 23sec.

August 20 NASA launches Voyager 2 spacecraft on multiplanet, gravity-assist, fly-by mission to: Jupiter (July 1979), Saturn (August 1981), and Uranus (January 1986) and Neptune (1989).

September 5 NASA launches Voyager 1 on fly-by mission to Jupiter (March 1979) and Saturn (November 1980).

September 13 Space Shuttle Orbiter *Enterprise*, flown by Col Joe H. Engle and Cdr Richard H. Truly, makes second free flight from back of Boeing 747. After separating at 24,000ft (7,315m), craft completes series of manoeuvres before landing on dry lake runway at 185kt (342km/h). Flight lasted 5min 28sec.

Engle (right) and Truly just prior to Enterprise's second free flight test.

September 29 Soviets launch Salyut 6 into orbit of 133 x 159 miles (214 x 256km) x 51·59°. Telemetry frequencies: 15·008 MHz/ 922·75 MHz. Lifetime: still operational mid-1981. Related missions: Soyuz 25, 26, 27, 28, 29, 30, 31, 32, 33, 34, Soyuz-T, 35, 36, T-2, 37, 38, T-3, T-4, 39, 40; Progress 1, 2, 3, 4, 5, 6, 7, 8, 9, 10, 11, 12; Cosmos 1, 267; LC Baikonur. LV D-1.

October 1 Lt-Gen Vladimir A. Shatalov, commenting on future Salyut missions, says Soviet scientists "contemplate future space stations much larger than present Salyuts with crews of 12 to 20 people". However, the potential of present stations will have to be exhausted first. Shatalov envisages orbital stations being increasingly used for producing "super pure metals, monocrystals, vaccines and other useful products".

October 9-11 Lt-Col Vladimir V. Kovalenok and Valery Ryumin (C) in Soyuz 25 fail to dock with Salyut 6 space station. Flight lasts 2days 46min. LC Baikonur. LV A-2. LT 0540 MT. R about 115 miles (185km) NW of Tselinograd.

September 23 Space Shuttle Orbiter *Enterprise*, flown by Fred W. Haise Jr (C) and Lt-Col Charles G. Fullerton, makes third free flight from back of Boeing 747. After separating at 23,800ft (7,254m), lands on dry lake runway some 5min 34sec later. Glide test includes a "hands off" manoeuvre with the Orbiter on autopilot—also test from 8,000 to 3,000ft (2,438 to 914m) of ground-based microwave device which controls glide path automatically.

Haise (left) and Fullerton who piloted Enterprise's third free flight test at Dryden Flight Research Center.

October 12 Space Shuttle Orbiter *Enterprise* with astronauts Col Joe H. Engle and Cdr Richard H. Truly, makes fourth free flight from Boeing 747; first in which streamlined tail fairing is removed and three dummy SSME rocket engines are exposed in "high-drag" configuration. Flight lasts 2min 34sec.

October 26 Space Shuttle Orbiter *Enterprise*, with astronauts Fred W. Haise, Jr (C) and Lt-Col Charles G. Fullerton, makes fifth and last flight from Boeing 747. After separating at 17,000ft (5,181m) directly in line with Runway 22, glide lasts 1min 59sec.

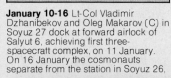

Inside Salyut 6: Grechko and Romanenko (right) with the Soyuz 28 crew—Gubarev and Remek.

December 10-March 16 1978 Lt-Col Yuri Romanenko and Georgi Grechko (C) in Soyuz 26 dock with Salyut 6 on 11 December. Soviet authorities reveal that orbital laboratory has two docking ports, one fore and one aft. Soyuz 25 attempted to dock at the front; Soyuz 26 docks at the rear in case the other port is faulty or has sustained damage. On 20 December, the cosmonauts perform an EVA lasting 1hr 28min, Grechko emerging from the actual docking hatch while Romanenko assists his activities from the depressurised transfer compartment. They find the docking unit undamaged. On-board experiments include use of MKF-6 multi-spectral camera, medical examinations, processing of materials, biological experiments, astronomical studies using sub-millimetre telescope. Flight lasts 96days 10hr, breaking US space endurance record of 84days 1hr 15min set by last Skylab crew between November 1973 and February 1974. Soyuz 26 returns Soyuz 27 crew; Romanenko and Grechko return in Soyuz 27. LC Baikonur. LV A-2. LT 0419 MT. R about 165 miles (265km) W of Tselinograd at 1419MT (Soyuz 27).

1978

January 10-16 Lt-Col Vladimir Dzhanibekov and Oleg Makarov (C) in Soyuz 27 dock at forward airlock of Salyut 6, achieving first three-spacecraft complex, on 11 January. On 16 January the cosmonauts separate from the station in Soyuz 26,

Dzhanibekov and Makarov head for the Soyuz 27 launch pad at Baikonur.

leaving the aft airlock free for another ferry mission. Their total flight time is 6days 4min. LC Baikonur. LV A-2. LT 1526 MT. R 1530 MT, about 192 miles (310km) W of Tselinograd (Soyuz 26).

January 20-February 9 Soviets launch unmanned, expendable, transport spacecraft Progress 1, containing 2,205lb (1,000kg) of propellants and 2,866lb (1,300kg) of compressed air, food, water, films and other cargo. After docking with Salyut 6 at 1312 MT on 22 January, the resident cosmonauts transfer supplies. Craft separates from station with waste material on 7 February and is made to re-enter the atmosphere and burn up over the Pacific Ocean. LC Baikonur. LV A-2.

Progress at the Paris Air Show.

March 2-10 Col Alexei Gubarev and Capt Vladimir Remek (first Czechoslovakian cosmonaut) in Soyuz 28 dock with Salyut 6/Soyuz 27 complex on 3 March. In conjunction with resident cosmonauts Romanenko and Grechko, they carry out medical examinations, conduct experiments in materials processing and make Earth resources observations. Flight lasts 188hr 16min. LC Baikonur. LV A-2. LT 1828 MT. R about 192 miles (310km) W of Tselinograd.

April 10 Fang Wi, deputy prime minister for science and technology, People's Republic of China, says plans over the next eight years include a major research centre, scientific and applications satellites, manned space flight and an orbital laboratory. National communications satellite project is planned for launch 1981-82.

May 18 British Interplanetary Society publishes *Project Daedalus*, a 192-page report on the world's first engineering study of an unmanned spaceship for exploring the nearer stars.

May 20 NASA launches Pioneer Venus 1 which swings into orbit round Venus on 4 December 1978. Conducts detailed survey of planet in conjunction with entry probes of Pioneer Venus 2.

June 8 Talks open in Helsinki between Soviet Union and United States on possible agreement to ban the use of anti-satellite weapons.

The Soyuz 29 capsule touches down.

June 15-November 2 Col Vladimir V. Kovalenok and Alexander Ivanchenkov (C) in Soyuz 29 dock with Salyut 6 on 17 June for extensive series of experiments. On 29 July they perform an EVA, from the hatch in the side of the forward transfer compartment, lasting 2hr 5min. Ivanchenkov replaces externally-mounted equipment and retrieves certain specimens which have been exposed to the space environment for nearly 10 months. Returning in Soyuz 31, their mission lasts a record 139days 14hr 48min. LC Baikonur. LV A-2. LT 2317 MT. R about 111 miles (180km) SE of Dzhezkazgan.

June 27-July 5 Col Pyotr Klimuk and Major Miroslaw Hermaszewski (first Polish cosmonaut) in Soyuz 30 dock with Salyut 6/Soyuz 29 complex on second airlock. Objectives: biomedical experiments using equipment made in Poland; Earth resources photography; materials processing. Total flight time 7days 22hr 04min. LC Baikonur. LV A-2. LT 1827 MT. R about 186 miles (300km) W of Tselinograd.

July 7-August 4 Soviets launch unmanned Progress 2 with 1,322lb (600kg) of propellant for Salyut 6 re-supply, plus scientific equipment, air, water, food and film. Docks 9 July; undocks 2 August and subsequently

is made to re-enter over Pacific Ocean. LC Baikonur. LV A-2. LT 1426 MT.

August 8-23 Soviets launch unmanned Progress 3 for Salyut 6 re-supply. Docks with Salyut 6/Soyuz 29 complex on second airlock 10 August; undocks 21 August and subsequently de-orbited over Pacific Ocean. LC Baikonur. LV A-2. LT 0131 MT.

August 8 NASA launches Pioneer Venus 2. On 9 December 1978, craft separates into five entry probes that measure Venus' atmosphere as they descend to the surface. Although not designed to survive after landing, one probe transmits data for 67 minutes after impact. LC Cape Canaveral. LV Atlas-Centaur.

August 26-September 3 Col Valery F. Bykovsky and Lt-Col Sigmund Jaehn (first East German cosmonaut) in Soyuz 31 dock with Salyut 6/Soyuz 29 complex 27 August, on second airlock. After carrying out joint experiments with resident cosmonauts (Kovalenok and Ivanchenkov), Bykovsky and Jaehn return in Soyuz 29. Total flight time 7days 20hr 49min. LC Baikonur. LV A-2. LT 1751 MT. R about 87 miles (140km) SE of Dzhezkazgan.

The A-2/Soyuz 31 launcher blasts off.

October 1 President Carter, during a visit to the Kennedy Space Center, Florida, states that US reconnaissance satellites have contributed immensely to international security and are an "important factor" in monitoring arms control agreements.

October 4-26 Soviets launch unmanned Progress 4 for Salyut 6 re-supply. Docks with Salyut 6/Soyuz 31 complex on second airlock, 6 October; undocks 24 October and subsequently de-orbited over Pacific Ocean. Before undocking, it is used to boost space station complex into higher orbit of about 230 miles (370km). LC Baikonur. LV A-2. LT 0209 MT.

Venera 11 descent module during test.

December 27 Capsules released by Venera 11 and 12 reach the surface of Venus some 497 miles (800km) apart. On-board instruments detect presence of key argon isotopes during descent phase: argon 40 and Argon 56, in 200 times the proportions found on Earth. Surface pressures about 88 atm, temperatures 466°C. Mothercraft continue in heliocentric orbit, Venera 12 parent also conducting Franco-German programme of research into solar and galactic gamma rays.

1979

February 25-August 19 Lt-Col Vladimir A. Lyakhov and Valery V. Ryumin (C) in Soyuz 32 dock with Salyut 6 on forward airlock, 26 February. During their protracted mission the cosmonauts perform a wide range of experiments and erect and deploy KPT-10 radio telescope delivered to them in kit form by Progress 7 supply craft. When 32ft (10m) antenna becomes hooked up on the end of the space station, they perform EVA to release it. Ryumin spends 1hr 23min in open space. Cosmonauts are eventually recovered in Soyuz 34 after spending record total of 175 days 36min in space. LC Baikonur. LV A-2. LT 1454 MT. R *Tass* reports re-entry module of Soyuz 32 "has been returned to Earth unmanned".

March 5 Voyager 1 flies within 177,720 miles (286,000km) of Jupiter's cloud tops providing startling new information about the Jovian system. Jupiter's atmosphere is complex, with layers of colourful clouds above a deep atmosphere of hydrogen and helium. The atmosphere, more turbulent than had been expected, appears to be controlled by forces far below the visible cloud tops. The Great Red Spot, large enough to swallow several Earths, is an

A gold disc of "sounds of the Earth" is attached to the side of Voyager 1.

immense atmospheric storm that rotates counter-clockwise, once every six days. A thin ring is discovered around Jupiter 18-20 miles (29-32km) thick. Biggest surprise: the moon Io has at least nine active volcanos, some with plumes extending 175 miles (280km). Other moons examined include Ganymede, Europa and Callisto.

March 12-April 5 Soviets launch unmanned Progress 5 for Salyut 6 re-supply. Docks with Salyut 6/Soyuz 32 complex second airlock, 14 March. Raises orbit of Soyuz 32/Salyut 6/Progress 5 complex, 30 March to 176 x 222 miles (284 x 357km); adjusts 2 April. Undocks next day and subsequently made to re-enter over Pacific Ocean. LC Baikonur. LV A-2. LT 0847 MT.

April 10-12 Nikolai Rukavishnikov, first Soyuz civilian commander, and Major Georgi Ivanov (Bulgaria) in Soyuz 33 fail to dock with Salyut 6/Soyuz 32 complex when a propulsion unit used to align the craft with the space station "was found to be deviating from the normal". Cosmonauts are recalled, landing in darkness. Flight time 1day 23hr 01min. LC Baikonur. LV A-2. LT 2034 MT. R about 199 miles (320km) SE of Dzhezkazgan. Failure to dock with Salyut 6 leads to Soyuz 34 being launched unmanned on 6 June 1979 to retrieve long-stay cosmonauts, whose original space ferry Soyuz 32 has exceeded safe period in orbit.

Two senior BIS members: Arthur C. Clarke and Secretary L.J. Carter (right).

April 30 British Interplanetary Society moves into new Headquarters Building in London (27-29 South Lambeth Road, SW8) as part of a Development Programme to promote international astronautics. HQ incorporates Golovine Conference Room and Arthur C. Clarke Space Library.

May 1 Space Shuttle *Enterprise* is rolled out of the Vehicle Assembly Building at the Kennedy Space Center, Florida, on the Mobile Launch Platform by the crawler-transporter and placed on Launch Complex-39A for compatibility checks with pad and service tower. It is returned to the VAB on 23 July 1979.

May 13-June 9 Soviets launch unmanned Progress 6 for Salyut 6 re-supply; 2·5 tonne payload includes propellant, food, water, scientific equipment and mail. Docks Salyut 6/ Soyuz 32 complex second airlock 15 May; undocks 8 June and subsequently de-orbited over the Pacific Ocean. LC Baikonur. LV A-2. LT 0717 MT.

May 17 Soviets launch first of new series of Earth resources satellites, Cosmos 1099, from Northern Cosmodrome into orbit of 134 x 153 miles (215 x 247km) inclined at 81·35° to the equator. Spacecraft apparently is based on Cosmos reconnaissance satellites, returning a capsule to Earth after 12 days.

June 6-August 19 Soviets launch unmanned Soyuz 34 which docks with Salyut 6/Soyuz 32 complex on second airlock, 8 June. Undocks 14 June; then re-docks to first airlock after space station "turn-around" manoeuvre. Undocks again 19 August, returning to Earth Soyuz 32 cosmonauts who have set new duration record for manned space flight of 175days 36min. LC Baikonur. LV A-2. LT 0913 MT. R about 105 miles (170km) SE of Dzhezkazgan.

June 28-July 20 Soviets launch unmanned Progress 7 for Salyut 6 re-supply. Docks with Salyut 6/ Soyuz 34 complex on second airlock, 30 June; undocks 18 July and subsequently de-orbited over Pacific Ocean. LC Baikonur. LV A-2. LT 1225 MT.

July 9 Voyager 2 flies within 399,560 miles (643,000km) of Jupiter's cloud tops. Examination is made of Jupiter's banded clouds, Red Spot, "white ovals", thin ring system (discovered by Voyager 1), and the moons Io, Europa, Callisto, Ganymede and Amalthea. Additional discoveries of joint mission included three new satellites, and auroras and cloud-top lightning bolts, like super-bolts on Earth.

Voyager 2 close-up view of Ganymede. The bright spots on the surface are "relatively recent" impact craters.

July 11 Skylab space station decays from orbit over the Indian Ocean and some debris falls on south western Australia. However, there is no damage to life or property.

September 1 Pioneer 11 flies within 13,000 miles (20,880km) of Saturn's cloud tops, some 1,000 million miles (1,600 million km) from Earth, after a six-year journey. The probe spends 10 days photographing and measuring the ringed planet. Discovers two new outer rings ("F" and "G") and a new—11th— Saturnian moon (1979S1), estimated diameter 250 miles (400km), near outer edge of Saturn's rings. Also confirms that Saturn has a magnetic field, magnetosphere and radiation belts. At the time of encounter, Saturn's gravity swings the probe almost 90° on a change of course toward the edge of the Solar System.

September 25-October 13 Soviets launch Vostok-type biosatellite Cosmos 1129 in first international experiment to breed mammals in space. Payload includes 38 white rats prepared by Soviet and Bulgarian scientists; also 60 Japanese quail eggs. Material from USA includes carrot seeds and carrot slices inoculated with bacteria which form tumours in plants. Capsule lands in Kazakhstan, 13 October 1979.

December 16-March 25 1980 Soyuz T-1 is launched unmanned and docks with Salyut 6 space station under computer control at 1405, 19 December, on forward airlock. Mission includes complete test of basic systems in conjunction with ground control. Previous spacecraft of this type were Cosmos 1001 and Cosmos 1074. Orbital module—a 2,778lb (1,260kg) spheroid, 7·5ft (2·3m) in diameter—separated from spacecraft before retro-fire; decayed from orbit about 28 May 1980. Flight time 100days 9hr 20min. LC Baikonur. LV A-2. LT 1230 GMT.

December 18 United Nations "Moon Treaty"—more properly the "Agreement governing the activities of States on the Moon and other Celestial Bodies"—is opened for signature.

December 24 European Space Agency (ESA) launches Ariane heavy satellite vehicle on maiden flight from Guiana Space Centre, Korou, at 1714·38 GMT. L01 mission is a total success, placing a CAT (Capsule Ariane Technologique) into an orbit of 125 x 22,217 miles (202 x 35,753km) inclined at 17·55° to the equator.

The 3-stage, liquid-fuelled Ariane L01 lifting off from the Kourou launch pad in French Guiana.

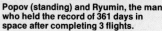

1980

March 27-April 26 Soviets launch Progress 8 unmanned cargo craft which docks with Salyut 6 on aft airlock at 2001 GMT, 29 March. Engine burn trims orbit of Salyut/Progress complex, 30 March, in readiness for launch of Soyuz 35. Orbit is 216 x 224 miles (348 x 360km) x 51·6°; period 91·4min. On 24 April, Progress engine fires again for 81sec to raise station's orbit to 211 x 228 miles (340 x 368km). Undocks at 0654 GMT, 25 April, and next day at 1654 GMT is made to re-enter the atmosphere and burns up over Pacific Ocean. LC Baikonur. LV A-2. LT 2153 MT; 1853 GMT.

Popov (standing) and Ryumin, the man who held the record of 361 days in space after completing 3 flights.

April 9-11 October Lt-Col Leonid Popov and Valery V. Ryumin (C) in Soyuz 35 dock with Salyut 6 on forward airlock at 1516 GMT, 10 April, to carry out servicing and maintenance tasks before starting long series of experiments. They transfer fuel and other supplies from Progress 8, which has docked automatically 29 March 1980. Ryumin (who only returned from record 175-day space mission the previous August) replaces Valentin Lebedev, who injured his knee in a trampoline accident during training in early March. Research programme includes more smelting experiments in Splav and Krystall furnaces and a new experiment, Lotos, to improve methods of obtaining structural materials from polyurethane foam under weightless conditions. Popov and Ryumin returned in the Soyuz 37 capsule on 11 October 1980, landing some 112 miles (180km) SE of Dzhezkazgan at 1250 MT and setting a new space endurance record of 184days 20hr 12min. LC Baikonur. LV A-2. LT 1638 MT.

April 27-May 22 Soviets launch Progress 9 unmanned cargo craft which docks automatically with Salyut 6/Soyuz 35 complex on aft airlock, 29 April. Supplies include food, water, clothing, dust collectors, regeneration equipment, spare parts, tools, scientific instruments, films and mail. Engine burn trims orbit of Salyut 6/Progress 9 to 216 x 229 miles (349 x 369km) x 51·6°, 16 May. After on-board cosmonauts have transferred cargo, craft is undocked at 2115 MT on 20 May, "with rubbish and used-up equipment", for disposal over the Central Pacific, 22 May. LC Baikonur. LV A-2. LT 0924 MT.

May US scientists prove by experiment that giant planet Jupiter could be a future source of huge quantities of hydrocarbon products to serve Earth's industries. A mixture of gases identified in Jupiter's atmosphere has been irradiated with UV rays, obtaining some 50 polymers and hydrocarbon components, including butane, ethane, propane, benzine and toluene from which fuel oil, plastics, fibres, lubricants, rubbers, solvents and explosives can be produced. Researchers: Professors Carl Sagan and B.N. Khare (Cornell University, N.Y.) and Eric Bandurski and Batholomew Nagy (University of Arizona).

May 18 People's Republic of China launches ICBM test vehicle CSS-X4 between space centre near Shuangch'eng-tzu and target area of 70 miles (112km) radius centred at 7°S, 171° 33'E in the South Pacific. Splashdown of inert warhead observed by Royal Australian Navy at approximately 0230 GMT, about 750 miles (1,207km) NNW of Fiji. A second test is made on 21 May, ending the test series. Distances travelled respectively are about 5,000 miles (8,046km) and 4,200 miles (6,759km).

May 23 Ariane space rocket (L02) launched from Kourou, French Guiana, crashes into the Atlantic after successful lift-off. One of four first-stage engines loses pressure, leading to pressure drop in other three and activation of "destruct" system. Lost with the rocket are two West German satellites, Firewheel and Amsat (Oscar 9).

May 26-June 3 Valery Kubasov (C) and Capt Bertalan Farkas (Hungarian) in Soyuz 36 dock with Salyut 6/Soyuz 35 complex on aft airlock at 2256 MT on 27 May for series of experiments in conjunction with resident crew (Popov and Ryumin). Flight time 7days 20hr 46min. Land in Soyuz 35 3 June at 1807 MT, 87 miles (140km) SE of Dzhezkazgan. LC Baikonur. LV A-2. LT 2121 MT.

Soyuz 37 crew: Gorbatko with the Vietnamese cosmonaut, Pham Tuan.

July 23-31 Col Viktor Gorbatko and Lt-Col Pham Tuan (Vietnamese) in Soyuz 37 spacecraft on 24 July at 2302 MT dock with Salyut 6/Soyuz 36 complex on aft airlock. Experiments with resident crew (Popov and Ryumin) included "applied problems of space medicine and biology, space technology, mapping of the surface of land and water". Gorbatko and Tuan returned in Soyuz 36. Total flight time 7days 20hr 42min. LC Baikonur. LV A-2. LT 2133 MT. R about 112 miles (180km) SE of Dzhezkazgan at 1815 MT.

September 18-26 Lt-Col Yuri Romanenko and Lt-Col Arnaldo Tamayo Mendez (Cuban) in Soyuz 38 spacecraft dock with Salyut 6/Soyuz 37 complex on aft airlock on 19 September. Experiments with resident crew (Popov and Ryumin) included observation of Cuba's natural resources, the crystallisation of sucrose and bio-medical tests. They returned in their own spacecraft at 1854 MT. Total flight time 7days 20hr 43min. LC Baikonur. LV A-2. LT 2211 MT. R about 108 miles (175km) SE of Dzhezkazgan.

September 28 Progress 11 is launched on 28 September and docks with Salyut 6 on 30 September under automatic control. After the resident cosmonauts had left the station, the cargo ship refuelled Salyut 6 automatically, finally separating on 9 December at 1323 MT after the Soyuz T-3 crew had boarded the Salyut 6/Progress complex. It re-entered the atmosphere over the Pacific Ocean on 11 December.

November 12 Voyager 1 flies within 77,000 miles (124,200km) of Saturn's cloud tops making detailed studies of the planet, its spectacular ring system and various moons. Ring system is more complex than previously believed, eg faint rings within Cassini division; dark radial "spokes" or "fingers" extend across B-ring. Some rings have eccentric paths, outer ring "braided like rope".

Voyager 1's 12 November picture of Saturn's braided F-ring.

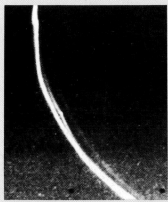

Yuri Malyshev in the Salyut cabin mock-up during pre-flight training.

June 5-9 Lt-Col Yuri V. Malyshev and Vladimir V. Aksyonov (C) in Soyuz T-2 spacecraft dock with Salyut 6/Soyuz 36 complex on aft airlock at 1858 MT 6 June. Intended docking was automatic under computer control but a suspected fault (spurious as it happened) made the cosmonauts control the docking manually from a distance of about 700ft (213m). Soyuz 36 had been re-docked 4 June on forward airlock by resident cosmonauts Popov and Ryumin who pulled away about 600ft (183m) while Salyut was turned through 180 deg. Soyuz T-2 re-entry module landed with cosmonauts Malyshev and Aksyonov about 124 miles (200km) SE of Dzhezkazgan at 1541 MT. Total flight time 3days 22hr 22min. Soyuz T-2 orbital module (separated before retro-fire) decayed from orbit about 5 September 1980. LC Baikonur. LV A-2. LT 1719 MT.

June 29-July 19 Soviets launch Progress 10 unmanned cargo craft which docks automatically with Salyut 6/Soyuz 36 complex on aft airlock 1 July. The ship "brought expendable materials and various cargoes" to the resident cosmonauts Popov and Ryumin and raised the orbit in preparation for next cosmonaut visit. Undocked 17 July and subsequently re-entered over Pacific Ocean. LC Baikonur. LV A-2. LT 0741 MT.

July 18 India becomes seventh nation after Soviet Union, USA, France, Japan, China and United Kingdom to launch an artificial satellite by independent effort. The 78lb (35·4kg) test-satellite is launched by the SLV-3-2 Rohini four-stage solid-propellant rocket from Sriharikota island, some 62 miles (100km) N of Madras.

Sizes of particles making up the rings cover a wide range, from microns to metres. Rings probably formed at different times, from different sources. Titan, Saturn's largest moon—"no more than 3,175 miles (5,120km) across"—has an atmosphere composed largely of nitrogen, not methane as previously believed. Atmospheric pressure near surface is 50 per cent greater than that of Earth; surface hidden by dense haze at least 175 miles (280km) thick. Titan believed to have roughly equal amount of rock and ice. Close-up observations of Saturn's smaller moons suggest that they consist of "dirty ice". Some are pockmarked by meteoritic craters collected over eons; others are smoother and therefore younger. Voyager 1 photographed six new Saturnian moons, some that had never been seen before, and some that had been reported as moons but not confirmed.

November 25 Space Shuttle Orbiter *Columbia* is moved from the Orbiter Processing Facility at the Kennedy Space Center, Florida, to the Vehicle Assembly Building for mating with the External Tank (ET) and Solid Rocket Boosters (SRBs). First flight is scheduled "no earlier than 17 March 1981".

November 27 Lt-Col Leonid Kizim Oleg Makarov and Gennady Strekalov in Soyuz T-3 dock with Salyut 6/Progress 11 complex on forward airlock, 28 November at 1854 MT. Described as a "new stage in the testing of space hardware and a logical continuation of the testing of the new generation of spaceships". Soyuz T-3 undocked from Salyut 6 at 0910 MT on 10 December and then separated the re-entry module before initiating retro-fire. The craft travelled some 6,090 miles (9,800km) to the landing area to touch down some 81 miles (130km) east of Dzhezkazgan. Parts fitted included a new four-pump hydraulic module for temperature control, telemetry, programming and timing modules. Research tasks include the growth of higher plants, the manufacture of semi-conductor

materials and the use of a portable helium-neon laser to obtain a hologram of a crystal being dissolved. A new converter was also fitted to Salyut's fuel system. LC Baikonur. LV A-2. LT 1718MT. R 81 miles (130km) E of Dzhezkazgan at 1226 MT.

The Soyuz T-3 crew: (left to right) Strekalov, Makarov and Kizim.

December 6 First of a series of Intelsat 5 satellites is launched by Atlas-Centaur from Cape Canaveral for stationing in Clarke orbit. The biggest communications satellite to date, it will relay 12,000 telephone calls and two colour TV programmes. This and others of the planned series of nine satellites will link 105 member countries of the Intelsat consortium.

December 29 Space Shuttle Orbiter *Columbia* and its launch system (STS-1) rolled out of Vehicle Assembly Building at Kennedy Space Center and positioned "hard down" on the pad at Launch Complex-39A in readiness for first flight by John W. Young (C) and Capt Robert L. Crippen. The journey along the crawlerway took 10½ hours.

Space Transportation System-1 on the crawlerway leading to LC-39A.

1981

January 24-March 21 Soviets launch Progress 12 unmanned cargo craft at 1718 MT which docks automatically with Salyut 6 on aft airlock at 1856 MT 26 January. Fuel and oxidant for station's main engine are replenished automatically on command from Earth. (Cosmonauts Kovalenok and Savinykh subsequently unloaded Progress 12 and placed used equipment in cargo compartment for disposal.) Undocked 19 March, re-entered atmosphere over Pacific Ocean 21 March. LC Baikonur. LV A-2.

March 12-May 26 Col Vladimir Kovalenok and Victor Savinykh in Soyuz T-4 dock with Salyut 6/Progress 12 complex on forward airlock at 2333 MT 13 March. Savinykh is world's 100th space traveller. Mission continues programme of occupation of Salyut 6 during which necessary repairs and maintenance are carried out and scientific experiments performed. By end of mission Salyut 6 has operated for total of 676 days with men on board. LC Baikonur. LV A-2. LT 2200 MT. R 1638 MT some 77 miles (125 km) E of Dzhezkazgan.

Kovalenok (left) and Savinykh in Red Square before the T-4 flight.

March 22-30 Col Vladimir Dzhanibekov and Jugderdemidiyn Gurragcha (Mongolia) in Soyuz 39 dock with Salyut 6/Soyuz T-4 complex at 1928 MT 23 March. Work with resident crew Kovalenok and Savinykh includes study of the adaptation of human organism to weightlessness and changes in the acuity and depth of cosmonauts' eyesight; also physical and technological experiments including use of holography for study of materials and seeds under micro-g conditions. For first time holographic images are transmitted by TV to and from the Earth. Mission also includes observation and photography of NW and Central Mongolia to locate possible mineral and water resources and assess condition of pasture land. LC Baikonur. LV A-2. LT 1759 MT. R 1442 MT about 106 miles (170km) SE of Dzhezkazgan.

Dzhanibekov (right) and Gurragcha during training activities.

April 12-14 First orbital test flight of Space Shuttle *Columbia* with John W. Young (commander) and Capt Robert L. Crippen (pilot) includes opening and closing of cargo bay doors in space, emergency donning of pressure suits and test of basic systems. Discovery that one complete thermal protection system tile and portions of others on the rear OMS pods are missing after

John Young (left) and Robert Crippen leave Columbia after touchdown at Edwards AFB on 14 April.

launch — fortunately they are not in critical areas that might endanger Orbiter during re-entry heating. Spacecraft flies planned 36 Earth orbits in mission lasting 54hr 21 min 57 sec, returning to Dryden Space Flight Center, Edwards AFB, California. Flight initially scheduled for 10 April was delayed two days by computer fault. LC KSC. LV Space Transportation System (STS)-1. LT 0700.03.98 EST. R Runway 23, Edwards AFB, California.

April 25- Soviets launch 33,069lb (15,000kg) Cosmos 1,267 which executes power manoeuvres before docking automatically with unmanned Salyut 6 space station on 19 June at 1052 MT. Tass News Agency reports that Cosmos 1,267 is testing new spacecraft systems and means of assembling large orbiting stations from modular units. Orbit of docked combination is 208 x 234 miles (335 x 377km) x 51·6°. LC Baikonur. LV D-1. LT 0201 GMT.

The Soyuz 40 crew: Leonid Popov (right) and Dumitry Prunariu.

May 14-22 Leonid Popov (C) and Dumitry Prunariu (Romania) in Soyuz 40 dock with Salyut 6/Soyuz T-4 complex at 2250 MT on 15 May. Work with resident crew Kovalenok and Savinykh includes bio-medical experiments, study of effects of outer space on construction materials, Earth resource observation and "methods of obtaining monocrystals of a set profile". (Before arrival of Soyuz 40, engine of T-4 was used to adjust space station's orbit.) LC Baikonur. LV A-2. LT 2117 MT. R 1437 MT 140 miles (225km) SE of Dzhezkazgan.

June 19 European Space Agency Ariane L03 launches Meteosat 2 and APPLE, an Indian experimental communications satellite, into geostationary orbit from Kourou Launch Site, French Guiana. Ariane data capsule is also carried to monitor vehicle performance. It is the third launch of the Ariane test series, and the second success.

Early July Soviet officials reveal that they will abstain from further manned flights for the rest of 1981 while work on a new space station is completed. The assembly will be conducted in orbit by attaching modular elements to a central core with multiple docking points. Cosmos 1,267 docked to Salyut 6 is performing interface tests directly related to this project. The manning levels will vary according to mission requirements, but the station may carry up to 12 cosmonauts at one time.

August 25 Voyager 2 passes within 63,000 miles (101,300km) of the cloud tops of Saturn, some 14,000 miles (22,500km) closer than Voyager 1. Spacecraft surveys the planet's ring

One of the first pictures of Saturn returned by Voyager 2 after the camera platform fault was rectified.

system and many of its moons during several days of close encounter. A camera platform fault — subsequently rectified — results in the loss of some pictures. Highlights of the encounter include more detailed examination of the complex ring system and the mysterious spoke-like features; discovery of a narrow ring in the Encke division; improved imagery of the satellite Hyperion; better pictures of Saturn's atmosphere; discovery of a 250 mile (400km) wide crater on Tethys, the largest yet observed in the Saturnian system. Spacecraft now on course for Uranus (1986) and Neptune (1989).

September Report on Soviet military power authorised by Caspar W. Weinberger, US Secretary of Defense, includes reference to Soviet Saturn V-class booster having close orbit capability of 390,000-455,000lb (176,870-206,350kg). It could launch heavy Soviet space station, large laser weapons. "The Soviet goal of having continuously manned space stations may support both defensive and offensive weapons in space with man in the space station for target selection, repairs and adjustments and positive command and control."

September 19 People's Republic of China launches three satellites—China 9, 10 and 11—from a single carrier rocket. Largest satellite is an octagonal prism, maximum diameter 3·9ft (1·2m) x 3·28ft (1·0m); carries four rectangular solar panels. Second satellite is cone shaped. Third is a balloon linked to metal sphere by a wire tether. Satellites one and two designed to study Earth's magnetic field, IR and UV radiation, charged particles, X-rays etc. Third satellite, which decayed from orbit in six days, for research into atmospheric density. Orbits: 242 x 994 miles (390 x 1,600km) x 59·4°. LC Shuang-ch'eng-tzu. LV FB-1 (CSL-2). LT 2132 GMT.

The FB-1 and its umbilical tower at the Shuang-ch'eng-tzu launch site.

Pioneer-Venus radar images of the planet supplied through US/Soviet co-operative scientific exchanges. LC Baikonur. LV D-1-e. LT 0530 GMT.

November 12-14 Second orbital test flight of Space Shuttle *Columbia* (STS-2) begins at LC-39A at Cape Canaveral at 1010 EST. Crew are Col Joe H. Engle (commander) and Capt Richard H. Truly (pilot). Mission includes five Office of Space and Terrestrial Application (OSTA)-1 experiments mounted in cargo bay on British Aerospace pallet to explore Earth's natural resources; also test of 50ft (15m) long manipulator arm remotely operated by the crew, built by SPAR of Canada. The flight—intended to last more than five days—is cut short because of a fault in one of the three fuel cells that supply electricity. *Columbia* lands at Edwards AFB, California, on 14 November, having completed some 90 per cent of its tasks. Mission elapsed

Bhaskara 2 mounted on top of its C-1 launch vehicle at the Kapustin Yar launch site in the Soviet Union.

radiometers operating at 19·35, 22·235 and 31·4 GHz. Orbit 324 x 337 miles (521 x 543km) x 50·64°. LC Kapustin Yar. LV C-1. LT 0825 GMT.

December 11 First flight unit of ESA Spacelab arrives at Kennedy Space Center, Florida, aboard Lockheed C-5A transport which lands on Shuttle runway. Some 80 Space Shuttle sorties with the laboratory are planned between 1983-1995, at first with the now-delivered unit and from 1984 with the second Spacelab.

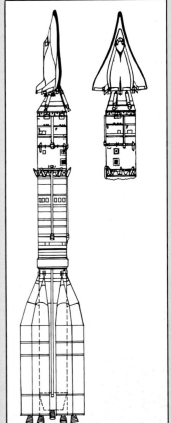

Charles Vick's drawing of a possible Kosmolyot testbed; the operational vehicle may take off horizontally.

(about $30-37·5). Project will be openly discussed in two to three years; first flight expected 1987. Perhaps Vladimir Shatalov best expresses the philosophy. "The horizontal or aircraft start," he said, "is definitely preferred for a re-usable spacecraft, and we are taking this standpoint. However, the Americans chose a useful and less costly alternative, namely a vertical rocket start which has the advantage that it can carry along a greater load each time. The design has undeniable advantages as well as disadvantages . . . We prefer the more advanced second shuttle which proceeds from a horizontal launching device. This gives the further advantage that the device can start from any airfield in the Soviet Union equipped for this purpose; this makes the system more flexible in mission operations."

The Marecs spacecraft undergoes pre-flight preparations at Kourou.

December 20 European Space Agency's Ariane L04 launches Marecs 1 maritime communications satellite for positioning in geostationary orbit at 26°W to provide fast, high-quality radio links between ships and shore stations. Payload also includes data capsule CAT to monitor vehicle performance. LC Kourou, French Guiana. LV Ariane L04. LT 0129 GMT.

1982

January NASA announces that data supplied by Voyager 2, during close encounter with Saturn August 1981, has led to discovery of four more moons and evidence suggesting possibly two more, making a total of 23. All estimated to be 6·2-12·4 miles (10-20km) across circulating within the orbits of larger moons, Mimas distance 115,580 miles (186,000km), Tethys 183,310 miles (295,000km), Tethys/Dione 217,490 miles (350,000km) and Dione 234,880 miles (378,000km).

January Anatoliy Skripko, Science and Technology attaché, Soviet Embassy, Washington DC, informs American Astronautical Society that USSR may begin development of space shuttle-type vehicle in about five years to support long-duration space station operations. The USSR had not urgently pressed for development of a shuttle because "it is no problem for us now to deliver fuel, food or other supplies" to space stations by using large boosters and Progress supply craft. Major interest surrounds concept of horizontal launching with full recovery of flight vehicles. Aim to reduce payload cost to a level one-tenth that of US Space Shuttle, ie 20-25 roubles per kg

January NASA announces study of an unmanned heavy launcher SRB-X utilising re-usable Space Shuttle components such as Solid Rocket Boosters and Main Engines. Will place 65,000lb (29,484kg) into low Earth orbit or 12,000lb (5,443kg) into geostationary orbit.

January 2 Subsidiary of US investment banking firm, William Sword Co., Space Transportation Co., reported to be considering the private procurement of a Space Shuttle Orbiter. Company states: "Our concept is to supply the fifth Orbiter and contribute it to the fleet, and then in effect to become ticket agency for the entire fleet."

January 5 British Aerospace announces that ESA has awarded Space and Communications Division a contract to lead industrial team from seven European countries and Canada in construction of L-Sat, one of world's largest communications satellites, which will beam television programmes into homes, or business communications into offices and factories, via small, roof-mounted, dish antennas. The 5,070lb (2,300kg) L-Sat 1, to be launched by Ariane 4 from Kourou, French Guiana, in 1986, will have solar arrays developing over

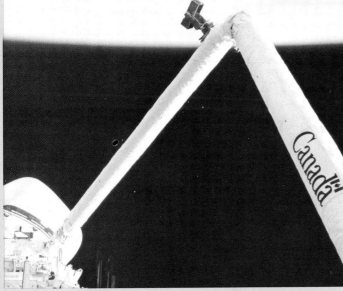

September 29 Salyut 6 space station (now unmanned) completes four years in space having made 23,029 revolutions of the Earth. Manned flights to the station have included five long-stay crews and 11 visiting missions. Since the docking of Cosmos 1,267 on 19 June, the orbit of the complex has been raised twice using engines onboard the attached module. It is now 292 x 324 miles (470 x 521km).

October 30 Soviets launch Venera 13 unmanned spacecraft with intention of landing a robot laboratory on Venus in March 1982. The craft is designed to be able to excavate a Venusian soil sample and bring it inside the lander for analysis. LC Baikonur. LV. D-1-e. LT 0602 GMT.

November 4 Soviets launch Venera 14 unmanned spacecraft, the sister ship of Venera 13. The two craft are expected to land in an area southeast of the Beta Shield volcano region. The choice of this site was determined by studying US

The remote manipulator system arm during first flight testing.

time is 54hr 13min 11sec. LC KSC. LV STS-2. LT Edwards AFB, California. Note: A previous attempt to launch STS-2 on 4 November was frustrated when overheating of *Columbia*'s auxiliary power units (APUs) caused by contaminated lubricating oil made the automatic ground launch sequencer stop the count-down at T-31 seconds. This was the second launch delay as a nitrogen tetroxide spill on 22 September, as the forward reaction control system was being loaded with oxidant, had necessitated the rebonding of some 370 silica tiles and the replacement of 26 thermal blankets in the nose RCS bay. This work delayed the launch from the scheduled date of 9 October.

November 20 Soviets launch Indian Earth Resources satellite Bhaskara 2. Embodies two TV cameras operating in 0·54-0·66 and 0·75-0·85 micrometres bands and three microwave

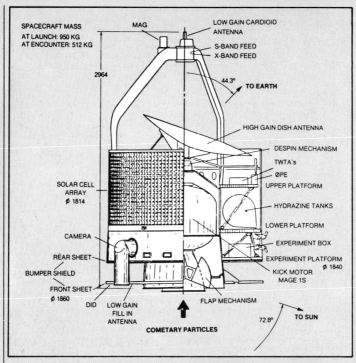

SPACECRAFT MASS
AT LAUNCH: 950 KG
AT ENCOUNTER: 512 KG

MAG
LOW GAIN CARDIOID ANTENNA
S-BAND FEED
X-BAND FEED
2964
44.3°
TO EARTH
HIGH GAIN DISH ANTENNA
DESPIN MECHANISM
TWTA's
ØPE
UPPER PLATFORM
SOLAR CELL ARRAY Ø 1814
HYDRAZINE TANKS
LOWER PLATFORM
CAMERA
EXPERIMENT BOX
REAR SHEET
EXPERIMENT PLATFORM Ø 1840
BUMPER SHIELD
KICK MOTOR MAGE 1S
FRONT SHEET Ø 1860
DID
LOW GAIN FILL IN ANTENNA
FLAP MECHANISM
COMETARY PARTICLES
72.8°
TO SUN

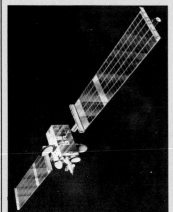

The British Aerospace design for the L-Sat 1 communications satellite.

3,500 watts. It will stand 18·4ft (5·6m) tall and span 88·6ft (27m) over the fully-extended solar arrays. L-Sat is expected to develop up to 7,000 watts in subsequent commercial versions with arrays extending up to 180ft (55m).

January 26 European Space Agency approves development of Ariane 4 in family of six launchers of differing capability. All versions to embody common, lengthened first stage having propellant capacity of 210 tonnes, powered by four uprated Viking engines operating at chamber pressure of 58·5 bar. Second stage, third stage and equipment bay same as Ariane 3. A new, large diameter fairing to be available in three sizes: normal, lengthened and 'dual-launch'. Versions of the launcher differ according to the number of strap-on boosters: either two or four solid-propellant boosters as those of Ariane 3, or two or four liquid propellant boosters using the Viking engine with 40 tonnes of propellant.

The six launch vehicles of the proposed Ariane 4 family. The rockets are identified according to the number and type of strap-ons used.

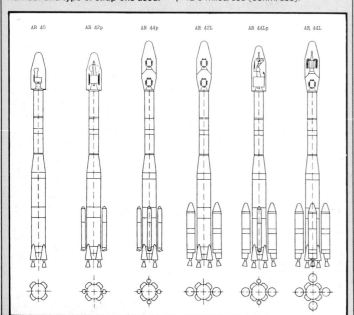

AR 40   AR 42p   AR 44p   AR 42L   AR 44Lp   AR 44L

There are also plans for a hybrid version having two solid-propellant. and two liquid propellant boosters, and finally one having no strap-ons. Ariane 4 family will place 2,425 to 9,480lb (1,100 to 4,300kg) into geostationary transfer orbit. Cost per kilogram in orbit should fall to 55 per cent of using Ariane I.

March European Space Agency initiates development of Giotto spacecraft to investigate Halley's comet. Optimum launch date, by Ariane from Kourou, French Guiana, 10 July 1985; Halley encounter 13 March 1986 with comet 0·89 AU from Sun and 1 AU from Earth; fly-by velocity 42·3 miles/sec (68km/sec).

Giotto: ESA's spacecraft to encounter Halley's Comet in March 1986.

Giotto: spin stabilised, overall height 116in (296cm), diameter over solar cell drum 71in (181cm), launch weight 2,094lb (950kg) reducing to 1,130lb (512kg) when "kick" motor has burnt out and hydrazine propellant used for mid-course attitude and trajectory correction manoeuvres. Cylindrical solar cell arrays (plus four silver cadmium batteries) provide 190W during encounter. High-gain dish antenna diameter 4·8ft (1·47m). Double bumper shield at nozzle end comprises 0·04in (1mm) aluminium front sheet and 0·47in (12mm) Kevlar rear sheet with 9·8in (25cm) gap. Instruments: camera, neutral mass spectrometer, dust impact detector, plasma analysers, energetic particles detector, magnetometer, optical probe. The other two Halley comet spacecraft are:
USSR: Two Venera-Halley spacecraft to be launched 22-28 December 1984 to drop landing modules on Venus 14-22 June 1985; first comet intercept 8 March 1986, second a week later. Fly-by velocity 48·3 miles/sec (77·7km/sec).
Instruments: Wide and narrow angle cameras; three-channel spectrometer; dust counter, plasma analyser.
Japan: ISAS Planet-A intended to penetrate Halley's coma. Launch date: 14 August 1985, Halley encounter 8 March 1986. Depending on trajectory achieved, miss distance will be between 6,214 and 62,140 miles (10,000 and 100,000km). Spacecraft is spin-stabilised, cylindrical, height 27·5in (70cm), diameter 55·1in (140cm), launch weight 298lb (135kg) including 22lb (10kg) scientific instruments, 11lb (5kg) hydrazine for attitude and velocity control. Instruments: UV (Lyman alpha) camera, solar wind analyser. Launch centre: Kagoshima. Launch vehicle: three-stage Mu-3C plus 4th stage "kick" motor.

A panoramic view of Venus taken by Venera 13. Note the shock-absorbing landing ring and discarded lens cap.

March 1 Descent craft of Venera 13 soft-lands on Venus, transmitting from surface for 127 minutes, four times longer than planned. Obtains first colour photographs of landscape; first remote analysis of soil samples. Mission sequence: encapsuled lander separates from Venera 13 mothercraft 27 February, some 48 hours before anticipated time of entry into atmosphere of Venus, the latter passing the planet at a distance of some 22,370 miles (36,000km). Lander enters dense layers of Venusian atmosphere at 0555 MT and 62 minutes later lands in a mountainous area east of Phoebe region at 7°30'S, 303°E. Entry speed about 7 miles/sec (11·3km/sec); after a period of aerodynamic braking and parachute descent to altitude of 29·2 miles (47km) capsule completes descent with help of aerodynamic braking disc. After landing two small television cameras obtain eight panoramic views of surrounding landscape from distance of 4·9ft (1·5m) revealing objects as small as 0·16-0·196in (4-5mm) across; some pictures taken sequentially through red,

blue and green filters to obtain colour. Pictures reveal shoots of ancient volcanic lava with traces of chemical erosion; scattering of sharp rocks partly covered with fine dust and sand. Landscape has a brownish hue. Soil sampling device drills the surface rock at the ambient temperature of 457°C (855°F) and pressure of 89 atmospheres. Soil samples are conveyed by suction to an hermetically-sealed chamber in the lander for X-ray and fluorescent analysis. To achieve this, pressure in the chamber is reduced to about one two-thousandth of that outside and a temperature of 30°C (86°F) is maintained by a cooling system. Discovers that soil contains highly alkaline potassium basalts, similar to those of lunar samples obtained by Luna probes, but which do not occur on Earth's surface. Planet's seismic activity and physical and mechanical properties of the ground are investigated by detachable device. The mechanical strength of rocks is determined by a rod powered by springs which impresses a metal stamp into the ground. The same rod is used to measure the electrical conductivity of the ground. During descent and after landing, studies are made of chemical composition of atmosphere and clouds, structure of the cloud cover, and diffused solar radiation. Electric discharges in the atmosphere are also registered. Lander instrument data are relayed to Earth via Venera 13 mothercraft during its close passage of Venus. En route to Venus, and subsequently, studies made of X-rays, inter-planetary plasma and characteristics of cosmic rays and solar wind. Franco-Soviet experiment also investigates location and characteristics of galactic sources of gamma rays. Interplanetary magnetic field studied using a magnetometer of Austrian manufacture.

March 4 UK Government gives approval for direct broadcasting by satellites from 1986, providing BBC with two additional TV channels and three extra high-quality stereo radio channels. Geostationary satellite will broadcast directly to homes with TV sets equipped with signal converters using 35·4in (90cm) dish antenna pointed at the satellite. Alternatively, service will be received by community cable system using a single dish antenna. Three satellites to be built initially based on ECS technology, two operational, one spare, for launch by Ariane rockets from Kourou, French Guiana. Partners in £150 million project to supply satellites—British Telecom, British Aerospace and Marconi—will set up joint company, United Satellites; also discussing with Rothschild Bank possibility of establishing leasing arrangements for the satellites, the three equally to share the equity and the risks.

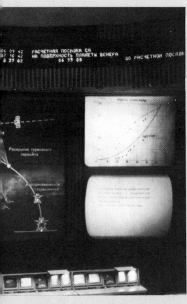

A view of the Soviet Flight Control Centre during the descent phase of the Venera 14 landing capsule.

March 5 Descent craft of Venera 14 soft-lands on Venus, transmitting from surface for 57 minutes. Obtains colour photographs of landscape; soil samples for on-the-spot analysis. Encapsuled lander entered dense layers of Venusian atmosphere at 0553 MT, landing 63 minutes later east of the Phoebe region at 13°15'S, 310°9'E. Surface temperature is 465°C (869°F), pressure 94 atmospheres. Probe lands on a hill about 1,640ft (500m) high. The surroundings, as observed by onboard TV cameras, show large boulders of dark grey rock covered with brownish-black fine-grained material; also small potholes covered by hillside debris. Sky colour is orange or reddish-brown, reflecting appearance of surface. For research objectives, see 1 March, Venera 13.

March 22-30 Third orbital test flight of Space Shuttle *Columbia* (STS-3) begins at LC-39A at Cape Canaveral at 1100 EST, one hour behind schedule because a heater that keeps nitrogen gaseous in the fuel lines failed to start automatically; it was subsequently switched on manually. Crew are Col Jack R. Lousma (commander) and Col C. Gordon Fullerton (pilot). Orbit achieved is 130 x 130nm (240·8 x 240·8km). Mission includes Office of Space Sciences (OSS-1) instruments devoted to astronomy and space physics mounted on British Aerospace pallet in cargo bay; also further test of Spar-built manipulator arm remotely operated by crew including first removal and replacement of a payload in the cargo bay, and test of Orbiter's reaction to thermal extremes at different attitudes with respect to the Sun. Flight preparations, following previous mission of November 1981, included replacement of 499 thermal insulation tiles with densified tiles; replacement of

STS-3 thunders aloft. Note the dark External Tank; elimination of the white paint saved 600lb (272kg).

fuel cell No 1 (which failed on STS-2 flight). Lift-off weight 4,478,787lb (2,031,578kg), about 17,000lb (7,710kg) heavier than STS-1 and 4,518lb (2,049kg) heavier than STS-2. Problems associated with mission include loss of or damage to some 38 thermal protection tiles from the nose area and aft section of *Columbia*, above the "sear line"; failure of certain radio communications channels; failure of part of close-circuit TV system used to monitor work with manipulator arm; minor drop in cabin pressure; overheated auxiliary power unit (APU 3) and a clogged toilet. Originally intended to land 29 March 1982 (at 1336 local time) at Army Missile Range, White Sands, New Mexico, mission extended by one day because of sandstorm conditions in the area.

Mission elapsed time is 192hr 4min 49sec instead of pre-planned 171hr 36min. Landing site was changed from Edwards Air Force Base, California, before mission began because of rainstorm damage to landing strip. Number of orbits: 128, re-entry on 129th orbit. LC KSC. LV STS-3. LT 1100 EST. R 0904·49 MST, Northrup Strip, Army Missile Range, White Sands, New Mexico.

March 24 Hughes Aircraft Company wins contract to build five Intelsat 6 communications satellites. Each will carry 33,000 telephone calls and four TV programmes. The spin-stabilised satellite has two nesting concentric cylindrical solar arrays 39ft (11·9m) long when fully deployed; diameter 12ft (3·65m). Launch weight 7,700lb (3,493kg); power 2·2kW; frequencies 4-6GHz and 11·14GHz. Intelsat has options for 11 additional satellites that could eventually raise programme value to $1,6000 million. Hughes' team

Intelsat 6 on station mounting its C-band and K-band reflectors.

includes British Aerospace (value of initial participation $100 million); MBB; Nippon Electric; Spar Aerospace; Selenia and Thomson-CSF.

April 10 Insat 1A, world's first combined communications and weather satellite, built for India by Ford Aerospace, is launched from Kennedy Space Center. LV Delta 3910/PAM.

Insat IA, the world's first combined comsat and weather satellite.

April 19 Soviets launch Salyut 7 space station into orbit of 136 x 173 miles (219 x 278km) x 51·6°: period 89·2 min At present unmanned, "it will be used, like Salyut 6, both in automatic mode and with a human crew". It can accommodate up to five people. Objective is to test modernized systems and equipment and conduct further technical experiments. Communications with the station are being maintained via tracking stations in the USSR and the research ship *Academician Korolev* in the Atlantic. Compared to Salyut 6 there are no fundamental design changes, main

Salyut 7 orbits the Earth with a Progress cargo ship docked to it.

consideration being to lighten work load of crew and making long-term living conditions more tolerable. New water supply system, "Rodnik" (Spring) operates as reliably as a domestic tap; hot water constantly available. Station embodies brightly coloured, washable, wall panels, more comfortable crew accommodation, better artificial lighting, "Stroka" teleprinter link Earth-to-space, Delta automatic navigator using on-board computers. Research programme includes studies of Earth's surface and atmosphere for various departments of the national economy; astrophysical and biomedical studies; technological and technical experiments; tests and adjustments of improved on-board systems and apparatus. "Aelite" multipurpose unit checks and evaluates cosmonauts' cardio-vascular systems, cerebral activity, blood pressure and circulation. Fresh foodstuffs brought from Earth in Progress cargo ships are stored in a refrigerator. Station has improved docking unit which will allow larger ships to link up in orbit. LC Baikonur. LV D-1.

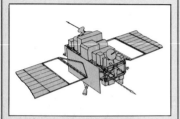

The baseline design for Eureca: European Retrievable Carrier.

May Member countries of European Space Agency (ESA) approve three new projects. 1. Unmanned Spacelab free-flight pallet, Eureca, to carry up to 3,307lb (1,500kg) experiments. Derived from British Aerospace standard pallet mounted in Space Shuttle Orbiter cargo bay, will have solar arrays for power, provision for remote operation, and attitude and thermal control. Flight duration up to six months before Space Shuttle retrieval. First launch 1986, material and life support experiments. 2. Improvements to existing Spacelab module. 3. Studies of manned and unmanned space stations benefitting from Spacelab technology. Participants: Belgium, Denmark, France, Italy, Spain, Switzerland, West Germany and UK. Estimated cost: $160 million (155·9 million accounting units) at mid-1980 prices.

May 13-December 10 Lt-Col Anatoly Berezovoi and flight engineer Valentin Lebedev in Soyuz T-5 dock with Salyut 7 space station on forward airlock at 1536 MT May 14. Orbit of combined vehicles 213 x 224 miles (343 x 360km) inclined at 51·6° to equator. Significant events: 17 May: Cosmonauts release 62lb (28kg) Iskra 2 amateur radio satellite from airlock compartment. 25 June-2 July: They receive Franco-Soviet cosmonauts (who arrive in Soyuz T-6). 30 June: After being in space for 78 days, Berezovoi and Lebedev spacewalk for 153 minutes to replace and fix new instruments on the exterior of Salyut 7; they also assess the use of "different mechanical joints which can be used in assembly work in space". 21-27 August: They receive three more cosmonauts, including the woman Svetlana Savitskaya (who arrive in Soyuz T-7). 18 September: Cosmonauts release amateur radio satellite Iskra 3 from airlock. During their long stay aboard the space station, four automatic Progress cargo ships kept them supplied with air, food, propellant, water, mail and equipment. Progress 16, still attached to the station when the cosmonauts left, was later released by remote control to burn up in the atmosphere. Berezovoi and Lebedev returned in the Soyuz T-7 spacecraft having travelled more than 80 million miles (129 million km) and setting a new duration record of 211 days 8 hours 5 minutes. Of 300 major

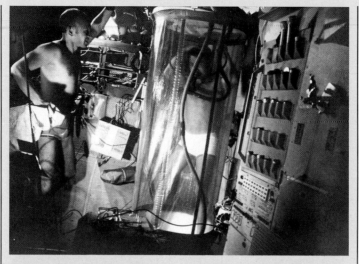

Berezovoi takes a shower inside Salyut 7 while Lebedev seems to be waiting his turn!

experiments, the crew made observations and surveys of Earth including potential areas of oil and mineral deposits and also mapped the distribution of glaciers. More than 60 sessions of photography logged by December included more than 2,000 pictures with the MKF-6M multispectral camera, more than 3,000 with KT-140 topographical camera. The cosmonauts also completed many astrophysical, medical and biological experiments. Astronomical studies included use of Soviet designed X-ray camera and Elena gamma-ray telescope for which fittings were supplied by Bulgaria and Czechoslovakia. Two French-made cameras, Piramig and PSN, obtained more than 1,100 photographs. Pilot production of semi-conductor monocrystals (cadmium selenide and indium antimonide) processed in 300lb (136kg) Korund electric furnace, described as the first manufacture in space for the electronics industry. Products were "highly uniform monocrystals with properties immensely better than those produced in gravity". Furnace operated at temperatures of 20 to 1,270°C to an accuracy of half a degree. First sample products stated to weigh up to 3·3lb (1·5kg). Cosmonauts landed in a snowstorm, their capsule rolling down a hillside before coming to rest. LC Baikonur. LV A-2. LT 1358 MT. R 2203 MT, 118 miles (190 km) east of Dzhezkazgan.

May 17 Cosmonauts aboard Salyut 7 release 62lb (28kg) artificial satellite Iskra 2 from airlock compartment. Satellite embodies transponder for experiments in amateur radio communications, a command radio channel and a telemetry system for relaying scientific and housekeeping information to ground stations. Designed by student design office, Sergo Ordzhonikidze Aviation Institute, Moscow. Orbit 212·5 x 222 miles (342 x 357km) x 51·6° inclination. A similar Iskra 3 was released from airlock on 18 September; orbit 224 x 229 miles (360 x 365km) x 51·6° inclination.

May 23-June 6 Soviets launch unmanned Progress 13 cargo ship which docks with Salyut 7-Soyuz T-5 complex on aft airlock at 1157 MT on 25 May, final link-up being controlled by on-board cosmonauts Berezovoi and Lebedev. Two tonnes of supplies transferred to space station include 1,455lb (660kg) propellants, 290 litres water, life support equipment, research and technical equipment and materials, some 551lb (250kg) being of French supply. Other items include Krystall furnace, electrophotometer EFO-7 (to obtain data from stars), improved Oasis plant growth unit (peas and onions). Modifications to Progress include a "more efficient system for delivering water to the station". Whereas water tanks of earlier

craft were internal, water is now contained in spherical bottles on the outside of both Progress and Salyut leaving space for other cargo. After manoeuvring space station complex into lower orbit by two stage engine burn, in readiness for arrival of Soyuz T-6, Progress 13 is separated on 4 June and two days later is de-orbited over Pacific Ocean. LC Baikonur. LV A-2. LT 0957 MT.

June Australia places contracts worth almost $175 million with Hughes Aircraft Company for three Aussat communications satellites, one a ground spare, plus controlling ground stations to be located in Sydney and Perth. Will provide direct-broadcast TV and radio to the outback, relay TV between Australian cities (also services to Papua New Guinea and offshore islands) and supply domestic and data links; also improve air traffic control services and maritime radio coverage. First launch anticipated June 1985; planned geostationary longitudes 156°E, 160°E and 164°E.

June Aérospatiale study looks beyond Ariane 4 to a new family of ESA launchers, some partly re-usable, which could put up to 33,069lb (15,000kg) into low Earth orbit. Three main

versions: Ariane 5B: for low Earth orbits. Ariane 5G, with H9 LO₂/LH₂ third stage, 19,840lb (9,000kg) thrust. Ariane 5H: two-stage variant for use with "Hermes" mini-shuttle studied by CNES.

June 3 Soviets launch test model of winged spacecraft—Cosmos 1374—into 140 miles (225km) circular orbit inclined at 50·7° to equator; makes wing-borne re-entry over Indian Ocean after 1¼ orbits. Royal Australian Air Force reports seven Soviet ships in recovery area some 350 miles (563km) south of Cocos Islands. Test model probably in 2,200lb (1,000kg) class launched by C-1 two-stage rocket from Kapustin Yar about 2130 GMT (est); flight lasts approximately 109 minutes. Project possibly related to planned 40,000lb (18,144kg) class Kosmolyot (spaceplane), designed to resolve thermal heating and control problems. Reminiscent of US Air Force Prime glide-vehicles flown on sub-orbital trajectories by Atlas boosters beginning 1966-70.

June 6 Radio Luxembourg reported to be planning to launch a £200 million satellite system by mid-1980s which could provide new TV channel for Europe, including the UK.

June 18 Soviets conduct successful test of a killer satellite by passing Cosmos 1379 close to target satellite Cosmos 1375. Target, launched from Northern Cosmodrome June 6, entered orbit of 615 x 634 miles (990 x 1,021km) x 65·9°. Interceptor, launched from Baikonur at about 1110 GMT executes plane change of 0·7° 76 minutes later, then manoeuvres into 607 x 628 miles (977 x 1,010km) orbit at 1226 GMT. Re-enters atmosphere 1450 GMT. LC Baikonur. LV F-1. LT 1110 GMT.

June 24-July 2 Soviets launch Soyuz T-6 with first Franco-Soviet crew comprising commander Vladimir Dzhanibekov (USSR), flight engineer Alexander Ivanchenkov (USSR) and Lt Col Jean-Loup Chrétien (France). Orbit before docking with Salyut 7/ Soyuz T-5 on aft airlock at 2146 MT

France's first "spationaute", J-L. Chrétien, enjoying the freedom of a microgravity environment.

25 June, 154 x 172 miles (248 x 277km) x 51·6°. Research programme, in conjunction with resident crew Berezovoi and Lebedev, includes medical experiments—cardio-vascular functions and sensory physiology—biological experiments, studies of Earth's atmosphere, the interplanetary medium and galactic and extra-galactic radiation sources. Also, work with Krystall Magma F electric furnace installed by resident crew including examination of processes of diffusion and crystallisation of metal alloys and improved "space production techniques". French attachment to the furnace measured temperatures at different points in and around the melting zone. Total participation cost to France about £5·5 million including instruments, training and personnel. Dzhanibekov replaced original crew member Yuri Malyshev on medical grounds. Back-up crew: Leonid Kizim (USSR), Vladimir Solovyov (USSR), Patrick Baudry (France). LC Baikonur. LV A-2. LT 1629 GMT. R 1821 MT, about 40 miles (65km) NE of Arkalyk.

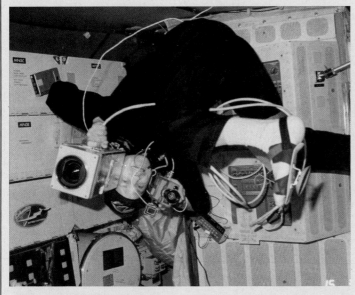

Mattingly in Columbia's mid-deck; note suction-cup-fitted footwear.

June 27-July 4 Fourth and final test flight of Space Shuttle *Columbia* (STS-4) with astronauts Capt Thomas K. Mattingly (commander) and Henry Hartsfield (pilot). First shuttle to fly due east into an eventual 201 x 184 mile (323 x 296km) x 28·5° orbit. Lift-off weight 4,484,585lb (2,034,207kg). Modifications to Orbiter included densification of about 800 thermal tiles and replacement of 10 attitude control thrusters which were contaminated by gypsum during previous landing at White Sands, New Mexico. Objectives include investigation of spacecraft capability under extreme in-orbit conditions of solar heating, and recording of environmental conditions in and around spaceplane; also further testing of Remote Manipulator System arm with which Induced Environment Contamination Monitor (IECM) was deployed away from spaceplane and returned. An 8,000lb (3,629kg) military payload, DoD 82-1, fixed in cargo bay, tested IR and UV sensors and space sextant for future surveillance (unofficially reported to include cryogenically cooled IR radiation detection telescope capable of identifying heat from enemy aircraft and missiles). Other experiments include tests of flight instrumentation, thermal effects on external tiles and tile gap heating. In *Columbia's* crew compartment were two materials processing experiments: Continuous Flow Electrophoresis System (CFES) to isolate and purify biological materials, in this case a blend of rat and egg albumins. Mission problems: SRBs failed to develop rated thrust and spaceplane entered orbit some 5 miles (8km) lower than planned; difficulty in closing cargo bay doors which had "warped" under extremes of

temperature; failure to salvage the two SRBs which broke up and sank in 3,100ft (945m) of water after main parachutes failed. Fault was traced to a "g" switch designed to close on water impact and release the main parachutes; instead parachutes were released from boosters at altitude, some 365 secs after lift-off, when the boosters' frustrums were due to separate. Orbiter's landing is made for first time on concrete runway of minimum length-15,000ft (4,572m). Mission elapsed time is 169hr 14min. LC KSC. LV STS-4. LT 1100 EDT. R 0914 PDT, Runway 22, Edwards Air Force Base, California.

June 30 Space Shuttle *Challenger* is rolled out at Rockwell's factory in Palmdale, California.

June 30 General Georgi Beregovoy, commander of Gagarin Cosmonauts' Training Centre, says two women are training for a space flight which most probably will be to the Salyut 7 space station. Both are married, about 30 years old and already experienced respectively as pilot and flight engineer of aircraft.

July Reagan Administration revives Widebody-Centaur as upper stage for Space Shuttle by approving FY 1982 supplemental of $80 million for conversion work to start. Will replace two-stage Inertial Upper Stage (IUS) in projects Galileo and International Solar Polar Mission (ISPM). Galileo-Jupiter mission will slip to May 1986 but transit time will be reduced to about two years. Estimated development cost: $250 million. Estimated cost of modifications to KSC launch pad and *Challenger* and *Discovery* Orbiters: $125 million. Each payload bay door of Orbiter will include orifice for LO_2 and LH_2 to allow fuelling on the pad; vents through rear of spacecraft will allow dumping of propellants for emergency landing.

July 10-August 13 Soviets launch unmanned Progress 14 cargo ship which docks with Salyut 7-Soyuz T-5 complex on aft airlock at 1141 GMT, 12 July. After replenishing the space station, Progress 14 was de-orbited over the Pacific Ocean on 13 August. LC Baikonur. LV A-2. LT 0958 GMT.

Landsat 4 undergoes inspection at the General Electric plant in Philadelphia, Pennsylvania.

July 16 NASA launches 4,273lb (1,938kg) Earth resources satellite Landsat 4 on its way into Sun-synchronous orbit of 422 x 435 miles (680 x 700km) inclined at 98·3° to equator. Objective to provide continuous remote sensing information and to encourage continued national and international participation in land remote sensing programmes; assess capability of new thematic mapper and exploit new areas of IR and visible light spectra at higher resolution. On-board thematic mapper provides 98·4ft (30m) resolution in six visible-light spectral bands; an additional IR band gives 394ft (120m). Scanning images processed at

Goddard Space Flight Center, Greenbelt, Maryland. After six months satellite turned over to National Oceanic and Atmospheric Administration, Department of Commerce. LC Vandenberg AFB. LV Delta 3920 (first use). LT 1059 PDT.

July 22 NASA announces that two mercury ion thrusters will be embodied in USAF research satellites Ion Auxiliary Propulsion System (IAPS). Built for Lewis Research Center by Hughes Aircraft, the small electric rocket engines will be used for attitude control and orbit manoeuvring.

July 29 Life of Salyut 6 space station is ended after four years ten months by attached "Star" module (Cosmos 1267) which uses its rocket engine to brake the station and direct it into the atmosphere over the Pacific Ocean. Five main expeditions of cosmonauts and 11 short-stay expeditions visited the station; nine included people of other socialist countries. Manned occupation lasted total of 676 days, and 35 dockings with manned and automatic spacecraft were made.

August Official China News Agency announces new multi-stage liquid propellant rocket CZ-3 designed to place large satellites into geostationary orbit.

August 19-27 Soviets launch Soyuz T-7 with cosmonauts Col Leonid Popov, flight engineer Alexander Serebrov and researcher-cosmonaut Svetlana Savitskaya (second woman in space). Docks with Salyut 7 space station on 20 August. Objectives: scientific, technological and bio-medical experiments jointly with resident cosmonauts Berezovoi and Lebedev. Serebrov is qualified engineer concerned in design and testing of spacecraft. Savitskaya, 34, has flown more than 20 types of aircraft, has 1,500 flying hours to her credit and is a qualified test pilot, second class. She holds 18 world records in aviation and was world aerobatic champion in 1970. Crew returned in the spacecraft Soyuz T-5 originally used by Berezovoi and Lebedev. Brought to Earth results of experiments performed on Salyut 7 by resident crew during previous three months, and by crew of five cosmonauts in the course of their joint work. Cosmonauts photographed selected regions of land and oceans, carried out astrophysical and geophysical

The USSR's second woman in space, Svetlana Savitskaya, as photographed by Popov on board Salyut 7.

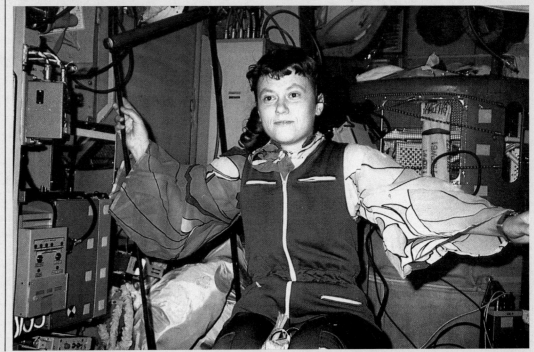

experiments using Soviet, Czech and French equipment. One experiment obtained "ultrapure biologically active materials" under conditions of weightlessness. Biomedical studies showed "no substantial differences in the reactions of the female and male organisms to space flight". LC Baikonur. LV A-2. LT 2112 MT. R 1904 MT, 43 miles (70km) north east of Arkalyk.

September 1 United States establishes Space Command within US Air Force to co-ordinate military uses of space including Space Shuttle missions and anti-satellite (ASAT) weapon to be launched from F-15 Eagle aircraft. Based at NORAD Cheyenne Mountain underground complex near Colorado Springs.

USAF Space Command F-15 carries an ASAT on vibroacoustic trials.

September 4 Contact with India's combined communications/weather satellite, Insat 1A, is lost, probably because of premature depletion of fuel for attitude control.

September 9 Chinese People's Republic launches 12th artificial satellite into orbit of 107 x 244 miles (172 x 393km) inclined 62·98° to equator. Satellite experiment, including recovery technique. Capsule recovered after four days. LC Shuang-ch'eng-tzu. LV FB-1 (CSL-2).

September 9 First US private venture space rocket, Conestoga 1, launched from Matagorda Island, Texas, completed scheduled sub-orbital flight lasting 10·5 minutes. After reaching altitude of about 195 miles (314km) splashes down about 260 miles (418km) downrange in Gulf of Mexico. The 37·5ft (12·7m) rocket, based on 46,500lb (21,090kg) thrust government surplus Aerojet M56A-1 Minuteman 2nd stage motor, sponsored by Space Services Inc of America and cost about $2·5 million (£1·3 million). Company plans to develop satellite launchers.

September 10 Fifth ESA Ariane 1 rocket, carrying first revenue earning payload, fails to achieve orbit due to third stage turbopump failure. After 560 seconds of flight, nearly

The Marecs B/Sirio 2/Sylda stack during payload integration at the ESA launch site, Kourou.

halfway into third stage burn, turbopump speed fell off followed by drop in chamber pressure. Lost was the Inmarsat Marecs B, Europe's second maritime communications satellite, and Sirio 2, a meteorological data distribution satellite. Marecs B insured for about $20 million, less than half its value. ESA investigating team concluded that most likely cause of turbopump failure was build-up of manufacturing tolerances in turbine assembly. LC Kourou, French Guiana. LV Ariane L05. LT 0212 GMT.

September 18-October 17 Soviets launch Progress 15 cargo spacecraft which docks with Salyut 7 space station on aft airlock at 1012 MT 20 September. Final approach and docking controlled by resident cosmonauts Berezovoi and Lebedev. Vehicle brought air, water, food, scientific equipment and propellant for Salyut's engines. After supplies are transferred, craft is separated to make a controlled re-entry over central Pacific. LC Baikonur. LV A-2. LT 0859 MT.

September 29 NASA announces agreement to have Canadians trained as Space Shuttle mission specialists.

October 30 USAF launches first Titan 34D from Kennedy Space Center, Florida, carrying two Defense Satellite Communications System spacecraft for transfer to geostationary orbit by Inertial Upper Stage (IUS). Satellites are last of DSCS 2 series and first of DSCS 3.

October 31-December 15 Soviets launch Progress 16 which docks with Salyut 7 space station next day. Initial orbit 120 x 163 miles (193 x 263km) x 51·6°. Aboard are various consumables and replacement equipment. Craft is used to adjust the orbit of space station and remained attached after long-stay cosmonauts Berezovoi and Lebedev have departed. It is finally separated by remote command on 13 December to make a controlled re-entry over the central Pacific. LC Baikonur. LV A-2. LT 1420 MT.

November 11-16 Space Shuttle Columbia (STS-5) makes fifth flight into orbit marking first operational use.

Allen tapes Lenoir to the mid-deck floor during biomedical tests on board STS-5 Columbia.

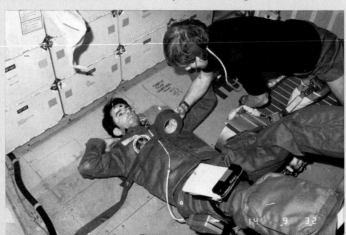

Astronauts: Vance D. Brand (commander), Col Robert F. Overmyer (pilot) and Dr Joseph P. Allen and Dr William B. Lenoir (mission specialists). Target lift-off weight is 4,494,556lb (2,038,730kg); operational orbit is 160 nautical miles (296km) circular. First revenue earning payload: two communications satellites for transfer to geostationary orbit, Satellite Business Systems SBS-3 and Telesat Canada's Anik C-3. SBS-3 is separated from cargo bay over Pacific 11 November; apogee motor PAM-D fires as planned by preset timer some 45 minutes after separation, when satellite is 20 miles (32km) behind Columbia and 16 miles (26km) above it. Anik C-3, separated above Atlantic the next day, is equally successful. Spacewalks by Lenoir and Allen to practise use of tools in cargo bay, delayed 24 hours from 14 November because of Lenoir's space sickness, are subsequently cancelled because of spacesuit problems. Lenoir's suit failed to fully pressurize because two plastic locking devices, each the size of a grain of rice, were omitted from pressure regulator during assembly. Oxygen circulation fan in Allen's suit failed because of a faulty magnetic sensor. Mission elapsed time is 5 days 2 hours 14 minutes. LC KSC. LV STS-5. LT 0719 EST. R 0633 PST, Runway 22, Edwards AFB.

December 22 NASA announces agreement to have Australians trained as Space Shuttle mission specialists. In 1985 an Australian will assist the launch from the Shuttle Orbiter's cargo bay of one of two communications satellites being developed for Aussat Pty Ltd., operator of Australia's national satellite system.

December 28 Soviet nuclear-powered satellite, Cosmos 1402, fails to eject section containing reactor into parking orbit at 600 miles (965km) altitude. Separates into three parts which re-enter Earth's atmosphere: rocket stage 30 December; reactor section (over Indian Ocean) 23 January 1983, and fuel core (over S. Atlantic) 7 February. One of a regular series of spacecraft designed to monitor

Western shipping using radar. Launched 1 September 1982 into orbit of 156 x 164 miles (251 x 264km) x 65° sustained by low-thrust on-board rocket engines. Tass stated ". . . the satellite, equipped with a safety system in accordance with international recommendations, completed its programme of work and ceased active existence . . . extraction of the fuel core with radioactive products of fission from the reactor guaranteed its complete incineration." LC Baikonur. LV F-1-m. LT 1005 GMT.

1983

January 10 NASA postpones maiden flight of Space Shuttle Challenger scheduled for 24 January because of suspected hydrogen leak in engine compartment following 20 second on-the-pad engine test firing at KSC. At first decision is made to replace one main engine but replacement is found to be defective. Eventually, all three main engines are removed following discovery of hairline cracks in fuel coolant lines, which leads to further delay.

Challenger's SSME no 2 has just been removed from the Orbiter on LC-39A: a hydrogen leak required repair.

Final checks on IRAS are run at the Jet Propulsion Laboratory, Ca.

January 25 NASA launches 2,365lb (1,073kg) Infrared Astronomical Satellite (IRAS) by Delta 3910 from Vandenberg AFB, California into near-polar circular orbit of 560 miles (900km). Designed to seek IR sources in surrounding Universe, it includes a sensitive liquid helium cooled telescope. The cryogenic liquid cools the IR detectors to 2 degrees above absolute zero which allows them to register the faintest impulses of IR from objects in space. First images reveal sources in Large Magellanic Cloud invisible to optical telescopes on Earth. Satellite is joint venture between NASA, the Netherlands and Britain which operates IRAS ground station at Rutherford Appleton Laboratory, Chilton.

April 9 Soviet spaceplane resembling NASA Space Shuttle is spotted at Ramenskoye airfield, SE of Moscow, mounted on back of My-4 Bison bomber. Airfield is associated with Central Institute of Aero-hydrodynamics (TsAGI). Soviet shuttle orbiter has double-delta configuration but omits main engines. Large shuttle booster is being developed as part of a family of modular boosters for application in both expendable and re-usable launch systems employing liquid propellants.

April 11 NASA announces that President Reagan has requested the Senior Interagency Group for Space to conduct a study to establish basis for an Administration decision on whether to proceed with NASA development of a permanently-based, manned space station. Issues addressed by study to include how such a station would contribute to the maintenance of US leadership and how a station would best fulfill national and international requirements versus other possible methods of satisfying them; also to be considered are foreign policy and national security implications and overall economic and social impacts.

April 17 India launches 91·5lb (41·5kg) satellite Rohini D2 by SLV-3 rocket from Sriharikota into orbit of 230·5 x 535 miles (371 x 861km) x 46·6°. Embodies two cameras with "smart" sensors, plus an L-band beacon for improved tracking.

March 2 Soviets launch Cosmos 1443 which docks automatically with Salyut 7 space station eight days later for "testing in various modes of flight a number of on-board systems, equipment and structural elements". Initial orbit of Cosmos 1443 123 x 167 miles (199 x 269km) x 51·6° Enlargement of space station permits wider range of experiments by cosmonauts. Said to resemble Cosmos 1267 which docked with Salyut 6 for engineering experiments 19 June 1981. LC Baikonur. LV D-1. LT 0932 GMT.

March 9 NASA announces programme SP-100 to assess and advance the technology required for nuclear reactor power systems for civil and military space applications. Cooperating are Department of Energy's Office of Nuclear Energy, NASA's Office of Aeronautics and Space Technology, and the Defense Advanced Research Projects Agency (DARPA).

March 15 Soviets repeat test of 2,205lb (1,000kg) class spaceplane research model. Flown under guise of Cosmos 1,445, delta winged vehicle is recovered by parachute some 200 miles (322km) south-west of Cocos Islands, Indian Ocean after 1¼ orbits. Orbit 98 x 129 miles (158 x 208km) inclined at 50·7° to equator. Seven-ship task force in recovery area comprises Kara class GM cruiser, Kashin class GM destroyer, three space vehicle recovery ships, support ship and missile range instrumentation ship. Similar flight test made 3 June 1982. LC Kapustin Yar. LV SL-8. LT 2235 GMT (est).

March US Defense Department publishes 2nd edition of *Soviet Military Power* which confirms that USSR "has under development a heavy-lift launch system, comparable to US Saturn V, and a re-usable space plane." Anticipated that expendable heavy-lift booster will place 330,688lb (150,000kg) into close Earth orbit; smaller vehicle will lift 28,660lb (13,000kg). A re-usable launch vehicle could be in regular use within a decade. Large manned space station expected by about 1990. Even larger station, possibly weighing more than 100 tonnes, possible by end of century.

March 23 President Reagan tells nationwide TV audience that United States should move away from nuclear deterrence in favour of a new kind of anti-ballistic missile (ABM) system—the beam weapon. "Until now we have

increasingly based our strategy of deterrence upon the threat of retaliation. But what if free people could live secure in the knowledge that their security did not rest upon the threat of instant retaliation to deter a Soviet attack: that we could intercept and destroy strategic missiles before they reached our own soil or that of our allies?"

March 23 Soviets launch observatory satellite, Astron, for UV and X-ray observation of Universe. Orbit 1,243 x 124,300 miles (2,000 x 200,000km) inclined at 51·5° to equator; period approximately 98 hours. Telescope, over 16ft (4·87m) long by 31·5in (80cm) diameter, weighs more than 3·5 tons and incorporates 31·5in (800mm) primary mirror; also X-ray spectrometers. Developed by Crimea Astrophysical Observatory; some equipment supplied by French specialists. Remotely controlled from Earth, Astron is designed to provide new information on the chemistry, temperature and density of stars and how matter is "leaked " from their surfaces. Also will investigate electromagnetic field associated with stars. First objects of study are star clusters and Crab Nebula in Taurus. LC Baikonur. LV D-1e. LT 1250 GMT.

April 4-9 NASA launches Space Shuttle *Challenger* on maiden flight from Cape Canaveral with commander Paul Weitz, a Skylab astronaut; pilot is Air Force Colonel Karol Bobko, and mission specialists Dr Story Musgrave and Donald H. Peterson. *Challenger* is about 2,490lb (1,130kg) lighter than *Columbia;* its main engines are power rated at 104 per cent (compared with 100 per cent). Prime object is to launch first of four Tracking and Data Relay Satellites (TDRS) nearly 10 hours after lift-off. Satellite, to be transferred from 175 miles (281km) high orbit of Shuttle Orbiter into geostationary orbit by attached Inertial Upper Stage, is mis-directed into elliptical orbit of 12,000 x 19,000 miles (19,300 x 30,580km) due to fault in second stage. Subsequently, NASA nudged the satellite higher by firing small on-board thrusters. STS-6 mission features: First Shuttle EVAs into the payload bay (by Dr Story Musgrave and Donald Peterson) on 8 April, EVA duration: 3hr 45 min. First use of two-stage Inertial Upper Stage (IUS) to boost TDRS from Orbiter's cargo bay. Use of thermal-insulation blankets instead of certain white silica-foam

Secured by tethers to safety wires, Musgrave (left) and Peterson float above Challenger's payload bay.

tiles on upper surface of Orbiter. (A blanket was lost and two others bent on starboard side; three small pieces missing on port side). Removal of ejection seats for commander and pilot; four fixed seats fitted. First use of headup displays. First use of lightweight External Tank, approximately 10,000lb (4,536kg) lighter than previous tanks. First use of lighter Solid Rocket Boosters, approximately 4,000lb (1,815kg) lighter than previous boosters. Small payloads include "Getaway Specials", an electrophoresis experiment by McDonnell Douglas Astronautics and a Monodisperse Latex Reactor. LC KSC. LV STS-6. LT 1330 EST. R 1053 PST, Runway 22, Edwards AFB, California.

April 20-22 Soviets launch Soyuz T-8 with cosmonauts Lt-Col Vladimir Titov (commander), Gennady Strekalov (flight engineer) and Alexander Serebrov (cosmonaut researcher). Fails to dock with Salyut 7/Cosmos 1443 complex on 21 April because of malfunction in rendezvous phase. Mission was intended to carry out "technical, medical and biological research." Strekalov—who flew in Soyuz T-3 in 1980—belongs to the spacecraft design bureau. Serebrov—who flew in Soyuz T-7 in 1982—is from the same bureau. LC Baikonur. LV A-2. LT 1711 MT. R 1729 MT, "several kilometres" SE of Arkalyk.

The T-8 crew (l to r); Strekalov, Serebrov and Titov. Despite Titov attempting a manually-controlled approach, the Salyut docking failed.

May Revealed that Vought anti-satellite (ASAT) will not be tested from F-15 Eagle with an active IR homing manoeuvring head until "early 1984". Two 6·5ft (2·0m) balloons to be launched by Vought Scout from Wallops Flight Center as orbiting targets; they can change thermal signature by louvres and assess ASAT miss distance by radar if head does not impact. Technique involves (following separation from Altair stage) spinning up manoeuvring head to 20 revs/sec for stability, utilising laser gyro and liquid helium-cooled IR sensor to fire small rocket correction motors to track and align with ASAT target.

May 26 Exosat, the European Space Agency's first X-ray observatory satellite, is launched by Delta 3914 from Vandenberg Air Force Base, California. Orbit ranges between 186 x 124,278 miles (300 x 200,000 km) inclined at 72·5° to equator. Exosat will explore cosmic X-ray sources in the energy range 0·04keV to 80keV, parts of the spectrum which are cut off from ground observation by the Earth's atmosphere. Was originally to have been launched by ESA Ariane but mishap to the 5th launch vehicle intervened and it was decided to switch to an American rocket. Exosat weighs approximately 1,124lb (510kg) including 278lb (126kg) of payload and is 10ft (3·3m) high including solar array. Built by Cosmos member companies led by Messerschmitt-Bölkow-Blohm (W. Germany) with Aérospatiale (France); CASA (Spain), ETCA (Belgium), MSDS (UK), Selenia (Italy). Exosat ground station developed by MBB in co-operation with Krupp (W. Germany). Experiments involve nine institutes or universities from four countries involved in project.

MBB technicians at work on the X-ray observatory Exosat.

June 2 Soviets launch Venera 15 for study of Venus from orbit. Unlike previous spacecraft of the series they do not have landing capsules but are designed to map the planet and investigate the atmosphere by radar. LC Baikonur. LV D-1-e. LT 0240 GMT.

June 7 Soviets launch Venera 16 for study of Venus from orbit. Objectives similar to those of Venera 15. LC Baikonur. LV D-1-e. LT 0240 GMT.

June 13 Pioneer 10, which departed Earth in March 1972, crosses orbit of Neptune at 30,552 miles/h (49,168km/h) on its way out of the Solar System. Designed to operate for 21 months, still relays data on solar wind more than 2,800,000,000 miles (4,506,000,000km) from Sun. It may pass a nearby star after 10,500 years.

June 16 ESA launches first European Communications Satellite (ECS-1) by sixth Ariane rocket. Satellite, weighing 2,300lb (1,043kg) at launch and

ECS-1 mounted on the Sylda containing Amsat, prior to launch from Kourou.

spanning more than 40ft (12·2m) with solar panels deployed, is subsequently positioned in geostationary orbit at 10° E longitude, above Gabon, Africa. Secondary payload is German-built satellite Oscar 10 for amateur radio enthusiasts. ECS-1, the first of five, is part of the Eutelsat network, providing telephone and telegraph services, TV distribution and (from ECS-2) specialised business services, covering Europe, the Middle East and Northern Africa; eg high speed data, audio and tele-conferencing, facsimile, remote printing of newspapers, computer-to-computer links, etc. LC Kourou, French Guiana. LV Ariane L06. LT 1159 GMT.

June 18-24 NASA launches space shuttle *Challenger* for second time on flight STS-7 from Kennedy Space Center, Florida, with Capt Robert L. Crippen (commander), Cdr Frederick H. Hauck (pilot) and mission specialists Lt-Col John H. Fabian, Sally K. Ride (first American woman in space) and Dr Norman E. Thagard. Deploys Telesat Canada Anik C2 and Indonesia Palapa B-1 satellites for subsequent positioning in geostationary orbit. First flight of German SPAS pallet satellite (commercially developed by MBB) deployed and recaptured by Canadian-built remote manipulator arm, in rehearsal for retrieval of failed Solar Maximum Mission (SMM) satellite during shuttle flight STS-13. First pictures of space shuttle in orbit by still, movie and TV cameras mounted on deployed SPAS pallet. Various experiments embodied in STS-7 were provided by the USA, Canada, Germany, Japan, Italy and Switzerland. One of several materials processing experiments was OSTA-2 provided by the USA and West Germany.

Sally Ride communicates with Earth from the flight deck of Challenger.

Payload included Continuous Flow Electrophoresis System (CFES) and Monodicporco Latex Reactor (MLR), two mid-deck mounted experiments flown on previous shuttle missions for developing materials with potential pharmaceutical and medical uses. In experiment devised by students of two US high schools, Camden and New Jersey, colony of 150 carpenter ants, including queen "Norma", were found to be dead after the flight although plexiglas container, microprocessor and power equipment appeared to have operated normally. Many may have died during seven-week period aboard Challenger before lift-off. Objective of landing a Shuttle for first time at Kennedy Space Center was frustrated by bad weather conditions in Florida; flight diverted to Edwards Air Force Base, California, making six extra revolutions of Earth. Brake assembly of main landing gear damaged on landing which was otherwise normal. Some 25 thermal-tiles damaged. At time of STS-7 mission total space shuttle costs—development and production—amounted to some $20,000 million including allowances for inflation. LC KSC. LV STS-7. LT 0733 EDT. R 0957 EDT, Runway 15, Edwards AFB, California.

June 27-November 23 Soviets launch Soyuz T-9 with pilot-cosmonaut Col Vladimir Lyakhov and flight engineer Alexander Alexandrov. Docks with Salyut 7/Cosmos 1443 complex 28 June at 1046 GMT; combined mass of these vehicles about 103,000lb (46,720kg); orbit 203 x 213 miles (328 x 343km) x 51·6°. Objectives include technical and scientific experiments and bio-medical research. Lyakhov, 42, took part in 175-day space flight in 1979. Alexandrov, 40, making his first space flight, is from a spacecraft design bureau, specialising in control systems. Cosmonauts conducted more than

300 geological, astrophysical, technological and other research experiments during the 150 day flight. Visual observation alone of Earth and oceans took up about 50 hours. More than 100 medical and biological experiments conducted, and many experiments connected with space technology (including the processing of sample materials) were made for the first time. Electrical power of Salyut 7 was increased by the attachment of two additional solar panels on mountings installed during manufacture by resident crew during two spacewalks, "considerably widening the possibilities for research and experiments with the space station". The solar panels had previously been delivered to the station by Cosmos 1443. The first EVA began on 1 November at 0747 MT when the cosmonauts retrieved from the airlock a container in which the solar panels were folded. The men spent 2 hours 50 minutes in space installing and deploying the panels using special tools and welding equipment. On 3 November a second spacewalk

Traditional gifts are offered to Lyakhov (l) and Alexandrov on their return from 150 days in space.

lasting 2hr 55min began at 0647 MT to instal second, additional, solar panel. Soviets pointed out that Salyut 7 already had three large directional solar panels totaling some 538ft² (50m²) providing about 5kW of energy. Two extra panels, each of about 53·8ft² (5m²), would provide the extra power for the larger furnaces to be used for making semi-conductor materials—also to compensate for the slow degradation of solar panels under micrometeoroid bombardment in space. Pre-flight training included identical experiment in water tank at Gagarin Cosmonauts' Training Centre, during which an exact time table was worked out. Work is preparatory to bringing Salyut 7 into commission "as a pilot plant for the manufacture of semi-conductor components for use in high technology projects." Results of the Soyuz T-9 mission" laid the basis for a quantitatively new step in outer space exploration—a transition from the present space stations periodically visited by crews, replacing each other, to a multi-sectional, permanently inhabited orbital complex." This future complex was described as "a single system of structures of large size, placed in orbits at an altitude of 124 miles (200km) to 24,855 miles (40,000km), LC Baikonur. LV A-2. LT 1312MT. R 2258 MT, about 100 miles (160km) east of Dzhezkazgan, Kazakhstan.

July 1 Tracking & Data Relay Satellite (TDRS-A), launched by *Challenger* STS-6 but misdirected into lower-than-planned transfer orbit by Inertial Upper Stage (IUS), completes transfer to geostationary orbit under propulsion from small thrusters used for manoeuvre and control. Retains sufficient fuel for 10 year life on station. After being initially located at 67° W longitude (where radio interference is best for testing communications), satellite is manoeuvred to final location just off NE coast of Brazil (41° W) between 23 September and 17 October 1983.

Charles Walker alongside the EOS electrophoresis separation chamber.

July 1 NASA names Charles D. Walker, 35, as payload specialist for shuttle's flight STS-41D. An engineer with McDonnell Douglas Astronautics, Walker will run equipment developed by his company as part of its Electrophoresis Operation in Space Project (EOS) which has the object of separating large quantities of biological materials in space for ultimate use in new pharmaceuticals. Aim to provide enough materials for clinical testing.

August 6 Japan launches Sakura 2B communications satellite by Japanese-built NII rocket from Tanegashima for positioning in geostationary orbit at 135° E longitude. Satellite is cylindrical, enclosed in a drum-shaped solar panel with de-spun antenna. Launch weight 1,477lb (670kg), including 782·6lb (355kg) fuel and tank pressurant. Objective: provide telephone, TV and data links for Japanese mainland and smaller islands. Satellite built jointly by Ford Aerospace and Mitsubishi Electric for Japan's National Space Development .Agency. (Sakura 2A launched 4 February 1983).

Sakura 2B: it can transmit 4,000 telephone calls simultaneously.

August 10 Soviets launch three Glonass navigation satellites, Cosmos 1490-1492, by Proton D-1-e rocket from Baikonur cosmodrome. Second scheduled mission to form global positioning system similar to US Navstar. Three other satellites launched 12 October 1982.

August 14 Cosmos 1443 separates from Salyut 7/Soyuz T-9 at 1804 under control of on-board cosmonauts Lyakhov and Alexandrov. Spends nine days in free flight before releasing re-entry capsule on

28 August which lands on target 65 miles (105km) SE of Arkalyk, Kazakhstan. Contains some 700lb (317·5kg) of exposed film, materials processing samples and expended hardware. Soviets describe Cosmos 1443 as "combined space tug and electric power module"—also a vehicle for transporting heavy cargo to and from large space facilities. Capable of returning 1,102lb (500kg) of cargo for water recovery. Module has about 430·5ft² (40m²) of solar panels providing some 3kW of electrical power. Propulsion system allows fuel and oxidant to be passed in either direction between tug module and Salyut. Cosmos 1443 had docked with Salyut 7 on 10 March 1983. "On-board systems, power systems and structural elements of prospective spacecraft were tested and methods of controlling large-dimension complexes were practised during the joint flight. Flight path of manned complex was repeatedly adjusted by propulsion unit of Cosmos 1443. Brought to orbit about three tonnes of various cargoes necessary for functioning of Salyut 7 and conduct of scientific research and experiments.

August 15 Disclosed that Soyuz T-8 docking with Salyut 7 was unsuccessful in April because Soyuz rendezvous radar failed to deploy from its launch position. Commander, Titov, attempted visual approach in conjunction with data from ground control but abandoned the effort when he decided risk was too great.

August 17-September 18 Soviets launch unmanned Progress 17 cargo craft which docks with Salyut 7 on 19 August. On-board cosmonauts had previously separated Cosmos 1443 and transferred their Soyuz ferry to Salyut's forward docking port to clear aft port for cargo ship. Orbit after docking: 198 x 210·6 miles (319 x 339km) x 51·6°. After transferring propellant and other consumables, Progress 17 was undocked September 17 and made to re-enter the atmosphere over the Pacific Ocean. LC Baikonur. LV A2. LT 1208 GMT (est).

August 18 Soviet President Yuri Andropov, during Moscow meeting with nine US senators, proposes treaty banning anti-satellite weapons in space. Indicates that USSR would not conduct further anti-satellite tests if US refrained from doing so, pending negotiation of a treaty (according to Sen Clairborne Pell).

August 19 China launches thirteenth satellite as part of development programme. Orbit 106 x 248 miles (170 x 400km) x 63·59°. Ejects capsule for recovery on 24 August. Objectives: possibly largely photo-reconnaissance with other more general applications. On 4 August *People's Daily* reported that photographs obtained by Chinese satellites have been used for exploration of raw materials and analyses of river and coastal geographical and tidal influences, earthquakes and archaeology. LC Shuang-ch'eng-tsu. LV CSL-2. LT 0603 GMT (est).

August 30-September 6 NASA launches *Challenger* STS-8 with Capt Richard H. Truly (commander), Cdr Daniel C. Brandenstein (pilot) and three mission specialists, Lt Cdr Dale A. Gardner, Lt Col Guion S. Bluford, Jr, and Dr William E. Thornton. Bluford has doctorate in aerospace engineering; he is the first US black astronaut. On second day of mission deploys Indian National Satellite (Insat 1B). Later discovered that satellite was struck by unidentified object as it left cargo bay; a solar array had deployment problems, later rectified. Flight days three and four devoted to operations with Payload Deployment and Retrieval System test article using Canadian-built remote manipulator arm. Another major object was in-orbit test of Tracking and Data Relay Satellite

0232 EST: the first night launch of a Shuttle—this time, STS-8.

System (TDRSS), mission being extended from five to six days for this purpose. (Proper operation of TDRSS was essential for STS-9 Spacelab mission launched 28 November 1983). Making its fourth flight was the Continuous Flow Electrophoresis System (CFES), the object of which is to develop techniques for the manufacture of pharmaceuticals under micro-gravity conditions. Live cell samples were used for the first time rather than simple protein samples used previously. Equipment, located on *Challenger's* mid-deck, weighed about 760lb (345kg) at lift-off. Six laboratory rats were carried in a special Animal Enclosure Module; the cage is to be used again in a subsequent student experiment. First night launch and landing. Post-flight analysis revealed that nozzle liner of Solid Rocket Booster almost burned through. LC KSC. LV STS-8. LT 0632 GMT. R 0440 GMT, Runway 22, Edwards Air Force Base, California.

September 27 Fire breaks out on Baikonur launch pad during final stage of countdown of Soyuz-T and two cosmonauts Lt-Col Vladimir Titov and Gennady Strekalov are forced to use emergency rocket escape system, which pulls their spacecraft clear of stricken A-2 launcher. Incident occurred shortly before 0140 local time. Their re-entry module lands within confines of cosmodrome after releasing recovery parachutes. Mission of Soyuz T-9 cosmonauts aboard Salyut 7 was extended by this incident, who had to fit two exterior solar panels by EVA without the help of the men whose launch was aborted.

September Laser fired from NKC-135 Airborne Laser Laboratory puts BQM-34A drone out of control over Pacific Ocean, some 20 miles (32km) from US Navy Pacific Test Center, Pt Mugu, California. Carbon dioxide gas dynamics laser in aircraft operated at wavelength of 10·6 micrometres in IR band. Experiment—last of series—was part of joint programme by US Air Force Weapons Laboratory and Naval Weapons Evaluation Facility.

September 28 In bid to make first inspection of a comet, NASA deflects path (10 June 1982) of existing ISEE 3 satellite in a series of planned gravity-assist swings round the Moon. Third pass of the Moon occurs today, fourth 21 October and fifth 22 December taking the craft within 120 miles (194km) of lunar surface, accelerating it away towards a rendezvous with comet Giacobini-Zinner 5 September 1985. Launched August 12 1978, the International Sun-Earth Explorer (ISEE-3) was the first spacecraft to orbit a point in space, i.e. Sun-Earth Libration Point—the first continuously to monitor solar wind conditions upstream from Earth; to explore distant geomagnetic tail between 317,000 and 990,000 miles (510,000 and 1,600,000km); to use multiple swingbys of Moon for orbital control and to use lunar gravity-assist manoeuvre to escape from Earth-Moon system.

October 10 Soviet space probe Venera 15 swings into orbit round Venus to begin joint radar mapping excursion with Venera 16 which arrives on 14 October. Images show objects little more than 0·5 mile (0·8km) across, including major fractures in crust,

Venera 15's radar mapper reveals the desolate volcanic face of Venus.

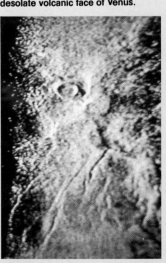

hills, mountain ridges and large impact craters. Plainly visible are traces of volcanic activity including hardened streams of lava. Continuous radar mapping covers an area 5,592 miles (9,000km) long by 93 miles (150km) wide. Analysis allows determination of heights of mountain ranges and individual mountains. Four maps prepared from this survey cover the northern geological structure of Venus; temperature distribution on the surface and composition of atmosphere and ionosphere.

October 13 Major expansion of Sentinel Project seeking evidence of intelligence elsewhere in Universe announced by Prof Carl Sagan. Organised by the Planetary Society, project will allow sky to be scanned on 8·4million radio channels simultaneously using radio receiver of advanced design. Already, the 84ft (27·5m) antenna of Harvard University Oak Ridge Radio Telescope is searching 131,000 channels. Prof Paul Horowitz (who built the new receiver) comments: "We shall have the biggest analyser on Earth. It will enable us to detect an extra-terrestrial civilisation that is not beaming a signal specifically at us."

October 17 TDRS-1 data relay satellite, launched by STS-6 in April, reaches final orbital position above Atlantic Ocean ready to link STS-9 Spacelab 1 mission with ground control.

October 18 ESA launches seventh Ariane rocket from Kourou, French Guiana with Intelsat V (F7) communications satellite for positioning in geostationary orbit.

October 20-November 16 Soviets launch unmanned Progress 18 cargo craft which docks with Salyut 7 on aft airlock on 22 October to transfer propellant and other expendables. Two of three oxidant tanks of Salyut are replenished following incident on 9 September which dumped fluids overboard and rendered inactive 16 of 32 control thrusters on the station. Progress 18 separates on 13 November and is made to re-enter the atmosphere over the Pacific three days later.

October 24 NASA renames Space Telescope, to be launched by Shuttle, as the Edwin P. Hubble Space Telescope, in honour of one of America's foremost astronomers.

A full-scale model of the Hubble telescope during dynamic testing.

November Revealed that USSR plans 1986 mission to explore Martian moon Phobos at close range by placing robot spacecraft into coincident orbit. Hopes to fly within "few hundred metres" of moon for high-resolution photography and chemical analysis. Other Soviet plans include 1987-1990 missions to explore Moon from polar orbit, possibly in co-operation with France.

November 22 Infra-Red Astronomical Satellite (IRAS), launched 25 January 1983, runs out of helium refrigerant used to cool the telescope. During 300 days of observations, IRAS conducted first complete survey of the IR sky. Discoveries included detection of a ring of solid material around star Vega, seven comets, and bands of dust around the Sun between orbits of Mars and Jupiter. Telescope provided a "new look" at Milky Way galaxy and detected many new mysterious objects; observations included more than 95 per cent of the sky, pinpointing the locations and intensities of more than 200,000 infra-red objects.

November 28 Following conclusion of 150-day mission by Soyuz T-9 cosmonauts aboard Salyut 7, *Pravda* describes future "multi-sectional, permanently inhabited orbital complex" as a single system linked to the Earth by transport cargo-passenger spaceships. The complex will include "specialised research laboratories, comfortable living modules, powerful energy systems, a refuelling station, repair workshops and even construction platforms for the manufacture and assembly of standard structural elements." Early objectives: round-the-clock observation of atmospheric conditions and agricultural crops, forest fires and "considerably increased effectiveness of prospecting for, and estimation of, mineral deposits." Subsequently, full-time monitoring of ships and aircraft, steady reception of TV programmes, batch production of electronic, optical and bio-medical materials and preparations having characteristics unattainable in usual terrestrial conditions. Looking further ahead, "it is possible to contemplate such vast projects as illuminating the long polar nights with reflected sunlight."

November 28-December 8 NASA launches Space Shuttle *Columbia* (STS-9) with astronauts Cdr John W. Young (USN retired), commander, Chief of Astronaut Office; Major

Scientific experiments in full swing on board Spacelab 1; crew (l to r) Merbold, Lichtenberg and Parker.

Brewster H. Shaw, Jr (pilot); Dr Owen K. Garriott; Robert Allan Ridly Parker (mission specialists); Dr Byron K. Lichtenberg and Dr Ulf Merbold (payload specialists). Marks maiden flight of European Spacelab which remains fixed in Orbiter's cargo bay; also first mission to include a European crew member (Merbold). Configuration Spacelab 1: long module plus pallet; total mass 34,612lb (15,700kg) including 6,173lb (2,600kg) experiments. Orbit: circular at 155 miles (248km) x 57°. Objectives: verify Spacelab engineering performance by flying a variety of experiments in five broad scientific and technological disciplines (71 principal investigators, 13 NASA and 58 ESA). Experiment objectives: examine Earth's atmosphere and the space environment; biology and medicine; astronomy and solar physics; Earth observations, and space technology. Spacelab represents a European investment of almost $1,000 million. Nine ESA members contributed in the following percentage proportions: West Germany 54·94; Italy 15·57, France 10·29; UK 6·51; Belgium 4·32, Spain 2·88, Denmark 1·54 and Switzerland 1·0. Austria, which has associate member status, contributed 0·79 per cent of the endeavour. During off-duty periods Garriott uses a small radio to contact radio hams around the world (including King Husain of Jordan) in the 2 metre band, in the range 145·51 to 45·770 MHz FM. Mission, originally planned to last nine days, is extended a day to complete experiment programme; then re-entry is delayed by five orbits when two of five IBM general purpose computers fail (about 3hr 49min before planned re-entry burn) coincident with firing of small nose thrusters used for attitude control. Subsequently revealed that small fire broke out unnoticed in SSME compartment, damaging two of three auxiliary power units (APUs), after Orbiter re-entered atmosphere. (Fuelled by catalytic decomposition of hydrazine, APUs produce hot gas which operates a turbine in each unit to drive an hydraulic pump. Hydraulic power is used to gimbal the SSMEs and orbiter control surfaces; hydraulic power also lowers the undercarriage. APUs operate independently, at least one being essential for flight.) Launch of STS-9 was postponed one month by discovery that nozzle of one of two Solid Rocket Boosters used on sister craft *Challenger* nearly burned through on 30 August lift-off, risking a disaster. *Columbia* was returned from launch pad to VAB for replacement of SRBs which had "new technology" nozzle liners. LC KSC. LV STS-9. LT 1100 EST. R 0347 PST, Runway 17, Edwards Air Force Base, California.

December Canada selects six Canadian scientists and engineers to train as payload specialists from

more than 4,300 applicants. Planned that two of the six will eventually fly aboard the Space Shuttle to conduct two different Canadian experiments in life sciences and robotics in 1985-86.

December 14-20 Soviets launch bio-satellite Cosmos 1514 containing small laboratory animals, fish, rats and (for the first time in .Soviet experiments) two monkeys "Abrek" and "Bion". Orbit: 140 x 179 miles (226 x 288km) x 82·3°. After recovery, animals are taken to Institute on Bio-Medical Problems of Ministry of Health. Objectives: development of manned space flight, study mechanisms of adaptation of living organisms to conditions of space flight, primarily weightlessness, in the first hours and days of flight.

December 20 Britain confirms decision to have two Skynet 4 military communications satellites launched by NASA Space Shuttles, late 1985 and 1986. Total cost about £60 million (See also 26 January 1984).

December 27 Soviets conduct third orbital flight test of sub-scale Kosmolyot (spaceplane) called Cosmos 1517. At end of mission model makes "controlled descent in pre-set area of the Black Sea," indicating growing confidence in guidance and control. Previous test models were recovered in the Indian Ocean. LC Kapustin Yar. LV C-1.

1984

January 21 US Air Force announces successful first launch test of anti-satellite (ASAT) missile from F-15 interceptor over the Pacific. The 17ft (5·2m) missile, which omitted IR guided warhead, was aimed at a point in space rather than an actual target. It then dropped into the ocean, as planned.

January 25 President Reagan, in State of the Union address to joint session of Congress, says America must rebuild on its pioneer spirit "and develop our next frontier—space". He directs National Aeronautics and Space Administration to develop "within a decade" a permanent manned space station. NASA had previously published details of a 6-8 person space station which could be in permanent orbit by 1992. Assembled 310 miles (500km) above the Earth from prefabricated sections carried up by Space Shuttles, it would become a repair depot for satellites and a departure point for spacecraft making journeys into deep space; also an orbiting industrial centre where international companies could learn to exploit near-weightless conditions to produce ultra-pure semiconductor materials, pharmaceuticals and new industrial alloys. Laboratories are planned that will be more advanced than Spacelab developed by the European Space Agency. Governments of Europe, Canada and Japan are invited to join project. Overall estimated cost about $8,000 million; a larger modular arrangement housing 12 to 18 astronauts $17,000-20,000 million.

January 26 Mr Larry Speakes, White House spokesman, confirms that President Reagan has "authorised a prudent research programme to determine if technology can be developed in the area of defence against ballistic missiles." The President's defence budget request includes $5·6 billion for this purpose (see also entry for 23 March 1983).

January 29 China launches 14th Earth satellite. New China news agency says "important results" were achieved but gives no further information. NORAD confirms that after entering a low parking orbit of 191 x 279 miles (307 x 449km) x 31·04°, satellite was injected into eccentric orbit of 223 x 4,025 miles (359 x 6,479 km) x 36·03°. Possibly first orbital test from new launch site of three-stage launcher CSL-X3, developed from FB-1, having LO_2/LH_2 third stage.

February 3-11 NASA launches Space Shuttle *Challenger* mission 41-B with astronauts Vance D. Brand (C) (commander); Cdr Robert L. Gibson (pilot); Robert E. McNair; Capt Bruce McCandless, II, and Lt-Col Robert Stewart (mission specialists). Astronauts deploy first of two communications satellites, Westar 6 for Western Union, 3 February but Payload Assist Module (PAM), intended to achieve geostationary transfer orbit, underburns leaving satellite in 218 x 872 miles (352 x 1,403km) orbit, too low for adjustment by on-board propulsion. Deployment of second satellite, Palapa B-2 for Indonesia, is delayed 48 hours while mishap to Westar is investigated but Palapa also goes off course ending in 172 x 748 miles (278 x 1,204km) orbit. (Cause may have been defective batch of

The world's first human satellite: Bruce McCandless flies his MMU up to 320ft (97·5m) away from Challenger.

nozzle material, which resulted in break-up of rocket nozzle). Total insurance loss of two satellites about $180 million (£128 million). On 5 February, a 6·5ft (2·0m) Mylar balloon, released from cargo bay, bursts during inflation; was intended as rendezvous target for Orbiter prior to forthcoming shuttle mission to retrieve and repair Solar Maximum Mission satellite (SMM). Mission also features first shuttle flight of Manned Maneuvering Unit, a self-contained, propulsive backpack that enables astronauts McCandless and Stewart to move around freely in space without being tethered. On 7 February, McCandless becomes first human satellite orbiting alongside *Challenger* for more than one hour at 17,400mph (28,000km/h) up to 320ft (97·5m) away. Quotes: "That may have been one small step for Neil, but it was a heck of a big leap for me." "My impressions were of the immensity of the entire universe . . . what a beautiful Earth, what a beautiful flying machine!" Second EVA on 9 February, by Stewart, had to be modified because of jammed wrist action of remote manipulator arm. Both men were to practise docking with a shuttle pallet satellite (SPAS-01A) and perform work in preparation for the retrieval, at a later date, of the SMM, now tumbling in space. This involved simulating the spin rate of the SMM using a mockup but the experiment had to be abandoned. Instead, Stewart and McCandless conduct more free-flight trials with MMUs. At the end of the mission *Challenger* achieved first Shuttle landing at Kennedy Space Centre, Florida. LC KSC. LV STS 41-B. LT 0800 EST. R 0716 EST, KSC.

February 8 Soviets launch Soyuz T-10 with cosmonauts Col Leonid Kizim (commander); Vladimir Solovyov (flight engineer) and cosmonaut-researcher Oleg Atkov. After docking with Salyut 7 space station at 1743 MT 9 February, crew perform essential maintenance operations. Mission objectives: study of Earth's surface and atmosphere; astrophysical, technological and technical experiments; medical and biological research in conjunction with qualified doctor (Atkov). Particular attention is given to function of the human organism considered most important for ensuring man's prolonged stay in space, e.g. study of cardio-vascular system and water and salt exchange. LC Baikonur. LV A-2. LT 1507 MT.

February 8-October 2 Soviets launch Soyuz T-10 with cosmonauts Col Leonid Kizim (commander); Vladimir Solovyov (flight engineer) and cosmonaut-researcher Oleg Atkov. After docking with Salyut 7 space station at 1743 MT 9 February, crew perform essential maintenance operations. Mission objectives: study of Earth's surface and atmosphere; astrophysical, technological and technical experiments; medical and biological research in conjunction with qualified doctor (Atkov). Particular attention is given to function of the human organism considered most important for ensuring man's prolonged stay in space, e.g. study of cardio-vascular system and water and salt exchange. Kizim, Solovyov and Atkov returned in Soyuz T-11 capsule after record-breaking flight of 236 days 22hr 50min. During their time in space, cosmonauts were visited twice by different space crews and five times by Progress freighters which docked automatically. Six EVAs were made lasting a total of 22hr 50min. LC Baikonur. LV A-2. LT 1507 MT. R 1357 MT, some 99 miles (160km) E of Dzhezkazgan.

February 21-April 1 Soviets launch Progress 19 unmanned freighter which docks at rear port Salyut 7 at 0821 GMT 22 February to replenish propellant, water, food and other expendables; also provides new items of scientific equipment. Separates at 0940 GMT 31 March and re-enters atmosphere over Pacific Ocean. LC Baikonur. LV A-2. LT 0646 GMT.

April 3-11 Soviets launch Soyuz T-11 with cosmonauts Yuri Malyshev, Gennady Strekalov and Major Rakesh Sharma (India). Docks at 1831 MT 4 April with Salyut 7/Soyuz T-10 complex which contains cosmonauts Leonid Kizim, Vladimir Solovyov and Oleg Atkov. Objectives within Terra programme: study of natural resources of Indian sub-continent (oil, gas, minerals), agricultural crops, forests, coastal erosion, ocean conditions, etc. Also medical studies (Vector, Ballisto 3, Yoga, Optokinesis, Questionnaire and Poll) and, within Isparitel programme, microgravity processing of three alloys investigating borderline dividing liquids and solids. Cosmonauts returned in Soyuz T-10. LC Baikonur. LV A-2. LT 1709 MT. R 1450 MT, 29 miles (46km) E of Arkalyk, Kazakhstan.

April 6-13 NASA launches Space Shuttle *Challenger* (41-C) with Capt Robert L. Crippen (commander); Major Francis R. Scobee (pilot); George D. Nelson, James D. van Hoften and Terry J. Hart (mission specialists). Orbit approximately circular at 280 miles (450km) x 28·5° is achieved by direct insertion; subsequently Orbiter achieved record altitude of 309 miles (497km). On day two of mission, astronauts deploy Long-Duration Exposure Facility (LDEF) containing 57 experiments for US, Canada, Denmark, W Germany, France, Ireland, Netherlands, Switzerland and UK. Launch mass 21,400lb (9,707kg), length 29·8ft (9·1m), width 14·1ft (4·3m). LDEF, which lacks electrical power, attitude control and space-to-ground communications, is largest craft yet to be deployed from Shuttle by remote manipulator arm. Purpose is to expose various materials to cosmic rays, UV radiation, temperature extremes, micrometeorites and vacuum, and then to recover LDEF for post-flight analysis in February 1985, possibly during mission 51-D. On day three of 41-C mission, EVA astronauts, van Hoften and Nelson, attempt to retrieve and repair Solar Maximum Mission Satellite (SMMS) orbiting in same plane as *Challenger* at some 304 miles (490km) altitude. After Orbiter is brought within 200-300ft (61-91m) of Solar Max, George Nelson, wearing MMU, performs untethered EVA to reach satellite and stabilize it so that it can be grappled by Orbiter's remote manipulator arm and berthed in cargo bay. However, Nelson's docking tool fails to engage satellite's docking fixture, and despite his valiant attempts to reduce satellite's rotation by manoeuvring and to grasp one of Solar Max's solar panels and using gas jets, he is forced to return to *Challenger* when

gas runs low. This action leaves satellite with slight "wobble". After scientists at Goddard Space Flight Center unexpectedly re-established communications with Solar Max, satellite is brought under control and on 10 April Crippen and Scobee edge *Challenger* to within 33ft (10m) of the slowly revolving satellite. Hart, using the RMS, secures Solar Max which is then lowered into prepared berth in cargo bay. On 11 April Hart and van Hoften make 6hr EVA to repair satellite, replacing attitude control unit and electronic control box of coronograph/polarimeter. On 12 April Solar Max is released to continue study of solar flares and other activity on the Sun; also to study Halley's Comet in 1986. Heavy cloud over KSC prevents *Challenger's* return to Florida and flight is diverted to Edwards AFB, California. LC KSC. LV STS 41-C. LT 0859 EST. R 0538 PST, Runway 17, Edwards AFB, California.

Lift-off of Long March 3 from Xi Chang with the China 15 payload.

April 8 Chinese People's Republic launches China 15, first experimental communications satellite for positioning (16 April) in geostationary orbit above 125°E longitude. Launch vehicle resembles Ariane 1 with "podded" nose fairing. Two liquid-propellant stages are derived from CSL-2/FB-1 launcher with LO_2/LH_2 third stage of smaller diameter. Base stage has four steerable fins. LC Xi Chang. LV Long March 3 (CSL-3). LT 1100 GMT approx.

April 15-May 7 Soviets launch Progress 20 unmanned freighter which docks with Salyut 7/Soyuz T-11 complex on rear port at 1322 MT 17 April. Orbit of space station complex is corrected by engine firing of Progress 20. Separates at 2146 MT 6 May and next day is de-orbited over Pacific Ocean. LC Baikonur. LV A-2. LT 1213 MT.

April 23 Cosmonauts Leonid Kizim and Vladimir Solovyov perform tethered EVA from Salyut 7 lasting 4hr 15min to begin repair of station's engine system. On 26 April the cosmonauts emerge again; using appropriate tools they open a protective cover on the engine bay and fit a new fuel valve in the pipe circuit. They re-enter station after some 5hr. Repairs are completed during two further EVAs, on 30 April and 4 May, each lasting about 2hr 45min. On the last occasion, the cosmonauts fitted a second pipe circuit and secured a thermal cover.

May 8 Soviets launch Progress 21 unmanned freighter which docks with Salyut 7/Soyuz T-11 complex on rear port at 0410 MT 10 May. Mission followed four record-breaking EVAs between 23 April and 4 May lasting a total of 14hr 45min by cosmonauts Kizim and Solovyov to repair station's engine. Progress 21 separated 26 May and was made to re-enter atmosphere over Pacific Ocean. LC Baikonur. LV A-2. LT 0247 MT.

May 18 Cosmonauts Leonid Kizim and Vladimir Solovyov make their fifth EVA from Salyut 7, this time to install additional solar arrays on solar panel no 2. They remain in open space for 3hr 5min. In total they have now spent a record 17hr 50min on EVA activity.

May 28-July 16 Soviets launch Progress 22 unmanned freighter which docks with Salyut 7/Soyuz T-11 on aft port at 1947 MT 30 May. On-board cosmonauts transfer propellant for repaired Salyut 7 propulsion unit, air, equipment, instruments, materials for scientific research including cassettes for MKF-6M multi-spectral camera and mail. On 11 July engine of Progress 22 is used to move station complex to new orbit of 198 x 222 miles (318 x 358km) x 51·6°. Separates at 1736 MT 15 July and is made to re-enter atmosphere over Pacific. LC Baikonur. LV A-2. LT 1813 MT.

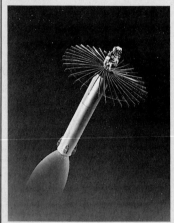

The June 10 intercept/kill vehicle.

June 10 Non-nuclear missile launched from Mech Island, Kwajalein Atoll, intercepts dummy warhead of Minuteman ICBM launched from Vandenberg AFB more than 100 miles (161km) out in space when travelling at 15,000mph (24,140km/h). Interceptor erected steel "umbrella" 15ft (24·1m) wide studded with weights, and locked onto its target by IR sensor which could theoretically detect heat emitted by a human body up to 1,000 miles (1,609km) away in space. Closing velocity 20,000ft/sec (6,096m/sec).

June 29 Soviet Union proposes talks on banning space weapons to begin in Vienna, September 1984; President Reagan agrees but states US intention to raise overall question of nuclear arms control. Soviets say this is unacceptable. In July US and USSR release joint statement affirming readiness to negotiate a ban on space weapons. Soviets want a moratorium on testing in space from the moment talks begin, but US Administration insists "no preconditions".

July 17-29 Soviets launch Soyuz T-12 with cosmonauts Col Vladimir Dzhanibekov (cdr), pilot cosmonaut Svetlana Savitskaya and researcher Igor Volk (world's 100th human space flight). Docks with Salyut 7/Soyuz T-11 complex on rear port at 2317 MT 18 July ; Dzhanibekov making his fourth space flight, Savitskaya her second. She now participates in tests of space vehicles and is attached to a design bureau. Volk, a newcomer to space, is a leading test pilot. Dzhanibekov and Savitskaya open the outer hatch at 1855 MT 25 July . Savitskaya, using a bulky 66lb (30kg) welder, then carries out three successive operations: 1) metal plate samples are cut and then welded together; 2) the plates are soldered; 3) a silver coating is

sprayed onto an aluminium plate. The cosmonauts change places and the cycle of operations is repeated with other samples. Results look towards "an era of extensive space construction" when large antennae of radio telescopes and solar arrays will be set up for supporting orbital factories and other objects employing large amounts of electricity. Other experiments are concerned with the effects of exposure of materials in outer space, the production of vaccines, electrophoresis, molecular physics, the effects of spaceflight on human eyesight and the cardio-vascular system, and the use of filters for the purification of the cabin atmosphere. A Resonance experiment determined dynamic characteristics of orbital complex Soyuz T-11/Salyut 7/Soyuz T-12. Investigation also made of structure of Earth's atmosphere and distribution of interplanetary matter in outer space. Cosmonauts returned in Soyuz T-12. LC Baikonur. LV A-2. LT 2141 MT. R 1655 MT, some 87 miles (140km) SE of Dzhezkazgan.

August 4 Arianespace launches Ariane 3 (V-10) on maiden flight from Kourou, French Guiana; carries two geostationary communications satellites mounted in tandem, ECS-2 for Eutelsat and Telecom 1A for French national telephone/TV network. ECS-2 geostationary above 7°E; Telecom 1A 8°W. Launching of Ariane 3, made without prior test flight, is described as "a calculated technological risk" at saving of nearly £40 million. LC Kourou, French Guiana. LV Ariane 3 (V-10). LT 1333 GMT.

The first launch of an Ariane 3.

August 14-28 Soviets launch Progress 23 unmanned freighter which docks with Salyut 7/Soyuz T-11 complex on rear port at 0811 GMT 16 August. It is fifth re-supply operation in support of long-stay cosmonauts. Separates at 1613 GMT 26 August and re-enters atmosphere over Pacific Ocean. LC Baikonur. LV A-2. LT 0628 GMT.

August 16 NASA launches Active Magnetosphere Particle Tracer Explorers (AMPTE) by Delta 3924 rocket from Cape Canaveral, Florida; triple payload studies interaction between solar wind and Earth's magnetic field. Three satellites mounted in tandem are: Charge Composition Explorer AMPTE 2 (US); Sub-satellite AMPTE 3 (UK) and Ion-Release Module AMPTE 1 (W Germany). LC Cape Canaveral. LV Delta 3924. LT 1448 GMT.

August 24 British Aerospace confirms existence of design study for pilotless spaceplane as satellite launcher which breathes air for burning in rocket engines. Code-named HOTOL (meaning horizontal take-off and landing), the delta-winged craft would propel itself into orbit without dropping off boosters and return under its own power. Assisting the study are Rolls-Royce and Royal Aircraft Establishment.

The OAST-1 solar array experiment at full extension above Discovery.

August 30-September 5 NASA launches Space Shuttle *Discovery* (41-D) on maiden flight with Henry Hartsfield, Jr (Cdr), Cdr Michael Coats (pilot), Lt-Col Richard M. Mullane, Dr Judith Resnik, Dr Steven A. Hawley (mission specialists) and Charles D. Walker (payload specialist). Orbit: 184 miles (296km) x 195 miles (314km) x 28·47°. On 30 August communications satellite Leasat 1 (Syncom 4-2) is released for transfer to geostationary orbit. Mission did not fly Anik communications satellite as originally planned because of unresolved problem with PAM stage (see 3-11 February 1984). Resnik, an electrical engineer, helped test extension and retraction of 103ft (31·4m) solar panel which is part of Office of Aeronautics and Space Technology Pallet (OAST-1). Walker, an employee of McDonnell Douglas Astronautics, monitored apparatus designed to separate biological material for use in new drugs for clinical analysis. On 5 September crew successfully dislodge lumps of ice which had formed on the waste outlet of the Orbiter's toilet using remote manipulator arm. There had been concern that ice might dislodge during re-entry and damage the spacecraft. Mission was much delayed, first by need to replace one of three main engines with engine taken from sister craft *Challenger*, following static testing early June. This caused postponement from 22-25 June. Launch that day was abandoned within 30 minutes of lift-off because of transistor fault in a back-up computer. This computer was exchanged for one from *Challenger*. Second launch attempt 26 June was aborted four seconds before lift-off when No 3 main engine failed to ignite, causing other two to shut down automatically. Small fire at base of Shuttle was quickly doused with water jets. Problem was faulty valve on the computer signal system that activates the valve. Launch finally delayed for 24 hours on 29 August because of computer indication that separation mechanism of external tank and SRBs might be suspect and then for seven minutes because two private aircraft had strayed into KSC airspace. Satellite payload was revised to avoid delay in launching communications satellites for fare-paying customers: Leasat (on original rosta) plus Telstar 3-C and SBS-D dropped from mission; both employed PAM motors which gave trouble in February 1984. LC KSC. LV STS 41-D. LT 1242 GMT. R 1338 GMT, Runway 17, Edwards AFB, California.

September 12-17 People's Republic of China launches China 16 (SKW-12) into orbit of 106 x 241 miles (171 x 388km) inclined at 67·94° to equator. Descent module recovered five days later. Service module re-enters after 17 days. LC Jiuquan. LV FB-1. LT 0543 GMT.

October 5-13 NASA launches Space Shuttle *Challenger* (41-G) with Capt Robert L. Crippen (cdr), Cdr John A. McBride (pilot), Dr Sally K. Ride, Dr Kathryn D. Sullivan, Lt Cdr David C. Leestma, Paul D. Scully-Power (mission specialists) and Dr Marc D. Garneau of Canada (payload specialist). Earth Radiation Budget Satellite (ERBS) deployed 5 October. Another primary payload was Shuttle Radar Laboratory (OSTA-3) named after the Office of Space Science and Terrestrial Applications. Designed to obtain radar images of Earth for map-making and interpretation of geological features, it comprised the Shuttle Imaging Radar (SIR-B), Large Format Camera, Measurement of Air Pollution from Satellites (MAPS) and Feature Identification and Location Experiment (FILE) which classifies areas according to water, vegetation, bare ground, snow and clouds. Tests also made of Orbital Reservicing System (ORS) which includes techniques for refuelling Landsat 4 in orbit. Scully-Power was added to crew at late stage to take advantage of 57° orbit which provided opportunity for a trained scientist to observe over three-quarters of Earth's surface. Opportunity was taken, with Large Format Camera, to photograph site of suspected Soviet nuclear accident in winter of 1957-58 located 56°N, 61°E. Several technical problems affecting communications were encountered which delayed planned EVA by Leestma and Sullivan for two days. An antenna did not fold back into place, delaying planned orbit-lowering manoeuvre. Ride used robot arm to fold antenna. On 11 October, Sullivan and Leestma spacewalked in Orbiter's cargo bay for more than three hours to test refuelling technique for restoring spent satellites to useful life. LC KSC. LV STS 41-G. LT 0703 EDT. R 1226 EDT, KSC.

November 8-16 NASA launches Space Shuttle *Discovery* (51-A) on second flight with Capt Frederick H. Hauck (cdr), Cdr David M. Walker (pilot) and Dr Anna L. Fisher, Lt-Cdr Dale A. Gardner and Joseph L. Fisher (mission specialists). Launched geostationary communications satellites Canadian Telsat-H (Anik D2) 9 November and Hughes Syncom 4-3

Dale Gardner flying back to Discovery having retrieved Westar 6.

(Leasat 2) 10 November and retrieved from orbit Palapa B-2 12 November and Westar 6 14 November. Recovery involved ground stations manoeuvring satellites from some 650 miles (1,046km) down to Shuttle orbit of about 225 miles (362km) by firing on-board thrusters. First retrieval entailed bringing *Discovery* within some 35ft (10·7m) of Palapa, enabling Allen wearing manoeuvring backpack (the MMU, manned maneuvering unit) to cross to it. He then inserted a 4ft (1·22m) "stinger" capture device into satellite's apogee rocket nozzle which expanded inside locking him to it. Thrusters in astronaut's backpack then stopped satellite's rotation and nudged man and satellite towards *Discovery*. After experiencing difficulty in attaching Orbiter's remote manipulator arm, method of securing satellite by means of a cradle device was abandoned and Allen and Gardner manhandled 1,200lb (544kg) Palapa into *Discovery*'s cargo bay. Second recovery involved similar procedure, with Gardner flying out to retrieve Westar with Allen assisting. The highly successful 51-A mission also included Radiation Monitor Experiment and Aggregation of Red Blood Cells experiment installed in the mid-deck. LC KSC. LV STS 51-A. LT 0715 EST. R 0700 EST, Runway 15, KSC.

November 10 Arianespace launches second Ariane 3 carrying two geostationary satellites mounted in tandem, GTE Spacenet 2 and ESA's maritime communications satellite Marecs B-2. LC Kourou, French Guiana. LV Ariane 3 (V-11). LT 0114 GMT.

November 13 US Air Force conducts second live firing of anti-satellite (ASAT) missile from F-15 Eagle aircraft over Pacific Ocean. Target is simulated by fixing IR guidance system on a star.

December 15 Soviets launch Vega 1 interplanetary spacecraft on dual mission to investigate Venus and Halley's Comet. Equipped by scientists from Bulgaria, Hungary, E Germany, Poland, USSR, Czechoslovakia and W Germany, it will drop off capsule on Venus June 1985, then intercept the comet March 1986. Descent module to investigate atmosphere, cloud layer and surface of Venus; during descent 11·4ft (3·47m) balloon sonde released to study atmospheric circulation and meteorological phenomena. LC Baikonur. LV D-1-e. LT 0916 GMT.

December 19 Soviets launch sub-scale model of Kosmolyot (spaceplane) of blended wing/body design (Cosmos 1614). After completing single orbit, it makes controlled descent to planned recovery area in Black Sea. LC Kapustin Yar. LV C-1. LT 0400 GMT approx.

December 21 Soviets launch Vega 2 interplanetary spacecraft on dual mission to investigate Venus and Halley's Comet (see also 15 December). LC Baikonur. LV D-1-e. LT 0914 GMT.

1985

January 7 Japan launches 300lb (136kg) probe Sakigake (Pioneer) to study conditions in deep space during approach of Halley's Comet. Closest approach of 4·35 million miles (7 million km) achieved 11-13 March 1986. Measured solar wind plasma and interplanetary magnetic fields. LC Tanegashima. LV Mu-3S. LT 1915 GMT.

January 24-27 NASA launches Space Shuttle *Discovery* (51-C) into circular orbit of approximately 186 miles (300km)

A KSC landing for STS-51C Discovery.

x 28.5°; is first dedicated military mission with DoD astronaut Major Gary E. Payton and four NASA astronauts Capt Thomas K. Mattingly, II; Lt-Col Loren J. Shriver; Major Ellison S. Onizuka, and Lt-Col James F. Buchli. Payton (mission specialist) assists deployment of "national security satellite" with Boeing Inertial Upper Stage (IUS). Among details originally withheld are launch time and mission objectives. In fact, satellite was 30,000lb (13,608kg) new-generation Sigint 5 (Aquacade) designed to monitor military and diplomatic communications in USSR and large parts of Europe and Asia, including missile telemetry, radio, radar, telephone and satellite re-transmission. Deployment occurred some 16 hours into mission. First stage IUS burned for 145sec injecting satellite into elliptical transfer orbit; second stage propelled it into geosynchronous orbit, probably about 90°E downlinked to ground station in Western Australia. On 26 January it was announced that

Discovery had completed its mission and would be landing at KSC the next day. NASA later reported that 13 protective tiles were damaged sufficient to need replacing. Launch was delayed 24 hours because of severe cold at the Cape, which raised concern that ice might form on External Tank. (At least four smaller Sigint satellites had been launched previously by USAF expendable rockets). LC KSC. LV STS 51-C. LT 1450 EST. R 1623 EST, Runway 15, KSC.

March 1 NASA announces cancellation of Space Shuttle *Challenger* mission 51-E because of problem with TDRS satellite installed in cargo bay. Proposed to merge mission with that of *Discovery* (51-D), eventually flown on 12-19 April. Crew of 51-E were to be Col Karol J. Bobko (commander), Capt Donald E. Williams (pilot), S. David Griggs (flight engineer) Dr Margaret Rhea Seddon and Jeffrey A. Hoffman (mission specialists), Lt-Col Patrick Baudry (France) and US Senator E. J. "Jake" Garn (R-Utah) (payload specialists). Garn, 52, an experienced jet-fighter pilot, is chairman of Senate appropriations sub-committee which oversees NASA's budget. Principal payloads: second Tracking and Data Relay Satellite and Anik C1 for Telesat of Canada. Baudry was to have monitored French echography experiment. Mission 51-E had already been delayed some weeks because of necessity to replace about 4,200 thermal insulation protective tiles following mission 41-G in October 1984.

April 12-19 NASA launches Space Shuttle *Discovery* (51-D) with Col Karol J. Bobko (cdr); Capt Donald E. Williams (pilot), S. David Griggs (flight engineer), Dr Rhea Seddon and Jeffrey A. Hoffman, mission specialists, Charles W. Walker, McDonnell Douglas payload specialist and Senator E. J. "Jake" Garn. Orbit: 196 x 285 miles (315 x 452km) x 28·52°. Mission lasted six days 23hrs 55min 23sec, following a one orbit delay caused by rain clouds over KSC. Successfully deployed are (12 April) Canada's Telesat-1 (Anik C-1) and (13 April) Hughes Syncom 4-3 (Leasat-3) leased to US Navy. Apogee motor of latter fails to ignite after 45min as planned. Mission is extended two days in unsuccessful attempt to fix inoperable satellite. Hughes engineers concluded that power switch

had failed. Leasat is deployed by low-energy "frisbee" action which imparts both stabilizing spin and separation velocity. Centripetal force generated is supposed to pull out a pin which activates satellite's systems and starts sequence of events leading to ignition of apogee motor. Pin did not pull out leaving satellite inert. Leasat was not fitted with grapple that would have allowed it to be recaptured and returned to cargo bay. Unplanned EVA repair mission began 16 April. Astronauts improvised "flyswatter" tool from a few centsworth of plastic and tubing. Handle was made of 4ft (1.2m) extendable rod used to reach inaccessible switches in Shuttle cabin. This was sheathed in a hose from a portable vacuum cleaner and a plastic flap (with rectangular holes cut into it) was attached to one end. Astronauts Hoffman and Griggs space-walked on 16 April to attach makeshift tool to end of manipulator arm but despite several attempts on 17 April to

snag the Leasat switch their efforts were in vain (however, Syncom was successfully repaired during mission 51-I in August/September 1985). LC KSC. LV STS 51-D. LT 0859 EST. R 0855 EST, Runway 33, KSC.

April 29-May 6 NASA launches Space Shuttle *Challenger* (51-B) with Spacelab 3 and crew of seven: Col Robert F. Overmyer, (cdr) Lt-Col Frederick D. Gregory (pilot), Dr William E. Thornton, Dr Norman E. Thagard (mission specialists) and Don L. Lind (physicist); Dr Taylor G. Wang (JPL fluid-mechanics specialist), and Dr Lodewijk van den Berg (EG&G specialist in materials processing) payload specialists. Considered first operational launch of Spacelab after Spacelab 1 check-out mission, 1983. Entered circular orbit of approximately 219 miles (352km) x 57°. Deployed "getaway special" sub-satellite NUSAT, 114lb (52kg), for air traffic control calibration, but GLOMR for DoD failed to leave its canister. LC KSC. STS 51-B. LT 1102 EDT. R 0912 PDT, Runway 17, Edwards AFB, California.

June 6-September 26 Soviets launch Soyuz T-13 with cosmonauts Col Vladimir Dzhanibekov and flight engineer Viktor Savinykh. Docks manually with Salyut 7 on forward port at 1250 MT 8 June using new range-finding device instead of ground-controlled automatic system. Objective: to repair space station which had been unmanned since October 1984 and was no longer responding to signals from mission control. Station was "lifeless" due to battery failure, with water and gas lines frozen. Cosmonauts began by examining antennas, solar batteries and other on-board systems and equipment. Over period of days they restored battery power and gradually restored the station to life. After repairs, cosmonauts participated with seven Intercosmos member-countries in major experiment, "Kursk-85", which tested new methods of forecasting crop yield. LC Baikonur. LV A-2. LT 1040 MT. R 1352 MT, 124 miles (200km) NE of Dzhezkazgan.

June 11 Soviet Vega-1 spacecraft en-route to rendezvous with Halley's Comet in March 1986 passes Venus after separating landing module two days earlier. After entering Venerian atmosphere releases 11·8ft (3·6m) diameter helium weather balloon which circulates around planet at some 33·5 miles (54km) altitude. Radio signals from balloon are received at JPL, California, who are co-operating in international venture. Soft-landing of descent capsule confirmed at 7° 11'N lattitude, 177° 48' longitude. Capsule made an hour-long descent measuring temperature, pressure and water content of clouds; also studied absorption and diffusion of light and gas composition of atmosphere. TV cameras not embodied because landing was made on night side of planet. Network of Soviet and international radio-telescopes in Europe, Asia, Australia, Africa and North and South America received balloon's signals (time interval in reception from probes nearly six minutes). Findings included: clouds around Venus were moving at 197-230ft/sec; balloon was blown 984ft (300m) up and down in atmosphere. Surface temperature 452°C (846°F); pressure 86 atmospheres. Experiment repeated 22 June with Vega-2. Both balloons drifted for approximately 46hr at average of 34mph (55km/hr) travelling some 7,450 miles (12,000km).

June 17-24 NASA launches Space Shuttle *Discovery* (51-G) with Cdr Daniel C. Brandenstein (cdr), Cdr John O. Creighton (pilot) and mission specialists Dr Shannon W. Lucid, Lt-Col Steven R. Nagel and Col John M. Fabian, and payload specialists Lt-Col Patrick Baudry (France) and Prince Sultan Salman Abdelazize Al-Saud (Saudi Arabia). Orbit is 219 miles (352km) x 28·5°. Successfully deployed 17 June are Mexican satellite Morelos-1A, geostationary above 113·5°W; 18 June Saudi-Arabian Arabsat-1A, geostationary above 26°E and 19 June AT&T Telstar 3-D, geostationary above 62°W. Also deployed and recovered by remote manipulator arm, day 4 and day 6 respectively, Spartan 1 which uses X-ray sensors to search for hot gas clouds in galaxy clusters and carry out a survey of X-ray sources in local galaxy (examine possible Black Hole in galactic centre). Maximum separation distance from *Discovery* 99 miles (160km). On 21 June experiment was made to bounce ground-based low-energy laser beam from 8in (20·3cm), retro-reflector mounted in window of Orbiter's mid-deck side hatch. Beam was projected from USAF base 9,000ft (2,953m) up on Mt. Haleakala on the Hawaiian island of Maui to discover if ground computers could adjust beam to counteract distorting effect of Earth's atmosphere; also to test ability of Laser Beam Director accurately to track an object in low Earth orbit. Beam, originally pencil thin, was estimated to be about 30ft (9·14m) wide when it hit the Orbiter which was moving at 17,400mph (28,000km/h) some 220 miles (354km) overhead. LC KSC. LV STS 51-G. LT 0733 EDT. R 0612 PDT, Runway 23, Edwards AFB, California.

June 21-July 15 Soviets launch Progress 24 freighter which docks with Salyut 7 on rear port at 0234 GMT on 23 June. Re-supply mission followed repair and servicing of space station by on-board cosmonauts Dzanibekov and Savinykh, rendezvous and docking being controlled by Flight Control Centre and the cosmonauts themselves. The freighter brought propellants, food, air, water and research materials and mail. This enabled crew of Salyut 7 to restore vital systems, including replacement of three storage batteries. Progress 24 undocked at 1228 GMT on 15 July and was made to re-enter atmosphere over Pacific. LC Baikonur. LV A-2. LT 0040 GMT.

July 2 ESA launches Giotto space probe at 1123 GMT by Ariane 1 (V-14) from Kourou, French Guiana to intercept Halley's Comet on 13-14 March 1986. Launch mass 2,116lb (960kg) reducing to 1,129lb (512kg) after propellant depletion.

July 16-August 30 Soviets launch Cosmos 1669 freighter in test flight of new Soyuz/Progress type vehicle with solar arrays. Docks automatically with Salyut 7/Soyuz T-13 complex at 1905 MT 18 July. Undocked 29 August and re-entered atmosphere next day. LC Baikonur. LV A-2. LT 1705 MT.

July 29-August 6 NASA launches Space Shuttle *Challenger* (51-F) with Spacelab 2 two-pallet train plus single pallet and "Igloo". Astronauts are Col Charles Gordon Fullerton (cdr); Lt-Col Roy D. Bridges, Jr (pilot); Dr Story Musgrave (payload specialist; also 3rd pilot); Dr Karl G. Henize (astronomer); Dr Anthony W. England (geophysicist); Dr Loren W. Acton (payload specialist, Lockheed Palo Alto Research Lab); and Dr John-David Bartoe (payload specialist, NRL). Launch resulted in first major in-flight Shuttle emergency when sensor action shut down one of Orbiter's main engines some six minutes into launch sequence, causing an "abort to orbit" situation. Craft achieved orbit of 196 miles (315km) x 49·48° – some 41·5 miles (67km) lower than planned. Necessitated jettisoning about 4,400lb (1,996kg) of OMS propellants and use of additional OCS propellant. The fail-safe procedure was entirely successful and, in fact, mission was extended one day to allow increased observation time. A sub-satellite, Plasma Diagnostic Package (PDP), was deployed alongside *Challenger* on 1 August to detect effects on movement through natural plasma; also to measure electron emissions from Spacelab experiments. Was successfully recovered by manipulator arm 2 August; further experiments were performed with PDP still attached to arm. Mission validated pallet-only configuration of Spacelab which embodied 13 experiments in seven scientific disciplines: solar, atmospheric, plasma physics, IR astronomy, technology research, life sciences. After overcoming early problems in working pallet-mounted ESA/Dornier instrument pointing system (IPS), good data was obtained by associated instruments. "Igloo", pressurized automatic supply module, housed computers, data-handling equipment, etc. Previous launch attempt on 12 July was aborted

because hydrogen chamber coolant valve on main engine no. 2 failed to close. LC KSC. LV STS 51-F. LT 1700 EDT. R 1245 PDT, Runway 23, Edwards AFB, California.

August 2 Cosmonauts Vladimir Dzhanibekov and Viktor Savinykh emerge from Salyut 7 airlock at 1115 MT to attach additional solar panels, delivered by Progress 24, to third solar array; now all three solar arrays have additional panels. EVA lasts total of 5hr.

August 16 Japan launches space probe Suisei (Planet A) by Mu-3S from Kagoshima for fly-by of Halley's comet. Spin-stabilized at 5rpm, 311lb (141kg) probe has low-thrust gas jets for minor course corrections; passed within 124,270 miles (200,000km) of the comet 8 March 1986. LC Kagoshima. LV Mu-3S. LT 2330 GMT approx.

August 27-September 3 NASA launches Space Shuttle *Discovery* (51-I) with astronauts Col Joe H. Engle (cdr), Lt-Col Richard O. Covey (pilot), Dr James D. A. van Hoften, John M. Lounge and Dr William F. Fisher (mission specialists). Deploys three communications satellites: Australia's Aussat 1, American Satellite Company's ASC-1 and Hughes Communications Services Leasat 4 (Syncom 4-4). Then, astronauts rendezvous with failed Leasat 3 and achieve capture by remote manipulator arm. Repair is effected during EVA by Hoften and Fisher and satellite is redeployed. When originally deployed during 51-D mission, 13 April 1985, satellite's automatic sequencer failed to initiate antenna deployment, spin-up and ignition of perigee kick motor. Orbits: 218 x 236 miles (351 x 380km) x 28·55° for satellite deployments; then manoeuvred to 195 x 279 miles (314 x 449km) x 28·53° for Leasat 3 retrieval. Leasat 3 geostationary above 175°W following boost motor firing 27 October. Conducted in *Discovery's* mid-deck was Physical Vapour Transport of Organic Solids (PVTOS) experiment for 3M Corporation. Mission duration: 170hr 18min 29sec. Mission was originally scheduled for 24 August but was postponed because of thunderheads over Cape Canaveral; and again on 25 August when back-up computer was "out of sync" with four primary computers. LC KSC. LV STS 51-I. LT 0658 EDT. R 0615 PDT, Runway 23, Edwards AFB, California.

September United States SDI test succeeds in directing ground-based low-power (4W) visible laser at missile target. Test is conducted from Air Force Maui Optical Site, Mt Heeakala, Hawaii, tracking a two-stage Terrier-Malemute launched from Pacific Missile Test Range, Kauai. Claimed to be first time that a laser beam, adjusted for atmospheric distortion, has been projected from the ground.

An ASAT test vehicle streaks skyward after launch from an F-15.

September 13 USAF launches ASAT from F-15 interceptor at 35,000-40,000ft (10,668-12,192m) over Vandenberg AFB, California. Target is DARPA test program satellite P78-1 orbiting some 345 miles (556km) out in space. Hit confirmed at 1632 EDT by telemetry from target satellite and Spacetrack network (P78-1, which was still returning scientific data at time of attack, contained gamma-ray spectrometer).

September 17-November 21 Soviets launch Soyuz T-14 with cosmonauts Lt-Col Vladimir Vasyutin (cdr), Georgi Grechko (flight engineer) and Aleksandr Volkov (researcher). Docks with aft port of Salyut 7 space station complex at 1414 GMT 18 September; orbit 210 x 219 miles (338 x 353km) x 51·63°. Grechko returned with Vladimir Dzhanibekov on 26 September 1985. LC Baikonur. LV A-2. LT 1239 GMT. R 1031 GMT, 111 miles (180km) SE of Dzhezkazgan.

September 27 Soviets launch Cosmos 1686 Star Module which docks with Salyut 7/Soyuz T-14 space station complex on forward port at 1016 GMT on 2 October. Was further test for

International Sun-Earth Explorer (ISEE-3) launched from Cape Canaveral in August 1974 to study solar wind from "halo orbit" about libration point one million miles (1·6m km) sunward from Earth where gravitational fields of Sun, Earth and Moon are in balance.

The ground-based laser used to track a Terrier-Malemute target rocket.

September 11 International Cometary Explorer (ICE) flies safely through tail of comet Giacobini-Zinner about 6,214 miles (10,000km) behind nucleus. Observed clear signatures of the interaction of comet with the solar wind within 18·6 million miles (30 million km) on sunward side of comet at end of March 1986. Before being re-directed, ICE was

assembling "orbital complexes of large size and mass". Cosmos 1686 also delivered miscellaneous freight items. Similar to Cosmos 1267 and 1443. LC Baikonur. LV D-1-e. LT 0841 GMT.

October JPL scientists reviewing findings of Mariner and Viking spacecraft conclude that early history of Mars was shaped by ice, snow, flowing rivers and vast lakes. Today, however, surface water is frozen because thin Martian atmos-

phere (95 per cent carbon dioxide) cannot effectively trap solar heat. Thin mantle of dry ice covers polar regions with underlying layers of water ice. Some evidence of water ice in places above 30 deg latitude, with evidence of "terrain softening" in regions of impact craters, indicating possibility of liquid water perhaps 0·6 miles (1km) down, subject to thermal heating.

October Second launch pad, ELA 2, is completed at Kourou Space Centre, French Guiana. Consecutive use of two pads allows Ariane 3/4 launch rate to rise to 10 per year. Construction has already started of third launch pad for Ariane 5.

The ELA 2 launch pad at Kourou.

October 3-7 NASA launches Space Shuttle *Atlantis* (51-J) on maiden flight with astronauts Col Karol J. Bobko (cdr); Lt-Col Ronald J. Grabe (pilot), Major David C. Hilmers and Col Robert L. Stewart (mission specialists) and Major William D. Pailes (payload specialist). Was dedicated DoD mision achieving orbit of 296 x 320 miles (476 x 515km), a new Shuttle altitude record. Launched by single IUS booster two geosynchronous satellites DSCS Phase 3. Mid-deck experiment studied damage to biological materials from high energy cosmic rays. LC KSC. LV STS 51-J. LT 1115 EDT. R 1000 PDT, Runway 23, Edwards AFB, California.

October 21-26 Chinese People's Republic launches China 17 (SKW-13) for Earth observation into orbit of 106 x 244 miles (171 x 393km) x 62·98°. Ejects capsule for recovery after five days. Satellite body re-enters after 17 days. LC Jiuquan. LV CZ-2 (Long March 2). LT 0504 GMT approx.

October 24 Austria and Norway are accepted by council of ESA into full membership; brings membership to 13.

October 25 Soviets launch Cosmos 1700 (Lutch) tracking and data relay satellite as part of triple satellite system in support of Mir space station. However, satellite drifts out of position over Indian Ocean. Was to be geosynchronous above 95°E. LC Baikonur. LV D-1-e. LT 1545 GMT approx.

October 30-November 6 NASA launches Spacelab D-1 aboard Space Shuttle *Challenger* on mission 61-A. Astronauts are Col Henry W. Hartsfield, Jr (cdr), Lt-Col Steven R. Nagel (pilot), Col James F. Buchli, Dr Bonnie J. Dunbar, Col Guion S. Bluford, Jr, Dr Reinhard Furrer (W Germany); Dr Ernst Messerschmid (W Germany) and Dr Wubbo Ockels (Netherlands). Spacelab experiments – primarily materials, life sciences, communications and navigation – are managed by W Germany and controlled from German Operations Control Centre, Oberpfaffenhofen, near Munich. Biorack experiments provided striking evidence of effects of microgravity on bacteria, unicellular organisms, white blood cells and insect development. Vestibular sled comprised a seat for a test subject that could be moved backward and forward with precisely adjusted accelerations along rails fixed to floor of Spacelab's aisle. Mission also launched 150lb (68kg) GLOMR message relay satellite which failed to deploy during Spacelab 3 mission (see April 29-May 6 1985). Was 22nd Shuttle mission; carried largest Shuttle crew; mission duration 168hr 44min 51sec. Orbit: 200 x 207 miles (322 x 333km) x 57°. LC KSC. LV STS 61-A. LT 1200 EST. R 0944 PST. Runway 17, Edwards AFB, California.

November 26-December 3 NASA launches Space Shuttle *Atlantis* (STS 61-B) with astronauts Lt-Col Brewster H. Shaw, Jr (cdr), Lt-Col Bryan D. O'Connor (pilot), Mary L. Cleave (mission specialist), Lt-Col Sherwood C. Spring, Major Jerry L. Ross, Rudolfo Neri Vela (Mexico) and Charles D. Walker (McDonnell-Douglas payload specialist making his third space flight). Orbit is 219 miles (352km) x 28·46°. Successfully deployed are: 26 November, Mexican satellite Morelos 2; 27 November, Australian satellite Aussat 2 and 28 November RCA Satcom K-2 with PAM D2 perigee boost stage. On-board experiments include: McDonnell-Douglas biological processing of erythropoietin (a red blood cell stimulant); 3M Corp commercial materials processing (development of materials for advanced light-powered communications and data handling); Alabama/Birmingham protein crystal growth. Spring and Ross, during two EVAs lasting more than 11hr, erected and dismantled 44·3ft (13·5m) tower (ACCESS) and 11·8ft (3·6m) pyramid (EASE). Mary Cleave, from *Atlantis'* mid-deck, controlled manipulator arm on which astronauts worked. LC KSC. LV STS 61-B. LT 1929 EST. R 1333 PST, Runway 22, Edwards AFB, California.

December Soviet Union establishes civilian space agency, Glavkosmos, to manage space science, space applications and co-operative international space programmes.

December 28 Pioneer 12 Venus Orbiter begins observations of Halley's Comet. Passes within 25 million miles (40 million km) of comet on 4 February 1986 (five days before comet's closest approach to the Sun). Pioneer's UV spectrometer observed comet's gas composition and water vaporisation rate. Particle field sensors observed solar wind.

1986

January 12-18 NASA launches Space Shuttle *Columbia* (61-C) with astronauts Cdr Robert L. Gibson (cdr), Col Charles F. Bolden, Jr (pilot), George D. Nelson (mission specialist), Steven A. Hawley, Franklin R. Chang-Diaz, Robert Cenker (RCA payload specialist) and Bill Nelson (Congressional flight observer). Communications satellite RCA Satcom K1 is deployed with PAM-D2; subsequently positioned in geostationary orbit above 85°W longitude. Astronauts conducted materials science experiments, tested SDI-related surveillance equipment and its ability to obtain atmospheric signature of USAF aircraft. Bill Nelson assisted protein crystal growth experiment sponsored by Alabama-Birmingham; obtained photographic documentation of crystal growth. Three days of bad weather at KSC resulted in mission terminating at Edwards AFB. LC KSC. LV STS 61-C. LT 0655 EST. R 0559 PST, Runway 22, Edwards AFB, California.

January 24 Voyager 2 passes within 66,500 miles (107,00km) of Uranus. The fly-by also features encounters with moons Miranda, Umbriel, Ariel, Titania, Oberon and the planet's ring system. Discovered 14 new moons by mid-January, including one of about 50 miles (80km) diameter midway between Miranda and outer rim of Uranus' ring system which orbits planet every 18hr 17min 9sec. Following thrust manoeuvre on 14 February, spacecraft is re-directed towards Neptune for 24 August 1989 encounter.

January 28 Space Shuttle *Challenger* (51-L) is destroyed in mid-air explosion 73 seconds after lifting off from KSC with total loss of crew, Francis R. Scobee (cdr), Cdr Michael Smith (pilot), Dr Judith Resnik, Lt-Col Ellison Onizuka and Dr Ronald McNair (mission specialists), Gregory Jarvis (Hughes payload specialist) and Christa McAuliffe (teacher observer). Primary objective had been to deploy TDRS-B in geostationary orbit for high capacity communications and data links between Earth, Shuttle and other spacecraft and launch vehicles in conjunction with previously-launched TDRS-1. TDRS-B was scheduled for Pacific station above 171°W longitude.

A telltale puff of smoke escapes from Challenger's defective right-hand SRB just seconds after launch.

Was first Space Shuttle launch from newly-activated Pad 39B, and 25th Shuttle mission, *Challenger's* tenth. Launch photographs revealed plume of flame coming from right hand SRB impinging on attachment structure. Jerrol W. Littles, assistant director of engineering Marshall SFC (7 March) gave the probable cause: 1) Damage to primary and secondary O-rings caused by out-of-round segment when boosters were stacked. 2) Blowby or leakage of primary O-ring 3) Putty sealant (asbestos-filled zinc chromate) that keeps pressure off primary O-ring. The question remained if sub-zero temperature at the Cape before 28 January had affected RH booster O-ring used to seal the aft booster segment. Recovered section of SRB had a 1·96ft (0·6m) x 0·98ft (0·3m) hole where hot exhaust gases had burned through destroying the base attachment of the SRB and allowing it to pivot into the External Tank. (A subsequent report suggested that the aft attachment might have failed because of a combination of abnormal side gust loads). Crew compartment, with astronaut remains, was recovered from a depth of some 85ft (26m) 16·8 miles (27km) NE of KSC. It had fallen practically intact from 72,200ft (22,000m) and broke up on impact with the water. Launch, originally scheduled 20 January, was delayed because of hydrogen leak during flight readiness firing 18 December 1985. LC KSC. LV STS 51-L. LT 1138 EDT.

February 12 Soviet scientists reported to be finalizing "Atlas of Venus" from radar and optical probing carried out by orbiting stations Venera 15 and Venera 16 between October 1983 and July 1984. Surface of Venus resembles that of Earth with mountain ranges and valleys, volcanic peaks and craters; there are signs of tectonic activity. Highest mountain stands 7·1 miles (11·5km).

February 19 Soviets launch core of permanent space station Mir (Peace) into staging orbit of 107 x 187 miles (172 x 301km) x 51·62°; subsequently raised by on-board propulsion to 201 x 211 miles (324 x 340km). Developed from Salyut, the overall length is about 42·6ft (13m); maximum diameter 13·6ft (4·15m); mass about 21 tonnes. At forward end a spherical docking unit will accept four laboratory modules on laterally disposed docking ports; fifth and sixth ports are located on the axis front and rear. The rear port is surrounded by the ODU engine compartment. A "lab" module to be attached radially will first dock on the forward axial port, then be transferred by manipulator arm to its final position. Inside the station much of the scientific equipment found in Salyut has been removed to the "lab" modules which arrive separately. Cosmonauts now have their own compartments with table, chair and intercom. Life-support and air-conditioning systems are improved and water is reclaimed from the atmosphere. After orbital adjustments, on 16 March, orbit is 206 x 220 miles (332 x 354km) x 51·6°; period 91·2min. Mir is officially described (*Pravda*) as "a test site for practising in-flight assembly and maintenance of large structures of different shapes... utilising new structural materials and fundamentally new approaches to durability estimates and design methods, and the use of multi-functional space robots". New training programmes have been prepared for future orbital stations – "continually growing and developing multi-functional complexes". It may be supposed, says Vladimir Shatalov, that crews will later be increased to six and even 12. LC Baikonur. LV D-1. LT 2119 GMT.

March National Commission on Space, tasked by President Reagan to formulate space policy for next 50 years, recommends establishment of permanent base on Moon by 2017 and base on Mars by 2027. Total estimated cost $7,000,000 million.

March 6 Soviet comet probe Vega 1 flies within 5,520 miles (8,889km) of Halley's Comet.

March 9 Soviet comet probe Vega 2 flies within 4,990 miles (8,030km) of Halley's Comet. Observations from Vega 1/2 suggest to Professor Yuri Makogon that heads of comets are made of gas hydrates in which methane and water are combined in a ratio of 200 to 1. Measurements made during comet fly-by suggest nucleus comprises a hydrate of carbon dioxide and water in the ratio of 300 to 1 by volume mixed with mineral dust and metals.

March 13/14 ESA's Giotto comet probe flies within 335 miles (540km) of nucleus of Halley's Comet. Discovers that nucleus is potato shaped about 9 miles (14·5km) long by 5 miles (8·05km) wide. Surface is uneven with valleys, hills and what appear to be impact craters. Maximum brightness is observed to be closest to the Sun; two bright dust jets spring from sunward side which pour tons of dust particles per second deep into space. Most of the activity of nucleus seems to come from only a few sources; the remainder of the surface appears to be sealed beneath a black crust. From launch 2 July 1985, Giotto travelled some 435 million miles (700 million km) to intercept the comet at a distance from Earth of 93 million miles (149·6 million km). Will arrive back in Earth's vicinity 1990, when it may be given another scientific task.

Giotto's multicolour camera reveals the dynamic nature of Halley's comet as it approaches its rendezvous.

March 13-July 16 Soviets launch Soyuz T-15 with cosmonauts Col Leonid Kizim and Vladimir Solovyov; docks with Mir core module on forward port 1638 MT 15 March. On 5 May, cosmonauts undocked and transferred to unmanned Salyut 7/Cosmos 1686 complex entering that station on 6 May. On 12 May Kizim and Solovyov checked the orientation system and replaced an instrument in the engine control loop. On 13 May they carried out a full check of electrical circuits. After performing other essential maintenance tasks, they were able to resume visual observations of Earth's surface seven days later. On 28 May, the cosmonauts spacewalked from the Salyut 7/Cosmos 1686/Soyuz T-15 complex, taking out segments of a 49·2ft (15m) truss from a cylinder and joining sections together by "automatic devices". The whole structure was then secured to a platform. On 31 May Kizim and Solovyov make their eighth spacewalk opening the hatch at 0857 MT. As before they unfolded a lattice and pin frame and with its help built a 36·5ft (12m) tower resembling an oil derrick; mounted on a platform atop the structure were the "Fon" wide-band instrument to measure atmospheric density and a seismic unit to monitor vibrations in the framework. The data obtained helped to forecast the behaviour of large structures and estimate their strength. For the first time an optical communications system, employing a low-power laser, relayed data to a ground station from the outside. Next the cosmonauts employed a portable beam-welder to weld lattice and pin frames. Altogether, in eight EVAs, Kizim and Solovyov worked on the outside of the station for 31hr 40min. In total they spent 50 days aboard Salyut 7/Cosmos 1686, leaving at 1858 MT on 25 June, and re-docking with Mir at 2346 MT the following day. On 2 July Kizim broke human space endurance record, having accumulated 362 days during three missions. LC Baikonur. LV A-2. LT 1533 MT. R 1634 MT, NE of Arkalyk.

Leonid Kizim chases an elusive film canister during his Soyuz T-15 visit to the Mir space station.

March 19-April 21 Soviets launch Progress 25 freighter which docks with Mir/Soyuz T-15 space station complex on aft port at 1416 MT 21 March with propellants, air, food, water and other expendables. On 25 March Progress 25 engine is fired to adjust orbit of station complex; other thrust corrections follow. Separates at 2324 MT 20 April and is made to re-enter atmosphere. LC Baikonur. LV A-2. LT 1308 MT.

April Japanese space agency NASDA, in 1986-87 budget, includes funds for study of unmanned spaceplane Himes. The highly manoeuvrable vehicle 42·6ft (13m) long, weighs about 14 tonnes; propellants are LO_2/LH_2. Objective: to carry sounding-rocket size payloads on sub-orbital trajectories but for periods longer than a conventional sounding-rocket. Also receiving financial support are plans to build two free-flying platforms, one for use in conjunction with NASA Space Shuttle and the other with US International Space Station.

April 7 NASA initiates Shuttle Crew Egress and Escape Review to be completed December 1986. Considers emergency escape possibilities for pad abort, bale out, ejection systems, water landings and powered flight separation.

April 12 On 25th anniversary of world's first manned venture into Earth orbit (Yuri Gagarin, Vostok 1), *Izvestia* reveals identity of eight previously unknown cosmonauts in group of 20 chosen in 1960. Includes Valentin Bondarenko, killed in a spacecraft fire during a ground test 23 March 1961 only 20 days before Gagarin's epic space flight.

April 23-June 23 Soviets launch Progress 26 freighter which docks with Mir-Soyuz T-15 complex on rear port at 0126 MT 27 April. Delivers propellant, water, food and "assorted cargo". Undocks 2225 MT 22 June and is made to re-enter atmosphere next day. LC Baikonur. LV A-2. LT 2340 MT.

May 21-30 Soviets launch Soyuz TM spacecraft, unmanned, into preliminary orbit of 124 x 149 miles (200 x 240km) x 51·6°. Docks with unmanned Mir/ Progress 26 complex on forward port at 1412 MT 23 May. Developed from Soyuz T, craft has new systems: approach and docking; radio communications; emergency rescue; new combined propulsion unit and a new lighter and stronger recovery parachute. Mutual search, rendezvous and docking were carried out with aid of onboard automatic systems of both space vehicles. Instead of the previous "Igla" (Needle) system, it involves new system "Kurs" (Course) in which only TM ship manoeuvres for docking and Mir expends zero propellant. New communications system allows communications with Earth via the Luch geostationary relay satellite. Before separating at 1323 MT 29 May, Soyuz TM used its combined propulsion unit to adjust orbit of Mir complex. LC Baikonur. LV A-2. LT 1222 MT. R 1049 MT, "designated area of Soviet territory".

May 31 Ariane launches Intelsat 5A (F14) but rocket's third stage HM-7 LO_2/LH_2 engine suffers ignition failure; rocket and satellite are destroyed by range safety officer. Rectification involved detailed study of ignition conditions, redefinition and qualification of more powerful third stage igniter. Testing of cryogenic engine with modified igniter began 4 August 1986. LC Kourou, French Guiana (ELA-1 pad). LV Ariane (V18). LT 0053 GMT.

June 19 Dr James C. Fletcher, NASA Administrator, cancels Shuttle-Centaur programme for reasons of safety.

July ESA responds to Arianespace request to up-rate design of Ariane 5 launcher to include capability of putting 5·2 tonnes into geostationary transfer orbit. New design also conforms to a CNES requirement to build extra safety provisions into Hermes spaceplane, increasing launch mass from 17 to 20 tonnes. Modifications to Hermes include: provision of second orbit manoeuvring engine; launch escape system of four solid propellant rockets mounted externally between second stage and spaceplane and, possibly, a crew compartment escape pod.

July W Germany considers design of two-stage re-usable spaceplane, Sänger 2, as competitor to BAe-Rolls-Rolls HOTOL project. Stage 1 is conceived as winged ramjet carrying a rocket-plane which separates at Mach 6 velocity 18 miles (30km) above the Earth. Like HOTOL it takes off horizontally and payloads are placed in low-Earth orbit for about one-fifth cost of NASA Space Shuttle. Spaceplane, designed by MBB, is named after German rocket pioneer Dr Eugen Sänger who designed rocket-powered "antipodal bomber" 1938-42.

July 30 Cosmos 1767 launched by "new type of rocket" (according to DoD) fails to achieve useful orbit; decays from orbit 15 August 1986. Orbit actually achieved: 123 x 140 miles (198 x 226km) x 64·9°. LC Baikonur. LV MLLV. LT 0830 GMT approx.

August Cockpit voice recording released by NASA reveals that *Challenger* astronauts were unaware of impending disaster until pilot Michael Smith's last words, "uh oh!" at the moment of the explosion at about 47,900ft (14,600m) altitude 73sec after launch. After crew compartment was torn away from Orbiter by aerodynamic forces, subjecting occupants to 12-20g for brief periods, it depressurised and crew members were probably conscious for between 6-12sec. Severed crew compartment, travelling at almost 2,953ft/sec (900m/sec), climbed on to altitude of 63,320ft (19,300m) before falling back towards Atlantic Ocean. It impacted the water at some 207mph (334km/h).

August Prime Minister Jacques Chirac confirms go-ahead for French TDF 4-channel direct-broadcasting satellite programme. Total programme cost FFr 3,500 million. First of two satellites, TDF-1, to be launched by Ariane 1988; TDF-2 1989.

August 12 Japan launches Ajisai (EGS) for geodetic studies into orbit of 919 x 930 miles (1,479 x 1497km) x 50·01°. Satellite is 7ft (2·15m) sphere covered with mirrors and retro-reflectors, mass 1,510lb (685kg). Secondary payload is Fuji (JAS-1), an amateur radio relay satellite placed in a similar orbit. Was first successful Western launch since *Challenger* disaster. Launcher was H-I with only first two stages live in test of Japan's new LE-5 cryogenic second stage engine which tested operation in orbit of flywheel with a magnetic bearing. LC Tanegashima. LV H-I (two stage version). LT 0845 GMT approx.

The Ajisai satellite which is used to improve geodetic surveys.

September 1 *Novosti* reveals that Soviet design team head investigating orbital mirror systems is Nikolai Lidorenko, a corresponding member of USSR Academy of Sciences. Object is to place mirrors in geostationary orbit so that they remain stationary above that part of Earth they illuminate. As a further development light energy will be converted into electricity for transmission to Earth at laser or microwave frequencies.

September 5 Delta rocket launched from Cape Canaveral Air Force Station releases two experimental satellites into different orbits as part of SDI programme. Object was to track a missile launch to the point where it released a "warhead" and an "interceptor". The latter was then to manoeuvre in a game of "space pursuit" and destroy the "warhead". Launch was first to be made successfully from the Cape since Shuttle disaster on 28 January.

September 8 Reported by *Pravda* that Salyut 7/Cosmos 1686 complex has been manoeuvred into higher orbit averaging 298 miles (480km) from Earth, extending lifetime by eight years. Although station is in "suspended animation", an expedition may be sent to it "in several years time" to examine conditions on board and to recover parts for analysis.

September 26 Soviets confirm that two Phobos spacecraft will be launched in summer of 1988 to study Mars and its moons. International project involves specialists from Socialist countries, as well as Austria, W Germany, France, Sweden and ESA.

September 27 NASA reveals "single-keel" space station re-design which allows assembly to be accomplished by eight Shuttle flights per year. More emphasis is placed on accommodating equipment *within* space station, reducing number of EVA's by astronauts.

November NASA/JPL scientists increase Voyager 2 miss-distance from Neptune in 1989 fly-by from 795 miles (1,280km) above cloud tops to 27,840 miles (44,800km) in case atmospheric drag causes significant diversion.

December NASA reveals details of Space Shuttle crew escape systems for emergency use in gliding flight. Favoured scheme involves "blowing" side hatch in crew compartment under deck, allowing astronauts to escape sequentially by attached tractor rockets. Alternative is telescoping pole down which astronauts slide for conventional parachute recovery. (The second technique was adopted).

December 26 Soviets launch Cosmos 1801, bringing total of year's satellite launchings by USSR to 91. Compares with twelve launched by rest of world. (The USSR total in 1985 was 98). Many satellites launched in the Cosmos programme have unspecified military objectives.

December 31 Total number of satellites and spacecraft in space, mainly in Earth orbit, is 1,655 plus 4,582 trackable items of debris including discarded rocket stages, payload shrouds, etc. There are also thousands of unrecorded fragments resulting mainly from deliberate or accidental explosions.

1987

January British Aerospace redefines HOTOL spaceplane concept following windtunnel model testing. Wing shape revised for improved aerodynamic performance, canard foreplanes deleted. Primary structure: titanium/Rene 41 sandwich, with carbon-carbon nose cone and wing leading edges withstanding up to 950°C (1,742°F). Launch weight 230-240 tons from laser-guided trolley at 334mph (537km/h). Landing weight 40-42 tons. Payload to 186 miles (300km) orbit 7-8 tons. Aims to reduce launch cost to $5 million.

January Caspar Weinberger, US Defense Secretary, requests "budget supplemental" of $2.8 billion to start development of heavy lift vehicle (HLV) capable of launching "heavy space structures" into low Earth orbit, including SDI experiments, up to 145,500lb (66,000kg) mass.

January 5 Debris of Space Shuttle *Challenger* is buried in two disused Minuteman ICBM silos at Cape Canaveral Air Force Station, Florida.

January 16-February 25 Soviets launch Progress 27 freighter which docks with Mir space station on aft port 1027 MT on 18 January, delivering propellant and other consumables. Engine fired to raise orbit of Mir complex to 204 x 225 miles (328 x 363km) 18 January. Undocks 1429 MT on 23 February and is made to re-enter atmosphere. LC Baikonur. LV A-2. LT 0906 MT

February US Air Force anticipates that Space Shuttle *Atlantis* will launch KH-12 reconnaissance satellite from KSC in May 1988 into orbit inclined at 57° to equator. Launch was originally to have been into near-polar orbit from Vandenberg. KH-12, designed to be serviced in orbit, will be capable of resolving surface objects less than 4in (10·2cm) across; also carries thermal IR sensors for night-time imaging. KH-12 was cancelled in 1988.

February Alexander Arkhipov of Moscow's Radio Astronomy Institute reveals that nine sites in Universe have been identified as possible locations of intelligent life, based on a "new approach" to SETI investigations. Assumes that any developed civilization will have an industrial base giving off radiation in a band of frequencies between 100 and 1,000MHz, similar to that of our own. Life is likely to be found, Arkhipov argues, where a radio source of this kind exists very close to a yellow dwarf star, like the Sun. A search near 4,500 stars of this type has discovered nine with an appropriate source nearby.

February 5 Japan launches 924lb (419kg) satellite Astro-C (Ginga) by Mu-3C at 0630 GMT from Tanegashima into 314 x 416 miles (505 x 670km) x 31.09° orbit. Object: detect X-ray emissions from neutron stars and black holes, believed to result from dust and gas being drawn into gravity wells. Largest satellite-borne X-ray detector yet flown weighs more than 220lb (100kg) and has a sensitive area of 5·38ft^2 (0·5m^2).

February 6-July 30 Soviets launch Soyuz TM-2 with cosmonauts Col Yuri Victorovich Romanenko (commander) and Alexander Leveykin (flight engineer). Docks with Mir/Progress 27 space station complex at 0228 MT on 8 February using new "Kurs" automatic docking system. Spacecraft has improved computers, upgraded propulsion, lighter launch escape tower. Flight crew "manual" is held in Strela information retrieval system. First tasks were to re-activate Mir's radio and TV communications, etc. On 11 February propulsion system of Progress 27 was used to adjust orbit of Soyuz TM-2/Mir/Progress 27 complex. Other improvements: engine assembly has new base unit of propellant tanks, feed system and sustainer engine with uncooled nozzle; power unit and altimeter for landing rockets. Inertial guidance system and computer diagnosis allows revision of flight programme. Main electrical system triplicated. Redundant hydraulic and pneumatic systems; back-up life support system provides oxygen during re-entry if main system fails. Weight reduced by 309lb (140kg). Weight and space saving allows capsule to carry 551lb (250kg) extra payload. LC Baikonur. LV A-2. LT 0038 MT. R 0504 MT.

February 11-12 Representatives of NASA, ESA, Japan and Canada concerned in US International Space Station programme meet at US State Department to discuss new draft intergovernmental agreement. Proposed accord gives NASA overall control of Station operations, bars ESA and Japan from using US laboratory module and allows only limited use of their own laboratory modules; US Defense Department retains option to use Station for "peaceful research purposes". New draft reflects fact that "foreign" participation in dual-keel Station is only about one-quarter of the original $8 billion estimate; latest estimates put total costs at $14·5-$20 billion.

February 18 Japan launches Marine Observation Satellite MOS-1 (Peach Blossom) at 0120 GMT by last N-II rocket from Tanegashima Space Centre. Orbit is Sun-synchronous at 561 x 570 miles (903 x 917km) x 99·10°. Returns surface images of quality comparable with NASA Landsat. Has multi-spectral electronic self-scanning radiometer (MESSR); visible and thermal IR radiometer (VTIR) and microwave scanning radiometer (MSR).

MOS-1 during qualification testing.

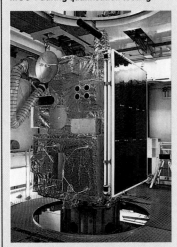

March Soviet plans for Mars exploration (yet to be approved in detail) according to Valery Barsukov, director USSR Academy of Geochemistry and Analytic Chemistry at 18th Lunar and Planetary Science conference, Houston, Texas: 1992 Large Mars orbiter carrying surface penetrators, balloon sonde, and possibly small roving vehicle. Landing module to contain two penetrators, double-walled "rise and fall" balloon to drift in thin Martian air up to 3·7 miles (6km) when heated by Sun, obtaining high-resolution images; where it lands at night soil type and composition are measured by on-board instruments. 1994 Large Mars Rover plus robot "mole" capable of tunnelling 66 to 98ft (20 to 30m) beneath soil to obtain samples for chemical and biological analysis. 1996/98 Sample return mission.

March Sixth edition of US Department of Defense publication *Soviet Military Power* claims that USSR spends $1 billion a year on laser weapons research. Most research is concentrated at Sary Shagan where anti-ballistic missile tests are made. Estimates that ground-based high-energy air defense laser could be deployed early 1990s and aboard ships mid-1990s. Prototype space-based particle-beam weapon capable of disrupting electronics of satellites might be tested 1990s.

March 3-28 Soviets launch unmanned Progress 28 freighter which docks with Mir space station complex on aft port 1443 MT 5 March. Delivers more than two tonnes of propellant, equipment, food, letters, newspapers and magazines for on-board crew. Payload includes Korund semi-industrial plant for growing industrial crystals under microgravity; KATE-140 topographic mapping camera. Engine used to raise orbit of station complex 26 March. Undocks at 0807 MT March 26 and is made to re-enter atmosphere. LC Baikonur. LV A-2. LT 1414 MT.

March 24 India's first attempt to fly Augmented Satellite Launch Vehicle (ASLV-DL 1) from Sriharikota ends disastrously when second stage fails one minute after lift-off; rocket and satellite descend into Bay of Bengal. Concluded that central core failed to ignite at T + 48·5sec, due either to electrical short-circuit or "random malfunction of safety arm device". Satellite was first of Stretched Rohini Series (SRS) with gamma-ray detectors, monocular optical scanner, and ionospheric monitoring and X-ray astronomy instruments.

March 31 Soviets launch astrophysics module Kvant (Quantum) into 110 x 199 miles (177 x 320km) orbit for subsequent docking with Mir space station central core. However, orientation problems cause temporary suspension of docking manoeuvres on 5 April when module is within 1,968ft (600m) of station. On-

board cosmonauts Romanenko and Laveykin had previously taken up positions in the Soyuz TM-2 ferry on the nose of Mir at the time of the planned docking at the station's rear, ready for an emergency breakaway. Second docking attempt 9 April was only partially successful; although Kvant functioned normally through every stage of rendezvous and docking before it finally linked up with Mir, the docking was not positive. Romanenko and Laveykin began 3hr 40min spacewalk 11 April at 2341 MT. By extending the boom of Kvant's docking unit, the two craft were pulled as far apart as possible; the cosmonauts found that a "foreign object" (a plastic bag) was impeding hard docking. After this was removed, Kvant was successfully docked with Mir by ground control under the cosmonaut's visual supervision. At 0018 MT on 13 April the 10·6 tonne service module or "tug" was detached, leaving the 12·1 tonne Kvant module attached to Mir with its axial docking unit exposed ready to receive Progress freighters. Combined mass Soyuz TM-2/Mir/Kvant 51 tonnes; overall length 114·8ft (35m). LC Baikonur. LV D-1. LT 0406 MT.

April Chinese People's Republic declares interest in marketing facilities aboard recoverable space-stabilised satellites FSW-I and FSW-II which have "useful loads" of up to 661lb (300kg) and 1,102lb (500kg) respectively. Re-entry capsules are 330lb (150kg) and 551lb (250kg) respectively.

April Feasibility study by Government of Queensland backs proposal to establish international launch centre on Cape York peninsula. Launch azimuths are ES-E over water for geosynchronous orbits; SW over Gulf of Carpentaria and thinly populated central Australia for polar orbits.

April 21-May 11 Soviets launch Progress 29 freighter which docks with Mir/Kvant/Soyuz TM-2 space station complex on rear port at 2105 MT on 23 April. The complex – almost 115ft (35m) long – has a total mass of nearly 50 tonnes. Undocked 0710 MT 11 May and re-entered atmosphere. LC Baikonur. LV A-2. LT 1914 MT.

May NASA delays re-launch of Space Shuttle *(Discovery)* until June 1988 to allow more time for validation testing. Following qualification of modified SRBs about six weeks before launch, a "wet" countdown demonstration test is planned on the pad followed by a 20 second flight-readiness firing of the three main engines. Under revised programme, three Shuttle flights are scheduled in 1988, seven in 1989, building up to 14 per year by 1992.

May 15 Soviets launch new generation heavy-lift rocket Energiya 1 (SL-W) (Energy) at 2130 MT from Baikonur cosmodrome. Carried side-mounted "dummy satellite" with apogee "kick motor" for orbital injection but orientation fault caused motor to fire in

Energiya awaits its maiden flight.

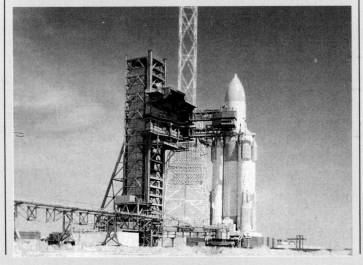

wrong direction; it fell into Pacific Ocean. Chief designer G. Gubanov blamed malfunction of circuit in an on-board instrument. However, according to *Tass*: "All the aims and objectives of the launch were met and the high standard of Energiya's design and engines were confirmed".

May 19-July 19 Soviets launch Progress 30 freighter which docks with Soyuz TM-2/Mir/Kvant space station complex on rear Kvant port at 0953 MT on 21 May with propellant, water, food, equipment, mail, etc. Undocks 19 July at 0420 MT and is made to re-enter atmosphere. LC Baikonur. LV A-2. LT 0802 MT.

The Mir/Kvant/Soyuz TM-3 complex.

June NASA sets up Office of Exploration with astronaut Sally Ride as acting associate administrator. Object to coordinate effort that could "expand the human presence beyond Earth", e.g. intensive use of Earth systems to protect the environment; robotic exploration of Moon and planets; permanent Moon base; manned expedition to Mars.

June International Council for Scientific Unions designates 1992 – 500th anniversary of Columbus' voyage to the New World – International Space Year, dedicated to a global understanding of the benefits of space to mankind.

June 12/June 16 Yuri Romanenko and Alexander Leveykin spacewalk from Mir/Kvant space station complex to erect third solar array on core module. Additional solar array boosts Mir's power supply by 10kW, needed to run gyroscopes which keep station correctly orientated; also to furnish additional power for Kvant astrophysics module and microgravity processing equipment.

July Sally Ride, former US astronaut, submits to Congress NASA Committee report on long-term space goals. Recommends "evolution and natural progression" rather than one-shot spectaculars: 1. "Mission to planet Earth", systematically examining global cloud cover, rainfall, vegetation, chlorophyll, ozone and carbon dioxide. 2. Solar System exploration, including Mars sample return mission 1996. Others, asteroid flyby 1993; Cassini probe to Saturn 1998. 3. Construction of lunar outpost around turn of century as part of

long-term strategy for human exploration of Solar System. 4. Manned mission to Mars. Favoured is two-stage mission in which cargo vehicle is followed by manned ship. Advocates series of three one-year missions culminating in manned landing 2010.

July 22-30 Soviets launch Soyuz TM-3 with joint Soviet/Syrian crew: Alexander Viktorenko (cdr), Alexander Alexandrov (flight engineer) and Mohammed Faris (Syrian Arab Republic). Docks with Soyuz TM-2/Mir/Kvant complex on Kvant aft port 0731 MT 24 July. Objectives, in conjunction with resident cosmonauts: comprehensive mapping of Syrian republic, study of Euphrates basin, Syrian desert, Arabian-African fissure, etc; experiments related to raw materials, mineral and oil exploration, energy and ecology; ionospheric studies, medical experiments, materials technology. Laveykin, the resident Mir flight engineer, whose electrocardiogram had indicated irregularities in heart rhythm during physical exercises, returned with Viktorenko and Faris in Soyuz TM-2 which had been docked to Mir complex for 174 days. Alexandrov was left behind as his replacement. After investigation at national heart research centre, Laveykin's heart function was declared to be sound. After TM-2 had departed from forward berth, cosmonauts undocked TM-3 from Kvant module on 31 July at 0328 MT; commands from mission control caused space station complex to turn through 180° and at 0348 MT crew re-docked TM-3 on forward port thereby releasing Kvant docking port for Progress freighters. LC Baikonur. LV A-2. LT 0559 MT. R 0504 MT in TM-2 capsule, 87 miles (140km) NE of Arkalyk, Kazakhstan. Parachute-supported capsule, blown off course by strong winds, came down within 1·2 miles (2km) of a village.

July 25 Soviets launch Cosmos 1870, a 20 tonne remote-sensing platform into near polar orbit; possibly large enough to be man-tended following rendezvous and docking operation. After adjustment, orbit ranges between 147 x 154 miles (237 x 249km) x 71·9°. Carries large imaging radar and array of scientific instruments related to hydrology, cartography, geology, agriculture and the environment. LC Baikonur. LV D-1. LT 0855 GMT.

August Confirmed that French 2.5 tonne military reconnaissance satellite Helios will be launched in 1993 by Ariane 4 into Sun-synchronous orbit at 528 miles (850km) altitude. Will have powerful optical telescope with electronic-scanning sensors capable of resolution about 3·3ft (1m). Italy contributing 15 per cent of estimated FFr 7·6 billion funding, Spain 5 per cent.

August Manufacture of new Shuttle Orbiter, estimated to cost $2.12 billion, begins at Rockwell's Palmdale facility. Possible that Vandenberg Shuttle operations could begin 1993, with delivery of first of 82 sets of Block II SRBs. This would allow 31,966lb (14,500kg) payload to be placed in polar orbit. Vandenberg facility, now mothballed, cost $3·6 billion to build.

August 3-September 23 Soviets launch Progress 31 freighter which docks with Mir space station complex on Kvant's rear port at 2028 GMT 5 August to replenish propellant, air, water, food and other supplies. Undocked 2358 GMT 21 September and made to re-enter atmosphere. LC Baikonur. LV A-2. LT 2044 GMT.

August 4 Roy Gibson, director-general of British National Space Centre (BNSC), resigns because of failure of UK Government to provide adquate funding for UK and ESA civilian space ventures.

August 25 Woomera rocket range in South Australia is re-opened for scientific research by sounding rockets under $A10 million up-grading programme. First launch campaign involves 11 NASA sounding rockets and at least one British Skylark.

The first H-I launcher lifts off.

August 27 Japan launches Engineering Test Satellite ETS-5 (Kiku 5), three-axis stabilized communications satellite, by first three-stage H-I rocket. Embodies C-band communications package and L-band transponders for use by aircraft in Pacific area and for navigation and search and rescue for ships. H-I launcher features Japanese LE5 cryogenic engine in second stage with Nissan solid propellant third stage. LC Tanegashima. LV H-I. LT 0920 GMT.

August 27 Criticism of SDI programme is voiced by Lawrence Livermore Laboratory specialists. Although it is conceivable that a "few thousand" kinetic projectiles could deal with an attack by presently operational Soviet SS-18s, defence will cease to be effective as Soviets deploy faster SS-24s and SS-25s in the 1990s.

September Japan reveals plans to replace Nissan Mu-3S2 launcher with new-generation M-booster in mid-1990s. Length 98·4ft (30m); diameter 8·2ft (2·5m). Will place 2 tonnes into low Earth orbit.

September 16 Arianespace launches satellites ECS-4 and Aussat K3 by Ariane 3 (V-19) from Kourou, French Guiana. Was first launch since V-18 which suffered third stage ignition failure 31 May 1986; for this launch a more powerful twin-jet engine igniter was substituted with delayed ignition start and faster LH_2 ignition valve opening. ESA spent £52 million to correct the fault. When positioned 10°E in geostationary orbit, ECS-4 on 1 November was re-designated Eutelsat I F-4. Complements ECS-1 and ECS-2 to extend communications services including telephone, business and TV distribution. Aussat K3, located 164°E, used to extend TV broadcasting for Australia's main networks. LC Kourou, French Guiana. LV Ariane 3 (V-19) LT 0045 GMT.

September 18 US Government declares intention of stepping up "Star Wars" anti-missile programme. Research "within constraints of 1972 Anti-Ballistic Missile Treaty" concentrates initially upon: space platforms capable of discharging rockets against incoming missiles; satellites capable of tracking missiles and discriminating real warheads from decoys; ground-based tracking system, including rockets that would be fired to the "edge of space"; computerised "battle management" system to coordinate various anti-missile defences.

September 23-November 18 Soviets launch Progress 32 freighter which docks with Mir-Kvant space station complex at 0108 GMT 26 September. After Mir cosmonauts have finished tranferring supplies, freighter undocks 0409 GMT 10 November, retreats some 1·55 miles (2·5km) and is re-docked 90 minutes later after two Earth orbits to check new computer software in Mir and stability of station's modified solar arrays. Finally, undocks 1925 GMT 17 November and re-enters atmosphere. LC Baikonur. LV A-2. LT 2344 GMT.

September 29-October 12 Soviets launch Vostok-type biosatellite Cosmos 1887 carrying two Rhesus monkeys, Yerosha (Trouble-Maker) and Dryoma; 10 rats, fish, single-celled organisms and plants. Mission is organised jointly with United States and ESA, including more than 50 NASA-sponsored scientists from Ames Research Centre and US universities participating in 27 major joint experiments. Experiments investigated effects of space flight on major body systems. One of the monkeys, Yerosha, succeeded in freeing its left paw from harness on day five and pulled off its name tag. Return of capsule on 12 October was misdirected, the intention being to land in Kazakhstan. LC Baikonur. LV A-1. LT 0050 GMT approx. R 0403 GMT near Kakut city of Mirny district some 1,988 miles (3,200km) off target probably because of misalignment at time of retro-fire.

September 30 NASA's Goddard Space Centre reveals that 3,668 payloads have been launched into space since 4 October 1957. Including trackable debris, there are some 18,400 man-made objects in space.

October 1 Yuri Romanenko aboard Mir space station breaks human space endurance record of 236 days 22 hours 50 minutes set by Soyuz T-10/Salyut 7 cosmonauts in October 1984.

October 29 Soviets achieve 2,000th satellite launch with Cosmos 1894.

November 20 Arianespace launches Ariane 2 (V20) at 2319 local time from Kourou, French Guiana, with Franco-German TV-Sat 1. Is Europe's first direct-broadcast satellite built by Aérospatiale and MBB under Eurosatellite label; has four TV channels and 16 digital radio links. Although successfully positioned in geostationary orbit 5°W, one of satellite's two solar panels fails to open. Subsequently, 14 January 1988, ground control reports failure to control satellite's momentum wheel. If backup fails attitude control thruster must be used, reducing operational life.

November 20-December 19 Soviets launch Progress 33 freighter which docks with Mir/Kvant complex 0139 GMT on rear port 23 November. Delivers propellant, food, water, equipment and mail including 1,000 envelopes with a stamp commemorating 30th anniversary of Sputnik 1. Cancellation of covers aboard space station is world's first such act performed for commercial purposes. Undocks 0816 GMT 19 December, and re-enters atmosphere. LC Baikonur. LV A-2. LT 2347 GMT.

November 29 US Air Force launches Defense Support Program early warning satellite into geostationary orbit by Titan 34D from Cape Canaveral. Joins five earlier satellites for early warning of ballistic missile attack (system requires three satellites operational at any one time). LC Cape Canaveral AFS. LV Titan 34D/IUS. LT 0327 approx.

December 1 NASA selects prime contractors to build NASA-International Space Station. Objectives: research and development of new technologies/private sector R&D activites. Later, staging base for continued manned and unmanned exploration of Solar System. Capable of growth both in size and capability; intended to operate well into the 21st century. First construction phase consists of a "single keel" complex to house eight astronauts, serving as a base for scientific and technological research, for commercial space activities and as a "springboard" for missions beyond low Earth orbit. Construction period spans 1994-1997 (20 Shuttle missions); station to be man-tended from 1995. Four work packages in 10-year Phase 1 program to establish single-keel complex (Phase 2 extends configuration to two-keel).

1. Boeing Aerospace Company responds to Marshall Space Flight Center, Huntsville, Alabama. Associated are Lockheed, Teledyne, Grumman Aerospace, ILC Industries. Laboratory and habitation modules, logistics elements, resource node structures, airlock systems, environmental control and life support, thermal, audio and video systems, etc. Contract value: $750 million (Phase 2 adds $2·5 billion to make station "dual-keel").
2. McDonnell Douglas Astronautics Co., Huntington Beach, California, responds to Johnson Space Center. Associated are IBM, Lockheed, RCA, Honeywell and Astro Aerospace. Integration, management, integrated truss, airlocks, propulsion and mobile servicing system, mobile transporter; also outfitting of resource nodes. Contract value $1·9 billion. Phase 2 adds $140 million.
3. General Electric, responding to Goddard Space Flight Center. Associated is TRW Incorporated. Free-flying, unmanned, polar-orbiting platform to carry scientific experiments in Sun-synchronous or other near-polar orbits plus two "attach points", including pointing system, for accommodating scientific instruments on the manned base; also integration of telerobotic service to the space station, software, planning NASA's role in satellite servicing, etc. Contract value $800 million. Phase 2 includes free-flying, unmanned, co-orbiting platform, three additional attach points, another pointing system and a satellite servicing facility. Phase 2 adds $570 million.
4. Rocketdyne, responding to Lewis Research Center. Associated are Ford Aerospace, Garrett, General Dynamics, Lockheed, Harris (solar dynamics mirrors). Electrical power system using photovoltaic arrays and batteries, with 75kW delivery. Also solar array, battery assemblies and common power management and distribution components for polar platform. Proof of concept for possible Brayton cycle solar dynamics power system. Contract value $1·6 billion. Phase 2 adds solar dynamics 50kW power system $740 million.

December 21-29 Soviets launch Soyuz TM-4 with cosmonauts Col Vladimir Titov (cdr), Musa Manarov (flight engineer) and Anatoli Levchenko (researcher/pilot). Docks with Mir/Kvant complex on rear port at 1551 MT 23 December. Levchenko returned with resident Mir/Kvant crew Romanenko and Alexandrov in Soyuz TM-3, undocking at 0555 GMT 29 December. LC Baikonur. LV A-2. LT 1418 MT. R 1216 MT, 50 miles (80km) from Arkalyk.

December 29 Soyuz TM-3 undocks from Mir-Kvant space station complex at 0555 GMT returning to Earth cosmonauts Yuri Romanenko, Alexander Alexandrov and Anatoli Levchenko. Romanenko had spent record 326 days in space exceeding previous record by some 90 days. Alexandrov was aloft 160 days and Levchenko 8 days. Romanenko, 43, had grown taller by 0·39in (1cm) but lost 3·5lb (1·6kg) in weight; circumference of his calf muscles had shrunk by 15 per cent.

The return of Soyuz TM-3 brought (l to r) Alexandrov, Romanenko and Levchenko back to Earth from Mir.

Alexandrov had grown taller by 10·59in (1·5cm), gained about 5lb (2·27kg).

December 29 Soviets launch Cosmos 1907 photo-reconnaissance satellite, bringing year's total of USSR launchings to 94. Total all other nations, 13.

December 30 Vladimir Titov and Musa Manarov aboard Mir/Kvant complex undock their Soyuz TM-4 at 1210 MT from Kvant module and pull clear. The station complex, on command from mission control, then turns through 180° allowing crew to redock at 1229 MT on Mir forward axial port. This is now routine procedure with Soyuz TM.

1988

January President Reagan approves go-ahead for Advanced Launch System (ALS) to place payloads of 100,000-150,000lb (45,360-68,040kg) into low Earth orbit by late 1990s. Under DoD funding, ALS will launch SDI and other military payloads but NASA will have vehicle use under separate funding; will also manage studies into liquid propellant engine systems and associated technologies. ALS could feature in early 21st century Mars expedition.

January 20-March 4 Soviets launch Progress 34 freighter which docks with Mir/Kvant complex on Kvant aft port at 0009 GMT 23 January. As well as replacing expendables, craft brought new systems equipment to replace parts of station complex which had completed their service life. Undocks at 0340 GMT 4 March and is made to re-enter atmosphere. LC Baikonur. LV A-2. LT 2252 GMT.

February 8 As part of Phase 1 SDI layered defense technology programme, DoD launches 6,000lb (2,722kg) SDIO Delta 181 in $250 million bid to improve knowledge (1) of ballistic missile characteristics before individual warheads are separated, and (2) backgrounds against which space sensors will view missiles, warheads and decoys. In test lasting 12hr satellite ejected 14 mock-up targets, each representing a Soviet missile, warhead or decoy which were observed both from the satellite itself and hundreds of ground stations using radars, lasers, optical, IR and UV sensors. Satellite made up to 200 attitude changes to observe objects it deployed; also tracked other launchings carried out from the ground. LC Cape Canaveral AFS. LV Delta 3910. LT 2208 GMT.

February 11 President Reagan announces National Space Policy, confirming recommendations of Sally Ride committee (July 1987). Also supports development of Advanced Launch System (ALS) and commercialization of space, including Industrial Space Facility (ISF), a Shuttle-launched free-flying space factory. FY 1989 budget contains $100 million request to study "enabling technologies" within Pathfinder Project.

February 16 NASA launches first Black Brant IX sounding rocket from Woomera, Australia. Observes supernova 1987A.

February 17 Air-launched anti-satellite missile programme is cancelled in US Defense Budget for FY 1989.

February 26 Mir/Kvant cosmonauts Vladimir Titov and Musa Manarov spacewalk to modify third solar array of Mir's core module; replaced one of two lower panels with new panel embodying samples of "photoelectric transducers of semi-conductors with improved energy properties". EVA lasts 4hr 25min.

March MBB confirms Sänger feasibility study for two-stage re-usable space-planes for the cost-effective transport of crews and freight into low Earth orbit. First stage is hypersonic aircraft powered by turbo-ramjets; can be used independently as passenger transport. Optional upper stages have rocket engines. Winged, re-usable, HOROS to have accommodation for two to six astronauts and payload of two to four tonnes. CARGUS, an expendable payload carrier, will take up to 15 tonnes into low Earth orbit and up to 2·6 tonnes to geostationary orbit.

An MBB concept of the Sänger two-stage re-usable aerospace plane.

March Soviets reveal that Cosmos weather satellites have tested "a new form of radar" which simultaneously gives a picture of cloud cover and underlying surface. Combination of the two images "improves flood predictions, Arctic navigation and monitoring of grain ripening".

March 7 People's Republic of China launches China 22, STW domestic communications satellite, into geostationary orbit by Long March 3 from Xi Chang. Geostationary above 87·5°E. Was fourth launch of rocket type: STW-1 1984 (not entirely successful); STW-2 1984; STW-3 1986.

March 17 Soviets launch India's remote-sensing satellite IRS-1A by A-1 Vostok rocket at about 0643 GMT from Baikonur. Was first launched under commercial arrangements negotiated with Glavkosmos but price (7·5 million roubles) did not reflect actual cost. Orbit is Sun-synchronous 539 x 567 miles (867 x 913km) x 99·03°; mass 2,072lb (940kg).

March 23-May 5 Soviets launch Progress 35 freighter which docks with Mir/Kvant complex on Kvant rear port at 2222 GMT on 25 March. Replenished propellants, air, water, food and other expendables. Engine used to lift orbit of station complex 22 April. Undocked at 0136 GMT 5 May and is made to re-enter atmosphere same day. LC Baikonur. LV A-2. LT 2105 GMT.

March 18 ESA announces that agreement has been reached with NASA to join development of International Space Station; also involves Canada and Japan. Britain is only major industrial nation abstaining. ESA's contribution comprises: attached lab module; man-tended free-flier; polar orbiting platform. (Later, see April 18, UK agreed contribution to polar orbiting platform).

April NASA submits to Congress plans for Advanced Solid Rocket Booster (ASRB) which retains segmented design features. Will boost Shuttle payload capability by 12,000lb (5,443kg). If rigorously pursued, could fly in 1994. Precludes necessity to throttle Shuttle's main engines during period of Max-q (maximum dynamic pressure).

April US Air Force elects to "mothball" Shuttle launch facility at Vandenberg AFB which currently costs some $50 million a year to maintain. Spending is limited to about $7 million p.a. to maintain Shuttle pad and main control centre.

April NASA approves use of telescopic pole for emergency escape from Shuttle Orbiter during gliding flight. Housed in the mid-deck, pole extends from open hatch (cover explosively released) to enable each astronaut, in turn, to slide out on a ring attachment sufficient to clear Orbiter's wings and tail for conventional parachute recovery. Pole-bale-out technique is effective during gliding flight following an "abort" between 24,000-11,000ft (7,315-3,353m) before water or ground impact. Astronauts wear Crew Altitude Protection System partial pressure suits, with emergency oxygen supply, parachute, flotation gear and survival equipment.

April 20 United States becomes 21st. nation to accept INMARSAT amendments to extend mobile satellite communications services to aircraft. Will include cockpit data and voice communications, as well as direct-dial global telephone services for passengers. INMARSAT is the 54-member-nation cooperative organisation currently providing satellite communications services to almost 7,000 ships and other units around the world.

May Japan reaches agreement with NASA to equip international space station with permanently attached Japanese experiment module (Jem) comprising: (1) pressurized module; (2) exposed experiment pallet; (3) experiment logistics module; (4) remote manipulator, and (5) science equipment airlock. Assembly requires two Shuttle flights with Japanese astronaut participation. Supplementary projects may include small re-entry capsule to return samples of processed materials and life-science experiments from space station directly to Japan. Communications to be relayed initially via Japanese ETS-VI satellite, later by planned data relay satellite.

May NASA reveals that three-stage commercial winged booster, Pegasus, being developed by Orbital Sciences Corporation and Hercules Aerospace, will be launched from B-52 No 0008, the same "mother" that air-launched X-15 research aircraft. Aims to place up to 900lb (408kg) payloads into low Earth orbit. Performance gains stem from use of new solid-propellant motors with lightweight cases of graphite composite construction. Lift generated by graphite composite delta wing of stage 1, combined with B-52 launch at 39,700ft (12,100m) at Mach 0·80, yields significant payload benefits.

May 13-June 5 Soviets launch Progress 36 freighter which docks with Mir/Kvant space station complex on rear port at 0213 GMT 15 May to replenish propellant, water, food and other expendables. Engine used to raise orbit of station complex 3 June. Undocks 5 June at 1112 GMT and is made to re-enter atmosphere. LC Baikonur. LV A-2. LT 0030 GMT.

June 7-17 Soviets launch Soyuz TM-5 with Anatoli Solovyov (cdr), Viktor Savinykh (flight engineer) and Alexander Alexandrov (Bulgaria) which docks with Mir/Kvant complex on Kvant rear port at 1557 GMT on 9 June. Forty-two experiments conducted under Shipka programme involved space physics, space biology and medicine, remote sensing and materials processing. Cosmonauts returned in Soyuz TM-4 with samples of alloys and computer disks containing results of astrophysical experiments; undocked Mir front port 0618 GMT 17 June. On 18 June Mir/Kvant resident cosmonauts Vladimir Titov and Musa Manarov entered Soyuz TM-5 and transferred it to the forward axial port of Mir in readiness for another Progress docking. LC Baikonur. LV A-2. LT 1403 GMT. R 1013 GMT, 125 miles (202km) SE of Dzhezkazgan.

June 15 Ariane 4 on maiden flight, in 44LP configuration, launches three satellites: Meteosat P2, Amsat IIIC (OSCAR 13) and PanAmSat 1, combined mass 7,745 lb (3,513kg). Spelda dual launch structure of 13ft (3·97m) diameter in nose of launcher allows two satellites stacked one above the other to be launched independently; third satellite mounted above Spelda's roof employs adaptor Apex (Ariane Passenger Experiment). LC Kourou Space Centre. LV Ariane 4 (V-22). LT 1119 GMT.

The first flight of Ariane 4; note two liquid and two solid boosters.

June 30 Soviet cosmonauts Vladimir Titov and Musa Manarov spacewalk from Mir space station for five hours in unsuccessful bid to repair X-ray telescope mounted on Kvant module built jointly by University of Birmingham and Netherlands Space Research Laboratory. However, a wrench broke in the hands of one of the cosmonauts who was using it to force off a clamp. The telescope was not designed for in-orbit repair.

July 4 Space Shuttle *Discovery* is rolled out to launch complex 39B at Kennedy Space Center in readiness for STS-26 mission to deploy NASA's Tracking and Data Relay Satellite, TDRS-D. Follows successful test-firing of modified Solid Rocket Booster (SRB) at Morton Thiokol on 14 June.

July 5 Soviets launch new satellite, Okean 1, for sea and ice survey by microwave sounders and side-looking radar. Orbit ranges between 404 and 422 miles (661 x 680km) inclined at 82·5° to equator. LC Plesetsk. LV F-2. LT 0946 GMT approx.

July 7 Soviets launch Phobos 1 which is course-corrected 16 July with object of being inserted into orbit around Mars on 23 January 1989. Intended to make close inspection of inner moon Phobos but incorrect signal sent by Soviet mission control immobilizes spacecraft's systems (see September 2); probe is officially declared "lost" 3 November. LC Baikonur. LV D-1-e. LT 2138 MT.

July 12 Soviets launch Phobos 2 with objectives similar to Phobos 1 (see July 7). Primary objective is the inner Martian moon Phobos which has dimensions of about 16·8 x 13·0 x 11·8 miles (27 x 21 x 19km). Flight into Mars orbit lasts about 200 days, spanning 118 million miles (190 million km). Mid-course corrections 21 July and one or two weeks before arrival 29 January 1989. Midcourse observations: X-ray, UV and visible of Sun's chromosphere and corona plus French experiments on plasma density, temperature, wave measurements. LC Baikonur. LV D-1-e. LT 2102 MT.

July 13 India's Augmented Satellite Launch Vehicle (ASLV), launched from Shriharikota, goes out of control following ignition of core stage after 48·5 seconds of flight. Propulsion continued but rocket was yawing and rolling; the top end, containing 330lb (150kg) SROSS-2 satellite, broke off and debris descended into Bay of Bengal.

July 18 President Reagan names US International Space Station "Freedom". Subsequently, he signs Bill fixing NASA's FY 1989 budget at $10·6 billion of which $900 million is allocated to space station.

July 19-August 12 Soviets launch Progress 37 freighter which docks with Mir/Kvant space station complex on rear port on 21 July to replenish propellant, water, food and other expendables. Also brings new tools for cosmonauts to use in second attempt to repair TTM telescope mounted in Kvant module. Undocks 12 August at 1232 MT and is made to re-enter atmosphere. LC Baikonur. LV A-2. LT 0113 MT.

July 25 British Government refuses further financial backing for Hotol spaceplane project. Mr. Kenneth Clarke, in one of his last acts as Industry Minister (he is newly appointed Secretary of State for Health) declares Hotol too expensive for Britain to develop alone. The Government, he said, would help British Aerospace and Rolls-Royce find "suitable collaborators" but would not provide further funds for "the foreseeable future".

August 5-13 People's Republic of China launches FSW satellite with recoverable capsule. Orbit 127 x 194 miles (204 x 312km) x 63°. Carried 104 experiments by 20 scientists including study of protein crystallisation to find new ways of making cancer drug Interferon. Crystal growth experiment sponsored jointly by MBB, the European Consortium Intospace, and West Germany's DFVLR. Capsule recovered after 8 days. LC Jiuquan. LV Long March 2C. LT 0730 GMT approx.

August 6 Cosmonaut Anatoly Levchenko, 47, dies in Moscow following surgery for removal of a brain tumour. Flew in Soyuz TM-4 to Mir space station and was training to fly Soviet space shuttle. Another cosmonaut training to fly the shuttle, Alexander Shchukin, was killed on 18 August in a Sukhoi Su-26M which crashed after aerobatic manoeuvres.

August 29-September 7 Soviets launch Soyuz TM-6 with cosmonauts Col Vladimir Lyakhov (cdr), Dr Valeri Poliakov (physician) and Capt Abdol Ahad Mohmand (Afghan researcher). Docks with Mir/Kvant space station complex at 0941 MT on 31 August on Kvant rear port. Main task of Dr Poliakov is to check health of resident cosmonauts Titov and Manarov attempting to break 326-day space endurance record set by Yuri Romanenko in 1987. Afghanistan is 20th nation to have a human being launched into space. Return is made in Soyuz TM-5

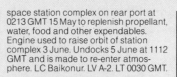

capsule. Mission went smoothly until cosmonauts started re-entry sequence when navigation computer received different readings from primary and back-up IR horizon sensors (possibly because of sunglare) which inhibited engine firing. Then computer accepts sensor readings indicating that spacecraft was oriented correctly, starting ignition sequence seven seconds late. After three seconds Lyakhov shuts down engine; it would have meant landing in Manchuria! Two orbits later Lyakhov tries retro-fire again using spacecraft's inertial measuring unit but engine cuts off again after six seconds (it should have burned for 230 seconds). Lyakhov re-starts manually and engine continues to burn for about 60 seconds when computer detects orientation error and stops engine again. Mission control advises waiting another day. After on-board back-up computer had been re-programmed, retro-fire at 0401 MT 7 September is successful and cosmonauts land in primary recovery zone. LC Baikonur. LV A-2. LT 0823 MT. R 0450 MT, about 100 miles (161km) SE of Dzhezkazgan.

September 2 Phobos mission controller sends incorrect signal to Phobos 1 space probe en-route to Mars, causing its de-stabilization. Solar panels lose lock on the Sun and electronic systems are deprived of power. According to Dr Roald Sagdeev, on-board computer chips were "probably damaged beyond repair . . ." He saw no hope of restoring craft to working order. Craft officially declared "lost" 3 November.

September 7 People's Republic of China launches metereological satellite Feng Yun (Wind and Cloud) which embodies both optical and infra-red sensors. Achieves Sun-synchronous orbit at 547 x 562 miles (881 x 904km) x 99·12°. This is first launch of Long March 4, from new launch site at Taiyuan, south of Beijing. Mass approximately 1,653lb (750kg); downlink frequency 137·78 MHz. LC Taiyuan. LV Long March 4. LT 2030 GMT.

September 10 Soviets launch Progress 38 freighter which docks at 0522 MT 12 September with Soyuz TM-6/Mir/Kvant complex on Kvant rear port. Replenished basic services and carried new X-ray detector and tools needed for repair of Anglo-Dutch X-ray telescope (see October 20). LC Baikonur. LV A-2. LT 0334 MT.

September 19 Israel becomes eighth nation to launch an artificial satellite by independent effort. Spin-stabilized 344lb (156kg) test satellite Offeq (Horizon) 1 ascends from site in Negev desert south of Tel Aviv, taking a north-westerly course over the Mediterranean (against the direction of Earth's rotation). Retrograde orbit ranges between 155 x 717 miles (250 x 1,154km) inclined at 142·86° to the equator. Shavit launcher is derived from Jericho II ballistic missile developed by Israel Military Industries. LC Palmachim, Negev desert, S. Tel Aviv. LV Shavit. LT 1132 local time.

September 29-October 3, NASA launches Space Shuttle *Discovery* (STS-26) on first US manned spaceflight since *Challenger* disaster in January 1986. Aboard are Capt Frederick H. Hauck (cdr); Col Richard O. Covey (pilot) and John M. Lounge, Lt-Col David C. Hilmers and George D. Nelson (mission specialists). Primary payload is Tracking and Data Relay Satellite (TDRS-C) deployed with associated Inertial Upper Stage 6hr 13min into the mission; satellite is subsequently located in geostationary orbit at 171°W longitude. Operated from the mid-deck was environmental experiment Oasis to measure TDRS vibration, strain, acoustics and temperature during Orbiter ascent, using transducers affixed to the payload. In addition to TDRS and Oasis, 11 mid-deck experiments involved the study of electrical storms, microgravity research and materials processing. Orbit approximately circular at 184 miles (296km) x 28·45° allowed photography of storm damage in East Mexico due to Hurricane Gilbert; flooding in Khartoum, and monitoring of drought conditions in Senegal. Flew 1·7 million miles (2·7 million km), completed 64 orbits. *Discovery* incorporated many modifications following *Challenger* disaster, affecting

The STS-26 crew pay lighthearted tribute to Hawaii's tracking station.

several major sub-systems including main rocket engines and solid rocket boosters (SRBs). In particular, changes were made to SRB field joints, case-to-nozzle joint, nozzle, local propellant grain contour, ignition system and ground support equipment. Crew, for the first time, had telescopic pole for emergency escape in gliding flight and new partial pressure suits. Re-design and testing to restore Shuttle programme cost some $2·4 billion. Shuttle launch costs now averaging nearly $500 million, several times original estimates. LC Pad 39B, KSC. LV STS-26. LT 1137 EDT. R 0937 PDT, Runway 17, Edwards AFB, California.

October Soviets confirm intention to launch two Mars orbiters by Proton D-1-e booster in October 1994, to arrive August 1995. Three components: Mothercraft orbiter, with 441lb (200kg) payload instruments. Landing module with 330lb (150kg) roving vehicle, range 62 miles (100km). Balloon with instrument gondola (released from landing module just before touchdown). Ascends during Martian day; descends to surface during Martian night. Employs Soviet/French technology. Embodies: cameras, radar altimeter, magnetometer, IR spectrometer, gamma spectrometer, meteorological instruments. (Roving vehicle later deferred until 1996 mission).

October 20 Mir cosmonauts Vladimir Titov and Musa Manarov repair Anglo-Dutch TTM X-ray telescope installed in attached Kvant module during EVA lasting 4hr 12min. The telescope, built by scientists at Birmingham University and the Space Research Laboratory at Utrecht, was not designed to be serviced in space and a defective X-ray detector had to be replaced using parts and tools flown up by Progress 38.

October 29 First attempt to launch Soviet space shuttle *Buran* (Snowstorm), unmanned, by Energiya 2 from Baikonur is aborted 51 seconds before planned lift-off when service gantry arm fails to retract properly. Launch attempt had previously been delayed four hours from 0623 MT because of difficulty with "support systems".

November 11 Cosmonauts Vladimir Titov, 41, and Musa Manarov, 37, aboard Mir/Kvant space station complex break space flight endurance record of 326 days set by Yuri Romanenko. Cosmonauts report small changes in weight and muscle sizes; otherwise in good health.

November 15 Soviets launch re-usable space shuttle Buran (Snowstorm), unmanned, by Energiya. Lift-off is made entirely under control of on-board computers switched on at 0549 MT. Human controllers no longer interfere with pre-launch preparations; "craft itself decides whether to go for launch or to abort". Within the last minute "escape" arm and external services disengage. Stages 1 and 2 of Energiya ignite together developing total thrust of some 3,500 tonnes. Unlike US Space Shuttle, *Buran* has no main engines and depends on Energiya to obtain high sub-orbital velocity. *Buran*'s manoeuvre engines burn as third stage to inject craft into preliminary orbit at 99 miles (160km) x 51·6°; then re-fire to circularise at 155 miles (250km). Elapsed time 47 minutes. At 0820 MT on second orbit, under computer control, craft turns through 180° and fires propulsion unit as braking engine. Re-enters atmosphere at 62 miles (100km) and at 24·8 miles (40km), with nose pitched up, begins re-entry glide using elevons and airbrakes. Return is made to Baikonur concrete runway 2·8 miles (4·5km) long x 275ft (84m) wide, located some 7·4 miles (12km) from launch pad. Completed two Earth orbits; flight duration 3hr 25min. LC Baikonur. LV Energiya. LT 0600 MT. R 0925 MT, Baikonur runway.

Buran, the Soviet shuttle, awaits first launch by Energiya booster.

November 26-December 21, Soviets launch Soyuz TM-7 (Aragatz) with cosmonauts Col Alexander Volkov (cdr); Sergei Krikalev (flight engineer) and Brig-Gen Jean-Loup Chrétien (French researcher). Docks with Mir/Kvant complex on Kvant rear port at 2016 MT, 28 November. Experiments: technological, astrophysical and medical. First West European EVA, by Chrétien, with Volkov 9 December; hatch opened 1257 MT. Set up on outside of Mir experimental carbon-fibre pin-jointed erectable structure (made by Aerospatiale) stowed as bundle of rods which springs open, by remote control, into 12·5 x 11·8ft (3·8 x 3·6m) lattice. However, EVA lasted approximately 6hr instead of 4hr 20min largely because lattice initially failed to open. Objective: evaluate vibration modes of structures suitable for large antennae and space station unit assembly. After tests completed, lattice structure is rejected overboard automatically at 1·64ft/sec (0·5m/sec). During spacewalk Chrétien and Volkov erected panel of materials samples with different coatings, paints and films; also experimental solar panel, Armedeus, to test deployment mechanism. Other mission experiments related to monitoring blood flow/ hormonal response using French-supplied echo-cardiograph and radiobiological apparatus; also measurement of radiation field inside Mir/Kvant complex. Chrétien was making his second space flight, having flown to Salyut 7 in Soyuz T-6 in 1982. Chrétien returned in TM-6 with Vladimir Titov and Musa Manarov whose total flight lasted record 366 days 18 hours 7 minutes. Re-entry was delayed some three hours because on-board computer was overloaded and automatically stopped preparations for descent sequence. However, following the problems with Soyuz TM-5, orbital module was retained until after retro-fire (reverting to earlier practice) to safeguard crew in the event of prolonged delay in achieving safe return. LC Baikonur. LV A-2. LT 1850 MT. R 1257 MT, 110 miles (177km) SE of Dzhezkazgan.

December Soviets modify plans to explore Mars with unmanned spacecraft (see also March 1987): *1994* Orbiter and Lander with penetrators "to be anchored to its surface". Instrumented helium balloon about 82ft (25m) diameter; will rise 2·5 miles (4km) during day and descend to ground at night. Objectives: photography, chemical analysis and electromagnetic soundings of Martian soil; study of atmosphere. *1996* Mars Orbiter plus Lander with 1,102lb (500kg) roving vehicle with soil sampler/analyser. Total mass 1994/96 spacecraft 14,330lb (6,500kg) of which scientific instruments aboard orbiter account for 441lb (200kg). *1998/2000* Sample return mission to lift off from Mars with up to 6·6lb (3kg) soil samples, returning to Earth or space station.

December 2-6 NASA launches Space Shuttle *Atlantis* (STS-27) with all-military crew: Cdr Robert L. Gibson (cdr); Lt-Col Guy S. Gardner (pilot); Lt-Col Jerry L. Ross, Cdr William M. Shepherd and Col R. M. (Mike) Mullane (mission specialists). Classified DoD military payload is Lacrosse radar imaging reconnaissance satellite deployed in space by manipulator arm on fifth orbit. Orbit approximately circular at 242 miles (389km) x 57°, later manoeuvred to 415 x 437 miles (668 x 703km). Crew observations related to ground and ocean surveillance. Insulation debris falling from Shuttle's right hand Solid Propellant Booster caused impact damage to some 170 thermal protection tiles about 85 seconds into the flight; one tile was lost beneath the crew compartment – also an insulation panel from the RH orbital manoeuvring system pod LC Pad 39B, KSC. LV STS-27. LT 1430 GMT. R 2336 GMT, Runway 17, Edwards AFB, California.

December 11 Ariane 4 launches double satellite payload using Spelda: Skynet 4B military communications satellite built for MoD by BAe with Marconi communications package, located 1°W; Astra 1A 16-channel TV direct-broadcasting satellite sponsored by SES Luxembourg, located 19·2°E. LC Kourou. LV Ariane 4 (V-27) LT 0038 GMT.

December 25 Soviets launch Progress 39 freighter which docks with Mir/Kvant space station complex on Kvant rear port at 0835 MT on 27 December. Brings propellants, water, food and other expendables; also equipment, mail and New Year gifts for resident cosmonauts. Undocks at 0946 MT on 7 February and is made to re-enter atmosphere over Pacific Ocean later that day. LC Baikonur. LV A-2. LT 0712 MT.

December 31 Total number of satellites (including Space Shuttles) launched in 1988: USSR 90; others 26, including USA 11, Arianespace 7, China 4; Japan 2; Italy/NASA 1 and Israel 1.

1989

January Oleg Borisov, Academy of Soviet Sciences, reveals Soviet plan for landing cosmonauts on Mars from two nuclear-electric powered spaceships between 2005 and 2010. Assembled in Earth-orbit after eight Energiya launchings, ships are propelled by 80-tonne nuclear-electric engines located 328ft (100m) behind 10-tonne crew compartments. Two men descend from Mars orbit in 60 tonne landing craft with roving vehicle, returning to Mars orbit in ascent stage for return flight.

January 11 Novosti confirms names of first pilots who will fly Soviet Space Shuttles: I. Volk; R. Stankevicius; U. Sultanov and M. Tolboyev.

January 12 Novosti confirms Soviet plan to put unmanned spacecraft into polar orbit round the Moon in 1992. Will photograph large areas of lunar surface, including polar regions, with a resolution down to a few metres. Also aboard will be gamma and x-ray spectrometers to analyse soil composition; infra-red spectrometer to study mineral composition, and magnetometer to measure magnetic fields, and other instruments. Spacecraft is based on Phobos spacecraft sent to Mars.

January 29 Phobos 2 swings into orbit round Mars having travelled nearly half a billion kilometres in 200 days. Braking engines switched on at 1555 MT operated for about 200 seconds to put craft into orbit of 497 x 49,710 miles (800 to 80,000km) inclined at 1° to equator. First orbit correction 12 February changes this to 3,977 x 50,457 miles (6,400 x 81,200km) x 0·9°.

February 10-March 5 Soviets launch Progress 40 freighter which docks with Mir/Kvant complex on rear port at 1330 MT on 12 February to replenish expendables. New equipment and scientific apparatus are also on board. On 24 February orbit of station complex is raised by Progress engine to 222 x 240 miles (358 x 386km) x 51.6°. Separates 0446 MT 3 March when two large "multi-link" structures are automatically deployed from sides of craft, testing "form-remembering" materials. Sequence is filmed from space station. After braking manoeuvre initiated 0408 MT 5 March, craft re-enters atmosphere and is destroyed. LC Baikonur. LV A-2. LT 1154 MT.

February 14 USAF launches Navstar 2-1 by Delta 2. First satellite of Global Positioning System Block 2 series. Full complement of 21 satellites (18 operational, 3 standby) to be launched at approx 60 day intervals. LC Pad 17, Cape Canaveral. LV Delta 2. LT 1329 EST.

February 21 Japan launches 660lb (200kg) auroral research satellite EXOS-D by Mu-3S-2 from Kagoshima. Orbit 168 x 6,520 miles (270 x 10,493km) x 75°.

March West German government allocates about £70 million towards "first phase" development of Sänger two-stage re-usable spaceplane.

March 13-18 NASA launches Space Shuttle *Discovery* (STS-29) with Capt Michael Coats (cdr); Col John Blaha; Col James Buchli; Col Robert Springer and James Bagian (physician). Launches data relay satellite TDRS-D by two-stage IUS for positioning 1°W. Secondary objectives: test within cargo bay of Space Station heat pipe advanced radiator

James Bagian juggling with elusive tape cassettes in the middeck area of Discovery during STS-29.

element (SHARE), only partly succeeds because of formation under micro-g of "bubbles" in ammonia fluid system preventing proper heat transfer. Also: Oasis payload bay environmental monitoring unit; protein crystal growth, chromosomes and plant cell division; IMAX camera; two student experiments. *Discovery* was rolled out 3 February. Mission was delayed because of requirement to replace liquid oxygen turbopumps of main engines following discovery of stress corrosion in pump bearing during STS-27 mission December 1988. LC 39B, KSC. LV STS-29. LT 1457 GMT. R 1436 GMT, Runway 22, Edwards AFB, California.

March 16-April 25 Soviets launch Progress 41 freighter which docks with Mir-Kvant complex at 2051 GMT on 18 March. After delivering supplies, including new storage batteries, engine is used to raise orbit of station complex to 231 x 248 miles (372 x 400km). Undocked 21 April at 0146 GMT, craft runs out of fuel during re-entry burn and decays naturally in atmosphere more than four days later. LC Baikonur. LV A-2. LT 1854 GMT.

March 24 US Air Force launches Delta Star satellite from Cape Canaveral by Delta 3920 (last of series) for Strategic Defense Initiative Organisation (SDIO). Comprises sensor module and attached McDonnell Douglas command/control module; total length 18ft (5·5m) x 7·6ft (2·3m) diameter; mass approximately 6,000lb (2,722kg). Sensor system designed and integrated by Johns Hopkins Applied Physics Laboratory, includes laser radar and seven IR and UV imaging sensors – also Laser Illumination Detection System (LIDS). Object: by precise manoeuvring, to point sensors to observe "rocket plumes and other phenomena from space".

March 27 Soviets lose contact with Phobos 2 spacecraft orbiting Mars during final manoeuvres to approach moon Phobos within 164ft (50m). With rendezvous achieved, craft was set to drift slowly past the moon for some 20 minutes while TV, radar, laser and ion-gun equipment probed the surface. Two landers were to be released, one static with TV and soil sensors, the other capable of hopping up to 65·6ft (20m) to investigate soil chemistry at different points.

April 1 Power depletion aboard Mir space station and late delivery of two 20 tonne "building block" modules for attachment to Mir's multiple docking unit, lead to abandonment of plans to launch Soyuz TM-8 with Alexander Viktorenko (cdr) and Alexander Balandin on 19 April. Moscow anticipates that Mir will be left unmanned after the return of resident crew Alexander Volkov, Sergei Krikalev and Valery Polyakov on 27 April. Before leaving the station, cosmonauts monitored a number of engine firings which raised the orbiting altitude. Mir could remain "mothballed" for "several months"

April 27 After "mothballing" Mir/Kvant space station for period of unmanned operation, cosmonauts Volkov, Krikalev and Polyakov leave in Soyuz TM-7 at 2328 GMT 26 April. They land safely at 0259 GMT 27 April south of Tikenekty, about 87 miles (140km) NE of Dzhezkazgan.

May 4-8 NASA launches Space Shuttle *Atlantis* (STS-30) with astronauts Capt David M. Walker (cdr), Col Ronald J. Grabe (pilot), Dr Mary L. Cleave, Norman E. Thagard and Major Mark C. Lee (mission specialists). Deploys Venus probe Magellan and attached two-stage IUS booster from cargo bay about 6hr 18min into mission; an hour later IUS fires to inject 7,604lb (3,449kg) spacecraft into transfer orbit to Venus, travelling 1½ times around Sun. After braking into orbit August 1990, object is to map 70 to 90 per cent of surface perpetually hidden by thick cloud using synthetic aperture radar revealing mountain areas, volcanoes, lava flows and impact craters in greater detail than achieved with Soviet spacecraft Veneras 15 and 16. For 37 minutes of each orbit, Magellan's radar will image 15 mile-wide (24km) swaths of Venus' surface while other instruments determine altitudes and temperatures of surface features. When craft moves towards zenith of its orbit, the large antenna will be turned towards Earth for 115 minutes, transmitting data to receiving stations at 268 kilobits/sec. Orbit ranges between 155 x 4, 989 miles (250 x 8,029km); imaging radar should discriminate objects down to 820ft (250m) across near equator and about 2,460ft (750m) near north pole. Secondary experiments aboard shuttle *Atlantis:* fluid research in general liquid chemistry and study of electrical storms in Earth's atmosphere. LC Pad 39B, KSC. LV STS-30. LT 1947 BST. R 2043 BST, Runway 23, Edwards AFB, California.

Magellan mated to its IUS motor at KSC. This is the first planetary probe to have been launched by a Shuttle.

June 6 Arianespace launches two communications satellite by Ariane 44L (V31) using Spelda: West Germany's 3,086lb (1,400kg) DFS-1 Kopernicus, and Japan's Superbird A. DFS-1 provides West Germany with direct-broadcast TV, digital data exchange and news services. Launch vehicle is first Ariane 4 to employ four liquid propellant strap-on boosters.

June 8 Soviets launch new-series communications satellite Molniya 3 into high elliptical orbit of 392 x 25,288 miles (631 x 40,696km) with apogee in northern hemisphere. Upgrades telephone, telegraph and TV services operating within Orbita network and international services.

June 14 US Air Force launches first Titan IV from Cape Canaveral with first Defense Support Program (DSP) Block 14 advance warning satellite; equipped with advanced 12ft (3·65m) infra-red telescope and other sensors to enhance warning against land and sea-based missiles and bomber aircraft. Established in geosynchronous orbit, includes some protection against ground-based lasers. Overall length 33ft (10m); with width with solar panels extended from base 13·7ft (4·17m); mass 5,200lb (2,359kg).

August 8 Arianespace launches West German TV-Sat 2 direct broadcasting satellite and Europe's Hipparcos astrometry observatory by Ariane 44LP from Kourou. While TV-Sat 2 achieves geostationary orbit, star-mapping Hipparcos is stranded in high elliptical transfer orbit when apogee motor fails to ignite to circularise orbit at 22,300 miles (35,880km). Mission is curtailed; partial remedy is to raise perigee by firing satellite's control thrusters.

August 8-13 NASA launches Space Shuttle *Columbia* (STS-28) with all-military crew: Col Brewster H. Shaw (cdr), Cdr Richard N. Richards (pilot) and Cdr David C. Leestma, Lt-Col James C. Adamson and Major Mark N. Brown (mission specialists). Deploys upgraded manoeuvrable KH-series strategic/tactical reconnaissance satellite some 7·5 hours after lift-off. Orbit is 188 x 196 miles (302 x 315km) x 57°. Also aboard *Columbia:* 275lb (125kg) science payload by Goddard SFC/JPL related to SDI plus seven other experiments. LC KSC. LV STS-28. LT 0837 EDT. R 0637 PDT, Runway 17, Edwards AFB, California.

August 22-24 At Second International Conference on Solar System Exploration, JPL, Pasadena, Soviets outline revised plans: **1994** Two probes to Mars launched October, arriving September 1995 to enter polar orbit of 124-310 x 12,427 miles (200-500 x 20,000km), each to release one research balloon plus small soft-landers or penetrators. Employs entry capsule smaller than originally planned. (Subject to final approval late 1989). **1996** Sample-return mission to moon Phobos. **1998** Orbit Venus, with surface penetrators. **2002-2003** Orbit Mercury, with surface penetrators. **2015** Manned mission to Mars: "deferred because of cost and technical difficulty."

August 24 Voyager 2 passes within 3,000 miles (4,830km) of Neptune's north pole following successful close encounters with Jupiter (1979), Saturn (1981) and Uranus (1986). Discoveries include Earth-size cyclonic storm (Great Dark Spot) about 21°S latitude, lesser dark spot about 54°S in blue-green atmosphere, mainly hydrogen/helium plus methane; 400 mph (644km/h) winds; wispy methane ice clouds, called "scooters", 30-60 miles (48-90km) above main cloud tops; strong magnetic field inclined at 50° to axis; six new moons, one 260 miles (418km) diameter, bigger than Nereid; other moons 30 and 60 miles (48 and 96km); three continuous rings, two associated with small moons at 17,000 miles (27,360km) and 23,300 miles (37,500km) from cloud tops, and a broad disc of diffuse ring material.

August 25 Voyager 2 flies within 24,000 miles (38,625km) of Neptune's largest moon, Triton, revealing methane/nitrogen glacier-like terrain, hummocky and rippling in pastel shades of red, pink and blue; surface temperature c. −186°C; thin atmosphere; evidence of icy volcanic flow, quake faults with ridges, rilles and some craters showing through. Spacecraft now heads out of Solar System.

Glossary

A

AAF Association Astronautique Francaise.
AAS American Astronautical Society.
ABL Allegheny Ballistics Laboratory.
Ablation The erosion of a solid body by a high-temperature gas stream moving with high velocity, eg, a re-entry vehicle's heat shield which melts or chars under the effects of air friction.
ABMA Army Ballistic Missile Agency (USA).
Abort To cancel or cut short a mission.
Absolute zero The temperature at which all heat action ceases, approximately −273·16°C (−459·69°F).
Accelerometer An instrument which measures acceleration or gravitational forces capable of imparting acceleration.
Actuator A device which transforms an electrical signal into a measured motion using hydraulic, pneumatic or pyrotechnic (explosive) action.
Aerodynamic heating The heating of a body due to the passage of air or other gases over the body; caused by friction and compression processes.
Aerozine 50 A storable liquid fuel: 50 per cent hydrazine; 50 per cent UDMH.
AIAA American Institute of Aeronautics and Astronautics (USA).
AIDAA Associazione Italiana di Aeronautica e Astronautica.
Airglow The visible light that appears at night in the upper atmosphere.
Algae A group of simple organisms, mostly aquatic, which contain chlorophyll and thus provide a means of photosynthesis. They could be used to absorb carbon dioxide and provide nourishment in a spaceship.
Ambient Environmental conditions, such as pressure or temperature.
Analog computer A computing machine that works on the principle of measuring, as distinct from counting, in which the measurements obtained (as voltages, resistances etc) are translated into desired data.
Angström A unit for the measurement of wavelength. Equals one hundred millionth of a centimetre (0·003937 millionth of an inch).
Annular Pertaining to, or having the form of, a ring.
Anti-matter A hypothetical form of matter of which the atoms are composed of anti-particles, as protons, electrons, etc, assumed to carry charges opposite to those associated with ordinary matter. Particles having such properties have been produced in particle accelerators.
Antipodal Pertaining to, or located on, the opposite side of the Earth.
Aphelion That point in a solar orbit which is farthest from the Sun.
Apogee That point in a terrestial orbit which is farthest from the Earth.
Apolune That point in a lunar orbit which is farthest from the Moon.
Arianespace A private limited company established for the purpose of producing, financing and marketing the ESA Ariane launch vehicle. Comprises European companies concerned in the rocket's development, CNES and several banks. US agent is Grumman Aerospace.
ARS American Rocket Society (USA).
Artificial gravity Use of centrifugal force to simulate weight reaction in a condition of free-fall. May be achieved by spinning the vehicle to make the centrifugal force of the outer periphery or bodies within the vehicle to replace the weight reaction experienced at the Earth's surface.
ASAT Anti-satellite.
Asteroid A small planetary body. Many thousands of them orbit the Sun between the orbits of Mars and Jupiter.
Astronaut A person who flies in space, whether as a crew member or passenger.
Astronautics The science and technology of space flight.
Astronomical unit The mean distance of Earth from the Sun, ie 92,907,000 miles (149,487,360km).
Astrophysics Study of the physical and chemical nature of celestial bodies and their environs.
ATDA Agena Target Docking Adapter.
Attenuation The decrease of a propagating physical quantity, such as a radio signal or sound wave, with increasing distance from the source, or from some obstruction.
Attitude Orientation of a space vehicle as determined by the relationship between its axes and some reference plane, eg the horizon.
Attitude control The system that turns and maintains a spacecraft in the required direction as indicated by its sensors.
Aurora Arcs, rays or swaying curtains of green, yellow or white lights seen in latitudes of about 70°, such as *Aurora Borealis* or Northern Lights, and *Aurora Australis* or Southern Lights; caused by streams of electrified particles, emitted by the Sun, trapped in the Earth's magnetic field.
Azimuth The angular position of a heavenly body measured in the observer's horizontal plane, usually from North through East. Bearing or direction in the horizontal plane.

B

Back-up An item kept available to replace an item which fails to perform satisfactorily.
Ballistic The science that deals with the motion, behaviour, appearance or modification of missiles acted upon by propellants, rifling, wind, gravity, temperature or other modifying conditions of force.
Ballute An aerodynamic braking device which is both balloon and parachute.
Binary star Two stars revolving around a common centre of gravity.
Bi-propellant A rocket propellant consisting of two unmixed or uncombined chemicals (fuel and oxidant), fed separately into the combustion chamber.
BIS British Interplanetary Society.
Bit A basic unit of computer information; abbreviation of binary digit.
Blackout (physiological) A temporary loss of vision and/or consciousness when a person is subjected to high accelerations.
Blackout (radio) A temporary loss of radio communications which occurs between a spacecraft re-entering the atmosphere and ground stations due to an ionised sheath of plasma which develops around the vehicle.
Boilerplate A metal replica of the flight model (eg of a spacecraft) but usually heavier and cruder for test purposes.
Boost The extra power given to a rocket or space vehicle during lift-off, climb or flight, as with a booster rocket.
Booster The first stage of a missile or rocket.

C

CAS Chinese Academy of Sciences.
CAST Chinese Academy of Space Technology.
CAT Capsule Ariane Technologique.
Centrifugal force A force which is directed away from the centre of rotation.
Centripetal force A force which is directed towards the centre of rotation.
CETI Communication with Extra-Terrestrial Intelligence.
Chaff Metallic foil ejected by a re-entry module to enhance its radar image.
Chlorella A genus of unicellular green algae, proposed for converting carbon dioxide into oxygen for use in spacecraft.
Cislunar Relating to the space between the Earth and the orbit of the Moon.
CNES Centre National d'Etudes Spatiales (France).
Combustion chamber The chamber in a rocket where the fuel and oxidant are ignited and burned. By common usage the expansion nozzle is included as part of the combustion chamber, particularly for liquid-propelled rocket engines.
Comet A body of small mass but large volume, compared to a planet, orbiting the Sun, often developing a long luminous and partly transparent tail when close to the Sun.
Command module The compartment of a spacecraft which contains the crew and main controls.
Composites Structural materials of metal alloys or plastics with built-in strengthening agents, eg carbon fibres.
Control rocket A vernier or other rocket used to control the attitude of, or slightly change the speed of, a spacecraft.
Coolant A medium, usually a fluid, which transfers heat from an object.
Coreolis effect Dizziness or nausea experienced when an astronaut in a spinning spacecraft moves his head in the opposite direction. Experiments are planned to establish if people can adapt themselves to such effects.
Cosmonaut The Russian term for an astronaut. A space traveller.
COSPAR The Committee on Space Research (established October 1958).
Countdown A count in inverse numerical order, in hours, minutes and finally in seconds, of the time remaining before the launch of a rocket.
Cryogenic A rocket fuel or oxidant which is liquid only at very low temperatures, eg liquid hydrogen which has a boiling point of −217·2°C (−423°F).
CSA Chinese Society of Astronautics.
CSAA Chinese Society of Aeronautics and Astronautics.
C-stoff A rocket fuel used by Germany in World War II: 30 per cent hydrazine hydrate, 57 per cent methanol, 13 per cent water with traces of potassium cuprocyanate. Used in conjunction with T-stoff oxidant: 80 per cent hydrogen peroxide with 1 to 2 per cent oxiquinoline as a stabiliser.
Cut-off The action of stopping a process abruptly, such as shutting off the flow of propellant to a rocket engine.

D

Data reduction Conversion of observed values into useful, ordered and simplified information.
DC Direct current, flowing in one direction and substantially constant in value.
Decay The action of air drag upon an artificial satellite causing it to spiral back into the atmosphere, eventually to disintegrate or burn up.
Deceleration Negative acceleration (slowing down).
Decompression The relief of pressure. Explosive decompression would occur if the cabin of a spacecraft was punctured in space.
Delta V Difference or change in velocity.
Density Amount of matter per unit volume.
DGLR Deutsche Gesellschaft für Luft-und Raumfahrt (German Company for Air and Space Travel).
Digital computer An electronic device for solving numerically a variety of problems.
Dish A reflector for radio waves, usually a paraboloid.
Docking The technique of connecting two or more spacecraft in space.
DoD Department of Defense (USA).
Doppler effect The apparent change in frequency of vibration (ie the pitch) of sound, light or radio waves, due to relative motion between the source and the observer.
Drag The resistance offered by a gas or liquid to a body moving through it.
Drogue A small parachute used to slow and stabilise a spacecraft returning to the atmosphere, usually preceding deployment of a main landing parachute.

E

Earth-sensor A light-sensitive diode which seeks the direction of the Earth and then informs the attitude control system of a spacecraft.
Eclipse The obscuring of one celestial body by the passage of another in front of it.
Ecliptic The great circle on the celestial sphere which traces the path of the Sun during the year.
ECM Electromagnetic countermeasures.
EDT Eastern Daylight Time.
ELDO European Launcher Development Organisation.
Electric propulsion A form of rocket propulsion which depends on some form of electrical acceleration of propellant to achieve low thrust over long periods of time. Eg, an ion or magnetohydrodynamic engine.
Ephemeris Table of predicted positions of bodies in the Solar System.
Equatorial orbit An orbit in the plane of the Equator.
ESA European Space Agency.
Escape velocity The precise velocity necessary to escape from a given point in a gravitational field. A body in a parabolic orbit has escape velocity at any point in that orbit. The velocity necessary to escape from the Earth's surface is 6·95 miles/sec (11·2 km/sec.).
ESMC Eastern Space and Missile Center.
EST Eastern Standard Time.
Eurospace Non-profit-making industrial association with headquarters in Paris (founded September 1961).
Exhaust velocity The velocity of the exhaust leaving the nozzle of a rocket motor.

F

Ferret Satellite using electromagnetic surveillance techniques, eg to identify and record emissions from another country's air defence and missile defence radars, and strategic and tactical communications, etc.
Fission The release of energy through splitting atoms.
Fly-by Space flight past a heavenly body without orbiting.
FOBS Fractional Orbit Bombardment System. A Soviet method of delivering a warhead from partial satellite orbit and thus approaching from any direction.
Free-fall The motion of any unpowered body moving in a gravitational field.
Fuel cell A cell in which chemical reaction is used directly to produce electricity.
Fusion The release of nuclear energy through the uniting of atoms.

G

g. The symbol for the acceleration of a freely moving body due to gravity at the surface of the Earth. Alternatively, 1 g.
Galaxy A very large system of stars, gas and dust isolated from its neighbours by an immensity of space; an "island universe".
GALCIT Guggenheim Aeronautical Laboratory of the California Institute of Technology.
Gamma rays Very short, highly-penetrative electromagnetic radiation with a shorter wavelength than X-rays: produced in general by emission from atomic nuclei.
GATV Gemini-Agena Target Vehicle.
Gauss CGS unit of magnetic induction (after the German mathematician. Karl F. Gauss).
GE General Electric Company of the USA.
Geodesy The science of the Earth's shape.
Geostationary orbit A circular orbit in which a satellite moves from west to east at such velocity as to remain fixed above a particular point on the Equator; sometimes referred to as the 24-hour orbit, or Clarke orbit after the proposer Arthur C. Clarke.
g-force A force caused by acceleration expressed in "g's".
Gimbal A mechanical frame for a gyroscope or power unit, usually with two perpendicular axes of rotation.
GMT Greenwich Mean Time. The mean solar time of the meridian of Greenwich, England. Used as the basis of standard time throughout the world.
GO Geostationary orbit.
GSFC Goddard Space Flight Center (Greenbelt, Maryland).
GTO Geostationary transfer orbit.
Gyroscope A device consisting of a wheel so mounted that its spinning axis is free to rotate about either of two other axes perpendicular to itself and to each other. Once set in rotation the gyro axle will maintain a constant direction regardless of the fact Earth is turning under it.

H

Hatch Door or doorway, usually hermetically sealed.
Heat shield A device which protects people or equipment from heat, such as a shield in front of a re-entry capsule.
Horizon scanner A scanner which automatically seeks the horizon for purposes of a spacecraft's orientation and control, eg one that detects the sharp discontinuity in infra-red intensity at the outer edge of the Earth's tropopause.
HTP High Test Peroxide.
H_2O_2 Hydrogen peroxide.
Hydrazine A rocket fuel (N_2H_4) which burns spontaneously, eg with oxidiser, RFNA or nitrogen tetroxide. Can also be used as a monopropellant: when passed through an iridium-bearing catalyst, it decomposes at high temperature into constituent gases of ammonia, nitrogen and hydrogen. Used in small thrusters for orbit modification and attitude control of spacecraft.
"Hydyne" A rocket fuel comprising 60 per cent UDMH and 40 per cent diethylene-triamine.
Hypergolic A term applied to an oxidant and a fuel which ignite spontaneously with each other.

I

IAA Indian Astronautical Association.
IAA International Academy of Astronautics (established 15 August 1960).
IAF International Astronautical Federation (formally inaugurated 1951).
ICBM Inter-continental Ballistic Missile.
IGY International Geophysical Year (1957-58).
Inclination The angle between an orbit path and the Equator.
Inertial guidance An on-board system for launch vehicles and spacecraft where gyroscopes, accelerometers and other devices satisfy guidance requirements.
Infra-red radiation Electromagnetic radiation of wavelengths between 7500 A – the limit of the visible light spectrum at the red end – and centimetric radio waves.
Injector Typically, a perforated plate through which liquid fuel and oxidant are injected into the combustion chamber at a controlled rate.
Intelsat Organisation of 105 countries (July 1980) owning or operating system of satellites used by 144 countries and territories around the world for international communications, and by 16 countries for domestic communications.
Interplanetary probe Unmanned instrumented spacecraft capable of reaching the planets.
Interstellar ark Hypothetical space colony capable of transporting human intelligence to the stars.
Interstellar probe Unmanned instrumented spaceship with artificial intelligence capable of reaching the nearer stars.
Ion An atom that has lost or acquired one or more electrons.
Ion engine A rocket engine, the thrust of which is obtained by the electrostatic acceleration of ionised particles.
Ionisation Formation of electrically charged particles. Can be produced by high-energy radiation such as light or UV rays, or by collisions of particles in thermal agitation.
Ionosphere The region of the Earth's upper atmosphere which reflects or absorbs radio waves.
IR Infra-red.
IRBM Intermediate Range Ballistic Missile
IRFNA Inhibited red fuming nitric acid.
ISAS Institute of Space and Aeronautical Science. University of Tokyo (Japan).
ISRO Indian Space Research Organisation.
IWFNA Inhibited white fuming nitric acid.

J

JPL Jet Propulsion Laboratory (Pasadena, California).
JSC Johnson Space Center (Houston,Texas).

K

Kelvin Scale of temperature named after the English physicist Lord Kelvin, based on the average kinetic energy per molecule of a perfect gas. Absolute zero is equivalent to −273·16°C (−459·4°F).
Kerosene A mixture of hydrocarbons distilled from crude petroleum; see RJ-1, RP-1.
KHz Kilohertz, equal to 1,000 Hertz.
Kosmobuksir Russian name for "space tug".
Kosmolyot Russian name for "spaceplane".
KSC Kennedy Space Center, Florida.
KT Kilotonne, equal to 1,000 tonnes.

L

Lanyard Small rope or cord.
Laser Light amplification by the stimulated emission of radiation. A device for producing a coherent monochromatic high-intensity beam of light.
Launch complex The complex of site, facilities and equipment used to launch a missile or space rocket.
Launch pad The load-bearing base from which a rocket or spacecraft positioned on its launcher is fired. Colloquially "the pad".
Launch window An interval of time during which a space vehicle can be launched to accomplish a given mission, eg a flight to Venus or Mars.
LC Launch centre.
LH_2 Liquid hydrogen; a cryogenic rocket fuel which becomes liquid at −423°F
Lift-off The start of a rocket's flight from its launch pad. Colloquially, "blast-off".
Light year The distance light travels in one year 186,282·39 miles/sec (299,792·458 km/sec ± 1·2 m/sec). U.S. National Bureau of Standards, 1971.
Longitudinal axis The fore-and-aft line through the centre of a space vehicle.
LO_2 Liquid oxygen; a cryogenic oxidant which becomes liquid at −279°F.
LRBM Long Range Ballistic Missile.
LT Launch time.
Lunar Of or pertaining to the Moon.
LV Launch vehicle.

M

Mach The ratio of the speed of a vehicle (or of a liquid or gas) to the local speed of sound.
Magnetic storm A disturbance of the Earth's magnetic field initiated by a solar flare or sunspot.
Magnetosphere That region of space surrounding the Earth which is dominated by the magnetic field.
Magnetron A vacuum tube in which the flow of electrons is subject to the control of an external magnetic field.
Maria Dark areas on the Moon—actually lava plains—once believed to be seas.
Mass The quantity of matter in a body. It can be determined by measuring the force of gravity (weight) acting on it and dividing this by the gravitational acceleration at that point. Thus, the mass of a given body remains the same everywhere, while its weight changes with the gravitational attraction.
Mass ratio Ratio of the total mass of a rocket vehicle to the mass remaining when all the propellant is consumed.
Max Q Maximum dynamic pressure; the point during launch when the vehicle is subjected to its greatest aerodynamic stress.
Memory The faculty of an electronic device to record and store data and/or instructions for future action on a command.
MeV One million electron volts.
MHz Megahertz, equal to one million Hertz.
Micrometeoroid Meteoroid less than $\frac{1}{250}$th of an inch in diameter.
Microwaves Radio waves having wavelengths of less than 20 centimetres.
Mixture ratio Ratio of the masses of the fuel to the oxidant at any given time.
MMH Monomethyyl hydrazine.
Mock-up A full-size replica or dummy of a vehicle, eg a spacecraft, often made of some substitute material such as wood to assess design features.
Module A self-contained unit of a spacecraft or space station which serves as a building block for the total structure.
Momentum The product of the mass of a body and its velocity.
Mono-propellant A rocket propellant consisting of a single substance, especially a liquid containing both fuel and oxidant, either combined or mixed together.
MRBM Medium Range Ballistic Missile.
MSFC Marshall Space Flight Center (Huntsville, Alabama).
MT Megatonne, equal to 1 million tonnes.
MT Moscow time.
Multiplexer A mechanical or electrical device for sharing a circuit by two or more coincident signals.
Multi-stage rocket A rocket having two or more stages which operate in succession, each being discarded as its job is done.

N

NASA National Aeronautics and Space Administration (USA).
NASDA National Space Development Agency (Japan).
Neutron Atomic particles having approximately the same mass as a hydrogen atom—very penetrating.
Newton That force which gives a mass of 1 kilogramme an acceleration of 1 metre per second per second.
Noctilucent clouds Weakly-luminous clouds, seen at night at heights of about 50 miles (80·5km) above the Earth.
NORAD North American Air Defense Command (USA).
Nose shroud A cover on the nose of a rocket or spacecraft which jettisons before insertion into orbit.
NRC National Research Council (USA).
N_2O_4 Nitrogen tetroxide.

O

OKB Experimental construction bureau.
Orbit The path of a body acted upon by the force of gravity. Under the influence of a single attracting body, all orbital paths trace out simple conic sections. Although all ballistic or free-fall trajectories follow an orbital path, the word orbit is more usually associated with the continuous path of a body which does not impact with its primary.
Orbital module That part of a spacecraft (eg Soyuz), which allows additional volume for crew relaxation and/or experiments. Discarded prior to re-entry.
Orbital period The time taken by an orbiting body to complete one orbit.
Orbital velocity The velocity necessary to overcome the gravitational attraction of the Earth and so keep a satellite in orbit, about 18,000 mph (28,960km/h) close to the Earth.
0-stage Rocket boosters which operate during part of the burning time of the first stage of a launch vehicle to provide additional thrust.
OTRAG Orbital Transport- und Raketen-Atktiengesellschaft.
Oxidants Alternatively oxidisers. Chemicals used for combining with fuels in rocket engines so as to enable combustion to be independent of the atmosphere.

P

Parking orbit Orbit in which a space vehicle awaits the next phase of its planned mission.
Parsec Measure of distance (1 pc = 3·26 light years approx).
P & W Pratt and Whitney (USA).
Payload Useful cargo.
PDT Pacific Daylight Time.
Pegasus A rocket-vehicle concept for transportation of commercial high-priority freight or 172 passengers.
Perigee That point in a terrestrial orbit which is nearest to the Earth.
Perihelion That point in a solar orbit which is nearest to the Sun.
Perilune That point in a lunar orbit which is nearest to the Moon.
Perturbation Modifications to simple conic section orbits caused by such disturbances as air drag, non-uniformity of the Earth, and the gravitational fields of more distant bodies such as the Moon.
Photon A quantum of radiant energy.
Photon propulsion The propulsion of a vehicle by the emission of photons, which possess momentum.
Photosphere The visible surface of the Sun.
Photovoltaic cells Crystalline wafers called solar cells which convert sunlight directly into electricity without moving parts.
Pitch Movement of a spacecraft about an axis (Y) which is perpendicular to its longitudinal axis; degree of elevation or depression.
Planet A satellite of a star. The only know planets are those of the Sun but others have been detected on physical (non-observational) grounds around some of the nearer stars.
Plasma An electrically conductive gas comprised of neutral particles, ionised particles, and free electrons, but which, as a whole, is electrically neutral.
Plasma engine A rocket engine in which thrust is obtained from the acceleration of a plasma with crossed electrical and magnetic fields.
Plug nozzle A doughnut-shaped combustion chamber which discharges engine gases against the surface of a short central cone (the plug). Adapted in the form of an LH_2 cooled heat shield, it can be used as a combination rocket/ aerodynamic braking device.
Polar orbit An orbit which passes over the poles.
Precession A change in the direction of the axis of spin of a rotating body.
Pressure suit A suit, with helmet attached, which is inflated to provide body pressure and air, worn by the crew of certain spacecraft and aircraft which fly at great altitudes.
Pressurised Containing air or other gas at a pressure higher than the pressure outside the chamber.
Primary The body around which a satellite orbits.
Probe An unmanned instrumented vehicle sent into space to gather information.
Propellant A liquid or solid substance burnt in a rocket for the purpose of producing thrust.
PST Pacific Standard Time.
Pulsar Discovered in 1967. Pulsars emit radio signals the pulsations of which are extremely precise. The evidence suggests that pulsars are fast-spinning neutron stars.

Q

Quasars Quasi-stellar objects. They are believed to be among the most distant objects in the observable Universe, emitting more energy than some of the most powerful galaxies.

R

Radio astronomy The science of astronomy using radio waves instead of light waves.
Radio guidance A system which is dependent on outside signals for information.
Radioisotopes Atomic particles which decay by natural radioactivity.
Radio telescope A radio receiving station for detecting radio waves emitted by celestial bodies or space vehicles.
RD Reaktivnyi Dvigatel. Russian for reaction motor.
Readout The action of a radio transmitter sending data either at the same time as data are acquired or by playback from an electronic memory.
Redundancy US term meaning that certain critical components in a space vehicle are duplicated.
Re-entry The re-entry of a space vehicle into the atmosphere.
Regenerative cooling Circulation of a propellant through a jacket around the combustion chamber in order to cool the chamber wall, the propellant subsequently being injected into the combustion chamber.
Relay An electrical switch employing an armature to open or close circuits.
Rem Roentgen equivalent man. A measure of nuclear radiation causing biological damage.
Rendezvous A place of meeting at a given time—for example, a spaceship with a space station.
Retro-rockets Rockets fired to reduce the speed of a spacecraft.
Revolution Orbital motion about a primary.
RJ-1 A hydrocarbon rocket fuel (a refined kerosene).
Rocketdyne A division of Rockwell International concerned with the design and development of rocket engines (USA).
Roll The rotational movement of a vehicle about a longitudinal (X) axis.
Rotation Rotary motion about an axis.
RP-1 A hydrocarbon fuel (a refined kerosene).
RV Re-entry vehicle.

S

Satellite A natural or artificial body moving around a celestial body.
Sensor An electronic device for measuring or indicating a direction or movement.
SEP Société Européene de Propulsion (France).
Sequencer A mechanical or electrical device which may be set to initiate a series of events and to make events follow a sequence.
Service module That part of a spacecraft which usually carries a manoeuvre engine, electrical supply, oxygen and other consumables external to the descent module. Discarded prior to re-entry.
SETI Search for Extra-Terrestrial Intelligence.
SIS Satellite Interceptor System.
Solar cell A cell that converts sunlight into electrical energy. The light falling on certain substances (eg a silicon cell) causes an electric current to flow.
Solar flare A sudden brightening in some part of the Sun, followed by the emission of jets of gas and a flood of ultra-violet radiation. The gale of protons which accompanies a flare can be very dangerous to astronauts.
Solar sensors Light-sensitive diodes which indicate the direction of the Sun.
Solar wind Constant stream of ionised gas atoms (mostly hydrogen) from the Sun.
Solid propellant A rocket in solid form; usually consisting of a mixture of fuel and oxidiser.
Sounding rocket A research rocket used to obtain data from the upper atmosphere.
Space colony Hypothetical extra-terrestrial habitat, for hundreds, thousands or even millions of people, perhaps established on a moon or planet or as an artificial construction in free space.
Space platform A large artificial satellite conceived as a habitable base in space with scientific, exploratory or military applications. A space station.
SPADATS Space Detection and Tracking System (USA).
SPASUR Space Surveillance System (US Navy).
Specific impulse Parameter for rating the performance of a rocket engine. Indicates how many pounds or kilogrammes of thrust are obtained by consumption of a pound or kilogramme of propellant in one second.
SRB propellant Composite propellant used in the Space Shuttle Solid Rocket Boosters. Consists mainly of ammonium perchlorate as the oxidiser, powdered aluminium as the metallic fuel, and PBAN— polybutadiene—acrylic acid-acrylonitrile terpolymer— as the polymeric fuel binder. A small amount of iron oxide is added to increase the burning rate. The final product is a rubbery material not unlike a typewriter eraser.
SRC Science Research Council (UK).
Static firing The firing of a rocket on a special test stand to measure thrust, etc.
Sub-orbital Not attaining orbit, ie a ballistic space shot.
Sub-satellite A secondary object released from a parent satellite in orbit, eg an electronic "ferret" released by a reconnaissance satellite.
Sunspots Dark regions on the Sun which are the centres of large vortices and possess powerful magnetic fields. Maximum sunspot activity occurs in cycles with a period of about 11 years.
Supernova A large dying star, the final collapse of which is a cataclysmic explosion, hurling its substance into space.
Sustainer engine An engine that maintains propulsion of a launch vehicle once it has discarded its boosters.

T

Telemetry The system for radioing information, including instrument readings and recordings, from an air or space vehicle to the ground.
Thermal tile Silica fibre insulation used to protect 70 per cent of the exterior of the NASA Space Shuttle orbiter against re-entry temperatures of up to 1430°C. Surface heat dissipates so rapidly that an uncoated tile can be held by its edges with the bare hand while its interior glows red hot.
Throat That part of a rocket engine between the combustion chamber and nozzle.
Thrust Propulsive force. Measured in lb, kg or Newtons.
TNT Trinitrotoluene, a high explosive.
Tracking station A station set up to track an object through the atmosphere or space, usually by means of radar or radio.
Trajectory The flight path of a projectile, missile, rocket or satellite.
Transponder Radio equipment that receives a signal, modulates it, and re-transmits it at a different frequency.
Trojan relay system A method of ensuring uninterrupted radio contact with the surface of any planet in the Solar System at any time first proposed by James Strong in March 1967 (*Wireless World*). Two radio satellites, keeping station along the Earth orbit, 60° ahead and 60° behind the Earth, transmit/receive signals from a similar pair of relay satellites at the Trojan equilaterals of another planet. Radio communication via these satellite links, from surface to surface, then becomes possible day and night, despite planetary rotation or orbital displacement. It could be used, for example, in steering a remotely-controlled vehicle on the surface of Mars.
TVC Thrust vector control.

U

UDMH Unsymmetrical Dimethyl Hydrazine.
Umbilical connector A flexible connector which maintains the ground supplies to a rocket before launch.
UTC United Technologies Corporation: Chemical Systems Division (USA).

V

Van Allen radiation belt A zone of high radiation density girdling the Earth, named after James A. Van Allen who instrumented the satellite Explorer 1.
Vector Contraction of velocity vector—magnitude of speed plus direction.
Vernier Rocket engine of small thrust used for fine adjustments in velocity and trajectory.
VfR Verein fur Raumschiffahrt e.V. (Germany).

W

Weightlessness A state experienced in a ballistic trajectory (ie in orbit or free fall) when, because the gravitational attraction is opposed by equal and opposite inertial forces, a body experiences no mechanical stress.

X

X-axis See roll.

Y

Yaw The rotation of a vehicle about its vertical (Z) axis, ie to a different azimuth.
Y-axis See pitch.

Z

Z-axis See yaw.
Zero-g See free fall, weightlessness.

Index

Page references occurring in captions to illustrations are in *italic*. Primary treatment of selected subjects is indicated by **bold type**.

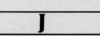

Picture Credits

The publisher wishes to thank the many individuals, aerospace companies, and institutions who have so generously supplied photographs for this book, here credited by page number. Particular thanks are due to Theo Pirard of the Space Information Center, Pepinster, Belgium, who supplied many rare photographs relating to Soviet, Chinese, Indian and Japanese activities, and to David Shayler of Astro Info Service, Halesowen, who provided several photographs of recent US manned flights from his personal archive.

Aérospatiale: 109, 128
Allgemeiner Deutscher Nachdienst: 39
American Rocket Society: 255
Arianespace: 7, 48, 49, 288
British Aerospace: 268, 277, 278
Bell Textron: 260
Bendix: 207 Boeing Aerospace: 146, 158, 168, 223, 236
BIS (K. W. Gatland): 15, 24, 28, 76, 91, 166, 167, 170, 191, 259, 273
CGWIC: 45, 46, 287
CNES: Jacket back, 96, 238, 274, 280
Convair: 196
CTK: 196
Department of Defense, Washington D.C.: 86, 87, 88, 290
Deutsches Museum, Munich: 20, 258
Dornier: 120
Carter Emmart: 250, 251
Rolf Engel: 256
ERNO: 224
ESA: 48, 109, 121, 135, 136, 235, 278, 284, 290, 295
Ford Aerospace: 279
G.D.T.A.: 120
GE Astro-Space: 100/1, 102
General Electric: 84, 110, 206, 260, 281
Glavkosmos: 293
Grumman Aerospace Corporation: 171
Harris Corporation: 164/5
Hasselblad: 73, 169, 171, 177, 179, 180, 181, 265
Dr Rupert Haydn: 111
Hughes Aircraft Company: 92, 93, 97, 108, 113, 142, 152, 264, 271, 279
ISA: 53
ISAS, University of Tokyo: 50, 267
ISRO: 52
IWM, London: 258
Jet Propulsion Laboratory: Jacket back, 121, 134, 137, 155, 160, 161, 163, 164, 274, 275, 276, 282
Lawrence Livermore Laboratory: 89
Lockheed Missiles and Space Co: 136, 137, 221, 228
LTV Aerospace and Defense: 87
Martin Marietta: 37, 69, 183, 222/3, 227, 242, 286
Matra: 137
MBB: 122/3, 196, 224
McDonnell Douglas Corporation: 238, 285
MOA PRC: 45, 46
NASA: Jacket front, 2-3, 4, 11, 17, 25, 29, 3, 33, 35, 38, 63, 66, 67, 70, 71, 72, 73, 74, 79, 82, 84, 90, 91, 98, 99, 100, 101, 102, 104, 111, 114, 115, 118, 119, 122, 124, 127, 129, 133, 135, 139, 140, 146, 148, 149, 150, 153, 154, 154/5, 158, 159, 160, 167, 169, 170, 176, 177, 178, 179, 180, 181, 182, 183, 186, 187, 188/9, 189, 192, 193, 204, 205, 206, 207, 210, 211, 212, 213, 218, 219, 220, 221, 222, 223, 225, 226, 227, 228, 229, 230, 231, 232, 233, 239, 243, 248, 249, 254, 256, 260, 261, 262, 263, 264, 265, 266, 267, 268, 269, 270, 271, 272, 273, 276, 277, 279, 281, 282, 283, 284, 285, 286, 287, 288, 289, 291, 296, 297
NASDA: 51, 285, 292, 293, 294
National Portrait Gallery, London: 253
New York Public Library: 253
Novosti Press Agency: 11, 16, 23, 28, 29, 30, 40, 41, 62, 67, 68, 126, 139, 141, 146, 151, 190, 198, 205, 206, 246, 261, 262, 265, 266, 268, 271, 272, 273, 274, 275, 276, 277, 278/9, 283, 284, 296
Panorama-DDR: 199, 273
Planeta Publishers, Moscow: 201
Orbital Sciences Corporation: 36
RAE, Farnborough: 115
RAF: 258
Rocketdyne: 226
Rockwell International: 85, 168, 169, 233, 234
Arthur Rudolph: 12-13
Abraham Schnapf: 103
Mitchell Sharpe: 20
SIC-Theo Pirard: 10, 31, 47, 62, 96, 272
David Skinner: 10 inset, 12, 13, 254, 256, 257
Smithsonian Institution: 1, 14, 16, 17, 20, 21, 24, 190, 253, 254, 255, 256, 257, 259
Stephen Smyth, Space Center Photos: 275
A. Sokolov (via SIC): 235
Soviet Academy of Sciences: 272
Space Services Inc: 53
Tass: Jacket front, 41, 196, 197, 199, 200, 203, 264, 279, 280, 281, 285, 291, 294
TRW: 128, 160
USAF: 1, 23, 25, 71, 75, 78, 83, 138, 264, 282
US Army: 23, 262
US Navy: 259, 260, 261, 265, 267
UTC: 79
Rice Sumner Wagner: 228
Xinhua News Agency: 44

NAME	DEVELOPMENT	LENGTH ft (m)	DIAM ft (m)	MASS lb (kg)	ENGINE S	Designator	Propellant	Thrust lb (kg)	REMARKS

USA

NAME	DEVELOPMENT	LENGTH ft (m)	DIAM ft (m)	MASS lb (kg)	S	Designator	Propellant	Thrust lb (kg)	REMARKS
Atlas (Score) 1958	General Dynamics/ Convair	85·0 (25·9)	10 (3·05) 16 (4·87) skirt	244,000 (110,660)	0 1	Rdyne LR89-NA5 (x2) Rdyne LR105-NA5 + LR101 verniers (x2)	LO₂/RP-1 LO₂/RP-1	330,000 (149,660) 59,000 (26,755)	Launched Score active communications experiment.
Atlas-Able 1959	General Dynamics/ Convair	98·0 (29·9)	10 (3·05) 16 (4·87)	260,000 (117,915)	0 1 2 3	Rdyne LR89-NA5 (x2) Rdyne LR105-NA5 + LR101-5 verniers (x2) AJ10-11B ABL X-248-3 Altair	LO₂/RP-1 LO₂/RP-1 IWFNA/UDMH Solid	330,000 (149,660) 59,000 (26,755) 7,500 (3,400) 3,100 (1,405)	Derived from Atlas D ICBM plus Able stages from Vanguard launcher. Launched early Pioneer spacecraft, all three were failures.
Atlas-Agena A 1960	General Dynamics/ Convair USAF	99·0 (30·2)	10 (3·05) 16 (4·87)	273,000 (123,810)	0 1 2	Rdyne XL89-NA5 (x2) Rdyne XL105-NA5 + LR101 verniers (x2) Bell 8048	LO₂/RP-1 LO₂/RP-1 IRFNA/UDMH	330,000 (149,660) 59,000 (26,755) 10,110 (4,585)	Used in both Midas and Samos programmes.
Atlas-Agena B 1961	General Dynamics/ Convair USAF, NASA	98·0 (29·9)	10 (3·05) 16 (4·87)	275,000 (124,715) Ranger	0 1 2	Rdyne LR89-NA5 (x2) Rdyne XL105-NA5 + LR101-7 verniers (x2) Bell 8096	LO₂/RP-1 LO₂/RP-1 IRFNA/UDMH	330,000 (149,660) 59,000 (26,755) 15,000 (6,800)	Various programmes including Midas and Ranger. Payload into 300 mile (483km) CO 5,000lb (2,268kg).
Atlas-Agena D 1963	General Dynamics/ Convair USAF, NASA	102·0 (31·1)	10 (3·05) 16 (4·87)	274,965 (124,700)	0 1 2	Rdyne LR89-NA5 (x2) Rdyne LR101-NA5 + LR101 verniers (x2) Bell 8096	LO₂/RP-1 LO₂/RP-1 IRFNA/UDMH	330,000 (149,660) 59,000 (26,755) 16,000 (7,255)	Various civil and military programmes: reconnaissance and surveillance: Mariner 4, 5, Ranger 7, Lunar Orbiter, GETV, ATDA etc.
Atlas-Burner 2 1968	General Dynamics/ Boeing USAF	78·7 (24·0)	10 (3·05) 16 (4·87)	286,440 (129,905)	0 1 2	Rdyne LR89-NA5 (x2) Rdyne LR105-NA5 + LR101 verniers (x2) P&W RL-10-A3 (x2)	LO₂/RP-1 LO₂/RP-1 Solid	370,000 (167,800) 59,000 (26,755) 8,800 (3,990) av	Launched DSMP payloads. STP72-1 Radcat etc. Burner 2A used post-1971 for data on that engine see Thor-Burner 2A entry.
Atlas-Centaur 1962	General Dynamics/ Convair	105·0 (32·0)	10 (3·05) 16 (4·87)	300,000 + (136,055 +)	0 1 2	Rdyne YLR89-NA7 (x2) Rdyne YLR105-NA7 + LR101 verniers (x2) P&W RL-10A-3-3 (x2)	LO₂/RP-1 LO₂/RP-1 LO₂/LH₂	367,000 (166,440) 59,000 (26,755) 30,000 (13,605)	Originally designed to launch Advent comsat into GO. Later developed to launch Surveyor lunar soft-landing spacecraft.
Atlas F 1977	General Dynamics/ Convair USAF, NASA	85·0 (25·9)	10 (3·05) 16 (4·87)	262,500 (119,050)	0 1 2	Rdyne LR89-NA5 (x2) Rdyne LR105-NA5 + LR101 verniers (x2) TE-364-4	LO₂/RP-1 LO₂/RP-1 Solid	330,000 (149,660) 59,000 (26,755) 14,330 (6,500)	Modified Atlas ICBM (1961). Launched Navstar, NOAA-7, Tiros-N, military payloads. Payload into 342 mile (560km) orbit 3,307lb (1,500kg).

The following Atlas vehicles can have either medium or long payload shrouds: the first length and mass are for the medium variant and the second for the long variant.

NAME	DEVELOPMENT	LENGTH ft (m)	DIAM ft (m)	MASS lb (kg)	S	Designator	Propellant	Thrust lb (kg)	REMARKS
Atlas 1	General Dynamics	137·8 (42·0) 144·0 (43·9)	10·0 (3·05)	361,300 (163,900) 362,200 (164,290)	1 2	MA-5 (x3) RL-10 (x2)	LO₂/RP-1 LO₂/LH₂	437,800 (198,600) sl 33,100 (15,000)	First of the new commercial Atlas series 13,000-12,570lb (5,900-5,700kg) to LEO 5,160-4,960lb (2,340-2,250kg) to GTO a 3,350-3,090lb (1,520-1,400kg) to escape
Atlas 2 1991?	General Dynamics	149·6 (45·6) 155·8 (47·5)	10·0 (3·05)	412,600 (187,170) 413,500 (187,560)	1 2	MA-5 (x3) RL-10 (x2)	LO₂/RP-1 LO₂/LH₂	468,300 (212,400) sl 33,500 (15,200)	14,950-14,510lb (6,780-6,580kg) to LEO 6,110-5,910lb (2,770-2,680kg) to GTO a 4,280-4,010lb (1,940-1,820kg) to escape
Atlas 2A 1992?	General Dynamics	149·6 (45·6) 155·8 (47·5)	10·0 (3·05)	412,900 (187,310) 413,800 (187,700)	1 2	MA-5 (x3) RL-10 (x2)	LO₂/RP-1 LO₂/LH₂	468,000 (212,400) sl 40,600 (18,400)	15,700-15,260lb (7,120-6,920kg) to LEO 6,390-6,195lb (2,900-2,810kg) to GTO a 4,630-4,365lb (2,100-1,980kg) to escape
Atlas 2AS 1993?	General Dynamics	149·6 (45·6) 155·8 (47·5)	10·0 (3·05)	434,100 (196,920) 435,000 (197,310)	0 1 2	Castor 2 (x4) MA-5 (x3) RL-10 (x2)	Solid LO₂/RP-1 LO₂/LH₂	209,000 (94,800) sl 468,000 (212,400) sl 40,600 (18,400)	19,000-18,500lb (8,610-8,390kg) to LEO 8,000-7,700lb (3,630-3,490kg) to GTO, 5,890-5,640lb (2,670-2,550kg) to escape
Delta B DSV-3B 1962	McDonnell Douglas NASA	87·9 (26·8)	8·0 (2·44)	114,170 (51,780)	1 2 3	Rdyne LR79-NA11 Aero AJ-10-118D X-248 A5DM	LO₂/RJ-1 IRFNA/UDMH Solid	172,000 (78,005) av 7,575 (3,435) 2,760 (1,250)	Launched Relay 1, Syncom 1, Explorer 17, Telstar 2 etc. Payload into 300 mile (483km) orbit 500lb (227kg).
Delta D DSV-3D 1964	McDonnell Douglas NASA	92·8 (28·3)	8·0 (2·44)	143,325 (65,000)	0 1 2 3	Thio Castor 1 (x3) Rdyne LR79-NA13 Aero AJ-10-118D Hercules X-258	Solid LO₂/RJ-1 IRFNA/UDMH Solid	156,775 (71,100) 175,075 (79,400) 7,715 (3,500) 2,755 (1,250)	Launched Syncom 2, Early Bird. Payload into GO 230lb (104kg).
Delta E DSV-3E 1965	McDonnell Douglas NASA	95·8 (29·2)	8·0 (2·44)	149,940 (68,000)	0 1 2 3	Thio Castor 1 (x3) Rdyne LR79-NA13 Aero AJ-10-118E Hercules X-258	Solid LO₂/RJ-1 IRFNA/UDMH Solid	156,775 (71,100) 175,075 (79,400) 7,805 (3,540) 2,755 (1,250)	Launched Explorer 29, Pioneer 6, ESSA 2, 3, 4, 5 etc. Payload into GTO 441lb (200kg).
Delta 1000 Config. 1913 1972	McDonnell Douglas NASA	116·0 (35·35)	8·0 (2·44)	295·470 (134,000)	0 1 2 3	Thio Castor 2 (x9)★ Rdyne LR79-NA13 Aero AJ-10-118F Thio TE-364-3	Solid LO₂/RJ-1 N₂O₄/Aerozine 50 Solid	470,325 (213,300) 175,075 (79,400) 9,810 (4,450) 9,505 (4,310)	This series introduced the "Straight Eight" Deltas. Config. 1913 launched Explorer 49 etc.
Delta 2000 Config. 2914 1974	McDonnell Douglas NASA	116·0 (35·35)	8·0 (2·44)	293,100 (132,925)	0 1 2 3	Thio Castor 2 (x9)★ Rdyne RS-27 TRW TR-201 Thio TE-364-4	Solid LO₂/RJ-1 N₂O₄/Aerozine 50 Solid	470,325 (213,300) 205,065 (93,000) 9,810 (4,450) 14,995 (6,800)	Launched SMS, Westar, Anik etc. Payload into GTO 1,550lb (703kg).
Delta 3914 1975	McDonnell Douglas NASA	116·0 (35·35)	8·0 (2·44)	420,269 (190,560)	0 1 2 3	Thio Castor 4 (x9)† Rdyne RS-27 TRW TR-201 Thio TE-364-4	Solid LO₂/RP-1 N₂O₄/Aerozine 50 Solid	766,015 (347,400) 205,065 (93,000) 9,810 (4,450) 14,995 (6,800)	Launched Satcom 1 etc. Payload into GTO 2,050lb (930kg).
Delta 3910 1980	McDonnell Douglas NASA	116·0 (35·35)	8·0 (2·44)	418,000 (189,570) SMM	0 1 2	Thio Castor 4 (x9)† Rdyne RS-27 TRW TR-201	Solid LO₂/RP-1 N₂O₄/Aerozine 50	766,015 (347,400) 205,065 (93,000) 9,810 (4,450)	Launched SMM. Payload into low CO 5,500lb (2,494kg); into SSPO 2,985lb (1,354kg).
Delta 3920/PAM 1982	McDonnell Douglas NASA	116·0 (35·35)	8·0 (2·44)	426,000 (193,200)	0 1 2 3	Thio Castor 4 (x9)★ Rdyne RS-27 Aero AJ10-118K-ITIR Thio STAR 48	Solid LO₂/RP-1 N₂O₄/Aerozine 50 Solid	766,015 (347,400) 205,065 (93,000) 9,810 (4,450) 18,500 (8,390)	Launched Landsat 4, Anik D etc. Upgraded 3910 with improved 2nd stage injector and larger tanks. Payload into GTO 2,750lb (1,247kg).
Delta 2 (6920) 1989	McDonnell Douglas	126·0 (38·4)	8·0 (2·44)	477,500 (216,600)	0 1 2	Castor 4A (x9) RS-27B AJ-110-118K	Solid LO₂/RP-1 N₂O₄/Aerozine 50	978,200 (443,700) 231,700 (105,100) 9,700 (4,400)	8,781lb (3,983kg) to 28·7°, 115 miles (18 6,669lb (3,025kg) to 90°, 115 miles (18 5,659lb (2,567kg) to 98·7°, 518 miles (83 Can also use PAMs for geosynchron orbit missions.
Delta 2 (7920) 1990?	McDonnell Douglas	126·0 (38·4)	8·0 (2·44)	502,900 (228,100)	0 1 2	CGEM (x9) RS-27C AJ-110-118K	Solid LO₂/RP-1 N₂O₄/Aerozine 50	998,000 (452,700) 237,000 (107,500) 9,700 (4,400)	11,109lb (5,039kg) to 28·7°, 115 miles (1 8,419lb (3,819kg) to 90°, 115 miles (18 7,000lb (3,175kg) to 98·7°, 518 miles (83 Can also use PAMs for geosynchron orbit missions.

★ Six ignite at lift-off, three later   † Five ignite at lift-off, four later.

NAME	DEVELOPMENT	LENGTH ft (m)	DIAM ft (m)	MASS lb (kg)	S	Designator	Propellant	Thrust lb (kg)	REMARKS
Gemini-Titan II 1964	Martin Marietta NASA	109·0 (33·2)	10·0 (3·05)	407,925 (185,000)	1 2	Aero LR-87 (x2) Aero LR-91	N₂O₄/Aerozine 50 N₂O₄/Aerozine 50	430,000 (195,010) 100,000 (45,350)	Modified ICBM. Launched Gemini two-man spacecraft into CEO.

NAME	DEVELOPMENT	LENGTH ft (m)	DIAM ft (m)	MASS lb (kg)	ENGINE S	Designator	Propellant	Thrust lb (kg)	REMARKS
Juno I 1958	Chrysler NASA, MSFC	71·25 (21·7)	5·83 (1·77) 13 (3·96) fin span	64,000 (29,025)	1 2 3 4	Rydne A-7 Thio sc Sergeant (x11) Thio sc Sergeant (x3) Thio sc Sergeant	LO₂/"Hydyne" Solid Solid Solid	83,000 (37,640) 16,500 (7,485) 5,400 (2,450) 1,800 (816)	Derived from Jupiter C (started under NRL "Orbiter" Project). Launched Explorer 1, 3 and 4.
Juno II 1958	Chrysler NASA, MSFC	76·6 (23·3)	8·75 (2·67)	122,000 (55,330)	1 2 3 4	Rydne S-3D Thio sc Sergeant (x11) Thio sc Sergeant (x3) Thio sc Sergeant	LO₂/RP-1 Solid Solid Solid	150,000 (68,025) 16,500 (7,485) 5,400 (2,450) 1,800 (816)	Derived from Jupiter IRBM and Jupiter C upper stages. Launched Pioneer 3 and 4 etc. Payload into 300 mile (483km) orbit 100lb (45·4kg).
Mercury-Redstone 1961	Chrysler NASA, MSFC	83·0 (25·3)	5·83 (1·77)	66,000 (29,930)	1	Rdyne A-7	LO₂/ethyl alcohol + water	78,000 (35,375)	Derived from Redstone MRBM. Launched Shepard and Grissom.
Mercury-Atlas 1962	General Dynamics NASA, MSFC	95·3 (29·0)	10·0 (3·05)	260,000 (117,915)	0 1	Rdyne LR89-NA5 (x2) Rdyne LR105-NA5 + LR 101-NA7 verniers (x2)	LO₂/RP-1 LO₂/RP-1	367,000 (166,440) 59,000 (26,755)	Derived from Atlas D ICBM. Launched first US astronauts into Earth orbit.
Pegasus/B-52 1989	Orbital Sciences Corp/ Hercules Aerospace	49·0 (15·0)	4·3 (1·3)	40,600 (18,400)	1 2 3	— — —	Solid Solid Solid	112,000 (50,800) 28,000 (12,700) 9,000 (4,100)	Carried to altitude by B-52 and then separates and continues to orbit: 595lb (270kg) to polar 286 miles (460km) orbit.
Saturn I 1961	Chrysler NASA	164·0 (50·0)	21·5 (6·55)	1,122,000 (508,845)	1 2	Rdyne H-1 (x8) P&W RL-10A-3	LO₂/RP-1 LO₂/LH₂	1,504,000 (682,085) 90,000 (40,815)	Used for R&D. Data relate to SA-5 which put 37,900lb (17,190kg) into EO.
Saturn IB 1966	Chrysler NASA, MSFC	224·0 (68·3)	21·7 (6·61)	1,295,000 (587,300)	1 2	Rdyne H-1 (x8) Rdyne J-2	LO₂/RP-1 LO₂/LH₂	1,640,000 (743,765) 225,000 (102,040)	Launched Apollo 7, Skylab and ASTP astronauts. 40,000lb (18,140kg) to EO.
Saturn V/Apollo 1967	NASA, MSFC Boeing/Rockwell McDonnell Douglas	363·0 (110·6) Apollo 17	33·0 (10·06)	6,423,000 (2,912,925)	1 2 3	Rdyne F-1 (x5) Rdyne J-2 (x5) Rdyne J-2	LO₂/RP-1 LO₂/LH₂ LO₂/LH₂	7,650,000 (3,469,390) 1,150,000 (521,540) 238,000 (107,935)	Launched Apollo astronauts to the Moon.
Saturn V/Skylab 1973	NASA, MSFC Boeing/Rockwell	333·7 (101·7)	33·0 (10·06)	6,222,000 (2,821,770)	1 2	Rdyne F-1 (x5) Rdyne J-2 (x5)	LO₂/RP-1 LO₂/LH₂	7,723,726 (3,502,820) 1,125,000 (510,205)	Launched Skylab space station into Earth orbit.
Scout 1960	Vought Corporation NASA	72·0 (21·9)	3·33 (1·015)	36,600 (16,600)	1 2 3 4	UTC Algol I Thio Castor I ABL X-254 Antares I ABL X-248 Altair I	Solid Solid Solid Solid	115,000 (52,155) 50,000 (22,675) 13,600 (6,170) 3,000 (1,360)	Launched Explorer 9, Explorer 13 etc. Payload into 300 mile (483km) CO 150lb (68kg).
Scout D 1972	Vought Corporation NASA, USAF	75·46 (23·0)	3·75 (1·14) UK-6	47,000 (21,315)	1 2 3 4	UTC Algol IIIA Thio Castor IIA HX-258 Antares IIA Thio Altair 3A	Solid Solid Solid Solid	108,300 (49,115) 63,200 (28,660) 28,500 (12,925) 5,900 (2,675)	Launched Meteoroid Technology Satellite, SAS-B, UK-6 etc. Payload into 300 mile (483km) CO 390lb (177kg).
Space Shuttle 1981	Rockwell International NASA	184·2 oa (56·1) 122·2 (37·2) Orb	78·06 (23·79) wing span	4,500,000 (2,040,815)	0 1	Thio SRB (x2) Rdyne SSME (x3) + Aero OMS (x2)	Solid LO₂/LH₂ N₂O₄/MMH	5,300,000 (2,403,630) 1,410,000 (639,455) 12,000 (5,440)	Max payload into CEO, due East launch Cape Canaveral, 65,000lb (29,478kg). First flight (STS-1) 12-14 April 1981.
Shuttle-C 1993-1994?	Rockwell International NASA	56·0 (17·0)	56·0 (17·0)	4,400,000 (2,000,000)	1 2	Thio SRB (x2) Rdyne SSME (x2)	Solid LO₂/LH₂	5,950,000 (2,700,000) 939,000 (426,000)	Uses pre-Challenger SRBs and SSMEs near the end of their lives. Will use 2 or 3 SSMEs as mission demands. With 2 SSMEs can place 176,000lb (80 tonnes) to 28.5°, 115 miles (185km) or 84,000lb (38 tonnes) to polar 255 miles (410km).
Thor-Able 1958	Douglas NASA, USAF	90·0 (27·4)	8·0 (2·44)	114,660 (52,000)	1 2 3	Rdyne LR79-NA9 Aero AJ-10-42 ABL X-248 Altair	LO₂/RJ-1 IRFNA/UDMH Solid	150,000 (68,025) 7,575 (3,435) 2,760 (1,250)	Launched first Pioneer Moon probes. Derived from Thor IRBM with modified Vanguard second stage.
Thor-Able Star 1960	Douglas USAF	79·3 (24·17)	8·0 (2·44)	117,900 (53,470)	1 2	Rdyne LR79-NA11 Aero AJ-10-104 with restart capability	LO₂/RJ-1 IR (or W) FNA/ UDMH	172,000 (78,005) 7,730 (3,505)	Launched Transit, Courier etc. Payload into 300 mile (483km) CO 1,000lb (453·5kg).
Thor-Agena A 1959	Lockheed/Douglas USAF	78·5 (23·9)	8·0 (2·44)	117,000 (53,060)	1 2	Rdyne XLR79-NA9 Bell Hustler 8048	LO₂/RJ-1 IRFNA/UDMH	150,000 (68,025) 15,500 (7,030)	Launched early Discoverers. Payload into 300 mile (483km) CO 300lb (136kg).
Thor-Agena B 1960	Lockheed/Douglas USAF	81·3 (24·8)	8·0 (2·44)	123,040 (55,800)	1 2	Rdyne LR79-NA11 Bell Hustler 8096	LO₂/RJ-1 IR (or W) FNA/ UDMH	172,000 (78,005) 16,000 (7,255)	Discoverer series. Payload into 300 mile (483km) CO 1,600lb (726kg).
Thor-Agena D 1962	Lockheed/Douglas USAF, NASA	76·3 (23·25)	8·0 (2·44)	123,040 (55,800)	1 2	Rdyne XLR79-NA11 Bell 8096	LO₂/RJ-1 IRFNA/UDMH	172,000 (78,005) 16,000 (7,255)	Various military and civil programmes.
Thor-Burner 2A 1971	Lockheed/ McDonnell Douglas/ Boeing, USAF	85·0 (25·9)	8·0 (2·44)	N/A	1 2 3	Rdyne XLR79-NA11 Thio TE-M-364-2 Thio TE-M-442-1	LO₂/RJ-1 Solid Solid	172,000 (78,005) 10,000 (4,535) av 8,800 (3,990)	Launched DMSP. Thor-Burner 1 used an Altair motor. Thor-Burner 2 omitted the third stage.
Titan II 1988	Martin Marietta	141 (43)	10 (3·05)	408,000 (185,000)	1 2	LR-87-AJ-5 LR-91-AJ-5	N₂O₄/Aerozine 50 N₂O₄/Aerozine 50	430,000 (195,000) sl 99,200 (45,000)	Titan missile adapted for satellite launch vehicle. 4,850lb (2,200kg) to polar 115 mile (185km) orbit.
Titan IIIA 1964	Martin Marietta USAF	108·0 (32·9) + payload	10·0 (3·05)	407,925 (185,000) + payload	1 2 3	Aero LR-87 Aero LR-91 Transtage	N₂O₄/Aerozine 50 N₂O₄/Aerozine 50 N₂O₄/Aerozine 50	430,000 (195,000) 100,000 (45,350) 16,000 (7,255)	Launched LES-1, 2, radar calibration sat. Payload into 100 mile (161km) EO 3,300lb (1,496·6kg).
Titan IIIB-Agena 1966	Martin Marietta USAF	160 max (48·76)	10·0 (3·05)	454,450 (206,100)	1 2 3	Aero LR-87-AJ-11 Aero LR-91-AJ-11 Agena	N₂O₄/Aerozine 50 N₂O₄/Aerozine 50 IRFNA/UDMH	463,200 (210,070) 101,000 (45,805) 16,800 (7,620)	Launched various payloads. Payload into 100 mile (161km) EO 8,550lb (3,877kg).
Titan IIIC 1965	Martin Marietta USAF, NASA	157 max (47·85) + payload	10·0★ (3·05)	1,392,000 (631,290)	0 1 2 3	UA 1205 (x2 x5 seg) Aero LR-87-AJ-11 Aero LR-91-AJ-11 Trans AJ10-138	Solid N₂O₄/Aerozine 50 N₂O₄/Aerozine 50 N₂O₄/Aerozine 50	2,360,000 (1,070,295) 532,000 (241,270) 101,000 (45,805) 16,000 (7,255)	Launched IDCSP, Vela, DSCS, ATS-6 etc. Payload into 100 mile (161km) EO 29,600lb (13,425kg); into GO 3,600lb (1,633kg).
Titan IIID 1971	Martin Marietta USAF	155 max (47·2) + payload	10·0★ (3·05)	1,300,000 (589,570)	0 1 2	UA 1205 (x2 x5 seg) Aero LR-87-AJ-11 Aero LR-91-AJ-11	Solid N₂O₄/Aerozine 50 N₂O₄/Aerozine 50	2,360,000 (1,070,295) 532,000 (241,270) 101,000 (45,805)	Launched "Big Bird", KH-11 etc. Payload into PO 13,000lb (5,895kg).
Titan IIIE-Centaur 1974	Martin Marietta NASA	160·0 (48·76)	10·0★ (3·05)	1,411,200 (640,000)	0 1 2 3	UA 1205 (x2 x5 seg) Aero YLR-870-AJ-11 Aero YLR-910-AJ-11 Centaur D-1T	Solid N₂O₄/Aerozine 50 N₂O₄/Aerozine 50 LO₂/LH₂	2,361,000 (1,070,750) 530,000 (240,360) 101,000 (45,805) 30,000 (13,605)	Launched Helios, Viking, Voyager etc. Payload into GO 7,400lb (3,356kg); to Venus or Mars 8,400lb (3,809kg); to outer planets 500-1,750lb (227-749kg).
Titan 34D 1982	Martin Marietta USAF	160·7 max (49·0)	10·0★ (3·05)	1,724,530 (782,100)	0 1 2 3 4	UA 1205 (x2 x5½ seg) Aero LR-87-OAJ-11 Aero LR-91-OAJ-11 IUS stage 1 IUS stage 2	Solid N₂O₄/Aerozine 50 N₂O₄/Aerozine 50 Solid Solid	2,498,000 (1,132,880) 532,000 (241,270) 101,000 (45,805) 62,000 (28,120) 26,000 (11,790)	Launched DSCS 2 and other military missions. Payload into 100 mile (161km) EO 27,500lb (12,470kg); into GO 4,200lb (1,905kg).
Titan III (Commercial Titan III) 1989	Martin Marietta	155·1 (47·3)	10 (3·05)★	1,500,000 (680,000)	0 1 2	Strap-on (x2) Aero LR-87-AJ-11 Aero LR-91-AJ-11	Solid N₂O₄/Aerozine 50 N₂O₄/Aerozine 50	2,792,000 (1,266,600) 1,092,200 (495,400) 104,100 (47,200)	Latest Titan III variant: can carry two payloads totalling 31,600lb (14,334kg) or a single payload of 32,500lb (14,742kg) to 28·6°, 92-161 mile (148-259km) orbit. Can also carry IUS or PAMs with payloads for GTO/GSO missions.
Titan III-T Available 1989	Martin Marietta	165·0 (50·3)	10 (3·05)★	1,532,000 (695,000)	0 1 2 3	Strap-on (x2) Aero LR-87-AJ-11 Aero LR-91-AJ-11 Trans AJ-10-118K	Solid N₂O₄/Aerozine 50 N₂O₄/Aerozine 50 N₂O₄/Aerozine 50	2,792,000 (1,266,600) 1,092,200 (495,400) 104,100 (47,200) 32,200 (14,600)	Titan III plus Transtage. Can place single 10,200lb (4,626kg) payload or two payloads totalling 9,500lb (4,309kg) into GTO or 2,100lb (952kg) into GSO.

NAME	DEVELOPMENT	LENGTH ft (m)	DIAM ft (m)	MASS lb (kg)	S	ENGINE Designator	Propellant	Thrust lb (kg)	REMARKS

USA continued

NAME	DEVELOPMENT	LENGTH ft (m)	DIAM ft (m)	MASS lb (kg)	S	Designator	Propellant	Thrust lb (kg)	REMARKS
Titan IV 1989	Martin Marietta	197 (60)	10 (3·05)★	1,760,000 (800,000)	0 1 2	Strap-on (x2) LR-87-AJ-11 (x2) LR-91-AJ-11	Solid N_2O_4/Aerozine 50 N_2O_4/Aerozine 50	3,567,000 (1,618,000) 1,100,000 (498,000) 106,000 (48,000)	Growth version of Titan 34D. 39,000lb (17,700kg) to 28·6° LEO or 32,000lb (14,500kg) to polar LEO. Can fly GTO/GSO or escape missions using Centaur or IUS.

★ Also carries two strap-on boosters each of the same diameter.

NAME	DEVELOPMENT	LENGTH ft (m)	DIAM ft (m)	MASS lb (kg)	S	Designator	Propellant	Thrust lb (kg)	REMARKS
Vanguard 1958	Glenn L. Martin US Navy	72 (21·9)	3·74 (1·14)	22,600 (10,250)	1 2 3	GE X-405 Aero AJ-10 ABL X-248 Altair	LO_2/kerosene IWFNA/UDMH Solid	28,000 (12,700) 7,500 (3,400) 3,100 (1,405)	First orbital attempt (TV3) failed. TV4 launched Vanguard 1 test satellite.

USSR

NAME	DEVELOPMENT	LENGTH ft (m)	DIAM ft (m)	MASS lb (kg)	S	Designator	Propellant	Thrust lb (kg)	REMARKS
A (SL-1) 1957	USSR (S.P. Korolev)	95·69 (29·167)	33·8★ (10·3) over fins	588,735 (267,000)	0 1	RD-107 (x4)† RD-108 (4 main chambers + 4 verniers)	LO_2/kerosene LO_2/kerosene	877,590 (398,000) 205,065 (93,000)	Derived from R.7 ICBM, SS-6 Sapwood. Launched Sputniks 1, 2 and 3. Dry weight 48,510lb (22,000kg).
A-1 (SL-3) 1959	USSR (S.P. Korolev)	109·9 (33·5)	33·8★ (10·3)	615,195 (279,000)	0 1 2	RD-107 (x4)† RD-108 RD-448	LO_2/kerosene LO_2/kerosene LO_2/kerosene	899,500 (408,000) 211,600 (96,000) 11,025 (5,000)	Launched Luna 1, 2 and 3. Additional Luna payloads were launched but went off course. Dry weight 52,920lb (24,000kg).
A-1 (SL-3, Vostok) 1959	USSR/Glavcosmos (Korolev Bureau)	126·0 (38·4)	33·8 max★ (10·3)	639,300 (290,000)	1 2 3	RD-107 (x4)† RD-108 RD-448	LO_2/kerosene LO_2/kerosene LO_2/kerosene	899,500 (408,000) 211,000 (96,000) 12,300 (5,600)	Carried first man into space (1961), now rarely used for SSO missions. 11,000lb (5,000kg) to LEO, 4,050lb (1,840kg) to 98°, 404 miles (650km), 2,540lb (1,150kg) to 99°, 572 miles (920km).
A-2 (SL-4, Soyuz) 1963	USSR/Glavcosmos (Korolev Bureau)	147·3 (44·9)	33·8 max★ (33·4)	676,800 (307,000)	1 2 3	RD-107 (x4)† RD-108 RD-461	LO_2/kerosene LO_2/kerosene LO_2/kerosene	899,500 (408,000) 211,600 (96,000) 66,100 (30,000)	Carries manned Soyuz, Soyuz-T, Soyuz-TM craft and Progress ferries, as well as reconnaissance satellites. 16,500lb (7,500kg) to 51·6°, 124 miles (200km), 15,200lb (6,900kg) to 50·5°, 124-280 miles (200-450km).
A-2-e (SL-6, Molniya) 1960	USSR/Glavcosmos (Korolev Bureau)	137·8 (42)	33·8★ (10·3)	679,000 (308,000)	1 2 3 4	RD-107 (x4)† RD-108 RD-461 RD-?	LO_2/kerosene LO_2/kerosene LO_2/kerosene LO_2/kerosene	899,500 (408,000) 211,600 (96,000) 66,100 (30,000) 14,800 (6,700)	Molniya and early warning missions 4,400lb (2,000kg) to 63°, 310-24,200 miles (500-39,000km), 3,750lb (1,700kg) to the Moon, 2,760lb (1,250kg) to Mars or Venus.

★ 1st stage core 9·67 (2·95); boosters 9·8 (3·0)   † Each with 4 main chambers and 2 verniers.

NAME	DEVELOPMENT	LENGTH ft (m)	DIAM ft (m)	MASS lb (kg)	S	Designator	Propellant	Thrust lb (kg)	REMARKS
B-1 (SL-7) 1962	USSR (M.K. Yangel)	98·4 (30·0)	5·4 (1·65)	94,815 (43,000)	1 2	RD-214 (4 chambers) RD-119 (4 exhaust ver)	RFNA/kerosene LO_2/UDMH	158,760 (72,000) 24,255 (11,000)	Derived from SS-4 Sandal MRBM. Launched Cosmos and Intercosmos family.
C-1 (SL-8, Cosmos) 1964	USSR/Glavcosmos (Yangel Bureau)	102·3 (31·2)	8·0 (2·44)	275,600 (125,000)	1 2	RD-216 (x2) RD-?	Nitric acid/UDMH N_2O_4/UDMH?	388,000 (176,000) 33,000 (15,000)	First stage derived from SS-5/Skean. 2,800lb (1,250kg) to LEO from Kapustin Yar, 1,800lb (810kg) to 83°, 620 miles (1,000km) from Plesetsk.
D (SL-9) 1965	USSR (Chelomei Bureau)	171·7 (52·33)	24·3 max (7·4)★	2,303,400 (1,044,625)	1 2	RD-253 (x6) RD-? (x4)	N_2O_4/UDMH N_2O_4/UDMH	2,355,000 (1,260,000) 529,000 (240,000)	Launched Proton 1, 2 and 3, all 26,900lb (12,200kg). Rumoured launch failure in early 1966.
D-1 (SL-13, Proton Three Stage Variant) 1968	USSR (Chelomei Bureau)	197 (60) 145·3 (44·3) without payload	24·3 max (7·4)★	1,540,000 (700,000)	1 2 3	RD-253 (x6) RD-? (x4) RD-?	N_2O_4/UDMH N_2O_4/UDMH N_2O_4/UDMH	2,355,000 (1,068,000) 529,000 (240,000) 141,000 (64,000)	Two stage Proton flew four times during 1965-1966 (one failure). Three stage variant used for Salyut series, 41,700-43,920lb (18,900-19,920kg), Mir core, 46,100lb (20,900kg) and Mir modules, 45,400lb (20,600kg): 51·6°, 130-155 miles (210-250km).
D-1-e (SL-12, Proton Four Stage Variant) 1967	USSR/Glavcosmos (Chelomei Bureau)	174 (53) 145·3 (44·3) without payload	24·3 max (7·4)★	1,540,000 (700,000)	1 2 3 4	RD-253 (x6) RD-? (x4) RD-? RD-?	N_2O_4/UDMH N_2O_4/UDMH N_2O_4/UDMH LO_2/kerosene	2,355,000 (1,068,000) 529,000 (240,000) 141,000 (64,000) 19,200 (8,700)	Three stage Proton with fourth stage (Block-D, now Block-DM) added: 4,675lb (2,120kg) to GTO, 10,250lb (4,650kg) to Mars, 11,685lb (5,300kg) to Venus and 12,630lb (5,730kg) to the Moon.

★ Central oxidiser tank 13·6ft (4·15m); fuel strap-on tanks 8·2ft (2·5m).

NAME	DEVELOPMENT	LENGTH ft (m)	DIAM ft (m)	MASS lb (kg)	S	Designator	Propellant	Thrust lb (kg)	REMARKS
F-1-r, F-1-m (SL-11, Tsyklon Two Stage Variant) 1966	USSR (Yangel Bureau)	115 (35?)	10 (3·05)	400,000 (180,000)	1 2	RD-? RD-219	Nitric acid/UDMH Nitric acid/UDMH	617,000 (280,000) 198,400 (90,000)	Ocean surveillance, ASAT and FOBS missions. 8,800lb (4,000kg) to 65°, 155-165 miles (250-265km).
F-2 (SL-14, Tsyklon Three Stage Variant) 1977	USSR/Glavcosmos (Yangel Bureau)	128·8 (39·27)	10 (3·05)	440,000 (200,000)	1 2 3	RD-? RD-219 RD-?	Nitric acid/UDMH? Nitric acid/UDMH Nitric acid/UDMH?	617,000 (280,000) 198,400 (90,000) 55,000? (25,000?)	Meteorological, oceanographic and minor military payloads. 8,800lb (4,000kg) to LEO, 2,870lb (1,300kg) to 82·6°, 746 miles (1,200km).
G-1-e (SL-15, Soviet name N-1) 1969	USSR (S.P. Korolev)	311·7 (95)	52·5 base (16·0) 13·6 (4·15) payload	7,300,000? (3,300,000?)	1 2 3	Main engines (clustered) N/A N/A	LO_2/kerosene LO_2/Kerosene LO_2/Kerosene	10,000,000 (4,500,000) sl N/A N/A	Super-booster for manned lunar flight. Launch failures 21 February and 3 July 1969; 2 more failures, 27 June 1971, 23 Nov 1972. Three stages to Earth orbit, plus a fourth escape stage.
J-1 (SL-16, Zenit) 1985	USSR (Korolev Collective)	187 (57)	13 (3·9)	1,014,000 (460,000)	1 2	RD-170 RD-?	LO_2/kerosene LO_2/kerosene	1,779,000 (807,000) 205,000 (93,000)	Medium lift launch vehicle: 30,290lb (13·74 tonnes) to 51·6°, 124 mile (200km) orbit from Baikonur.

A three stage version of Zenit is being developed: this will be able to place 8,420lb (3,820kg) into a 51·6° GTO or alternatively 1,320lb (600kg) into GSO from Baikonur.

NAME	DEVELOPMENT	LENGTH ft (m)	DIAM ft (m)	MASS lb (kg)	S	Designator	Propellant	Thrust lb (kg)	REMARKS
K-1 (SL-17, Energiya) 1987	USSR (Korolev Collective)	197 (60)	59 max (18)	5,290,000 (2,400,000)	1 2	RD-170 (x4) RD-? (x4)	LO_2/kerosene LO_2/LH_2	7,108,000 (3,224,000) 1,764,000 (800,000)	Heavy lift launch vehicle, first flown 15 May 1987. Can theoretically place 309,000lb (140 tonnes) into 51·6°, 152-158 miles (245-255km) orbit.
K-1 (Energiya, Three Stage Variant)	USSR (Korolev Collective)	197 (60)	59 max (18)	4,630,000 (2,100,000)	1 2 3	RD-170 (x4) RD-? (x4) RD-?	LO_2/kerosene LO_2/LH_2 LO_2/kerosene	7,108,000 (3,224,000) 1,764,000 (800,000) 110,000? (50,000?)	39,700lb (18 tonnes) to GTO, 61,700lb (28 tonnes) to Mars and Venus, 70,500lb (32 tonnes) to the Moon.
K-1 (Energiya, Two Strap-on Variant) 1995	USSR (Korolev Collective)	197 (60)	59 max (18)	3,836,000 (1,740,000)	1 2	RD-170 (x2) RD-? (x4)	LO_2/kerosene LO_2/LH_2	3,554,000 (1,612,000) 1,764,000 (800,000)	Standard Energiya, but with only two strap-on boosters: 143,300lb (65 tonnes) to 51·6°, 124 mile (200km) orbit.
K-1/VKK (SL-17, Energiya/Shuttle) 1988	USSR (Korolev Collective)	197 (60)	59 max (18)	4,630,000 (2,100,000)	1 2	RD-170 (x4) RD-? (x4)	LO_2/kerosene LO_2/LH_2	7,108,000 (3,224,000) 1,764,000 (800,000)	First flight with Buran shuttle orbiter, 15 November 1988. Orbiter maximum mass 231,500lb (105 tonnes): payload 66,100lb (30 tonnes) to 51·6°, 155 miles (250km).

Note: a six strap-on variant of Energiya is planned for introduction before 2000, being capable of 330,700lb (150 tonnes) to low Earth orbit and an eight strap-on variant could fly with a tandem payload of 441,000lb (200 tonnes) between 2000-2010.